# A GALLERY OF GREETINGS

A Guide to the

Seddon Collection of Greeting Cards in

Manchester Polytechnic Library

Compiled by Laura Seddon

Manchester
Manchester Polytechnic Library

1992

Design and Typography
Rachel Davies Cooper and
John Hartshorne

Printed by Revell & George,
Manchester

# CONTENTS

The colour pictures , numbered for
identification are inserted between
section 5 and 6 and section 18 and 19

# PREFACE

Until recently, it was considered below the dignity of a learned library to acquire and retain printed ephemera. Indeed, in some quarters, such attitudes still exist, although increasing public awareness of the importance of the John Johnson and other collections will in time eradicate these.

It is fortuitous that the value of ephemeral printing as a resource for historical research was largely realised within the University of Oxford, one of the world's great centres of learning. By putting its seal of approval on the activities of John Johnson, the University printer, the systematic collecting of what Johnson called "everything which a museum or library would not ordinarily accept if it were offered as a gift" was legitimatised.[1] Not unnaturally, christmas cards, valentines and other pictorial cards feature strongly in this collection which was transferred to the Bodleian Library from the University Press in 1968.

Again, until recently, it has been fashionable to denigrate "commercial" art. Since the second world war, however, the contribution made by "commercial" artists and designers has been increasingly recognised and the boundaries between high culture and popular culture have become increasingly blurred. Important collections of greetings cards have long been held in the British Museum and the Victoria and Albert Museum although some art gallery curators still regard such material as "not legitimate".

Probably the largest and certainly the most exciting collection of greetings cards in the United Kingdom still in private hands in 1991 is that which Laura Seddon has carefully and systematically amassed and refined over twenty years. Unsurpassed in breadth and depth, this is one of the most visually exciting sources of design history in the United Kingdom, characterised by fine draughtsmanship, sumptuous colour and the use of interesting materials.

The Collection comes to Manchester Polytechnic Library, not only as a generous gift, but also endowed with this catalogue which Mrs Seddon has compiled over the last five years. At the age of 76 she embarked on a herculean task which would have daunted many younger people and has saved Manchester Polytechnic the task of employing a professional cataloguer in order to provide the key to this collection. As a result of her work, individual items will be readily made available to collectors and those interested in design history.

Manchester Polytechnic has the largest faculty of Art and Design in the United Kingdom. The Faculty can trace its history back over 100 years through the Regional College of Art. Many well known designers have taught here including Herbert Cole, Lewis Day and the great illustrator and art educator Walter Crane, who was Director of Design from 1893 until 1896. It is, therefore, most appropriate that a collection built in the North West of England should be deposited in a leading local academic institution where it will play an important role in stimulating creativity in those students who are tomorrow's designers.

Collecting is not necessarily virtuous, but when planned and executed in the scholarly manner carried out by Laura Seddon, with clear objectives in view, where modest, individual pieces of ephemera have been brought together in a monumental tour de force, then collecting becomes an art. The Director and Governing Body of the Polytechnic are deeply conscious of the value of this gift.

The physical preparation of this catalogue has been an exhausting task, not only for Mrs Seddon but also for Pat Kelly and Nicola Clarke who have conscientiously keyboarded the work throughout the project and also for Dr Rachel Davies-Cooper who has designed the catalogue and seen it through the press. The photography is by Peter Fletcher Photography and the staff of the Educational Services Unit of Manchester Polytechnic. Messrs Revell and George, our printers, have been most helpful and patient. To all these I owe a debt of gratitude.

IAN ROGERSON
September 1991

# ACKNOWLEDGEMENTS

Laura Seddon acknowledges with much gratitude her appreciation for the help and support received from the following people and organisations:

The late Sir Harry Page, who started it all.

The late George Buday for his invaluable "**History of the Christmas Card**, and for his encouragement and support for this project.

The Ephemera Society and its founders, in particular Maurice Rickards who has given much helpful advice.

David Taylor of the Manchester Local History Library, whose research into the Hildesheimer records has provided much useful information for the catalogue.

Mrs Elisabeth Worth for her account of the Hildesheimer family.

Brigadier Stephen Goodall, Michael Goodall, and Mrs Julia Woodward for help with Goodall cards.

Patrick Withers for detailed information about De La Rue.

Mrs Joyce Tonge, who generously shared her wide knowledge of Victorian artists.

Stockport Corporation and the Museum staff, who hosted five exhibitions of cards from the Seddon Collection between 1972 and 1985, with special thanks to former Curator Harry Fancy who suggested the first one.

The staff of the Hallmark Cards Historical Collection at Kansas City USA, the Boston, Mass. Public Library, and the American Antiquarian Society in Worcester, Mass. for allowing access to their collections.

The British Museum Print Room staff for assistance with access to archives and provision of photocopies, and Mrs Anne Flavell of the John Johnson Collection in the Bodleian Library, Oxford for similar help.

The Librarian of Windsor Castle archives for permission to examine Queen Mary's card collection.

The Public Record Office, Kew, for access to Stationers' Hall Records, and members of staff for timely assistance to one with limited experience of computers.

Edith Hibbert and Nita Hornsby, whose warm and comforting hospitality made bearable the long days in the Public Record Office handling heavy volumes, peering at microfilms, and looking through dusty bundles.

The RSPB, and Michael Seddon, for much needed assistance in identifying bird cards.

Mrs Barbara Renshaw, Mr and Mrs Vernon Shaw, and the late Mrs Alison Yates who responded nobly to frequent appeals for help in identifying flowers.

The National Trust and Mrs Susan Denyer for information about Beatrix Potter cards.

Professor Anthony Crane for help with Walter Crane cards.

The Seddon family for unfailing support and enthusiasm, both for the Collection and for the catalogue.

It has been a pleasure and an education in modern publishing technique to work with Dr Rachel Davies-Cooper who has designed the catalogue and seen it through the press.

Last but by no means least, Manchester Polytechnic Library and Professor Ian Rogerson for the effort, time and patience needed to complete this publication, with special thanks to Pat Kelly and Nicola Clarke who had the onerous task of transferring a handwritten script to the word processor with continual complications of peculiar names, figures, and references.

LAURA SEDDON
September 1991

# GREETING CARDS
# THROUGHOUT THE YEARS

This brief history of Victorian greeting cards shows their development from 1843 when greetings for Christmas began. Seasonal greetings, which form the greater part of the Seddon collection, are the main theme but the valentine, birthday and Easter cards included in the catalogue are also considered.

New Year greetings, gifts and tokens, have been known from Roman times, and valentines were exchanged between lovers long before the first commercially produced Christmas card appeared in England. This is now recognised as the card designed by J C Horsley in 1843 for Henry Cole, known to collectors as the Cole-Horsley card. Cole, who was later knighted for his public work, notably for the Great Exhibition of 1851 and for the South Kensington Museum, published the card at Felix Summerly's Home Office, an enterprise he had started to produce children's books and toys. A thousand copies were lithographed, coloured by hand, and sold for a shilling each (five new pence), a very high price at a time when a labourer might earn little more for a day's hard work. There are perhaps fifteen examples still known to exist, and two were sold at Sotheby's in November 1989 for £6,600 and £3,300. The card illustrated on plate 1 of Buday's History of the Christmas Card is held in the National Art Library at the Victoria and Albert Museum whilst that shown on plate 2 is at the British Museum. Two examples are in the Hallmark Historical collection in Kansas City, USA and several more are in USA collections.

A close contender for priority was the card designed by the artist William Maw Egley in 1848. Both designs show Christmas family festivities along with scenes of charity to the poor, the Egley card also showing Harlequin and Columbine; these themes ignored the basic religious meaning of the Christmas festival. A similar card was issued about 1850 as a trade card for the Albany, New York, firm of R H Pease, designed by Edwin Forbes. This shows an American family attended by a negro servant, with the addition of Santa Claus bearing a sack of presents presiding over the party. The well-known poem by Dr Clement C Moore, published in America in 1822 (see Volume 63) perhaps inspired this, and the Santa Claus and Father Christmas tradition seems to have appeared earlier in America than in Britain. The writer has no record of any other copy of this card in public or private collections, and the Seddon collection is fortunate and perhaps at present unique in possessing all three "firsts".

A few small Christmas and New Year cards, usually showing robins or holly, appeared in the 1850's when the production of valentines was perhaps at its peak, with an occasional birthday card on similar decorative lace paper mounts. Some were specially made for mother, father, brother or sister. But nearly twenty years elapsed before the commercial possibilities of seasonal greetings were

developed. In 1862 Charles Goodall & Son issued a series of small cards resembling visiting cards, die-stamped with seasonal motifs or flowers and with simple greetings, usually with hand-coloured edges. Similar cards soon appeared from Canton, Dean, Sulman, Windsor, J Mansell & Rimmel, who had made valentines for many years. The New Year greeting appeared alone as well as with Christmas wishes.

By 1870 these small cards had become more elaborate, with scraps, gilt and silver decoration and embossing, and the valentine makers were using lace paper for Christmas and New Year cards. Commercial production was now in full swing, meeting increased popular demand, though still from the more affluent families. The penny charge introduced in 1840 had encouraged the sending by post of valentines and early greetings cards, and by 1870 they could be sent for a halfpenny in unsealed envelopes. By this time Marcus Ward, originally in Ireland, was established in London and making goods of a high artistic standard; soon Raphael Tuck, De La Rue, Prang in U S A, Eyre & Spottiswoode, the Hildesheimers, and a host of other firms, many of German origin, were supplying the growing market.

Robins and holly were joined by children in family scenes, and anthropomorphic birds and animals and the humanised Christmas dinner provided comic relief. The religious motif appeared more often in the accompanying greetings or sentiments, though illuminated designs based on mediaeval manuscripts conveyed religious feeling; Marcus Ward made some delightful Easter cards in this style. "Mechanical" cards, consisting of layers of lace paper with coloured scraps and prints joined by paper springs, were made to open to give a three-dimensional effect or rotate to show new pictures, and these often featured Nativity scenes as well as floral bouquets.

By 1880 card production was big business, and designs were recognised to some extent as important art forms, products being regularly reviewed in leading journals and often satirized in Punch. Valentine production declined as the Christmas card market grew. Competitions for designs organised in 1881 and 1882 by Prang, Raphael Tuck, S Hildesheimer and Hildesheimer and Faulkner attracted well known artists, including Royal Academicians and many women. Portraits of charming maidens and elegant ladies appeared, along with the earlier seasonal motifs, though an untimely invasion of scantily dressed girls, flower children and fairies, prompted a Punch cartoon showing Father Christmas telling them they had no business to be out at this season.

Cards with flowers continued the tradition of the New Year greeting with its hope for the coming of spring, though roses were used as much for Christmas greetings as for New Year. Although religion played a prominent part in family life, cards with sacred themes were comparatively rare; Christmas was celebrated chiefly as a time of family reunion and festivity and the secular aspect of the occasion was usually portrayed. The conscience of the well-to-do was perhaps appeased by cards showing the humble pleasures of the poor and the timely charity of their "betters". However, the growth of the Sunday School movement created a larger demand for appropriate cards and texts which was met by an increasing number of publishers who specialised in religious themes.

Designers' themes were extended to meet all tastes, with hunting, shooting, the army and navy portrayed often in comic situations. The artistic tastes of the 1880's encouraged cards with Japanese designs and aesthetic subjects; cards with negroes brought comic situations as well as a reminder of increasing contact with the New World. Town and country scenes were popular, many with churches, and sailing ships provided suitable material for the artist's brush. Children appeared in summer scenes as well as in winter, with a variety of birds and animals often portrayed in humorous vein. Traditional themes with Christmas in the olden days and clowns and pantomime were popular subjects.

By 1890 cheaper means of production, with some cards selling for a penny a dozen or less, meant that Christmas greetings were no longer the preserve of the more affluent society. Many cards were made specially for children to send or receive, with amusing cut-out and shaped designs of children at play with birds and animals. Topical events were caricatured, an occasional political scene appeared, and cards with pictorial humour and punning verses not always in the best of taste appeared in quantity in response to popular demand. The "naughty nineties" were depicted in saucy cards opening to show frills and laces. This was a flamboyant period with decoration often carried to excess on elaborate tinselled flower cards. Most of the cards were folders, tied with cord or ribbon. Before the end of the century the coloured postcard had appeared, new manufacturers were taking over and many of the older firms had abandoned card production.

Technique of production can be followed throughout the collection from the early wood-block colour printing of Baxter licensees including Dickes, Kronheim and J Mansell, to the later chromolithography and the use of photographic processes. Die stamped early small cards were succeeded by elaborate embossing, and the frosted, tinselled and jewelled cards which first appeared in 1867 were at their best in designs of the 1880's from Wirth Bros, S Hildesheimer and Hagelberg. Black, red and gold backgrounds were introduced in the 1870's, perhaps originally in the U S A by Prang, and these were soon used

by other firms. The lace paper of the early valentines gave way to coarser designs in the 1880's, though some attractive patterns appeared in the 1890's. The mechanical cards, on springs, opening to make three-dimensional scenes, appeared throughout the period, with some interesting nativity designs lighted by an arrangement of transparent coloured paper in the 1890's.

Cards made from photographs appeared in the 1880's, though these were of small artistic interest. However, they included some interesting topical pictures of children in typical Victorian pursuits. Cards were now printed by suppliers for personal use and some were specially designed for or by the senders. Silk insets (which had been earlier used for valentines) were introduced to Christmas cards in the 1870's, and some pictures were printed on silk backgrounds. Many cards from French firms have been found in albums, made for the English market using silk, paper lace, and mother-of-pearl. Machine embroidered insets were used on cards made by Stevens and Bollans, both firms well known to collectors of silk bookmarks.

The simple greetings of the 1860's later extended to verses, often signed by their authors, and were sometimes accompanied by texts or quotations from the classics. The larger sizes allowed more space, and often long poems were printed on the backs of the cards, sometimes in narrative form describing the pictures. These were sometimes issued in folders of four or six scenes with poems describing a sequence of comic events. The writing of "sentiments" must have been an extensive commercial enterprise. H M Burnside was said to have written over 6,000 between 1874 and 1900; quotations from the religious verse of Frances Ridley Havergal often appear, with her poem "The Bells" used in many different contexts. A number of writers were in Holy Orders, including E H Bickersteth, Bishop of Exeter. Buday suggests that the writers record was achieved by Samuel K Cowan, MA, who wrote 1,005 verses in 1884 for eleven different firms. Cards in the Seddon Collection from ten publishers are signed by him, as well as many others unattributed.

All this provides a fascinating picture of Victorian social customs and popular artistic taste, even though it was reflected in a comfortable middle class mirror. Greeting cards must not, of course, be considered in the same context as great art, although in Victorian times they were regarded as products of some artistic importance. Gleeson White wrote a detailed serious study "Christmas Cards and their Chief Designers" for the Studio Magazine of 1894, based largely on the collection of publisher Jonathan King, who filled two houses in Islington with cards and associated material. These were largely destroyed in 1918 by a disastrous fire and much that survived went to the United States of America. It is sad that so much of our

social heritage has left, and is still leaving, this country.
However, much remains and there are signs that public
bodies are now recognising the importance as social
heritage of ephemera that not long ago would have been
discarded. The Ephemera Society, started in London and
now flourishing in U S A, Canada, and Australia, has done
much to promote this attitude.

# THE LAURA SEDDON COLLECTION OF GREETING CARDS

This collection began after hearing a lecture by Sir Harry Page, whose fine collection of albums and associated ephemera is now in the archives of Manchester Polytechnic.

Collecting is a contagious disease, and this introduction to a fascinating new field, at a time when hunting in bookshops and fairs could produce lucky finds, fostered a growing interest in old albums and their contents. Many of these included greeting cards tastefully embellished with coloured scraps and prints, and were compiled by young people to whom the preservation of such treasures gave pleasant occupation in the days before radio, cinema, and television.

After neglected years in cellars or attics, the background paper of many of those albums proved more vulnerable to the ravages of time than the cards making their removal advisable from shabby volumes and Victorian glue. This, and the purchase of cards for which dealers had already provided this service, made a systematic mounting and grouping advisable. The acquisition of George Buday's book "The History of the Christmas Card", and of the three "first" cards - Cole Horsley, Egley, and the first American card - encouraged their owner to consider building up a worthwhile collection, and in the following eighteen years that objective has been achieved and is now accompanied by the compilation of a detailed catalogue. This would never have been accomplished without Buday's book with its extensive lists of publishers and artists and its comprehensive illustrations. His letters and personal Christmas cards have been a great encouragement for the work on the catalogue, which has involved abandoning many other activities. Collections in the British Museum, Queen Mary's collection, the Victoria and Albert, the John Johnson collection in the Bodleian Library, and the Greenaway collection in Hampstead, have all been visited and studied, as well as a number of private collections; visits to the USA have included the Hallmark collection in Kansas City, the American Antiquarian Society in Worcester, Mass, and the Boston Public Library with their collections of Prang cards. The paper chase has continued for over twenty years though four years work on this catalogue has slowed down recent acquisitions, and there are some important gaps in the collection. However, there are two thousand seven hundred and seventy six Marcus Ward cards, two hundred and ninety four by Kate Greenaway and Walter Crane, a fair representation of De La Rue cards, a large number of early Goodall cards, and a collection of four hundred and eighty nine in the visiting card style of the 1860's and early 1870's, as well as a large number of "valentine" style and "mechanical" cards. Most of the cards have Christmas and New Year greetings, with some birthday, valentine and Easter examples; many designs were used with variant sentiments for all these festivals.

The Ephemera Society has provided happy hunting grounds with its frequent bazaars, as well as many friends, both dealers and fellow collectors, among whom Joyce Tonge must be ranked as the most knowledgeable, always prepared to share her wide knowledge of artists. Five major exhibitions have already been staged from the collection in Stockport, two at Vernon Park Museum in 1972 and 1974, and three at Stockport Art Gallery in 1980, 1984, and 1985 (Christmas cards in 1972, 1980, 1985, and valentines in 1974, 1984), under the auspices of Stockport Metropolitan Borough Council, and have created much interest, with television and radio coverage. This has included BBC North West and Granada, Manchester BBC and Piccadilly Radio, Woman's Hour, and programmes for Channel 4's Years Ahead and ITV. A card from the collection was used by the Victorian Society as its Christmas card for 1985 and a number have been reprinted by two leading card manufacturers for present day use. Cards have also been used by David Taylor in three exhibitions in the 1980's in the Manchester Local History Library. His research has provided much valuable information for this catalogue, notably in connection with Hildesheimer records.

The collection began with Christmas and New Year cards but a number of Easter, birthday, and valentine cards are included which widen the range of design. A few memorial cards are included in the religious section, as well as Reward cards and texts which were often sent as Christmas cards. The building of this collection has given its owner much pleasure and many new friends, as well as much interesting purposeful travel and lecture and article material.

# THE CATALOGUE

The filing and arrangement of this collection has evolved during twenty years of work on the cards as the simplest method for personal study. It should be easily followed from the list of section and volume headings and from the following explanations.

At least six avenues of classification could be followed, leading to dating, publishers, subjects, artists, style and technique of production, and writers of sentiments. It is obvious that all these are interlinked, and that unless a collection was formed with one particular objective, no one trail could be followed exclusively. With the contents of this particular collection in mind it seemed advisable to start with sections of early cards up to the 1870's, including cards from some early publishers, many on valentine style paper, most of which were unsigned by their designers though a few could be traced. The earliest cards are followed by selections from publishers where sufficient cards were available to show representative collections, including Goodall, Marcus Ward, De La Rue, Prang, Raphael Tuck, and the Hildesheimers, varying from six to twenty seven volumes each. These have sub-sections for subjects, and for artists, with the cards as far as possible filed chronologically. Cards designed by Kate Greenaway and Walter Crane, however, have been given a separate two volume section to themselves in view of the interest they arouse, though most of them were published by Marcus Ward.

From this stage, the sections are classified under subjects - Religion, Children, Family Scenes, Ladies, Fairies, Humour, Birds, Animals, the Good Old Days and so on to a large group with Flowers, Fruit, and Foliage. These sections include cards from publishers not previously dealt with in detail, of which the more prominent were Eyre and Spottiswoode, Hagelberg and Castell Bros, mainly with cards of the 1880's and 1890's; although there are a large number of cards from these publishers in the collection, in view of so many similar cards of this period being unmarked it was considered wiser to group these cards for comparison with others of similar style that could not be firmly attributed. Artists have been sorted where identified. The final sections have cards from the later Victorian era grouped mainly by consideration of style and technique, followed by a small selection of early 20th century cards, including some postcards and First World War cards, showing changes in artistic values and in popular taste.

Sentiments have not been taken into account in the classification, but enough names of writers are given in the catalogue to demonstrate the number and variety of composers of greeting card verses, including some prominent clerical gentlemen.

The collection began with Christmas cards, but the inclusion of valentine, birthday and Easter cards as well as New Year greetings gives a much wider range of artists and designs and sometimes completes sets of designs. Many cards in the collection with New Year greetings were also issued for Christmas, though some cards were specifically designed for New Year including a number for use by Scottish people. Cards other than Christmas or New Year are listed in the text; where no description of variant sentiment is given, they are Christmas or New Year or both. Some duplicate designs are included where sentiments vary, and in this case the number of different pictorial designs is given in the text.

The cards are mounted, either on sheets in loose leaf files or in dropside boxes for the more delicate examples which need careful handling, with 274 volumes (files and boxes) in all. Measurements are given in centimetres, width first, height second, a form which seems logical to the mathematician for whom the horizontal x precedes the vertical y. With cards of varying sizes on one sheet, individual measurements are given if considered of sufficient importance, or as "sizes up to ...." if there is little difference. Where sizes vary significantly the smallest and largest are listed.

It is hoped that collectors and students will find the hitherto unpublished material in this catalogue both useful and interesting. Identification of publishers and artists has been carefully controlled. Much of this is based on personal research into Stationers' Hall Registrations, which are stored at the Public Record office in Kew. This involved going through a number of large volumes listing date, publishers, with a description of the drawing and the name of the artist in some cases, and all the registrations traced to cards in the Collection have been included in the catalogue. This was a difficult and sometimes wearisome experience extending over many years; the original drawings, though in store, were not easily available, and microfilms, though helpful and time saving but hard on elderly eyes, are not always clear enough for positive identification. Some previously accepted attributions have been corrected from positive source information.

There is of course always room for further discoveries, and more work could be done on cards of the later Victorian era.Where identifications have been taken from other sources - eg Gleeson White, Buday - these are given. Publishers are named from signatures or trademarks, and occasionally from similarity, though this has been done with caution; the same applies to artists. It should be noted that incorrect attributions can be handed down from one source to another until they are accepted as fact.

Dating is only precise when taken from Stationers' Hall or publishers' records, though Gleeson White, price lists and newspaper articles provide reasonably reliable contemporary figures. Dates written on the cards, or in the albums from which they were taken, are given in the text, but these only show that the cards were issued before that date. Publishers' numbers on the cards can help, and these are given when present and readable - some are so small and indistinct that even strong spectacles plus magnifying glass cannot decipher them. However, one must be cautious, as there are several examples in the collection of identical cards marked with different publishers' names, probably from another source which supplied several firms.

Access to public collections has given valuable support for research on the collection, and great help has been given by the staff of the British Museum Print Room, the John Johnson Collection in the Bodleian Library, the Hallmark Collection in Kansas City, the Boston (Mass.) Public Library, and the Reading University Library. The American Antiquarian Society in Worcester, Mass., produced in one day 70 volumes of Prang material and valentines for examination, with two patient members of staff in constant procession to and from the storeroom. Nearer home, much valuable information and help has come from David Taylor at the Manchester Local History Library. The items of Manchester interest are particularly important for a collection to be housed in the Library of the Manchester Polytechnic.

# BIBLIOGRAPHY

Allan, Alastair, and Hoverstadt, Joan. **The History of Printed Scraps.** New Cavendish Books, 1983.

Buday, George. **The History of the Christmas Card.** Rockliff Publishing Corporation, 1954, Spring Books, 1964.

Cole, Sir Henry. **50 Years of Public Work.** Bell, London 1884.

Crane, Walter. **An Artist's Reminiscences.** Methuen & Co, 1907.

Houfe, Simon. **Dictionary of British Book Illustrators and Caricaturists 1800-1914.** Antique Collectors' Club, 1978.

Ingram, John. **Flora Symbolica - or the Language and Sentiment of Flowers.** Frederick Warne & Co, c1880.

Jones, Owen. **The Grammar of Ornament.** Day & Son, 1856.

Lewis, C Courtney. **The Story of Picture Printing in England during the 19th Century.** Sampson Low, Marston & Co Ltd. nd.

Lockwood, M S and Glaister, E. **Art Embroidery.** Illustrated by Thomas Crane. Marcus Ward & Co, 1878.

McLean, Ruari. **Victorian Book Design.** 2nd Edition. Faber & Faber, 1972.

Nahum, Peter. **Monograms of Victorian and Edwardian Artists.** Victoria Square Press, 1976.

Punch.

Schuster, Thomas E, and Engen, Rodney. **Printed Kate Greenaway, a Catalogue Raisonné.** T E Schuster,1986.

Spencer, Isobel. **Walter Crane.** Macmillan, 1975.

Spielmann, M H and Layard, GS. **Kate Greenaway.** Adam and Charles Black, 1905.

Staff, Frank. **The Valentine and its origins.** Lutterworth Press, 1969.

Staff, Frank. **The Picture Postcard and its Origins.** Lutterworth Press, 1968.

Thomson, Susan Ruth. **The Catalogue of the Kate Greenaway Collection in the Detroit Public Library.** Wayne State University Press, 1977.

Times, The.

White, Gleeson. **Christmas cards and their Chief Designers.** Studio Christmas number 1894.

White, Gleeson. **Children's Books and their Illustrators.** Studio Winter number 1897-98.

Wood, Christopher. **Dictionary of Victorian Painters.** Antique Collectors' Club, 1971. Reprinted.

Worth, Elisabeth. **The Hildesley Family.** Privately printed, 1981.

**Love Knots & Bridal Bonds.** Raphael Tuck 1882. (Verses illustrated by actual Tuck greeting cards).

# SOURCES OF INFORMATION

American Antiquarian Society, Worcester, Mass, USA.

Boston (USA) Public Library.

British Museum, and Queen Mary's Collection of Greeting Cards.

City of Manchester Local History Library.

Hallmark Historical Collection, Hallmark Cards, Kansas City, USA.

John Johnson Collection, Bodleian Library, Oxford.

National Trust, Cumbria.

Reading University Library.

Stationers' Hall Records, Public Record Office, Kew.

Victoria and Albert Museum.

# EARLY CARDS

*Section*

*1*

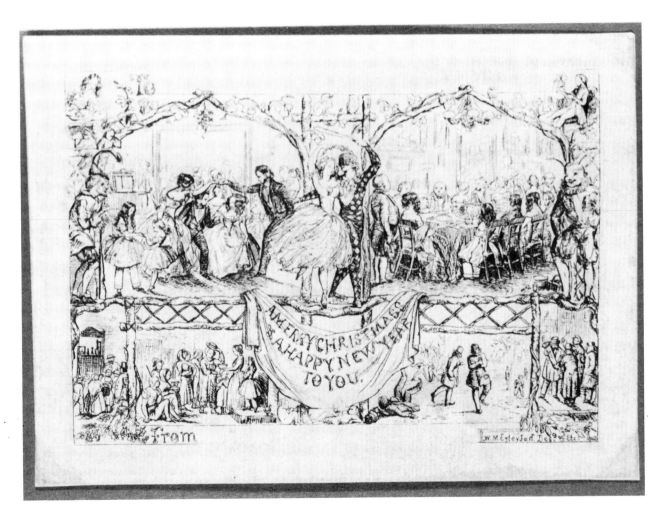

1.2

# VOLUME 1:
## THE "FIRST" CARDS AND SOME FORERUNNERS

**New Year greetings, gifts and tokens have been known since Roman times, but the commercially produced Christmas card, as we know it, would appear to date from 1843 when the card designed by JC Horsley for Henry Cole was issued, closely followed by Egley's card of 1848. Here are copies of the "first" three cards, with some earlier New Year greetings, and associated material.**

The Cole Horsley Card
1. This copy was sent by George Bell (probably the publisher) to a Mrs Trapnell. The card was designed by J C Horsley (later to become a Royal Academician) for Henry Cole, who was later knighted for his many public services, notably to the Great Exhibition of 1851 and to the South Kensington Museum, (now the Victoria & Albert Museum). It was lithographed and hand coloured and published by Felix Summerly's Home Treasury Office, a business enterprise of Cole's, and sold for one shilling, a very high price at the time. The theme is secular, of happy family feasting and charity to the poor. The date is now firmly established as 1843 by the existence of cards with that date upon them, though Cole himself in his later memoirs of 1884 showed some confusion giving both 1845 and 1846. (Ref. Buday, Cole).
There are at least twelve signed copies still in existence and three unused. The authentic cards should not be confused with proof copies (see below).
13 cm x 8.1 cm.

The Egley Card
2. This was designed in 1848 by the artist William Maw Egley, and is similar in theme to the Cole Horsley card, but includes Harlequin and Columbine. At one time, the date on the card, which is rather indistinct, was taken to be 1842, but Egley himself established the date as 1848, five years later than the Cole Horsley card.
13.7 cm x 10 cm.

The "First" American Card
3. This card, reputedly the first commercially produced American Christmas greeting, was issued about 1850 as an advertising or trade card for the firm of R H Pease of Albany, New York State. It was designed by the artist Edwin Forbes, and again there is the theme of family festivity, here with a negro servant helping at the table. 20 cm x 13.5 cm.

4. Two copies of the Cole Horsley card comprising:
a) A proof copy printed in red.
b) The De la Rue reproduction of 1881, series no. 459.

5. Two reproductions
a) The Raphael Tuck reproduction of 1954 of a Cole Horsley card from John Washbourne, 1843.
b) A Hallmark reproduction of an unused Cole Horsley card in their collection.

6. Two reproductions
a) Another Hallmark reproduction of a Cole Horsley card.
b) An uncoloured Victoria and Albert Museum reproduction of a Cole Horsley proof copy.

7. An early reproduction of the Egley card by the British Museum, made soon after acquisition in 1931. The date of the Egley card is incorrectly given as 1842.

8. Nine cards, five of comic folk (one marked J King) and four of ladies' faces. One of these is illustrated by Buday and dated in the 1840's, but this has not been confirmed. The J King card is hand coloured and could be 1850's, and has been repeated later in colour printing. This design has also been used for a visiting card. 6 cm x 9 cm.

9. Dobbs Kidd. A lace motif with applied Christmas scraps and handwritten message, obviously adapted from valentine material. 1850's. 9 cm x 12 cm.

10. Windsor. Five cards, probably 1850's-60's.
a) Silver lace paper with paper cage (one missing). 18 cm x 11.5 cm.
b) Silver lace paper with die-stamped motif, message on silk. 6.5 cm x 9.5 cm.
c) Embossed on silver with die-stamped motif. 6.5 cm x 9 cm.
d) A folding card with embossed winter scene and lace paper robin, with die-stamped Christmas motif within. The sender's date appears to be 1840. As, however, the motif is characteristic of the '50's or even '60's, the date could have been added later. 5.1 cm x 19.5 cm open.
e) A similar card, with gold embossing on scenes of house and woodland, with die-stamped motif of girl.
5.1 cm x 19.5 cm open.

11. J C Erhard. A German New Year Greeting. From an etching on copper dated 1818. 16 cm x 14.4 cm.

12. J A Klein. A Viennese New Year Greeting for 1818. Etching of little girl with calendar. 23 cm x 16 cm.

13. A Swiss letter folder with space inside for a New Year letter. 1850's.
13.6 cm x 20.5 cm.

14. Seven lace paper German "Namenfeste" cards of the 1840's and 1850's, some with gilt decoration.
8.5 cm x 5 cm to 8.8 cm x 11 cm.

15. Three cards.
a) "Carte de visite" style, German New Year, published by C Naumann, Frankfurt. c1845.
b) Etching "Prosit Neujahr", H Dorn, Leipzig. An early postcard.
c) Greeting "Herzliche Gluckwunsch" on gilt and lace paper. c1865.
8.7 cm x 5.8 cm to 8.7 cm x 14 cm.

16. De La Rue, a leaflet showing the envelope folding machine shown at the Great Exhibition of 1851.

# VOLUME 2:
## EARLY SMALL CARDS 1850's - EARLY 1870's

**The commercial possibilities of Christmas greetings were not exploited for some time after the Cole Horsley and Egley cards appeared in the 1840's, but a few small cards, with holly, robin and festive scenes, appeared in the 1850's and 60's. Occasional ones found in scrapbooks are signed by Pinches & Co., or Lambert of Newcastle; Petter & Galpin are credited by Buday with producing some between 1851-1859. Some were lithographed and hand coloured, and the development of chromolithography, following Baxter's colour process, stimulated production. These cards are small, measuring up to 10 cm x 7 cm, the majority being about 9 cm x 6 cm. They have brief seasonal greetings, but occasionally verses appear, and sometimes frosting. In the absence of publishers marks or signatures, no attempt has been made to assign the origins of the majority of these cards, though some might be guessed.**

1. Pinches & Co, dated by the sender Dec. 11, 1860, with embossed robin and a window scene.

2. M & M W Lambert of Newcastle. Six cards, with holly designs in red, green, one with envelope. One is signed, the others are similar. c1860.

3. Seven similar cards, with holly and robin designs, one featuring a lady at a window. Early 1860's.

4. Four cards, with more elaborate colouring, of festive and winter scenes. Early 1860's.

5. Seven cards, showing winter scenes and holly, one marked Bishop & Co. 1860's.

6. Two cards, embossed with holly in red and green, and a Christmas verse printed on similar paper. 1860's.

7. Four cards, two designs, one with envelope, of holly and ivy. 1860's.

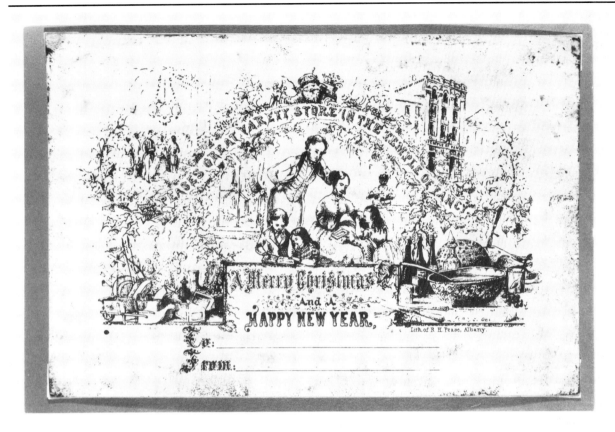

1.3

8. Six cards, with various decoration of holly and scenes, two having verses, one a photographic print, and one "remembrance from dear old York". c1870.

9. Sheet of notepaper with die-stamped robin motif, printed with Christmas verses. 1860's.

10. Five cards with scalloped edges, printed with scenes, holly, ivy and an open book. c1870.

11. Seven cards, with various designs of holly, flowers, scenes, two on yellow card with scalloped edge. 1870's.

12. Five small cards with holly and robin designs and serrated blue edges, one on fancy mount. 1870's.

13. Four cards, all with the same flower design but different style greetings - one birthday. 1870's.

14. W T Harris. Three cards with robin print in circle and one other similar style, edges hand coloured red. 1860's.

15. Eight cards of robins and holly, with various styles of embossed border. c1870.

16. Six cards with plain edges, and scenes of robins with holly, one with a cross and a church, and one of woodman cutting holly. 1860's.

17. Seven cards with scalloped edges featuring robins, one on oval mount with embossed border. 1860's.

18. Six cards, with robin pictures on plain mounts with red hand coloured edges. 1860's.

19. Nine cards, with robins and holly, three having serrated edges. Late 1860's.

20. Two cards, robins, holly, with green borders. c1870.

21. Four cards of robins in winter scenes, with embossed serrated edges. c1870.

22. Five similar cards.

23. Six cards, robins in winter scenes, one with scalloped edge. c1870.

24. Four cards, robins in winter scenes, with embossed scalloped edges. 1870's.

25. Nine similar cards, one with plain edge, three different designs with various captions. 1870's.

26. Ten similar cards, eight of robins with four different designs, two of holly and winter scenes. 1870's.

27. Eight similar cards on blue grounds. 1870's.

28. Seven cards of robins, four with embossed borders, three with pale blue and white borders. 1870's.

29. Nine cards with blue serrated borders, showing robins in human situations. Seven different designs. 1870's.

30. Six similar cards, with robins in oval vignettes, and red line border on cream ground. 1870's.

31. Five cards of robins, two with embossed borders, three with blue or red line borders. 1870's.

32. Four cards, robins in holly borders, two different designs. 1870's.

33. Six cards, robins with holly wreaths, five with scenes. 1870's.

34. Six cards with embossed scalloped borders, showing robins, bird's nest, flowers, scenes and dogs, four different designs and various captions and verses. 1870's.

35. Eight similar cards, four flowers, four birds, six different designs. 1870's.

36. Eight similar cards, winter and summer scenes, six designs. 1870's.

37. Six cards, winter scenes with robins in vignettes. 1870's.

38. Eight miscellaneous cards of robins. 1870's.

## VOLUMES 3 & 4: VISITING CARD STYLE, 1860's-70's

By the early 1860's, small cards, like the visiting cards which had been in use for many years, were being made by stationery manufacturers including Goodall, Sulman and C E Layton. These were die-stamped or printed with Christmas motifs and brief seasonal greetings, and some had coloured "scraps". Later, the cards became more elaborate with gilt and silver decoration, and increased in size, before giving way to the more pictorial cards of the 1870's. Publishers can sometimes be identified from embossed or printed trade marks, and from similarity of design, though identical unmarked cards were sometimes used by different firms. John Leighton (Luke Limner) designed many motifs for Goodall's earlier cards, some of which were used for Christmas stationery. No Stationers' Hall registrations of the cards have been traced, though a number of "scraps" were registered by Sulman in the late 1860's. The cards measure from 5 cm x 8 cm to 6 cm x 10 cm, and are mostly on white card, with simple Christmas and New Year greetings. An occasional cross or an appropriate verse, marks the religious significance of the Christmas greeting.

## VOLUME 3: VISITING CARD STYLE - 1ST VOLUME 1860's- EARLY 1870's

1. Single card, die-stamped motif of holly, dated by sender Jan 1/60.

2. Goodall. Notepaper and card, with identical motif.

3. Goodall. Nine cards c1864, with plain edges hand-coloured in red or blue, die-stamped and embossed with Christmas motifs of holly, robin etc, in red and green.

4. Goodall. Nine cards, as above.

5. Goodall. Nine cards, as above.

6. Goodall. Nine cards. Three cards as above, two with added Christmas verses, four with embossed borders.

7. Goodall. Nine cards, with humorous motifs of robins, clowns, jesters etc, five of these with hand coloured edges, four with embossed borders. 1860's.

8. Goodall. Five cards, four with embossed flower motifs, one with printed robin. Two of these have plain hand coloured edges, three embossed borders. 1860's.

9. Goodall. Eight cards with elaborate gold and silver decoration, and brief seasonal greetings. c1870.

10. Goodall. Nine cards, five having gold and coloured borders, four with lace borders, two of which have coloured scraps. c1870.

11. Goodall? Ten cards, with gold embossed borders, five having coloured scraps and five printed motifs. c1870.

12. Goodall. Eleven cards, five with coloured scraps, six with prints of children. All have greetings printed in black, on embossed white mounts. 1870's.

13. Goodall. Seven similar cards, one with envelope, with small prints or scraps, on embossed white mounts.

14. Goodall. Ten similar cards.

15. Writing paper and two envelopes, one postmarked Dec. 25 1866.

16. Card, rather badly printed, with two envelopes. 1860's.

17. Sixteen motifs, cut from notepaper or envelopes, as found in scrapbooks. 1865-70.

18. Writing paper, with robin and holly heading, with humorous message dated 1863.

19. Sulman. Nine cards, with embossed trade mark, and die-stamped and embossed motifs of holly, robin, ferns etc., and edges hand coloured in red or blue. 1860's.

20. Sulman. Nine cards, as no. 19 including motifs of jesters, Red Riding Hood, Sailor etc.

21. Sulman. Nine cards, three of the cards as no. 19 but not marked, with flower and leaf motifs.

22. Sulman. Nine cards as before, but with serrated embossed borders and miscellaneous motifs. Late 1860's.

23. Sulman. Six cards, as no. 22, on embossed mounts.

24. Sulman. Seven cards, with a variety of embossed mounts, two having coloured robin scraps and five die-stamped motifs. Late 1860's.

25. Sulman. Seven cards, with embossed or printed motifs and scraps, six on embossed mount and one with serrated border. Late 1860's.

26. Sulman. Nine cards with religious verses, five with scraps, four with die-stamped motifs. Late 1860's.

27. Sulman. Seven cards, with die-stamped motifs of flowers, shells and a Turk, four having plain coloured edges and two serrated borders. Late 1860's.

28. Nine cards with die-stamped robin motifs and plain hand coloured edges. Late 1860's.

29. Seven similar cards, one with horse, jockey and 1869 label. Late 1860's.

30. Nine cards with comic and grotesque die-stamped motifs, c1870. One on thicker card is an 1888 product from De La Rue, who took over dies from earlier publishers. See photocopies of sales lists in the John Johnson Collection.

31. C & E Layton. Ten cards on fancy embossed mounts, with die-stamped motifs of robin, holly or flowers, some with hand coloured edges. 1865-70.

32. C & E Layton. Seven similar cards, two having coloured scraps.

33. C & E Layton. Nine larger cards, two with plain borders, seven fancy embossed.

34. C & E Layton. Six cards, four with hand coloured serrated borders, and two plain cards with photographic oval prints. 1865-70.

35. Pinches & Co, Marion. Eight Cards with embossed die-stamped holly and bird motifs, five having embossed borders. Four of these are marked "Marion" but an identical one is labelled "Pinches & Co". 1860's.

36. Nine similar cards with embossed borders. (Compare with Goodall cards on sheet six).

37. Sheet of notepaper, with seven cards, having holly and robin motifs, and plain hand coloured edges. 1860's.

38. Ten cards, holly, robin and flower motifs, variety of edges. 1860's.

39. Eleven cards with embossed hand coloured borders and coloured scraps. c1870.

40. Five cards on embossed mounts with printed and die-stamped motifs. c1870.

## VOLUME 4: VISITING CARD STYLE - 2ND VOLUME 1860's-1875

1. Windsor. Folder of notepaper with embossed lace border, robin motif and greeting, and a card with robin motif and fancy embossed border. 1860's.

2. Windsor. Nine cards with a variety of embossed borders and robin and flower motifs. 1860's.

3. Windsor. Three cards with fancy silver edge and die stamped motifs. 1860's.

4. J Mansell. Ten cards, seven oval, three rectangular, with embossed and serrated borders and die stamped or printed motifs. 1860's.

5. J Mansell. Nine rectangular cards, with printed or die-stamped motifs. Eight have embossed plain or serrated borders and one has a lace border. 1860's.

6. Four oval cards with coloured scraps on embossed mounts. c1870.

7. Rimmel. Five cards on pink or grey mounts with small coloured prints and attached greetings. 1870's.

8. Three small cards with pink or blue border and coloured scraps. 1870's.

9. Five plain rectangular cards with various die-stamped or printed motifs. 1870's.

10. Nine cards with embossed borders and die stamped or printed holly, robin or leaf motifs. 1860's.

11. Six cards on embossed mounts, with coloured scraps and hand coloured scalloped edges. c1870.

12. Nine cards, hand coloured edges, with coloured scraps, two having printed verses. Late 1860's.

13. Nine cards on plain or embossed mounts, with coloured scraps. Late 1860's.

14. Ten similar cards with embossed borders and printed motifs, six having added scraps. Late 1860's.

15. Five cards with printed scenes of flowers, robins or children. Late 1860's.

16. Nine similar cards, with embossed borders, and scraps over printed motifs. Late 1860's

17. Six cards with various printed motifs or scenes. Late 1860's.

18. Nine similar, three with added scraps. Late 1860's.

19. Ten cards on embossed mounts with coloured scraps, one dated 1872.

20. Six cards with coloured scraps, all bearing scraps dated 1871, 1872 or 1873.

21. Eight cards on fancy mounts, four having gilt embossing. Early 1870's.

22. Four cards on white and beige embossed mounts, with coloured scraps. Early 1870's.

23. Six embossed cards, four with scraps of birds or flowers, two with printed motifs. Early 1870's.

24. Eight cards with prints of children, scenes, or robins, fixed to embossed mounts. Early 1870's.

25. Five cards with printed winter scenes. Early 1870's.

26. Seven embossed cards with scraps or printed winter scenes, some with coloured grounds. Early 1870's.

27. Seven cards with gilt or silver decoration, three having greeting scraps on monotone holly ground. c1870.

## VOLUMES 5 & 6: EARLY CHILDREN'S CARDS, 1870's

**Small cards, about 6 cm x 9.5 cm, began to appear in the late 1860's featuring children and family scenes. The publishers Sulman, Dean, J Mansell and Kronheim made substantial contributions to similar cards in the period around 1870, and they have been included in this section, with similar unattributed cards. Winter scenes predominate, with Christmas celebrations, though an occasional floral motif appears. Captions are usually brief seasonal greetings, with an occasional verse. A few cards can be traced from Stationers' Hall registrations. During the 1870's, cards increased in size, and measurements of larger ones are given. Some of the unidentified cards in Volume 5 might by Canton.**

## VOLUME 5: 1ST VOLUME - CHILDRENS CARDS - SULMAN & SIMILAR CARDS, ALL EARLY 1870's

1. Sulman. Six cards designed by J Nixon, winter scenes with scalloped borders. Five out of eight designs registered by Stationers' Hall, 31-8-1871. (Copy of registration appended).

2/3. Sulman. Sixteen similar cards, eight designs.

4. Sulman. Eight similar cards.

5. Sulman. Eight similar, with some indoor scenes.

6. Sulman. Seven similar, showing street vendors and winter scenes.

7. Sulman? Six similar, with indoor and outdoor winter scenes.

8. Sulman. Eight similar, seven designs, with children out-of-doors.

9. Sulman. Three cards, two designs of girls, one with gilt border and one with caption in German.

10. Sulman. Eight cards, scalloped edges, with indoor Christmas scenes on dark grounds, four designs.

11. Sulman? Nine cards, scalloped edges, with children in outdoor winter scenes. One card is frosted.

12. Sulman? Eight similar cards with different style scalloped border.

13. Sulman. Eight cards with pink, blue or white borders, with children in costume. Seven designs, all marked.

14. Sulman. Six small cards of children in costume. 8 cm x 5.5 cm.

15. Sulman. Set of six cards of children playing, on gilt ground.

16. Sulman. Seven cards, scenes with birds and animals, white border.

17. Sulman. Three larger cards, single children with verse in vignette, flowers or leaves in background. 12.5 cm x 9.3 cm.

18. Sulman. Two cards, one a snowman, one children by Christmas tree, from a set of four registered at Stationers' Hall, designed by C Eade, 31-8-1871. (Copy of registration appended). 7.5 cm x 11 cm.

19. Sulman. Three cards, holly and mistletoe designs on gilt border, with children in vignette. 7.5 cm x 11 cm.

20. Sulman. Four cards, three with children outdoors, and one of a child in bed with toys. 7 cm x 10 cm.

21. Four cards with single children, scalloped borders (one on Meek paper).

22. Nine cards, embossed printing in red, black and yellow, showing six designs and varied captions, family scenes.

23. Five cards, children at play in snow, two with embossed scalloped borders.

24. Five cards, with three designs of winter scenes, embossed scalloped borders.

25/26. Eighteen similar cards, with eight designs showing varied greetings and frosting.

27/28. Eighteen similar cards, with nine designs showing varied greetings and frosting.

29/32. Thirty-two similar cards, with twenty designs showing varied greetings and frosting.

33. Eight similar cards, six designs, showing children with parents or grandparents.

34. Five similar cards, children with mother or dolls.

## VOLUME 6:
## 2ND VOLUME, CHILDREN'S CARDS, ATTRIBUTED TO KRONHEIM, J MANSELL, DEAN & SIMILAR. EARLY 1870's UNLESS OTHERWISE STATED

1/5. Kronheim? Twenty cards, Baxter process, with family Christmas scenes, gilt line border and appropriate verse in panel. c1870. 12.5 cm x 9.3 cm.

6/7. Kronheim? Seven similar cards, with verse on reverse.

8. J Mansell. Six cards, small girls in snow, two designs, showing varied greetings.

9. J Mansell. Two similar - girl and boy riding on turkey.

10. J Mansell. Four cards, outdoor scenes.

11. J Mansell. Ten cards with girls and children, indoor and outdoor scenes.

12/13. J Mansell. Eight cards with children's outdoor games, on fancy mounts with holly or patterned border. Five designs. 10.7 cm x 7.4 cm.

14. J Mansell. Five cards, with red and blue border, children with animals or birds.

15. J Mansell. Four cards, a set of Christmas scenes with children.

16. J Mansell. Six similar cards with various borders of blue, gilt, or white.

17. J Mansell. Five cards, four designs of children playing, with fancy corners in red and brown.

18. J Mansell. Four cards, three designs of children with flowers on cream ground, embossed borders, c1875. 11.2 cm x 7 cm.

19. J Mansell? Three similar, with family party scenes. c1875.

20. J Mansell. Six cards, five designs, embossed scalloped borders, winter scenes. 7 cm x 10 cm.

21. J Mansell? Four cards, embossed scalloped borders, winter scenes.

22. J Mansell. Two small cards, plain edge with red line, featuring Father Christmas and a turkey. 6 cm x 5.5 cm.

23. J Mansell. Four cards, single children with birds or animals, on gilt or black ground. c1875. 7.3 cm x 10.5 cm.

24. J Mansell. One card, girl in red cloak and hood, with verse, and border of Greek key pattern in gold on black. 8.9 cm x 13.5 cm.

25. J Mansell. Four similar size cards, girls in winter or summer scenes, with Greek key border in gold or black, or blue cross on gold. c1875.

26/28. Dean. Twenty-three cards, embossed scalloped edges, children and families in Christmas scenes, with verse or captions at top and bottom. (Nineteen designs).

29. Dean? Eight similar, seven designs with simple greetings.

30. Dean. Five cards, scalloped edges, children and robins, four with verses in vignettes.

31. Dean. Seven various cards, six designs with ladies and children in vignettes, encircled by flower or berry decoration.

32. Dean. Four cards, three designs of children in Christmas or outdoor scene with swan sledge, embossed scalloped border. 8.4 cm x 11.5 cm.

33. Two covers from "The Circle of the Year", Almanack 1876, with one similar card, designs from the set in no. 32.

34. Dean. Two cards, with cherubs in blue print on gold ground, one with music scroll, (the other trimmed). c1875.

35. Dean. Three cards, printed in sepia on gilt ground, one a girl's head and two with children at party and play. c1875.

36. Dean. Two cards, winsome children in scanty garb, poor design, probably valentines. 7.8 cm x 11.8 cm.

37. Dean? Six cards, two designs of girls in vignettes with holly, four of decorative initial letters with cherubs or girls. c1875.

38. Dean? Eight cards, scalloped borders, children in winter scenes or Georgian dress. c1875.

39. Dean? Seven cards, scalloped borders, six designs of family or country scenes. c1875.

40. Dean? Five similar cards, winter scenes. c1875.

41. Dean? One card with two young people in flower surround. c1875.

## VOLUME 7:
## EARLY SCENES

**These small cards, published around 1870, reflect the traditional view of life at Christmas time, with children feeding robins, parents gathering winter fuel and holly, skating, snowballs, and church going, though the religious theme does not predominate. Examples from Sulman, Dean, Mansell and Canton are shown here, with others not yet attributed, and are dated in the early 1870's. They are mostly about 7 cm x 10 cm, with an occasional larger or smaller set, for which measurements are given.**

1. Two elaborate cards with vignettes of winter scenes and berry surrounds, gilt ground, geometric coloured borders. 6.6 cm x 11.6 cm.

2. One card, Red Riding Hood in vignette, surrounded by holly and ivy border on gilt. 7.7 cm x 12.3 cm.

3. Three cards, holly borders enclosing family scenes (one larger with gilt ground).

4. Six similar cards, two designs, three with gilt borders, three plain.

5. Nine cards, coloured "scraps" on monochrome backgrounds with four different designs.

6. Eight smaller cards five designs of winter scenes and robins. Four have plain edges, four are scalloped, all with red line border. 9.5 cm x 5.7 cm.

7. Six similar cards, with "scraps" on monochrome backgrounds.

8. J Mansell. Five cards of one design of mother and children used in different ways.

9. J Mansell. Five cards, winter scenes, with pink borders. 7.5 cm x 11.4 cm.

10. Canton. Three cards, plain red line border, different captions on same design of mother and children.

11. Canton. Seven similar cards, three designs, one reversed to show trade mark.

12. Canton. Six similar cards, three designs, woodland scenes.

13. Canton. Seven cards, four designs, outdoor scenes, three with gilt borders.

14. Canton. Seven cards, three designs, with church and house.

15. Canton. Four cards with vignettes of church or house. Two of these designs, in

gilt picture frame, were registered at Stationers' Hall on 30-8-1875, but name of artist was not given.

16. Canton. Five cards, two designs, winter scenes bordered by wreath of holly, mistletoe, and flowers. Four are on black grounds. 11.8 cm x 8.4 cm.

17. Canton. Two cards, one design, with monochrome picture in different shades.

18. Sulman. Six cards, winter scenes, with embossed scalloped borders.

19. Sulman. Three cards with serrated edge, blue scroll pattern round scene with robin.

20. Dean. Three cards, two of winter scenes, one of unusual summer boating scenes, blue and red border.

21. Six cards, four designs, with winter scenes on blue ground. 7 cm x 11 cm.

22. Three cards, two designs, winter scenes in arch or semicircle, two having applied coloured scraps. 7.4 cm x 11.2 cm.

23. Six cards, four designs, winter scenes with wide grey border. 7 cm x 11 cm.

24. Three similar cards, two standard size with vignette views, one larger with mauve border.

25. Four cards, set of four designs, winter scenes with gilt fancy border and captions worked in brown branches.

26. Three cards, country scenes, with various gilt borders.

27. Five miscellaneous cards, winter scenes.

28. Three miscellaneous cards, with wreaths of holly, flowers or branches.

## VOLUMES 8 & 9: ILLUMINATED CARDS

**The use of gold and silver on cards from the 1860's embellished designs based on mediaeval manuscripts, and spread to some elaborate flower designs, with decorated initial letters and the development of the robin and holly themes. Cards here include some from early lithographers, from Sulman, Canton and Dean, with a few from the perfumery firm of Rimmel. More can be seen in the volumes devoted to the cards of Marcus Ward and De La Rue, and some have been included in the Religious card section. Most of these were published in the early 1870's, and the usual size was about**

**12 cm x 7.5 cm. Measurements are given where size varies significantly from this.**

## VOLUME 8: EARLY LITHOGRAPHERS, SULMAN, CANTON, DEAN, RIMMEL, J MANSELL

1. Five smaller cards, holly and flower designs with coloured greetings, one card marked E Fuller & Co. Lith. Probably late 1860's.

2. Day & Son. Four cards, with cross and holly border around religious verse. late 1860's.

3. Three similar cards, unmarked, incorporating flowers.

4. Four similar cards.

5. Three cards with text and floral decoration. Late 1860's.

6. M Chatterton & Co. Finely illuminated card with angel in initial C, geometric decoration and flowers in vase. Late 1860's.

*The following cards are all early 1870's.*

7. Sulman. Seven cards, smaller than average, with intricate mosaic designs, two with figures. Two of these cards were registered at Stationers' Hall on 31-8-1871, and designed by Thos. Sulman (brother of publisher Ben?). Copy of original registration is appended.

8. Sulman. Set of four cards, vignettes with church, flowers or holly, and the ubiquitous robin. All registered at Stationers' Hall, 13-7-1871, designed by T Sulman. Copy of original registration is appended. (The fourth card was used by the Victorian Society, by permission of Laura Seddon, as their official Christmas Card for 1985).

9. Sulman. Set of four similar cards, registered at Stationers' Hall on 3-3-1873, probably by Tom Sulman, but the artist's name was not given.

10. Sulman. Three cards, varying geometric design, one with robin.

11/13. Sulman. Six large cards, geometric design in border surrounding religious verse. There are three different designs, each in two different colour versions, and four cards have coloured scraps attached at edge so that verse beneath may be read. 10 cm x 15.2 cm.

14. Sulman. Four nativity cards, three designs, with decorated corners and religious captions, one frosted. 12.8 cm x 9 cm.

15. Sulman. Four cards with angels on gilt grounds, and texts. 12.6 cm x 8.2 cm.

16. Sulman. Four cards, three designs, one frosted, one with angels and floral or holly background and scene.

17. Sulman. Four cards, Georgian style children with flower or holly backgrounds, greetings on scroll or boxes. 11 cm x 7 cm.

18. Sulman? Four cards, two with maidens on flowers or mistletoe, two with scroll and flower design.

19. Sulman. Five cards, holly or flowers round label with Christmas or New Year verse. 11.9 cm x 8.7 cm.

20. Sulman. Two cards, one a bird, one with sheep, in scene with flowers around, embossed scalloped edge.

21. Sulman? Four cards, each with Christmas verse and holly and flower wreath around.

22. Canton. Six cards of varying sizes with geometric designs in deep colours.

23. Canton. Five cards with stylised leaf borders enclosing Christmas or New Year greeting in verse.

24. Canton. Five cards with coloured stylised lacy borders enclosing greeting verse on gilt ground.

25. Canton. Three cards with holly scrolls, two with flowers in vases, enclosing greetings in verse. The latter were registered at Stationers' Hall on 3-12-1875, designed by Albert Henry Warren.

26. Dean. Four cards, with scenes or holly or flower designs and inset verses.

27. Dean. Four cards with variety of scroll, flower and birds' nest designs, one larger than average.

28. Rimmel. Six cards with stylised flower and scroll designs, two having 1871 date.

29. Rimmel? Three similar, two designs, one with holly. 12 cm x 8.5 cm.

30. J Mansell. Four cards, holly, flowers, and illuminated initial with Christmas and New Year verses.

31. J Mansell. Three cards, one with holly, one with wine and fruit, one with boars head, all having Christmas or New Year verses.

32. W F Meade. Three smaller cards, illuminated border round Christmas verse, two with robin scrap.

## VOLUME 9: ILLUMINATED CARDS FROM UNIDENTIFIED PUBLISHERS c1875

1. Six cards, five with sprays of holly or spring flowers on gilt ground, around Christmas verse on white. One similar on black ground.

2. Five cards with holly entwined with initial letters, coloured borders, Christmas or New Year verse on gilt, white or beige ground. Two designs.

3. Four cards with holly, mistletoe and flower designs on gilt, around Christmas verse.

4. Four similar cards.

5. Four cards, three designs, stylised scroll and holly patterns on blue, green or silver ground, enclosing Christmas or New Year verse.

6. Four cards, scenes with robins and stately home, in vignettes with holly or vine borders. 10.5 cm x 7 cm.

7. Six cards, one trimmed, with holly, flowers, robins and scrolls in white border with red lines. 10 cm x 7 cm.

8. Four cards, with red, blue, gold and grey scroll designs.

9. Three cards, one frosted, two designs of holly with inset Christmas verse.

10. Four miscellaneous cards, fancy borders, inset verse.

11. Four miscellaneous cards, two smaller with holly designs, two average size with applied scraps over verse.

12. Two cards, in Gothic style with heraldic designs, one with angel and children, one with King figure and lion. 7 cm x 11 cm.

13. Three cards with arabesque and geometric designs, one smaller having "Emmanuel" on stylised cross.

14. Three cards with flowers or vines, one being larger (13 cm x 9 cm) with illuminated N and New Year greeting.

15. Six smaller cards with scrolls and arabesque designs. 6.5 cm x 9.5 cm.

16. Five cards, with flower sprays or holly, one with New Year verse. 6.5 cm x 10 cm.

17. Six miscellaneous cards, with birds, holly and stylised flower designs.

18. Three small cards with robin and stylised borders, two with Christmas verse. 9.8 cm x 5.9 cm.

19. Three cards, with holly and forget-me-not spray, simple verse, gilt border.

20. Four cards, illuminated initial, and various holly, ivy and flower designs, one with robin.

21. Two cards, one with children and scroll design, one with old man and verse.

22. Eight smaller cards with scroll patterns, four designs, seven having applied scraps over verses. 6.5 cm x 9.6 cm.

23. Four similar, with scraps, two larger cards with the same design.

24. Four similar, with scraps over New Year greeting verse. 8.4 cm x 11.8 cm.

25. Two distinctive cards with stylised colourful border around Christmas verse. Date unknown? 9 cm x 13 cm.

26. Two cards, one with illuminated border enclosing verse, and one small card with holly.

27. Four cards, all with the same interlaced design in different colours, enclosing greeting.

28. Six miscellaneous cards with various border designs.

## VOLUME 10: EARLY HUMOUR 1850's-1875

**Much early Victorian humour was based on the personified Christmas dinner and the antics of humanised birds and animals, with turkey and Christmas pudding revenging their annual ordeal on human consumers. Clowns contributed their frolics to the scene, and tumbles on the ice and snow battles provided fun and games for all. These early cards were usually small, increasing in size over the years, and had simple captions or brief verses. A few appear on black grounds. Some publishers have been included here. Except where otherwise stated, the cards are early 1870's.**

1/3. J S & Co. (not identified by Buday or LS). Twenty-one sepia greeting cards and cartes de visite, designed by Thomas Onwhyn, in 1850s, including Christmas scenes (two coloured), humorous sea side scenes with great play made over crinolines. One card is labelled "Rock", and one "Simmons & Co". 6.2 cm x 9.4 cm.

4. Three cards with robin and winter scenes and decorated borders in red or gold. One is stamped "Osborne, New St". 6 cm x 9.3 cm.

5. Set of four cards embossed in gilt and green, with small comic drawings of Christmas pudding. 5.3 cm x 8.9 cm.

6. Five cards, embossed serrated edges, Christmas scenes with clowns, prize bull, Father Christmas etc. Two have the Sulman mount. 6 cm x 9.2 cm.

7. Two cards, one of clown on embossed mount, one of pudding on bottle legs. 9 cm x 6 cm.

8/9. Eight cards, five designs, embossed scalloped edge, comic scenes with pudding, bottle, ghost, fox, skating. 7 cm x 10 cm.

10. Four cards, three plain edge 5.8 cm x 9.2 cm of sailor and stout gentlemen, and one with embossed edge showing artist sketching pudding. 10.5 cm x 6.2 cm.

11. Four cards, humorous winter scenes of robin, children, Jack Frost, and cracker, on plain card with coloured line edge. 11.5 cm x 7.8 cm.

12. Three similar cards with silhouette figures in vignette on coloured ground. 11.8 cm x 8.2 cm.

13/14. Canton? Eight cards, seven designs of comic figures in party, outdoor and kitchen situations, one reversed to show the sender's home made verse. 7.5 cm x 11 cm.

15. Canton? Eight similar smaller cards, seven designs, two embossed on cream or brown ground with gilt decorations.

16. Canton? One similar card on black ground with grained border. 6.7 cm x 10.2 cm.

17. J Mansell. Seven cards, six designs, personified Christmas dinner, with patterned coloured pink or blue borders and humorous captions and greetings. 10.2 cm x 6.8 cm.

18. J Mansell. Six cards of varying sizes, four designs, with clowns, monkeys, puddings. Two have gilt embossed borders, the others blue.

19. J Mansell? Set of four cards with comic birds and animals, in vignettes encircled by holly and mistletoe in vases on gilt. 11.2 cm x 7.6 cm.

20. J Mansell? Three cards with clowns and personified Christmas dinner, two with blue border, one scalloped edge. 11.6 cm x 7.8 cm.

21. J Mansell? Seven similar small cards. 9 cm x 6.3 cm.

22/23. J Mansell. Eight cards, seven designs on gilt grounds of clowns, Father

Christmas, puddings, turkeys and cherubs,
including the New Year on a train.
11.2 cm x 7.6 cm.

24. J Mansell. Five similar (two are
marked) with comic figures in bygone
dress. 11.6 cm x 8 cm.

25. Rimmel. Five cards, comic figures,
clowns, puddings etc., on gilt ground, with
verse. 11.2 cm x 7.6 cm.

26. Dean. Seven cards, embossed scalloped
edges, with clowns, pudding, frogs etc.,
and verse top and bottom. 6.1 cm x 9.2 cm.

27. Dean. Eight similar larger cards, some
repeating designs from no. 26.
7 cm x 9.8 cm.

28. Dean. Five cards, including set of four
with foxes, Christmas dinner etc., and
single smaller card of man chasing goose,
all with Christmas verses. 11.5 cm x 8 cm.

29. Rimmel. Six cards with embossed
scalloped edge, five designs, including set
of four animal designs with similar card of
boy playing concertina. 7.1 cm x 11 cm.

30. Three cards, birds, animals and people
in outdoor scenes on gilt ground.
7 cm x 10.8 cm.

31. Seven cards, with personified
Christmas dinner etc. 9.5 cm x 7 cm.

32. Four similar, with gold line border.
10.8 cm x 7.3 cm.

33. Four cards, three designs, black and red
festive figures on gold or silver.
9.5 cm x 6.8 cm.

34. Rimmel. Four cards, Envie, Fear, Grief
and Joye, mediaeval figures on gold
ground with verse. 6.8 cm x 9.8 cm.

35. Three cards, pen and ink grotesque
figures in black and white, one card with
gilt border. Signed, but monogram
untraced. 13.2 cm x 9.3 cm.

36. Two cards with gilt border, line
drawings in red and blue. 11.8 cm x 9 cm.

37. Seven cards on fancy gilt grounds,
featuring nursery rhyme figures with
verses, Rob Roy, jester, knight and squire.
Two dated 1871, 1873 by the senders.
(approx) 10 cm x 7 cm.

38. Three cards, two designs with rows of
small mediaeval figures spelling "Happy
Christmas" and "Happy New Year". (Two
designs). 11.5 cm x 7 cm.

# EARLY CARDS ON LACE AND FANCY MOUNTS, INCLUDING NOVELTIES, MECHANICAL CARDS, FANS ETC, MAINLY EARLY 1870s

*Section 2*

Lace paper, made for earlier valentines, was also used for other greeting cards, although large examples are hard to find, and most of the earlier cards are on smaller mounts, featuring paper lace with gilt and silver, scraps and greetings, often with elaborate embossing. Layers mounted on paper "springs" converted the flat card, which fitted into an envelope for posting, into a three-dimensional scene. There were many intricate mechanical cards, including paper fans and complicated flower arrangements. This section includes cards which so far have not been attributed to a definite publisher, but further study and comparison with known products might place some of them. Similar cards may be seen in the volumes of the publishers Canton, Sulman, Goodall, J Mansell and Marcus Ward. A few cards in this section are on mounts marked with the names of some publishers of earlier valentines, including Windsor, Wood, Mullord and Rimmel.

13.3

## VOLUME 11:
## CARDS WITH HOLLY, MISTLETOE, ROBINS, TRADITIONAL WINTER SCENES

**All are dated in the early 1870's, unless otherwise stated.**

1. Five cards, embossed borders, one gilt, with holly, mistletoe and robin scraps. 10.1 cm x 7 cm.

2. Wood. Five cards with lace borders. 8.9 cm x 6 cm.

3. Five cards on elaborate lace and gilt mounts, four with holly berry greeting in red, one with forget-me-nots. 9.5 cm x 6 cm up to 12.5 cm x 8.2 cm.

4. Two cards, Mr & Mrs Dicky Bird, she wearing cloth cape and lace bonnet, on a holly branch, with hand written greetings for Christmas and New Year. 11.6 cm x 7.7 cm.

5. Five cards, on lace mounts with gilt or silver, and scraps, three of these being the same, used differently. Sizes up to 10 cm x 7 cm.

6. Nine cards, on fancy gilded mounts with robin scraps. Sizes up to 7.5 cm x 10.5 cm.

7. Six similar cards. Sizes up to 12 cm x 8 cm.

8. Six cards on white or gold lace fancy mounts with scraps, three with opening doors. Sizes up to 7 cm x 10.5 cm.

9. Five cards on white lace mounts with robin scraps and scenes, two opening. Sizes up to 8 cm x 11 cm.

10. Ten cards on embossed mounts with gilt or silver, three with verses, robin scraps and scenes. Sizes up to 10.3 cm x 7.1 cm.

11. Eight cards on embossed and coloured mounts with robin scraps. Sizes up to 10 cm x 7 cm.

12. Five cards, various mounts, with robin scraps, showing use of same scrap in different ways. 9 cm x 6 cm to 8.7 cm x 13.2 cm.

13. Six cards with embossed borders and robin scraps. Sizes up to 10.3 cm x 7 cm.

14. Nine cards on elaborate lace paper mounts, with robin and scenic scraps. 8 cm x 4.5 cm to 9 cm x 6 cm.

15. Six cards with robin scraps, three having silver lace paper. Sizes up to 8.2 cm x 12.8 cm.

16. Ten small cards, with serrated borders and robin scraps. Sizes up to 9.5 cm x 6 cm.

17. Nine cards on various mounts with scraps, five with verses. 4.5 cm x 8.3 cm to 7.5 cm x 11 cm.

18. Six cards with scraps on paper springs, and gilt and lace mounts. Approximately 11 cm x 7.5 cm.

19. Seven cards, three with a circular robin scrap on embossed mount, three with holly and robin scraps on bordered embossed mount, and one on gilt lace with similar scrap. Sizes up to 9.2 cm x 6.5 cm.

20. Three cards, holly and robin on pale blue mount with gilt and embossed border. 10 cm x 7 cm.

21. Seven cards, scraps and prints of winter scenes and robins on various mounts. Sizes up to 6 cm x 9.5 cm.

22. Four cards, bird scraps on fancy mounts. Sizes up to 8.5 cm x 11.5 cm.

23. Three cards, scraps of turkeys, on gilt and embossed mounts. 10 cm x 6.5 cm.

24. Three cards, scraps of scenes on "springs", and gilt or silverlace. 13.5 cm x 9.7 cm.

25. Five cards, scraps of scenes on gilt and embossed mounts. Sizes up to 11 cm x 8 cm.

26. Five cards, scenes on lace mounts, two with gilt. Sizes up to 12 cm x 8 cm.

27. Four cards, with gilt borders, and lift-up scraps mounted on scenes. 8 cm x 12 cm.

28. Six cards, scenes on various mounts with gilt. 6.2 cm x 9.2 cm to 8.8 cm x 13.2 cm.

29. Four cards, winter scenes on "springs", on various mounts. 8.8 cm x 13.2 cm.

30. Four cards, party and snow scenes in oval vignettes with floral or holly surround, two gilded. 7.7 cm x 11.5 cm.

31. Nine cards, various scraps, on mounts with embossed or lace borders. Sizes up to 10.2 cm x 7 cm.

32. Seven cards, scenes with lift up scraps including windmills and houses, on various mounts. Unfortunately, with time, the small figures in the scraps often lost their heads. 9 cm x 6 cm to 8 cm x 12 cm.

33. Five similar cards. Sizes up to 8.5 cm x 12.5 cm.

34. Nine cards, with oval prints, six on mounts with gilt border, 5.5 cm x 9.5 cm, and three with serrated edge and blue pattern, 6.2 cm x 9.1 cm.

35. Seven cards, scenes on mounts with embossed or lace border. Sizes up to 6.5 cm x 9.4 cm.

36. Four cards, scraps of children on two tone winter scene with embossed border. 10.5 cm x 7 cm.

37. Eight cards, rectangular scenes with scalloped embossed border. 9.5 cm x 6.5 cm.

38. Four similar with robin scenes (three designs). 9.5 cm x 6.5 cm.

39. Eight similar with various scraps. 9.5 cm x 6.5 cm.

40. Three similar. 9.5 cm x 6.5 cm.

41. Three cards, scenes of animals in snow, lace borders. 9 cm x 6.5 cm.

42. Four cards, children or ladies in vignettes surrounded by holly or ivy and robins, three with scalloped border, one with lace. Sizes up to 11 cm x 14.7 cm.

43. Six cards, various scenes, three with holly and robins, three with flowers. 5.6 cm x 9.2 cm to 8.1 cm x 11.2 cm.

44. Six cards with scenes and people, on gilded mounts. Sizes up to 12 cm x 8.4 cm.

## VOLUME 12:
## CARDS WITH CHILDREN, WINTER SCENES AND FATHER CHRISTMAS

**These cards of the early 1870's are similar in form to those in Volume 11. They include a few with Father Christmas, not always in the traditional red robe, but seen in green, brown, and even white, with holly wreath, perhaps linking him with the Lord of Misrule. The children as before, are mostly well-fed and well-clothed, but sometimes a less fortunate one is out in the snow. An occasional summer scene appears, with floral decoration.**

1. Nine cards, mounts embossed or paper lace, some with gilt and silver. All have Father Christmas scraps in red, green or brown costume. Sizes up to 7.7 cm x 11.2 cm.

2. Five cards, children with dress of real cloth, on various mounts. Sizes up to 9 cm x 12 cm.

3. Four cards, on lace and silvered mounts, with scraps of a single child. 7 cm x 9.5 cm.

4. Seven cards, winter and summer scenes with children, on various mounts. Sizes up to 7 cm x 10.5 cm.

5. Seven cards, elaborate gilt or silver borders, prints of children in winter or summer scenes. Sizes up to 8 cm x 12 cm.

6. Five similar cards, prints or scraps, one marked Mullord. Sizes up to 8 cm x 12 cm.

7. Six similar cards. Sizes up to 8.5 cm x 13.5 cm.

8. Six similar cards. Sizes up to 8 cm x 12 cm.

9. Seven cards, with gilded borders and prints or scraps. Sizes up to 7.3 cm x 11 cm.

10. Six cards of a set, scalloped border and gilt double line, with pictures of children in all seasons. 7.3 cm x 10.7 cm.

11. Ten smaller cards on a variety of lace edged, scalloped, or gilded mounts with scraps and prints of children. Sizes up to 9.5 cm x 6.5 cm.

12. Six cards on coloured mounts, with scraps and prints of children. Sizes up to 8.5 cm x 12.5 cm.

13. Seven similar (two on white embossed mounts). Sizes up to 7.7 cm x 12 cm.

14. Nine small cards, scraps and prints on coloured and gilded mounts. 6 cm x 8.5 cm.

15. Six cards, with scraps, on white embossed mounts. One is marked S Marks & Sons, with lace edge, size 4.8 cm x 8 cm, one is marked Windsor, two Mullord, one Dickinson. Sizes up to 7 cm x 10 cm.

16. Eight cards, scraps and prints of children on lace edge embossed mounts (one coloured ground). Sizes up to 7.5 cm x 11.3 cm.

17. Eight cards on various coloured and embossed mounts, with scraps and prints, one with amusing reversible scrap of man's head. (cf. Rex Whistler "Oho"). Sizes up to 11.3 cm x 7.7 cm.

18. Four cards, on coloured embossed mounts, one with lift-up flap showing scene on "springs", and one of "The Boy who lost his Christmas pudding through being naughty". 8 cm x 13 cm.

19. Six cards of a set, with white lace border (three with border damaged) with oval prints of girls and a boy in winter. J Mansell? 6.7 cm x 10 cm.

20. Six cards of a set, scalloped border, four with coloured line around oval prints of children., 6.2 cm x 9.4 cm.

21. Four cards, with scraps of girl, or mother and child, with holly, scalloped borders, one more elaborate. 7 cm x 10 cm.

22. Seven cards, with various embossed borders, and scraps and prints of children. One has a learned fox reading a book. Sizes up to 7.5 cm x 11 cm.

23. Nine cards, scraps and prints of children, on various white embossed cards. Sizes up to 6.5 cm x 9.2 cm.

24. Nine cards, embossed borders, scraps of children, grotesque small figures, Father Christmas and a martial Cock. Sizes up to 6 cm x 9 cm.

25. Twelve similar on various mounts, including a comic dog and stork. Sizes up to 6 cm x 9 cm.

26. Six miscellaneous cards on coloured fancy mounts, two having verses. 6.2 cm x 10 cm to 9 cm x 16 cm.

27. Five cards of children, three designs, three on mounts with gilded borders, two with wide gilt bands making crosses at the corners. One scene of a girl feeding a dog is shown in three versions. 7.5 cm x 10.5 cm.

28. Four cards on elaborate lace and gilded mounts, as used for valentines, but adapted for Christmas and New Year with suitable scraps. 14 cm x 9 cm.

29. Six pieces, as found in Victorian albums, four being ovals or scraps, and two lace pieces with prints of girl in winter scene.

30. Four cards on coloured mounts. Two are marked W F M (W F Meade) and two have gilt border and scraps, one with valentine caption "To my Love". Sizes up to 12.5 cm x 9.6 cm.

31. Nine cards of an amusing set, showing French style children in festive scenes, each with applied matching scrap which lifts to show space for message. 10.9 cm x 7 cm. Marked F & S, not traced.

32. Six pieces of a sheaf of oval cards with Christmas scenes. Note the "Christmas Aged King" dressed in white. Found in a scrapbook, but would have been issued tied like a fan. 7 cm x 13 cm.

33. Six pieces of a similar sheaf "Little Miss Dollikins". 7 cm x 13 cm.

# VOLUME 13: PERFUMED SACHETS AND CARDS, SOME WITH WOVEN GREETINGS

**Elaborate padded perfumed cards were made by many earlier manufacturers for valentines, and these were later extended to Christmas, New Year, and birthday cards, many being adorned with woven silk motifs made by Stevens & Bollans; these motifs also appeared on valentine style lace cards. Eugene Rimmel, the well known perfumer, made many of those sachets, but his products cannot always be traced as the small gold discs with their name were easily lost, along with the original perfume. The sachets were sometimes in envelope form, perhaps enclosing a card, or in two, three, or four sheet folders. Birthday greetings appear here. The cards are dated about 1875.**

1. Valentine style card with woven winter scene and Happy New Year, on an elaborate lace paper folder marked "Wood", with silver lace and flower scraps. 12.2 cm x 18.5 cm.

2. Six cards, all with woven greetings, scraps and pictures, three in sachet form. 5 cm x 7 cm up to 7.2 cm x 11 cm.

3. Three sachets. The first is an elaborate four fold on silk and embossed mounts with silver, the eight sides showing pictures of angels, fairies, a cross, with flower scraps and prints. 38 cm x 13.5 cm opened. The other two have scrap crosses on "doors" opening to show cards with scraps and greetings on silk. 8 cm x 12.5 cm.

4. Four cards, including one folder and a similar single sachet with silk greeting or scraps, on Sulman mount. The other two have the same blue flower scrap, one being a sachet, and one a card with greeting in German. Sizes up to 9 cm x 12 cm.

5. Rimmel. Four sachets, three with silver decoration, one of these a folder, and one on white lace. Sizes up to 10 cm x 14 cm.

6. Four sachets, with silver lace and scraps, one opening to show the card inside. Sizes up to 9.5 cm x 14 cm.

7. Three sachets, with envelope opening to show cards, two having prints of sailing boat, the other with a flower motif. 9.5 cm x 13 cm.

8. Four sachets on elaborate mounts with scraps, three having a greeting printed on silk. Sizes up to 9.5 cm x 13 cm.

9. Four sachets, three with prints of children, one with verse "To my Father". Sizes up to 7.4 cm x 11 cm.

10. Six miscellaneous sachets, with flower scraps, robins, and angels. 9.5 cm x 7.2 cm to 8 cm x 12.3 cm.

11. Five sachets on lace, gilt and silver mounts, two opening to show cards and scraps. Sizes up to 8.3 cm x 12.5 cm.

12. Four sachets, on elaborate mounts with flower scraps and silk, one opening three-fold and one two-fold. 8 cm x 12 cm.

13. Four folding cards on silver lace mounts, two with "doors" opening to show scenes and scraps, one a three-fold sachet with tassels, and one a two-fold with elaborate rose scraps on green silk. Sizes up to 9 cm x 13.5 cm.

14. Three folding sachets, on lace and silver mounts, with flower scraps. Sizes up to 9 cm x 12.5 cm.

15. Two sachets with pleated ribbon borders, one single with floral prints on both sides, the other folding with two applied cards of children and two of flowers. 13.5 cm x 10 cm.

16. Five sachets, on various mounts. Sizes 7 cm x 10 cm to 10 cm x 16 cm.

## VOLUME 14:
## ELABORATE CARDS WITH FLOWERS AND GREENERY, INCLUDING SOME MECHANICAL DEVICES

**Flower scraps and prints were used in large quantities to embellish fancy cards, and many ingenious mechanical devices were employed. Although such cards were more appropriate for New Year greetings or Valentines, many appear as Christmas cards. The publishers of most of these cards have not yet been traced, but many are similar to Goodall, Canton, Sulman and Mansell cards. They are dated from late 1860's to about 1875, and all have flowers, with an occasional sprig of holly or evergreen.**

1. Two cards, with the same flower print in an elaborate embossed edge, one dated 1867, found in the envelope shown. The motif on this is similar to those on early Windsor or Sulman cards. 8 cm x 11.7 cm.

2. Four cards on elaborate gilded mounts, one with pull out paper "cage" revealing picture of girl, one with an envelope and pull out flowers, and two with ribbon which pulls to reveal further pictures. Sizes up to 8.8 cm x 13.4 cm.

3. Four similar cards with various mechanical devices, one a pull out fan. Sizes up to 8.8 cm x 13.4 cm.

4. Six similar cards, one a bouquet marked E B (Bollans), two with rotating pictures, the others with tabs which reveal more pictures. Sizes up to 8.2 cm x 11.4 cm.

5. Four similar cards, with large floral scraps, lifting to show pictures or greetings. Sizes up to 8.2 cm x 12 cm.

6. Seven similar smaller cards. Sizes up to 6.5 cm x 10 cm.

7. Four cards on gilded or silvered mounts, with opening flaps. Sizes 6.5 cm x 10 cm to 8 cm x 12 cm.

8. Three cards with fancy gilded borders, one with lifting bird and flower scrap, one with flower fairies in a wheatfield with an inappropriate Merry Christmas greeting, and one with scraps of flowers and shells on "springs". 6.4 cm x 11 cm.

9. Seven cards, with oval flower motifs on embossed and gilded mounts, some lifting to show greetings. 6 cm x 9.4 cm to 7.5 cm x 10.8 cm.

10. Five cards on white and coloured mounts, with flower scraps, three having holly and robin scraps as well as flowers. Sizes up to 11 cm x 7.5 cm.

11. Four cards, with lifting flower scraps on gilded mounts. Sizes up to 7.8 cm x 11.5 cm.

12. Four similar, one with forget-me-nots and holly. Sizes up to 8.8 cm x 13.4 cm.

13. Seven cards on various mounts, with scraps in the form of flower wreaths over greetings. Sizes up to 8 cm x 12 cm.

14. Four decorative motifs from cards, as found in scrap books, consisting of gilt or silver lace with floral scraps. The compilers of Victorian albums often removed those from their original mounts to make decorated pages. 7.8 cm x 13 cm.

15. Four similar. 7.8 cm x 13 cm.

16. Six similar cards, including two with cover only. Sizes up to 7.6 cm x 12 cm.

17. Four cards, with gilt borders. Two have a small envelope holding a card of greeting, one has a movable flap over verse, and one has a lady holding a movable scroll. Sizes up to 12 cm x 7.7 cm.

18. Seven lacy cards with flower scraps and wreaths. 7.2 cm x 5 cm up to 10.5 cm x 7.5 cm.

19. Eight cards on various mounts, with flower, leaf or shell scraps. 6.7 cm x 7.5 cm up to 7.2 cm x 10 cm.

20. Two cards on plain gilt edge mounts, one with elaborate lifting flower, the other with bird and flower bouquet. Sizes up to 12 cm x 7 cm.

21. Six cards, one with 1872 motif surrounded by cherubs and floral wreath, the others having cards mounted on elaborate gilt and silver edge mounts, these being late 1870's. 9.7 cm x 6.2 cm to 10 cm x 13.8 cm.

22. Five cards, with flower scraps and greetings on mounts with decorative gilt or silver borders. 6.5 cm x 10 cm up to 12 cm x 8.7 cm.

23. Six cards, varied borders, and flower prints. Sizes up to 8 cm x 12 cm.

24. Nine cards on a variety of mounts, five coloured, eight having flower scraps and one a flower and leaf collage, this perhaps late 1860's. 5.3 cm x 8.3 cm to 7.8 cm x 12 cm.

25. Eight cards, winged cherubs and flowers, two with scraps, six printed. 6 cm x 9 cm to 8.1 cm x 11.1 cm.

26. Nine shaped and cut out greetings, eight with flowers, one with holly, two perhaps by J Mansell. Sizes up to 9.5 cm x 6.3 cm.

27. Mullord. Three cards on white mounts, one with embossed border and flower scrap, 7.5 cm x 11.3 cm, and two with serrated embossed border and flower wreaths. 7.5 cm x 5.5 cm.

28. Eight cards with gilded borders, four having illuminated style designs with verses, and four with various flower motifs and greetings. Sizes up to 10.1 cm x 6.5 cm.

29. Six miscellaneous cards with prints, scraps, or illuminated greetings. 9.5 cm x 5 cm to 8.8 cm x 13.4 cm.

30. Seven cards, flower scraps on embossed mounts, two on beige grounds. 6 cm x 9.6 cm to 11.6 cm x 7.7 cm.

31. Eight cards, lace or scalloped edges, with floral motifs and greetings (one birthday). Sizes up to 7 cm x 11 cm.

32. Six similar cards, two with scraps, and two with oval motifs and floral scraps. Sizes up to 9.6 cm x 6.7 cm.

33. Ten cards, eight with floral scraps, two with printed motifs. Sizes up to 10.2 cm x 7 cm.

34. Ten cards, three with floral scraps and scalloped edges, three small with lace edges and scraps, and four similar to visiting cards, with scalloped edges and printed flower motifs. 5.7 cm x 8 cm to 6.5 cm x 9.5 cm.

## VOLUME 15:
## MECHANICAL, OPENING AND MOVABLE CARDS, WITH SOME IN VALENTINE STYLE

**These cards show many interesting mechanical devices, including paper cages, layers with "springs" making three-dimensional scenes of nativities and parties, discs rotating to change pictures, and opening "doors". Valentines were adapted for use at Christmas by the addition of suitable scraps and greetings to the**

lace paper mounts of earlier days. A few of these cards have known publishers, and more can be seen in the publishers' files. They are dated in the early 1870's except where otherwise stated.

1. Two cards
a) A paper cage, opening to show a greeting. 10.8 cm x 7.3 cm.
b) A Christmas Toy Box in the form of an envelope mounted on a holly ground, opening to show a selection of cut out paper toys. 11.2 cm x 7.8 cm.

2. Two cards
a) A Christmas box, which opens to form a box in which another card can be seen. 7.5 cm x 10 cm.
b) Another, with gilt borders opened out to show a winter scene. 7 cm x 9 cm.

3. Three cards
a) A card with floral scrap and small book, which opens to show a Christmas tree on springs on a gilded mount, with angel background, and table beneath.
b) A Christmas tree lifting to show party scene.
c) A floral scrap on silvered mount with party and children scenes.
Sizes up to 8 cm x 12 cm.

4. Three cards on embossed or lace edged mounts.
a) Ye Christmas Pantomime, with a scene outside the theatre opening to show a three-dimensional harlequinade and fairy scene on springs.
b) A Victorian house with waits and children outside. A tab, when pulled, reveals people at the windows.
c) An Elizabethan house, opening to show the party inside.
Sizes up to 12.5 cm x 9 cm.

5. Two cards
a) A winter scene with coach.
b) Father Christmas arriving outside a house on a flap which opens to show him with the children indoors. Sulman? 11.5 cm x 7.7. cm.

6. Three cards
a) A curious mixture of Thomas Stevens Chinese style card, lifting to show rows of summer children on springs, with an Eskimo scene at the back, probably Sulman.
b) A card with a flower scrap, opening to show children and lovers in a summer scene, with a holly scrap (perhaps an adapted valentine).
c) A very elaborate card with a heart and dove, which can be manipulated to make a three dimensional scene of a church with tower, a couple, and angels etc.
Sizes up to 12.6 cm x 8.8 cm.

7. An elaborate card, with a picture of children and flowers on the front, opening to make a three dimensional party scene with six figures. The greeting is "Bonheur et Prosperité". A single card is included from the same series as the cover. 11.5 cm x 8 cm.

8. Five humorous cards, on the same lace and gilded mount, with greetings in cursive writing (as in early Dobbs valentines).
a) "Home Brewed" with barrels.
b) A Christmas Hamper, with kittens.
c) The Bill File.
d) A Bundle of Sticks.
e) Winter Quarters. Probably 1860's.
Sizes 7.5 cm x 11 cm.

9. Five similar cards on various mounts. a) A dog with a blue bow.
b) The Christmas Joint.
c) A Cosy Party (with kittens).
d) A Pair of Paris Kids (gloves).
e) A willow pattern plate with knife and fork. Sizes up to 7.8 cm x 12 cm.

10. Six cards on fancy lace, gilt and silver mounts (one coloured blue) with various lifting scraps - shell, robin on holly, children with corn etc.
Sizes up to 9.5 cm x 13 cm.

11. Two cards with opening doors.
a) A lifting panel reveals a device for rotating scenes.
b) A wedding scene and floral scraps on springs, signed E B - probably E Bollans. 7.7 cm x 11 cm.

12. Three cards on gilded mounts, with tab to pull a panel which moves four pictures seen through oval windows, and changes them to greetings. 7.7 cm x 11.2 cm. (These cards might have Sulman mounts with J Mansell prints).

13. Four cards with scraps and prints of children and Christmas scenes. One is a six-page folder, the others have lifting flaps. Sizes 6 cm x 9 cm to 7.5 cm x 10 cm.

14. Five cards, two on gilded mounts opening to show further scenes, and three lace edged cards showing the same scenes. Sizes up to 7.5 cm x 11 cm.

15. Three cards, opening to show three dimensional nativity scenes. 10.5 cm x 10.5 cm and 7.7 cm x 11.7 cm.

16. Two cards
a) A gilded bell, opening to show three dimensional scene of church and churchgoers (German design). 16 cm x 11 cm.
b) A table, unfolding to stand up and show bouquet of flowers, with greeting in small envelope. 12.5 cm x 10 cm.

17. Three cards
a) A gilded chest with cherubs, opening to show eight small pictures of "The Language of Flowers". 8.7 cm x 8 cm.
b) A ladies dressing chest, opening to show labelled drawers, which in turn open to reveal desirable virtues - e g Perfumery -

15.8

"The richest perfumes are virtue and love". 7.7 cm x 12 cm. (This was probably a valentine but has a Happy New Year label affixed).
c) A theatre stage, with curtain moving to show children. 8 cm x 12 cm.

18. S Hildesheimer - five cards.
a) A set of four embossed cards showing German style goblets, glass tankard, helmet etc (one with a German greeting). Series 259.
b) A card with one of the above on the front, opening to reveal a delightful bouquet of fabric and scrap flowers and leaves. Series 5712. 12 cm x 8.3 cm.

19. Four cards with opening doors.
a) Robin and children pictures on blue and gilt mount. 9.7 cm x 6 cm.
b) Doors with ivy and vine decoration, opening to show a child in red cloak gathering holly, on gilt edged mount. 7.7 cm x 11 cm.
c/d) Two cards with illuminated crosses on doors, with robins inside. 7.7 cm x 11 cm.

20. Two similar cards with opening doors, one with a father at cottage door and family within, the other with a church door, and child and congregation inside. 7.7 cm x 11.5 cm.

21. Four similar cards with a casket on holly ground, with various greetings and prints inside, two marked Canton. 11 cm x 7.5 cm.

22. Four cards, late 1860's, on lace mounts, one marked Mossman, and one a lace envelope holding an elaborate card, marked Wood. Sizes up to 7.5 cm x 10 cm.

23. Four cards, late 1860's, on embossed mounts, one a folder with coloured scrap, and two with Christmas greeting on silk. Sizes up to 7 cm x 10 cm.

24. A valentine style folding card with gilt lace paper on springs, converted for Christmas by the application of a small floral card with seasonal greetings. 12.5 cm x 19 cm.

25. Two folder cards, late 1860's, on valentine style lace paper.
a) With a Christmas figure on white and silver lace. 14.5 cm x 9.6 cm.
b) With a Christmas verse on silk on pink and gilt lace. 9 cm x 11.8 cm.

26. Two cards.
a) A pair of gilded doors on a green and white lace mount, opening to show children in snow. 11.8 cm x 7.6 cm.
b) A pair of doors with scenes in vignettes, opening to show children in snow, on a gilt edged lace mount. 11.8 cm x 7.6 cm.

27. Two cards, one an elaborate frame of flowers and fans on springs, mounted over a card with a girl in a shell, surrounded by scraps, and a single identical card of the girl in shell.
15.5 cm x 11.5 cm, 12 cm x 8 cm.

28. Two cards, with cork pictures, on gilt lace mounts, one a folder with a windmill in cork and a Father Christmas scrap, the other a cork castle framed by holly and mistletoe scraps. 7.7 cm x 11.5 cm.

29. Two cards, prints of children and fairies framed by elaborate gilt and silver lace, one marked Rimmel. 11 cm x 13 cm, 9 cm x 13 cm.

30. Six cards on valentine style paper lace with various scraps and prints on springs, one with opening doors.
Sizes 5.3 cm x 7.5 cm to 8.5 cm x 12.2 cm.

31. Two large identical valentine style folder cards with scrap of the Christ Child, on gilt lace mounts, one with a German greeting. Each has a letter inside, dated respectively 1894, 1895, from Marie Annie Herbst to her mother "My gift of love to you is a promise to be a good, obedient child". The lace is very fine for this period, if the sender's date gives approximate time of publication, but the scrap is definitely 1890's. These cards are included here, though late, as fine examples of Valentine style cards. 14 cm x 20.6 cm.

## VOLUME 16: GLOVES AND FANS

**Valentine greetings in the form of gloves were known long before the days of Christmas Cards, and, like other valentine novelties, were adapted for other forms of greetings. By 1870 fans which could be folded flat and sent by post were being made for all kinds of greetings. Some were printed as Almanacs and Calendars, and sent at Christmas. Perfect specimens are hard to find, as many were broken up to be used in**

**Victorian albums. Three later pieces are included, to show developments up to 1900.**

1. Two and a half pairs of paper gloves.
a) A purple pair, with "A Happy New Year to You" inside.
b) A similar pink pair, with the same greeting outside.
c) A single piece in blue. These are replicas of similar valentine gloves. 1860's? 11.5 cm.

2. Two fan almanacs with original hinges.
a) Canton's Perfumed almanac 1871, six pieces, with flower decoration on gilt ground on both sides.
b) Canton's 1874 Illuminated almanac, six pieces, with printing on one side only. 11 cm closed.

3. Two fan almanacs, printed on one side only.
a) Almanac for 1874, six pieces, printed with flowers, with the dates in blue (hinge missing).
b) Almanac for 1874, seven pieces, printed with flowers on gilt ground (hinged). 11.2 cm closed.

4. Two fan almanacs, printed on both sides, with original hinges.
a) Sulman, 1876, six pretty leaf shaped pieces with flowers and sporting pictures. 10.6 cm closed.
b) S D Ewins & Sons, 1874, six identical pieces with flowers, wheatsheaves, and old man on gilt grounds. (This might be a trade card, as the name of Ewins has not been traced as a publisher). 11.8 cm closed.

5. Two fans, pieces as found in scrap books, printed on one side only.
a) J Mansell, five pieces, with roses, forget-me-nots and carnations, scalloped edges, with verses and greeting "Wishing you the Compliments of the Season". 1877. 12.3 cm closed.
b) "The Perfumed Almanac", 1876, six pieces, ladies and children in vignettes surrounded by flowers. 11.7 cm closed.

6. Fan, "A New Year wish", five pieces printed on one side with rose bouquets on pale blue, and greetings in verse, with original yellow tassel. c1875. 12.2 cm closed.

7. Two birthday fans, one printed on one side only. c1875.
a) Six pieces, with verses and flower and ivy sprays, having original tassel and button. 11.5 cm closed.
b) Five pieces as found in scrap book, with flower prints, scene and birthday verse. 12.4 cm closed.

8. E Bollans & Co. Two fans, five pieces with identical flower printing on four leaves and original tassels and buttons. c1875.
a) Inscribed: "I wish you a Merry

Christmas" on the first piece, and verses linked with the flowers on the others.
b) "With best wishes" on the first panel, and "I wish you many happy returns of the day" on the second. The same design was used for valentines. 12 cm closed.

9. Two fans, c1875, pieces as found in scrapbooks, printed on one side.
a) T Stevens, five pieces "A Happy Christmas", scenes and verses for Spring, Summer, Autumn, Winter. 12 cm closed.
b) Six pieces, "A Happy Christmas to You", flowers and verses on embossed and scalloped mount. 7.6 cm closed. (Perhaps taken from a bouquet fan as in no. 10).

10. Bouquet fan 1870's probably by Rimmel. There are seven pieces in the fan, printed with rose and forget-me-not sprays, and the edge is gilded. Size overall when open 20 cm.

11. Bouquet fan 1870's with robin scrap and "Happy New Year" over Christmas greeting, and five panels in leaf form printed with lily of the valley, violets, and roses, which fold away into a flower scrap. 18.5 cm open.

12. Two folding souvenir pieces.
a) Wood. "A Present from Lewisham", four leaves of silver lace paper with small flower prints.
b) A similar unmarked piece, five leaves of gilt lace paper, one with "Marguerite" printed, the others with scraps and prints. Probably 1860's. 18 cm open.

13. Two similar pieces.
a) Wood, four leaves of silver lace paper, greeting "A Merry Christmas and a Happy New Year" on one.
b) A similar unmarked piece in white lace, five leaves, with scraps, and a birthday greeting on silk. Probably 1860's. 18 cm open.

14. A very elaborate fan c.1875, with seven pieces, on silver embossed paper, with oval vignettes bearing greeting "A Happy New Year", flower scraps, and verses, one beginning "This little Christmas gift.....". 18 cm folded.

15. A fan calendar "The Circling Months", for 1894, opening to a circle, the twelve pieces having pictures of flowers, scenes, animals, people etc., above the month dates, on white card with gilt scrolls. 15.3 cm folded.

16. Twelve pieces of another similar calendar, cut down for scrap book, with pictures of children, dressed as flowers of the month. 10 cm.

17. A five piece fan in celluloid, each stick having a hand-painted picture of a flower or a bird. c1900. 9.6 cm.

# VOLUME 17:
## EARLY CARDS WITH MISCELLANEOUS GREETINGS FOR BIRTHDAYS, FRIENDS, AND FAMILY, 1850's to 1880

These cards are similar to others in this section, but have varied greetings, with verses reflecting Victorian family sentiment and friendship, and remind us of the Reward cards given in Sunday Schools to regular attenders. Many were mounted on valentine style paper, and some are marked with the names of valentine manufacturers, including Windsor and Mossman. The verses on the cards were regarded as the most important part of the greeting.

1. Nine cards, with verses for brother, sister, father, school-fellow, etc. One is lavishly decorated with gilt embossing and "jewels", two are oval, and there is a variety of gilt, silver and coloured decoration. 1860's.
7 cm x 5 cm to 10.7 cm x 7 cm.

2. Nine similar cards with verses entitled "Providence", "Trouble", "A wish", "The Parting" published by J Newman, "A Blessing", "To a Friend", "Welcome Home", "Flowers". 1860's.
8.5 cm x 5.8 cm to 11 cm x 7.2 cm.

3. Seven similar cards, with birthday verses. 1860's.
8.5 cm x 5.8 cm to 7 cm x 9.8 cm.

4. Five similar cards, including two sachets, one dated 1856 by the sender.
9 cm x 5.8 cm to 8 cm x 12.5 cm.

5. Eight cards on white lace paper, with miscellaneous verses, three printed on silk. The paper is in Wood or Windsor style.
1850's-60's. Sizes up to 9 cm x 6.8 cm.

6. Windsor. Five cards, all marked, on white lace paper. Four are envelopes holding fancy cards with various greetings, and one is a folding card with a birthday greeting on silk. One envelope has embossed heads of Royalty. 1850's-60's.
Sizes 10.5 cm x 7.6 cm, 9.5 cm x 12.8 cm.

7. Four sachet cards in white lace paper, one marked "Meek", three being in envelope form (one with a card) and one in the shape of a heart. 1850's-60's.
Sizes up to 12.7 cm x 8 cm.

8. Five motifs with verses, on silver or gilt lace paper, probably originally in envelopes. 1850's-60's. 9.6 cm x 7 cm.

9. Six similar with birthday greetings on silk, 1850'S-60'S. Sizes up to 9 cm x 7 cm.

10. Four cards on silver embossed paper, with coloured scraps and ribbon decoration and birthday greetings on silk, two being sachets and two opening cards (one marked Mossman). c1870.
Sizes up to 8.4 cm x 12 cm.

11. Four novelty cards, with birthday greetings, c1870.
a/b) Cards on white embossed mounts, opening to form a three-dimensional scene on springs. 8.8 cm x 7 cm.
c) Gilt lace with doors, opening to show a floral print and verse, with another card slotted in behind. 8 cm x 12 cm.
d) An ingenious mechanical card with prints of cherubs on oval windows which open to show more pictures; tabs at top and bottom can be pulled to reveal greetings behind. 7.6 cm x 11 cm.

12. Four cards on embossed gilt or silver mounts, three having birthday greetings. One is a sachet. c1870.
9.3 cm x 10.8 cm and 9 cm x 11.5 cm.

13. Six miscellaneous birthday cards on valentine style paper with scraps of children and flowers. c1870.
7 cm x 9.6 cm to 8 cm x 12 cm.

14. Three cards, with "A Blessing" verse on silk, under flower scraps, one on white lace paper and two on gilded mounts. c1870.
9.7 cm x 13.5 cm and 7.8 cm x 11 cm.

15. Three cards on valentine style lace paper with gilt, each one having a verse in woven silk beginning respectively "A wish.....", "Good wishes to my little friend" and "To a daughter". c1870.
Sizes up to 9 cm x 14 cm.

16. Six miscellaneous cards on fancy gilt and silver mounts with scraps and birthday greetings or verses. c1875.
6.3 cm x 9.7 cm to 8.8 cm x 12.3 cm.

17. Five others, c1875.
Sizes up to 8 cm x 12 cm.

18. Five cards, birthday greetings on various lace, gilt, and embossed mounts, with scraps of children.
5.5 cm x 8 cm to 7.5 cm x 11 cm.

19. Five cards
a/b) Two cards on green and white lace paper with scraps "For a Good Boy".
c) "To my Sister", on white embossed paper, edged green.
d/e) Small cards on white embossed paper with scraps and greetings "Remember me", and "For a Good Girl". Late 1870's.
6.7 cm x 9.2 cm to 9.6 cm x 16 cm.

20. Seven birthday cards with floral prints, or scraps on mounts with embossed edges.
1870's. 8.3 cm x 4.8 cm to 6.5 cm x 10 cm.

# THE PUBLISHERS R. CANTON, B. SULMAN, J. MANSELL, DEAN & SON

This section contains identified cards from publishers, some of whose cards have already appeared in Sections 1 and 2. Canton, Sulman, & Mansell had already adapted their production of early valentines for the growing Christmas card trade. The publishers are identified from trademarks, impressed names, and similar lace edged mounts, though some of these are very similar and can be easily confused. Scraps and prints also were interchanged between publishers, and mounts made by other firms were sometimes used, which makes precise attribution difficult.

*Section*
*3*

22.20                          18.33

## VOLUME 18:
## CANTON & SULMAN, LACE EDGED, FANCY AND MOVABLE CARDS

**These cards are dated in the early 1870's except where otherwise stated. The greetings are simple Christmas and New Year, with an occasional verse. The Canton borders are lettered, to show their number and variety, fourteen in all.**

1. Canton. Four open out cards, three with religious prints, showing two styles of lace border, three in type A, one in type B. 11 cm x 7.3 cm.

2/3. Canton. Nine cards, with lace border A, and prints of robins, winter and summer scenes, two with attached scraps. 11 cm x 7.3 cm.

4. Canton. Six cards, three being oval with lace border C and robin prints, 9.5 cm x 7.3 cm. Three have embossed borders, two of these having a negro picture with holly, and the other a scrap mounted on silk. 11.2 cm x 7.7 cm.

5. Canton? Ten cards, eight on embossed white cards with serrated borders, and scraps or prints, one oval with lace border D, and one rectangular with a print of a girl and holly. 9.2 cm x 6.7 cm, 10.6 cm x 7 cm.

6. Canton? Four cards on similar mounts, with gilt or silver embossed decoration, and scraps of robins and scenes. 9.2 cm x 6.7 cm.

7. Canton. Three cards with elaborate cut out robin scraps on springs, opening into three-dimensional scenes, on blue two-tone mounts, with lace border B. 11 cm x 7.3 cm.

8. Canton. Two cards with prints of a girl with flowers and holly, one with lace border A, the other with plain border and scalloped corners. 11 cm x 7.3 cm.

9. Canton. Three cards, lace border E, and prints of Father Christmas, robin, or boy. (This border resembles a Goodall border). 8.5 cm x 12.3 cm.

10/11. Canton. Ten cards, eight designs, lace border B, with various prints, two as in no. 9. 11 cm x 7.3 cm.

12. Canton. Five cards, lace edge border F, four with gilt or silver. One card is a folder with flower and child scraps, and two have J. Mansell prints, but the border is identified as Canton from a marked card with a printed picture. 11 cm x 7.3 cm.

13. Canton. Five cards, lace edge border G (one card marked Canton) with holly, flower and humorous prints. The flower print is the mirror image of a marked Goodall card, Volume 25 no. 32. 11.3 cm x 8 cm.

14. Canton. Two cards with layers of scraps on springs opening to make three-dimensional scenes, one with silver lace on lace edge mount A, and another on lace edge H. 7.3 cm x 11 cm.

15. Canton. Five cards, two scenes on lace edge mount B, 11 cm x 7.3 cm, and three smaller on similar mount, 9.2 cm x 6.5 cm.

16. Canton. Three cards, on lace edge mount I, with various winter scenes. 10.5 cm x 7 cm.

17. Canton. Two cards, one a winter scene with children on lace edge mount J, the other a Georgian group on the same mount with gilt. 8.7 cm x 12.4 cm.

18. Canton. Five cards of little girls in winter scenes, four being on lace edge mount K. Sizes up to 7.10 cm x 12.8 cm.

19. Canton? Four cards, with scraps on springs opening into three-dimensional scenes, with robins and children. One is on lace edge mount L. Sizes up to 11.3 cm x 8 cm.

20. Canton.
a) Two cards, of clowns and Christmas figure, with rotating discs which change the faces, on lace edge mount B. 7.6 cm x 11 cm.
b) A folder "How I spent a Happy Christmas" containing ten pictures of a family party with appropriate verses. 12 cm x 8.2 cm.

21. Canton. Four cards with crosses, opening to show Biblical prints. Two are on lace edge mount A, and one on another style M. A fifth cross is shown open. 11 cm x 7.3 cm.

22. Canton. Five cards, on embossed mounts, two with white edges, three with gilt and colour. One card has a cross opened by pulling a tassel, three have a cross with holly or flowers, and one has a clock which opens to show an angel. 7.6 cm x 11.3 cm.

23. Canton? Eight cards on background printed scenes. Seven have scrap crosses (three registered at Stationers' Hall by S Hildesheimer), entwined with flowers or holly. The borders, with gilt pattern on various colours, are similar to one on Marcus Ward cards. 7.6 cm x 11.3 cm.

24. Canton? Six similar cards with flower scraps or prints, one being a folder with a New Year greeting on silk. Sizes 7.3 cm x 11.3 cm and 6 cm x 8.8 cm.

25/26. Canton. Fourteen humorous cards from eight designs with personified animals and Christmas dinner in oval

prints on white embossed cards, showing the use of different captions for Christmas, New Year and Compliments of the Season. 9.3 cm x 6.1 cm.

27. Canton. Ten similar cards on more elaborate mounts, with humorous prints of people, animals and Christmas dinner, and suitable captions. 6.1 cm x 9.3 cm.

28. Canton. Eight lace edge cards, border N. Six have background pictures of house, church, robin or mill, two with attached scraps. Another has a robin scrap on a plain ground, and one a holly and scroll design on a gilt ground. 6.2 cm x 8.7 cm.

29. Canton. Eight plain cards with similar background pictures, two with scraps. Sizes up to 6.4 cm x 9 cm.

30. Canton. Seven cards, six designs of fine blue and white china with gilt borders, bearing seasonal greetings. The set of six was registered at Stationers' Hall by Anna Maria Donnelly, on 24-8-1880. 9.3 cm x 9.3 cm.

31. Sulman. Eight cards. Five are on octagonal serrated edge embossed cards, and three on plain edge cards. All have robin scraps, or prints of children, robin, holly, or flowers. Sizes up to 10 cm x 6.8 cm.

32. Three elaborate cards of Christmas trees with presents.
a) Two faces below scrap of a tree, probably the design registered by A Laidlaw designed by A. Pernot, 9-4-1866. This is grouped here for similarity, being the only one attributed to Laidlaw, and having much in common with b) and c).
b/c) Two Christmas trees on different mounts, with a tab to pull which reveals more pictures under the branches. Three children are below at a table with toys. Sizes up to 8.5 cm x 13.6 cm. This is probably the design by Mr Buckley registered by Sulman, 18-4-1867.

33. Sulman. Three cards on lace edge mounts.
a) St. Paul's Cathedral. This opens to show a three-dimensional scene of the thanksgiving for the recovery of the Prince of Wales from typhoid. Registered at Stationers Hall, 2-12-1872.
b) The Great Exhibition of 1851, opening to show the scene inside. Registered at Stationers' Hall, 3-3-1873.
c) The Great Exhibition, print of scene within. All 7.8 cm x 11.3 cm.

34. Sulman. Six cards, three designs, showing children in Georgian dress with Christmas tree or holly. Three of the cards have prints, and three have scraps in the same designs. Four designs were registered at Stationers' Hall 13-7-1871, by J Nixon. Sizes up to 7 cm x 10 cm.

35. Sulman. Three cards, with oval prints of children at play on lace edged cards. 9 cm x 6 cm.

36. Sulman. Seven cards.
a) A six-page elaborate folder, with one side of three pages having gilt embossed designs, and the other three designs of children on white embossed mounts.
b/d) Three single page cards with scraps on springs opening into three-dimensional scenes with children.
e/g) Three single cards with designs the same as the prints used above. Sizes up to 7.3 cm x 11 cm.

37. Sulman. Four cards.
a) A cross and anchor on a gilt and ribbon edged mount, over a flower scrap.
b/c) "Excelsior" print of climbers, on a gilt edged mount. Compare Volume 8 no. 13.
d) A scrap of children and a tree on a gilt edged mount. Sizes up to 7.7 cm x 11 cm.

38. Sulman? Five cards with prints of men and dogs rescuing snowbound climbers; four of these open to show a party inside a monastery. There are five different versions of greetings, and two varieties of gilded borders. The mounts would appear to be Sulman, but the prints might be by J Mansell. 11.2 cm x 7.7 cm.

39. Sulman? Two similar cards, with ship picture opening to show sailors at their Christmas feast. 11.2 cm x 7.7 cm.

40. Sulman? Six cards, (one opening) with prints of angels and children. One card is marked Sulman and the others are similar, but the same prints also appear on Marcus Ward mounts. Sizes up to 8 cm x 12 cm.

41. Sulman. Nine cards on white mounts with embossed edges, and prints or scraps of children, Red Riding Hood and scenes. 5.3 cm x 8 cm up to 7.7 cm x 11.2 cm.

42. Sulman?
a) Two cards with embossed edges. one marked, with scraps of children and people.
b) Four scraps from the same set. Sizes up to 7.5 cm x 10.5 cm.

43. Sulman. Seven cards, with three designs of a Christmas tree and angels on six styles of gilded embossed mounts with floral border. Three cards have attached scraps of children. Registered at Stationers' Hall, designed by Tom Sulman, 3-7-1869. 7.7 cm x 11.7 cm.

44. Sulman. Six similar cards, six designs. Three, of angels, were registered at Stationers' Hall, 1-1-1876, designed by Tom Sulman. 7.7 cm x 11.7 cm.

45. Sulman. Six miscellaneous cards. Five have prints or scraps, and one is a moonlight scene with a verse in red print. Sizes 9 cm x 5.7 cm to 7.6 cm x 10.5 cm.

## VOLUME 19:
## CHILDREN'S CARDS
## PUBLISHED BY R. CANTON

**These cards are from the mid 1870's. There could however, be earlier ones in Section 1 which have not yet been identified. The cards here have brief seasonal or birthday greetings, with an occasional verse.**

1. Four cards, with vignettes of children with flowers or holly surrounds, on black, gold, or green mounts. 10.3 cm x 6.7 cm.

2. Three cards on embossed edged mounts, children at Christmas. These are three out of a set of five registered at Stationers' Hall, designed by Mrs C A Saltmarsh, 17-3-1876.
11.5 cm x 7.5 cm up to 12.5 cm x 8.5 cm.

3. Four cards, Christmas messengers holding greetings, two boys and one girl. Three designs out of a set of four, registered at Stationers Hall 28-9-1874, designed by S Rosenthal. 6.2 cm x 9.7 cm.

4. Three cards, winter scenes with children on embossed edge scalloped cards. 11.2 cm x 7.8 cm.

5. Two cards, vignettes of girls in winter, surrounded by a scroll design, with Christmas verse by Eliza Cook. 11.3 cm x 7.5 cm.

6. Six cards, four designs of single children in winter scenes, with holly surrounds. Three cards have plain white borders, three embossed. One card has the Canton trade mark on reverse. 7.8 cm x 11.2 cm.

7. One card - Canton? Small girl with floral bouquet in scroll design on embossed edge card. 10.3 cm x 6.6 cm.

8. Five cards with children on cards with scalloped corners. Three have a gilt edge. These are not marked, but identified by having the same picture as the lace edged marked card in Volume 18, numbers 8, 10 and 11. 7.6 cm x 11.6 cm.

9/10. Nine cards on black or brown backgrounds, boys and girls with scrolls, and peepholes, with somewhat winsome verses and greetings. Registered at Stationers' Hall 2-8-1877, designed by Mrs C A Saltmarsh. These cards appear to have been popular and appear frequently in albums of the time. 7.2 cm x 10.8 cm.

11. Five cards, four designs, head and shoulders of winsome children on black, pink, or white embossed mounts, greetings such as "I tiss you tos its Tismas". Registered at Stationers Hall, 2-8-1877 by Mrs C A Saltmarsh.
Sizes up to 8 cm x 11.1 cm.

12. Four cards, scenes with children on plain cards. Three out of eight designs, registered at Stationers Hall by Mrs C A Saltmarsh, 27-11-1877. 7 cm x 10 cm.

13. Four cards with designs of a boy and girl, showing scenes in Spring, Summer, Autumn and Winter, used for a calendar 1878. 6.8 cm x 10 cm.

14. Seven cards.
a) Four with a boy or girl peeping through a curtain. Two designs, different captions. 6.8 cm x 10.2 cm.
b) Three with the head of a boy or girl looking round a curtain, and pink or blue line in the border. 7.8 cm x 11.2 cm.

15. Four cards, with plain white border.
a) Two have a girl with crackers or a doll. 8 cm x 11 cm.
b) Two have a girl with a dog. 10 cm x 7 cm.

16/17. Nine cards of children, four designs, in leafy surrounds, with holly and robins. Five have grey serrated borders, four plain white. Sizes up to 12.5 cm x 7.8 cm.

18. Canton? Five cards, four designs, with boys and girls at play, on black grounds with orange borders. 7.3 cm x 10.4 cm.

19. Canton? Eight cards, six designs, with plain white borders, of children in winter scenes. 6.8 cm x 10 cm.

20. Canton? Nine cards, seven designs, children in winter scenes, with red line borders, signed J I R. 6.7 cm x 9.5 cm.

21. Canton? Two cards with blue line borders, girls in winter scenes, one with a child posting a letter. 6.9 cm x 9.9 cm.

22. Canton? Six cards, five designs, with white borders, children and robin in winter scenes, indoors and out. 7 cm x 10 cm.

23. Canton? Five cards, four designs, poorly drawn children in winter scenes, one dated 1871 by the sender. 7.5 cm x 10.7 cm.

24. Canton? Seven cards
a) Three with poor children in winter scenes, line border.
b) Four with children in winter scenes, indoors and out, and double red line border. 6.5 cm x 9.3 cm.

25. Canton? Four cards.
a) Two cards, unattractive children in winter scene.
b) Two cards, Scottish figures, red line in border. Sizes up to 7 cm x 10.5 cm.

26. Canton? Four cards on black or blue ground, two with Scottish figures, two with fisher girls. 6.2 cm x 9.2 cm.

## VOLUME 20:
## R CANTON, DEAN AND SONS - REMAINING CARDS

**This volume contains most of the remaining cards attributed to the publishers Canton and Dean, including birds, animals, flowers, Christmas scenes and religious cards, all published in the 1870's. They have brief seasonal greetings or appropriate verses, and some Easter and birthday cards are included.**

1. Canton. Four gilt-edged cards with holly, robins and flowers. 6.4 cm x 9.2 cm.

2. Canton. Two cards, hunting scenes with white border. 8.5 cm x 12.5 cm.

3. Canton. Four miscellaneous cards with robins. One has an opening envelope with greeting inside. One with a robin between curtains and holly was registered at Stationers Hall 1-4-1875.
Sizes 10 cm x 6.3 cm up to 11.4 cm x 7.5 cm.

4. Canton. Three cards, two designs, with flower wreaths and robin on branch, and brief Christmas verse. 10.5 cm x 6.4 cm.

5. Canton. Three cards, two designs, with robin in holly wreath, embossed edges, and Christmas or New Year verse. 11 cm x 7.5 cm.

6. Canton. Four cards, three designs, with robins on holly or mistletoe, and wide coloured borders. 11.1 cm x 7.5 cm.

7/8. Canton. Fifteen cards with robins, four designs, various mounts and captions, some with gilt borders and some coloured. Sizes up to 7 cm x 10.4 cm.

9/10. Canton. Eleven cards, six designs of parrot, cat, mice, chick and dogs, in circular vignette on beige, blue, or green ground, with a holly, mistletoe or ivy spray, and humorous captions for Christmas, New Year, and birthday. A popular set, often found in Victorian albums, they were registered at Stationers' Hall, 9-10-1878, by Jean Gabriel Faustin Belbeder. 8 cm x 11.5 cm.

11. Canton. Two cards with birds, one flying over water, the other with two wrens in snow, on a dark mount. 12.2 cm x 5.3 cm.

12. Canton. One card with white border, a dog by a fireside. 11 cm x 7.6 cm.

13. Canton. Three cards, two designs, one with flower and holly wreath and two with holly on a blue ribbon, around New Year or Christmas verse.
Sizes up to 11.2 cm x 7.3 cm.

14. Canton. Five cards with flower designs on gilt bordered cards, and greetings on

gold panel, one dated 1879 by the sender. 12 cm x 8.4 cm.

15. Canton. Three gilt edged cards, two designs of flower sprays on coloured ground surrounding greeting. 8.5 cm x 5.6 cm.

16. Canton. Three cards with flowers. 8 cm x 5.3 cm up to 12.2 cm x 7.3 cm.

17. Canton. Two cards, with holly branch in snow around pictures of hands. 11 cm x 7 cm.

18. Canton. Four cards with flower designs, two on gilt grounds, two with gilt borders around greetings. A fifth card reversed, shows the Canton trade mark. 7.2 cm x 10.3 cm and 8.8 cm x 11.8 cm.

19. Canton. Three Easter cards with crosses, decorated with birds, flowers, and gilded rays, on plain ground. 7.6 cm x 11.3 cm.

20. Canton. Four cards with various crosses, three being illuminated designs for Easter, and one with Happy New Year greeting and a cross on a holly, fern and lily of the valley bouquet. Sizes up to 7.8 cm x 11.3 cm.

21. Canton. Four cards, three designs, with flower wreath around gilded cross with texts, one labelled "Easter offering" and one "Happy may thy Birthday be". 7.6 cm x 11.8 cm.

22. Canton. One card with green and red border and small oblong vignette of people in a snow scene, and verse below. 7.3 cm x 10 cm.

23. Canton. A large card with flower spray of crimson passion flower and Christmas rose, and a text. 16 cm x 22.7 cm.

24. Dean. Five cards, four designs, a gilt cross entwined with flowers, three on black ground, two on mauve, with scalloped embossed borders. 8.5 cm x 11.5 cm.

25. Dean. Eight cards, five designs, embossed birds and flowers on coloured grounds. 8 cm x 4.5 cm.

26. Dean. Three embossed cards, two with leaves and berries and one with branch of white flowers and leaves. 11 cm x 7 cm.

27/29. Dean. Five cards, probably from packets containing a series. Two are from a set of "English birds", one from "Butterflies of all countries", one from "English flowers", and one from a set of "Shells of all countries". All are in bright colours with white border. 11 cm x 14.9 cm.

20.9

## VOLUME 21:
## B SULMAN. REMAINING CARDS

**This volume contains most of the remaining cards in the collection attributed to Sulman, including religious, Scottish, flowers, birds etc. They have brief seasonal greetings and occasional verses, and were published in the 1870's. An interesting feature here is the card in no. 12 marked both for Sulman and Marcus Ward, illustrating the practice of some early publishers of using the same cards from another source (probably W Hagelberg, at this time in Berlin). Several more identical cards, marked Marcus Ward, are shown in that publisher's files. (See also volume 193).**

1. Three cards with mock heraldic devices showing cross, boar's head and angel. Eight designs were registered at Stationers' Hall by E Jackman, 13-7-71. 9.2 cm x 6 cm.

2. Four cards, three designs, two of New Year Scottish themes and one of Father Christmas with a humorous verse. 12 cm x 7.4 cm.

3. Three cards, black ground, one Punch and Judy, and two with dogs and cats. 7.7 cm x 11.5 cm and 12.1 cm x 8.8 cm.

4. Three cards, two designs, one with dogs and cat, one with cow and bird. 12.1 cm x 8.8 cm.

5. Three religious cards with holly, snowdrops, and mistletoe on gilt borders, around pictures of the three Kings, the Shepherds, and the Nativity. 14.8 cm x 9.5 cm.

6. Two cards with leaves and berries in a gilt frame, and verse. 12.9 cm x 9.3 cm.

7. Four cards.
a) Two with a bird and nest on a rose branch, one on gilt ground and one on black, with verse. 12 cm x 7.3 cm.
b) Two designs on black ground, one showing a kingfisher by a lake with flowers, the other a mouse eating corn in a surround of poppies and daisies. 16.3 cm x 10.3 cm.

8. Two cards with verse in panel, one of roses and buttercup with a ladybird, the other a spray of roses and ferns, both on black backgrounds. 16.7 cm x 11 cm.

9. Three cards on gilt backgrounds, robins and blue tit on holly or flower spray, with verse in panel. 14.4 cm x 10.4 cm.

10. Four miscellaneous cards of birds, including a robin on holly, two parrots on a gilt ground, a robin with a yellow ribbon and a blue tit on a berried branch. 9.5 cm x 6.3 cm up to 12 cm x 8.5 cm.

11. Six cards with black background, two with robins, three with flowers, and one showing a cornfield. One card shows an open envelope with a stamp and London, '76, on the postmark, with address "A Christmas greeting to you", and an insect. 10.2 cm x 7 cm.

12. Six cards with black backgrounds, five designs. One has a swan design, and one holly. 12.5 cm x 4.8 cm. Four have flower sprays and a greeting in verse on white panel. Two of these have the same lily of the valley design, but one is marked Sulman, one Marcus Ward. This card is put here to indicate the practice in earlier times of different firms obtaining the same design from another source (perhaps Hagelberg) and publishing under their own names. Sets of the same designs are shown in the Marcus Ward files, Volume 44. 10.4 cm x 6.3 cm.

13. Four cards with black backgrounds, with flower sprays, insects, butterflies, and ducks, and greetings on white panels, two dated 1876 by the senders. 9.4 cm x 6.6 cm.

14. Three cards with black backgrounds, one a squirrel, one a hare, the third two doves and forget-me-nots, with a Christmas verse in a panel. 10.8 cm x 6.2 cm.

15. Two cards with black background. a) Oak leaves and acorns, with gilt border. 12.2 cm x 7.4 cm. b) Boy on skates, pulled by dog. 12.5 cm x 4.8 cm.

16. Three cards, gilt backgrounds, with flower and bird sprays, and verses in panel. 11.5 cm x 7.4 cm.

17. Six cards, three with gilt backgrounds, three grey, birds and floral wreaths around a panel with verse. 9.3 cm x 5.9 cm.

18. One card showing a lake scene in a panel surrounded by gilt border and scroll design with a New Year greeting. 11.5 cm x 7.4 cm.

19. Five cards, flower and fruit sprays on dark ground with verse in a scroll. 8.5 cm x 11.8 cm.

20. Four cards with gilt backgrounds, two with white borders, flower sprays and verse in panel. 10 cm x 14 cm and 8.7 cm x 12.4 cm.

21. Three cards, two with a leaf and flower spray and seasonal verse, the other with a holder lying on the ground with flower bouquet. Sizes up to 13 cm x 8.8 cm.

22. Six cards, three designs, robins with nest, berries or flowers. One is the macabre picture of a dead bird, surprisingly popular at this time, and was sent to "Auntie" by "Fred", obviously a child! 11 cm x 7.5 cm.

23. Five cards, three designs. One has a nest with leaves, one has ferns, and the other has roses and a butterfly, all on a grey ground with greeting in a white panel. 11 cm x 7.5 cm.

24. Two cards, each with four figures in Elizabethan and Stuart dress in Christmas scenes, with a seasonal verse. 10.5 cm x 7.2 cm.

25/8. Eight cards, four designs of gilt crosses entwined with forget-me-nots, lily of the valley and harebells, violets, or passion flower. The captions are for Easter, Christmas and perhaps valentine, "Affection's Offering". 11 cm x 16 cm.

29. One card, a wild rose spray on white ground, with verse. 10.8 cm x 16 cm.

30. Two cards, a folding card with the music of "God Rest Ye, Merry Gentlemen" inside, and another with a festive Elizabethan scene. 11.6 cm x 7.6 cm, 12.8 cm x 9.7 cm.

31 One card on beige ground, with a winter scene in a circular vignette, a spray of poppies, lily of the valley and cornflowers, and a New Year greeting. 13 cm x 9 cm.

32. Three cards with bird and flower sprays, around religious texts. 10.5 cm x 6.5 cm.

## VOLUME 22: JOSEPH MANSELL, FANCY, MECHANICAL AND LACE-EDGED CARDS

**Joseph Mansell was a prolific producer of early valentines on elaborate lace paper, and the firm continued producing greeting cards into the 1870's. Though entries under his name appear in the Stationers' Hall Records up to 1900, this collection has found none positively identified after about 1880, and few of the entries in the Records appear to be cards. The attribution of the cards in this section has been difficult, as many of the markings are indistinct, and, as with other publishers, scraps and prints were interchangeable between firms. The cards are arranged in an order which it is hoped will help the student to follow the system of identification, and perhaps further discoveries may be made. The cards are all of the 1870's.**

1. Seven cards on embossed bordered mounts, with prints of holly, robins, flowers, seaweed, ferns, and an old man, two with a silver edge and one blue. Four cards have attached scraps, and one is marked 1872 by the sender. 9.4 cm x 6 cm.

2. Ten cards, on lace or embossed edged mounts, with various prints. Three have attached scraps, and one is marked 1869 by the sender, perhaps the earliest in the volume. 9.5 cm x 6.4 cm.

3. Seven cards.
a) Three have snow scene prints on blue and gold mount.
b) Four have prints on scallop edge cards, two with scraps.
8 cm x 5.4 cm, 6.4 cm x 9.5 cm.

4. Seven cards, four designs, winter scenes on fancy edge embossed cards. Sizes up to 10.5 cm x 6.8 cm.

5. Five lace edge cards, three varieties, showing two designs in oval prints of a handshake. 9.6 cm x 6.4 cm.

6. Six cards, four with lace borders (two versions) and two with embossed scalloped borders. Five cards have scraps on springs, opening to give three-dimensional scenes. Three cards are marked, from which all these, and subsequent cards, can be attributed to J Mansell. 6.9 cm x 10.2 cm, 8.2 cm x 11.2 cm.

7. Six cards with black background, four designs, personified Christmas dinner - including pudding, wine bottle, roast beef, oysters and pineapple. One card has a lace border like one in no. 6. 9.5 cm x 7 cm.

8. Seven cards with scalloped borders, four with prints, one with Father Frost scrap,

and two with scraps of children on a scenic background; five cards have indistinct impressed marking from which subsequent cards can be identified. 6.9 cm x 10.2 cm.

9. Six cards, four designs.
a) Four have double gilt line borders, and two of these have scraps of children in real cloth garments.
b) Two cards, with children, on embossed edge mounts. Sizes up to 7.6 cm x 11.4 cm.

10. Six cards with various lace edge and embossed mounts, with scraps attached to scenic background as in no. 8. One scrap, however, was registered by Sulman, 31/8/1871. Sizes up to 8 cm x 12.4 cm.

11. Three cards, one a print of a boy with book on gilt edged mount, and two folder cards with prints of girls. 7.6 cm x 11.4 cm.

12. Three cards, two designs, with prints of a girl and a boy. One has a gilt edged border, and two are on coloured mounts with flower surround. 7.6 cm x 11.4 cm, 8.8 cm x 12.5 cm.

13. Five cards, robins and Christmas figure, all clearly marked, with holly and mistletoe surrounds. Two are on beige mounts with convoluted border, two plain rectangles. The fifth card is on a gilt edged mount. 9.5 cm x 6 cm up to 11.2 cm x 8 cm.

14. Four cards.
a) Gilt edged mount as in no. 13, with scrap of coach and horses on print of horsemen and snowy mountains.
b) Three cards, with prints of winter scenes on scallop edge mount with wide gilt line, one print being the same as a). Possibly Sulman. 11.2 cm x 7.6 cm.

15. Four cards.
a) Three fold card with gilt illuminated decoration, opening to show print of Madonna and Child. 7.4 cm x 13 cm folded.
b) Two cards on scallop edge mounts, with two gilt lines (as in no. 9) and print "Light of the World". 7.6 cm x 11.4 cm.
c) A floral cross on a gilt edged marked card. 8 cm x 11.2 cm

16. Two cards.
a) Another three fold card as in no. 15a with print of the Angel appearing to the Shepherds. 7.4 cm x 13 cm.
b) An illuminated card with gilt decoration on terracotta enclosing a print of the Nativity. 7.6 cm x 11.4 cm.

17. Six cards, with prints of angels on various mounts. 6.9 cm x 10.2 cm up to 8.5 cm x 11.6 cm.

18. Six cards, crosses entwined with flowers, two designs, on four varieties of gilt edged mounts.
Sizes up to 7.5 cm x 13.2 cm.

19. Two cards.
a) A New Year folder, with scraps of a bird and flowers on the exterior, and two pictures within, one a girl with holly, one with two plants in pots, tied by a purple ribbon. 8.5 cm x 12 cm folded.
b) A single card on the same mount, with print of angel and child and a Christmas verse beneath. 8.5 cm x 12 cm.

20. Five cards, four designs, on gilt edged mounts, showing single children in winter scenes, with verse beneath. 8 cm x 12 cm.

21. Four cards, three designs, two as in no. 20, plus one with a boy and girl on a swing, these with gilded scallop edge. 8.5 cm x 12.5 cm.

22. Four cards.
a) Mechanical card with flower scraps opening on springs to show pictures beneath, on a mount as in no. 21.
b) Another, on silvered mount, with oval lace edge print over an opening flower fan.
c) Two others with the same attached oval scrap. Sizes up to 8.5 cm x 12.5 cm.

23. Four cards on various coloured mounts, three with single children, one a fairy holding a Christmas pudding. Sizes up to 8.7 cm x 13.2 cm.

24. Four cards, three designs, on gilt edged mounts, with prints of an angel with children or flying over a ship, and verses below. 8 cm x 12 cm.

25. Four cards, two designs, children at a window with robin.
a) Two on a scallop edge card. 8.8 cm x 6 cm.
b) Two on a gilt edged mount. 11.2 cm x 8 cm.

26. Six cards, four designs, children in leafy surrounds with robin. Five have a gilt edge and one a white embossed border. 7.6 cm x 10.5 cm, 8 cm x 11.2 cm.

27. Two cards.
a) A boy pushing a girl in a swan sleigh. 8.8 cm x 11.8 cm.
b) A boy and girl building a sandcastle. 13 cm x 8.7 cm.

28. Four cards on lace or embossed edge mounts.
a) A folding card with elaborate flower scrap, opening to show picture of two children as in no. 9.
b) A girl in a red cloak, in gilt lace border.
c) Father Christmas with fairies.
d) Roses and forget-me-nots.
Sizes up to 8 cm x 11.5 cm.

29. Six cards, with various lace and gilt borders, and prints or scraps of flowers. Sizes up to 8 cm x 11.2 cm.

30. Four cards, single boys and girls on fancy mounts.
7.5 cm x 10 cm up to 11 cm x 15.3 cm.

31. Six cards, cats and dogs, four designs, on two styles of gilded mounts. These four designs were registered at Stationers' Hall, 3-7-1873. 6.1 cm x 9.4 cm, 7.3 cm x 10.7 cm.

32. Seven cards, cats and dogs on various coloured and gilded mounts, four designs, one as in no. 31.
Sizes up to 7.8 cm x 10.7 cm.

33. Ten cards, seven with cats and dogs and three with children, on various white embossed mounts, two of which are marked Meek and one Mullord, but with Mansell scraps, three repeating designs as in no. 31. 7.4 cm x 11 cm, 5.5 cm x 8.5 cm.

34. Four cards, two with chicks on white lace edged mounts and two with dogs on gilded scallop edge mounts. Sizes up to 12 cm x 8.3 cm.

35. Four cards, one a cat, three with dogs, on gilt embossed mounts. 8.6 cm x 11.4 cm.

36. Five cards, four designs of flowers on various fancy mounts. 13.6 cm x 8.3 cm.

37. Five cards, one design of heather and azalea. Three are on various fancy mounts with different greetings, and two have plain borders. One is marked E B & Co (Bollans), and one Mansell, another example of two firms getting supplies from a common source.
12.5 cm x 8.5 cm, 11 cm x 6.5 cm.

38. Four cards with serrated edge borders, with gilt or silver, and flower scraps. One is a folder, with verses, and a white ribbon tie, and one has a robin scrap on silk. 11.7 cm x 7.8 cm.

39. Four cards on gilt and silver scallop edge mounts, two with floral sprays and verse, and two with embossed roses. 8.4 cm x 12 cm.

40. Five cards with prints of flowers or fruit on various mounts. Sizes up to 8.2 cm x 12 cm.

41. Four cards with flower prints on white embossed edge mounts. Sizes up to 7.5 cm x 10.5 cm.

42. Two folder cards with elaborate gilt or silver lace paper, with flower vase. No greetings, perhaps manufacturers samples. 8.5 cm x 11.5 cm.

# VOLUME 23:
# JOSEPH MANSELL,
# REMAINING CARDS

**This volume contains cards attributed to J Mansell dated from about 1875 to the early 1880's, with pictures of birds, animals, flowers, scenes, religious cards, most in plain printed styles with simple greetings or verses, some being adapted for valentine or birthday use by suitable sentiments. Although some cards are marked J Mansell, they might have been supplied by another maker, as shown in identical cards with another name.**

1. Five cards, robins and flower sprays, with pink, blue or grey borders. One has a black background. c1875.
Sizes up to 12.3 cm x 7.5 cm.

2. Five cards, four designs of insects following human pursuits, making music, cooking etc. Four have gilt backgrounds and one has a black background. c1875.
11 cm x 7.8 cm.

3. Five cards, four designs, hens, ducks and chicks in farm scenes, four with a brown border and one gilt. c1875.
9.8 cm x 6 cm.

4. Three cards, birds with roses and holly or ivy.  c1878.  7.5 cm x 10.7 cm.

5. Six cards, five designs, birds in flight or on branches. Five are plain, one is on a silvered mount. c1878.
Sizes up to 11.7 cm x 7.6 cm.

6. Three gilt-bordered cards, two designs of a summer and a winter scene, with people, flowers, holly, birds and animals, and Christmas or New Year verses. c1880.
13.2 cm x 10.2 cm.

7. Seven cards, animals and hens.
a) Three cards, with cat or dog in circular vignette, and Christmas or New Year verse (one trimmed).
b) Two cards, one with cat and tortoise, the other fox and hens on black backgrounds.
c) Two cards, dogs in Christmas scenes, with verse. 1880-1885.
Sizes up to 10.3 cm x 7.5 cm.

8. Six cards, four designs, one black background, showing a handshake in a rectangular vignette, with flowers around. c1880. Sizes up to 10.5 cm x 7.5 cm.

9. Three cards with beige border, a handshake with ferns and flowers. One was dated 1879 by the sender.
12 cm x 8.5 cm.

10. Six cards, crosses in four designs with flowers or holly, on blue, green, or beige grounds, with Christmas or New Year greetings. c1875. 6.6 cm x 10 cm.

11. Three cards with prints of crosses on gilt-edged mounts, and holly, ferns or flowers. c1875. Sizes up to 7.9 cm x 11 cm.

12. Five cards, elaborate gilded crosses with various designs of flowers, ivy, an open book, and heart and anchor. Four have texts and a plain edge, and one has a gilded border and a Christmas greeting. c1878. 7.5 cm x 11.7 cm.

13. Five cards, crosses, with verses.
a) Three have a rustic cross with flowers or ivy, gilt line borders, one dated 1878 by the sender. 7.2 cm x 11 cm.
b) Two have gilded crosses, entwined with violets and gentians, on a plain white card. 7.5 cm x 10 cm.

14/15. Thirteen cards, seven designs, with flower sprays, and beige and brown line border. Six have Christmas or New Year greetings, seven texts. c1880.
7.8 cm x 11.2 cm.

16/17. Twenty-two cards with various embossed flower sprays, eight designs, with pink or blue ribbons, and greetings for Christmas, New Year, birthday or valentine. Two cards are marked Mansell, but this set was perhaps from another maker. The description of a set from Falck, in Jonathan King's stock book no. 207 in the John Johnson Collection, tallies with these cards. c1880. 4.7 cm x 8 cm.

18/20. Nineteen cards, eight folders, eleven single, incorporating six designs of mixed flower sprays. The folders are brown outside with flower sprays and greeting in a panel, and the cards have greetings in verse, or texts. c1879.
6.3 cm x 9.5 cm.

21. Six embossed cards with gilt borders, four designs, flower sprays and greetings in bordered panels. c1880. 13 cm x 6.7 cm.

22. Four cards, three designs, flower sprays on beige backgrounds with Christmas or New Year greetings. These are marked J Mansell, but the same set appears marked T S (Thomas Stevens) and A H (Albert Hildesheimer). One is on a gilt edged mount. c1880. 10.5 cm x 6.5 cm.

23. Five cards, all the same design of a rose spray on a beige ground, with different greetings in a bordered panel. One is marked J Mansell, one E B & Co (Bollans). One was marked 1878 by the sender.
10.8 cm x 6.5 cm.

24. Seven cards, six on black backgrounds, one on beige, with three designs of flower sprays, and greeting in verse on scrolls. c1880. 10.8 cm x 6.5 cm.

25/26. Eleven cards, five on black backgrounds, five gilt and one on brown with five designs of flower sprays and various greetings on panels. c1880.
11 cm x 7.4 cm.

27. Four valentine cards. c1880. a) Three with children on flowers, with loving greetings. 7 cm x 10.7 cm. b) One with flower sprays, and hearts transfixed by arrows, with verse in vignette.
8 cm x 12.8 cm.

28. Eight cards with a variety of flower and holly designs on bordered mounts. c1880. Sizes up to 7.2 cm x 11.6 cm.

29. Four cards, with grey borders, flower sprays. One has a superimposed silver lace border. c1880. 7.2 cm x 11.6 cm.

30. Six cards, four designs, with flower pictures of edelweiss, gentians and spring blooms. Four are on black backgrounds. One is marked J. Mansell, but they resemble a set of Marcus Ward cards. c1880. 10.8 cm x 7.1 cm.

31. Four cards of winter scenes, three having lace borders. All have Christmas or New Year verses. c1875.
Sizes up to 8.2 cm x 12 cm.

32. One card, scallop edge, with a child looking out of a window at a cherub with a Christmas tree, c1875. 8 cm x 11.8 cm.

# CHARLES GOODALL & SON

Charles Goodall & Son were pioneers in the production of playing
cards in the early 1870's. They made illustrated Christmas stationery
from 1859, and issued what were probably the first visiting card styles
from 1862 (see volume 2). They continued producing Christmas cards
for thirty years, using well known artists and illustrators, and were
noted for outstandingly fine printing. All identified Goodall cards are
included here, with the exception of the early visiting cards in volumes
2 and 3, and a few cards by Kate Greenaway included in the volumes
devoted to her work. There are very few entries in Stationers' Hall
records, and none have been traced to this collection. The cards are
identified by the Goodall trade mark, a heart with Goodall within, or
signature "C G & Sons" or "Goodall" beneath the picture, and a few
later ones have been attributed by similarity of production.

*Section*

*4*

26.26                                29.13

## VOLUME 24: GOODALL, CARDS MAINLY DESIGNED BY CHARLES BENNETT, ALFRED CROWQUILL, ROBERT DUDLEY

**Some cards are plain, others with lace borders, and the same design was used in different ways. Folding cards tell a story. They were issued from 1870-1875 with a few exceptions as stated.**

1. Two cards from the set of four designed by Charles Bennett in 1866. This set, and the 1865 set, are illustrated in Gleeson White's "Christmas Cards and their Chief Designers". 6.6 cm x 9.5 cm.

2. Two cards.
a) A feathered robin on a winter landscape. 11 cm x 7 cm.
b) A surprise or "voiced" robin on postcard size mount with concealed whistle, patent 1877.  14 cm x 9.5 cm.

3. Six cards with robins or scenes, four on lace embossed mounts with scraps, two smaller with embossed borders.
6 cm x 8.8 cm up to 10.5 cm x 7.2 cm.

4. Four cards on fancy lace mounts, one design of a robin with a letter.
Sizes up to 8.5 cm x 12 cm.

5. Robert Dudley? Two cards on gilt embossed mounts, each with a print of two robins and a Christmas pudding, one lifting to show a knight attacking a turkey. Sizes up to 12.2 cm x 8.7 cm.

6. Four cards.
a) A folder telling the tale of "Our Goose".
b) A folder "The Old English Gentleman" on a gilt edged mount, opening to show music and verses, with four pictures illustrating the story.
c) Two cards, each with one picture from b, with verses on reverse.
Sizes up to 8.3 cm x 12 cm.

7. Three cards.
a) A folder telling the story of The Queen of Hearts in four pictures.
b) Two separate cards with Christmas and New Year greetings. 13 cm x 9 cm.

8. One card, a folder including four illuminated flower and holly cards with silk fringe edge. 11.7 cm x 7.2 cm.

9. Alfred Crowquill. Four cards.
a) A triptych, with Father Christmas and humanised pudding, with verses.
b) Three cards of "the pudding that got away" in different mounts. 7 cm x 10.5 cm.

10. Alfred Crowquill. Four humorous cards, with appropriate verses on reverse - The Pig Rig, The Oyster, The Turkey, The File of Bills. 7.2 cm x 10.2 cm.

11. Robert Dudley? Five cards with the same picture of cats, kittens and ice cream, used in various ways. Four are on embossed or gilded mounts, and one on a plain correspondence style card, this dated c1888.
8.6 cm x 5.5 cm up to 11.7 cm x 9.4 cm.

12. Robert Dudley? Five cards.
a) Triptych card, joined by ribbons, with Father Christmas, holly, and a Georgian group. 8.7 cm x 13.3 cm.
b) Four cards on gilt grounds, on embossed edge mounts, (including two of the Georgian group).  6.5 cm x 9.4 cm.

13. Robert Dudley. Six cards, three of personified pudding, two of Sir Loin, and one a later blank folder with Georgian figures, perhaps for a programme of the 1880's. Sizes up to 6.5 cm x 9.8 cm.

14. Robert Dudley. Five cards, three designs, of elves, clowns, and Harlequin and Columbine, on lace edged cards. The signed original of one, in the possession of a descendant of the Goodall family, has been seen by the writer.
Sizes up to 8 cm x 11.3 cm.

15. Robert Dudley. Seven cards of humanised robins, three designs on lace, coloured, or gilded mounts.
Sizes up to 12.1 cm x 8.3 cm.

16. Robert Dudley. Eight cards on various gilt, embossed, and lace edged mounts showing humanised Christmas dinner, snapdragon, pigs etc.
5 cm x 7.8 cm up to 11.5 cm x 8 cm.

17. Robert Dudley. Five cards, with small rectangular or oval prints of humorous situations, on gilt, blue or red background mounts with floral design. (Note Goodall Trade Mark in design). 10 cm x 6 cm.

18. Robert Dudley. Twelve cards on various embossed mounts, some with gilt, showing comic situations, personified Christmas dinner etc. 5.5 cm x 8.5 cm.

19. Robert Dudley. Eleven cards with lace or scalloped borders, humorous situations with people and animals. 5.5 cm x 8.4 cm.

20. Robert Dudley. Eleven similar, with coloured border designs.
Sizes up to 5.5 cm x 8.2 cm.

21. Robert Dudley. Ten similar, with lace or scalloped edge.
Sizes up to 9.4 cm x 6.1 cm.

22. Robert Dudley. Seven cards on fancy lace, embossed, gilded or coloured mounts, repeating previous designs.
9.6 cm x 6.5 cm up to 12 cm x 8.3 cm.

23. Robert Dudley. Eight cards, five designs on various fancy mounts, with oval pictures of people, or robins, and

greeting in border. 7.6 cm x 5.2 cm up to 9.3 cm x 6 cm.

24. Robert Dudley. Twelve cards, nine designs on lace, gilt or embossed mounts, with prints or oval vignettes of robins. Sizes up to 5.5 cm x 8.5 cm.

25. Robert Dudley. Nine cards, five designs on various mounts, lace, gilt or embossed, of robins in Christmas situations. Sizes up to 10.5 cm x 7.2 cm.

26. E Duncan, R W S. Two cards, with the same picture of peasants gathering holly. One is on a lace mount which lifts to show a picture of children, the other on a plain embossed mount. The writer has seen the original drawing.
Sizes up to 11.2 cm x 7.8 cm.

27/8. Thirteen cards, nine designs, various pictures of winter scenes in oval or rectangular vignettes on embossed or coloured mounts.
Sizes up to 10 cm x 7 cm.

29. Eleven cards, eight designs on white embossed or lace edge mounts, with oval or rectangular prints of country scenes. 7.6 cm x 5.3 cm up to 6.2 cm x 9.5 cm.

30. Six cards, four designs on lace edge mounts, of family, children, or Father Christmas in Alpine scenes, one dated 1869 by the sender. 7.2 cm x 10.5 cm.

31. Five cards, three designs on lace edge mounts, with scenes of school, watchman, and Father Christmas. 7.2 cm x 10.5 cm.

32. Three cards, two designs, chicks on gilt edge or embossed mounts.
Sizes up to 12.5 cm x 8.5 cm.

33. Six cards, two of mediaeval indoor scenes, four of outdoor scenes, on various mounts. Sizes 6.5 cm x 9.4 cm up to 10.5 cm x 7.2 cm.

34. Three cards, c1888, with pictures by Robert Dudley used on plain correspondence cards. (see no. 11). Probably from a set of six.
11.8 cm x 9.2 cm.

35/36. Eleven calendars. "Time's Footsteps" probably all by Robert Dudley. Complete issues for 1874, 1877, 1880, 1881, 1882, 1888. Covers only for 1872, 1873, 1875, 1876, 1879. Closed 5.9 cm x 9 cm.

## VOLUME 25: GOODALL - MORE CARDS OF THE EARLY 1870'S

**Most of these are on fancy mounts and some are mechanical.**

1. One card, a lady in a brown dress, with holly, printed on silk.  9 cm x 13.8 cm.

2/3. Seventeen cards, eight designs on various gilt, embossed and coloured mounts, with half figures of girls in oval vignettes, two lifting to show another picture beneath. 6 cm x 9.5 cm up to 7.3 cm x 10.8 cm.

4. Seven cards, five designs of girls, head and shoulders, on various fancy mounts. Sizes up to 7.2 cm x 10.7 cm.

5. Ten cards, with girls or children on various gilded and embossed mounts. Sizes up to 6.7 cm x 9.2 cm.

6. Six cards, on various lace and gilt mounts, four with Georgian style children, one with three oval prints, and one of a dancer which lifts to show greeting below. 6.2 cm x 9.3 cm up to 11.3 cm x 9 cm.

7. Four cards with the same background of four oval prints with verse "Tis Flora's page...". Two have four lifting flaps with pictures of children. 7.3 cm x 10.7 cm.

8. Four similar, three with three lifting flaps, and one with flower scraps over picture, and cherubs. 7 cm x 10.5 cm.

9. Two cards with gilt edge, and design of water lilies and shells, one embossed. One has an oval scrap lifting to show picture below. 7.7 cm x 11.2 cm.

10. Four cards, with gilt edge borders, three designs. Two have cherubs and a garland, one an oval print of a family by a cross, and one a flower motif which lifts to show cherubs beneath. 7.9 cm x 11.2 cm.

11. Six cards, with lifting flower scraps on various fancy mounts. Sizes up to 8.7 cm x 12.5 cm.

12. Three cards with lace border, two of these with gilt, with various designs of flower scraps, a girl, a tree with birds and holly, lifting to show a winter scene. The lace border is similar to one by Canton. 8.5 cm x 12.3 cm.

13. One card on a plain mount with a picture of fungi. A scrap of a vase in aesthetic style lifts to show an owl - a curious mixture! c1880. 9.2 cm x 12.3 cm.

14. Four cards.
a) An elaborate card with an oval print of a lady on a swimming horse, which lifts to show flowers and a verse of greeting. 12.3 cm x 8.5 cm.
b) Three plain cards of the same set with flowers and greetings. 11 cm x 7.5 cm.

15. Five cards.
a) An elaborate card with an oval print of a summer scene with scraps of people, lifting to show another card with robin and holly. 12.3 cm x 8.5 cm.
b) Four lace edge cards, of the same set with robin and holly. 10.2 cm x 6.7 cm.

16. Seven cards, three with romantic style figures, four with flower wreaths on lace or embossed mounts, one dated 1867 by the sender.
9 cm x 6 cm up to 8 cm x 11.6 cm.

17. Three cards, one design with a Twelfth Night theme. Two have lace borders, and one has elaborate gilt and lace surrounding the oval print.
10.3 cm x 7.2 cm, 12 cm x 8.5 cm.

18. Six cards on different mounts, the same design of Red Riding Hood on five cards and the sixth with a mother and children. 7.2 cm x 10.3 cm up to 11.5 cm x 8 cm.

19. Six cards on embossed edge mounts, four with scraps of grotesque figures or jesters, one with a dog, and one with children in a swing. 8.4 cm x 12 cm.

20. Six assorted cards on various mounts with scraps or prints, one showing the Goodall trade mark.
Sizes up to 7.4 cm x 11 cm.

21. Six assorted cards on various mounts with scraps or prints of cherubs, or Holy Family. Sizes up to 7.7 cm x 11.5 cm.

22. Five cards.
a) Three with children, or flowers, on fine gilt lace edged mounts.
b) One with opening envelope and floral print.
c) One with a pansy, which opens to show a girl's face. 7 cm x 10 cm.

23. Four cards (three designs).
a) An envelope, enclosing a lace edged flower card.
b) Three similar cards, one dated 1872 by the sender. 7 cm x 10.5 cm.

24. Three cards, lace edge, with large flower scraps, which lift to reveal message. 7.2 cm x 10.5 cm.

25. Five cards on gilt and embossed mounts, with lifting oval motifs. 7.3 cm x 10.5 cm.

26. Three cards, lace edge, two with flower scraps, one with a scene. The border resembles one used by Canton.
Sizes up to 7.3 cm x 11 cm.

27. Six cards, embossed lace edge, with flower scraps or prints.
Sizes up to 8 cm x 11.3 cm.

28. Ten cards, oval flower scraps or prints on various mounts. 6.1 cm x 9.4 cm.

29. Ten cards, flower prints on embossed or lace edge mounts, nine designs.
Sizes up to 6.7 cm x 10.2 cm.

30. Nine cards, flower prints on embossed or lace edge mounts, seven designs 6.5 cm x 9.7 cm.

31. Nine cards, flower prints on various mounts. 5 cm x 7 cm to 7.4 cm x 10.7 cm.

32. Four cards, lace or embossed edges with flower prints. One design, on two cards, is the mirror image of a Canton card in Volume 18, no 32. 10 cm x 14.2 cm, 8 cm x 11.2 cm.

33. Six cards, flower prints on gilt edged mounts. Sizes up to 7.7 cm x 11.3 cm.

## VOLUME 26: GOODALL - EARLY PLAIN CARDS

**These cards are early 1870's, and have brief Christmas or New Year greetings, with occasional verses. The subjects include humour, animals and birds, with the humanised robin and personified Christmas dinner.**

1. Seven cards, c1870. Two have verses "The Yule Log" and "Snapdragon" with appropriate pictures, another shows the "Ancient Armorial Bearings of the Yule family", with pig, turkey, pudding and robin. Four are on similar mounts with pictures of holly and a handshake, two people kissing under mistletoe, people going to church, and carol singers. Sizes up to 6.7 cm x 10 cm.

2. Two cards, c1870, one of a sunrise, the other with a Georgian couple under mistletoe. 4.8 cm x 7.4 cm.

3. Five cards with embossed edges. Four have verses and robins with holly, mistletoe, ivy or flowers, and one is a holly spray with greeting. 6.6 cm x 9.6 cm.

4/5. Ten cards, six designs, four of robins, one Father Christmas, one the Old Year. Eight have a white embossed edge, and two a brown pattern. R Dudley? 6.5 cm x 9.2 cm, 7 cm x 9.9 cm.

6. Seven cards, showing the personified Christmas dinner and birds and animals on embossed edge cards. R Dudley? 7 cm x 9.9 cm, 9.9 cm x 7 cm.

7. Four cards, two designs of robins, three with embossed edge, and one with brown line pattern. 10.2 cm x 7 cm.

8/10. Fifteen cards, eleven designs with two different pattern line borders in brown, with pictures of birds and animals in comic situations, Christmas scenes, personified Christmas dinner, snowballs. 9.9 cm x 7 cm.

11. Six humorous cards, Christmas scenes with triangular brown line pattern border. R Dudley? 9.9 cm x 7 cm.

12. Six humorous cards, four with a boy and birds and animals, two with

Christmas dinner scenes and robin. Two different brown line borders.
9.9 cm x 7 cm.

13. Six cards, five designs bordered by brown line, five of personified birds and pudding, one of deer on a mountain. R Dudley? 10.3 cm x 7.5 cm.

14. Five humorous cards with personified robins, bordered by gilt and blue line. R Dudley? 10.2 cm x 7.4 cm.

15/16. Fourteen cards, eleven designs of people and children in Christmas scenes, and humanised animals. Two different borders. 7 cm x 9.9 cm.

17. Six cards with scalloped embossed borders, children and Christmas figures in Christmas scenes. One is a figure in red riding a goat "When Capricorn doth bring us colde", a recurrent theme in cards of this period. c1870.
6 cm x 9.5 cm, 7 cm x 10 cm.

18. Four lace-edged cards, two with figures in Georgian dress, one with a mother and babe, one with two children in snow.
7 cm x 10.5 cm.

19. Six cards with pictures of pigs, Little Jack Horner, Red Riding Hood, the New Year and the Old Year, in gilt backed vignettes with patterned surrounds.
6.5 cm x 9.2 cm.

20. Six humorous cards with pink and gilt line border, showing the personified Christmas dinner, clown, Father Christmas and children in snow. 9.4 cm x 6.5 cm.

21. Nine cards.
a) Set of six with small children in fancy dress in various pursuits. 9.2 cm x 5.4 cm.
b) Three others with Christmas scenes in snow and ice. 6.5 cm x 9.4 cm.

22. Two cards. A fox leading a goose to dinner, and people in a storm outside an umbrella repair shop, both with patterned borders. 10.3 cm x 7.2 cm, 11 cm x 7.7 cm.

23. Four humorous cards with personified robins and Christmas dinner, three on a fancy blue border. R Dudley? Sizes up to 9 cm x 12.5 cm.

24. Set of four humorous cards of clowns in circus antics. c1880. 11.3 cm x 7.8 cm.

25. One card, Father Christmas figure with tray of cards, handing these out to children, possibly Goodall. c1880.
7.3 cm x 11.8 cm.

26. Two humorous cards, one with boy and goose, the other showing the New Year and the Old Year on a seesaw over Earth, possibly Goodall. c1880.
11.8 cm x 7.3 cm.

27. One card, a party of humanised bears in a snow scene, c1875. 11.6 cm x 8 cm.

## VOLUME 27: GOODALL - ANGELS AND ILLUMINATED CARDS

**These cards are exceptionally well printed, showing Goodall at this time as far ahead of most of his competitors in artistic achievement and design. Most are dated in the early 1870s.**

1/3. Thirteen cards, eleven designs probably by Robert Dudley, with angel scenes on gilt or coloured grounds. One is reversed to show a Christmas greeting verse. 7.2 cm x 11.8 cm.

4. Three similar cards. 7.2 cm x 11.8 cm.

5. Three illuminated cards, with angels and Christmas or New Year verses. Perhaps by Luke Limner? c1870. 10.2 cm x 7 cm.

6. Five cards with gilt ground or border, and nativity or religious scenes. Sizes up to 11.8 cm x 7.2 cm.

7. Four cards with Christmas verses and illuminated scroll designs, one dated 1867 by the sender. 11.6 cm x 6.7 cm.

8. Four cards with illuminated designs and verses. 11.4 cm x 6.7 cm.

9/10. Eight cards, attractive stylised flower designs on gilt ground, with Christmas or New Year greeting and verse.
11.8 cm x 7.2 cm.

11. Four miscellaneous illuminated cards with flowers, religious scene, holly, or deer, two with verses. 11.8 cm x 7.2 cm.

12. Four illuminated designs with robin, bird, squirrel, or holly set in illuminated initial. Probably by Luke Limner.
11.8 cm x 7.2 cm.

13. Two cards, birds, holly or flowers, on gilt ground with verse on scroll.
11 cm x 7.2 cm.

14/15. Eight cards, miscellaneous flower and holly designs on illuminated ground, with inset verses, two dated 1868, 1871 by the senders. Sizes up to 11.8 cm x 7.2 cm.

16. Four miscellaneous illuminated cards with Christmas or New Year verses, two with a robin, one with a duck, one with flowers. 7.2 cm x 11.8 cm.

17/18. Eight cards, seven designs with various flowers and holly on illuminated ground, with verses, one dated 1870 by the sender. 11.8 cm x 7.2 cm.

19. Five card, three designs, one reversed to show verse by W B Atkinson, with

flower, holly and robins on illuminated ground. 11.8 cm x 7.2 cm.

20. Two cards, one a folder with holly and snowdrop panels and Christmas and New Year verses, the other a single card of the snowdrop design with New Year greeting. 11.8 cm x 7.2 cm.

21. Three cards, one a folder with holly and flower motifs and Christmas and New Year verses, with two other identical single cards. 11.8 cm x 7.2 cm.

22. Three cards, flower designs with illuminated initial and verses by S C Hall, one dated 1878 by the sender.
8.1 cm x 17 cm.

23/24. Fourteen cards, twelve designs, verses set in flower surrounds, with various coloured line borders.
6.4 cm x 9.4 cm.

25. Eight cards, bird scenes on gilt grounds, one dated 1880. 6.4 cm x 9.4 cm.

26. Four cards, two designs, flowers set in to crosses, two reversed to show acrostic verses. 7.2 cm x 11.8 cm.

27/29. Eleven cards, seven designs, flowers and butterflies with panels enclosing Christmas or New Year verses, one with holly, later 1870's.
7.2 cm x 11.8 cm.

30. Four miscellaneous similar cards, with swans, fruit, or flowers. Sizes up to 6.5 cm x 9.3 cm.

## VOLUME 28: GOODALL - FLOWERS, BIRDS AND ANIMALS, 1870-1880

**This volume of plain cards features black backgrounds, flower subjects, and a few birds and animals in conventional style, with brief seasonal greetings or verses.**

1. Nine cards, five designs on black backgrounds of fruit, two with grotesque faces. One is marked "Spalding, Cambridge", perhaps the distributor. c1875. 10.8 cm x 6.5 cm.

2. Five cards, with flowers and verses in scrolls on black background. c1875. Sizes up to 10.5 cm x 6.5 cm.

3. One card, a shell and seaweed design on a black ground, around a birthday greeting verse, c1875. 11.2 cm x 16.5 cm.

4. Eight cards, with five designs of shells and seaweed, on black background. c1875. 8.8 cm x 5.7 cm.

5. Six cards, flower and fruit designs with greeting on scrolls, c1875. 10.8 cm x 6.5 cm.

6. Three similar, flower designs, with verses signed F R H. c1875. 10.5 cm x 5.8 cm.

7. Eight cards, seven designs of flower sprays, three with black backgrounds, c1875. 5.8 cm x 9.2 cm.

8. Nine cards, four designs of flower bouquets in a lace paper holder. Four have black backgrounds and one has a greeting in German. c1875. 6.8 cm x 10.2 cm.

9. Two identical cards, advertisement for "Good Words for 1877", with a flower design on a black ground. One is reversed to show the text. 13.3 cm x 8 cm.

10. Two cards with flower sprays on blue or yellow ground, one marked 1878 by the sender. 12.8 cm x 8.7 cm.

11/12. Nine cards, six designs, one on black background, with flowers and butterfly, and verse of greeting, some with botanical names on reverse. c1875. 11.8 cm x 7.2 cm.

13/14. Eight cards, five designs, one on black background with flowers and insects and panels with verse of greeting, c1875. 11.8 cm x 7.2 cm.

15/17. Eleven cards, eight designs, flowers or berries around a scroll with greeting. Three were marked 1878 by the sender. 11.8 cm x 7.2 cm.

18. Four cards, three designs of flower sprays. Late 1870's. 11.8 cm x 7.2 cm.

19. Three cards, two designs, exotic flowers on a blue ground with greeting in panel. Late 1870's. 11.8 cm x 7.2 cm.

20. Three cards, flower sprays on a wood pattern ground, c1880. 12.8 cm x 8 cm.

21. Three cards with highly coloured fruit designs and a Greek key border, c1880. 12.8 cm x 9.5 cm.

22. Three cards, two designs of fruit and flower sprays, one with a ladybird, around Christmas or New Year verses, c1880. 9 cm x 13.2 cm.

23. Four miscellaneous flower cards, c1880. Sizes up to 13 cm x 8 cm.

24. Four cards with farmyard subjects of ducks, hens, cats and rabbits, one marked 1879 by sender. 14 cm x 9.3 cm.

25. Two cards, one mice and acorns, the other a nest with eggs and a butterfly, with fancy gilded border and inscription to friends. c1880. 11.2 cm x 17.3 cm.

26. Three cards, two designs as in no. 25 with plain gilt border and simple greeting, c1880. 8 cm x 13.7 cm.

27. Three cards, two designs of birds in vignettes with flower or berry border, c1880. 13.2 cm x 10 cm.

28. One card with birds and a nest in reeds, c1880. 7.5 cm x 18.3 cm.

29. Two cards, a duck or a heron in a water scene, one dated 1879 by the sender. 15 cm x 9.1 cm.

30. One card, a bird on a rose branch, possibly Goodall. c1880. 11 cm x 16 cm.

31. Three cards, two designs, a robin on a flower spray, bullfinches, with verse, c1880. 11.5 cm x 7.2 cm, 7.5 cm x 14 cm.

32. Three cards, two designs, exotic birds on a tree branch, with verse, c1880. 7cm x 15.2 cm.

33. Three cards, birds in water scenes, c1880. 13.5 cm x 7.5 cm, 8.8 cm x 12.7 cm.

34. Two cards, showing grasshoppers and mice having a party, dated 1879 and 1880 by the senders. 16.4 cm x 6.8 cm.

35. Three cards, Scottish country scenes, with a flower spray, c1880. 14.5 cm x 7.8 cm.

## VOLUME 29:
## GOODALL - CHILDREN, LADIES, ETC, LATER CARDS

**This volume contains cards featuring children, ladies, scenes etc., of an artistic standard not always comparable with that of previous volumes, though the printing is still good. They are dated c1880, except where otherwise stated.**

1. Six cards, four designs, three with children, one with a lady in a snowscene. 7.2 cm x 10.3 cm.

2. Two cards, one design of a girl in a swing with wisteria, pansies and auricula, and panels with a Christmas or New Year verse. 10.5 cm x 17 cm.

3. Five cards, three designs of nursery rhymes, Hush a bye, Baby, Little Jack Horner, Bo-peep, with verses for Christmas and New Year. 7.9 cm x 12 cm.

4. Three cards, children in party scenes. 8.7 cm x 12.5 cm.

5. Three cards, skating and sledging scenes. 9 cm x 12.2 cm.

6. One card, peasants with a sleigh. 9.7 cm x 13 cm.

7. Two cards, one with two children in a winter scene, another holly (dated 1877 by sender). 7.2 cm x 11.8 cm.

8. Two cards, one with an angel and birds, the other with three cherubs, in a Greek key border. 12.7 cm x 9.8 cm.

9. Four cards, three designs of ladies on a gilt or silver background, with flowers. 7.5 cm x 11.3 cm.

10. Four cards, three designs, two with a jester and a lady in a red dress, two on a gilt ground with a girl or boy with a letter in a floral surround. 8.5 cm x 11.7 cm and 9.3 cm x 13.3 cm.

11. One card, a Georgian party in a country scene with a fountain. 9.3 cm x 14 cm.

12. Two cards, girls, one indoors, one outdoors by the sea. 10.2 cm x 12.7 cm.

13. Five cards, four designs of children seated variously on an egg, a drum with a pudding, or floral sprays. 8.3 cm x 11.8 cm.

14. Three cards, one a seaside scene, one a lady in classical dress, and the third a girl in a winter scene. Sizes up to 9 cm x 13.7 cm.

15. Two cards, an elf with puppets, and a boy riding on a humanised cat in boots. 9 cm x 12 cm.

16. Three cards with unprepossessing girls' heads in circular vignettes with floral surrounds. 7.6 cm x 11.5 cm.

17. Three cards, girls in classical dress. 7.5 cm x 12.2 cm.

18. Four cards, small children in indoor and outdoor scenes.12.2 cm x 8.8 cm.

19. Six cards, babies and children in outdoor and indoor scenes, some with birds and animals. Sizes up to 8 cm x 11.6 cm.

20. Two cards, one a child at a piano, and another under the mistletoe. These have an unusual large trademark and are numbered 201. 8.8 cm x 12 cm.

21. Three cards, boys in snow on a pale blue ground. 8 cm x 11.2 cm.

22. Three miscellaneous cards, a cherub with a large fish, a girl in the snow, and a girl in an autumn scene. Sizes up to 7.5 cm x 11 cm.

23. Four "In Memoriam" cards, all marked, folders with black and white decoration and silver borders, dated 1889, 1899, 1902, 1905. These indicate that card production of some description continued under the name of Goodall into the 20th century, though Buday gives the dates of Christmas card production as 1862 to about 1885. 11.5 cm x 7.8 cm.

# MARCUS WARD & CO

The firm of Marcus Ward was originally at the Royal Ulster Works in Belfast where they printed cards for other publishers. These included the Charles Bennett cards of 1865 and 1866 for Goodall. They opened in London in 1867, where they published cards with their own imprint. With Thomas Crane (brother of Walter) as artistic director, their products while satisfying popular taste, achieved a high artistic standard which they maintained till the 1890's when cheap German products took over much of the market. They employed many well known illustrators including Walter Crane and Kate Greenaway and published many well illustrated books. The cards are marked, either with their trademark on reverse, or later with the name of the firm, or initials. Large numbers were registered at Stationers' Hall in the 1870's and many of the cards in this collection can be precisely dated and often attributed to their designers, from the Stationers' Hall entries in the Public Record Office at Kew. Marcus Ward employed many sentiment writers, of whom the most prominent was Frances Ridley Havergal, whose Christmas and religious verses are found on many cards and in the numerous packets of Reward cards issued by the firm, perhaps celebrating the centenary of the Sunday School movement in 1880.

*Section*
*5*

38.32

## VOLUME 30:
## MARCUS WARD.
## ILLUMINATED CARDS WITH
## SCRAPS & PRINTS

**It is probable that most of the designs of these cards were by Thomas Crane, but his name seldom appears in the Stationers' Hall records. Many have prints manufactured in Germany. They are c1875, except where otherwise stated.**

1. Twelve cards with oval prints of children or nativity scenes, on various coloured backs with gilt patterns. 4.7 cm x 8.3 cm and 7 cm x 10 cm.

2. Seven similar cards, six designs, with scraps of children at play. Sizes 8.3 cm x 4.7 cm up to 10 cm x 7 cm.

3. Twelve cards, ten designs with illuminated borders and attached scraps of children or nativity scenes, over verses. 5.7 cm x 7.7 cm.

4. Six cards, three designs. Four are folders, and two are similar single cards, with verses set in to illuminated floral or holly borders. 5.2 cm x 6.7 cm closed.

5. Twelve cards, six designs with Christmas or New Year verse in a panel surrounded by floral border on gilt ground, four having attached rectangular prints. The set of six was registered at Stationers' Hall 12-6-1876. 6 cm x 8.7 cm.

6. Ten cards, two folders, six designs in flower or berry borders with a bird on gilt ground, around a print of birds or children. Two were registered at Stationers' Hall on12-6-1876, and one on 15-6-1876. 5.6 cm x 7.5 cm, 6 cm x 8.3 cm.

7. Eleven cards, four designs including two folders, all with attached prints in floral borders on gilt. 5.6 cm x 7.5 cm closed.

**30.23**

8. Six cards with one border design of mistletoe on gilt, with rectangular prints of children and Christmas, New Year, or birthday verses at the top. 5.2 cm x 8.8 cm.

9. Eight cards, three border designs. One is a two page folder with conventional style border of fruit, with three similar single cards; four have a border design of birds on blossom around attached prints over verses. 8.2 cm x 5.8 cm, 7 cm x 9.9 cm.

10. Three cards, two being identical three page folders (one reversed to show back), with illuminated designs including a Christmas tree in a pot, and a single similar card. 7.5 cm x 11.2 cm closed.

11. Seven cards with illuminated border designs around attached prints over verses, one on black-background. 7.5 cm x 10.8 cm, 8.2 cm x 6 cm.

12. Six cards with the same border design of Christmas roses around rectangular prints of angels, cherubs, nativity, or Georgian figure. 8.2 cm x 11.8 cm.

13. Six cards, all the same design, three being folders with bird and flower designs on reverse in red or blue, and three single similar cards with attached prints of children and flowers over verse. 7.5 cm x 11 cm closed.

14. Three cards, two designs, three page folders, with flower designs on gilt ground and illuminated backs. One has a Christmas verse by J Green. 7 cm x 11 cm, 7.5 cm x 7.5 cm closed.

15. Five cards with the same floral border design on gilt around a panel with Christmas or New Year verse. Three have attached prints. 11.7 cm x 8.2 cm.

16. Four cards with the same holly border design on gilt, and prints over Christmas

greeting verse. Three of these prints, with robins, were published separately as cards.11.7 cm x 8.2 cm.

17. Four cards
a) Two with conventional border designs of flowers or holly and mistletoe, aroundprint. 12 cm x 8.3 cm.
b) Two with holly border around Christmas verse with attached print. Registered at Stationers' Hall 15-6-1876. 12 cm x 8.3 cm.

18. Three cards with border design of violets around a verse (two with attached prints). Registered at Stationers' Hall 15-6-1876. 12 cm x 8.3 cm.

19. Six miscellaneous cards with different border designs, around prints. Three of these with red lilies, periwinkle, ivy and primula were registered at Stationers' Hall 14-6-1876. 7 cm x 10 cm up to 9.8 cm x 13.2 cm.

20. Four cards with the same conventional border design in pink and blue, around prints of Georgian couples. 8.4 cm x 12 cm.

21. Nine cards with three border designs in red, blue, mauve and green, around Christmas or New Year verses. Four have attached scraps of children. 7.6 cm x 11 cm.

22. Five cards. Two are folders with an illuminated border design and a bird design on reverse, and three are similar single cards. The coloured scraps are probably from Kinze Bros, Meissner, of Leipzig. 7.2 cm x 11 cm closed.

23. Four cards, all with the same border design of toys in bright colours on gilt with different captions, around German style prints of babies, three versions. 13.5 cm x10.1 cm.

24. Seven cards, or prints, six designs with pictures of a baby as in no 23. Registered at Stationers' Hall 15-9-74, by Kinze Bros & Meissner, Leipzig. Sizes up to 10.5 cm x 6.2 cm.

25. Four cards, three designs as in no 23, with embossed lace edges. Babies as above. One has a greeting in German. 11.3 cm x 8 cm.

26. Four cards, two border designs, one of daisies and forget-me-nots, one of red jasmine on blue, around attached prints. The jasmine design was registered at Stationers' Hall 24-7-1876. 13.7 cm x 10.2 cm.

27. Three cards with a border design of hawthorn and berries, greeting in a scroll, around attached prints over verses by S C Hall. Sizes up to 12.9 cm x 9.7 cm.

28. Four cards, all triptych folders, with pink and green scroll border design on gilt around prints attached over Christmas or New Year verses. 7.2 cm x 11 cm closed.

29. Three similar cards with the same design in green and mauve, showing verses by S C Hall and others. 7.2 cm x 11 cm closed.

30. Four cards, two designs, with flower borders on gilt around Christmas or New Year verses by Julia Goddard. Two cards have attached prints of two children carrying a large bouquet. 10 cm x 13 cm.

31. Four cards, two designs, with conventional floral borders around attached prints. Two cards have Christmas and New Year verses. Sizes up to 10 cm x 13 cm.

32. Two cards, triptych folders, with illuminated designs and country scenes. 10 cm x 14.2 cm closed.

33. Five cards, four designs with angel and nativity scenes, one with a lace border marked 1871 by the sender, another 1876. Sizes 7.6 cm x 11 cm up to 10 cm x 14.2 cm.

34. Three cards, one a triptych folder with carol singers, two with illuminated borders around angel prints. Sizes up to 9.5 cm x 12.8 cm.

35. Three cards, one a folder with the Lord's Prayer, and the others triptych folders with illuminated floral and catkin designs, one an Easter card, one Christmas. 8 cm x 11.7 cm, 9 cm x 11.7 cm closed.

36. Four cards, triptych folders, with identical illuminated designs and attached religious prints over four different Christmas verses. The exterior has a Gothic style design. 6.6 cm x 11.8 cm closed.

37. Four cards, triptych folders, with identical pink and blue scroll border design, and attached prints over two different verses by S C Hall. The exteriors are in pink, blue or green. 7.4 cm x 10.8 cm closed.

38. Three cards and seven scraps of crosses. The cards have the same design of angels and shepherds, with circular religious prints on a scrap cross over a greeting; the crosses, three designs, are similar, with illuminated designs and attached scraps. 8.3 cm x 11.6 cm, 6.8 cm x 8 cm.

39. Three cards
a) A border of lilies on a red ground around a gilt doorway with a cross, opening to show an angel print (Sulman).
b) A similar border on a blue ground, with a cross and passion flower - unmarked. 9 cm x 12.8 cm.

c) A three-fold cross, with religious print and illuminated scroll design. 6.8 cm x 8 cm closed.

40. Six cards, three versions with crosses on embossed bordered mounts. Two of these also appear on Canton cards, and one is in a set, published by S Hildesheimer, registered at Stationers' Hall 17-3-1875. 8 cm x 11.8 cm.

41. Six cards, four designs, gilded crosses entwined with flowers or ivy, on embossed bordered mounts. Registered at Stationers' Hall 20-6-1876. Sizes up to 8 cm x 11.8 cm.

42. Five valentine cards with Cupid prints, four designs, in a floral border on gilt ground, with valentine verse below. 8.2 cm x 11.7 cm.

43. Four valentine cards with two border designs with Cupids, around panels with valentine verse. Two have attached prints. 7.5 cm x 11.2 cm.

44. Six valentine cards, two border designs, three with attached prints of Georgian figures, the other three having prints over valentine verses. 7.7 cm x 11.2 cm.

45. Four cards, three border designs around prints with valentine verse below, and one a Happy New Year card with print. 11 cm x 7.7 cm.

46. Seven valentines.
a) Four with two border designs of lilies and buttercups, daffodils and primroses, around four different valentine verses, one with attached print.
b) Three cards with conventional passion flower design on gilt, and attached prints over three different valentine verses. 7.8 cm x 11.2 cm.

47. Six valentines, with the same illuminated border design on silver in pink or mauve, with attached prints of Georgian figures with captions below. 8.6 cm x 12.3 cm.

48. Two folding valentine cards with illuminated floral designs on the outside (one with a print), and scroll border designs inside with verses in vignettes. 8.8 cm x 13 cm closed.

49. Seven miscellaneous valentine cards with various borders around verses, and attached prints. Sizes 7.4 cm x 10.7 cm up to 9.7 cm x 13 cm.

50. Nine miscellaneous valentine cards with various borders around verses, and attached prints. Sizes 5 cm x 8.5 cm, 5.9 cm x 8 cm.

51. Six valentine cards, three designs.
a) With cupid and flower border around two prints. 11.8 cm x 8.2 cm.

b) One with two figures and print over verse. 7.8 cm x 5.9 cm.
c) Four with illuminated border design of birds on a branch, around prints with captions in scrolls. 7.8 cm x 5.9 cm.

52. Two elaborate folding valentines, with cherub figures, flowers and butterflies, in gilt border. The outside has a design of flower sprays on a gilt ground with verse by H A D. 25.2 cm x 10.3 cm opened.

53/54. A set of twelve Reward of Merit cards, with envelope (packet no 153), and flower designs and butterflies on coloured grounds. c1880. 7.1 cm x 13.5cm.

55. Six similar cards, with moral precepts in verse. 7.1 cm x 13.5 cm.

56. Set of four cards "Everlasting flowers" with envelope, no 142A, with flower sprays, and texts and verses on reverse by Frances Ridley Havergal. c1880. 10.2 cm x13.5 cm.

## VOLUME 31: MARCUS WARD. SOME ARTISTS' CARDS, FOLDING CARDS, ALMANACS, BOOKLETS, LACE EDGE.

**Marcus Ward published few "mechanical" cards, but relied more on artistic merit than on tricks. They produced many interesting folding series, and calendars, some of which are included here. The cards are mid 1870's, unless otherwise stated, and as in Volume 30, many of the illuminated decorations were by Thomas Crane.**

1/2. Seven cards (all four designs of the series are here), by H Stacy Marks, R A, of "Christmas in olden times". Three cards are 15.4 cm x 10.9 cm, and four smaller are 10.5 cm x 7.5 cm.

3. Three cards by W Tasker Nugent.
a) A boy in fancy Royalist dress, with a bouquet, on a lace bordered mount, over a folder with a Valentine verse. 15 cm x 18.8 cm.
b) Two cards, of a boy dressed as a Georgian soldier. 9.7 cm x 13.6 cm, 9.2 cm x14 cm.

4. A calendar by W Tasker Nugent, for 1880, eight pages, showing four pictures of girls dressed for Spring, Summer, Autumn, Winter, with calendar material on reverse. 7.3 cm x 10.3 cm closed.

5. Four cards, three designs, by W Tasker Nugent, of girls in fancy bonnets, with outsize plum, grapes, or chili. Registered at Stationers' Hall 19-11-1879. 9.5 cm x14.1 cm.

6. Four cards by Miriam Kerns, a girl by a stile, a couple on a wall, a lady with a bird,

a lady with a fairy. The first two cards are frequently attributed to Walter Crane. Registered at Stationers' Hall 26-5-1879. 9.8 cm x 13.5 cm.

7. Two cards by Miriam Kerns, one of the girl by a stile with a gilt border, the other of the couple on a lace edge mount on a folder with a valentine verse. 10.5 cm x15.8 cm, 15 cm x 18.8 cm.

8. Two eight-page calendars, one for 1878 with four pictures of maidens in mediaeval dress, the other for 1879 with four pictures of couples in mediaeval dress, and calendar details on reverse. 6.8 cm x 10 cm, 7.2 cm x 10.1 cm.

9. Three calendars.
a) 1874, four pages with elaborate floral decoration outside, bird card and calendarwithin. 8 cm x 12 cm
b) 1879, eight pages with four pictures of family scenes in mediaeval times, calendar details on reverse. 6.7 cm x 10.2 cm.
c) 1885, eight pages with four pictures of girls' heads in circular vignettes with floral borders. 6.5 cm x 10.4 cm.

10. A twelve page calendar for 1878 "Time Flieth", with five pictures of cherubs or children, and decorative cover, with verses on reverse. 7.7 cm x 11.7 cm closed.

11. Six cards and a folder with pink cover of the same cards "Father Christmas and his Little Friends", showing pictures of Father Christmas with children. Cards 10 cm x 6.7 cm.

12. Six similar cards with red border, and a folder cover in green. Cards 9.7 cm x 7 cm.

13. Six cards, with cover "Christmas with Punch & Judy". Cards 10 cm x 6.9 cm.

14. Six cards and a folder of the same cards in gilt and yellow cover. "A Christmas Pantomime". Cards 11.2 cm x 7.2 cm.

15. Eight cards and a green cover, six designs in the series, "Ye Newe Yeare Greetynge". A set of six cards shows mediaeval figures and has a silver border. Two other cards show a blue border. Cards 10.1 cm x 6.8 cm.

16. Four cards and a folder of six cards, "Fairies and Elves at Christmastide", with a gilt and yellow cover. The drawings are reminiscent of Richard Doyle, but have also some similarity to Kate Greenaway's fairies in "Puck and Blossom". No artist is given in the registration at Stationers' Hall, 30-4-1874. Folder 10.6 cm x 7.2 cm.

17. A folder of six cards telling "The Story of the Nativity" with two similar separate cards. This was perhaps the set registered at Stationers' Hall 15-10-1877. Cards 11.8 cm x 8 cm.

18. Three very fine illuminated folding cards.
a) Four flaps folding on to illuminated card, with four pictures of cherubs by E Carrière - registered at Stationers' Hall 27-11-1879. 14 cm x 11 cm. "A Fantasy in four phases".
b) A similar card, with four flaps, which have bird and floral pictures. 11 cm x 11 cm.
c) A similar card, with four flaps with bird pictures, and greetings "Health" "Wealth" "Happiness". 9 cm x 12 cm.

19. Three folding cards.
a) A folder made up of nine cards, including the Father Christmas set, and Thomas Crane designs of flowers and holly. 10.3 cm x 7 cm.
b) "Jack the Giant Killer's Christmas Conflict", an eight page folder with six pictures of humorous encounters of a boy with personified Christmas dinner. 7.2 cm x 10.4 cm.
c) Four flaps on an illuminated base, made up of nine cards of flowers, holly and birds. 8.9 cm x 11.9 cm.

20. A folder birthday card, with four flaps on an illuminated base, made up of eight floral cards around a picture of sheep. 15.4 cm x 11.3 cm closed.

21. Two cards.
a) A folding card, with floral pictures within and a nativity outside, on a lace bordered mount on a blue silk base. 12.7 cm x 8.11 cm.
b) A similar card on a lace edged mount with illuminated design and a New Year verse. 12.7 cm x 8.11 cm.

22. Three cards.
a) A folding card with children in an oval vignette on lace ground on the outside, and two pictures of children with flowers within, mounted on blue silk with frilled edge.
b) Two similar cards of children with flowers, with lace borders. 12 cm x 8.2 cm, and 11.7 cm x 8.2 cm.

23. Two cards.
a) A sachet, with oval vignette of a girl lifting to show a Christmas verse, on a blue and gilt ground with floral design. 8.5 cm x 12 cm.
b) A folding card, with four cards mounted on white silk with frilled edge. c1880. 11.5 cm x 9 cm. Two of these cards were registered at Stationers' Hall 19-11-1879 by Agnes Lewis.

24. Three silk-fringed cards, all folders with tassels, c1880.
a) Two pictures of birds, two of children. 13.4 cm x 9.5 cm.
b) Four pictures of roses with birthday greetings. 8.6 cm x 12.7 cm.
c) Three pictures of flowers with decorated illuminated cover. 8.1 cm x 10.3 cm.

25. Six miscellaneous cards including two folders with scraps or prints of children or flowers. Sizes up to 8 cm x 11.8 cm.

26. Two Christmas booklets.
a) A folder with two pictures of cats and dogs on gilt ground, with a decorative cover, probably by S T Dadd, dated 1888 by the sender. 11.5 cm x 15.4 cm.
b) A folder "Two Convivial Mice", by A M Lockyer, with two pictures of festive mice. 16.3 cm x 13.5 cm.

27. Seven cards, six designs, hexagonal in shape, with a folder of the six cards, showing pictures of dogs in circular vignettes with a floral border on a gilt ground. Registered at Stationers' Hall 19-11-1879 by George Pederson. 9.3 cm x 9.3 cm.

28. Three folding cards in the form of wicker baskets opening to show a cat, dog, or hamster. 11 cm x 8.7 cm.

29. A gilt-edged card of Christmas roses, with a verse, which was enclosed in a sachet with green and gilt design and a floral card on the front. The envelope in which this was sent is dated 18-12-1874. Card 10 cm x 13.7 cm.

30. Two folding cards with embossed scalloped edges, one made up from four floral cards, the other from two floral cards and two of romantic style couples. 13.7 cm x 9.7 cm closed.

31. Three cards with blue or red border designs on gilt, two with floral scraps attached over verses, and one showing a birthday greeting. 8.7 cm x 13.2 cm. The border resembles a Canton border.

32. One card, a floral spray of asters on a lace mount, on a folder containing a Shakespeare verse suitable for a valentine. 15 cm x 19 cm.

33. Six cards, with silk flowers or Father Christmas designs on rice paper. These are marked Marcus Ward but were probably made in France to order. Sizes 5.7 cm x 7 cm up to 7.7 cm x 11.5 cm.

34. A five piece fan with tassel, showing New Year greetings, with bird and flower designs. 6.7 cm x 13 cm closed.

## VOLUME 32: MARCUS WARD. EARLY CARDS WITH ROBINS, FESTIVE SCENES, CHILDREN, EARLY 1870's UNLESS OTHERWISE STATED

1. Ten visiting cards, two with scraps and gilt borders, eight with illuminated embossed designs on scallop edge cards. 4.6 cm x 8.5 cm.

2. Six scallop edge cards with borders hand-coloured red or blue and illuminated scroll designs. 6 cm x 9.5 cm.

3. Three scallop edge cards, borders hand-coloured, one on a lace mount, with scenes of Father Christmas, Christmas dinner, or a clown. 9.5 cm x 6 cm.

4. Five cards with blue hand-coloured edge, and various humorous designs, including snowballs and pudding. Two designs are as no. 3. 9 cm x 5.5 cm.

5. Eight cards, four designs with various embossed or coloured borders, and pictures of robins, including four versions of a robin pulling a holly cart, a very popular card.
9 cm x 5.7 cm, 10 cm x 6.9 cm.

6. Six cards with hand-coloured blue edge, and pictures of robins and small figures, four designs as in no. 5. 9.5 cm x 6.2 cm.

7. Five cards, three designs with gilt embossed borders and mediaeval Christmas scenes. Two cards have the early shamrock trade mark.
10.2 cm x 7 cm.

8. Five cards, children in winter scenes. 8 cm x 6.5 cm.

9. Three cards, two designs, Georgian style figures. 11.5 cm x 7.3 cm.

10. Three cards, quaint figures in costume. 8 cm x 6.7 cm.

11. Four cards, the set "Christmas Dreams", showing the progress of man from boyhood to old age, with verses on reverse. This was published as a folder. 7 cm x 10.3 cm.

12. Five cards with various embossed and gilt borders, of a Georgian couple, a lady in a boat, three children in church and two of three children - these registered at Stationers' Hall 15-6-1876. Sizes 6.6 cm x 10 cm up to 8 cm x 11.7 cm.

13. Five cards, four designs of Christmas scenes, three with embossed borders, one dated 1877 by the sender. Verses on reverse by J Hain Friswell. Sizes up to 7.3 cm x10.7 cm.

14. Six cards, four designs, winter scenes with a girl and boy, and a Christmas or New Year verse in a panel. Four have embossed borders. One card is dated 1872 by the sender. Sizes up to 11.8 cm x 8 cm.

15. Four cards, a girl and boy in fancy costumes with a bird, and greetings in verses. 5.7 cm x 8.5 cm.

16. Six cards, four designs, festive scenes, with verses, one with an angel, and one with a brown garbed Father Christmas figure. 12.7 cm x 8 cm.

17. Four illuminated cards, two designs of nativity scenes, with religious verses. 12 cm x 7.6 cm.

18. An envelope marked 1877, with a card found in it which has children playing with snowballs, and a duplicate card reversed to show verse. This card is one of the set registered at Stationers' Hall, 5-9-1877.

19/22. Twenty cards, eight designs, with various borders, greetings and verses. The four designs of a woman and children in a cottage, an ass and a foal with children, two calves and girls, a goat with a kid, were registered at Stationers' Hall 25-6-1876. The four designs of children snowballing, two boys fishing, two girls in a field with sheep and children at play in the corn, were registered at Stationers' Hall 5-9-1877. Probably designed by Harry Arnold.
10.9 cm x 7.8 cm up to 12 cm x 8.9 cm.

23. Five cards of single children in summer scenes, four designs, with gilt pattern borders. Registered at Stationers' Hall 21-11-1879, by Harry Arnold.
10.9 cm x 8.1 cm.

24/25. Sixteen cards, by J Moyr Smith, R A, mediaeval festive scenes on a gilt ground, with a red line border. 10.5 cm x 7 cm.

26. Six similar cards with gilt or green borders. Three cards have the shamrock leaf trade mark.
10.3 cm x 7 cm, 12.5 cm x 7.7 cm.

27. Five similar cards, with fancy borders, probably by J Moyr Smith, festive scenes in olden times. 10.3 cm x 7.2 cm.

28. Six cards, comic figures in Christmas scenes with geese, a set, registered at Stationers' Hall 11-7-1876. 7 cm x 10 cm.

29. Five cards, one a folder, with verses by J Hain Friswell and H S on Marcus Ward embossed edge cards. Two are dated 1877, 1878. 8.2 cm x 13 cm, 7.2 cm x10.6 cm.

30. Three cards, hand painted on Marcus Ward embossed edge cards.
8.2 cm x13 cm, 10.5 cm x 14 cm.

## VOLUME 33:
## MARCUS WARD. NEW YEAR CARDS, ANGELS AND NATIVITIES, FAIRIES AND CHILDREN, WITH SOME ARTISTS' CARDS, 1875-1880

1. Two cards, showing the Old Year departing, and the New Year arriving by train, with verses on reverse by G P M. 14.4 cm x 18.2 cm.

2/3. Four cards, three showing the New Year as a cherub arriving in a mediaeval house, with the Old Year departing, and one showing two children watching their ancestors stepping out of picture frames, with story verses on the reverse. 13.3 cm x17.8 cm.

4. Two cards by W Tasker Nugent "Old Port" and "Roast Beef" from a set of four called "Christmas Advances". (The two missing ones are "Hot Mince Pie" and "Plum Pudding"). 8.3 cm x 11.5 cm.

5. Three cards from a set of four - "The Story of Cinderella" - with pale blue borders and gilt holly leaves. (This was published also as a booklet). 12.7 cm x 13.3 cm.

6. Five nativity cards on gilt ground, four designs, Shepherds, Angels, Star in the East, The Adoration. This is perhaps the set by Thomas Goodman, said by Gleeson White to be "four cards on a gold ground". 12 cm x 8 cm.

7/8. Three nativity cards with gilt border, "Glad Tidings", "Eastern Star", "Emmanuel", with verses on reverse by Cecilia Havergal. 13 cm x 15.5 cm.

9. Two cards, Shepherds and Angels, Baby Jesus. 13 cm x 15.3 cm.

10. Two cards, one design, with different borders and captions, showing an angel watching over a child, from the picture by J K Thompson.
Sizes up to 20.4 cm x 14.5 cm.

11/12. Three cards after Fra Angelico, illuminated scenes of angels on gilt ground. 14cm x 14 cm, 8.3 cm x 17.4 cm.

13. One card "Noel", a boy in a cloak with a staff, and a verse "Christmas" on reverse, by Tennyson. 10 cm x 17.5 cm.

14. One card, drawing of the Virgin and Child on a blue ground, with silver border. 11.5 cm x 14 cm.

15. Five cards, four designs by Harry Arnold, cherubs or children in pastoral scenes. Nine designs were registered at Stationers' Hall 21-11-1879. 11.5 cm x 8 cm.

16/17. Eight pieces from a Christmas folder, four designs by Harry Arnold as in no. 15 with design in gilt and brown on yellow on reverse. Seven designs from the nine registered are in numbers 15, 16, 17. 8.7 cm x 13.2 cm.

18. Three cards, cherubs with flowers in summer scenes, in fancy gilt borders. 9.1 cm x 11.9 cm.

19/20. Six cards, four designs, fairies on butterflies, four with grey geometric border patterns, two in lunettes on an illuminated ground. Three are valentines. 13.9 cm x 10.5cm, 12.5 cm x 7.4 cm.

21/23. Five cards, four designs, fairies in boats or pastoral scenes, with blue and gilt borders. One card is Christmas and New Year, with a different border, four are valentines, with verses on reverse. 14.9 cm x 11.1 cm.

24. Two cards, one with two children with a Grecian temple and a lady, and one with two children in the sea. 12.7 cm x 9.4 cm, 12.1 cm x 10 cm.

25/26. Four cards, fairies and elves with butterflies, in blue and gilt borders. 15.2 cm x 11.5 cm.

27. Three cards, gilt edged, two with fairies with butterflies or insects, and one with two fairies on a peacock feather. 9 cm x 5.5 cm, 11 cm x 8.5 cm.

28. Three similar cards, fairies with butterflies or insects on plain white cards, with greeting in gilt. 10.2 cm x 8.2 cm.

29. Two cards by E Carrière, babies on flowering branches. Registered at Stationers' Hall 27-11-1879. 9.2 cm x 6.2 cm.

30. Four cards, three designs by E Carrière and A Gobran of children in floral settings. One is a valentine with a "True Lovers' Knot" on reverse. Registered at Stationers' Hall 19-11-1879. 9.7 cm x 13 cm.

31/33. Seven cards, three designs, of a girl or boy in party dress with bouquets, in summer scenes. Four have fancy gilt borders, three white borders with a gilt line design. Four designs were registered by W Tasker Nugent, 23-4-1879. 10.7 cm x14.4 cm, 10 cm x 13.5 cm.

34/38. Twenty-two cards, four designs of a girl with a basket, a girl with two books, a boy with a letter, and a boy with a jug, in Kate Greenaway style clothes. Ten cards are on a gilt ground with Thomas Crane style floral design, the others on white with borders like tree branches. Some have captions in French and verses on reverse. These are probably by W Tasker Nugent, but the registration has not been traced. 9.2 cm x13.7 cm, 7 cm x 10.5 cm.

39. Three cards, two designs of a boy or a girl with cards and toys, and a verse on reverse. 11.5 cm x 15.4 cm.

40. Three cards, two designs, a girl with a broom, and a lady in elaborate gown with fan, and verses on reverse. Two cards out of three registered at Stationers' Hall 23-4-1879, by W Tasker Nugent. 10.7 cm x 14.4 cm.

41. One card, a girl in blue skating, probably by W Tasker Nugent. 7.8 cm x 11.7 cm.

33.26

42. Six cards, four designs, children in party clothes (one playing the piano), with red and gilt borders. 8.1 cm x 12.1 cm.

43. One card by Alfred Ward, lady's head in red and yellow. 1878 according to Buday. 13 cm x 13 cm.

## VOLUME 34:
## MARCUS WARD. CHILDREN AND LADIES, 1880's

**The last Stationers' Hall registration by Marcus Ward appears to be in 1882, but the cards of this period can sometimes be traced from initial signatures, and some appear on the1885 trade list of which a copy, by courtesy of the John Johnson collection, is enclosed here.**

1. Five cards, four designs with advertisements for the National Medical Aid Company on the reverse, and pictures of two children in summer scenes. 12.3 cm x 9.5 cm.

2. Two cards, one with two children by the sea, as in no. 1, and another a child with a dog. 16.2 cm x 11.2 cm, 16.5 cm x 12 cm.

3. Four cards, a small boy with a Japanese doll and a dog in a Thomas Crane border. This is in the 1885 list as "Our Baby Jolly and his Japanese Dolly", no 1232, price 1/- for the four. 14 cm x 10.4 cm.

4. Four cards with various greetings, small children going to school, or at play. 12.7 cm x 10.2 cm.

5. Five cards with gilt borders, girls and boys in summer scenes, one dated 1883 by the sender. 6.7 cm x 11 cm to 11.5 cm x 14.8 cm.

6. Four cards with wide gilt borders, two with a small girl and boy, two a girl

outdoors. 9.2 cm x 12.8 cm, 9.2 cm x 13.6 cm.

7. Three cards, two with a girl and boy at play, the other a small girl with deer. 13.2 cm x 9.7 cm, 15.2 cm x 10.8 cm.

8. Two cards, boys in period costume, one with a bouquet, the other as a trumpeter. 11.2 cm x 16.5 cm.

9. Two cards, one a girl with umbrella, the other a boy with a sword and shield. 11.4 cm x 15.7 cm.

10. Six cards, four designs of a boy or girl in outdoor scenes, signed P T. The style appears to resemble that of Patty Townshend rather than Percy Tarrant. 8.9 cm x12 cm, 9.9 cm x 14.2 cm.

11. One card, a girl with a hay fork and a pitcher in the sunset. 9.6 cm x 14.7 cm.

12. Two cards, one a boy with a shuttlecock, the other a girl in riding habit, both of the Stuart period. 10.2 cm x 15.9 cm.

13. Two cards, one a lady in Greenaway style dress with a basket of apples, the other two men and a boy in Georgian costume. 10.1 cm x 15.5 cm, 11.5 cm x 16.3 cm.

14. One card by Edith Scannell, a girl's head in a fancy border, with a verse by S K Cowan M A, on reverse. This is one of four in the 1885 list, no. 656 "Happy and Careless", price four for 2/-. 11.1 cm x 13.4 cm.

15. Three cards in a similar border, two designs by Edith Scannell, one a girl with a kitten, the other a boy with a letter, both in Georgian dress. The reverse has a Thomas Crane design. 10.5 cm x 17.7 cm.

16. Two cards, a lady and gentleman on the ice, in rather curious pursuits, having tea, and playing a form of tennis. 17.9 cm x 12.8 cm.

17. Two cards, ladies in classical dress in floral settings. 10.2 cm x 15.7 cm and 11.5 cm x 15.7 cm.

18. Two cards, one a child on the seashore, the other a girl writing at a desk. 11.2 cm x 15.8 cm.

19. Three cards, two with girls in summer scenes, and one a caged cupid with a laburnum spray around a verse. 7.4 cm x 10.5 cm, 9.8 cm x 12.5 cm.

20. Two cards, a mother and child, with a Thomas Crane style border on a yellow ground. 10.8 cm x 12.8 cm.

21. Two cards, children in a meadow, with a birthday verse. 11.8 cm x 8.8 cm.

22/23. Six cards, four designs, small girls in bonnets, amongst summer flowers, with two border styles. 10.2 cm x 13.3 cm, 8.2 cm x 11.3 cm.

24. One card, a girl's head in a vignette, with flowers and birds around. 15.4 cm x10.1 cm.

25. Three cards, girls' heads, one in a circular vignette with ivy around, and two with a verse beneath. 6.2 cm x 6.2 cm, 8.8 cm x 11.8 cm.

26 Three cards.
a) A child in a circular vignette, perhaps by Edith Scannell? 11.3 cm x 15.2 cm.
b) Two cards, boys in vignettes with leafy branches, and Christmas verses. 8.7 cm x12.5 cm.

27. Five miscellaneous cards of children, two with girls' heads, three with boys, probably all by the same artist. Sizes 8.6 cm x 10 cm up to 10 cm x 17.2 cm.

28. Four cards, girls outdoors, two playing games. 7.7 cm x 11.7 cm, 10 cm x14.9 cm.

29. Two cards with boys, in blue borders, one with a drum, the other with a fishing net. 9.5 cm x 12 cm.

30. Three cards, quaint children, with a robin, butterflies, blackberries, or cowslips. Sizes up to 9.4 cm x 13.3 cm.

31. Four cards of outdoor scenes, a man ploughing, a girl in snow, and two of ladies in spring or winter. Sizes up to 13.5 cm x 11.4 cm.

32. Three cards, two designs, farmyard scenes with sheep or geese. 9.3 cm x13 cm, 10.4 cm x 14.3 cm.

33/34. Three frosted cards, little girls in summer and winter scenes. 11.8 cm x15.2 cm.

35. Three cards with children in circular vignettes surrounded by gilded sprays. Perhaps by E J Ellis? 8.2 cm x 10.7 cm, 9.2 cm x 11.4 cm.

36. Four miscellaneous cards, small children in summer scenes with flowers. The style resembles that of J M Dealy. 7.1 cm x 10.2 cm up to 11.3 cm x 12.8 cm.

37. One card, monochrome, two children, one in a swing. Dated 1891 by the sender. 10.3 cm x 13 cm.

38/40. Six cards with elaborate embossed gilded borders, ladies in fashionable '90's dress, one with a bicycle. Two are signed, but the signature has not been deciphered.1890's. 11.8 cm x 15 cm.

## VOLUME 35: MARCUS WARD. CARDS WITH BIRDS, 1870's

**Some artists here can be traced from Stationers' Hall registrations. Birds were a popular subject with many artists and these are dated in the mid 1870's except where otherwise stated. An occasional animal strays in, when appearing in a set of cards with birds.**

1/5. Thirty cards, mostly robins with an occasional blue tit or chaffinch. Five are mounted on gilt or embossed borders, and there are six designs with a variety of verses by S C Hall, Charlotte M Yonge, Coleridge, J Hain Friswell and others, for Christmas and New Year. One is dated 1874 by the sender. 10.3 cm x 7 cm.

6/7. Three folding cards, robins and other birds, with Christmas or New Year verse. There is a design of the Old and the New Year in blue and silver, or red and gold, on reverse. 12.2 cm x 16.5 cm open.

8/10. Twelve cards, nine designs, embossed scalloped edges, with a border of birds, flowers, and berries, on gilt or silver, around a panel with a Christmas or New Year verse or a valentine greeting. 10 cm x 13.5 cm.

11. A similar valentine card on a large decorative mount. 18.3 cm x 23.3 cm.

12/14. Fourteen similar cards, nine designs with plain borders, five with Christmas or New Year verses, and nine with hymns. 9 cm x 13 cm.

15. Three cards with similar designs on silver, and verses for New Year, January, and July (part of a set for the months). 8.5 cm x 12.4 cm.

34.15

16. Three cards, two designs, birds with floral sprays and religious verses. 9 cm x13 cm.

17. Four cards, three designs on embossed scalloped borders, a robin, chaffinch and goldfinch with verses in panel. Four designs (including a bullfinch) were registered at Stationers' Hall 15-6-1876. 10 cm x 14 cm.

18/20. Twelve cards, four designs of birds with flowers, nests and berries. One is on a scalloped embossed edge card, and eleven are on gilt edge cards. Some have verses on reverse for Christmas, New Year, or valentine. Registered at Stationers' Hall 10-9-1877. 10 cm x 14 cm, 9 cm x 12.8 cm, 7 cm x 10.3 cm.

21. Three cards, with texts, using designs as above. Two were registered at Stationers' Hall 15-6-1876, and one 10-9-1877. 7.3 cm x 13.3 cm.

22/24. Ten cards, four designs, birds on trees or in flight. Four have elaborate gilt and coloured borders, four a plain gilt edge and two a blue border with flower design. Registered at Stationers' Hall 28-4-1879 by George Pederson. 11 cm x 14 cm, 7.6 cm x10.4 cm, 10.6 cm x 14 cm.

25. Four cards, birds on branches and with nests. The four designs were registered at Stationers' Hall 19-11-1879 by George Pederson. 16.3 cm x 8.4 cm.

26. Two cards, one of an exotic bird in a Chinese scene, the other of a nightingale, in gilt borders with a leaf design. Verses by Tennyson and Frederick Langbridge, are on the reverse. 10.8 cm x 12.7 cm.

34.28

27. Three cards, two designs, one a tropical bird, the others a dead goldfinch, with verses for Christmas, New Year, or birthday, on reverse. Registered at Stationers' Hall 23-4-1879 by Helen Coleman Angell, (sister of W S and Rebecca Coleman). 11.8 cm x 8.6cm.

28/29. Six cards, three designs, birds with nests on gilt backgrounds with elaborate borders. Three cards, reversed, show verses for Christmas, New Year and valentine. Registered at Stationers' Hall (four designs) by J Daudin, 23-4-1879. 9.7 cm x 13.3 cm.

30. Four similar cards on silver background, registered at Stationers' Hall 18-11-1879 by A Daudin. Buday does not list either Daudin amongst his artists, and the writer has not been able to trace them in available reference books. 10.3 cm x 13.6 cm.

31. Four cards, three designs, "The Country Mouse", "The Cock and the Jewel", "The Fox and the Stork", with appropriate verses on reverse. These were amongst six designs registered at Stationers' Hall 12-5-1879 by J Daudin. 12 cm x 8.2 cm.

32. Three cards, birds and fishes, with elaborate scroll border. These were amongst ten designs registered at Stationers' Hall 19-11-1879 by A Daudin. 13.3 cm x 9.4 cm.

## VOLUME 36:
## MARCUS WARD. CARDS WITH BIRDS, FROM THE LATE 1870'S TO 1890

**Those cards not dated were probably published about 1885. A popular set of butterflies and moths is included.**

1/3. Seventeen well printed cards, nine designs, birds, animals and fishes on gilt grounds, with embossed scalloped, brown, or blue and gold borders. They have verses, in panels, for Christmas, New Year and Valentines, or moral precepts, including one "God Bless Bands of Hope". One card was dated 1880 by the sender, but they appear to be about 1875. The registration at Stationers' Hall has not been traced. 8 cm x 11.8 cm, 9 cm x 12.8 cm.

4/6. Ten cards, four designs, single birds, with flower or holly sprays on gilt grounds, and a variety of verses for Christmas, New Year, or Valentine. Registered at Stationers' Hall 5-10-1877. 13.3 cm x 10 cm, 10.3 cm x 7.7 cm.

7/8. Nine cards, four designs, single birds in winter or summer scenes, on gilt grounds. Eight have coloured borders, one an orange and gilt edge. Two cards were dated 1878 by the sender. 11.7 cm x 8 cm.

9/10. Ten cards, five designs, birds in black, gilt or silver vignettes encircled by flowers, with captions for Christmas and Valentine, or texts. One card was dated 1879 by the sender. 9 cm x 13.3 cm, 7.7 cm x 10.4 cm.

11. Two cards with two birds on flowering branches on gilt grounds, with a panel containing a verse for valentine or Christmas. 13.6 cm x 9.8 cm.

12. Five cards, tropical birds and flowers, with a gilt patterned border. Two have greetings in panel, three texts. Two cards were dated 1881 by the sender. 9 cm x 13 cm, 8.2 cm x 12 cm.

13. Four cards, birds and flowers with gilt patterned border and a greeting verse in panels. One was dated 1881 by the sender. 10 cm x 13.5 cm

14. Two cards, one design, two birds on a flowering branch with silver patterned border, and greeting. 13.4 cm x 9.6 cm.

15. Three cards, exotic birds on branches, with silver border and greeting verses. 8.4 cm x 15.2 cm.

16. Four cards, three designs with texts and religious verses on reverse, from Marcus Ward packet "Little Words of Wisdom" no 145. From the same set of designs as no. 15. 8.1 cm x 12.3 cm.

17. Three cards, two designs, birds in water scenes, with hymns on reverse. One card is from packet 166 "Hymns for learning by heart", and two cards are from packet167 "Hymns for committing to memory". 12.3 cm x 8.1 cm, 13 cm x 8.4 cm.

18. Three cards, two with birds, and one with a cat and dead birds, with greetings. Verses by Frederick Langbridge are on the reverse. 8.6 cm x 13 cm.

19. Four cards, robins in winter scenes, one mounted on a larger green card with a holly branch border. 9.8 cm x 5.8 cm, 14.8 cm x 10.8 cm.

20. Two cards, birds on a rooftop, with a rope scroll border, and verses on reverse for Christmas and valentine. 10.2 cm x 13.4 cm.

21. Two cards, the same robin on a snowy branch, one in a circular vignette with a green patterned border, the other on a plain card with a green edge, and verse on reverse. 10.8 cm x 11.5 cm, 9.9 cm x 14.8 cm.

22. Three cards, two birds in a snow scene, one with a verse on reverse. Late 1880's. 9.3 cm x 13 cm, 9.7 cm x 15.5 cm.

23. Two cards, with a robin and blackbird on leafy branches, and a verse by Sarah Doudney on reverse. Late 1880's. 12.2 cm x 9.7 cm.

24. One card, three chicks on a mount with pink pattern border. Late 1880's. 11.2 cm x 17.2 cm.

25/32. Thirty-four cards of three or four moths and butterflies, on blue, black, gilt, or silver ground with verses in panels for Christmas, New Year, Valentine, or texts. An envelope is included for twelve "Moth Lessons, with texts chosen by Frances Ridley Havergal", though the contents have not been identified precisely. There appear to be seven designs with butterflies, and six with moths. Eight designs were registered at Stationers' Hall on 16-11-1877. 7.7 cm x 11.8 cm, 5.5 cm x 8.5 cm.

## VOLUME 37:
## MARCUS WARD. CARDS WITH ANIMALS, AND HUMOROUS CARDS WITH BIRDS AND ANIMALS

**Some of the earlier cards can be dated c1880 from Stationers' Hall registrations and by style. The comic cards, some by S T Dadd and A M Lockyer, have a naive and sometimes cruel humour.**

1/2. Seven cards, five designs in brown and blue with Thomas Crane style borders, various animals in winter scenes. Six designs were registered at Stationers' Hall by Hannah B Barlow, 23-4-1879. This artist is not listed by Buday. 10.5 cm x 13.6 cm.

3. Four cards, three designs of cats, three with Thomas Crane style borders, one with gilt. These are three of twelve designs registered by Hannah B Barlow, 19-11-1879.
12.4 cm x 8.6 cm, 13.1 cm x 9.4 cm.

4. Three cards, two designs, deer and rabbits in snowy scenes. These are from packet 152 "Kindness to Animals", with verses or stories by Hesba Stratton on reverse. c1880. 12.4 cm x 8.6 cm.

5. Four cards, three designs with Thomas Crane style border, rabbits and fox and hound, in country scenes. c1880.
11.6 cm x 8.2 cm.

6/7. Eight cards, five designs, dogs in circular vignettes in a Thomas Crane style border on a coloured ground. Seven cards have seasonal greetings, and one, with a verse by Crabbe, is from packet no 153A "Dogs' Heads & What's in them", with a story on reverse by Frederick Langbridge. Six pictures of dogs were registered at Stationers' Hall 19-11-1879 by George Pederson (see Volume 31).
13.6 cm x 9.6 cm.

8. Five cards, farm and country scenes with gilt borders, c1880. 12 cm x 7.6 cm.

9. Two cards, one design with wide gilt patterned borders, two dogs by a fireside, with a kennel. c1880. 15.5 cm x 11.8 cm.

10. Four cards, pelicans and other long-billed birds, on a gilt ground, with a file of unpaid bills, and appropriate captions, "May the weight of your bills prove no longer than your pouch". c1880.
10.4 cm x 14.2 cm.

11/12. Six cards telling the tale of a robin chased by a cat, but saved by a friendly dog. c1880. 14.7 cm x 9.9 cm.

13. Three cards, two cats with birds' nests, and a beetle. c1880. 15.5 cm x 7.9 cm, 7.5 cm x 20.8 cm.

*The following cards are dated from 1884-90, and show animals and birds in comic situations.*

14. Four cards from a folder, "Mr Fox's Christmas Goose, and how it was cooked", telling the story of a fox hunting a goose, but caught itself by a dog. By S T Dadd. 13 cm x 9.5 cm.

15/16. Five cards by S T Dadd with green borders, showing cats, dogs and birds in comic situations. 9.2 cm x 12.3 cm up to 14.5 cm x 11.5 cm.

17. Two cards by S T Dadd with green borders, monkeys, cats and birds. These

are two out of three in the 1885 list, with captions "Possession is nine points of the law", and "Do you see anything in it?".
11.8 cm x 15.6 cm.

18. Two cards by S T Dadd with green borders, cats and dogs. 17.5 cm x 12.9 cm.

19. Three cards by S T Dadd, two with cats and mice. The third has ducks and a frog and is no. 3 of the set in no. 17, but in a smaller version, with the caption "Beware of Quacks". 8.7 cm x 11.5 cm up to 15.2 cm x 11.5 cm.

20. Two cards by S T Dadd in green borders, cats with a mouse, and a dog with a crab. 16.4 cm x 11.8 cm.

21. Three humorous cards with dogs, cats and a pig. 13.5 cm x 9.4 cm up to 15.5 cm x 11.4 cm.

22. Two cards, one with four cats looking at eggs, and one a cat with birds.
16 cm x 12 cm.

23. Four cards, three designs in green borders, cats and a dog with birds and a crab. 12.5 cm x 9.3 cm.

24. Four cards with blue borders, two frogs, an owl with three kittens, a cat and mouse, and cocks and hens riding a donkey. 14.6 cm x 10.1 cm.

25. Three cards, two designs by A M Lockyer, kittens tangling with a ball of wool. Two cards have a Thomas Crane style border on reverse. 11.3 cm x 9 cm, 12.3 cm x 11.5 cm.

26. Two cards by A M Lockyer, birds skating on the ice. 19 cm x 10.1 cm.

27. Three cards by A M Lockyer, one showing five mice with tails tied together, and two with birds skating (one as in no. 26). 14.5 cm x 10.5 cm, 14.3 cm x 8.1 cm.

28. Two cards, frogs sledging.
12.9 cm x 10.3 cm.

29. One card, a humanised crocodile family walking. 16.5 cm x 11.3 cm.

30. Two cards, one a group of feline waits, the other a goose in evening dress and top hat, with a begging mouse.
14.1 cm x 10.3 cm, 14.5 cm x 12 cm.

31. Three miscellaneous cards, a monkey with banjo, a pig, and a dog with a cello, accompanied by appropriate verses. Sizes up to 13.3 cm x 10.3 cm.

32. Two cards, moonlit scenes with frogs, owls and mouse. 15.4 cm x 10 cm.

33. One card, two ducks in a tug-of-war with a frog. 14.8 cm x 11.5 cm.

37.10

34. Two cards "Early birds", tits and chicks with a worm and a grub. 12.7 cm x 9.7 cm.

35. Two cards, dogs, one peeping over a scroll, the other a hound. 10.2 cm x12 cm, 15.8 cm x 12 cm.

36. Four cards, cats and dogs in sporting garb with guns, fishing rod, and a fox's brush. Sizes up to 7.7 cm x 10.5 cm.

37. Four cards, kittens at play and at school, two dated 1887 and 1888 by the senders. 9.7 cm x 7.8 cm.

38. Six miscellaneous cards, robins, rabbits, ducks, cats and dogs. c1890. Sizes up to 10.2 cm x 12.8 cm.

## VOLUME 38: MARCUS WARD. FOLDING CARDS

**This volume contains a number of well printed illuminated cards, some with quotations from Shakespeare, some with texts. They are c1880 unless otherwise stated.**

1/2. Five folding cards, with a picture of Shakespeare and "Shakespeare Greeting" "with the Compliments of the Season" on the outside, opening to show floral borders on a gilt ground encircling a panel with a quotation from Shakespeare.
10 cm x 15 cm open.

3. Three similar cards with Shakespeare greetings.
11.8 cm x 9.2 cm, 16 cm x12.5 cm open.

4/5. Four folding cards with blue and gold illuminated designs outside and a Shakespeare picture. Inside, a design of flowers and butterflies encircles a panel with a Shakespeare quotation. These are four designs from six registered at Stationers' Hall 26-11-1879 by A Daudin, Paris. 10.2 cm x 18.5 cm open.

6/7. Four miscellaneous cards with Shakespeare greetings.
a) Fruit design on silver outside, and large illuminated greeting within.
b) Leaf design outside, and catkin picture within.
c/d) Berry design outside, flowers and mouse with greeting within.
17 cm x 11.8 cm,18.2 cm x 12 cm, 15.3 cm x 11.5 cm open.

8/9. Two folding cards with flowers and greeting outside, and floral border, birds nests and a verse within. 22.5 cm x 12.8 cm open.

10/11. Three folding cards.
a) The outside has a blue and gold design with sun and moon, and a Christmas greeting. Inside are two pictures of barefooted children, and two of a church and a windmill, with the poem "Bells across the snow" by Frances Ridley Havergal.
b/c) Two folding cards, with pictures of houseleek, cyclamen, cowslip and windflower outside, on a gilt ground, and the same pictures as a) within, with verses by F G H and G H S. The four pictures were registered at Stationers' Hall 28-4-1879 by Harry Arnold.
22.5 cm x 16 cm, 11.2 cm x 15.2 cm open.

12. Three cards with illuminated designs of holly and robin on blue grounds outside, and pictures of three quaint children in outdoor scenes within, and verses by G P Meade below encircled by a flower and butterfly design. 12.2 cm x 16 cm open.

13. Two folding cards.
a) The outside has an illuminated greeting with red and yellow and a Thomas Crane style floral design. Inside is a girl in a wreath of violets, with a Christmas verse below on a silver ground. This is one out of six designs, registered at Stationers' Hall 26-11-79 by H Oulevray (Paris).
12.3 cm x 14.7 cm open.
b) Violets and herb robert are around panels with New Year verses by Frances Ridley Havergal, with silver borders inside, and a berry design outside.
15.3 cm x11.5 cm open.

14. Two folding cards, with floral branches on a gilt ground outside, and floral sprays within around illuminated texts from St Luke. 16.5 cm x 14 cm open.

15. A similar single card, with flowers on a gilt border around an illuminated text from Revelations. 20.8 cm x 16.1 cm.

16. Four folding cards.
a) The outside has an illuminated floral spray on a green ground, and a robin and children within. 12.3 cm x 8.3 cm open.

b/d) Three cards with illuminated crosses entwined with flowers outside, and an illuminated text from St Luke within. 13.4 cm x 10.2 cm open.

17/19. Six folding cards, four designs. These have "Mizpah" on the outside, with an illuminated design in blue, red and gold, and a butterfly on a floral spray with an illuminated text or verse by Frances Ridley Havergal within. 12 cm x 14.9 cm open. ("Mizpah" or "The Lord watch between thee and me when we are absent from one another", Genesis 31:49, is often used on cards with a religious flavour).

20/22. Eight cards, six designs with birds on trees or with nests, surrounded by floral sprays, over verses by Frederick Langbridge or Frances Ridley Havergal. Five are folders with red and silver "Mizpah" greeting and design outside, and three are plain cards. 10.3 cm x 14.2 cm open.

23. Two folding cards, with "Mizpah" and an ivy design on blue outside, and crosses with flower sprays and a text inside. 10 cm x 16 cm open.

24. Two folding cards with "Mizpah" and an ivy design in silver and red on a yellow border outside, and an ivy or floral spray within with "Mizpah" in silver and a verse by Frances Ridley Havergal. 10.3 cm x 15.5 cm open.

25/26. Four folding cards, three designs with gilt borders, and country scenes with people, around a verse for Christmas, New Year, or birthday. A Thomas Crane style design is on the outside. These are three out of four designs registered at Stationers' Hall 28-4-1879 by Harry Arnold. 13.2 cm x 14.8 cm open.

27. Two single cards from the same set as above, including the fourth design. These have panels with valentine verses from Shakespeare & Burns. 14 cm x 18.2 cm.

28. One three-fold card with an ivy design on green outside, with New Year greeting, and three pictures inside of carol singers and boys in mediaeval dress, with illuminated ivy design and verse. Two pieces from another card with Christmas greeting, and pictures and verse of Good King Wenceslas, are included. c1885? 11.5 cm x 12.6 cm closed.

29/30. Five cards, two designs with fruit sprays and butterfly on blue ground. Three are folders with a "horn of plenty" design and a verse on the outside, and two are single with a verse on reverse. 10 cm x 13 cm open.

31. Two folding cards with floral spray outside, and two pages of verse by Frances Ridley Havergal within. c1885. 16.7 cm x 12.2 cm open.

32. One folding card with flowers on gilt border around a panel with "Glad Tidings of Great Joy" - music from Handel's Messiah. 19.5 cm x 15 cm open.

33. Two folding cards.
a) Two-fold, with "Hail Christmas Day" music, and illuminated border. 22 cm x 7.3 cm open.
b) A four-fold card, with music for "Hark the Herald Angels Sing", with illuminated pictures by J Moyr Smith (cf Volume 32). c1875. 12.6 cm x 7.6 cm closed.

34. Two three-fold cards, with illuminated designs of a troubadour and four heads with "arranged for four voices", one on yellow, one on pink, ground. Music inside for "Christmas bells are ringing out", encircled by a holly design. c1875. 7 cm x 10.8 cm closed.

35. Four miscellaneous folding cards with music, three two-fold and one two-fold. c1875. Sizes 10.1 cm x 7 cm up to 20.5 cm x 10.1 cm open.

36/37. Eight single cards with music for carols, ornamented by illuminated designs. c1875. 11.5 cm x 7.6 cm.

# VOLUME 39: MARCUS WARD. VALENTINES, SPORT & HUMOUR

**This volume contains three sections: Valentines, made in sets for the purpose and not adapted from Christmas or New Year designs, Hunting and Sporting scenes, and Humour of the late 1880's. Few if any Marcus Ward cards have been found, for this collection, dealing with the army, navy, negroes, or Japanese scenes, and none of these subjects appear in the 1885 list of cards appended in Volume 34, though oriental pottery appears.**

1. Two valentines in scalloped borders, with pictures of two lovers in romantic flower-decked settings. One has a verse by Shelley "Love's Philosophy",the other an anonymous poem which also appears in the "Quiver of Love". c1875. 12.4 cm x 17 cm.

2. A similar valentine, with plain edge, and verses by W Allingham, also quoted in "Quiver of Love". c1875. 14 cm x 21.7 cm.

3. Four valentines, three designs with four varieties of embossed gilded borders. Two have floral designs, two exotic birds. c1875. 13.7 cm x 10 cm.

4. Two valentines, with embossed scalloped borders, and flowers in oval vignettes surrounded by a scroll design. The verses are by Enis Herne. c1875. 10 cm x 13.7 cm.

5. Two valentines, with butterflies and roses, and True Lovers' Knot designs with Cupids, on reverse. c1875.
11.1 cm x 15 cm.

6. Four valentines, with four different embossed gilded borders, showing country girls with flower sprays, and verses on reverse. c1875. 10 cm x 13.8 cm.

7. Three valentines, with figures in costume - a girl with a Cupid, a boy with a letter at a window, and a girl with a hound - and verses on reverse. These are three out of eight designs registered at Stationers' Hall by E Carrière 26-5-1879.
9.7 cm x13.5 cm.

8. Two valentines, showing girls' heads and shoulder in oval vignettes, surrounded by Cupids on a gilt ground with valentine verses. c1880.
12.5 cm x 7 cm.

9. Four valentines, girls in outdoor scenes, with verses in panels or scroll, printed in violet or orange, with gilt borders. c1880.
10 cm x 13.3 cm.

10/11. Three folder valentines, with pictures of fashionable ladies on the outside, and Thomas Crane style border. There are appropriate valentine style verses inside, printed in gold. c1880.
12.3 cm x 17.2 cm.

12. Three cards of hunting scenes, registered at Stationers' Hall 19-11-1879.
15.2 cm x 8.9 cm

13/14. Four cards by Georgina Bowers, picturing humorous hunting scenes, with holly design on a pale green border. One card is dated 1884 by the sender.
15.1 cm x 11 cm, 11 cm x 15.1 cm.

15. One card by Georgina Bowers, with a white border, of a boy riding over a field. c1885. 12 cm x 16.5 cm.

16. Two cards by Georgina Bowers, with white borders, of comic hunting scenes. c1885. 16.3 cm x 11.7 cm.

17. Four cards by Georgina Bowers, with holly or oak leaf patterned borders, and humanised dogs and foxes in sporting scenes. c1885. 8.8 cm x 13.5 cm.

18. Two cards, hunting scenes with pale blue borders. c1885. 13.3 cm x 12.5 cm.

19. Three cards, two huntsmen with pigs and geese, and one a sailor riding backwards. Late 1880's. 13.5 cm x 10.5 cm.

20. Three cards, two designs, children in hunting costume, with large horseshoe around. One is dated by the sender 1896. 11.7 cm x 16 cm.

21. Two cards, Georgian beaux, one seated at a spinet and one with a violin, with suitable verses. Dated by the senders 1886, 1888. 14.7 cm x 11.6 cm.

22. Four humorous cards, a Christmas pudding, a man with a scarecrow, a clown and pantaloon, and an Elizabethan gentleman by a table. c1890. Sizes up to 11 cm x 16 cm.

23. One "card"-a mock telegram, from "Good Cheer Messenger's Co. Unlimited". Late 1880's. 21.2 cm x 14 cm.

24. One card, a house in moonlight. A tab at the back is pulled and shows a brush emerging from a chimney and a lady in a nightcap at a window. 11.3 cm x 13.7 cm.

# VOLUME 40:
## MARCUS WARD. SCENES, VIGNETTES WITH FLOWERS, SHIPS AND SEA PICTURES

**These cards can be dated as c1885 with a few earlier as stated. There are indoor and outdoor scenes, some with Biblical connections and some with music. A few registrations in Stationers' Hall have been traced and some appear on the 1885 Marcus Ward list, but these could have been published earlier. At some time before 1885 Marcus Ward & Co became Marcus Ward & Co Limited and it is interesting to note that Stationers' Hall registrations for Marcus Ward have not been found after about 1882.**

1. Four cards, three designs with embossed borders, winter scenes in blue and brown shades. One card was dated by the sender 1876. 10.2 cm x 7 cm.

2. Five cards, four designs, country scenes with figures, in gilt or silver borders. Registered at Stationers' Hall 19-11-1879 by Harry Arnold.
8 cm x 13 cm, 7.4 cm x 11.5 cm.

3. Two folding cards, one Christmas, one New Year, with "A four-fold Greeting" on the outside with a bird and flower design in silver, and winter scenes with figures in four designs. 18.3 cm x 13.3 cm open.

4/5. Six cards, five designs by Patty Townshend, with pictures of cottages. One is an eight page folder with four vignettes inside and verses by Mrs Hemans, and on the outside is "Cottage Homes of England", with a flower and ivy design. 8.8 cm x 10.8 cm closed. Five are single cards, four having verses by Tennyson for Christmas and New Year on reverse. Sizes 10.5 cm x 13.8 cm, 9.7 cm x 11.8 cm. Buday gives the date of the folder as 1878-80, but it appears on the 1885 list as no 664, price 1/-.

6. Four cards with country scenes, and verses for Christmas and New Year by G P M, R L O, F G H. Early 1880's. 13.3 cm x 10 cm.

7. One card, a view of Glen Rossa, Arran, with grey border. 15 cm x 11.5 cm.

8. Two cards, lake views with stormy skies in an interesting colour combination of browns and greens. 10 cm x 14.4 cm.

9/10. Five cards with rectangular vignettes of Como or Venice with feluccas and floral sprays. Two have gilt borders and texts and three have verses by Frances Ridley Havergal or G P Meade. One was dated by the sender 1882.
10 cm x 14 cm, 9 cm x 12.8 cm.

11. Two cards, one with a vignette of a sailing ship and an orchid spray, the other a moonlit sea view with a gilt holly border pattern, perhaps one of the series "Moonlight and Twilight on the Deep" by H S C Wright. 10 cm x 15.3 cm, 14 cm x 10.8 cm.

12. Four cards with seascapes, one of rocks and birds, three of sailing ships. Three cards have verses on reverse.
7.9 cm x 10.8 cm up to 14 cm x 9.1 cm.

13/14. Five cards with Alpine scenes in vignettes, sprays of flowers, and music for Christmas, by Helga von Cramm. These are five out of six designs registered at Stationers' Hall 19-11-1879.
14.5 cm x 11.3 cm.

15. Three cards with three of the above designs by Helga von Cramm, but with texts instead of music, and verses by Frances Ridley Havergal on reverse. This set is on the Marcus Ward 1885 list.
14.5 cm x 11.5 cm.

16/17. Four cards with vignettes of Jerusalem views, and floral sprays on a pale blue ground, c1880. Two have music and a heading "Flowers from the Land of Jesus' birth", and two have "For a Christmas offering", and a descriptive sentence. 11.4 cm x 14.8 cm and 14.8 cm x 11.4 cm.

18. Two cards, one Christmas, one birthday, each with two vignettes of country scenes, and flowers around, with the same verse on each. Early 1880s.
10 cm x 15.4 cm, 9.9 cm x 14.1 cm.

19. Two cards.
a) Circular, in quodlibet fashion with overlapping vignettes. 11.9 cm diameter.
b) A vignette of country folk in a garden, with a floral spray around. Early 1880's.
12.4 cm x 10.7 cm.

20. Two cards, one Christmas, one New Year, each with two vignettes of country scenes and a floral spray in oval frames. Early 1880's. 11.5 cm x 15.6 cm.

21. Two cards, with views of elegant rooms in oval vignettes, with a peacock feather and greetings around. 11.5 cm x 15.4 cm.

22. Two cards.
a) "Bells across the Snow", Frances Ridley Havergal's well known poem on reverse, with a view of Linton Church, Herefordshire, which inspired the poem. On the 1885 list, no 686, price 6d. 11.8 cm x 16.4 cm.
b) A river scene in a circular vignette, with poppies, and a verse by F R H. 10.1 cm x 15.5 cm.

23. Three cards.
a) A folder card, "Folding Forget-me-nots", no 653 on the 1885 list, with two miniature scenes on each inside leaf and a floral spray and forget-me-nots outside. 8.8 cm x 11.8 cm closed.
b) Two similar single cards.

24. Three cards.
a) Two with a text, forget-me-not sprays, and two small vignettes of a fountain and a river. A poem of prayer is on the reverse, and the cards are from packet no. 210 "Prayer and Peace". c1885.
b) Two lovers in a sunset scene, dated by the sender 1890. 8.8 cm x 12 cm.

25. Four miscellaneous cards with vignettes and flower or leaf sprays. Sizes up to 10.4 cm x 13 cm.

26. Three cards, summer scenes in vignettes with floral sprays, one with a verse by Frances Ridley Havergal, late 1880's. 9.3 cm x 10.5 cm up to 16.3 cm x 10.2 cm.

27. Four cards, scenes in circular or oval vignettes, one with a spray of roses. Sizes up to 12.4 cm x 10.2 cm.

28. Three cards.
a) A river scene with boats, and a gilt ivy spray around, dated by the sender 1886. 15.5 cm x 10.9 cm.
b) Two cards, river and fishing scenes, with verses. 10 cm x 2.3 cm.

29. Two cards, river scenes, with a "trompe l'oeil" effect of the picture fitting into slots, and verses on reverse by Frances Ridley Havergal. 13.9 cm x 9.2 cm, 9.2 cm x 13.9 cm.

30. Two cards, sea and river scenes with gilt border and texts, verses on reverse by A R C. 14 cm x 9.5 cm.

31. Three cards, children at cottage door, one with a verse on reverse. 10.1 cm x 12.2 cm, 9.2 cm x 12 cm.

32. Three cards, country and village scenes, late 1880's. 12.6 cm x 10.2 cm, 11.5 cm x 9.2 cm.

33. Four miscellaneous cards, seascapes, lady and child, village scene with couple. Late 1880's. 7.8 cm x 10.3 cm up to 15.3 cm x 11.4 cm.

34. One card "Life in the Far West", Canadian Ice Boat. 1885 list 678a, four for 2/-. 11.8 cm x 18.7 cm.

35. Two cards - "Life in Australia", tree cutting and cattle herds. 16.9 cm x 11 cm, 11 cm x 16.9 cm.

36. Three cards. "Australian Flowers", with red border, and a greeting in a gilt edged vignette. 16.7 cm x 10.8 cm.

37. Four cards, country scenes with ladies, man and woman, a family in a garden, and a shepherd, with white borders and verses. One is a valentine. 15.6 cm x 8.8 cm.

## VOLUME 41:
## MARCUS WARD. MORE ILLUMINATED CARDS

**Many of these cards were probably designed by Thomas Crane, but most of the registrations traced are anonymous and cards have only been credited to him when the style makes an attribution fairly certain. The cards can be dated in the early 1870's, except where otherwise stated. The quality of printing and design is excellent.**

1. Nine cards, with four illuminated designs with greeting or brief verses by Francis Davis, including a birthday and a valentine card. One was dated by the sender 1871. 9.5 cm x 6.2 cm.

2. Nine cards, with two illuminated missal type designs with various fancy borders and seasonal verses by Francis Davis and S C Hall. 9.5 cm x 6.2 cm.

3. Five cards, two designs in illuminated missal style with holly and snowdrops, and verses for Christmas and New Year by Francis Davis. 6.2 cm x 11.5 cm.

4. Five cards, two illuminated designs with verses by S C Hall. Three have a robin with a floral spray, two have a robin with mistletoe, and two were dated by the sender 1874, 1875. Buday illustrates the latter design as a "characteristic Luke Limner - John Leighton design of the early 60's", but the writer would date it as early 1870's, and feels it might be by Thomas Crane. 7.5 cm x 11.4 cm, 8 cm x 12 cm.

5. Three illuminated cards, two designs, one with robin, holly and mistletoe, the other with ivy. Verses by S C Hall. 7.5 cm x 11.4 cm, 12 cm x 8 cm.

6. Seven illuminated cards, two designs, with verses by Tennyson and F Davis.

Possibly Thomas Crane or Luke Limner. Three cards were dated by the senders 1872, 1873, 1874. 10.2 cm x 6.8 cm, 10.5 cm x 7 cm.

7. Three illuminated cards, one design, a Christmas rose around a panel with verse, two of the cards dated by the senders 1873, 1876. 11.5 cm x 7.4 cm.

8. Three illuminated cards, one design of holly and mistletoe around panels with three different verses by S C Hall and Francis Davis. 11.5 cm x 7.4 cm.

9. One card, illuminated border pattern around a spray of wild arum with berries, and a greeting on a scroll. Perhaps by Thomas Crane. 7.7 cm x 12.4 cm.

10. Eight illuminated cards, two designs of snowdrops and primroses by Thomas Crane, with various greetings in verse for Christmas, New Year, birthday. Two cards were dated by the sender 1872 and 1877. 10 cm x 6.8 cm.

11. Four cards, two designs with illuminated missal type borders in red and blue around panels with four different verses, two with attached prints. Two cards were dated by the senders 1874, 1876. 10 cm x 15 cm.

12. Four similar cards, with two border designs, and four attached prints, two of nativity and two of festive Christmas, with three different verses in panel. 15 cm x 10 cm.

13. Four illuminated cards, with texts in large ornamental print. 11.2 cm x 7.2 cm.

14. Five cards, four designs with fleur-de-lys border around panel on red, blue, or green, with silver. Two have attached prints of saints and three have The Lord's Prayer, or the Apostle's Creed, in the panel. One card was dated by the sender 1874. 7.4 cm x 13.3 cm.

15. Ten cards, with greeting in gilt and colour over sprays of holly, flowers, or fruit. The four larger cards were registered at Stationers' Hall 13-6-1876. 10.1 cm x 6.2 cm, 10.1 cm x 4.3 cm.

16. Three similar cards, two with birthday greeting, one with a text. 10.1 cm x 6.2 cm, 12 cm x 7.5 cm.

17/19. Twelve illuminated cards, six designs, registered at Stationers' Hall 17-4-1877. Two of these have a mixture of wild flowers. Four have flowers with butterflies and a bee and are used in the set "Forging the Ring" attributed to Kate Greenaway (see Volume 51). The attribution of the flower design is controversial. 9.3 cm x 13.2 cm.

20/21. Twelve illuminated cards, six designs, also registered at Stationers' Hall 17-4-1877 with the previous set. These have flowers or berries around oval vignettes, with greetings or texts, and verses in a scroll. Some of this set were used for the smaller versions of Kate Greenaway's "Puck and Blossom" (see Volume 51). 7.4 cm x 11.4 cm.

22. Four cards in illuminated missal style with texts in ornamental script, one dated by the sender 1879. 11.2 cm x 7 cm.

23. Six cards, as in no. 22, some with silver. One card was dated by the sender 1882, but one was found in an album with the date 1876. 7.2 cm x 11.5 cm.

24. Five cards as above, with illuminated panels around religious verses of greetings, some by Frances Ridley Havergal. Late 1870's. Sizes up to 11.5 cm x 7.2 cm.

25. Six illuminated cards with scroll or geometric designs around panels with texts in large print. c1880? 11.5 cm x 7.2 cm.

26/29. Sixteen cards with embossed gilded scalloped borders and ten different flower designs, some with butterflies or mouse. They have greetings or verses in oval vignettes, scrolls, or panels, for Christmas, New Year, birthday or valentine. c1875. 8 cm x 11.8 cm.

30. Four similar cards with butterflies hovering on sprays of flowers or strawberries. Three have valentine, one a birthday greeting. c1875. 11.8 cm x 8 cm.

31. Six cards, three gilt-edged designs, with spring flowers on dark green backs, one a broom spray with a mouse (as in no. 28). c1875. 11.3 cm x 7.7 cm.

32. Four cards with illuminated initials and flower sprays. Registered at Stationers' Hall, 5-9-1877. 8 cm x 14.6 cm.

## VOLUME 42:
## MARCUS WARD. FLOWERS OF THE MONTH, AND SIMILAR

**This volume is a good example of the way that Marcus Ward used the same design in a variety of forms - large, small, gilt edge, coloured edge, and with different uses for Christmas, New Year, valentine and texts. It includes a number of designs that were used on known Kate Greenaway cards, as in Volume 41.**

*The cards numbered 1-17 are all variations on twelve designs of flowers and berries.*

1/3. Twelve cards "The Months", flowers and berries, with blue and gilt patterned border and appropriate verses. The reverse gives a description of each month. The flowers chosen to represent each month are: snowdrop, crocus, primrose, daffodil, hawthorn, ox-eye daisy with butterfly, convolvulus, poppy and wheat, blackberry, rose-hips with butterfly, chrysanthemum, holly. Six of these were registered at Stationers' Hall 30-4-1874. 8.9 cm x 12.5 cm.

4. Four similar, with red and gilt borders, for January, February, March and August. 8.9 cm x 12.6 cm.

5/6. Six cards, with texts - primrose, daffodil, blackberry, hawthorn, rosehip, chrysanthemum, five blue and gilt border, one red and gilt border, dated by the sender 1880. 8.9 cm x 12.5 cm. Also eleven small gilt backed text cards, 3.5 cm x 4.8 cm.

7. One card, ox-eye daisy on embossed scalloped mount, with Christmas greeting in verse. 10 cm x 13.8 cm.

8/10. Twelve smaller cards, embossed scalloped borders (one plain, one trimmed), with the month flowers, and Christmas or New Year verses. Two cards were dated by the sender 1872, 1873, which might show that some cards were published before being registered. 8 cm x 11.6 cm.

11. Six similar cards with birthday or religious verses. 8 cm x 11.6 cm.

12/14. Eleven cards of the flowers of the months, each named (rosehip missing), with Christmas or New Year verses, one dated by the sender 1876. 8.9 cm x 12.7 cm.

15. Four similar, three with valentine greeting, one with a New Year verse, two with attached scraps. 8.9 cm x 12.7 cm.

16. Six cards, snowdrop, primrose (two), crocus, rose-hip, holly on black ground with texts. 7 cm x 11 cm.

17. Eight cards, snowdrop, daisy, hawthorn, poppy, convolvulus, rose-hip, chrysanthemum, holly, on gilt ground with coloured borders and texts in panels. 7.4 cm x 11.2 cm.

18/20. Twelve cards and a cover "Pictures of Birds' Nests, Morning and Evening Hymns". The cards have six designs of nests and flowers, registered at Stationers' Hall 5-10-1877. Five cards have texts and pink or blue borders, seven have embossed scalloped borders, five with Christmas or New Year greetings and two with valentine greetings and verses on reverse. 9.3 cm x 13.2 cm.

21/27. Twenty six cards with six designs of primroses, violets, cyclamen, honeysuckle, snowdrops, white hibiscus, wood anemone. Five have embossed scalloped borders and flowers on gilt grounds, three plain borders, gilt grounds, sixteen are on black or brown grounds, all with verses for Christmas and New Year or texts in panels. Two smaller cards have gilt border and ground, and texts in panels. These designs were registered at Stationers' Hall 27-4-1874 and are the Kate Greenaway backgrounds (without the figures) illustrating "Cruise in the Acorn". Possibly her design, see Volume 51. 10 cm x 13.8cm, 9 cm x 12.8 cm, 7.7 cm x 10.7 cm.

## VOLUME 43:
## MARCUS WARD. FLOWER CARDS, c1875

**These cards are mostly large, similar to those in Volume 42, with the same design used with variations of captions, verses and mounts. The sizes are usually from 9 cm x 13 cm to 10 cm x 13.8 cm and will not be given below unless there is a significant difference.**

1/8. Thirty-one cards with six designs of flowers on gilt grounds, cornfield flowers, primulas, roses, geraniums, carnations, the borders being scalloped and embossed, plain, or coloured. Sixteen have greetings on the front, fourteen of these with verses on the reverse, and fifteen have a Christmas, New Year, birthday verse or a text, in a panel on the front. c1874.

9/10. Nine cards, two designs of Christmas roses or hyacinths, primroses and daisies, with Christmas or New Year verses or texts on panels. Six have a red line border, three a patterned red and blue border. These are two out of six designs registered at Stationers' Hall 30-4-1874. The other four are in Volume 45. 8 cm x 12.8 cm up to 9 cm x 13 cm.

11/13. Eleven cards, three designs of woodland flowers and ferns, with embossed scalloped borders on red and blue patterned edges. There are brief greetings or panels with verses on the front, and two have verses on the reverse. c1875.

14/15. Nine cards, four designs of holly, blackberries, primroses and violets, or roses. Four have scalloped embossed borders with Christmas or New Year verses in panels, four have patterned borders with texts in panels, and one has an advertisement for "Accomplished Drawing Room Attainments for Young Ladies and Gentlemen". Registered at Stationers' Hall 20-6-1876.

16/17. Seven cards, scalloped embossed borders and large flower designs. Four of red roses, carnations, berberis and plumbago have verses by Agnes R Howell on reverse and were registered at Stationers' Hall 22-6-1876. Three of tea roses, chrysanthemums and clematis have verses by Frances Ridley Havergal on reverse and were three out of four designs registered at Stationers' Hall 10-9-1877.

18/20. Thirteen cards of flowers on gilt grounds with greetings or texts in panels, five with patterned borders, five smaller with scalloped borders and three with red borders. There are seven designs, of which four, of Canterbury bells, nasturtiums, geraniums, and lilies were registered at Stationers' Hall 11-7-1876, and one of China asters on 12-7-1876. Sizes 9 cm x 13 cm, 8 cm x 12 cm, 7.5 cm x 11.3 cm.

21/22. Eight cards, scalloped embossed edges, with four designs of narcissus, crocus, apple and pear blossom, and heath, on gilt grounds, bordering panels with verses. Five are valentines, three birthday cards. Registered at Stationers' Hall 18-9-1876.

23. Six small cards of the same four designs, with texts, Christmas, or New Year verses in panels and blue patterned borders. 7.8 cm x 11 cm.

24. Five cards, four designs of pink and white flowers, with verses or text in panels and a blue and gilt patterned border. c1875.

25. Four similar cards with red, pink or yellow borders, various flowers around panels with Christmas or New Year verses. c1875.

26/27. Seven cards, four designs of fuchsias, pansies, pear and apple blossom, Christmas roses. Four have ornamental greetings in panels with Greek key borders in pink or blue, and three have birthday verses. One was dated by the sender January 1877.

28. Six smaller cards, two designs of asters or berries on gilt with blue patterned borders, and greetings or text on panels. Two are valentines. One was dated by the sender 1880, but the design was probably earlier. 7.8 cm x 11 cm.

29. Three cards, embossed scalloped edges, with verses in panels. Two are Easter cards with designs of passion flowers or vines on gilt grounds, the verses being by John Keble & Bishop Richard Mant; the other is a valentine with a bunch of mixed chrysanthemums. c1875. 9.8 cm x 13.7 cm.

30/32. Thirteen cards, four designs of roses and flower sprays, with verses on scrolls or panels and one other with mixed flowers. Six have embossed scalloped borders, six plain white, and one is trimmed. The four rose designs were registered at Stationers' Hall 15-6-1876. 6.9 cm x 10.2 cm up to 9 cm x 12.8 cm.

33/34. Nine similar cards with plain white borders. These are not marked Marcus Ward, but the rose designs and the greetings on scrolls by Julia Goddard permit the attribution. Late 1870's. 8.3 cm x 12.8 cm.

## VOLUME 44: MARCUS WARD. FLOWER CARDS, 1876-77

**This volume includes mainly smaller cards without borders or embossing on various coloured backgrounds including black and gilt. Most of the Stationers' Hall entries have been traced, but no artists are named. Ferns and berries appear with the flowers, and holly and mistletoe.**

1/5. Forty-five cards, with six designs of flower sprays - rose, moss rose, violets, daisies, forget-me-nots and carnations - around panels with brief seasonal greetings. Sixteen are on beige grounds, four on gilt and twenty-five on black, one of these on a gilt-edged mount. These designs were actually registered at Stationers' Hall by S Hildesheimer, with W Hagelberg, Berlin, 22-4-1876, but many are marked Marcus Ward, so they may have been commissioned by Marcus Ward from S Hildesheimer. cf cards in S Hildesheimer Volume 100. 8.3 cm x 5.5 cm.

6/9. Thirty cards with six designs of flowers and fruit - heather and ferns, forget-me-nots and lilies of the valley, red roses, blackberry, daisies, harebells and berries around scrolls with greetings or texts. Twenty-three are on various coloured grounds, seven on gilt. These are six out of eight designs registered at Stationers' Hall by Marcus Ward, 15-10-1877. 8.2 cm x 5.5 cm, 9 cm x 6.3 cm.

10/11. Nineteen cards with six designs of flowers and fruit, around panels with greetings. Three are on dark blue, nine on black, and seven on gilt grounds. Registered by Marcus Ward at Stationers' Hall, 13-6-1876. 10 cm x 4.4 cm.

12/13. Sixteen cards, with ten designs of flower sprays around panels with brief greetings or verses. Ten are on beige, five on black, and one on gilt grounds. 10.5 cm x 6.3 cm.

14. Five cards, with one design of yellow rose with stem piercing a panel withverse or greeting, one a valentine. Two are on beige, three on black grounds. Sizes up to 10.5 cm x 7.4 cm.

15. Nine cards, with five designs of flower sprays around panels with greeting or verse. Six are on beige, three on black grounds. 10.5 cm x 6.4 cm.

16/18. Seventeen cards, eight designs of flowers, holly and mistletoe, with greetings or verse on a panel. Eight are on

black grounds, nine on gilt. These are eight out of twelve designs registered at Stationers' Hall 14-6-1876. Sizes up to 11.6 cm x 7.5 cm.

19. Five cards, three designs of roses, primroses, or daisies, and panels with greetings or verse, on various coloured mounts, including silver. Sizes up to 11.2 cm x 7 cm.

20/21. Nine cards, five designs with flower or holly sprays around panels. Five have verses including one by Charlotte M Yonge, (two of these on gilt ground) and four have greetings. Six designs were registered at Stationers' Hall, 15-10-1877. 12 cm x 7.2 cm, 10.8 cm x 6.3 cm.

22/23. Fourteen cards with four designs of flower sprays, forget-me-nots, apple blossom, garden anemone, pyrus japonica, around panels of verses for Christmas, New Year and birthday. Nine are on gilt grounds, five on black. Registered at Stationers' Hall 13-6-1876. 10.3 cm x 6.3 cm.

24. Six cards on various coloured grounds, with five designs of yellow broom, thistles, lime, forget-me-nots and a butterfly, and a branch with rosehips. Registered at Stationers' Hall 15-10-1877. 10.7 cm x 6.6 cm.

25. Four cards, three designs of fungi, wild rose and berries, with greetings or text on panels. 10.7 cm x 6.6 cm.

26. Eight cards, with various flower and berry sprays, and greetings or verse on panels, including valentines. Six are on black grounds, two on beige. 10.3 cm x 6.3 cm.

## VOLUME 45: MARCUS WARD. FLOWER CARDS, 1874-1890

**This volume contains more unbordered cards, many with registration dates, and continues with bordered cards up to 1890.**

*The following cards have no borders.*

1/5. Twenty-five cards with nine designs of flower sprays and greetings or verses on sloping panels. Nine are on beige grounds, eight on black and eight on gilt. Although several are marked Marcus Ward, the designs were registered at Stationers' Hall by S Hildesheimer with W Hagelberg, Berlin, 22-4-1876. See Volume 44, numbers 1-5, and cards in S Hildesheimer Volume 100, nos. 1-5. Sizes approximately 12.2 cm x 7.3 cm.

6/7. Twelve cards, four designs of holly, mistletoe and berries, on various coloured grounds including silver, with greetings and verses on reverse. Registered at Stationers' Hall 5-9-1877. 10.6 cm x 6.5 cm.

8/9. Twelve cards, five designs of floral sprays. Five are on gilt or black grounds with greetings in scrolls, seven have coloured borders and texts. Six designs were registered at Stationers' Hall 20-6-1876, of which four are here, with one of crocuses from a different set. 11.6 cm x 7.6 cm, 9.8 cm x 6.9 cm.

10. Nine small cards, five designs, six on black grounds, three on gilt, with greetings, of which four designs are as 8/9, with one from 6/7. 8 cm x 5.4 cm.

11/13. Nineteen cards with black grounds, texts in panels, showing six designs of spring flowers and moss rose. c1875. 10.8 cm x 6.8 cm.

*The following cards are bordered (except where otherwise stated).*

14. Seven cards, four designs, as in 11/13, with Christmas and New Year verses in panels, and gilt borders. One was dated by the sender 1875. 10.8 cm x 6.8 cm.

15/17. Thirteen cards, with four designs of snowdrops, violets and berries, and Christmas and New Year verses or texts in panels. Five cards have fancy red or blue borders, eight red or blue lines. These are four out of six designs registered at Stationers' Hall 30-4-1874. 12.8 cm x 9 cm, 11.8 cm x 8 cm.

18. Four cards, with three designs of oak leaves or berries on gilt grounds, with Christmas or New Year greetings in panels. One was dated by the sender 1877. 11.8 cm x 8 cm.

19/22. Twenty cards, white borders, with seven designs of flower sprays and a variety of greetings or verses on scrolls, ten being on black grounds. These are not all marked Marcus Ward but are attributed by similarity. Two cards were marked 1876 by the senders. 11.2 cm x 7.2 cm.

23. Six cards with black backgrounds. Three are unbordered, with designs as in 19-22 and three are smaller with white borders and floral designs around panels with greetings. Late 1870's. 10.4 cm x 6.4 cm, 9 cm x 5.2 cm.

24. Seven cards, with six designs of floral sprays on a brown ground, and Christmas verses or texts on reverse. Two are larger with gilt edge, and five smaller ones have a blue border. Late 1870's. 12 cm x 9.6 cm, 9.8 cm x 7.5 cm.

25. Seven valentine cards, with flower pictures, captions below and scalloped edges. There are finely printed verses on the reverse of the cards, one by Julia Goddard, a prolific writer of verses for Marcus Ward. Four of these were registered at Stationers' Hall 15-9-1876. 7.2 cm x 10.9 cm.

26/29. Twenty-nine cards using the designs from no. 25, with five more, twelve designs in all. They have texts, or greetings, or verses in panels, and various borders. Sizes up to 6.6 cm x 9.3 cm.

30. Seven cards with scrolls bearing seasonal verses on two designs of spring flowers. Late 1870's. 6.2 cm x 9 cm.

31. Seven similar cards with scrolls on two designs of roses and berries. 9 cm x 6.2 cm.

32. Six gilt-edged cards with flower designs on gilt grounds, including passion flowers and scrolls with texts. Three cards with verses on reverse are from Packet no. 16 "Songs and Sunbeams" and Packet no. 164 "Favourite Hymns". These are probably late 1870's, but a racing programme written in French "Courses de Maurice" is dated 1890, and has a similar picture. 6 cm x 9.1 cm.

33. Four cards with flowers on gilt grounds with texts in panels, and red line borders. One card is dated by the sender 1881. Sizes up to 8 cm x 11.2 cm.

34. Three cards, two designs of Christmas roses and narcissi, with greetings in a Gothic style window. One card was dated by the sender 1878. 11.8 cm x 8.4 cm.

35. Seven cards, five designs of floral sprays on dark grounds with text in panel. c1880. 5.8 cm x 7.4 cm.

36. Six cards with three designs of wreaths of roses, primroses and blackberries, with another card dated 1883 bearing a verse, probably cut from its neighbour, originally a folding card. 6.5 cm x 10.3 cm.

37. Three cards, two designs of floral borders around panels bearing a greeting. One is a birthday card with a verse on reverse by Frances Ridley Havergal, from Packet no. 173 "Greetings for Birthdays". Two cards were dated by the sender 1884. 12.2 cm x 8.5 cm.

38. Three cards with bird and floral border designs, printed with sender's name and address and dated 1880, 1882, 1883. Sizes up to 15.5 cm x 11.7 cm.

39. Three hand-painted cards on Marcus Ward mounts, one dated 1881. 15.8 cm x 10.4 cm, 8.5 cm x 13 cm.

## VOLUME 46:
## MARCUS WARD. FLOWERS & CHINA, 1876 - EARLY 1880'S

**This volume includes some cards with named artists' registrations. Marcus Ward did not appear to name their artists till late in 1878. Many of the cards have well printed verses on**

**46.2**

**the reverse by Frances Ridley Havergal, Frederick Langbridge, and S K Cowan, M A and are mostly in larger sizes.**

1. Thomas Crane. Two gilt-edged cards (probably a folder) with blue patterned vases holding bunches of forget-me-nots, honeysuckle, sweet peas and pinks, in an ornamental border. These are two out of four designs registered at Stationers' Hall by Thomas Crane, 19-11-1879. 10.2 cm x 15.8 cm.

2. Thomas Crane. Two cards, of spotted lilies and pink flowers on a mosaic ground with ornamental borders top and bottom. These are two out of six designs registered at Stationer's Hall 19-11-1879. 10.5 cm x 16 cm.

3/4. Thomas Crane. Eight cards, signed T C, four designs of flower sprays, seven on blue grounds, one on orange, with greetings, text or a blank space for the sender to use. c1880. 10.2 cm x 15 cm.

5. Thomas Crane. Three cards, sprays of holly, mistletoe and ivy on mosaic ground with greetings. c1880. 10 cm x 12.8 cm.

6. Six square cards of flowers and butterflies, probably by Thomas Crane, with simple greetings. Sizes up to 10.4 cm x 10.4 cm.

7. Two cards with ornamental borders by Helen Coleman Angell, one of three roses, the other a blue vase with prunts (described as china but probably glass) holding flowers, with a camellia by its side. These are two out of four registered at Stationers' Hall by Helen Coleman Angell, 23-4-1879. 11.6 cm x 15.3 cm, 15.3 cm x 11.6 cm.

**47.6**

8/10. Seven cards by Percy Tarrant with various flower designs (one with birds) on gilt or silver mosaic ground. Three designs are from four registered at Stationers' Hall 28-4-1879, three from four registered 19-11-1879, and one from four registered 21-11-1879.
16 cm x 11.5 cm, 11.5 cm x 16 cm.

11/15. Fourteen cards with eleven designs of mixed flower bouquets. Three have embossed scalloped borders, two ornamental borders and nine are on white card with a gold line border and a Shakespeare quotation, with verses by Frances Ridley Havergal on reverse. Six of these designs illustrate "Floral Poetry and the Language of Flowers", published by Marcus Ward in 1877. Four of the designs were registered at Stationers' Hall 29-8-1876.
10 cm x 13.6 cm, 11.3 cm x 15.4 cm.

16/17. Seven cards with six designs of flower sprays and butterflies around panels, six bearing Christmas or New year verses, the other with a text and a blue border. Three of these designs are from eight registered at Stationers' Hall 5-9-1877, which appear in "Bards & Blossoms" by F E Hulme, FLS, FSA, published by Marcus Ward in 1877.
8.4 cm x 14 cm.

18. Four square cards with circles containing flower or berry sprays, and ornamental corners, in very bright colours in a brown border. Verses by Frederick Langbridge are on the reverse. c1880.
12.5 cm x 12.5 cm.

19. Four cards, three designs, with a mistletoe or floral wreath on a gilt lattice ground, around greetings. Verses by Frances Ridley Havergal are on the reverse. c1880. 9.8 cm x 11.8 cm.

20. Two cards on an emerald ground, one with a peony and an ornamental back, the other of flowers with a Thomas Crane style border. c1880. 12.5 cm x 16.7 cm, 12.4 cm x 15.5 cm.

*The following cards are early 1880's.*

21. Two cards, floral sprays on silver or gilt ground, one with Christmas greeting, one birthday. Both have verses on reverse, one signed by S K Cowan, M A.
10.3 cm x 16 cm, 11.2 cm x 16.6 cm.

22. Two cards, garden flowers on brown ground with a lake scene in a vignette encircled by a horseshoe, one with a verse on reverse by Frances Ridley Havergal. 15.3 cm x 11.2 cm.

23/24. Five cards, three designs of floral sprays on brown or blue ground. Two are valentines, one Easter, one birthday, and one Christmas, with verses on reverse by Frances Ridley Havergal. 17.1 cm x 9 cm, 18.4 cm x 10.9 cm.

25. Two cards with tulips and syringa on pale blue ground, and ornamental design on reverse in silver on yellow.
11 cm x 14.8 cm.

26. Two cards, apple blossom and pelargoniums, on a brown ground with a border imitating a wooden frame and Christmas verses on the back by Frances Ridley Havergal. 15.3 cm x 11.2 cm.

27. Two cards, Christmas roses and spring flowers, with ornamental initial to the greeting in red. 15.8 cm x 7.7 cm.

28. Two cards, everlasting flowers on a pale blue ground, with religious verses on reverse by Frances Ridley Havergal. 15.8 cm x 11.3 cm.

29. Two cards, violet and rose sprays with ornamental gilt border and verses on reverse by Frances Ridley Havergal. 13.3 cm x 10.3 cm.

30. Three cards, flowers in bowls or a stone jug, on a dark ground with gilt border and varied greetings, one with a verse on reverse by Frances Ridley Havergal.
12.5 cm x 10.3 cm.

31. Two cards with the same design of hyacinths in a bowl, and verse below, one a valentine, one New Year.
7.5 cm x 18.5 cm.

32. One card, ferns in a blue and white bowl on a dark blue ground.
18.5 cm x 10.4 cm.

33. Four cards with three designs of fine china and flowers. Two are in circular vignettes on a gilt ground. Sizes up to 12.2 cm x 9 cm.

34. One card with an oriental pot, bowl and vase, against a curtain with a stained glass window above and an ornamental border, and more pottery on reverse. 12.1 cm x 18.7 cm.

35. Two cards, snowdrops and evening primrose on a dark ground, the latter with "Bells Across the Snow" by Frances Ridley Havergal, on reverse. 9 cm x 13.5 cm, 12.7 cm x 20.3 cm.

36. Three cards, cyclamen, Christmas rose and double daffodils, growing against a brick wall. 10.3 cm x 13.3 cm.

37. Three miscellaneous cards with roses, two with verses by Frances Ridley Havergal on reverse.
Sizes up to 10.5 cm x 14.3 cm.

38. An illuminated "In Memoriam" tribute to Frances Ridley Havergal, 1837-1839. She wrote "Bells Across the Snow", probably the most quoted Christmas card poem, and Marcus Ward used many of her verses on cards. 18 cm x 25 cm.

## VOLUME 47:
## MARCUS WARD. FLOWERS WITH CROSSES AND EASTER CARDS 1875-1885

**These cards all have religious significance, and many were made specially for Easter greetings, which were popular in late Victorian times. The crosses which appeared at Easter were also used for Christmas and New Year cards; while celebrating the Birth of the Christ Child, they foreshadowed His end.**

1/5. Twenty-three cards with four designs of passion flowers, wild roses and convolvulus entwined round crosses, and two designs of sprays of white lilies and arum lilies. Seven are on dark backs, nine on beige, and seven on blue. Five are Easter cards, twelve Christmas or New Year, and six birthday. The two sprays and two of the crosses were registered at Stationers' Hall 20-6-1876. Sizes 8 cm x 11.7 cm, 7.2 cm x 11 cm, 5.7 cm x 8.7 cm.

6. Three cards, illuminated crosses, with passion flowers, camellias and convolvulus designs around Easter verses in scrolls. c1875. 9.2 cm x 13 cm.

7. Four Easter cards, two designs of illuminated borders, one with the four Apostles' symbols, all with verses in panels. c1875. 9.5 cm x 13.2 cm.

8. Four illuminated Easter cards, two with gilded floral crosses surrounded by symbols of the Passion, with verses on reverse, and two with gilded crosses encircled by floral designs with Easter verses. Two were dated by the sender 1876, 1877. 7 cm x 11 cm, 7.5 cm x 11.5 cm.

9. Four illuminated Easter cards, two with wallflowers on crosses and Thomas Crane style borders (one grey, one orange), one with illuminated cross and lily spray on Gothic background and Easter verse on reverse, and one with a border of poppies and wheat around an Easter verse. c1876. 7.1 cm x 15 cm, 9 cm x 13 cm.

10. Four illuminated cards, two with crosses, two with goblets, probably communion cups, interlaced with flower sprays on various coloured grounds. Late 1870's. 7.4 cm x 11.3 cm.

11. Three cards, roses and pansies with forget-me-nots on gilt ground with decorative black and white border. Two are Easter cards, one Christmas, probably two designs out of four registered at Stationers' Hall 21-11-1879. 9.7 cm x 12.8 cm.

12. One Easter card, floral spray on black ground in a Gothic arch, with a gilt border on a yellow ground. Late 1870's. 10.5 cm x 20 cm.

13. Four cards, two with lilies and snowdrops around greetings in panels, one with convolvulus and text in a Gothic window, and one with a leaf border around an Easter greeting verse. Late 1870's. 7.9 cm x 12.2 cm.

14. Two illuminated cards with crosses decorated with flowers, surrounded by captions and verses for Christmas and Thomas Crane type borders. Late 1870's. 8.8 cm x 13.7 cm.

15. One illuminated card with a gilt cross covered in violets and primroses, on a yellow ground with gilt decoration and an Easter verse on reverse. Late 1870's. 12 cm x 18.6 cm.

16. Four Christmas cards with crosses, entwined with flowers or catkins, on blue ground. Three have verses on reverse by Frances Ridley Havergal and one has gilt decoration round a cross with I H S. Late 1870's. Sizes up to 9.3 cm x 13 cm.

17/18. Four Easter cards, three designs with silver crosses entwined with passion flowers, lilies, or narcissus, on red grounds, and verses by F Langbridge, H M B and J E on reverse. c1880. 11.8 cm x 17 cm.

19. Three cards with three designs of the same set as in 17/18, including a fourth design of orange blossom, on gilt crosses on beige grounds with a blue border. All have verses on reverse by Frances Ridley Havergal. c1880. 11.8 cm x 17 cm.

20. Two small cards, designs as above of narcissus and passion flowers on crosses, on beige grounds with blue border. 1880. 7.6 cm x 11 cm.

21. Three Easter cards on beige grounds, one with an almond blossom spray and Frances Ridley Havergal verse on reverse, two with pelargonium and foxglove sprays and Easter verse by F Langbridge with illuminated initial. Early 1880's. 15.3 cm x 10.5 cm, 9 cm x 11.7 cm.

22. Three miscellaneous Easter cards, one with lilies and scroll, one with a butterfly, and one an illuminated cross. Two have verses on reverse. Early 1880's. Sizes up to 9.5 cm x 11.7 cm.

*The following cards are c1885.*

23. Two cards with gilt crosses, one with red climbing flowers, perhaps sprekelia, and one with violets. 11.8 cm x 16.3 cm, 11.4 cm x 11.4 cm.

24. Two Easter cards on pale blue grounds, one with anemones and small silver cross, the other with a rose on a decorated silver cross in a red panel. 10.5 cm x 14.1 cm, 10 cm x 14.6 cm.

25. Two Easter cards, tiger lilies on gilded cross with a greeting in a scroll. 11.1 cm x 15 cm.

26. Two Easter cards with crosses, one on silver with a pansy wreath, the other with lilies of the valley on a yellow ground. 10.1 cm x 12.2 cm, 11.3 cm x 15.2 cm.

27. Four miscellaneous Easter cards with crosses decorated by flowers. Sizes up to 10 cm x 14.3 cm.

28. Four miscellaneous Easter cards, two with floral sprays, one a basket of violets and one with a cross and flowers on a silver ground. Sizes up to 12.6 cm x 12 cm.

## VOLUME 48:
## MARCUS WARD. FLOWERS, FRUIT AND FUNGI

**These cards include some illuminated texts and a few of fungi, as well as some with butterflies and insects on the flowers or fruit. They are dated from 1876 to about 1880.**

1. Four cards with sprays of passion flowers, cyclamen, geraniums, and roses and greetings in gilt on black grounds. Registered at Stationers' Hall 20-6-1876. 13.2 cm x 9 cm, 9 cm x 13.2 cm.

2/3. Eight cards, with various gilt embossed edges, and four designs of wild strawberries and flower sprays. Four are valentines, four Christmas or New Year, with verses or greetings in panels. One was dated by the sender 1878. 9 cm x 12.8 cm.

4/5. Eight cards, four designs of wild flower sprays on various coloured grounds, with greetings or texts in gilt or

brown letters. One card has a biography of Robert Raikes, 1735-1811, on the reverse, headed "Sunday School Centenary, 1880". Another card was dated by the sender 1880. 8.3 cm x 12.2 cm.

6. Four cards on brown or peach coloured grounds with gilt borders, and two designs of fungi. c1878. 8.3 cm x 12.2 cm.

7. Three cards with sprays of wild strawberries, blackberries, or cherries, on silver grounds with a blue border. One card was dated by the sender 1882. 8.3 cm x 11.7 cm.

8. Six cards with designs of fruit and flowers on ornamental grounds, with greetings in panels or scrolls. c1880. 7.7 cm x 12.3 cm.

9. Four cards with texts "Be ye holy" etc, on black or silver grounds, and flower or fruit sprays with a bee. Perhaps three out of six registered at Stationers' Hall 17-4-1877. 7.5 cm x 11.4 cm.

10/13. Eighteen cards with conventional designs of periwinkles, cyclamen, lilies, poppies and Christmas roses on latticed gilt or silver grounds. Six are valentines, four have texts, two are birthday cards and six have Christmas or New Year greetings. One card has a bee on the text "- of Good Courage" and is from Packet no 149 "More Bees", with a verse on reverse. Two cards were dated by the senders 1878, 1879. 6.8 cm x 10.8 cm.

14/16. Twenty-two text cards, six designs of brightly coloured flowers on blue, red or purple grounds with various texts in panels and gilt borders. c1880. Two sizes, 7.7 cm x 11.5 cm, 4.5 cm x 6.5 cm.

17/19. Eleven cards on cream coloured grounds with green borders and gilt and silver embossed flower sprays, and Christmas or New Year greetings. These cards, unusually for Marcus Ward, are not signed, but were registered by Marcus Ward at Stationers' Hall, six on 19-11-1879 and ten on 21-11-1879, the cards here being eleven out of these sixteen. Similar cards were published by Eyre & Spottiswoode. Three sizes, 6.5 cm x 12 cm, 6.5 cm x 13.9 cm, 10.8 cm x 7.5 cm.

20/21. Seven cards of waterlilies and butterflies, four designs, with brown and yellow borders. Five have verses on the front, and a Thomas Crane style design in brown and white on reverse, with a greeting. Two are from Packet no. 63 "Lilies from the Waters of Quietness", with a verse on reverse. Late 1870's. 10 cm x 13.2 cm, 13.2 cm x 10 cm.

22. Two cards of orchids and a butterfly, with gold and brown borders and a verse in a panel, one dated by the sender 1881. 9.4 cm x 13.5 cm.

23/24. Six cards of butterflies and wild flowers, four designs. Three are on dark blue grounds with paler borders, and three in panels on pale green borders. c1880. 7.4 cm x 7.4 cm, 9.7 cm x 13.7 cm.

25. Three cards, two designs of syringa and Solomon's seal with a butterfly, on pale blue grounds in a white border. 7.7 cm x 13.5 cm.

26. Three cards, butterflies or dragonflies with scenes of wild flowers or waterlilies, one a valentine, one Christmas and one New Year with appropriate verses in panels. These are three out of six designs by Lewis F Day, registered at Stationers' Hall 27-11-1879. 11.2 cm x 7.5 cm.

27/28. Six miscellaneous cards of butterflies or dragonfly with flowers, and greetings in panels or scrolls. c1880. Sizes 10.1 cm x 6.5 cm to 14.7 cm x 10.7 cm.

## VOLUME 49:
## MARCUS WARD. FLOWER CARDS 1880-1890'S

**No registrations have been traced for these cards, many of which feature boldly drawn flower sprays some with holly and berries. Few marked Marcus Ward cards of the 1890's have been found by the writer, but perhaps some unmarked cards in subsequent volumes might be identified.**

*The following cards are early 1880's, marked Marcus Ward & Co.*

1/2. Twelve cards, five designs of flower sprays on symbolic arrows, with greetings or texts in panels. Four have a gilt edge and eight are plain. 6.4 cm x 13.4 cm, 5.6 cm x 12.7 cm.

3/4. Eight cards, four designs of hanging baskets of spring flowers with bamboo borders (one gilt) and greetings on small labels. One was dated by the sender 1882. 8 cm x 16.5 cm.

5. Two cards, chrysanthemum and primrose sprays on dark grounds, with gilt borders and greetings in scrolls. There are verses by Frances Ridley Havergal on the reverse. One was dated by the sender 1882. 9 cm x 11.8 cm.

6. Two cards, sprays of small flowers and fern on a brown ground, with verses by Frances Ridley Havergal. One card was dated by the sender 1882. 8 cm x 19.5 cm.

7. Three cards, gilt borders, two having rose sprays on a mosaic ground and crysanthemums in an oval vignette, first two registered at Stationers' Hall 21-11-1879 by Agnes Lewis. 9 cm x 14.7 cm, 10 cm x 15.8 cm.

8. Three cards, gilt borders, with sprays of lupins, soapwort and rockrose, one with Christmas greeting, one with text, the third a valentine. 8.6 cm x 12.5 cm.

9. Five cards with verses for Christmas, New Year and birthday in large panels, with spring flowers around and blue line borders. 9.5 cm x 9.1 cm.

10. Three cards with greetings in panels over bunches of anemones, forsythia, and berries, and coloured line borders. 8.6 cm x 12.5 cm.

11/12. Nine cards, eight designs of flower and berry sprays on various coloured grounds. Three are octagonal, with greeting verses and pink borders, six rectangular with greeting or verse in panel. 9.8 cm x 12.5 cm, 9.6 cm x 10.5 cm.

13. Three miscellaneous cards, flower sprays with coloured borders. 5.5 cm x 12.5 cm up to 15.7 cm x 11 cm.

14. Three cards, two with sprays of berries and forsythia on dark grounds with gilt border and greetings, the other with pink and white hawthorn and a red border. One card is dated by the sender 1884. 8 cm x 15.3 cm, 11.3 cm x 11.3 cm.

15. Three cards in mock postal form, with Father Christmas "stamp" on the pink back, and two designs of holly and ivy for Christmas and the New Year. 9.8 cm x 15.3 cm.

16. Five cards in two styles, featuring three designs of pansy, primula and soapwort(?), with Christmas and New Year greetings. Perhaps by Charlotte Spiers. 9 cm x 9 cm, 7.5 cm x 11.2 cm.

17/18. Nine cards, three designs of bunches of violets or primroses and a basket of primroses. Five are on dark backs with greetings in panels, three have green borders (one trimmed) and one a white border. 9 cm x 9 cm, 8.2 cm x 10.4 cm, 12.8 cm x 11.2 cm.

19. Four miscellaneous cards, one with a design in blue on gilt of flowering plants. Sizes up to 8 cm x 13.3 cm.

*The following cards are c1885-90, marked Marcus Ward & Co Limited.*

20. Four cards, open envelopes with spring flowers and Christmas postmark on reverse, one card perhaps earlier, marked Marcus Ward & Co. Probably the cards referred to by Gleeson White as "well known series of open envelopes" by Charlotte Spiers. 10.8 cm x 15.3 cm.

21. Six cards with sprays of spring flowers in coloured borders, in three styles, probably by Charlotte Spiers, one dated by the sender 1885. 7.7 cm x 7.7 cm up to 10.3 cm x 15.3 cm.

22. Four cards on green or blue grounds, with flower sprays and Christmas greetings. Two have verses by Frances Ridley Havergal on reverse. Sizes up to 9.7 cm x 13.2 cm.

23. Three cards, two designs of cotton and flax plants. Two cards are educational with descriptions of flax and cotton cultivation and manufacture on reverse, the other is a New Year card with greeting. 9.7 cm x 15 cm.

24. Three cards, chrysanthemum, rose and pansy sprays, two with poems by Frances Ridley Havergal and Sarah Doudney on reverse. Sizes up to 10.2 cm x 15.3 cm.

25. Two cards, one on a green ground with a spray of almond blossom, the other sunflowers on a black ground with Frances Ridley Havergal verse on reverse. 15.3 cm x 10.3 cm, 8.3 cm x 14.5 cm.

26. Three cards, holly, blackberry and rosehips, the latter with a poem by Hartley Coleridge on reverse. Sizes up to 11.2 cm x 15.2 cm.

27. Four cards, two with pink borders and rose and violet and lily-of-the-valley sprays around birthday verses, the other two with rose and orchid sprays on green ground with Christmas greetings. 11.2 cm x 10.6 cm, 10.8 cm x 9.5 cm.

28. Five miscellaneous cards, including two small folders with flower sprays and verse within, and holly or ivy designs on a brown ground on cover. 7 cm x 7 cm up to 9.3 cm x 13.5 cm.

29. Four miscellaneous cards with flower sprays and gilt or silver decoration, one an octagonal card with country scene in small vignette. Sizes up to 11.5 cm x 14 cm.

30/31. Seven shaped cards, one a fan, five circular, and one octagonal. Two of the circular cards are a return to the early type of illuminated decoration. Sizes 16.5 cm x 9cm, 10 cm diameter, 11 cm x 11 cm.

32. Two cards and a print.
a) A folding card with flower spray and a river scene. 10 cm x 15.3 cm.
b) A print, the coat-of-arms of Blair Smith, Londonderry dated 1898. 10 cm x 13.3 cm.
c) A folding card with illuminated design on cover and verse within, which might be twentieth century from its appearance. 12.7 cm x 9 cm.

## VOLUME 50:
## MARCUS WARD. FLOWERS AND BERRIES, MANY WITH TEXTS AND RELIGIOUS VERSES, 1879-90

1/2. Ten cards on gilt or silver grounds, nine with four designs of rose sprays, one with convolvulus. Five have texts in scrolls or panels, five have Christmas or New Year greetings or verses. One card was dated by the sender 1879. 11.7 cm x 7.6 cm.

3. Three cards with borders of berries or wild flowers on cream grounds, around panels with poems by Frances Ridley Havergal. One card was dated by the sender 1881. 10.5 cm x 14.2 cm.

4/5. Eight cards with gilt borders and four designs of wild flowers, roses and berries. Four have texts, four birthday or affectionate greetings. One was dated by the sender 1881. 9 cm x 12.8 cm.

6/10. Nineteen cards, six designs of flower sprays, cowslip, auricula, heliotrope and butterfly, gloxinia, delphinium, cantana, as given in Stationers' Hall registration, 28-4-1879, by Agnes Lewis. Six have Christmas greetings and verses by Frances Ridley Havergal, ten have various greetings with texts, these all with gilt borders; three have texts and blue borders. 9 cm x 12.8 cm, 8.4 cm x 12 cm.

11. Three cards with blue borders, and flower sprays and texts on various coloured grounds, c1880. 8 cm x 12 cm.

12. Six cards with three designs of poppies, roses and blackberries, on beige grounds with texts and illuminated initials and verses by Frances Ridley Havergal on reverse. Two cards are from Marcus Ward Packet no 19 "Light after Darkness". c1880. 12.5 cm x 9.5 cm.

13. Six cards, green and gilt borders, with rose, leaf, or clover sprays and texts. Four have "Christmas" or "New Year" in gilt panels, the others "Reward of Merit", and "Purity". One card was dated by the sender 1882. 9 cm x 11.5 cm.

14. Four small cards with flower borders around panels with texts or greetings. 9.4 cm x 7 cm.

15/19. Nineteen cards, gilt, yellow, or blue borders, with thirteen flower or spray designs. Eight of these, maidenhair, harebells, oats, periwinkle, lilac, knapweed, daffodil and cowslip were registered at Stationers' Hall 19-11-1879 by Agnes Lewis and there are also in the same sets daisies, mistletoe, primrose, lily-of-the-valley and pansy, in four varieties of card design. All have Christmas or New Year headings, with texts or religious verses, and two have poems on reverse. 11.7 cm x 9 cm, 11.7 cm x 8.5 cm.

20. Four cards, various flower sprays on beige grounds, with Christmas or loving greetings. One was dated by the sender 1880. 11.7 cm x 9 cm.

21. Four miscellaneous cards, flower sprays and texts, one with a butterfly. Early 1880's. Sizes up to 11.7 cm x 9 cm.

22. Six cards with four designs of flower sprays partly covered by large panels. Four have birthday or advent verses by Frances Ridley Havergal. Two have texts on the front panels, and are from Marcus Ward Packet no. 41a, "Memorable Words" with quotations from the poets or famous men on the reverse. c1880. 9.5 cm x 12.7 cm.

23. Large card with a spray of rosehips on white ground around a text from Romans in gilt letters. c1880. 11.3 cm x 18.5 cm.

24. Four miscellaneous cards with wreath or flower sprays; three have texts and one a verse by Frederick Langbridge. c1885. Sizes up to 10.5 cm x 13.2 cm.

25. Three cards, all with religious poems, one with birds in reeds by a stream, one with a mistletoe spray, one with a flowering branch. c1885. Sizes up to 10.5 cm x 16.5 cm.

26. Three cards, flower sprays on white grounds, one an acrostic with initial letters "God Speed". c1885. Sizes 7.7 cm x 9.7 cm to 13.7 cm x 10 cm.

27/28. Four gilt edged cards with pictures of the Madonna and Child and texts in large script with illuminated initials. Late 1880's. 19.6 cm x 12.5 cm.

29. Four cards with an advertisement for the "Sale of Marcus Ward's collection" date unknown. The cards illustrate trade marks and signatures from c1879-1890's, including the early wreath and crown, Marcus Ward & Co, Marcus Ward & Co - ent. Stationers' Hall and Marcus Ward & Co Ltd. Sizes 9.2 cm x 6.2 cm up to 11 cm x 9.5 cm.

30. Two examples of envelope and folder used to enclose cards, probably mid 1870's, with illuminated Thomas Crane style designs on pink or green. 10 cm x 13.5 cm.

31. A card dated 1891 by the sender, apple blossom over a gilt lunette with a poem by Frances Ridley Havergal on reverse. Marked M.W. cards of this period rarely appear. 11.5 cm x 13.3 cm.

32. Four cards from a calendar for 1883, showing girls in winter and summer, from the same set as two cards in volume 34, no. 6. 10 cm x 15.2 cm.

33. Four cards from a calendar for 1884, showing a man and a woman in Georgian style dress, in spring, summer, autumn, and winter. 9.5 cm x 14.5 cm.

To Mrs Trapnell

A MERRY CHRISTMAS AND A HAPPY NEW YEAR TO YOU

Published at Summerly's Home Treasury Office, 12 Old Bond Street, London.

From George Bell

To Emma Fletcher Norton

A MERRY CHRISTMAS AND A HAPPY NEW YEAR TO YOU

From Her Husband 1881

A MERRY CHRISTMAS AND A HAPPY NEW YEAR TO YOU

**3.22**

**4.14**

**3.4**

**3.3**

**3.30**

**3.25**

Visiting Cards 1860's

A MERRY CHRISTMAS AND
A HAPPY NEW YEAR

5.26

Welcome as the flowers in May
To share our Christmas joys to-day.

5.5

A MERRY
CHRISTMAS.

6.8

DANGEROUS

A HAPPY NEW YEAR TO YOU

6.10

A MERRY CHRISTMAS TO YOU

6.39

A CHRISTMAS GREETING NOW I SEND
MERR
CHRISTM

UNTO
US
A CHILD
IS
BORN

NEW YEARS
CARDS

CHRISTMAS
CARDS

TO YOU MY DEAR & LOVING FRIEND.

6.26

24.1

A MERRY CHRISTMAS AND A HAPPY NEW YEAR.

26.13

24.1

24.9

CHRISTMAS.

THE COLLECTOR.

The Turkey, the Pig, and the nice Roast Beef,
With Ducks all so prime you see;
Who wish to be dressed in the very best style,
Come up from the far country.

Old Christmas gives them as they come in,
A welcome you may be sure;
And gathers from out each goodly load,
A little for all the poor.

The little Pigs grunt, and the Ducks all quack,
And the Beef runs on to the roast,
Knowing that Charity blesses the feast,
And will give to those who want most.

THE PUDDING THAT CUT AWAY.

To such a pudding! now what do you say?
A hasty pudding that would run away,
He was in a hurry, so could not walk,
But hastened on with his knife and fork.

It was a good pudding you may be sure,
That sliced himself up for the old and the poor;
And left not a crumb on his silver dish,
So from all good people the like I wish.

Remember that when your pudding time comes,
You scrape the dish of the very last crumbs;
If you truly relish your own, I say,
You must make a pudding to cut away.

A HAPPY NEW YEAR

24.10

A HAPPY NEW YEAR

24.10

A HAPPY NEW YEAR

24.10

Cards designed by Charles Bennett, Alfred Crowquill, Robert Dudley

THERE SURELY IS NOT ANY REASON

WHY WE SHOULD NOT ENJOY THE SEASON

10.26

A MERRY CHRISTMAS & A HAPPY NEW YEAR.

26.8

A MERRY CHRISTMAS TO YOU ALL

10.26

MERRY CHRISTMAS AND A HAPPY NEW YEAR

TWO HEADS ARE BETTER THAN ONE

54.4

WHEN WINE SINKS WORDS SWIM.

A HAPPY NEW YEAR

54.4

A MERRY CHRISTMAS!

10.6

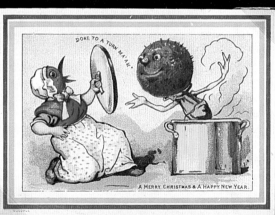

DONE TO A TURN MA'AM

A MERRY CHRISTMAS & A HAPPY NEW YEAR.

26.14

THE COMPLIMENTS OF THE SEASON

10.10

JOYFUL ANTICIPATIONS

A MERRY CHRISTMAS TO YOU.

10.17

HAMPERED BY THE ENEMY.

WISHING YOU A MERRY CHRISTMAS.

10.17

**121.5**

**138.1**

**138.1**

**121.14** ▶

**121.7**

**121.5**

**121.20**

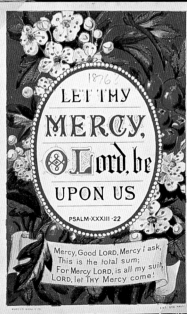

**121.13**

**41.21**

A Merry Christmas

A Happy New Year

8.13

A merry Christmas to you

8.9

A HAPPY XMAS

TO YOU

8.9

A Christmas Greeting

Plenty of Fun at
Christmas tide
Plenty of Friends at
Your Fireside
Plenty of Happy
Years beside.

8.7

THE COMPLIMENTS OF THE

SEASON TO YOU

8.9

A MERRY CHRISTMAS AND A HAPPY NEW YEAR

8.7

8.9

Illuminated cards published by Sulman early 1870's

15.27

25.8

195.14

195.

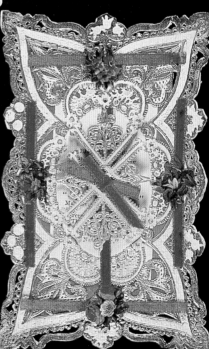

13.12

195.15

17.10

Silk, lace paper, scraps, early 1870's

22.22

22.22

16.11

14.2

14.3

Mechanical cards with fans and bouquets c 1875

2.23

2.26

2.3

26.4

2.3

26.4

26.14

26.14

20.3

20.5

Robins and Holly 1860's -70's

A MERRY CHRISTMAS AND A HAPPY NEW YEAR.

166.1

WITH TRUMPETS AND WITH DRUMS
LO! MOTHER CHRISTMAS COMES.

166.3

A HAPPY,
NEW-YEAR.

166.1

Wishing you a Merry Christmas.

166.2

MERRY CHRISTMAS

LINLEY SAMBOURNE. INV.

166.4

A Happy New Year.

166.2

A Merry Xmas

A Happy New Year.

166.3

Laden
with
fairy gifts may Christmas meet thee.

99.3

Hurrah! for the jolly Christmas tree,
And welcome, yes, thrice welcome he
Who bears this type of mirth and glee,
This emblem of felicity.

10.22

**Father and Mother Christmas**

MIDSUMMER'S EVE.

52.1

SPRINGTIME.

52.1

COME DANCE in the meadows:
The cowslips are there,
Nodding their heads
In the sweet scented air:
THE BLUE BELLS make music
Which we cannot hear,
And play for the fairies,
Whose delicate ear
Can catch all the talk
Of each insect and flower,
And see in my eyes
Love increasing each hour.

51.8

EASTERTIDE.

52.1

AUTUMN GAMES.

52.1

THE SPRING awakes,
And Winter takes
Its last adieu,
Bees softly hum,
And birds, long dumb,
Carol anew.

MY LOVE and I
Together hie,
To watch the Spring:
And gently walk,
Or sit and talk,
And blithely sing.

51.14

THERE IS A GARDEN IN THY FACE

MAY NEW YEAR BRING FROM LOVERS TRUE
LOTS OF VALENTINES FOR YOU!

52.24

WELCOME NEW YEAR, WELCOME MAY!
WE'LL CROWN THEE FLORA'S QUEEN TO-DAY!

52.24

51.25

TO MY LOVE

WITH CAROL SWEET AND MERRY LAY
WE GLADLY WELCOME NEW YEAR'S DAY!

52.24

MAY NEW YEAR BRING THEE PEACE AND PLENTY!
BARNS AND CELLARS NEVER EMPTY!

52.24

51.26

**Cards designed by Walter Crane**

A Merry Christmas To You.

147.10

147.5

I Wish you a Merry Christmas

147.5

Wishing You a Merry Xmas

147.10

A HAPPY CHRISTMAS!

BRIGHT SPIRITS ATTEND THEE!

67.7

WITH THE SEASON'S GREETING.

PEACE AND PLENTY CROWN THE YEAR.

Prize Design.    Nº 377. Copyright.

# BELLS ACROSS THE SNOW

WRITTEN BY

## FRANCES RIDLEY HAVERGAL

Christmas, merry Christmas!
Is it really come again,
With its memories and greetings,
With its joy and with its pain?
There's a minor in the carol,
And a shadow in the light,
And a spray of cypress twining
With the holly wreath to-night.
And the hush is never broken
By the laughter light and low,
As we listen in the starlight
To the "bells across the snow!"

Christmas, merry Christmas!
'Tis not so very long
Since other voices blended
With the carol and the song!
If we could but hear them singing,
As they are singing now,
If we could but see the radiance
Of the crown on each dear brow;
There would be no sigh to smother,
No hidden tear to flow,
As we listen in the starlight
To the "bells across the snow!"

Christmas, merry Christmas!
This never more can be;
We cannot bring again the days
Of our unshadowed glee.
But Christmas, happy Christmas,
Sweet herald of good-will,
With holy songs of glory
Brings holy gladness still.
For peace and hope may brighten,
And patient love may glow,
As we listen in the starlight
To the "bells across the snow!"

# CHRISTMAS GIFTS FOR THEE

WRITTEN BY

## FRANCES RIDLEY HAVERGAL

Christmas gifts for thee, fair and free!
Precious things from the Heavenly store,
Filling thy casket more and more;
Golden love in divinest chain
That never can be untwined again;
Silvery carols of joy that swell
Sweetest of all in the heart's deep cell;
Pearls of peace that were sought for thee
In the terrible depths of a fiery sea;
Diamond promises sparkling bright,
Flashing in farthest-reaching light.

Christmas gifts for thee, grand and free!
Christmas gifts from the King of love,
Brought from His royal home above,
Brought to thee in the far-off land,
Brought to thee by His royal hand.
Promises held by Christ for thee,
Peace, as a river flowing free;
Joy that in Christ's own joy must live,
And love, that infinite love can give;
Surely thy heart of hearts uplifts
Carols of praise for such Christmas gifts.

MARCUS, WARD & CO.

Folder card designed by Harry Arnold for Marcus Ward with poem by Frances Ridley Havergal

30.28

# CARDS DESIGNED BY KATE GREENAWAY & WALTER CRANE

Kate Greenaway designed a number of cards for Marcus Ward from 1868, many of these being used also for calendars or book illustrations. Some registrations at Stationers' Hall have been traced, but the designs were not entered in her name as artist till 1879. By this time she had begun to work for other publishers, and had become well known as a book illustrator. Walter Crane designed a few cards and calendars for Marcus Ward, the best known being the four Valentine designs in the "Quiver of Love". Volumes 51 and 52 contain cards designed by these two artists, mostly for Marcus Ward, with a few by Kate Greenaway published by Goodall.

Section

6

52.37                51.30

## VOLUME 51:
## CARDS DESIGNED BY KATE GREENAWAY & WALTER CRANE PUBLISHED BY MARCUS WARD, INCLUDING THOSE ALSO USED AS BOOK ILLUSTRATIONS

*Numbers 1-5 are from six designs by Kate Greenaway, also used as illustrations for "A Cruise in the Acorn", by Alice Jerrold, published in 1875 by Marcus Ward; the designs were registered at Stationers' Hall 27-4-1874, but not credited to Kate Greenaway. These cards are not signed, with the exception of Volume 51, no 46.*

1/2. Set of six valentine cards with embossed scalloped borders, showing two small figures in vignettes, with panels containing valentine verses, superimposed on flower designs with a gilt background; the flowers are snowdrops, primroses and violets, honeysuckle, wood anemone, cyclamen, hibiscus. An envelope with green and gold floral design holds a duplicate card. The flower backgrounds were also used separately - see Volume 42. 9.8 cm x 13.8 cm.

3. Two cards from the set with birthday verses.  9.8 cm x 13.8 cm.

4/5. Two cards from the set on large coloured mounts.  15.2 cm x 19.6 cm.

*Numbers 6-11 are from six designs by Kate Greenaway, also used as illustrations for "Puck & Blossom" by Rosa Mulholland, published by Marcus Ward. c1875; the designs were registered at Stationers' Hall 27-4-1874 but not credited to Kate Greenaway.*

6/8. Set of six valentine cards with embossed borders, each showing two children in oval vignettes and valentine verses in panels, with a surround of elves playing amongst spring flowers - primroses, narcissus, wild arum, lily of the valley, forget-me-nots and bluebells in a border of daisies. 12.5 cm x 17 cm.

9. One card from the set mounted on a large ornamental border with cupids. 18.5 cm x 23.5 cm.

10/11. Seven cards, with scalloped borders, one on a mount, with three designs of the same figures in oval vignettes, four having Christmas or New Year greetings in scrolls and three valentines. The borders, however, have three designs of flowers and berries, from six registered at Stationers' Hall 17-4-1877, not credited to Kate Greenaway. 8 cm x 12 cm.

*Numbers 12-14 have six designs by Kate Greenaway, used also as illustrations for "Melcomb Manor" by F Scarlett Potter, published by Marcus Ward in 1875.*

12/14. Set of six cards, embossed edges and coloured borders, two of a girl in Georgian dress seated with a dog and at a window with a dove, one of a lady in mediaeval dress with a dove and three of loving couples in romantic situations. These were registered at Stationers' Hall 27-4-1874 by Marcus Ward but not credited to Kate Greenaway. 12.5 cm x 17 cm.

*Numbers 15-18 have cards and calendars with four designs, also used as illustrations for "Flowers and Fancies, Valentines Ancient and Modern", compiled by B Montgomerie Ranking and Thomas K Tully F R H S, with illustrations in colour by Kate Greenaway, published by Marcus Ward in 1883 after Kate had left the firm.*

15. Eight cards, two sets of four designs showing girl and boy in Spring, Summer, Autumn, and Winter settings. The cards have gilt backs and scalloped edges, with various greetings for Christmas or New Year. c1875. 6.5 cm x 9.4 cm.

16. Three calendars, one for 1876, two for 1883, using these four designs. The 1883 version varies from the original in colour and background and was adapted after Kate left Marcus Ward. One of these is for American sale with appropriate entries. 7 cm x 9.6 cm, 7.2 cm x 11 cm.

17. Six cards, the same four designs with gilt and blue border, and valentine verses on the backs, two duplicates being reversed to show these. 8.2 cm x 12 cm.

18. Four cards, three with scalloped border and one with a pink patterned edge on brown, two having valentine greetings, and two Christmas or New Year. 6.5 cm x 9.4 cm, 7 cm x 10 cm.

*Numbers 19-27 have seven designs of valentine cards, used also as illustrations to "The Quiver of Love", a book of valentine verses published by Marcus Ward in 1876, with four pictures by Kate Greenaway and four by Walter Crane. One design by Kate Greenaway is missing.*

19. Lace-edged folder with valentine verse within, and picture by Kate Greenaway of two ladies, one plucking daisy petals. 18.5 cm x 22.5 cm.

20. Similar, with picture by Kate Greenaway of a lady looking at a heart carved on a tree. 18.5 cm x 22.5 cm.

21. Similar, with picture by Kate Greenaway of a lady holding roses in her skirt, and a parrot on a stand nearby. 18.5 cm x 22.5 cm.

22. A variant of no. 21 on a scallop edge card with a valentine poem on reverse. 14 cm x 18.2 cm. A photograph of the missing fourth design is included.

23. Lace-edged folder with valentine verse within, and picture by Walter Crane of a couple by a stile, on a gilt ground, with verse by Sylvester. 18.5 cm x 22.5 cm.

24. Similar, with picture of a lady with a cupid.  18.5 cm x 22.5 cm.

25. A scallop edge card, on a gilt ground, with design by Walter Crane of a lady picking flowers from a tree, with verse by Richard Allison on reverse. 14 cm x 18.2 cm.

26. Similar, with design by Walter Crane of a herald greeting a lady at a window. This was omitted from the second edition of "Quiver of Love" by order of Walter Crane. A sonnet by Spencer is on the reverse. 14 cm x 18.2 cm.

27. Two variants of nos 23 and 25, with ornate gilt and pink borders and verses on reverse. 10.8 cm x 13.8 cm.

28. Four cards, three designs out of four by Kate Greenaway for a second smaller volume "Quiver of Love", compiled by B Montgomerie Ranking and Thomas K Tully F R H S, published in 1880 by Marcus Ward. They show loving couples in spring, harvest and moonlight scenes, in two varieties or borders of wild rose sprays on a brown or black ground, the borders being possibly the registration for 15-9-1876. "three-quarter borders of dog roses". 9 cm x 12.7 cm. A photograph of the missing design is included.

*Other sets of cards by Kate Greenaway, published by Marcus Ward*

*Numbers 29-34 are four designs of a set known as "Children on Flowers". These are a small girl on a primrose, one sleeping on a pansy, a boy and girl on peach blossom, and a boy and girl on daffodils. Late 1870's.*

29. Set of four valentines as above, with scalloped and gilt edges and appropriate poems on reverse. 10 cm x 14 cm.

30. Four similar, peach blossom with New Year and birthday verses, and daffodil and primrose with variants of valentine verses, one signed F G H. 10 cm x 14 cm.

31/32. Eight cards, two sets of four as above, with gilt pattern borders. One set has verses for Christmas and New Year, the other birthday verses, signed J G, R I O, G P M, F G H. 9.2 cm x 12 cm.

33. Three cards using the Kate Greenaway figures as above with some variation in the flowers and colours, over country scenes in vignettes, with greeting below. 1885- 90. 8.4 cm x 11.4 cm, 7 cm x 9 cm.

34. Four cards, a set of four as above, trade cards for Dives, Pomeroy and Stuart of Harrisburg, P A, U S A, printed by the Sunshine Publishing Co, Philadelphia. These were probably pirated designs. 8.3 cm x 13.4 cm.

35. Four cards with scalloped edges, a set known as "Forging the Ring", from the verses on the cards. There are four designs of figures in oval vignettes, a smith forging a ring for a youth, Cupid with a letter riding on a fly, the youth giving the ring to a maiden, and Cupid with heart and bow and arrow; these are surrounded by designs of flowers and butterflies on gilt, with verses in panels. These backgrounds also appear separately as flower cards, with greetings or texts replacing the figures (see Volume 41), and these four designs were registered at Stationers' Hall (without the figures).
17-4- 1877. 9.7 cm x 13.8 cm.

*Numbers 36-40 show cards with four gilt-backed designs known as "Children by Ponds". They are of two children sitting on a wall by a pond feeding ducks, three girls by a window with a boy looking out, a boy and girl by a nest with eggs, and a couple under a rose arch - all in Georgian style dress. They were registered at Stationers' Hall 29-8- 1876 but not credited to Kate Greenaway.*

36. Set of four as above with fancy scalloped borders, Valentine poems on reverse. 10 cm x 14 cm.

37. Set of four as above with ornate border top and bottom and Christmas or New Year captions. 8.1 cm x 13.8 cm.

38. Three of the set as above with variant greetings. 8.1 cm x 13.8 cm.

39. Two folder cards, each with two of the above designs within, and red and gilt design of flowers and birds on cover, one Christmas, one New Year. 7 cm x 10.2 cm closed.

40. Two of the designs on a lace edge mount, one a folder with Valentine verse inside, the other the cover only.
13 cm x 18.7 cm.

*Numbers 41-46, all gilt-edged cards, have eight designs from a set entitled "Feed My Lambs". The cards here are all greeting cards, but they were also issued as texts, in an envelope illustrated in the Detroit Public Library catalogue on page 145. The designs were registered at Stationers' Hall 10-9-1877, but not credited to Kate Greenaway and are as follows: -*
*a) Girl in green with a rose.*
*b) Child in red dress, in landscape.*
*c) A boy and girl.*
*d) A girl in Gainsborough dress.*
*e) Two little girls.*
*f) A boy in a tree, girl below.*
*g) A baby girl in pink and white.*
*h) A boy with an umbrella.*
*The pictures are to the left of the cards, with verses with fancy initials to the right.*

41/42. Eight designs as above, all with Christmas verses, signed G P M, G B, J G, R I O, M R, R. 12.7 cm x 9 cm.

43/44. Eight cards as above, e), f), g), with New Year verses, b), h), with Christmas verses, h), c), g), with other verses.

45. Four smaller cards, b), c), d), h), with Christmas or New Year greetings.
9.6 cm x 6 cm.

46. A menu card, dated 20th February 1883, with a small drawing e) in bottom left hand corner, for the St Cuthbert's Preceptory of Knights Templar, No 139.
17.7 cm x 11.5 cm.

*A similar set of four designs with pink line borders was registered at Stationers' Hall 1-1-1879, by Marcus Ward and credited to Kate Greenaway as artist. The designs were:- a) Back view of a girl with a basket of roses. b) A small boy and girl. c) A boy in a check suit with a high hat. d) A girl with an umbrella.*

47. Four cards as above with verses for Christmas and New Year and Best Wishes.
14.3 cm x 10.2 cm.

48. c) and d) with birthday and New Year verses.

## VOLUME 52:
## CARDS DESIGNED BY KATE GREENAWAY & WALTER CRANE, MOST PUBLISHED BY MARCUS WARD, A FEW BY GOODALL

*Numbers 1-12 have cards designed by Kate Greenaway, all published by Marcus Ward; they were used for calendars, with different versions for greetings cards.*

1. Calendar for 1875 (cut), four pages with information on reverse, and pictures of small figures in scenes of Springtime, Easter, Midsummer Eve, and Autumn Games. 10.4 cm x 7.5 cm.

2. Three cards with three of the above designs, and greetings for Christmas and New Year. 10.4 cm x 7.5 cm.

3. Two Calendars of the Seasons for 1877, with four pictures on gilt grounds of a girl and boy in seasonal pursuits, with a bird's nest, fishing, at the seaside, and at Christmas. One calendar was intended for the American market with appropriate information for the United States.
6.8 cm x 10 cm closed.

4. Four cards as above, with Christmas and New Year greetings, three with scalloped or lace borders, and one with a pink and brown pattern. 6.6 cm x 9.4 cm.

5. An elaborate pull out birthday card, with picture of a girl and boy at the seaside as above and four tabs with flower pictures. 6.6 cm x 9.4 cm closed.

6. Calendar of the Seasons for 1881, with four pictures in fancy borders, showing:
a) Girl in pink by rose tree.

b) Girl in pink with parasol.
c) Three girls in the snow, backview.
d)Three girls in winter, front view.
All registered at Stationers' Hall, 21-11-1879 and credited to Kate Greenaway as artist. 7 cm x 10.5 cm.

7. Eight cards with pictures as above, Christmas, New Year and Valentine greetings. Six cards have a) and b) as above in panels on white gilt-edged cards; two have figures a) and b) on white cards with blue borders, signed K G.
7.5 cm x 10.7 cm and 4.5 cm x 9.5 cm.

8. Eight cards, with versions of c) and d) as above, with Christmas and New Year greetings and various borders, two signed K G. 9 cm x 7.8 cm, 7 cm x 9 cm and 7.5 cm x 9 cm.

9. Six small cards, three of a girl in blue with lilies, three with two girls sitting in a garden, with various borders. These two designs were also registered at Stationers' Hall 21-11-1879 and appear to have been issued in sets with the 1881 calendar designs. They were credited to Kate Greenaway as artist. 7.5 cm x 10.7 cm, 7.5 cm x 9.2 cm, 9 cm x 7.8 cm.

10. Calendar of the Seasons for 1882, complete as issued, with four pictures for Spring, Summer, Autumn and Winter.
a) A girl in blue by a cherry tree.
b) A girl, with panniers, by a rose tree.
c) A boy in red by an apple tree.
d) A boy in a long coat with hat and whip and a tree in Winter.
Also a card with a) in an oval vignette (no background), signed KG, with Christmas and New Year greetings on reverse.
9.3 cm x 11 cm closed, 10.7 cm x 15 cm.

11. Four similar cards, with the figures of a), c) and d) above in oval vignettes on beige ground and greetings for Christmas, New Year on reverse. The figure in d) is reversed. 10.7 cm x 15 cm.

12. Two cards, with the figures from a) (reversed) and c), in Wedgwood style, white on a blue vignette in gilt border with New Year greetings. 1885 on.
9 cm x 13.4 cm.

*The following eighteen sheets show miscellaneous cards published by Marcus Ward, designed by Kate Greenaway.*

13. Set of six cards, "Red Riding Hood's Christmas", with blue and gold border. This was published in 1868, according to Jonathan King as reported by Gleeson White, and was issued in a folder as well as individual cards. 7 cm x 10.3 cm.

14. One card from Red Riding Hood set with pink, blue and gold border, also a photo-copy of the cover taken from the specimen in the John Johnson Collection, by kind permission of the curator.

15. Four cards, from "Robin Hood and the Blackbird", telling the sad story of how the bird was hunted and killed for the Christmas feast. Three have a holly border in green and brown, and one a brown border from a different set. These were also issued in folders with accompanying poem. Two cards were dated by the senders 1882.
14.2 cm x 9 cm, 12.8 cm x 7.4 cm.

16. One card from a set of four, "Christmas Procession of Mirth and Good Cheer". c1880. 15 cm x 8.6 cm.

17. Two cards "Dainty Airs", showing a procession of children at a party, on gilt ground. One is a three-fold card with verses by G P Meade and music, and Thomas Crane style decoration back and front; the other is a single card, signed Kate Greenaway, with holly border and music continuing on reverse. This design is one of a set of two, the other showing the children outside "Going to the Party". c1880.
16 cm x 9 cm folded, 16 cm x 10.1 cm.

18/19. Ten cards, with four designs of small figures in red and green on backgrounds of snowdrops and violets, Christmas roses and mistletoe, ivy and narcissus, snowdrops and holly, with white or brown borders. Registered at Stationers' Hall 31-10-1877, not credited to Kate Greenaway.
8 cm x 12 cm, 7.4 cm x 11.3 cm.

20. Six cards with three designs, one of a boy in outdoor clothes with umbrella and two of little girls in red or green coats with muffs and hats, set in fancy borders with greetings. The set is known as "Children in Ulsters". One card was dated by the sender 1880.
7.5 cm x 14.8 cm and 9.8 cm x 13.9 cm.

21. Four cards with three designs of children's heads in vignettes, a boy in a cap and a frilled collar, a girl with a wreath, and a girl in a bonnet. Three cards are square, with a Thomas Crane style border; the fourth is larger, showing the girl in a bonnet with a Christmas verse below. The designs were registered at Stationers' Hall 19-11-1879, with Kate Greenaway as artist.
9.5 cm x 9.5 cm and 10.7 cm x 13.3 cm.

22/24. Thirteen cards of the set known as "Christmas Messengers", with four designs of children in costume, on gilt grounds with blue and gold borders and verses by J G on reverse. They show a girl with a letter, a boy at a door, a girl in a frilled hat and fichu and a boy with a plumed hat. The five smaller cards have birthday or valentine verses. Registered at Stationers' Hall 14-6-1876, but not credited to K G. 9 cm x 13 cm, 7 cm x 10.5 cm.

25/26. Ten cards of the set known as "Youth of Sir Joshua's Time", on gilt or brown grounds with various patterned borders, six with verses by G P M or E K on reverse. They have a girl with a muff or a fan, and a boy with a dish of fruit or a goblet, and two have valentine verses. c1880. 9 cm x 13.2 cm, 7.3 cm x 10.7 cm.

27/28. Nine cards, signed K G, with three drawings known as "Party Girls". One is in a blue bonnet with a tennis racquet, one has a parasol and a bouquet, and the other is in red and orange with a basket of roses. Seven cards have pale blue borders and various greetings on the front and back, and two are smaller with figures in vignettes on a beige ground. c1880. 10.9 cm x 15.3 cm, 6 cm x 8.7 cm.

29. Six cards with four probably from the set known as "Good Old Times" showing three designs of traditional Kate Greenaway style figures in early nineteenth century dress, and verses. Two others have a girl in blue with a parasol. c1880. Sizes up to 13 cm x 9.7 cm.

30. Two cards, signed K G, of six girls with garlands, in a patterned border, with greetings in verse for Christmas or valentine. c1880. 15.8 cm x 8 cm.

*Numbers 31-33 show cards by Kate Greenaway from other publishers.*

31. Three cards without greetings, with white embossed figures of girls with garlands, two designs, two on green ground and one on orange. Unmarked, but as one design is the same as one in no. 32, they were probably published by Goodall. 1880's. 14.7 cm x 6.2 cm.

32. Two cards on thick board, published by Goodall. One is of five small girls amongst roses and lilies, with Christmas greeting and verse, signed Kate Greenaway and marked on the back K G Series 504. The other is of six girls with garlands (as no. 31), signed Kate Greenaway, but the rear markings are not visible. 1880's.
18.7 cm x 7.8 cm, 18.7 cm x 8.8 cm.

33. Eight American Trade Cards, with various Kate Greenaway pictures, probably pirated designs. c1890?
6.3 cm x 11.6 cm.

*Numbers 34-37 have cards by Walter Crane published by Marcus Ward. (See also Volume 51 for Quiver of Love).*

34. Eight-page calendar for 1874 in four pieces, showing four designs on gilt grounds for St Valentine, May Day, Harvest, and Christmas Day, with a page from a similar calendar with a different border. Also a set of four cards with the same designs and a New Year greeting. This set has been often mistaken for Kate Greenaway, but the original design and a cover signed with the Walter Crane rebus (a crane) is in the possession of Professor Anthony Crane, Walter Crane's grandson. 10.3 cm x 7 cm.

35. Time's Garland for the Year, two eight-page folders with four pictures of rustic couples in Spring, Summer, Autumn and Winter, on blue or green backgrounds with captions in silver or gilt, and signed on the front by Walter Crane. c1875.
7.3 cm x 11.5 cm folded.

36. Six cards, probably 1874-5, perhaps from a folder. Four designs, of Fortuna, Return of Mr Christmas, Christmas Stocking, A Christmas Figure, have the Crane rebus and two of a Christmas pudding and a stork and clowns, are signed W C. 11 cm x 7.9 cm.

37. Two cards with Cupids, signed with a flying crane on reverse, and a personal card, with an invitation on reverse from "Mistress Beatrice Crane", c1895.
11.5 cm x 17.8 cm, 9.1 cm x 12.3 cm.

*Other material designed by Walter Crane.*

38. Notice of exhibition, for the Royal Institute of Painters in Watercolours, 1887.
14.4 cm x 22.4 cm.

39/40. Complete series of Scottish Widow Bookmarks, twelve designs for each month of the year. c1913. 5.7 cm x 15.3 cm. Two others, of a different series with coloured pictures, incorporating a Crane design.
6.4 cm x 17.9 cm.

41. Advertisement for Scottish Widow Life Assurance Fund. c1892. 14.4 cm x 22.4 cm.

# THOMAS DE LA RUE

Founded in 1835, the firm was famous for its fancy papers, banknotes and playing cards using design by, among others, Owen Jones and his pupil Aubert. De La Rue patented the first envelope-making machine. Their greeting card production was mainly from 1874- 1885, and these cards are easy to identify as all but a few of the early cards were signed and numbered. Production was revived later with the R series, when some earlier designs were reissued, and dies from other firms were also re-employed, as in the reproduction of a Sulman design in Volume 3. The cards can be dated approximately as follows : -

*Section*
*7*

| **Letters** | |
|---|---|
| A, B, C, D | 1872-1874 |
| **Numbers** | |
| 1 - 35 | 1874-1876 |
| 36 - 84 | 1876-1877 |
| 85 - 134 | 1877-8178 |
| 135 - 183 | 1878-1879 |
| 184 - 302 | 1879-1880 |
| 303 - 365 | 1880-1881 |
| 366 - 465 | 1881-1882 |
| 466 - 565 | 1882-1883 |
| 566 - 648 | 1883-1884 |
| 649 - 713 | 1884-1885 |

Like Marcus Ward, De La Rue emphasised the importance of the picture rather than using animation or tricks. Many well known artists were employed, including Aubert, W S Coleman, Rebecca Coleman, Ernest Griset, Robert Dudley and Gordon Browne. The same design was rarely used with different greetings, though sometimes one was issued later, on a mount with a different series number, not always visible. A series could contain one, two, three, four, six or twelve cards. They have Christmas or New Year greetings except where otherwise stated.

It has been thought advisable to file the cards with regard to subjects and artists rather than in a continuous number sequence, though each volume as far as possible is in numerical series order. There are a few De La Rue entries in Stationers' Hall records, but none have been traced to cards in this collection. Most of the cards have gilt or brown line borders, some inside a white edge, with a few on elaborate decorated mounts. The series all appear to have had titles, sometimes humorous or whimsical, and these are given where they are known.

# VOLUME 53:
# DE LA RUE. EARLY ILLUMINATED CARDS, RELIGIOUS CARDS, CHERUBS, ANGELS AND FLOWER CHILDREN, SOME BY ROBERT DUDLEY

1. Four illuminated cards, unmarked, probably Series B, elaborate flower designs on gilt grounds. Two cards have scenes in vignettes, the others have verses in panels. 10.3 cm x 6.9 cm.

2. Two three-fold cards, with pictures of rose and poppy on gilt grounds, and appropriate verses. The covers have an ivy design, in red on yellow. Series 2 (six in set). 10.1 cm x 6.8 cm closed.

3. Two similar, with pictures of plum and cherry, and purple covers. Series 3 (six in set). 10.1 cm x 6.8 cm closed.

4. One valentine card, with the same plum design on a mount with pink and gold design on blue. Series 101 (six in set). 14 cm x 10.7 cm.

5. Five illuminated cards, elaborate holly, mistletoe and spring flower designs on gilt, with verses for Christmas and New Year in panels. Series 4 "Floral Greetings" (six in set). 12.2 cm x 7.8 cm.

6. Eight illuminated cards.
a) Four with holly and floral designs and verse on reverse. Series 7 (six in set). 10.2 cm x 7 cm.
b) Four with fruit designs, and floral borders. Series 18 (six in set). 10.2 cm x 7 cm.

7. Three cards.
a) One folder card, with border and verses printed in gilt. Series 11. 6.4 cm x 9.8 cm closed.
b) Two illuminated cards, with verses in panels and floral and holly borders. Series 17 "Floral Greetings". 8.9 cm x 12 cm.

8. Two cards, birds on reeds or fruit branches in Japanese style, perhaps by Aubert. Series 16 (six in set) "Japanese Greetings". 13.6 cm x 10 cm.

9. Two cards, large illuminated greetings with floral or holly sprays. Series 15 (six in set). 19.6 cm x 11.8 cm.

10. Two cards, panels with double acrostic, in a three-sided border of flowers on black. A card giving the answer to one acrostic is included. Series 26 (six in set). 14.5 cm x 10.3 cm.

11. Four triangular cards, three designs, illuminated fruit and flower designs in Chinese style, one card on a green and gilt mount. One design is taken from Owen Jones' "Grammar of Ornament" and the

**53.6**

set is probably by Aubert. Series 65 "Chinese Fruits". 13.3 cm x 9.5 cm x 9.5 cm.

12. Five cards with black backgrounds.
a) A dahlia spray over a panel with greetings. Series 63 "Chinese flowers on black". 10 cm x 6 cm.
b) A scarlet pimpernel border around a greeting. Series 64 "Dark panels". 10 cm x 6 cm.
c) Three triangular cards with Japanese birds in gilt, red and green. Series 66. 13.3 cm x 9.5 cm.

13. Two illuminated cards, peacock feathers with red or yellow birds with human heads on stylised grounds. Series 72. 9.6 cm x 9.6 cm.

14. Two cards.
a) An illuminated card, similar to no. 6, with floral border around a picture of children and snowman, but 10 years later from series 536.
b) A similar two-sided card, with silk fringe, probably from the same series. 10.3 cm x 7 cm.

15. Set of three Easter cards, with pink, blue or brown eggs on a dish, basket, or cushion, in illuminated borders. Another card is reversed to show the De La Rue trade mark. Series 83. 9.6 cm x 9.6 cm.

16. Two cards.
a) A valentine with illuminated honeysuckle design, Series 79. 8.7 cm x 12.7 cm.
b) A Chinese style design of leaves, bird, fan and a hand, one from three in series 187 "Fruitful Branches" by E H Fahey. 12.7 cm x 8.7 cm.

17. One card with a large illuminated text and pictures of angels, St John the Baptist, and the Nativity. Series 75 "Heavenly Harbinger". 15.3 cm x 22 cm.

18. Four Easter cards, crosses with flowers and religious verses. Series 6 (six in set). 7.7 cm x 12 cm.

19. Two similar cards on fancy mounts, one design as above. Series 109. 12.4 cm x 16.5 cm.

20. Four Easter cards, hanging crosses, three having borders of ivy, speedwell, or convolvulus, and one on a spray of scarlet pimpernel. Series 20 "Emblematic". 7.7 cm x 12 cm.

21. Two Easter cards.
a) One triangular with a gilt cross and a peacock, and an advertisement on reverse. Series 181. 13.3 cm x 9.5 cm x 9.5 cm.
b) One rectangular with a jewelled cross surrounded by narcissi. Series 458. 8.3 cm x 12.2 cm.

22. Set of three valentine cards, cupids on branches, one card with a flower and faces of a man and a woman. Series 78. 8.7 cm x 12.7 cm.

23. Four cards, showing faces in flowers.
a) A child in a rose, valentine greetings. Series 23.
b) Three cards, one with the same child in rose, one with a girl and boy in sunflower and one with girl and boy in rose. Series 57. 7 cm x 10.4 cm.

24. Three similar cards.
a) Two cards, one with two faces, the other with one. Series 98. 7 cm x 10.4 cm.
b) Same picture as in no. 23, b), on elaborate mount, with leaf pattern, numbered 106. 11 cm x 15.5 cm.

25. Set of three cards, angels watching over mother and children with a border of holly and flowers and Christmas or New Year verse in scrolls top and bottom. Series 87. 7.9 cm x 12.2 cm.

26. Two Easter cards.
a) An angel by an altar. Series 100.
8.8 cm x 12.8 cm.
b) Two ladies kneeling by a cross. Series 133, "Message of the Cross".
12.8 cm x 8.8 cm.

27. Easter card on elaborate mount, with an angel by an altar, series number not visible. 13 cm x 17.4 cm.

28. Set of three valentine cards, Cupids making arrows. Series 135.
10.4 cm x 6.9 cm.

29. Set of three cards, angel heads, with Christmas greetings on a cross, a shield, or an open book. Series 191 "Celestial Whisperings". 9.7 cm x 9.7 cm.

30. One card "He took the young child and his mother by night", Joseph and Mary with donkey, and a Christmas greeting on reverse. Series 565. 10.2 cm x 16.4 cm.

31. One card, a cherub with flaming torch, and fairies flying above, verse on reverse. Series 680 or 690. 10.8 cm x 15.8 cm.

*The cards in numbers 32-38 are probably all by Robert Dudley.*

32. Three cards.
a) Barefoot carol singers. Series 443.
b) Two cards of cherubs, one with camera, verses on reverse. Series 474 "Cupid's Studio".16 cm x 10.5 cm.

33. Two Easter cards, a lady in a garden, one with lilies, one with clematis, with a text below. Series 417. 7.6 cm x 16.2 cm.

34. Two Easter cards.
a) Three small angels with harps and dove. Series 420. 9.7 cm x 10.2 cm.
b) An angel with large wings, holding a palm branch. Series 465. 12 cm x 12.2 cm.

35. Two cards, "Earth" (trimmed), with four winged sprites, and "Air", with a winged flying figure. Series 453 (four in set). 16 cm x 10.5 cm.

36. Two valentine cards.
a) Cupid on a raft. Series 526.
10 cm x 16.5 cm.
b) Grecian style ladies in a garden with a garland, signed R D. Series 629.
16.5 cm x 10 cm.

37. Two cards, signed R D, one of the Nativity, one of angels. There are verses on the backs from Milton's "Hymn to the Nativity", with a blue line border of passion flowers. Series 628.
16 cm x 10.5 cm.

38. Two cards, small naked children in gondolas, signed R D, with verse on reverse. Series 630. 16 cm x 10 cm.

39. Three photocopies of De La Rue advertisements in the John Johnson collection are included here, showing later visiting cards printed after earlier Sulman designs, perhaps from their dies. These are: -

Series R 1036 "Comic Series" 1888/89,
Series R 1040 "Jesters",
Series R 1039 "Castles",
Series R 1041 "Pantomime",

Some of the earlier Sulman originals may be seen in Volume 3, together with one which is probably De La Rue.

## VOLUME 54:
## DE LA RUE. PROVERBS, HUMOUR, GROTESQUES, ELVES & FAIRIES

**Most of these cards have greetings incorporated into the design, in small print. "Compliments of the Season" is often used.**

1/3. Set of twelve cards, probably by Griset, consisting of pictured proverbs in humorous style, some with personified animals and Christmas dinner. On mounts with Greek key borders, the pictures have greetings incorporated in the design, with the proverb below. Series A.
11.5 cm x 8 cm.

4/6. Twenty similar cards, probably by Griset. Ten have a chain line border, from Series C (twelve in set) and ten have a holly leaf border, nine Series A (twelve in set), one Series 49. 10.3 cm x 7 cm.

7. Four similar cards with a wavy line border. Series 35 (six in set).
10.3 cm x 7 cm.

8. Seven humorous cards, with people and humanised puddings. Probably from Series D (twelve in set). 8.2 cm x 5.8 cm and 5.8 cm x 8.2 cm.

9/10. a) Set of six folder cards showing contrasts such as Work and Play, with verse on inside. Series 9 "Pictorial Contrasts". 5.9 cm x 8.3 cm folded.
b) Four single cards, with country folk in various ploys, perhaps cut from folders. Series 21 (six in set). 5.8 cm x 8.2 cm.

11. Set of six cards, fairies and elves with toad stools. Series 31. 12.8 cm x 8.7 cm.

12. Set of six cards, fairies and elves with flowers, and tents made from inverted lilies. Series 47. 12.8 cm x 8.7 cm.

13. Set of six cards. Series 39 "Watersprites at Play". 11.5 cm x 7.8 cm.

14. Set of three cards, elves with cacti. Series 111. 12.8 cm x 8.7 cm.

15. Two mounted cards, water nymphs with sea anemones. Series 112 "Sea Bowers". 17.3 cm x 13.3 cm.

16. Set of three cards, probably by G G Kilburne, imps in acorn chariot drawn by rats, hunting a rabbit, roasting a rat. Series 60 "Impish Sports". 12.8 cm x 8.5 cm.

17. Six cards.
a) A triangular card, elves with a laughing gas machine. Series 55. 13.7 cm x 9.5 cm
b) Two birthday cards, elves in a kitchen, or with a rocking horse (trimmed). Series 150.
c) A card with elves on a stage in animal heads. Series 188. 10.4 cm x 7 cm.
d) Two cards. Series 50 "Pigmy Frolics".
11.5 cm x 7.8 cm.

18. Five cards.
a) Two with imps on board ship. Series 123 "Impish Sports at Sea".
6.7 cm x 10.5 cm.
b) Set of three with imps in a shell toboggan. Series 340. 7 cm x 10.5 cm.

19. Three cards, fairies and elves with tropical trees and flowers, one mounted. Series 210. 8.7 cm x 12.8 cm, 13.3 cm x 17.3 cm.

20. Three cards, two with elves with fruit and insects, series 345 and one with elves and a large egg, series 413. 10.4 cm x 7 cm, 9.6 cm x 9.6 cm.

21. One card, elves in evening dress climbing on a dining table. Series 596.
9.1 cm x 13.7 cm.

22. Two cards, frogs by a stream, one on a waterlily. Series 28. 10.4 cm x 7 cm.

23. Set of three cards, ants at war. Series 45 "Ant Life". 10.4 cm x 7 cm.

24. Set of three cards, dogs in human pursuits as magician, hunters, sportsmen. Series 56 "Canine Parodies".
10.4 cm x 7 cm.

25. Two cards, prehistoric animals in human pursuits, skating and studying fashion. Series 69 "Antediluvian Studies" by Griset. 10.4 cm x 7 cm.

26. Three cards.
a) Two with dogs and a wheelbarrow, and dogs as fishermen. Series 91 "Canine Parodies 2". 10.4 cm x 7 cm.
b) One with a chained dog barking at another showing a card with greeting. Series 189 "Canine Displeasure".
10.4 cm x 7 cm.

27. Set of three cards, triangular, with comic fishes and crabs. Series 93 "Under the Sea". 13.7 cm x 10 cm x 9.5 cm.

28. Set of three cards, probably by Griset, showing robins skating. Series 125.
10.4 cm x 7 cm.

"THERE SHALL COME A STAR OUT OF JACOB, AND A SCEPTRE SHALL RISE OUT OF ISRAEL."

**53.34**

29. Two cards, a man riding an ostrich, and a cat and an owl hunting mice. Series 128 "Animal Drolleries". 10.4 cm x 7 cm.

30. Four cards.
a) A stork with egg, and a stork with fledgling. Series 122. 7 cm x 10.4 cm.
b) Two birthday cards, birds with fledglings in nests. Series 166.
10.4 cm x 7 cm.

31. Set of three cards, mice catching a cat, feasting on it, and drinking at table, by Griset. Series 199 "Mice at Play".
10.4 cm x 7 cm.

32. Set of three cards, a magpie with birds, a bear, and a boar. Series 372 "Inquisitive Magpie". 10.4 cm x 7 cm.

33. Three cards, probably by Griset.
a) Two with humanised monkeys at the village pump and in the kitchen. Series 344 "Monkey Tricks". 10.4 cm x 7 cm.
b) Monkey orchestra and actors on stage. Series 445 "Animal Orchestras".
8.8 cm x 12.7 cm.

34. Two cards, polar bears sledging. Series 373. 12 cm x 7.8 cm.

35. Six cards of various animals and insects. One from each of the series 387, 429, (Griset) 433, 446, 624, 625.
10.4 cm x 7 cm.

36. Three cards.
a) Imps with a telescope "Earth seen from the Moon". Series 119. 9.6 cm x 9.6 cm.
b) Two cards, a man with a telescope and a woman with a candle, looking at the moon. Series 194. 7.8 cm x 7.8 cm.

37. Set of three cards, people at the zoo having problems with the animals. Series 92 "Pranks at the Zoo". 10.4 cm x 7 cm.

38. Three cards.
a) Three men buying roast chestnuts, by Griset. Series 193 "Wayside Caterers".
10.4 cm x 7 cm.
b) Two boys drawing birthday greetings on a gate. Series 296. 10.4 cm x 7 cm.

c) Geese attacking three cherubs - a valentine card. Series 484. 13.8 cm x 7.6 cm.

# VOLUME 55:
# DE LA RUE. CARDS BY THE ARTISTS W S COLEMAN, REBECCA COLEMAN, E G THOMSON

*Numbers 1-13 have cards designed by Rebecca Coleman. They have plain borders, with brown or gilt line and greetings below, and are all of girls with similar pink cheeks and wide eyes, varying only in the colour of their hair and the style of their costumes and headgear. Most of the series had sets of three cards.*

1. Two cards, girls, head and shoulders, one in a shawl, one in a bonnet on golden hair. Series 224 (three in set).
9.7 cm x 9.7 cm.

2. Two birthday cards with girls, head and shoulders, one in a straw hat, the other in Tyrolean costume. Series 263.
11.7 cm x 11.7 cm.

3. Two cards, girls in hats, with flowing hair, frilled collar, or fichu. One card is on an illuminated mount with valentine greeting. Series 273. 8.7 cm x 12.8 cm, 13 cm x 18 cm.

4. Set of three cards, girls with flowing hair, in frilled caps, with birthday greetings. Series 308. 11.7 cm x 11.7 cm.

5. Set of three New Year cards, girls, one with a peacock feather, one with a doll, the third in cap and shawl. Series 314.
9.7 cm x 12.9 cm.

6. Set of three New Year cards, girls holding shells to their ears, with a sea background. Series 399. 10 cm x 10.4 cm.

7. Two cards, girls, head and shoulder, in Elizabethan costume, with flowery backgrounds. Series 467 "Elizabethan Studies". 12 cm x 14.9 cm.

8. A similar card on a brown mount, unnumbered, probably the third design of series 467. 16 cm x 16 cm.

9. Two cards on mounts, unnumbered, a valentine with a girl in Stuart dress and a New Year card with a girl in frilled collar. 15 cm x 15 cm.

10. Two cards, fairhaired girls, head and shoulders.
a) In cap and fur edged jerkin on a leafy background, with verse on reverse. Series 568. 12 cm x 15 cm.
b) In hat, with fur jacket and muff, winter background. Series 594. 10.3 cm x 13 cm.

11/12. Set of three cards, girls with flowers in a country scene, one with a blue bonnet, one holding a flowering branch, the third with a basket of primroses, all on fancy mounts. Unnumbered, but probably Series

503. 13.7 cm x 16.4 cm. A photocopy of an advertisement for Silber & Fleming, agents for De La Rue's cards, illustrates the third card, described as R 503 and this could have been a later publication of this series. The advertisement is in the John Johnson Collection.

13. One card with white border, a small girl, head and shoulders, in a white dress and hat on a blue ground, with flowering branches. Series 707. 9 cm x 11 cm.

*Numbers 14-34 have cards designed by W S Coleman (brother of Rebecca). These were the cards which inspired Punch's comment of 1878 "Punch must protest.... against nudities at Christmas - it is too cold for them, if there were no other reason". They were, however, very popular with the card-buying public. The cards have brown line borders and greetings below; a few are on mounts. Many of these cards were also printed on silk.*

14. Two cards, naked girls by the sea, with flowing golden hair. Series 132.
9.8 cm x 12.9 cm.

15. Four cards, three designs, probably the set, two with brown borders, two on green and gilt mounts, showing scantily clad maidens by orange, lemon, or rose trees. Series 134 "Youthful Beauties".
6.5 cm x 14.5 cm, 10.8 cm x 18.6 cm.

16. Set of three birthday cards, a mother and child with blue and white china, a cherub and a little girl picking oranges, and a girl picking oranges. Series 149 "Harvest of Beauty". 9.8 cm x 12.9 cm.

17. Set of three birthday cards, winged cherubs with birds' nests. Series 156 "Sylvan Sports". 11.6 cm x 11.6 cm.

18. Set of three valentine cards, winged cherubs with flowers and butterflies. Series 174 "Cupid's Gambols". 9.7 cm x 9.7 cm.

19. A valentine card, one of the above designs, on a pink and gold illuminated mount. 15 cm x 15 cm.

20. Set of three New Year cards, scantily draped girls, one by a sofa with fan and cherry tree, one with goldfish and orange tree, and one looking at a lizard on a tree. Series 202 "Youthful Graces".
8.7 cm x 12.8 cm.

21. Set of three New Year cards, girls in diaphanous draperies in exotic settings. Series 214. 8.7 cm x 12.8 cm.

22/23. Four cards, set of three designs, two on plain brown edged cards, two on elaborate blue and gold illuminated mounts, title of series self explanatory. Series 219 "Girls in Muslin".
8.1 cm x 15 cm, 13 cm x 20.3 cm.

24. One birthday card, Cupid and a girl in a shell boat. Series 262. 11.6 cm x 11.6 cm.

**55.22**

25. Set of three cards, a girl asleep on a cushion, a naked child asleep on a sofa, and a girl with a lute. Series 307. 11.6 cm x 11.6 cm.

26. Three cards.
a) A girl with a goldfish. Series 306. 11.6 cm x 11.6 cm.
b) A girl with a cat.
c) A girl on a bench with a parasol. Series 317 "Jocund Youth". 8.7 cm x 12.8 cm.

27. Set of three cards, young ladies fully dressed, one with a rose tree, one picking apples, and one in a garden with a bowl of flowers. Series 262. 9.3 cm x 16.5 cm.

28. Four cards, more scantily dressed girls.
a) A girl seated by pool. Series 398. 10 cm x 13.5 cm.
b) A girl on a swing. Series 415. 7.5 cm x 15.9 cm.
c) A girl with fan and tambourine. Series 400. 8.1 cm x 17.5 cm.
d) A girl with a lizard. Series 394. 10 cm x 13.5 cm.

29. Four cards, scantily dressed girls.
a) Two girls by sea. Series 414.
b) A girl in a lake picking waterlilies. Series 468 "The Bathers". 10.5 cm x 14.2 cm.
c) A girl asleep by a lake. Series 699.
d) A girl making a garland. Series 581

30. Set of three cards, elegantly dressed maidens, one by the sea, one in a garden with parasol, and one in a field with a basket of flowers. One card is on a green patterned mount. Series 425. 9.3 cm x 16.5 cm, 12.6 cm x 19.7 cm.

31. One card, girl in lace dress on swing. Series 471.  9.3 cm x 16.5 cm.

32. Three cards, a girl catching shrimps, a girl with a dog, a Japanese girl. Series 557, 568, 580. 10.5 cm x 14.2 cm.

33. Three cards, two designs (set of two), winged cherubs blowing bubbles. Series 661. Two cards have plain borders, but the third has the top part of one of those designs mounted on an elaborate gilded thick card, probably produced about 1890, after the numbered series from 1874-1885. 9 cm x 17.6 cm, 12.5 cm x 17.4 cm.

34. One card, unnumbered, with a pink silk fringed border. One side has a girl draped in muslin sitting by the sea, the other has an elaborate stylised illuminated design of roses on pink and gold and green. 15 cm x 15 cm with fringe.

*The next two sheets have cards designed by E G Thomson, of more naked children, some under water. All the cards have gilt backgrounds.*

35. Two cards, one with winged children in a bubble encircled by flowering branches, and one of a child riding on a crab with fishes around. Series 639 (three in set). 16.2 cm x 11.4 cm.

36. Set of three cards, two naked children in a boat driven by seahorses and a child (inset) listening to a shell, two children in a shell boat, two children on the bottom of the sea with fishes and crabs around. Series 649. 16 cm x 11.4 cm.

## VOLUME 56:
## DE LA RUE. CARDS WITH CHILDREN AND FAMILIES, IN WINTER AND SUMMER SCENES

**Some of these cards were designed by GG Kilburne and J Lawson.**

1. Four cards with white borders, children in happy Christmas scenes, with holly and mistletoe decoration. Series 34 (six in set). 12.8 cm x 8.7 cm.

2. Four cards, two from series 54 with boys making a snowman and people skating, and two from series 89 with boys snowballing and sailors eating Christmas pudding. 14.3 cm x 9.2 cm.

3. Five cards.
a) Set of three, mother and daughter in Christmas scenes, verse below, one on a mount. Series 88 "Nursery Favourites". 7 cm x 10.4 cm and 10.8 cm x 14.3 cm.
b) Two cards, children playing with bricks, spelling "A Merry Christmas and a Happy New Year". Series 124 (three in set) "Children at Play". 7 cm x 10.2 cm.

4. Set of three cards, ladies in snowy landscape. Series 97 "Wintry Weather". 10.4 cm x 7 cm.

5. Set of three cards, mother, children and choirboys in church, in quaint costume, with illuminated Gothic style backgrounds. Series 127 "Christmas Choristers". 7 cm x 10.4 cm.

6. Three valentine cards.
a) Lady in Grecian dress with babies in nest. Series 137. 9.3 cm x 9.3 cm.
b) Two cards with ladies in a garden, with faces in the flowers. Series 140. 8.8 cm x 12.8 cm.

7. Three birthday cards, boys at school opening and eating a hamper of food. Series 157. 9.7 cm x 9.7 cm.

8. Two birthday cards, children writing birthday greetings on scrolls by a table with ink pot and feather pen, one on a pink, gold and violet mount. Series 161. 7 cm x 10.4 cm, 11.1 cm x 14.4 cm.

9. Four New Year cards.
a) Two cards of a sailor boy and girl on board ship, with greetings on a flag. Series 200. 7.8 cm x 13.2 cm.
b) Two cards of little girls and large dogs, one dressed in pink, one in grey. Series 227. 7 cm x 10.4 cm.

10. Set of three cards, a transparent Father Christmas bringing a pudding, a snowball, or snapdragon to children in a handsome brass bedstead. Perhaps by G G Kilburne. Series 216. 13.8 cm x 8.7 cm.

11. Set of three cards, two girls and a boy wading in stream, looking at boats of tiny fairies, by G G Kilburne. Series 220 "Fairy Skiffs". 7.9 cm x 12.3 cm.

12. One card, the boy from Series 220 on a mount of yellow and gold. 12.8 cm x 17.2 cm.

13. Two birthday cards, unprepossessing babes swimming in a river and in reeds on the bank. Series 261. 15.3 cm x 10 cm.

14. Three cards.
a) Two cards, rustic ladies with pitcher. Series 267. 9.7 cm x 12.8 cm.
b) One card, of two ladies with roses. Series 300+, mark indistinct. 16 cm x 7.7 cm.

15. Set of three cards, ladies with fans and greetings in the shape of butterflies. Series 310. 9.7 cm x 12.9 cm.

16. Three birthday cards, family scenes with babies, mothers and children. Series 280, 378, 379. 9.7 cm x 9.7 cm, 9.7 cm x 12.9 cm.

17. Two cards.
a) Lady in wood looking at two fairies. Series 304. 15.3 cm x 10.2 cm.
b) Little girl wheeling Father Christmas over snow. Series 318 (three in set). 12.8 cm x 8.7 cm.

18. Two cards, on illuminated patterned mounts, with children in night clothes knocking at a door, and putting up a Christmas greeting. Possibly by G G Kilburne. The designs are series 313. 13.6 cm x 16.7 cm.

19. Four cards.
a) Two of Eskimos, in sledge, and playing in wood. Series 320. 12.8 cm x 8.7 cm.
b) Set of two cards, fur clad children in a boat, in winter. By G G Kilburne? Series 627. 10.5 cm x 7 cm.

20. Two cards, elegant ladies, one in evening dress with two small naked cherubs, the other out-of-doors in the snow with fur clad cherubs. Series 325. 7.8 cm x 12.2 cm.

21. Two cards, boys, with dogs jumping through a hoop. Series 385. 9.7 cm x 9.7? cm.

22. Three cards, girls in transparent dresses with a plant in a vase. Perhaps by J Lawson. Series 395. 7.8 cm x 16.6 cm. (Set?)

23. Two cards, one with mother and three children in snow, the other with the family at the door of their home. Perhaps by J Lawson. Series 434. 10 cm x 13.5 cm.

24. Two cards, one of a girl on a pony, the other a baby on a pony in a special seat, with a groom. Possibly by G G Kilburne. Series 455. 9 cm x 13 cm.

25. One card, a little girl dreaming of her parents decorating the Christmas tree, with a verse on reverse. Design by G G Kilburne. Series 507 (two in set). 13.2 cm x 9.5 cm.

26. Two cards.
a) Three children fishing, possibly by J Lawson. Series 558. 13.2 cm x 10.5 cm.
b) Children in a field, with geese and view of distant village. Series 570. 15 cm x 10.5 cm. The card bears Christmas greetings on the picture, but an incongruous sombre verse is on the back.

27. One card, a Grecian lady in green, with flowers, before a pink curtain. Series 541. 10 cm x 16.2 cm.

28. Set of three cards, possibly by F S Walker R E, with Grecian style ladies, one in yellow with a mirror and a Greek vase, one in blue in a swan boat, the third in pink with a vase to match, in a garden. Verses are on the reverse. Series 572. 9.5 cm x 16.5 cm.

29. Set of three cards, each with three children in winter scenes. Series 582. 14 cm x 10.3 cm.

30. Two cards, a girl in snow with a muff, and a girl in yellow indoors with plants in pots, possibly by J Lawson. Series 587. 10 cm x 14.3 cm.

31. Two cards, girls by the sea, in flounced dresses. Series 598. 8.9 cm x 14.5 cm.

32. Two cards by J Lawson, with children in the snow carrying greenery. Series 601. 13.2 cm x 9.5 cm.

33. Two cards by J Lawson, each with a sleeping boy, one in the nursery, one in a hayfield, with a verse on reverse. Series 607. 16.2 cm x 7.7 cm.

34. Three cards.
a) Two cards, a boy at a table painting a model Father Christmas, and a girl dressing one, with a mirror and holly above. Series 615. 8.3 cm x 12 cm.
b) A husband and wife with Christmas presents, the wife with her hands over the husband's eyes. Series 616. 8.3 cm x 12 cm.

35. Set of two cards, each with three children playing in a snow fort, by G G Kilburne. Series 626. 10.3 cm x 7 cm.

36. One card, a girl at the gate of a house, with an apron full of flowers. Series 637. 10 cm x 15.7 cm.

37. Two cards, monochrome with plain white borders, one with a lady in a field, the other two children with a pipe and music. Series 648 and 704. 11.9 cm x 15.8 cm.

38. Two similar cards, brown and cream, with a girl and a boy out-of-doors. Series 705. 11.9 cm x 15.8 cm.

39. Two cards, on coloured mounts, one a girl picking flowers in a field, the other a girl with a hayrake. (No visible number). 11.4 cm x 15.8 cm.

40. Valentine card, a lady in white with a basket of roses and a verse below, on a pink and gold mount. (No visible number). 10.9 cm x 15.5 cm.

41. Two cards, both a boy with a flock of geese, one with a trumpet, the other with a dead fox. Series 709. 14 cm x 10.8 cm.

42. Two cards, with indistinct numbers.
a) Four musicians at a gate, in snow. 14 cm x 10.4 cm.
b) Hens on a table outside an inn. 14.5 cm x 9.7 cm.

43. Six miscellaneous cards, with people and children - one of each of the series 175, 281, 283, 338, 533, 679. Sizes 8 cm x 8 cm up to 9 cm x 12.6 cm.

44. Five miscellaneous cards. Three are triangular, with mermaids, a girl in a hammock, and a baby in an egg, from series 349, 358, 147. One square card has mermaids, series 327 and the other is a lady in a farmyard with rabbits, series 409. Sides from 7.8 cm to 13.6 cm.

## VOLUME 57:
## DE LA RUE. FESTIVE SCENES, THE GOOD OLD DAYS, FOREIGN FOLK, HUNTING, COACHES AND COUNTRY SCENES

1. Two cards, a mediaeval scene with peacock, series 51, and a herald in eighteenth century dress on illuminated mount (no number visible). 12.5 cm x 8.8 cm, 11 cm x 14.5 cm.

2. Three cards, clowns.
a) Two triangular cards with clowns lying on the ground holding greetings. Series 41. 13.5 cm x 9.5 cm x 9.5 cm.
b) A card with a blue and white border and a vignette with a clown's head, Christmas music below, surrounded by tiger lilies on gilt. Series 110 "Songs of the Seasons". 8.6 cm x 12.8 cm.

3. Two cards, comic dwarfs on a gilt ground, balancing greetings on long noses. Series 323. 6.5 cm x 14.4 cm.

4. Four cards on gilt grounds.
a) Two cards, Father Christmas (or Lord of Misrule?) and a lady with a mask, holly and evergreen branches behind. Series 186 "Masked Faces". 9.7 cm x 9.7 cm.
b) Two cards, a man and a woman with fans as wings. Series 328. 9.7 cm x 9.7 cm.

5. Four cards.
a) Two have jesters with blank space for message, one lying down in a garden, the other playing tennis. Series 29. 10.7 cm x 6.5 cm.
b) Two triangular valentine cards, Elizabethan groups with harp or lute. Series 177. 13.5 cm x 9.5 cm x 9.5 cm.

6. Three cards.
a) Shepherds and shepherdesses making music. Series 46. 12.7 cm x 8.6 cm.
b) Two cards, Georgian couples, one with the man playing a flute to a lady at a spinning wheel, the other with a man playing a lute and a lady with a fan. Series 67. 12.7 cm x 8.6 cm.

7. Two cards, on pink and blue illuminated mounts, with captions in French, one a Georgian party, the other a Georgian skating scene. Series 74. 20.1 cm x 14 cm.

8. Four cards.
a) Two cards, mediaeval servants bearing Christmas dinner. Series 117 "Christmas Cheer". 7.8 cm x 12.3 cm.
b) Valentine card, a knight in armour on horseback and a lady at a castle door, caption in French. Series 142. 8.7 cm x 12.8 cm.
c) A birthday card, showing a mediaeval court with a queen on a throne. Series 148. 12.3 cm x 7.8 cm.

9. Two birthday cards, Georgian family scenes with children and babies, one in the nursery, one in the drawing room. Series 151. 12.8 cm x 8.6 cm.

10. Two cards.
a) Birthday card, with Georgian musicians, music in panel below. Series 158. 12.8 cm x 8.7 cm.
b) Georgian couple dancing, gilt ground. Series 221. 9.7 cm x 9.7 cm.

11. Two valentine cards, Georgian costume, a man on a terrace, a lady in a garden, looking at the new moon. Possibly by J Lawson. Series 176. 8.6 cm x 12.8 cm.

12. Two cards, peasants in mediaeval dress drinking round a table. Series 206. 9.7 cm x 9.7 cm.

13. Four cards.
a) Two cards of monks, drinking at table, and bringing geese in a basket through the snow, with dogs. Series 198.
b) An old lady, looking at elves in Georgian dress on a table, by G G Kilburne. Series 217.
c) An old lady at table, with a dog bearing a label "A Happy Christmas". Series 392. All 12.8 cm x 8.7 cm.

14. Two cards, one on a yellow and gold mount, showing ladies in Stuart garb playing with Father Christmas in the snow. By G G Kilburne. Series 215. 12.8 cm x 8.7 cm, 17.4 cm x 13.3 cm.

15. Two cards, one of ladies in Stuart dress having a tug-of-war with Father Time, the other, four men in Stuart dress having a tug-of-war with Father Christmas. Series 450. 14.3 cm x 8.3 cm.

16. Two cards, Georgian scenes of a gentleman conducting a family singing, and a lady accompanying the singing on a harp. Series 212. 9.7 cm x 13.8 cm.

17. Two cards, a Georgian gentleman with a child, one out of doors, the other inside with a cat. Series 515. 7.8 cm x 14.6 cm.

18. Two cards, a mediaeval tournament with knights on horseback and ladies watching. Series 577. 15.3 cm x 10.6 cm.

19. Two cards, Elizabethan heralds, one on horseback blowing a trumpet, another beating a drum carried on a horse led by a child. Series 612. 10.1 cm x 10.1 cm.

20. Two cards on elaborate gilded mounts, Elizabethan Christmas with "King Christmas" in a fur trimmed robe, and courtiers around. Design series 441. 13.3 cm x 17.4 cm.

21. Eight cards, Eastern ladies in various leisure pursuits: making music, playing a game, eating fruit etc. Series 42 "Greetings from the Orient" (twelve in set). 10.4 cm x 6.5 cm.

57.1

22. Five cards.
a) Two cards, Christmas waits, the New Year sending out the Old Year, in mediaeval costume. Series 90 (three in set) "Antique Drolleries". 8.4 cm x 6 cm.
b) Two Japanese ladies, greetings written in Japanese style. Series 96 (three in set). 6 cm x 8.4 cm.
c) A valentine card, with a Japanese bridal procession. Series 136. 12 cm x 7.8 cm.

23. Set of three cards, Roman ladies blowing bubbles, showing greetings. Series 113. 8.7 cm x 12.8 cm.

24. Set of three cards, Russians sledging, one of a lady drawn by two dogs, one of a lady with a sail, and one of a man pushing a lady's sleigh. Series 115. 12.8 cm x 8.7 cm.

25. Set of three cards, Japanese ladies in boats, one drawn by swimming men, one by swans, and one by rowers, with greetings on their sunshades. Series 183. 16 cm x 10 cm.

26. One card, a Turk with a hookah, greetings in the smoke. Series 346 "In the Clouds". 7.7 cm x 7.7 cm.

27. Two cards on pink or green decorated mounts, showing a party having dinner out of doors, with Christmas pudding, perhaps in Australia, though one card has a Jap or Chinese servant. No number. 16.4 cm x 12.6 cm.

28. One card, the Pyramids, with man and woman on a camel and a donkey, perhaps Joseph and Mary? Series 584. 14 cm x 10.3 cm.

29. Two cards, the hunt, with men in pink coats and a lady in black receiving the brush. Series 222. 9.7 cm x 9.7 cm.

30. Set of three cards, each with a lady in uniform on horseback. Series 309. 11.8 cm x 11.8 cm.

31. Two cards, the hunt, the chase and the kill, with gilt borders decorated by whips, and greetings on reverse. Series 512. 14 cm x 10 cm.

32. Two cards, a jockey in blue on a brown horse. Series 517. 10 cm x 10.5 cm.

33. Three cards.
a) Two cards, the hunt, the chase and the kill. Series 603. 12.2 cm x 9.5 cm.
b) One card, a lady hunting, on a dapple grey horse. Series 681. 12 cm x 12.5 cm.

34. Set of three cards, monkeys hunting, riding on dogs, the meet, the fall, the kill. Series 686 "Monkey Riders". 13.2 cm x 10.4 cm.

35. Set of three cards, the Stagecoach, At the Inn, the Toll gate, Snowed up. Series 218. 12.7 cm x 8.7 cm.

36. One card, two grooms in a pony cart with a hamper. Series 454. 13.2 cm x 10.5 cm.

37. Two cards, a stage coach in Summer, on the way and changing horses. Series 574. 15.3 cm x 10.5 cm.

38. Set of two cards, a family at Christmas dinner with boar's head and wine, and country folk with Christmas drinks at the inn. Series 578 "Joyous Fellowship". 15.3 cm x 10.5 cm.

39. Two cards, a man and woman in a boat in summer. Series 397. 14.3 cm x 6.4 cm.

40. One card, a lifeboat in a stormy sea with appropriate verse on reverse. Series 600+? 15.7 cm x 10.5 cm.

41. One card, a house and bridge in snow, with a grey background, unbordered. Series 698. 13 cm x 9.8 cm.

42. Two cards in black and white, winter scenes of a farm and a manor house. One is signed E W, one V B. Series 437. 10.7 cm x 7.6 cm.

43. Two cards.
a) A farm in a rectangular vignette, with a plant with seeds in the background, and a verse on reverse. Series 496. 10 cm x 14.4 cm.
b) A castle and river scene in a circular vignette, background of reeds and stream. Series 631. 11.8 cm x 15.6 cm.

44. Four cards.
a) Two cards, winter scenes. Series 129. 8.3 cm x 6 cm.
b) Two cards, rural summer scenes. Series 660. 15.5 cm x 11 cm.

## VOLUME 58:
## DE LA RUE. CARDS DESIGNED BY E H FAHEY, AND CARDS WITH ANIMALS AND FLOWERS

*Most of the cards in numbers 1-15 were probably designed by E H Fahey, with three cards per set. Possible exceptions are noted.*

1. Two cards, ladies in classical dress with appropriate period background, and greetings on gilt panels. Series 71 "Pompeian Studies". 8.7 cm x 12.8 cm.

2. Two birthday cards, an old lady in cap and shawl, an old man by a table laid for dinner, with greetings in verse below. Series 145. 7.8 cm x 12.3 cm.

3. Two birthday cards, two boys in antique setting making shadow pictures with fingers on the wall. Series 160 "Finger Shadows". 9.7 cm x 9.7 cm.

4. Two birthday cards.
a) Mother and child in tropical forest. Series 163. 8.7 cm x 12.8 cm.
b) Lady in boat, fanning a toy boat, with a greeting in French on the sail. Series 192 "Friendly Waftings". 12.8 cm x 8.7 cm.

5. Two cards, Elizabethan men playing bowls or quoits inscribed with greetings. Series 201. 10.3 cm x 7 cm.

6. Eight cards.
a) Two cards, an old man, and a woman, with pedlar trays inscribed with greetings. Series 200.
b) Three cards, each of a lady in a garden shaking a sheet, with a verse below explaining its significance. Series 238.
c) Three cards, savages with bow, arrow, and sling, the verses below having a neat reference to each. Series 239.
All 4.4 cm x 8.7 cm.

7. Four cards.
a) Two cards, ladies and girls skipping and playing battledore and shuttlecock. Series 241. 14.3 cm x 6.3 cm.
b) Two cards, Roman ladies in classical background, by a pool. Series 242. 6 cm x 10.7 cm.

8. Five miscellaneous cards.
a) Boy in Elizabethan garb carrying a flag with birthday greeting, riding on a dog. Series 164. 7.8 cm x 7.8 cm.
b) Two varlets in mediaeval dress, one carrying a pie on his head. Series 190 "Dainty Viands". 10.3 cm x 7 cm.
c) Two cupids in boots, jerkin and feathered hats, valentine greetings below. Series 257. 7 cm x 10.3 cm.
d) Man in Elizabethan dress lying on a sofa, knitting. Series 322. 14.3 cm x 6.5 cm.
e) Artist painting a picture of a Christmas procession, in a gold frame. Series 335 "Christmas Scenes". 12.5 cm x 6.8 cm.

9. Six cards, all with gilt backgrounds.
a) Two cards, Italians in boats, one with two men raising the sail, the other two men and a girl on a barge. Series 230. 11 cm x 6 cm.
b) One card, two comic men, one carrying dumbells with greetings. Series 233. 8 cm x 6.3 cm.
c) Two cards, jesters, one with bladder, the other with cup and ball game. Series 360. 8 cm x 6.3 cm.
d) One card, a man playing a cello. (This might be by Griset). Series 261. 8 cm x 6.3 cm.

10. Six cards.
a) Two cards, boys playing by a stile, with kite, or on a seesaw. Series 244. 7.8 cm x 7.8 cm.
b) Dutch scene, with man with meerschaum pipe looking askance at a stork offering him a baby, with birthday greeting below. Series 292. 12.3 cm x 7.8 cm.
c) Two triangular cards, a comic man, with a newspaper greeting, or before a fire. Series 259 "Uncle Jonathan". 13.5 cm x 9.5 cm x 9.5 cm.
d) A triangular card, Indian maid in canoe. Series 412. 13.5 cm x 9.5 cm x 9.5 cm.

11. Seven miscellaneous cards.
a) Eskimo showing Christmas greeting to polar bear. Series 235. 8.3 cm x 6 cm.
b) Father Robin and son skating. Series 236. 8.3 cm x 6 cm.
c) Mother and son skating. Series 237. 6 cm x 8.3 cm.
d) Professor in museum watching an imp giving a birthday greeting to a stuffed chimpanzee. (Perhaps by Griset?) Series 246. 7 cm x 10.3 cm.
e) Man in Elizabethan costume juggling. Series 252. 7 cm x 10.3 cm.
f)g) Boy chasing his hat in the snow, with the basket on his back losing its contents, and a girl with umbrella. Series 353. 7 cm x 10.3 cm.

12. Six cards.
a) One card, seventeenth century lady pouring water over drunken monk, possibly by Griset. Series 228. 7.8 cm x 7.8 cm.
b) Two cards, fishermen in classical times with catch of plaice. Series 354. 7.8 cm x 7.8 cm.
c) Two cards, a tailor fitting clothes on a boy and working on a coat, with boy beside him. Series 355. 7.8 cm x 7.8 cm.
d) One card, Egyptian porter with trunk bearing greetings on his back. Series 356. 7 cm x 10.3 cm.

13. Two cards, imps attacking squirrels with arrows and spear. Series 357. 12.5 cm x 6.8 cm.

14. Four miscellaneous cards.
a) Birthday card, with small children playing in a shoe. Series 295. 12.5 cm x 6.8 cm.

b) A lady paddling a canoe. Series 336. 12.5 cm x 6.8 cm.
c) A man punting a boat towards a girl on stepping stones, with a basket of clothes, some blowing away. Series 350. 12 cm x 7.8 cm.
d) Gypsies in the snow decorating their tent with holly, possibly by Gordon Browne. Series 406. 12 cm x 7.8 cm.

15. Two cards, mediaeval festive scenes, with a child in red carried in a chair by three revellers. Series 410. 10.3 cm x 7 cm.

*Numbers 16-33 have cards of animals, most from sets of three.*

16. Two cards, two dogs on a cliff by the sea. Series 27 "Field Sports". 12.8 cm x 8.7 cm.

17. Five cards, four with dogs in various outside activities, one with a fox. Series 51. 12.8 cm x 8.7 cm.

18. Set of three cards, dogs, one in kennel, one holding a greeting in mouth, the third in a coat with a pipe and a flag with greeting. Series 116. 9.7 cm x 9.7 cm.

19. Two cards from Series 116 on a green mount with red and gold pattern. 14.4 cm x 14.4 cm.

20. Two birthday cards, dogs, one by an overturned ink stand with a greeting on paper, the other tearing up a greeting. Series 159. 10.3 cm x 7 cm.

21. Set of three cards, horses, one with groom in stable, one with two dogs, the third with three horses in stable. Series 197. 16.2 cm x 10 cm.

22. Two triangular cards, cows and goats in snow. Series 205. 13.5 cm x 9.5 cm

23. Set of three cards, dogs, one by the sea holding a piece of driftwood with greeting, the other two indoors holding a paper with greetings. Series 223. 14.3 cm x 6.5 cm.

24. Two triangular cards, bulls' heads. Series 243. 13.5 cm x 9.5 cm x 9.5 cm.

25. Set of three cards, dogs, one by a kennel in snow, looking in window, two on the doorstep, one in snow at the door. Series 330. 9.7 cm x 9.7 cm.

26. One card, mountain scene with three dogs. Series 451. 15.3 cm x 10.5 cm.

27. Two cards, dogs chasing a rabbit and a squirrel. Series 514. 14 cm x 7.8 cm.

28. Set of three cards, two dogs in a farmyard, a dog by a fireside, and a donkey braying at a scarecrow with geese amongst the crops. Series 588. 14.5 cm x 9.7 cm.

29. One card, two bulldogs dressed as boxers. Series 613. 10.5 cm x 10.5 cm.

30. Set of three cards, summer scenes with a cow, horse and donkey at a gate. Series 621. 8 cm x 10.1 cm.

31. Set of two cards, each with cat or dog in circular vignettes on gilt ground with red line pattern and white border. The centre vignette has the head of the cat or the dog, and various cat and dog activities are shown in the four others. Series 708. 13 cm x 13.5 cm.

32. Four miscellaneous cards.
a) A cat on a snowy roof, on a trimmed gilded mount. Series 99. 13 cm x 9 cm.
b) A squirrel on a triangular mount. Series 388. 13.5 cm x 9.5 cm.
c) Two giraffes, head and neck, with collar. Series 430. 7 cm x 10.5 cm.
d) Two dogs swimming, with driftwood bearing greetings in mouths. Series 532. 12.5 cm x 6.8 cm.

33. One card, frogs, in red, green and gold lacquer on thick yellow card. This is unmarked, but is probably the Series R 1094 "Procession of Frogs". c1888. 17.2 cm x 12.3 cm.

*Numbers 34-46 have cards with flower designs.*

34. Two cards, country scenes with hollyhocks etc. Series 126. 10.3 cm x 7 cm.

35. Two cards.
a) Peonies. Series 444. 12 cm x 12 cm.
b) Wild roses in a circular vignette, border of a gilt rose pattern on yellow. Series 553. 11.7 cm x 11.7 cm.

36. Two cards, Christmas roses, and orange blossom, against a rainbow background. Series 554 "Floral Rainbows". 10 cm x 13 cm.

37. Two cards, yellow, orange, and white flowers, cloudy background. Series 559 (three in set) "Floral Clusters". 11 cm x 16 cm.

38. Two cards, pink and yellow roses, with leaves and bud. Series 561. 12 cm x 12.4 cm.

39. One card, oval vignette with flowers in a blue glass vase, on a cream ground with gilt decoration. Series 586 (two in set). 10.5 cm x 14.5 cm.

40. Two birthday cards, yellow and pink dahlias with ferns. Series 602 (three in set). 13.2 cm x 9.7 cm.

41. Four cards.
a) Two cards, tulips and crocuses in pots. Series 609. 8.2 cm x 12.7 cm.
b) Two cards, roses in blue and yellow vases. Series 618. 8 cm x 12.5 cm.
All perhaps by M E Butler.

42. Two cards, carnations on a grey card and cornflowers on green, both with green line frames and white edge. Series 673. 10.6 cm x 15.1 cm.

43. One card, three fans with floral decoration, arranged as in a picture frame, with grey border, and greetings, and floral design in red on reverse. Series 685. 10.6 cm x 14.4 cm.

44. Four miscellaneous cards.
a) Easter card, with primroses. Series 462. 13 cm x 9 cm.
b) Roses and sweet peas. Series 551. 12 cm x 7.7 cm.
c) Pelargoniums with wooded background. Series 583. 14 cm x 10.3 cm.
d) Easter(?) card, flowering branches, thorn border. Series 605. 13 cm x 10 cm.

45. Three miscellaneous cards.
a) Narcissus and cineraria. Series 595 "Floral Gems". 9 cm x 13.5 cm. b) Hawthorn and butterfly. Series 614. 10.2 cm x 10.4 cm. c) River scene with village and branches of blackberry. Series 632. 9.5 cm x 16.8 ?cm.

46. Four cards.
a) Two cards, irises and butterfly, and anemone japonica, against blue sky, on plain white mount. Series 440. 8.1 cm x 15.3 cm.
b) Two cards, edelweiss and gentians, cydonia japonica and apple blossom on plain beige cards. Series 671. 10.3 cm x 15.3 cm.

# VOLUME 59.
# DE LA RUE. BIRDS, BUTTERFLIES, WITH A FEW MISCELLANEOUS CARDS

**Some of the earlier cards here are on plain white mounts, but the majority have the usual brown or gilt border, or line. W S Coleman probably designed some of the unattributed bird studies.**

1/2. Three similar three-fold cards, with bird picture and verses, in a decorative ivy border, the outsides being brown or blue with "trompe l'oeil" pictured hinges. The first card shows herons, from Series 1, the second storks, from Series 14, and the third robins, from Series 70. All three series are similar with six cards per set and are titled "Alfresco Studies" 1, 2 and 3. 24.2 cm x 9 cm open.

3/4. Eight cards, birds on branches, robin, goldfinch, lovebird, waxbill, titmouse, kinglet, bullfinch, blue honeysucker, with verses and greetings below, on plain white mounts. The first five are from Series 5, the other three from Series 19 (six in each set). 7.8 cm x 12.2 cm.

5. Three cards, colourful birds on flowering branches, on plain white mounts. Series 30. 8.7 cm x 12.8 cm.

6. Three cards, birds with nests, redstart, long-tailed titmouse, reed warbler, on plain white mounts. Series 44 (three in set). 12.2 cm x 7.8 cm.

7. Two similar, turtle dove and linnet. Series 68. 12.2 cm x 7.8 cm.

8. Three cards, macabre pictures of dead birds and hare hanging against wall or window. Series 36 "Gifts for Larder" (six in set). 7 cm x 10.4 cm.

9. Five cards, groups of birds on branches with flowers and butterflies, with inset panels for verse and New Year greetings below. Series 43 (six in set) "Woodland Songsters". 8.7 cm x 12.8 cm.

10/11. Five valentine cards (four designs), birds in flight carrying a verse of greeting. Three are on plain white cards from Series 40 (six in set) and two are mounted on pink illuminated cards, Series 103 "Winged Post", with the same designs. 10.3 cm x 7 cm and 14.5 cm x 11.3 cm.

12. A set of three cards in Japanese style, with birds or mice in a floral background with red and green border. Series 86 "Japanese Studies" 12.8 cm x 8.7 cm.

13. Two valentine cards, birds in circular vignettes on elaborate illuminated mount with leaf design and verse in panel. Series 107 (three in set). 11.3 cm x 15.5 cm.

14. One valentine card, a cockatoo picture on a green illuminated mount, with verse in panel below. Series 108 (three in set). 11.3 cm x 15.8 cm.

15. Set of three cards, birds and nests by the water. Series 120 "Water Birds". 9.7 cm x 9.7 cm.

16. Two cards, swans and ducks in lake scenes in oval vignettes, with border of illuminated leaf design on red ground, and greeting below. Series 130 (three in set). 12.8 cm x 8.7 cm.

17. Set of three cards, colourful birds on floral branches, with New Year greeting below. Series 203. 8.7 cm x 12.8 cm.

18. One birthday card, green woodpecker on a branch, with illuminated yellow mount, perhaps by W S Coleman. Series 209? 10.7 cm x 16.3 cm.

19. Set of three birthday cards, blackbird, thrush and yellow hammer, with nests or chicks. Series 211. 9.7 cm x 9.7 cm.

20. Set of three cards, gulls and herons in sea or river scenes. Series 225. 12.2 cm x 7.8 cm.

21. Two cards, robins in snow, one on illuminated pink mount. Series 229. 10.3 cm x 7 cm and 14.4 cm x 11 cm.

22. Two cards, water wagtails in river, and martins in flight over water lilies. By W S Coleman? Series 329. 9.7 cm x 9.7 cm.

23. Two cards on pale green mounts, birds on floral branches. Series 380 (three in set). 12 cm x 7.8 cm.

24. Two cards, tropical birds on flowering branches. Possibly by W S Coleman. Series 382 "Humming Birds". 9.7 cm x 9.7 cm.

25. Set of three cards, tropical birds with nests, possibly by W S Coleman. Series 384 "Honey Gatherers". 13.3 cm x 10.4 cm.

26. Two cards, a parrot in a tropical forest, and a humming bird with flowers. Series 402. 7.8 cm x 12.2 cm.

27. Three cards (two designs), groups of birds on snowy branches at sunset, with church in background. Two are on green patterned mounts. Series 498. 16.4 cm x 8.4 cm and 18.9 cm x 10.9 cm.

28. Two cards, birds on branches.
a) Three birds on fir tree in winter. Series 504. 13.2 cm x 10.4 cm.
b) Blue tits in autumn. Series 676. 14.8 cm x 10.4 cm.

29. Four cards.
a) Blue feathered bird on flowering branch. Series 405.
b) Two cards, birds on branches, one card with mountain scenery, the other with butterflies, both having corners with peacock feather design. Series 555 "Songsters' Retreat".
c) Two colourful birds on tropical tree branch. Series 617. All 12.2 cm x 7.8 cm.

30. One card, humming birds taking honey from tropical flowers. Series 500 "Tropical Splendour". 13.2 cm x 10.4 cm.

31. Two cards, robins on a snowy fence or ivy branch. Series 535. 8.3 cm x 8.8 ?cm.

32. Two cards, humming birds with flowers and butterflies. Series 516 (three in set). 10 cm x 10.4 cm.

33. One card, three robins with terns and blackberries, in elaborate pink and gold border with butterfly design in corners. Series 638. 12 cm x 12.4 cm.

34. One card, two humming birds with nest, on a plain grey background, and a greeting in panel below. Series 647. 11.9 cm x 16.7 cm.

35. Two cards, birds in oval vignettes with patterned border, on plain beige ground with greetings below in panel. Series 656. 11 cm x 15.8 cm.

36. Two cards, one with hobby or merlin perching on a post with martins in flight around, the other with a magpie on a fence. Series 675. 10 cm x 15.4 cm.

37. Two cards, yellow wagtails, redwings, in snow. Series 695. 12.2 cm x 9.2 cm.

38. Four miscellaneous cards.
a) A chick in a wood with blue butterflies. Series 389. 12.8 cm x 9.2 cm.
b) Eagle on rock, in a mountain scene (trimmed). Series 396. 8 cm x 12 cm.
c) Ducks, swimming, carrying a greeting to a robin. Series 593. 16.3 cm x 8.3 cm.
d) Baby bird on garden flowers. Series 608. 8.3 cm x 16.7 cm.

39. Two cards, butterflies on flowers. Series 538. 10.4 cm x 7 cm.

40. Three cards in Chinese style, similar pen and ink design with grey or green borders. One is of a heron, the other two show coolies in the snow. No numbers. 10.3 cm x 13.3 cm.

41. Two cards showing contrasting styles over thirteen years.
a) Shells. c1875. Series 32 "Gems of the Deep". 8.5 cm x 6 cm.
b) Illuminated peacock feathers with heavily gilded Christmas greetings on a thick cream coloured mount. This has no number, but is probably a design listed in the John Johnson records. c1888. 13.2 cm x 9.5 cm.

# ARTHUR ACKERMANN, LONDON, AND THE AMERICAN  PUBLISHERS LOUIS PRANG, J H BUFFORD & SONS, AND JOHN A LOWELL & CO OF BOSTON, USA

*Section*
*8*

Ackermann is grouped here with Prang as the firm was the sole agent for Prang's cards, which were shipped to England from the mid 1870's; they appear frequently in scrap books of the 1870's and 1880's. Prang was the leading producer of American prints from the 1840's, and had a high reputation as a lithographer. The firm began producing greeting cards, in addition to trade cards, in the early 1870's. They were marked with the name of the firm and the year of production, with the exception of a few early ones, though some were sold in England marked Ackermann.

There is a fine collection of 70 volumes of Prang material, (seen by the writer), in the American Antiquarian Society in Worcester, Mass., also a good selection of prize cards in the Public Library in Boston. Prang, like many English firms, introduced prizes for card design in 1881, bringing many American artists of repute into the business, including, amongst many others Elihu Vedder, Rosina Emmet, and D Wheeler. Prang is generally credited with the innovation of black and red-backed cards, but like Marcus Ward and De La Rue, the firm did not favour elaborate mechanical cards, though silk fringes were used in the 1880's. The decorated backs are an interesting feature.

The firm of Ackermann was noted for sporting prints, and there are many registrations for these in Stationers' Hall records, a few being traced to cards in this collection. According to John Ford's history of the firm, Ackermann began producing cards in 1881, but a registration has been found in the Seddon Collection dated 1878, for Ackermann's own productions.

There are a few cards in this section from two less well known publishers, Bufford and Lowell, who both competed with Prang in Boston, but it would appear, from the small number of their cards found in scrapbooks that they were not brought into England in quantity, like those of Prang.

For those interested in the development of the St Nicholas, Santa Claus, Father Christmas theme, it might be noted that in the poem by Dr Clement C Moore, as published and illustrated by Prang (see volume 63, 2(b)) St Nicholas is wearing brown; it is noted elsewhere in this catalogue that many of the Father Christmas figures are so attired.

# VOLUME 60:
# ACKERMANN, PRANG, BUFFORD

*Numbers 1-9 were published by Ackermann, and include a number by E G Thomson (see similar cards for De La Rue in Volume 55).*

1. Two cards by E G T, one of a naked baby riding on a turtle and a girl swimming behind, the other two babies riding on snails pursued by wasps, on a gilt ground, with greeting and verse. Registered at Stationers' Hall 28-6-1878. 17.5 cm x 10.7 cm.

2. Two cards by E G T, unbordered, one with two naked children riding on a seahorse, the other with four little girls in a shell with seaweed around, and a gilt surround. Registered at Stationers' Hall 18-6-1880. 17.5 cm x 12.4 cm.

3. Two cards by E G T with gilt borders, one with four naked fairies in a nest onapple blossom, the other with three naked children on a sea-shell seasaw. Registered at Stationers' Hall 3-5-1881. 17.9 cm x 12.4 cm.

4. One card by E G T, small girl on lily leaf with dragonfly above, with a gilt line border and greeting and verse. c1880. 16.1 cm x 10.7 cm.

5. Two cards by E G T, one with four naked babies on magnolia blossom, the other a maiden sitting on a crab shell with seaweed nearby, both on gilt grounds, with greeting and apt verse from Shakespeare in white border. c1880. 16.1 cm x 10.7 cm.

6. Two similar cards by E G T, a small naked fairy on honeysuckle with bees, and

**60.10**

four naked children under a mushroom. c1880. 16.1 cm x 10.7 cm.

7. Two similar cards by E G T, three naked children around a log fire with ivy leaves behind, and two with a peacock feather by a log fire. c1880. 16.1 cm x 10.7 cm.

8. Three cards by E A S Douglas, titled "A false start" (racing), "Taking a pipe and a drain" (The fox going into a hollow pipe), and "The girl I left behind me" (lady refusing to take a fence). These are three out of twelve registered at Stationers' Hall.14-2-1881.14 cm x 9.7 cm.

9. One card, a soldier on a donkey followed by a boy, titled "En route". This is one out of twelve registered 5-4-1881, by Orlando Norie. 11.5 cm x 14.7 cm.

*Numbers 10-17 have cards marked "Ackermann", but these were probably imported from Prang and made in USA.*

10. Three cards, the New Year seeing the Old Year off the stage, Jo's dream - a child in bed on Christmas Eve, and two angels on a cloud, all on black background. c1880. 14.7 cm x 8.5 cm. (The angel card is in the Prang collection in Boston Public Library).

11/12. Ten cards, on plain beige grounds, fine printing in gold and colours with designs of flowers, holly, and autumn leaves with illuminated greetings. c1875. 10.6 cm x 6.6 cm, 6.6 cm x 10.6 cm.

13. Nine cards, three designs of autumn leaves with various greetings in panels or scrolls, all on black background. c1876.10.4 cm x 6.2 cm, 6.2 cm x 10.4 cm.

14/15. Eighteen cards, with four designs of roses, violets, daisies, escallonia(?) etc, all on black back ground and varied greetings on beige coloured scrolls. c1876. 10.5 cm x 6.3 cm.

16. Seven cards, four designs of roses and escallonia, with varied greetings or texts in panels, all on black background. c1876. 10.5 cm x 6.3 cm, 6.3 cm x 10.5 cm.

17. Seven cards, two on white ground with small flower motif and Christmas verse in red, and five on blue or beige ground with flower or oak leaf design and verse or greeting in panel. Two of the latter are marked with the names of both Prang and Ackermann. c1876. 9.5 cm x 5.8 cm, 10.3 cm x 6.2 cm.

*Numbers 18-28 have early Prang flower and bird cards, most unmarked, probably c1875, on plain white mounts, with greetings in embossed gilt script unless otherwise stated.*

18. Two cards, one Easter, of pelargoniums, the other crocuses with Christmas and New Year greeting. This

card has an interesting inscription. "Entraced (sic) to Act of Congress in the yèar 1873 by L Prang & Co in the Office of the Library of Congress at Washington". 10.5 cm x 14.1 cm and 9.3 cm x 13.1 cm.

19. Four cards, roses. Sizes up to 10 cm x 13.5 cm.

20. Four cards, snowdrops, carnations, lily of the valley and forget-me-nots. Sizes up to 10 cm x 13.5 cm.

21. Four cards, roses. Sizes up to 10.2 cm x 14.2 cm.

22. Three cards, birds on oak and maple branches, two with birthday greetings. Sizes up to 9.9 cm x 14 cm.

23. Four cards, three designs, birds on nests or berried branches. Sizes up to 10.2 cm x 13.3 cm.

24. Four cards, two designs, strawberry plant and primula. Sizes up to 10 cm x14 cm.

25. Four cards, two designs, holly and grasses. Sizes up to 10 cm x 13.3 cm.

26. Three cards, one a valentine, with various flowers, one on a brown ground. Sizes up to 10 cm x 14 cm.

27. Three cards on beige grounds, camellias, with greetings printed in red. These are marked "Copyright 1879 L Prang & Co, Boston, USA". 10.3 cm x 14.7 cm.

28. Five cards on green or beige grounds, various flowers, with greetings in red. Two cards are marked 1880, one 1881. Sizes up to 9 cm x 12.5 cm.

*Numbers 29-32 have cards published by Bufford.*

29. Three cards with various flower sprays, two on black background with greetings in panel, dated 1876, the third on a grey ground with text, no date. All are marked "Copyrighted by J H Bufford & Sons", 8.3 cm x 5 cm up to 12.5 cm x 6.5 cm.

30. Four cards, three with floral patterns on black backgrounds over a blank space for a message, or perhaps a menu. The fourth has roses and a butterfly around a black envelope space. All marked as above, dated 1876. 7 cm x 13.3 cm, 10.8 cm x 6.4 cm.

31. Three cards, elegant ladies in blue, one leaning on a fence, one on a cliff, and one feeding robins in the snow. There is a panel below with greetings and verse, and a well designed illuminated border in blue and gold. Marked as above, 1879. 7.8 cm x15.8 cm.

32. An elaborate card with silver border, robins in rectangular vignette, bordered by holly and a group of children with toys, c1880, marked Bufford, and another with a Japanese scene.
10.3 cm x 14.4 cm, 8.5 cm x 13 cm.

## VOLUME 61:
## PRANG. SMALL CARDS WITH HOLLY, GREENERY, FLOWERS, BIRDS & BUTTERFLIES

**Most of these cards are signed "Copyright L Prang & Co, Boston, USA" with the date of manufacture, except for a few early ones. Some have "AA Copyright" as well as a Prang marking, but the cards are clearly Prang products. The majority of these cards show flowers, and many have a caption which might explain the use of flowers at Christmas time "Bright as a flower may thy Christmas be".**

1. Six cards, two designs of holly and autumn leaves, on blue, grey, or black ground with greeting in panels. Unmarked. c1875. 10.3 cm x 6.3 cm.

2. Eight cards, three designs of rose and flower sprays, with varied greetings in panels. The marking where present is integrated with the design and difficult to see. c1875. 10.3 cm x 6.3 cm.

3/4. Eleven cards, six designs, a hanging gilt edge plaque with various greetings over flower sprays, autumn leaves, and strawberry plant, one a birthday card, one with a text. 1875. 10.3 cm x 6.3 cm.

5. Five cards, two designs, two sizes, violet and fern spray, and lily of the valley and forget-me-nots, with verses in white panel on cream ground, for valentine, birthday, New Year and a text. All are marked Prang 1875 but four have A A as well.
13.5 cm x 7.9 cm, 13.5 cm x 6.4 cm.

6/7. Eighteen cards, blue ground, four with a rose spray, four apple blossom and bee, and ten with butterflies on floral sprays (eight designs). They have varied greetings, Christmas, New Year, birthday and texts, fourteen being in panels. 1875 and 1876. 10.3 cm x 6.3 cm.

8/9. Thirteen cards, blue, beige, or grey ground, with various greetings in a scroll over four designs, sprays of spring flowers, including three birthday cards. One visible date 1876. 10.3 cm x 6.3 cm.

10/11. Nineteen cards, six designs of birds on branches and of birds' nests with flowers and fruit. The greetings are in red brown script on white panels. 1876.
8.6 cm x 4.8 cm.

12. Two cards, one design of a moss rose spray with a greeting in a panel, on blue ground. 1876. 10.3 cm x 4.8 cm.

13. Six cards, five designs of various flowers on cream ground, with embossed silver greetings in panel. 1876.
10.3 cm x 5 cm.

14. Seven similar on blue ground, six designs. 1877. 10.3 cm x 5 cm.

15. Four cards on blue ground with three designs of small rose or strawberry spray and greetings in red cursive style. 1876.
8 cm x 4.2 cm.

16. Ten cards, various flower sprays, all with greetings in panels. Seven are on cream ground, dated 1876, and three on gilt and violet, dated 1879 (one a valentine). Sizes up to 8 cm x 4 cm.

17/19. Eighteen cards, twelve designs on cream ground, with greetings, verse, or text in panel. There are six designs of various flowers with a panel corner turned down, and six different designs with a plain panel. Three cards have a birthday greeting or text and three with strawberry flower and fruit show varied Christmas and New Year greetings in characteristic red brown style. Some cards have "A A copyright" as well as the Prang marking. 1876. Sizes up to 13.5 cm x 6.4 cm.

20. Five larger cards on cream ground, using three of the designs in no. 18, with two others. All have verses for Easter in panels. 1876. 13.5 cm x 7.9 cm.

21/22. Twelve cards, five designs of various flowers including roses, violets, fuchsias, carnations, pansies, on cream or

60.31

grey ground. Four have Christmas greetings, two birthday, and six quotations from the poets, in panels. 1877.
14.5 cm x 5.5 cm, 15.5 cm x 4.9 cm.

23. Four cards, two designs of roses and forget-me-nots, on grey ground with greetings or verse in panel, one for birthday. One card has "A A copyright", but a very dim "Prang 1877" can be discerned. 1877. 14.5 cm x 5.5 cm, 15.8 cm x 4.9 cm.

24. Two cards, cream ground, daisies and buttercups, and crocuses, with Happy New Year greeting on decorative scroll. 1877. 13.5 cm x 6.4 cm.

25. Two cards, one design of thistles and autumn leaves on pale green ground, with greeting and verse on brown scroll. 1877.
11.3 cm x 7.7 cm.

26. Nine cards, green ground, five designs of various spring flowers and catkins threaded into brown panel with greetings. 1877. 6.3 cm x 10.5 cm.

27. Seven cards, cream ground, four of birds eggs with sprays of fern or berries, one of birds' nests and two of catkins and fern, all with greetings in panel. 1877.
10.7 cm x 6.5 cm.

28. Five cards, four of colourful birds with fern or flower spray on grey ground with greeting and verse in panel, 1878, and a gilt edged card with a robin, undated.
10.8 cm x 5.5 cm, 8.5 cm x 5 cm.

29. Three cards, bunches of spring flowers and ferns on cream ground, behind a panel with greeting and verse. 1878.
10.8 cm x 6.9 cm.

30. Four cards, three designs of roses and fuchsia, on cream ground, behind large panels with greeting and verse. One panel was left blank for the sender's message. 1878. 11.9 cm x 7.8 cm.

31. Three cards, roses, holly and mistletoe, and convolvulus on cream ground, with greetings in red brown on a scroll. 1878.
9.4 cm x 6.8 cm.

32. Six miscellaneous cards, five designs of flower sprays on cream or beige ground with greeting in panel. None are marked. c1876-1880. 11.2 cm x 6.7 cm.

33. Seven miscellaneous cards with flower sprays. Four are dated 1878, one 1883, and two with a red, white and blue ribbon, 1876.
9.5 cm x 4.5 cm up to 13.3 cm x 6.5 cm.

## VOLUME 62:
## PRANG. BLACK, RED, & GILT BACKGROUNDS

**Most of these cards are marked, as before, with name and date which is**

**sometimes difficult to decipher. Many designs in Volume 61 are repeated here.**

*Numbers 1-20 have black backgrounds.*

1. Four humorous cards, with three designs of a huntsman, two children with an outsize cigar and an Irishman with two pigs. There are verses in panels, marked A A copyright, but the cards are signed Prang, 1875. 12.8 cm x 8.8 cm.

2. Three cards, one of three children with a turkey, and Christmas verse on a banner, one of the New Year as a baby emerging from an egg, and an angel announcing the birth of our Lord. 1875 and 1877. 8.9 cm x 12.8 cm, 8 cm x 13.3 cm.

3. Four cards, one design of an angel sitting on a rose ringing a bell, inscribed with greeting. 1876. 14.3 cm x 7.8 cm.

4. Four cards, two designs of roses and holly, roses and carnation, with a bell inscribed with greeting. 1876. 14.3 cm x 7.8 cm.

5. Four cards, turkey, lobster, fish, dessert, on a table with white cloth inscribed with greetings, one for Thankgiving and the others for Christmas. Signed both Prang and Ackermann, 1876. 12.5 cm x 6.4 cm.

6. Five cards, three designs of naked cherubs with flowers, and verses in panels, three being valentines, one Christmas and one New Year. 1876. 14.3 cm x 6.4 cm, 7 cm x 11.3 cm.

7. Four cards, two with groups of angels 1877, and two with sporting scenes and trees, 1878. 13.5 cm x 7.6 cm, 14 cm x 6.3 cm.

8. Thirteen small cards, three designs of moss rose, carnations, and amelanchier, with greetings in panels, three for birthday. The moss rose design repeats that in Volume 61, no. 16. c1876. 8.2 cm x 3.8 cm.

9. Seven similar small cards, two designs of autumn leaves and buttercups, c1876, and one larger with forget-me-nots, and Christmas verse, 1875. 8.2 cm x 3.8 cm, 6.3 cm x 10.5 cm.

10. Nine cards, three designs of roses, carnations, and amelanchier, with greetings in panel, one a text, one birthday. c1876. 10.4 cm x 6.3 cm.(Note: Amelanchier is a N E American tree. It appears to have been a popular subject for Prang artists).

11. Six cards, four of spring flowers, as in Volume 61, no. 8, and two others with flower sprays, with greetings on scrolls or panel. 1875. 10.4 cm x 6.3 cm.

12/15. Twenty-two cards, thirteen designs, various flower sprays and greetings on panels. Some of these designs are repeated from those in Volume 61, nos. 17, 18, 19.1876. 13.5 cm x 6.4 cm.

16. Two cards, the same strawberry design, as in Volume 61, no. 19, one on a yellow mount marked Trussell, Brighton, probably the dealer. 1876. 13.5 cm x 6.4 cm,15.5 cm x 8.3 cm.

17. Four cards, with three designs of rose sprays and greetings in panels, one oval. One design is also in Volume 61, no. 18. 1876. 13.5 cm x 6.5 cm.

18. Five cards, four of oak leaves, greetings in panels, and one of maple leaves in autumn with text in oval vignette. 1876. 13.5 cm x 6.5 cm

19. Three cards, one with oak leaves as in 18 above, the others with forget-me-nots and violet sprays as in 15, with verses or greeting in panel. Marked Prang 1876, but two cards have A A copyright as well. 13.4 cm x 8 cm.

20. Six cards, with designs of spring flowers and berries, the stems threaded into beige scrolls with greetings and verse. 1878. 10.7 cm x 7.5 cm.

21. Six cards, four designs of flower sprays on gilt ground, with greetings on a white scroll. 1877. 13.1 cm x 6.6 cm.

*Numbers 22-27 have cards with red backgrounds, with one exception in no 27.*

22. Five cards, four designs of barefoot children, out of doors with decorative greenery and flowers, and verses and greetings on white panels. 1878. 11.2 cm x 7 cm.

23. Three cards, probably meant for valentines, each with two barefoot children, one with a lacy shawl and flowers, one holding a mirror, the third encircled by an outsize jewelled diadem. 1878. 10.7 cm x 6.4 cm, 6.4 cm x 10.7 cm.

24. Two cards, one with Father Christmas holding a Christmas verse over two sleeping children, the other an Easter card with three children playing with eggs. 1878. 9 cm x 21 cm.

25. Two similar, children in vignettes with holly and mistletoe wreaths around, and Christmas verse printed in red on white panel. 1878. 9 cm x 21 cm.

26. Two similar Easter cards, one with a boy holding a cross with lilies, the other with five children and a cross with passion flowers and lilies, and an Easter verse printed in red on white panel. 1878. 9 cm x 21 cm.

27. Two cards, one on red background with four children holding palms and flowers, the other on a green background with the Virgin Mary and Child in a vignette and children singing in church below, with a Christmas verse in a decorative panel.1878. 9 cm x 21 cm.

## VOLUME 63: PRANG, FOLDERS, RELIGIOUS CARDS, FAIRIES. LOWELL, ALL THE CARDS IN THIS COLLECTION.

**By about 1880 Prang began to print attractive patterned backs to the larger cards appearing then, and many of these cards are so decorated. The Lowell cards are included here to fill the volume. They are monochrome steel engravings, and bear the inscription "John A Lowell & Co, Boston, USA" sometimes preceded by "Engraved & copyrighted by ...".**

*Numbers 1-21 have cards by Prang.*

1. Eight page folder in blue and beige, showing the complications of the early telephone system in humorous style, with apt quotations from Shakespeare. The outside has a Christmas greeting. 1877. 10.8 cm x 5.7 cm.

2. Two folders.
a) A four page calendar for 1882 with New Year greeting, pictures of New Year as a child, and the Old Year as an aged man, in bright blues, greens and orange. There is a calendar inside and a verse by J Whittier, with flower and berry designs in green and cream. 9 cm x 9.8 cm closed.
b) "A visit from St Nicholas", a multi-page folder with verses from the well known poem written in 1822 by Dr Clement C Moore, illustrated by pictures. No date is visible, but this was probably printed before the Christmas card era, as it has the inscription "Published according to Act of Congress 1864", with advertisements on the outside for Prang's "Album cards", at 50 cents per dozen. 8.6 cm x 10.7 cm closed.

3. One card, Christ child sleeping, in circular vignette with lattice and holly around, and verse in wood style panel. 1878. 9.2 cm x 14.6 cm.

4. Five cards, on pale green ground with Christmas greeting in panel, one of an angel, one of a boy with a tree and robin, and three of winged cherubs with a bell and holly. One of these was used for a U S stamp in 1975 (example included). No date, but one was dated by the sender 1878. 6.4 cm x 13.2 cm.

5. One card, Christ child in the manger with gold star behind in a gold border with winged cherub heads, by Alfred Fredericks. The back has the inscription

"Prang's American 3rd prize, 1880, $300".
14.8 cm x 18.4 cm.

6. Easter card, fairies riding on butterflies
in a border of violets and buttercups, with
verse below. 1883. 10 cm x 15.8 cm.

7. One card, head of an angel with holly
and a Christmas verse and greeting, and a
sepia design of a church scene on reverse.
1884. 12.8 cm x 16.4 cm.

8. One card, elves on snowy branches in
gilt border with greetings and verse by
E S F, and a mistletoe design on reverse.
1881. 15 cm x 17.8 cm.

9. Two cards, winged cherubs, one in a
moon chariot drawn by an owl, the other
on a flowering branch feeding birds, with a
design of cherubs on reverse.  1882,
1883.15.7 cm x 11 cm, 16.5 cm x 11.5 cm.

10. Three cards, two of elves with
snowflakes set in winter scenes, one of
dwarfs hanging icicles on roof. They have
a decorative flower pattern on reverse.
1884. 18 cm x 12.8 cm.

11.Three cards, fairies on flowers. Two
have grey borders and the other is a
birthday card on silver ground. All have
verses in a panel. c1885. 11.4 cm x 7.4 cm,
13.6 cm x 8 cm.

12. Three cards on a beige ground printed
in light pastel colours, two of elves, the
third a group of six children. 1886.
11.2 cm x 8.6 cm, 18.2 cm x 8.7 cm.

13. Two illuminated Easter cards, children
and cherubs in floral settings, no date,
perhaps c1880. 15.8 cm x 10.5 cm.

14. A text card, with "Precepts" by Thomas
Randolph in a panel bordered by roses,
fuchsia, etc. 1877. 15 cm x 19 cm.

*Numbers 15-20 have cards with crosses on
plain unbordered mounts.*

15. Four Easter cards, three designs,
crosses with flowers, on grey or cream
ground, with text below. 1876.
8.9 cm x 15.5 cm.

16. Three Easter cards, floral crosses on
cream ground, text below. c1877.
11.6 cm x 19.4 cm.

17. Three cards, one Easter with a cross
covered with moss and flowers, two
Christmas with a gilt cross, and flowers
and ferns. 1876.
8.7 cm x 15.4 cm, 8.1 cm x 17.7 cm.

18. One card, a gold cross with lilies and
ferns. 1880. 12.3 cm x 18.5 cm.

19. Three cards, on pale blue ground, with
gold or silver crosses entwined with

**63.22**

flowers or ferns. 1880. 6 cm x 14.7 cm,
8.7 cm x 16.3 cm.

20. Three Easter cards on cream ground,
crosses with flowers, two with butterflies.
1878, 1879, 1881. Sizes up to
9.3 cm x 17 cm.

21. Four miscellaneous Easter cards, with
floral sprays, three with verses and one
with text. 1881 and 1885. 11.2 cm x 6.2 cm
up to 12.3 cm x 17 cm.

*Numbers 22-27 have cards published by J A
Lowell, all steel engravings in black and white.
They are marked "John A Lowell & Co, Boston
U S A", sometimes preceded by "Engraved and
copyrighted by ...", and are numbered. Where
date is not given, they can be taken as early
1880's.*

22. Four cards, two of comic children in
fancy dress, no. 22A, two of little girls
playing in snow, no. 22L. 1882.
11.7 cm x 7.8 cm, 14.4 cm x 10 cm.

23. Two cards, country scenes, one with
floral border, no. 425, one with two
cherubs in vignette, number illegible.
17.9 cm x 12.7 cm, 19.8 cm x 12.7 cm.

24. Four cards, two of country and sea
scenes, no. 276, and two of scenes in
vignettes, with holly or flowers, no. 9A.
11.6 cm x 7.2 cm, 11 cm x 10.7 cm.

25. Two cards, scenes in vignettes, with
bird on a branch, or child with umbrella.
Nos. 400, 401. 16.1 cm x 11.3 cm.

26. Two similar cards, no. 402.
15.1 cm x 10.3 cm, 16.1 cm x 11.3 cm.

27. Two shaped cards, one with a girl's
head and a stormy scene arranged in three
joined circles, no. 502, the other with a bird
and fan in a border with circular corners,

dated 1879. 15 cm x 12 cm,
10.5 cm x 10.5 cm.

## VOLUME 64:
## PRANG. CARDS WITH CHILDREN, LADIES, HUNTING, HUMOUR, AND ANIMALS

**Many of these cards have decorated
backs, and a number have verses of
widely varying quality.**

1. Four cards, signed E F M, plump happy
children in party and winter scenes, one
having Santa Claus in a brown robe, all
with greetings and verse on white border.
1878. 9.3 cm x 13.6 cm, 13.6 cm x 9.3 cm.

2. Two cards, one a girl with a doll on a
sledge, the other a boy pulling a girl on a
sledge with dog running beside. 1878,
1885.  9.1 cm x 14.6 cm,10.9 cm x 10.9 cm.

3. Four cards, quaint children in winter
scenes, on panel with a gilt patterned
border. 1879. 11.8 cm x 7.7 cm.

4. Three gilt-edged cards, two designs,
with Christmas and New Year verses in
panels with borders showing children in
Christmas scenes. Unsigned, c1880.
13.3 cm x 9.7 cm.

5. Two cards, grey border, one with two
children and sledges, the other with little
girl looking at Christmas stocking, in
illuminated borders with holly or flowers
and verses in panels. Unmarked, one dated
by the sender 1880. 11.2 cm x 14.1 cm.

6. A folding card, winged cherubs in blue
and gold with Christmas verse outside,
and a lady with dog and vignettes with
Christmas scenes and more verses inside.
Unmarked, c1880. 5.2 cm x 16 cm closed.

64.11

7. Three cards, two with children playing round a Christmas tree, the other with three children gathering holly. 1880. 14 cm x 9.1 cm.

8. One card, two well dressed children with carriage in waiting giving presents to poor children, in a gilt border with lilies, and a Christmas verse below and a picture on the back of a tree in snow. 1881. 16.6 cm x 13.2 cm.

9. Two identical cards, a baby's head in a circular vignette with Santa Claus behind, adorned by gilt toy bells. The second card is reversed to show a pattern of mistletoe with a bell. 1881. 14 cm x 17 cm.

10. Two cards, gilt borders, each showing three children in a square vignette, one with berries and bells, the other with holly and birds. The backs have a two-tone design of holly, with Christmas verses by E S F and K S B. 1881. 12.7 cm x 15.5 cm.

11. One card, "A modern Father Christmas", showing a negro servant delivering presents, with a glimpse of a lady's foot and sleeve emerging from a carriage. 1881. 12.7 cm x 15.5 cm.

12. One valentine card by Rosina Emmet, the picture of a lady in a red-brown dress picking roses, with gilt border and background. The reverse has a design of flowers in a vase, with Robert Burns poem "O my luve's like a red, red, rose". 1882. 10.7 cm x 17 cm.

13. One valentine card, a seated lady in mediaeval gown and a verse by Longfellow in a panel, with an attractive design on reverse. Marking indistinct, probably c1881. 11.7 cm x 18.3 cm.

14. One card, child by a fire, with verse and flower design on reverse. 13 cm x 19.4 cm.

15. Two valentine cards with gilt borders and verses, designed by L B C, one a girl with tulips, the other a boy and girl on a tree branch, with chrysanthemums. 1883. 10.9 cm x 12.9 cm, 15.4 cm x 11 cm.

16. Two valentine cards, one a boy offering flowers to a girl, the other a boy in a boat holding out a basket of waterlilies to a girl in another boat. 1884. 15.4 cm x 10.7 cm.

17. Two cards, one a girl's head in a circular vignette with daisies on a dark ground with red border, the other two girls in a summer scene with a holly design on reverse. 1883 and 1886. 12.2 cm x 13.2 cm, 10.7 cm x 13.7 cm.

18. Five miscellaneous cards of children, one Easter, dated 1877-1889. 8.9 cm x 8.9 cm up to 8 cm x 12.5 cm.

19. Two cards, one silk-fringed with country scene, and a design with girls head on reverse, and Christmas greeting. The other has the same country scene with New Year greeting, and is shown reversed to display the design. 1885. 11 cm x 13.7 cm.

20. Two cards, one with two children playing violins, the other with a little girl showing her presents to a group of rabbits. Perhaps by F S Church. 1883, 1881. 9.5 cm x 13.3 cm, 15.2 cm x 13.3 cm.

21. Two cards, one with two children and a baby in a cabbage patch, printed in red, the other two little girls carrying a satchel with a Christmas greeting. 1881 and 1886. 15.3 cm x 10.5 cm, 12.5 cm x 13.3 cm.

22. Three cards, a little girl and a dog chasing a lamb, a girl on a branch with an owl and a turkey, and a baby on a branch. 1885, 1883. Sizes up to 16.5 cm x 11.5 cm.

23. Two cards by Lizbeth B Humphrey, both of little girls with flowers, and two-tone designs on reverse. 1886. 9.6 cm x 13.8 cm and 9.2 cm x 15.9 cm

24. Three cards by Lizbeth B Comins, one of two girls singing carols, the others of little girls in snow scenes, two having decorative backs. 1885, 1887, 1889. (Buday queries whether these two artists are the same, but these dates appear to overlap). 13.9 cm x 9.5 cm, 6.4 cm x 10.2 cm, 9.3 cm x 17.1 cm.

25. One card, two girls in elegant hats and coats, on blue background with mistletoe sprays, and a chrysanthemum design on reverse. 1887. 13.9 cm x 18.9 cm.

26. Three cards, plain white ground, one an Easter card with children singing, one of a child with two cats, the other a cat in a doll's pram with the doll on the floor. 1886, 1888, 1890. Sizes up to 12.3 cm x 10 cm.

27. Five cards, hunting scenes with mishaps, by Phiz (H K Browne). 1879. 14 cm x 9.7 cm.

28. Two cards, one with a negro hat in hand signed F L B, the other a Japanese doll hanging from a mistletoe bough, with an unknown monogram. 1886 and 1885. 8.8 cm x 15.4 cm, 10 cm x 16.5 cm.

29. One card, a man and umbrella in snow, with verse. 1888. 10.7 cm x 13.7 cm.

30. One card, a sponge on a slate, with humorous verse. 1886. 15.1 cm x 9 cm.

31. Three comic cards, people and a bear in comic situations on the ice. 14 cm x 8.6 cm, 8.6 cm x 14 cm.

32. One card, "Baby Elephant's 1st Christmas", mother elephant giving toy elephant to baby elephant. 1881. 15.3 cm x 12.7 cm.

33. Three cards, one with a rabbit painting portraits of an elephant and a rhinoceros, signed F B, two others with rabbits and owls playing in moonlight and foxes and an owl with Christmas dinner. 1883, 1884. 12.9 cm x 9.5 cm, 16.6 cm x 9.9 cm.

34. One card, Bruin family with holly in a wood. 1884. 13.7 cm x 15.3 cm.

35. Two cards, one a pug dog with a lace collar, the other three foxes riding on the Yule log. 1878, 1888. 8 cm x 13 cm, 12.7 cm x 10.3 cm.

36. Three cards with humorous verses, a merry band of frogs, cats playing tricks on humans and a cat with kitten on its back harnessed to a sledge with a Christmas pudding. 1887, 1888, 1889. 9.7 cm x 6.8 cm, 13.3 cm x 9.2 cm, 15.3 cm x 8.7 cm.

37. A coy kitten in girlish dress "I merily wish with tender mew...". 1891. 9.6 cm x 16.3 cm.

38. Two cards with even worse verse - five pigs singing "This is the porcine carol clear", and a hamper of chicks "With tiny chirp and feeble trill ...". 1891. 15.7 cm x 9.3 cm.

39. Five miscellaneous cards including a trade card, 1879, and a rebus, 1889. 6.4 cm x 9.9 cm up to 14 cm x 7.9 cm.

## VOLUME 65: PRANG. BIRDS AND NESTS, SCENES, FINE CHINA WITH FLOWERS, SHELLS, SEAWEED

**The earlier cards here are small, but by 1880 are replaced by larger cards, some with well designed patterns on the reverse, and a number with curious combinations of flowers, vases and scenery.**

1. Two cards, water scenes of small birds with a heron, and a greeting in a central scroll. 1877. 6.2 cm x 10.5 cm.

2. Five cards, most likely from a set of six by Walter Satterlee, of various birds in flight or on branches, with greeting verses in panels. 1879. 12.2 cm x 7.8 cm.

3. Three cards, two designs of storks and nests with violets and hawthorn, against a scenic background, with a verse and greeting. 1879. 13.3 cm x 9 cm.

4. Four cards, similar to above, colourful Alpine flowers against a mountain background. 1879. 12.8 cm x 8.6 cm.

5. Three cards, birds' nests with eggs, on branches of blackberry, hawthorn, rose, and fir. 1879. 12.8 cm x 7.5 cm.

6. Four cards, two the same design of a bird on winter branches, signed O E W, probably Mrs O E Whitney, the others Easter cards with flowers, ferns, bird and butterfly. 1879.
7.1 cm x 15.2 cm, 7.4 cm x 16 cm.

7. Three cards, two of robins and other birds in snow, the other a brightly coloured bird on a flowering branch, this overprinted "Mawson, Swan and Morgan", a Newcastle-on-Tyne firm. 1879. 9.2 cm x 14.5 cm up to 10.3 cm x 14.6 cm.

8. Two cards, in Japanese style, birds on floral branches with purple borders. 1880. 13.2 cm x 11 cm, 13.5 cm x 11 cm.

9. One card, birds on frosted branches, with gilt border, and Christmas verse on gilt panel, the reverse with a design of birds and flowers. 1881. 12.4 cm x 20.1 cm.

10/11. Four cards, three designs of birds with nests surrounded by flowers and ferns, with greetings on a beige border and flower design on reverse. 1881.
10.8 cm x 16.2 cm.

12. Three cards, birds in winter scenes with verse below, and attractive design of apple blossom on reverse. 1882.
12.4 cm x 16.2 cm.

13/14. Five cards, two designs of two birds in circular vignettes, with a winter scene in a square panel, and verses by E S F, with a rose design on reverse. One card has a silk fringe. 1882. 12.8 cm x 17 cm.

15. Three birthday cards, two designs of river scenes in circular vignettes with flying swallows on blue ground, and design of birds in flight and trees on reverse. 1882. 16.8 cm x 10.4 cm.

16. Three cards, two of sea scenes with flying gulls, by F B, i.e. Fidelia Bridges, the other swallows against a red sunset, all

with interesting designs of birds on reverse. 1883. 20 cm x 9.6 cm, 9.6 cm x 18 cm.

17. One card, three exotic birds with blue plumage in a pleasing winter scene, with silver border, and a design of birds in flight on reverse. 1884. 17.8 cm x 12.9 cm.

18. Two cards, birds on floral branches, with green borders and a daffodil design on reverse, one by Giacomelli, the other by Fidelia Bridges. 1884. 11.5 cm x 19 cm.

19. Two cards, one by Fidelia Bridges with a bird on a branch entwined with convolvulus, the other of swallows on a thorny branch with a sea view, both with flower design on reverse. 1882, 1885. 11.7 cm x 17.7 cm, 11.1 cm x 20.7 cm.

20. Six miscellaneous cards, birds and birds' eggs, five dated 1878-1884, and one humorous card of two fowls, 1889. Sizes 9.2 cm x 6.3 cm up to 9.5 cm x 13.5 cm.

21. Three cards, two designs of ships in circular or fan-shaped vignettes, with trails of sea-weed on a pale green ground, with greeting in red below. 1880.
10.1 cm x 20.3 cm.

22. Two cards, one design of a two handled vase, and a winter scene in a vignette, with greeting below, on a pale green ground. One card is overprinted "Baird, Kelvinbridge, Glasgow", who was listed as a publisher by Buday. 1881.
10.7 cm x 16.9 cm.

23. Two cards, one a river scene in a circular vignette with a bunch of grapes, 1884, the other a sea scene in a circular vignette with a vase and a bowl of flowers, 1882. 17.9 cm x 12.7 cm, 19.3 cm x 10.2 cm.

24. Three cards, vases with flowers or feathers, one with a New Year verse, the others with a vase and flower design on reverse. 1882, 1881. 8.7 cm x 16 cm, 12 cm x 10.3 cm.

25. Three cards, with vases. Two have intricate background designs of flowers, ivy, and mistletoe, the other has a space for the sender's message. 1882, 1883. Sizes 12.5 cm x 7.8 cm up to 13.8 cm x 8.5 cm.

26. Three cards, two with winter scenes, the other with river scenes in two vignettes with waterlilies in the background. 1885, 1887, 1883. 15.1 cm x 10 cm, 15.4 cm x 9 cm, 16.2 cm x 11 cm.

27. Three birthday cards with shells and seaweed. 1878.
9.3 cm x 6.5 cm, 13.4 cm x 8.2 cm.

28. Three miscellaneous birthday cards, two with a river scene in vignette, the other with chrysanthemums and a flight of birds. 1882, 1884. 7.7 cm x 11 cm up to 12.8 cm x 10.7 cm.

29. A folding valentine card, silk fringed, the outside with two illuminated designs of flowering branches in vases against a highly decorated background of a window with curtains. Inside is a picture of a girl with a flowering tree, and a valentine verse, in silver borders. This could be by C C Coleman (see Volume 66, no. 22). 1882. 12.1 cm x 17.2 cm, closed, without fringe.

## VOLUME 66: PRANG. FLOWERS AND FERNS, HOLLY AND MISTLETOE

1. Four cards, on blue or beige ground, sprays of various flowers with greetings, verse or text in large panel. 1876.
10.4 cm x 15.6 cm.

2. Three cards, including a valentine, on pale green ground, one design of an open fan with roses on a lace shawl, and various greetings. 1876. 13.6 cm x 7.5 cm

3. Four cards, two designs of closed fans on a cream ground, one with roses and feather, the other with a cross and a vase of flowers, both on lace draperies. 1877.
13.6 cm x 7.5 cm.

4. Three birthday cards, pink flowers on a grey background, with greetings in a panel. 1877. 13.5 cm x 8 cm.

5. Five cards, (one Easter), four designs of spring flowers, and verses with illuminated initial. 1877. 13.6 cm x 8 cm.

6. Four cards, three designs of berries and flowers, with greeting below. 1877.
13.5 cm x 8 cm.

7. Two similar, with pansies and appleblossom. 1877. 13.5 cm x 8 cm.

8. Three cards, two with wreaths of spring flowers around a greeting verse, the other roses, with greeting on a ribbon scroll and a verse in a panel, on cream and blue grounds respectively. 1877, 1878.
12 cm x 13.3 cm, 15.9 cm x 10.5 cm.

9. Three cards, ferns, flowers, and berries on pale green ground with greetings on a log or a stone. 1878. 13.6 cm x 6.8 cm.

10. Three cards on beige ground, two with flower sprays, one with holly, and greetings and verses. 1878.
12.9 cm x 8.8 cm.

11. Three cards, flower sprays on gilt panel, with greetings and verse. 1879, 1880. 8.8 cm x 10.7 cm, 15.2 cm x 12 cm.

12. Seven cards (one birthday), on coloured ground with pink border, sprays of flowers, grasses, and catkins, probably from three different sets. Three have Christmas verses on scrolls, one a greeting

on a scroll and three have quotations from
Shakespeare. 1879. 5.7 cm x 14.4 cm.

13. Six cards, grey borders, Japanese style
designs of flower sprays with butterfly or
bee, picked out with gilt, on cream ground.
1880. 7 cm x 14 cm.

14. Six cards, spring flowers on a
background part black, part brown, with
greeting and verse. 1880.
7 cm x 3.2 cm up to 14.5 cm x 9 cm.

15. Five cards, sprays of flowers, ferns, and
holly, on coloured ground, with greetings.
Two cards have Shakespeare quotations.
1880. 6.2 cm x 17.3 cm.

16. Two cards, lily of the valley and
carnation sprays on small gilt panel, with
verses on a grey ground, one by A H B.
1880. 17.6 cm x 11.6 cm.

17. Four cards, three designs of spring
flowers on blue panel, in beige border,
with Christmas verses in red below. 1879,
1880. 11.2 cm x 15.3 cm.

18. Two cards, pansy and ivy, pinks and
ferns, on grey ground, one with
Shakespeare quotation. 1880.
17.7 cm x 11.5 cm.

19. Two cards (one birthday), bunches of
flowers and leaves on pale green ground.
Both have interesting backs, one a
landscape, the other an intricate design of
birds, pink flowers, and medallions, with
Christmas greeting. 1882, 1881.
18.1 cm x 10.5 cm, 18.8 cm x 12.2 cm.

20. One card, a bunch of pink flowers and
leaves on cream ground. 1881.
12.5 cm x 17.7 cm.

21. Five cards, three designs of baskets of
flowers, on fringed cushions, with
decorated backs. 1881. 11 cm x 10.6 cm.

22. Two cards, with gilt borders, butterfly
with crocuses, dandelions with insect.
c1880. 12.3 cm x 8.6 cm.

23. One card, the third prize design by C C
Coleman of $500, 1881. This is an elaborate
design of a cherry branch in a vase, with a
book, glass and flagon, against a highly
decorated background. The back shows
the prize award, with a verse by Celia
Thaxter. 18 cm x 23 cm.

24. Two folding cards, sprays of Spring
flowers and berries inside, and a leaf and
fern design in green and brown outside.
1881. 7.3 cm x 14.6 cm closed.

25. Two folding cards, one with flowers
and ferns inside with Christmas and New
Year verses in panels, and a leaf design
and greeting outside, the other silk
fringed, horseshoes with pansies and lily
of the valley inside and a conventional

design outside. 1881. 9.2 cm x 13.2 cm,
8.4 cm x 11 cm closed.

26/28. Three cards, each with a spray of
white flowers and grasses, on a blue panel
with a verse and a New Year greeting on a
beige border. The backs have a
monochrome design of berries and a girls
head. 1881. 12.3 cm x 22.2 cm.

29. One card, hollyhocks against a blue
sky, with an iris design and a verse by
E S F on reverse. 1882. 11.5 cm x 21.7 cm.

30. Two cards, pansies and daisies on a
cream ground, with a monochrome design
of birds on reverse. 1882.
12.1 cm x 14.6 cm.

31. Three cards, ferns and fungi on a plain
cream ground. c1880. 10.2 cm x 20.2 cm.

32. Two cards, one dog roses on a
background of ferns, the other carnations
with a border of berries, by E T F, and a
monochrome design on reverse. 1881.
10.2 cm x 12.7 cm, 12.9 cm x 11 cm.

33. One card, dog roses on a fern
background with greetings in a scroll, and
a design of berries on reverse. 1882.
10.4 cm x 19.4 cm.

34. Three cards, on coloured grounds, with
various flower sprays, one a birthday card
with decorated back. Early 1880's.
10.2 cm x 13.2 cm up to 10.2 cm x 18 cm.

35. One Easter card, pink and white
viburnum, by Ellen T Fisher, with a design
of irises on reverse. 1884. 12 cm x 21 cm.

36. One card, thistles with a bee, and a
monochrome design of birds outside a
curtained window on reverse. 1884.
13.2 cm x 22.3 cm.

37. Two cards, one a mixed bunch of
flowers with a bee, the other white berries
and a quotation from Shakespeare, by
Lizbeth B Humphrey. Both have decorated
backs. 1884, 1885. 16.5 cm x 13.2 cm,
18.2 cm x 9.5 cm.

38. Two valentine cards, clematis in a
cream border, and roses and violets on
gold and green, 1886, both with designs on
reverse.
15.3 cm x 13.7 cm, 18.5 cm x 13.3 cm.

39. Six miscellaneous cards with various
flower sprays, two having birthday
greetings. 1881-1884.
7.8 cm x 8.8 cm up to 7.5 cm x 17.7 cm.

# RAPHAEL TUCK

*Section*
*9*

The firm of Raphael Tuck published greeting cards from the early 1870's but few before 1880 have been found for this collection. In that year they held a prize competition for designers, followed by an exhibition in the Dudley Galleries in October 1880. In 1882 they commissioned a series from Royal Academicians, published for Christmas as the Royal Academy Series. Most of their cards are clearly marked and can be roughly dated. "Raphael Tuck, London" appears till about 1882, and the familiar easel and palette trade mark, with "London registered", is seen from about 1880-83. The prize winners of 1880 were distinguished by the addition of "Prize design" to the trade marks, and those cards chosen for publication from the exhibition had "Prize Exhibition design", or series, added. There was a "Prize Painters" series in the early 1880's, "Artist series" at various times, "Mizpah" series of religious cards, and the cards were also labelled "Artistic Series" (abbreviated in the text as A.S.) from the early 1880's and sometimes numbered. By the late 1880's, the easel and palette trade mark was often accompanied by cherubs. Cards marked "Raphael Tuck and Sons" appear here dated from 1881 by the senders.

In 1893 the firm received the Royal Warrant as publishers to Queen Victoria, and this appears on the backs of cards from this date, and was continued in the 20th century for King Edward and Queen Alexandra. By 1890 cards included "Designed at the Studios in England and printed at the Fine Art Works in Saxony" (later Germany, Bavaria, or Berlin). Many artists have been identified, including most of the prizewinners listed by Gleeson White, but some monograms have not been traced. The verses, or sentiments, were made an important feature by this firm, and the writers have been listed in detail, by initials, most of which can be identified by reference to the appendix of writers included with this catalogue. More than 60 names have been noted, apart from quotations from classical writers.

Tuck frequently issued the same design in different sizes over a period of years. Dating from the series numbers is difficult, as many cards had no numbers, and different series had fresh sets of numbers, but it is hoped that the approximate dates as given here are reasonably accurate, and that the twenty-seven volumes following, only a small fraction of Tuck's tremendous output, will give a fair idea of its range and scope. The firm continued well into the 20th century, but has now been incorporated into the Fine Arts Developments Company.

67.1

## VOLUME 67: RAPHAEL TUCK. PRIZE DESIGNS, 1880, & PRIZE EXHIBITION CARDS, FEATURING PEOPLE & CHILDREN

**The attributions here are deduced from Gleeson White's "Christmas Cards and their Chief Designers".**

1. An advertisement folder for 1883-4, with press comments on Tuck's recent cards. 10.2 cm x 13.5 cm closed.

*Numbers 2-11 have designs that won prizes in Tuck's 1880 competition. The trade mark on the reverse has "prize design" inserted.*

2. Four cards by Alice Squire, 1st prize, showing single children or lady in woodland scenes, with verses on reverse by E H, F L and J M S. 10 cm x 13.8 cm.

3. Three cards by Harriett M Bennett, 3rd prize, with single ladies in spring, summer and winter on gilt ground. 11.4 cm x 16.5 cm.

4. Three cards by Patty Townshend, 3rd prize, groups of village children in various scenes, with verses by E H and J M S on reverse. 9.6 cm x 13.8 cm.

5. Folding card by R.J.Abraham, 5th prize, two ladies in classical dress outside, verse by F L inside. Registered at Stationers' Hall 2-5-1881. 8.3 cm x 15.2 cm closed.

6. One card by K Terrell, 6th prize (set of three?), a lady and child in Greenaway style in a garden, with verse by F R on reverse. 12.8 cm x 10.4 cm

7/8. Six cards by Rebecca Coleman, from a set of three designs of angel's heads which won a 7th prize. There are two sizes, with various captions, and the verses on the back are by E H and A J F. These are the cards which Gleeson White said "almost broke the record for popular success". 11.6 cm x 13.5 cm, 9.7 cm x 11.2 cm.

9. Two cards by George Clausen, R A, 7th prize, country folk in summer and winter, one with verse by F L on reverse. 16.3 cm x 11 cm.

10. Two cards by Helen J Miles, 7th prize, circular vignettes with grandmother or mother and child, on illuminated background, and verses by J C and F L on reverse. 10.5 cm x 10.5 cm.

11. One card by Marian Croft, 7th prize, a child on a leafy background, with verse by F L on reverse. 10.1 cm x 15.3 cm.

*Numbers 12-26 show cards exhibited in the Dudley Gallery after the prize competition. The trade marks have "prize exhibition design" inserted, but these must not be confused with the actual prize winning cards.*

12. Six cards, a set of figures in historical dress, one reversed to show an advertisement for the exhibition. The others have verses by F R on reverse. 7.5 cm x 13.8 cm.

13. One card, Mother and Child in vignette in an illuminated border with angels, and a design on reverse in the manner of Prang. Possibly by H J Miles. 11.8 cm x 16.4 cm.

14. Three cards, one Easter, angel figures in romantic lake and mountain scenes, with verse and greeting. 16.3 cm x 11 cm.

15. Two cards, female figures in classical dress in romantic scenes, with verse and greetings. 11.8 cm x 16.3 cm.

16/17. Four cards, three designs, with groups of Cupids engaged in making music and cooking the Christmas dinner. Verses by F R and F L are on the backs. 16.3 cm x 11 cm.

18. Five cards, three designs with varied captions, attractive child figures in red and brown in snow, with silver sky and gilt border, and verses by F R on reverse. 11.7 cm x 8.9 cm.

19. Set of four cards, girls and boys in party games, with appropriate verses on reverse by F R. 13.3 cm x 10.1 cm.

20. Three cards, two designs of children, in summer, or skating in winter, with greetings in illuminated borders. 17.4 cm x 5.4 cm.

21. Two cards, single ladies in snow against a gilt sky. 9.7 cm x 14.5 cm.

22. One card, a lady in an apron with a Japanese parasol, holding flowers, in a silver border. 10.8 cm x 14 cm.

23. Six cards, four designs perhaps by J M Morse, little girls in snow or at play. Two cards are reversed to show verses by F L and F R. 9.5 cm x 14 cm.

24. Three cards, two designs, garden boys in vignettes with a house in the background, and verses by E H on reverse. 15.3 cm x 7.3 cm.

25. Two cards, boys in a hammock, with drum or trumpet on ground, in illuminated border, and verses by L W on reverse. 14 cm x 8.2 cm.

26. Two cards by A L Vernon, one with a couple under the mistletoe, the other a lady in a fur trimmed coat with a robin. The first card is illustrated in "Love Knots and Bridal Bonds", published by R Tuck, and the other was one out of four registered at Stationers' Hall 27-6-1882, not a prize exhibition card, but labelled "London registered". 11 cm x 15 cm, 12.4 cm x 18.4 cm.

*Numbers 27-39 have cards designed by the prizewinners, and are mostly labelled "Artistic Series" (A S) dated from 1883 on, though some were registered before this.*

27/28. Six cards by Alice Squire in two sizes, ladies in woodland scenes, with verses by F L, E H, on reverse. These are six out of eight designs registered at Stationers' Hall 27-6-1882. 12 cm x 16.5 cm, 9 cm x 11.8 cm.

29. One card by H M Bennett, a child in bed, with a black cat, one out of two designs registered at Stationers' Hall 27-6-1882. 11 cm x 13.7 cm.

30. Four cards, three designs by H M Bennett, single children in outdoor scenes, with gilt borders and flowers. 11 cm x 14 cm.

31. Four cards by H M Bennett, children in outdoor scenes, with floral borders. 10.3 cm x 13.4 cm.

32. Two cards, possibly by H M Bennett, one a girl and boy in a field, the other a girl in a swing, with verses by F L and S K C. 10.2 cm x 13.7 cm, 11.7 cm x 13.5 cm.

33. Three cards by H M Bennett, loving couples in country scenes or by the sea. One is marked A S 1568 with verse by E H on reverse, another is marked "London registered", with verse by F L. 11.7 cm x 16.4 cm.

34. Five cards by H M Bennett, two designs of heads of boy and girl on gilt ground,

with blue, red, or black borders. 11.7 cm x 11.7 cm.

35. Three similar, heads of boy or girl, signed H M B, with wide blue or brown border. 11 cm x 11 cm.

36. One card, possibly by H M Bennett. Child's head in frilled bonnet, on gilt ground, with blue fancy border, and verse by F L on reverse. 9.4 cm x 9.4 cm.

37/38. Eleven cards possibly by H M Bennett. Six designs of a single boy or girl in snow, with a gilt sky, in two sizes. Verses by E H, F R, F L, are on the reverse. 10.7 cm x 13.7 cm, 7.4 cm x 10.5 cm.

39. Four cards, possibly by Marian Croft. Two designs of girls on a leafy background, and one of a sailor boy. 9 cm x 12 cm.

## VOLUME 68: RAPHAEL TUCK. THE ROYAL ACADEMY SERIES, AND MORE CARDS BY WELL KNOWN ARTISTS

*Numbers 1-6 have cards by Royal Academicians, five specially designed for the R A series of 1882. "The sales were not perhaps as high as expected, but they raised the popular reputation of Christmas card art." (Buday). The cards are in the "Royal Academy Series".*

1. A folding card by W F Yeames R A, with two designs of a lady with caged cupids within, and two designs of single cupids on the outside. These are four designs from eight registered at Stationers' Hall 27-6-1882. 11.8 cm x 16.3 cm closed.

2. A card by Edward John Poynter, R A, "Winter Cherries", a lady at her toilet in an elaborate gilded setting, with verse on reverse by E H. This is one of two cards registered at Stationers' Hall 27-6-1882. 11.9 cm x 18 cm.

3. Four cards, two designs in two sizes, by W C T Dobson, R A, R W S, one of a girl with a Christmas rose head-dress, the other with holly, registered at Stationers' Hall 27-6-1882. 11.8 cm x 16.3 cm, 8.8 cm x 11.8 cm.

4. Three cards by J Sant, R A, heads of small angels against a blue sky, with gilt borders, and a verse by E H on the back of the larger cards. 13.7 cm x 13.7 cm, 10.5 cm x 10.5 cm.

5. Two cards, one design, by Marcus Stone, R A, a lady in white seated in a garden, one out of four registered at Stationers' Hall 27-6-1882. 11.8 cm x 16.3 cm.

6. Three cards, (one birthday), ladies in spring, summer, and autumn, with appropriate flowers in a panel, perhaps three out of four registered at Stationers' Hall 1-6-1886 by Marcus Stone, R A. There

are verses by E H in elaborate gilded borders on the reverse. 10.5 cm x 15.5 cm.

*The following cards are by other well known artists and illustrators; most are marked "Artistic Series", some with numbers, and are dated in the 1880's.*

7/8. Two large cards by Alice Havers, 1881, boy and girl picnicking in a wood, with verses by E H and F L and a floral design on reverse. London registered. 22.8 cm x 12.9 cm.

9. One large card by Alice Havers, the Madonna and Child, with a verse by W W. A S 2725. 24.1 cm x 18.4 cm.

10. One card, a coy fairy child by W S Coleman, with a bird picture on reverse. 15.7 cm x 12.5 cm.

11. Two cards by Louisa, Marchioness of Waterford, a girl holding flowers, and a boy with holly, both in period costume. 9.5 cm x 14.5 cm.

12. Three cards, two designs in two sizes, by Emily Barnard, girls in white draperies, with verses by F L and E H and a monochrome design on reverse and verses by E H and F L. A S 1556. 18.2 cm x 11.5 cm, 11.6 cm x 8.9 cm.

13. Three cards, two designs in two sizes, by Emily Barnard, boys in sailor dress, with verses by E H and F L on reverse. A S 1282. 12 cm x 16.5 cm, 8.5 cm x 12 cm

14. Two cards by Emily Barnard, young girls in party dress holding holly or mistletoe, with verse by E H and monochrome picture on reverse. These are labelled A S 109, 1540, though similar in format and design, but different sizes. 10.3 cm x 17.7 cm, 7 cm x 12 cm.

15. Four cards, two designs, scantily draped maidens in the W S Coleman manner, two being reversed to show verses by F R, E H. These answer to the description of two cards registered at Stationers' Hall 27-6-82 by Robert Herdman, R S A. 7.7 cm x 15.3 cm.

16. One card by W Dendy Sadler, a convivial gentleman by a table, with a bottle of wine and a glass, one out of four registered at Stationers' Hall 12-10-1881. 13 cm x 17.3 cm.

17. One card signed J M Morse, a girl in white with a dove, the reverse having a floral design and a verse by S K C. A S 1483. 10.2 cm x 15.2 cm.

18. Four cards signed C P, probably Caroline Paterson, three designs of a girl and a boy with a doll. A narrative verse by S K C tells the story of how the boy cut the doll's hair. One card is a later version with holly. 13.5 cm x 11.5 cm, 11 cm x 8 cm.

**68.20**

19. Two cards, one of a girl with toys and a Christmas stocking, by R F McIntyre, the other of a girl with a basket of flowers, signed I Mc, numbered A S 248, with a verse by H M B on reverse.
10.7 cm x 12.8 cm, 9 cm x 13.5 cm.

20. Two cards, cut-out and pierced designs of children, one by H S with a verse by H M B on reverse, the other two sided, by R F McIntyre, both c1890. 11.7 cm x 16.8 cm, 16.4 cm x 11.8 cm.

21. One card by M E Edwards, a girl and a dog in an autumn scene, with verse by E H on reverse in a patterned border.
9.5 cm x 12.9 cm.

22. Two cards, attractive girls in red in snow scenes, probably by M E Edwards, with the same design as Vol 68 no 21 on reverse and verses by F E E H and L M L.
10.3 cm x 13.5 cm.

23/24. Two large cards by Edith B Salaman, girls head and shoulders, "Juliet", "Marguerite", with well designed illuminated borders of peacock feathers, and a flower and bird design on reverse. The border has the monogram C A P.
16 cm x 22.3 cm.

25. Three cards by Edith B Salaman, girls' heads with leaf behind - "Mignon", "Marguerite", "La Sonnambula".
9.2 cm x 13.7 cm.

26. Two cards by Edith B Salaman, one plain with a girls head in autumn leaves "Autumn", the other a folder, "La Sonnambula", with verses and design of grasses in gilt at the side and on the outside. 9.9 cm x 15 cm, 10 cm x 15 cm closed. These four sheets show four out of eight designs registered at Stationers' Hall 1-6-1886.

27. Two cards signed G S, possibly George Sadler, a boy in snow, and a girl with a Punch figure. 9.2 cm x 14.2 cm, 10.3 cm x 13.5 cm.

28. Two cards by E J Harding, on thick pasteboard, girls representing Scotland and Ireland, probably from a set of four, with two-tone picture on reverse. c1890.
11.6 cm x 16.2 cm.

29. Five cards, Kate Greenaway style figures, four reward cards unmarked and a fifth Happy New Year card repeating one design, signed E H - Emma Hardy. This set has been recorded as by Kate Greenaway, but the fifth card establishes its provenance. A S 2048.  6.6 cm x 4.9 cm, 4.9 cm x 6.6 cm, 11.7 cm x 8.8 cm.

30. Two cards, one by W J Webb of Father Christmas with a sleeping child, the other by J W Grey, of children hanging up stockings. 10.5 cm x 15 cm

31. Two cards by W Gilbert Foster, two girls in a country scene, with a verse of greeting by F G. Late 1880's.
14.9 cm x 11 cm.

32. Four cards, monochrome designs by Helena J Maguire, one a girl hanging Christmas greenery, and three with children in outdoor summer scenes, marked A S 247, A S 328, with verses on reverse by H M B.
11 cm x 15.7 cm, 11 cm x 13.5 cm.

33/34. Nine cards by Eliza Ann Cook, children at school and in outdoor scenes. Some unnumbered, others marked A S 256, 355. Late 1880's.  9.5 cm x 8.2 cm up to 14.5 cm x 10.6 cm.

35. Three cards by Eliza Ann Cook, two with a couple on a park bench, A S 2106, and one a girl in Georgian dress playing the harp, A S 3345.
13 cm x 9.3 cm, 9.3 cm x 14.4 cm.

## VOLUME 69:
## RAPHAEL TUCK. WINTER AND CHRISTMAS SCENES WITH CHILDREN

**This volume has cards with seasonal subjects, though a summer scene may be included in a set. They are dated mainly from 1880-90, with various trade marks, and an occasional prize exhibition design.**

1. Four cards, three designs of children skating or sledging, with verses by F L on reverse. Prize exhibition design, 1880. 11.3 cm x 7.7 cm.

2. Six cards, five designs of children outdoors, one with a penny-farthing bicycle. These could be by Felix Dussert, who designed many cards for Augustus Thierry. Late 1870's. 7 cm x 11 cm.

3. Four cards, unprepossessing figures of children, on gilt ground, marked no. 1940. 7 cm x 10.4 cm.

4. Six cards, four designs of children, in a boat, blowing bubbles, by a wall, and on a high chair with doll. Two cards are reversed to show verses by F R. 8.8 cm x 11.7 cm.

5. Six cards, four designs of children with toys, on gilt and silver ground. Two cards are reversed to show verses by F R. Marked "original design". 7.5 cm x 11.3 cm.

6. Three cards, two designs, one of two children on ice, the other three children in their nursery, with verse by F R on reverse. One marked London registered. 8 cm x 12.2 cm.

7. Two cards, a girl with a hoop, a boy with a football. 8 cm x 12.2 cm.

8. Two cards, a girl circus rider, a girl in a goat carriage, with verses by F L on reverse. A S. 11.7 cm x 8.8 cm.

9. Two cards, small children playing at shop, and having a tea party. A S 1203. 8 cm x 6.9 cm.

10. Three cards, children, with a blackboard, singing carols, playing in a band. A S. One card was dated 1883 by the sender. 8.7 cm x 8.2 cm.

11. Three cards, girls in rectangular vignettes, with holly, ivy, or mistletoe surround. Two have verses on reverse by E G, A S 232, the third has a snowman and a verse by S K C, A S, K series no. 440. 9 cm x 14 cm, 10.2 cm x 15 cm.

12. Three cards, demure children, two with girls in fur trimmed coats, one of two boys on a swing, perhaps by J M Morse. No trade mark. 10.8 cm x 12.8 cm.

13. Four similar cards, three with groups of girls and boys, London registered, and one of a girl skipping, marked "Prize Exhibition". Possibly by J M Morse. 10.8 cm x 12.8 cm.

14. Two similar, one with group of children at a party, the other a girl with battledore and shuttlecock, and verse by F R on reverse. Possibly by J M Morse. 10.8 cm x 12.8 cm.

15. Three cards, children with Christmas provender, signed E M R, London registered, girl knocking at door marked M C or C M, A S 323, and a boy's head with light curly hair, by Emily J Harding, with verse by S K C on reverse, A S 113. 13.2 cm x 9.5 cm, 9.1 cm x 15.2 cm, 8 cm x 11.1 cm.

16. Four cards (one a valentine), three designs of girls' heads and shoulders, one in a blue bonnet, A S 1284 and verse by S K C, one in a mob cap, and one with a bandeau, verse by H M B, prize exhibition design. 9 cm x 12 cm, 9.6 cm x 13.3 cm, 8.7 cm x 11.8 cm.

17. Two cards, babies' heads in a colourful background, with verse by F L on the back of one. These are signed E F, possibly Elizabeth Folkhard and marked A S, D. 10.1 cm x 12.4 cm.

18. Four cards, all the same design of a small girl head and shoulders. One is larger, in a circular vignette with flower and butterfly border, and the others have varied greetings. London registered, c1881. 10 cm x 15 cm, 7 cm x 10.5 cm.

19. Two cards, one of two children making and arranging holly garlands, with verse by H M B and a bird design on reverse, A S, 13.8 cm x 10.3 cm, and another of boys teasing a dog, A S, with verse by Helen of Troy, 16.8 cm x 8 cm.

20. One card, boy in tree with robin nearby, and a verse by E H on reverse with a design of two children in a circular vignette. A S, 11 cm x 11.2 cm.

21. Five miscellaneous cards, children and babies in various indoor situations, all with verses on reverse, three numbered 1202, 110, 2025. Mid 1880's? 7.4 cm x 10.3 cm up to 12.7 cm x 7.7 cm.

22. Three cards, girls', head and shoulders, one marked London registered 7.7 cm x 11 cm.

23. Four cards, two of children with dogs, verse by H M B on reverse, A S 129, one of a girl by a window looking at snow, A S 1269, and one of a girl riding, A S 151. 9.3 cm x 12 cm, 8.8 cm. x 11.7 cm.

24. Four miscellaneous cards of boys, one riding, verse by H M B, A S no 95H, one

**68.29**

feeding a donkey, verse by H M B, dated by sender 1889, one on ice with a dog, A S 2123, the fourth a Harrow boy, A S. 8 cm x 10.5 cm up to 13 cm x 15.4 cm.

25. One card with serrated edges, by W J W Nunn, two boys on ice, marked A S. c1890. 9 cm x 13 cm.

26. Five miscellaneous cards, two in correspondence style with space for sender's name (one A S 283), one in Japanese style, A S 3088, and two of elegant maidens, with serrated edges (one with Royal Warrant Trade Mark). Late 1880's to 1895. Sizes up to 8 cm x 12.8 cm.

27. Set of four cards, serrated edges, girls with garlands or a shuttlecock, or dancing with a boy, signed J W, c1895. 8.5 cm x 12.5 cm.

28. Five cards, serrated edges, three of girls at play, with Royal Warrant Trade Mark, c1895, and two of Georgian couples, A S. c1890. 8 cm x 12 cm, 14.3 cm x 7.8 cm, 12.5 cm x 9 cm.

29. One postcard, by Florence K Upton, procession of dolls with golliwog (by permission of Longman Green and Co). Postmark 22-12-1904. 13.9 cm x 9.3 cm.

## VOLUME 70: RAPHAEL TUCK. CHILDREN WITH FLOWERS, AT THE SEASIDE AND IN COUNTRY SCENES.

**Most of these cards were published in the 1880's with a few exceptions as stated. Some artists are identified, though a few monograms have not been traced. Some cards are labelled "Prize Exhibition Series".**

1. Two embossed cards, little girls with flowers, one marked R T London. Late 1870's. 7.2 cm x 10.7 cm.

2. Four cards, girls in flowing draperies, with verses on scrolls and flower decoration, one labelled R Tuck, all numbered 1885. One was dated by the sender 1879. 7.8 cm x 13.3 cm.

3. Four cards, two sizes, three designs of children's faces in flowers, with verses by E H, F L , F R on reverse. c 1881. 11 cm x 15.6 cm, 7.8 cm x 12.3 cm.

4. Four cards, two designs of a small girl in a cornfield or a field with flowers, with varied greetings, marked R T London registered.12.8 cm x 10.7 cm.

5. Two cards, children in a garden with dogs, one dated by the sender 1881. London registered. 11.8 cm x 8.3 cm.

6. Two cards, children in a summer scene with geese, signed F A R, with verse by F L on reverse. A S 1292. 12.8 cm x 10.1 cm.

7. Two cards, one a boy attacked by geese, the other a boy in a hayfield playing a pipe, with a mother and baby. A S. 13.6 cm x 10.3 cm, 15.3 cm x 10.3 cm.

8. Two cards, children playing by the sea, signed E C G '81, possibly E C Gardner, but marked A S 1335. 13.5 cm x 10.3 cm.

9. Two cards, children at seaside, monogram W G H, with a bird picture on the reverse of one card. A S. 13.5 cm x 11.7 cm.

10. Three cards (one birthday), two designs of children wading in the sea, signed with monogram W G H. A S 1294. 9.5 cm x 9.5 cm.

**70.3**

11. Two cards, boys by the sea, one with a toy yacht, and verses by F F and S K C and a floral design on reverse. A S 1309. 9.5 cm x 12.6 cm.

12. Two cards, girls seated on a bench with a dog or cat, marked "prize painter series". 10.2 cm x 15.2 cm.

13. Three cards with girls, two in a garden by a wall with birds, and the third a girl skipping. One card is marked "prize exhibition series", with a verse by E H on reverse. 8.5 cm x 14 cm, 9.4 cm x 14.3 cm.

14. Three cards, plump little girls in bonnets in a garden, with verses by E H, F R, on reverse. One is marked "prize exhibition series". 9 cm x 13.5 cm.

15. Two cards, the same design of "Bo Peep", one with a Christmas verse by H M B, the other with a birthday verse by S K C. A S 2113. 8.9 cm x 13 cm.

16. Four cards, two with small girls and geese, or a doll, marked "London registered", two of girls in a garden by a fence, one with a cat, marked A S. 7 cm x 10.3 cm.

17. Two cards, children by the sea with a lighthouse, jetty, and bathing van in the background, and verse by F R on reverse. Prize exhibition series. 11.7 cm x 8.9 cm.

18. Four cards, two with a girl and a cat in a garden and a boy by the sea with a dog, and two with a single boy by the sea. All are signed with a monogram E C G (not the same signature as in no. 8), possibly E C Gardner. A S 1351, A S 1212. 9 cm x 14.3 cm, 8.2 cm x 12 cm.

19. One card, boy in sailor suit, signed H S J. A S 2167. 8.9 cm x 13.5 cm.

20. Five cards, two with children on a bridge sailing a toy boat, three others with two children by a stile. London registered. 8.9 cm x 12.5 cm, 6.2 cm x 11.3 cm.

21. Four cards, three with boys and flowers, one a girl with a fan. London registered. 5.4 cm x 8.8 cm.

22. Two cards, the same design of two girls with a horse, signed by a monogram E C A, with a verse by S K C on reverse. A S. 13.6 cm x 10.3 cm.

23. Three cards, two of girls by the sea, one of a sailor boy in a ship's rigging, signed Harry Payne. The first two have verses by E H and S K C on reverse, marked A S 1218, the third is A S 385. 7 cm x 11 cm, 11 cm x 15 cm.

24. Two cards, one a girl by the sea wearing flower wreaths, with a butterfly, the other a girl and a dog by a pond with ducks. London registered. 8 cm x 10.8 cm, 8.9 cm x 11.8 cm.

25. Two cards, one a girl in a wood with a butterfly, A S 1229, the other a Kate Greenaway style girl with a lily of the valley border, and a verse by F L, A S 1296. 7 cm x 10 cm, 8.5 cm x 11.8 cm.

26. One card, a boy harnessed to a two wheel cart, pulling two girls, with verse by H M B on reverse. A S 1233. 11.7 cm x 9 cm.

27. Three cards, a part set of single children, two of girls by the sea, the other a boy with umbrella. This is marked with the Royal Warrant to King Edward VII and Queen Alexandra, probably c1902. 8 cm x 11 cm.

## VOLUME 71:
## RAPHAEL TUCK. CHRISTMAS SCENES, COSTUME, SCENES WITH PEOPLE, ELEGANT LADIES, PHOTOGRAPHIC

1. Three cards, two sizes, a Santa Claus face framed in holly and branches. Though these appear to be one set, they are numbered differently, AS 420, signed Mc, with verse by F L on reverse, AS 2356, with verse by H M B, and a smaller size AS 2081, signed Mc, with verse by H M B. 12.3 cm x 16.4 cm, 9.3 cm x 12.2 cm.

2. Two cards, watchmen in snow, one with a dog. One is marked A S 1550 with a verse by F L on reverse. 11.6 cm x 16.5 cm.

3. Two cards, men in the snow, one with a wooden leg carrying a goose, the other with two dogs and a bag of game. One is marked A S 1485, with an unsigned verse on reverse. 10 cm x 15.2 cm.

4. Three cards, two designs, one two boys dragging a Christmas log, the other an old man playing the violin, with a small child, outside an inn in the snow. London registered.14 cm x 10.7 cm.

5. Two cards, one a man driving a donkey cart, verse by F L on reverse, A S, the other

a stage coach, dated by the sender 1883. 13.4 cm x 10.3 cm, 13 cm x 10.3 cm.

6. A card showing carol singers outside a window with people looking out. Verse by Canon Bell on reverse. A S 408. 10.8 cm x 14.2 cm.

7. A folder card, with two pictures outside of scantily draped cherubs bearing the Christmas feast, and decorating the hall, and a snow scene with birds inside. 11.6 cm x 16.5 cm closed.

8. Three cards, colourful scenes from Shakespeare, c1880. 11.6 cm x 15.5 cm.

9. One card, a lady and child in classical dress by a column, looking out to sea. London registered. 9 cm x 16.8 cm.

10. Set of four cards, Elizabethan characters in festive scenes, with gilt backgrounds, and appropriate quotations from Shakespeare. Marked R T London. c1880. 16.2 cm x 9.6 cm.

11. One card, Georgian ladies by a fireside. A S, late 1880's. 11.5 cm x 16 cm.

12. Three cards, two designs of ladies in autumn and winter on gilt ground with floral or holly decorations. One has a verse by E H on reverse and is marked London registered. 16.5 cm x 8.3 cm.

13. Four cards, three of milkmaids with cows and one of farmer feeding calves, with verses by H M B on reverse. A S. 11 cm x 13.7 cm.

14. Two cards signed W F C, one of two horsemen riding through snow, the other a man on horseback greeting a lady with a basket, verses by F L on reverse. A S. 13.5 cm x 11 6.cm.

15. One card, by G F Wetherbee, R I, R O I, a man and woman on a bridge over a stream, with verse by F L on reverse in a two-tone design of a palette with flowers. A S. 11 cm x 16.4 cm.

16. Two cards, family groups, one in autumn, one in winter, with a verse by F R on reverse, one dated 1882 by the sender. Marked "original design". 10 cm x 13 cm.

17. Two cards, the same design of two ladies sitting by a river, one reversed to show verse by F R. Marked R T, London. 9 cm x 12 cm.

18/19. Three cards, country scenes in summer with mother and children, signed with monogram C M or M C. Verses by H M B and J E W are on the back. A S 2456. 16.5 cm x 11 cm.

20. Two cards, ladies and children in country scenes, with verse by F L on the

back of one which was dated by the sender 1882, marked London registered. 10.4 cm x 4.2 cm.

21/22. Four cards of extremely elegant ladies, two with dogs, one with a baby, one in aesthetic pose before an easel. Two cards have verses by H M B on reverse. A S, I series 495. 12 cm x 16.5 cm.

23. Two cards, elegant lady in the centre surrounded by five comic figures, with verse by E H on reverse. A S. 12 cm x 11 cm.

24. A set of three cards, ladies in a garden in heart-shaped vignettes, with verse below. Two are marked A S, one London registered. 10.2 cm x 15 cm. (See Vol. 89, no 22 for a fourth card in this set).

25. Two cards, ladies in elaborate evening dress in richly decorated rooms. One has a verse by F L on reverse, the other was dated 1888 by the sender. 11 cm x 15.8 cm.

26. One card, head and shoulders of a pensive lady leaning on a table, with a gushing verse of praise on reverse. A S. 16.4 cm x 12 cm.

27. One card, a pen and ink design of a lady's head, entitled "Vivien", signed Creswell Woollett, dated by the sender 1887. This is not marked, but was probably published by R Tuck. 12 cm x 16.4 cm.

28/29. Four cards, various groups of children in photographic style, coloured, with greetings below on brown borders. One card, marked A S 2305, was dated by the sender 1891. 10.8 cm x 16.6 cm.

30. Three miscellaneous cards, a couple in church, with verse by F L on reverse, marked A S 29, a couple kissing behind a fan, with verse by E M C, marked A S 1307, and a couple with a tricycle, by G H Edwards, marked A S 2225. Sizes up to 9.7 cm x 13.8 cm.

## VOLUME 72: RAPHAEL TUCK. CARDS DESIGNED BY R F MCINTYRE, W J HODGSON, AND W J WIEGAND, WITH PEOPLE AND CHILDREN, DATED IN THE 1880'S

*Numbers 1-10 have cards by R F McIntyre, signed unless otherwise stated.*

1. Three cards, two designs, Christmas without and within, outdoor scenes of churchgoers and watchman with vignettes showing party scenes. One card is reversed to show one of three verses by F L. A S 1573. 11.7 cm x 16.3 cm.

2/3. Four cards, three designs, two of a man struggling in a snowdrift, and one of

**71.1**

an old man and a girl waving from the door of a cottage. Three cards are proof copies with design only, the fourth has a verse by F L on the back, and is marked A S 1583. 16.3 cm x 11 cm.

4. One card, a man leading a donkey laden with holly. A S. 13.5 cm x 10.2 cm.

5. A set of four cards, telling the story of two boys in their Sunday suits who fell in the water while fishing, with verses by F L on reverse. A S 215. 9.5 cm x 12.6 cm.

6. Three cards, two designs, "A trip to the Moon", showing the adventures of two men in a boat. The backs of the cards, with verses by F L telling the story, are damaged. A S. 9.8 cm x 13.4 cm.

7/8. Five cards, unsigned, four of these with an old man and a boy in a snowstorm appear to agree with the Stationers' Hall registration 27-6-1882, though one is labelled "Prize exhibition design" with a verse by F L on the back. The fifth card has a verse by F L on the back, and is marked A S 1464. 14.4 cm x 11 cm, 15.3 cm x 10.1 cm.

9. Two cards, an elderly man sleeping by the sea, and being rescued from the incoming tide by a sailor, with verses by F L on the backs telling the story. A S. 9.4 cm x 14.5 cm.

10. Four cards, one of a man with a donkey, A S 398, one a man with a pig, A S 2288, one of two sandwich board men, A S 120, and the fourth two boys snowballing an elderly man, A S 2024. All have verses by F L on reverse. 10.1 cm x 15.3 cm, 7.8 cm x 11 cm.

*Numbers 11-16 have cards by W J Hodgson.*

11. Four cards, The Hunt, showing the mishaps of a rider. Prize exhibition design, c1880. 15.2 cm x 10.1 cm.

12. One card, a country couple in a donkey cart. London registered. 16.5 cm x 11.4 cm.

13. Three cards, one an old lady in a cart, London registered, and two of two men overturning their cart at a gate, one London registered, the other A S 448. 15.2 cm x 10.1 cm.

14/15. Four cards "The Rocket", adventures of a mail coach. 11.2 cm x 14.5 cm, 14.5 cm x 11.2 cm.

16. Three cards, probably from two series, with a bucolic couple in village scenes. Two have verses by F L on reverse, the other by A J F. One is marked A S 918. 16.4 cm x 11.3 cm.

*Numbers 17-30 have cards by W J Wiegand, and are all signed W J W except where otherwise stated. The children are in Kate Greenaway style dress, though this artist could hardly be classed as an imitator or follower.*

17. Two cards, "Sir Roger de Coverley", colourful scenes with quotations from Addison, and attractive vignettes below. These are marked A S 320, and are identified as Wiegand. Buday gives 741 as the number for this series, but it was probably re-issued later on thicker card. (see below). 10 cm x 13.8 cm.

18/19. Seven cards, colourful scenes from Dickens, with quotation and drawing below. Two are from "Martin Chuzzlewit", numbered A S 321 and A S 4015, two from "David Copperfield", A S 4015, and three from "The Old Curiosity Shop", A S 2214 and 2215. It would appear (see above) that some of these series were re-issued on thicker card. 10 cm x 14 cm.

20. Three cards, one of two children and a dog, with verse by F L on reverse, London registered, one of "The Man in the Moon", dated by the sender 1883, A S, the third a family waiting for a coach, with verse by H M B on reverse, A S 15 cm x 10.2 cm, 13.5 cm x 10.2 cm, 11 cm x 11 cm.

21. Three cards, two children in the snow, a little girl at a gate, and a girl with a vase of flowers, one dated by the sender 1883. A S. 8.5 cm x 12.6 cm.

22. Three cards, nursery rhymes, with figures in gilt circular vignettes, two designs of "Baby Bunting", the other "One, two, three, four, five, Once I caught a fish alive". One card was dated 1883 by the sender. A S. 9.4 cm x 14.5 cm.

23. Four cards, proof copies with silver borders, nursery rhymes. 9.5 cm x 14.5 cm, 14.5 cm. x 9.5 cm.

24. Four cards, silver borders, children and nursery rhymes, with verses below. A S. 9 cm x 14.2 cm.

**72.29**

25. Four cards, silver borders, a different version of nursery rhymes, Tom Tucker, Baby Bunting, Hey Diddle Diddle, and Cock-a-doodle-doo. A S 173. 14 cm x 9 cm.

26. Three cards, one of a mother and children waiting for a coach, with two small girls in a silver vignette, A S 139, one with an old man and a boy with a snowball, the third a boy chasing a dog with a fowl in his mouth, A S 392. Though these two are different in style from others in this volume, they are more likely to be by Wiegand than by W J Webb (compare Vol 68, no 30). 14.5 cm x 9.4 cm, 12.4 cm. x 9 cm.

27. Four cards, single children, a girl with a doll, or a dog, or flowers, and a boy in hunting kit. A S 1236. 7 cm x 11 cm.

28. Two cards, children in snow, with verse by F L on reverse and a country scene. A S 1299. 13.3 cm x 9.2 cm.

29. Two cards, silver borders, one with three children in snow, the other with a girl and an old lady in poke bonnets. Each card has children in a vignette and a verse by F L on reverse. A S 1503. 10.3 cm x 15.2 cm.

30. Three cards, one with two children and a coach, A S 1442, one with a girl on a stile, the third a boy with holly, and a verse by F L on reverse, A S 1366. 16.2 cm x 8.9 cm, 9.2 cm x 13.8 cm, 9.4 x 12.5 cm.

# VOLUME 73:
# RAPHAEL TUCK. HUMOROUS CARDS, WITH PEOPLE AND ANIMALS, 1880-1895

1. Three cards, two designs of groups of men and boys sliding on the ice. Prize exhibition design, c1880. 16.2 cm x 6.5 cm.

2. Set of four cards, "Boys in a Bedroom", telling the story of six boys in one bedroom and the resulting chaos, with narrative on the back by A J F. Prize exhibition design, registered at Stationers' Hall 15-12-1881, by Alfred Bouchette. 16.2 cm x 10.5 cm.

3. Two smaller cards from the same set, one with a different verse by F L. 12.8 cm x 8.3 cm.

4/5. Seven cards, showing an orchestra conductor in different tempos, from pianissimo to an exhausted finale. No others have been seen in this set, but perhaps it contained eight or twelve cards. London registered, c 1882. 9 cm x 14.4 cm.

6. Three cards, one frosted, signed F A R, boys in the snow, with verse by F L on reverse. A S 129. 11 cm x 7 cm.

7. Three cards by Marguerite Ludovici, two designs, one of Pierrot on a snowball, the other a negro boy in snow, with verse by F L on reverse. A S 130. 8.5 cm x 12.1 cm.

8. Five cards, three designs of a boy with a donkey cart, the two smaller cards being frosted. The verse by F L on the back tells the story. A S 141, A S 1504. One of the latter larger set was dated 1884 by the sender. 10.7 cm. x 7.2 cm, 15.2 cm. x 10.1 cm.

9. Set of four cards, a boy snowballing an elderly gentleman. A S 152. The A S trade mark with the easel and cherubs, and the one with the easel alone, both appear on this set. 8 cm x 12 cm.

10. One card, a donkey and geese on a railway line with an approaching train, and a verse on the back by F L. A S 166. 12.5 cm x 8.7 cm.

11. Two cards, signed F G Lewin, the first showing a bull tossing a man into a boat with two people in it, the second with them all in the water. A S 220. 13.2 cm x 9.5 cm.

12. Two cards, signed George Cruikshank Junior, barristers in wig and gown, one drinking, holding a client's will, the other with a red brief bag. A S 272. 10.2 cm x 13.3 cm.

13. Three cards, one with a man fishing in the centre losing his hat with four pictures of its retrieval in the corners, and two smaller with silver borders with a man

sleeping on the bank, and falling into the water, all with verses by F L on reverse. A S 2083, A S 426. 13.6 cm x 13.6 cm, 9.8 cm x 9.8 cm.

14. One card, silver border, an artist in a field with a bull approaching, and a verse by F L on reverse. A S 2098. 9.8 cm x 9.8 cm.

15. Three cards, boys in winter weather, a crossing sweeper, a boot black, and a letter carrier. A S 1233. 7.7 cm x 11.2 cm.

16. Four cards, three designs, two of boys snowballing, one an old man with a snowman and a ship design on reverse. A S 1237. 11 cm x 7 cm.

17. Set of four cards telling the story of a goose escaping, and how it was caught. A S 1414. 10 cm x 12.6 cm.

18. Five cards, a set of four designs of mischievous boys with snowballs, and a spare card with a different caption. A S 2163. 12.5 cm x 9.7 cm.

19. Three miscellaneous cards, an old man playing a violin while a cat steals his dinner, a soldier looking at a shadow, and a lady buying a goose. All A S. Sizes up to 10.5 cm x 13.8 cm.

*Numbers 20-23 are by an unidentified artist. All have humorous captions to the pictures, and are probably dated in the late 1880's.*

20. Three cards, a fat lady with a broken chair, a couple with a small girl, and a bathing machine being pulled into the sea. Marked 181 on front, A S on back. 11.7 cm x 8.9 cm.

21. Two cards, ballroom scenes. D series 383. 10.3 cm x 13.5 cm.

22. Four cards, a couple walking out, ending in a proposal in a quiet spot overlooked by small boy. Y series 227. 9.2 cm x 13.7 cm.

23. Four cards, scenes with ladies and mistletoe. Y Series 277. 9.2 cm x 13.7 cm.

24. Two cards by Ellam, a man with a bull and an umbrella, one card with serrated edge, and verses by F L on reverse. Artist Series A S. c 1890. 11.1 cm x 14.2 cm.

*Numbers 25-32 are all marked with the Royal Warrant - "Publishers to Her Majesty Queen Victoria", and are dated about 1895.*

25. Two cards, serrated blue borders, small children playing in a giant egg and a huge plum pudding, with a verse by H M B on reverse. 14.2 cm x 10.5 cm.

26. Two cards, serrated edge, "Living Picture", with Yvette Guilbert and Ada Reeve on a bright red background. 9.8 cm x 14.3 cm.

27. Three similar, on a brown ground, caricatures of soldiers, "The Black Watch", the "10th Hussars", and the "17th Hussars".
14.3 cm x 9.8 cm, 9.8 cm x 14.3 cm.

28. Four cards, serrated edges, a humanised pot and pudding, a buoy, and a sack of flour, with humorous captions. Sizes up to 12.3 cm x 9.2 cm.

29. Three cards, clowns. Sizes up to 9.7 cm. x 13.8 cm.

30. Three cards, one a nutcracker with comic verse, another John Bull with two pipes dressed in Scottish and Irish costume, the third "An Ice Christmas greeting". 12.5 cm. x 8.7 cm, 12.8 x 9.8 cm.

31. Three cards, one a folder with a man falling off a bicycle, another with a woman in bloomers and a man on bicycles, the third a bicycle with a rebus verse.
8.7 cm x 14.1 cm, 9 cm x 12.5 cm.

32. Three humorous cards, a boy spying on a flirtatious couple, a pudding escaping from two wooden dolls, and a man in evening dress avoiding his mother-in-law. Sizes up to 8.5 cm x 12.2 cm.

33. Two cards, comic elves, having Christmas feast with roast beef and Christmas pudding. A S Artist series. 13.3 cm x 9.7 cm. c1890.

## VOLUME 74:
## RAPHAEL TUCK. CARDS WITH NEGROES, THE HUNT, AND THE ARMY, DATED 1885-90 EXCEPT WHERE OTHERWISE STATED

1. Three cards, cheerful negroes, one serving Christmas dinner, one with a bottle of champagne, the third emerging from an egg, all on a bright red background. Marked "copyright 1878". 7.7 cm x 12.8 cm.

2. Two cards, curious pictures of a coloured boy on a fragile sailing craft. Late1870's. 7.5 cm x 11.5 cm.

3. Six cards, five humorous designs of a negro boy with a donkey and a snowman. London registered c1882. 11.3 cm x 6.7 cm.

4. Six cards, antics of a negro in a red coat and top hat with a snowman. London registered. c1882. 6.7 cm x 12 cm.

5. Two cards, one a valentine, a negro in a blue suit and a negress in a cap, in a circular vignette, with gilt surround. A S, one no. 794. 11.5 cm x 11.5 cm.

6. Four cards, negro children in elaborate costume, on a leaf patterned background with silver border. A S. 9 cm x 11.8 cm.

7. Four cards, (one a valentine), three designs of negroes having fun with statues, one dated by the sender 24-12-1886. A S 692. 6.8 cm x 11.4 cm.

8. Two cards, one design of a negro holding a small girl with a bouquet. A S 1222. 7.6 cm x 10.7 cm.

9. Three cards, two designs of racing and hunting. Prize exhibition design, c1880. 14 cm x 7.5 cm.

10/11. Four cards, the tribulations of a rider to hounds. London registered c1882. 16.5 cm x 11.7 cm.

12. Two cards, hunting, a fall in the brook, and the reluctant mount. A S. 15.2 cm x 10.3 cm.

13/14. Four cards, more hunting vicissitudes, described on reverse in poems by F L. A S. 11.6 cm x 16.5 cm.

15. Two cards, signed George Cruikshank Junior, hunting men - one eating sandwich on a gate, the other falling into brook. A S 304. 10.5 cm x 14.9 cm.

16. One card, signed George Cruikshank Junior, a rider thrown by his horse, in a blue border. A S. 11 cm x 15 cm.

17. Two cards, a rider to hounds in a central vignette with four pictures of his adventures around. A S. 12 cm x 12 cm.

18. Three cards, of hunting scenes -
a) Signed Ernest Griset, Y series 332. 14.5 cm x 9.5 cm.
b) With the hunt in a vignette, set in a picture with a man shooting with a dog, and a verse by F L on reverse. A S 382. 15.1 cm x 10.1 cm.
c) Signed G G K (indistinct), with the Royal Warrant trade mark, c1895. 13.6 cm x 8.6 cm. Possibly by G G Kilburne Junior.

19. One card, the Hunt, signed I R Kennedy, three riders, one in the water, with a verse by E Kennedy on reverse. Artist Series A S 9.5 cm x 13.6 cm.

20. Two cards, one design "Getting Ready", showing hounds emerging from kennels. A S 2270. 14 cm x 10.8 cm.

21. One card, signed R F McIntyre, Highland soldiers, "The Thin Brown Line". A S 2347. 16.6 cm x 10.6 cm.

22. Three cards, signed Harry Payne.
a) The Band of the Royal Horse Guards, with verse by S K C, dated by the sender 1885. 15.1 cm x 10.2 cm.
b) Tilting at the Ring, A S 3591 (?). 10.6 cm x 13 cm.
c) The Black Watch, A S, possibly one of those registered at Stationers' Hall 10-5-1893. 9 cm x 13.5 cm.

**73.5**

23. Three cards, signed Harry Payne, a sentry on horse back, and a redcoat on a brown horse with a flag, A S, 9.2 cm x 13.7 cm, and a Lancer, A S 2386, 10 cm x 15 cm.

24. Two cards.
a) Signed Arthur C Payne, Highland soldiers with bagpipes. A S. 10.7 cm x 13.4 cm.
b) Signed Harry Payne, two soldiers bringing the Christmas holly. A S 2363. 10.2 cm x 13.2 cm.

25. One card, a soldier in a plumed helmet and red coat. The face has a feminine appearance, and might be a woman in uniform. Trade Mark not visible. 10.3 cm x 17.7 cm.

26. Two folding cards,
a) A marine with a rifle, and caption "England expects every man to do his duty", dated by the sender 1903, but with the Royal Warrant to Queen Victoria. 13.5 cm. x 8 cm.
b) A Highlander with bagpipes, dated by the sender 1898, with Royal Warrant to Queen Victoria. 6.5 cm x 16 cm.

27. A folding card with a lady riding a horse side saddle, with the caption "May you take a lead in the New Century", and Royal Warrant. c 1900. 8 cm x 10 cm.

28. Four embossed cards, three designs of hunting scenes, one a folder with a verse by F R, c1885.
11 cm x 7.5 cm, 13 cm x 9.6 cm folded.

## VOLUME 75: RAPHAEL TUCK. RELIGIOUS CARDS, MAINLY CHRISTMAS AND NEW YEAR

**Many of these cards are signed, in full or with monograms, and some are marked "Artist Series" as well as Artistic Series (A S) with an occasional "Mizpah" series appearing. Most of the cards have texts on the front as well as verses on the back.**

1. Seven cards, four designs, on black, blue or cream ground, two with anchors, two with crosses, both entwined with flowers. Late 1870's. 7 cm x 10 cm.

2. Seven cards, crosses entwined with flowers. One card with silver border is marked Prize Exhibition design; the other six, all of one set, have four designs, two being Easter cards, and one of these is marked Prize Exhibition design. c 1880. 7.7 cm x 11 cm, 6.7 cm. x 10.1 cm.

3. Four cards, angels in the clouds.
a) One with golden hair, dated by the sender 1883, A S, with a moonlight scene on reverse. 11.2 cm x 13.6 cm.
b) A cherub's head. c1881. 12 cm x 16 cm.
c) Two cards with cherubs and doves. A S. c1883. 11 cm x 7 cm.

*Numbers 4-18 are dated from 1885-90*

4. Two cards, one design with a medieval couple by a gilt cross, one an Easter card with verse by S K C on reverse, the other Christmas with verse by S K C. A S 321. 10.2 cm x 13.4 cm.

5. Three cards, two designs, one of the Holy Family, the other the Virgin and Child with angels, with verse by H M B below. One card is reversed to show a design of three cherubs with the Star. These appear to be the same set, but two are marked A S 400, and one A S 2450. 11.1 cm x 16.3 cm.

6. Two cards, signed W J Webb, one of angels, children, and robins, the other two scenes of the Holy Family, with texts and verses by H M B and F R H. The Mizpah, A S 39, A S 35. 15.5 cm x 12.4 cm.

7. Two cards, one signed W J Webb, the Good Samaritan, with text and greeting, and verse on reverse by E P. The Mizpah, Artist Series, A S 1. 13.3 cm.x 17.5 cm. The other, an angel with a cross, by Alice Price, "with deepest sympathy", is apparently a card of condolence. A S. 12.5 cm x 16.5 cm.

8. Two cards, signed W J Webb, one a black and white picture of Jerusalem with verse by Dr Mansell on reverse, Mizpah, Artist Series, the other the Good Shepherd, with verse by H M B on reverse, Artist Series, A S. 10.7 cm x 15.6 cm, 10.2 cm x 14 cm.

9. Six cards, from three sets, five designs of the Holy Family by Fanny Bowers, all Mizpah Series, A S, with verses by F R H or J V on reverse. 8.8 cm x 11 cm, 11.2 cm x 8.7 cm, 14.7 cm x 11 cm.

10. Two cards, signed Fanny Bowers, Christ with the children, and Palm Sunday, with verses by J V on reverse. Artist Series, A S. 12 cm x 15.3 cm.

11. Three cards of angels in clouds.
a) Signed by Creswell Woollett, verse by Dr G M on reverse. The Mizpah Series, Artist series. 10.9 cm x 16 cm.
b) With a verse by W D on reverse. A S 1279. 11 cm x 12 cm.
c) With a verse by H M B on reverse. Artist series, A S 6. 6.3 cm x 11.7 cm.

12. Four cards of angels in clouds.
a) With a verse by W D A on reverse. A S 539. 6.5 cm x 15 cm.
b/c) Two cards signed Florence Prince, with verses by C H on reverse. Artist Series, Mizpah Series. 10.6 cm x 7.3 cm.
d) Angel with baby on a cross-shaped card, with a design of lilies on reverse. A S. 12 cm x 18 cm.

13. Two cards, one signed A M Clausen, angels appearing to the shepherds, with verse by H M B on reverse, A S 559, the other with five angels and a star, and a verse by Canon Bell on reverse, A S 402. 12.5 cm x 15.8 cm, 12.5 cm x 12.

14. Two cards both Artist Series.
a) The Nativity, with angels and villagers, after Corregio, La Notte or Holy Night, with verse by Canon Bell on reverse. 11.8 cm x 17 cm.
b) The shepherds seeing the Star, signed R F McIntyre, with verse by H M B on reverse. A S 557. 17.5 cm x 12.3 cm.

15. Two cards both Artist Series.
a) The Flight into Egypt, watched over by the Face of the Almighty in the sky, with verse by C H on reverse. A S X70. 12 cm x 16.4 cm.
b) The Flight into Egypt, signed R F McIntyre, with verse by H M B on reverse. A S 538. 16.4 cm x 12 cm.

16. One card, signed A Erskine, angel with doves, and a verse by F W F on reverse. Artist Series, A S. 12 cm x 16.6 cm.

17. Two cards, by R M Erskine, versions of the Virgin and Child, after Titian. The first is marked A S 2127, the second Artist Series, A S, with a verse by Canon Bell on reverse. 9.4 cm x 9.4 cm, 10.5 cm x 13.8 cm.

18. One card, the Baby Jesus with symbols of the Crucifixion, on an embossed card with lily, passion flower, and vine border - c1890. A S. 6.7 cm x 10.7 cm.

*The following cards are dated from 1880-85. Many have crosses, and resemble Easter cards.*

19. Two cards, crosses, one entwined with passion flowers, marked Prize Exhbition (1880), the other with roses, A S, c1883. 9.2 cm x 13.6 cm, 16.4 cm x 11.1 cm.

20. Two cards, one design of rustic crosses with white flowers, signed with a monogram S H or H S. A S. 15.9 cm. x 9.5 cm.

21. Two cards with crosses, one a frosted rustic cross with lily of the valley, A S, the other with white flowers and grasses, marked Prize Exhibition. 11.7 cm x 13.5 cm, 13.5 cm. x 10.3 cm.

22. One card, a gilt cross with ivy and lily of the valley, and a monochrome design on reverse, by the same artist as no. 21 above. A S. 11.8 cm x 16.4 cm.

23. Two cards, gilded crosses, with grasses and pansies or passion flowers, and wide gilt borders, signed with a monogram E M or M E. A S. 11.8 cm x 16.4 cm.

24. Two cards, silver crosses, one signed Bertha (Maguire), with lily of the valley and verse by F L on reverse, the other with a bunch of mixed flowers. A S. 10.2 cm x 13.5 cm, 14.5 cm. x 11 cm.

25. Five miscellaneous cards with crosses.
a) One with a landscape signed C N (Noakes) Artist Series, and a verse by W B A. 9.3 cm x 13.8 cm.
b) One on a gilt ground with a shield. A S 1419. 11 cm x 14.2 cm.
c) A rustic cross with white flowers, A S. 8 cm x 12 cm.
d) A silver cross with pansies, signed M H, A S 1281. 11.8 cm x 9 cm.
e) A rustic cross with mixed flowers, marked "Original design".
11.6 cm. x 7.8 cm.

26. Two cards.
a) Arum lilies, dated by sender 1883. A S. 12 cm x 16.5 cm.
b) Wild flowers on a bank against a silver sky, with a verse by S K C on reverse. A S 1331. 13.5 cm x 10 cm.

27. Two cards.
a) Pansies and ivy with a verse by H M B in a panel. Mizpah Series, A S 104. 8.8 cm x 12 cm.
b) A bunch of mixed pansies, signed B Reinhart, with verse by H M B below. "The Mizpah". A S 36. 11.8 cm. x 16.3 cm.

28. Three later cards.
a) An angel with birds, verse by H M B. The Mizpah, A S 7, c1890. 8.7 cm x 11 cm.
b) The Holy Family, in vignette in Gothic window, with verse by Rt Rev E H V B. Artist Series, A S 13. 8.2 cm. x 12.9 cm.
c) A folding card, Virgin and Child in vignette, with verse within. Artist Series, Royal Warrant, c1895. 7 cm x11.2 cm.

## VOLUME 76:
## RAPHAEL TUCK. RELIGIOUS CARDS, EASTER UNLESS OTHERWISE STATED

**Most of these cards have a text on the front, and some have verses on the back. They are dated from 1880 to early 1890's.**

1. Two cards, one a churchyard, prize exhibition series, the other a lake scene with "Christ our Passover" in silver, unmarked. 11.8 cm x 16.4 cm, 15.5 cm x 10.7 cm.

2. One card "An Easter Souvenir", with a bunch of white flowers, dated by the sender 1882. Prize exhibition design. 10 cm x 14 cm.

3. Three cards, children in white surplices, with a cross and flowers. The two larger are London registered, the smaller A S. 11.4 cm x 16.3 cm, 8.5 cm x 12 cm.

4. One card, two angels by a gilt cross, signed A M C, possibly A M Chambers. There is a verse by S K C on reverse. A S c1883. 16.6 cm x 12 cm.

5. Two cards, sprays of lilies or convolvulus, with music from the "Messiah". A S, B79. 14 cm x 9.1 cm.

6. Two cards, one a cross with white crysanthemums, signed H S or S H, the other a bunch of violets with catkins. Both London registered. 10 cm x 13.5 cm, 9.1 cm x 13.5 cm.

7. Four cards, one with violets and catkins over a global map, the other three with flowers and butterfly on a cross. London registered. 9.1 cm x 13.5 cm, 13.3 cm x 9.5 cm.

8. Two cards, one a cross with pansies, and a flower design on reverse, London registered, the other Christmas roses on a crown of thorns with a verse by A M B on reverse, A S 867. 12 cm x 16.5 cm, 13.5 cm x 11.7 cm.

9. Two cards, one a cross with snowdrops, A S, the other a spray of brown leaves and white flowers, dated by the sender 1881. 8.9 cm x 11.8 cm, 12.8 cm. x 10 cm.

10. Three cards, two with gilt crosses and flowers on a blue ground, one Christmas, one Easter, marked A S, the third a gilt cross surrounded by thorny japonica, A S 729 1/2, perhaps one out of a set of two. 8.2 cm x 13.8 cm, 7 cm x 13.2 cm.

11. Two cards, narcissi or Christmas roses with coloured leaves on a gilt cross, with verses by A R H and F E E H on reverse. A S. 13.2 cm x 13.2 cm.

12. Three cards, two with the same design of floral crosses and a verse by R J on reverse, London registered, the third with a silver cross and "Easter Joys" spelt in flowers. A S 754. 7 cm x 10.3 cm, 12 cm x 8 cm.

13. One card, primroses and forget-me-nots on a silver ground, with verse by S K C in an egg-shaped vignette. A S 1475 1/2. 10.3 cm x 15.2 cm.

*Numbers 14-26 have cards on thicker board, dated in the later 1880's.*

14. Two cards by Bertha Maguire, one a honeysuckle spray, the other cyclamen with a cross, each having verses in silver script by C H and H M B. A S. 12.3 cm x 17 cm.

15. Two cards, one signed Bertha Maguire having a cross with cyclamen and ferns and a verse by Canon Bell on reverse. Artist series, Mizpah series no. 30. The other is signed B M possibly Maguire, and has a silver cross with ferns and narcissi, A S 1257. 10.2 cm x 15.1 cm, 11 cm x 15.1 cm.

16. Two cards by Helena Maguire, embossed designs of doves flying through an archway, with verses by Canon Bell on reverse. Artist series, A S. 12.3 cm x 12.1 cm.

17. Two cards by Helena Maguire, the same design of doves flying in a cross formation, with text and verses by H M B. A S Mizpah series no. 54. 11.7 cm x 14.3 cm.

18. Two cards by Helena Maguire, doves flying round standing crosses, one with a verse on reverse by C H, dated by the sender 1891, the other with a verse by S K C. A S. 11 cm x 16 cm, 12 cm x 15 cm.

19. A well designed card by Helena Maguire, a celtic style cross with flying doves and narcissi at the base, and a pierced gilt border with bells and ivy. Artist series. A S. 11.5 cm x 16.3 cm.

20. Three cards, with flying doves and pierced borders with bells and ivy. Two are by C Noakes with verse by H M B on reverse, A S; the third is by Helena Maguire, with verse by Canon Bell on reverse, Artist Series, A S. 9 cm x 13 cm, 14.5 cm x 10.6 cm.

21. Two similar cards by C Noakes, with text only. A S. 12 cm x 10 cm.

22. Three cards, all for Christmas, by C Noakes, two with cut out crosses, and sheep by a lake, and verse by C M on reverse, Artist Series, A S 1274, the third a shepherd with sheep in a mountain scene, and verse by H M B on reverse, A S 19. 10.2 cm x 12.8 cm, 12.5 cm x 13.5 cm.

23. Three cards by Annie Simpson. Two are embossed, with flowers or birds, and cut out and pierced borders, one with a verse by H M B on reverse marked Artist series, A S, the other A S only. The third has a lily and forget-me-nots with a verse by H M B beneath, A S only. 9.7 cm x 13 cm.

24. Two cards, one of an anchor with forget-me-nots, signed J M, A S 712, the other by Annie Simpson with cross, flowers and dove, and verse by H M B, A S. 9.5 cm x 11.8 cm, 13.6 cm x 10.5 cm.

25. One card, a silver cross with waterlilies and forget-me-nots, and a hymn by Rt Rev J C R. A S 747. 13 cm x 16.5 cm.

26. One card, a rustic cross entwined with lilies and fern, and a verse by F R on reverse with a two-tone country scene. A S 1348. 10.1 cm x 15.1 cm.

27. Three cards, one with a silver cross and wreath of snowdrops and a verse on reverse by S K C, A S 1539, one with a woodland scene and ivy, dated by the sender 1885, A S 1462, the third with a cross of forget-me-nots, A S 1332. Sizes up to 11.6 cm x 13.3 cm

28. Four miscellaneous cards, one with a spray of white flowers and a verse by S K C on reverse, A S 1223. The other three have crosses with various flowers, one marked A S 1205, one unmarked, and one with a verse by S K C on reverse, A S 1318. Sizes up to 11.6 cm x 9 cm.

29. Three cards. Two have a lamb before a cross, one with a verse by E P on reverse, A S Mizpah series no. 36, the other a verse by H M B, A S Mizpah series 5. The third shows a lamb in a field with a border of flowers and branches, London registered. c1882. A set of four of these cards is in volume 77, no. 30. 14 cm x 10.5 cm, 8 cm x 11 cm, 9.2 cm x 14.2 cm.

30. Five shaped cards. Two have cut-out anchors and doves, A S 3053, one has a cross with doves and waterlilies, A S, and two have crosses with roses or forget-me-nots, and a text on reverse, A S. c1890. 7.5 cm x 12 cm, 8.5 cm x 12 cm, 17 cm x 6 cm.

31. Four cards, three with angels. Two have verses on the back by S K C and the third is a folder, marked with Royal Warrant, dated 1898 by the sender. The fourth is an embossed cross with passion flowers. 8.2 cm x 13.2 cm, 8.5 cm x 11.5 cm, 7 cm x 12 cm.

**77.17**

## VOLUME 77:
## RAPHAEL TUCK. ANIMALS, FARMYARD SCENES, PORTRAITS OF PETS, 1880-1890

**These cards vary from straightforward portraits to comic humanised situations. Many are by Helena Maguire.**

1. Three cards, one with three horses, two with dogs, and a verse by F L or F R on reverse. Prize exhibition designs. 13.5 cm x 11 cm.

2. Three cards, two designs of stags or rabbits, in woodland, with verses by F R on reverse. R T London. 12.1 cm x 8.2 cm.

3. Four cards, two designs of stags or deer, three with verses by F R, one with greeting only. R T London. 15.3 cm x 6.8 cm.

4. Three cards, two with playful cats, one with cows in snow. London registered. 9 cm x 12 cm, 14 cm x 8.2 cm.

5. Seven cards, cats and dogs in oval vignettes on grey bordered cards, with greeting below. Three have verses by F R on reverse, two verses by E H. London registered. 7 cm x 10 cm.

6. Six cards, five designs of dogs' heads, two marked R T London. Perhaps by Helena Maguire? 10 cm x 7 cm.

7. Six cards, four designs of donkeys' heads, one dated by sender 1883. Possibly by Helena Maguire. A S. 10.3 cm x 7 cm.

8. Three cards, farmyard scenes with donkey and poultry, verses on the back by E H, F L. One of these has been printed on the wrong picture. A S. 11.8 cm x 8.8 cm.

9. Four cards, farmyard scenes with horses and poultry, only one being marked R T & Sons, A S. 12.4 cm x 10 cm.

10. Four cards, farmyard scenes with poultry, signed F A R, possibly Frank Arthur Ramsey. Two have verses by F L on reverse, A S 1292, two have verses by H M B, A S. Y series 307. 12.8 cm x 10 cm, 13.4 cm x 10 cm.

11. Four miscellaneous cards.
a) Donkey and caravan, signed F A R, verse on reverse by F L, marked A S.
b) Horse in farmyard, signed E A, verse by F L, marked A S.
c) Horse and cart with holly, marked R T & Sons only.
d) Horse and dog, marked R T & Sons only. Sizes up to 13 cm x 9.8 cm.

12. Three cards, snow scenes with donkeys and geese, verse by F L on reverse. A S 197. 11.6 cm x 7.8 cm.

13. Four cards, snow scenes with cat, rabbits and robins, one dated by the sender 1884, and verses by E H, F L on reverse. A S 1443. 15.3 cm x 10.1 cm.

14. Two cards, farmyard scenes with horses, pigs and poultry. A S 1562. 15.5 cm x 11.8 cm.

15. Two cards, a market stall with poultry and dogs, and a farm kitchen with dog and cats and a donkey at the door. Verses by S K C are on the backs.
A S. 16.4 cm x 11.6 cm.

16/17. Five cards, four larger, unmarked, with designs of a donkey in winter and summer, and verses by F L on reverse. A small card with one of these designs is marked R T & Sons, A S. 16.4 cm x 11.8 cm, 10 cm x 7 cm.

*Numbers 18-29 have cards designed by Helena Maguire.*

18. Seven cards. Three have two designs of rabbits' heads, one dated by the sender

1883, A S, and four have three designs of cats and dogs with verses by H M B in a panel. A S 100.
10.3 cm x 7 cm, 8.7 cm x 5.5 cm.

19. Two cards, two kittens wrapped in a shawl, with mistletoe, and verses on the backs by F L, H M B. A S 303.
13.7 cm x 10 cm.

20. Two cards, a camel, possibly by Helena Maguire, a polar bear. A S 363, 1485.
9.5 cm x 14.5 cm, 13.3 cm x 11.4 cm.

21. Four cards, all the same design of a dog with a basket of flowers in its mouth, with different greetings including birthday and valentine, and a verse by E H on the backs of two cards which are marked A S 715.
11.8 cm x 9 cm.

22. Four cards, elephants, one with head only, marked A S, the other three in a woodland background, A S 1240.
13.5 cm x 11.7 cm, 10.3 cm x 7 cm.

23. Four cards, two with goats' heads, A S 1252, two with cats, A S. 10.3 cm x 7 cm.

24/25. Seven cards, donkey and kitten, four designs, with verses by H M B, S K C on reverse. The four larger are marked A S, Y series 314, the three smaller A S 2029.
9.1 cm x 13.8 cm, 6.1 cm x 9 cm.

26. Five cards, three designs of cats under mistletoe. Four are larger, one dated by the sender 1886, marked A S. The small card has a flower design on reverse and is marked Artist series, A S 2033.
9.1 cm x 13.7 cm, 6.7 cm x 10.2 cm.

27. Three cards, cats, one in a flower basket, two in shells. One is marked A S 2143. 11.7 cm x 8.9 cm.

28. Four cards, two with single rabbits in woodland, two with six rabbits on grass. A S. 10.2 cm x 6.9 cm, 16.5 cm x 7.3 cm.

29. Five miscellaneous cards, dogs and cats.
a) Dog on fence, with verse by H M B on reverse. Artist series, A S 2254.
13.7 cm x 9.5 cm.
b) Cats playing Blind Man's Buff, verse by H M B on reverse, A S 2318.
15.4 cm x 10.3 cm.
c) Head of Newfoundland dog, anonymous verse on reverse. A S 2131.
11.1 cm x 11.1 cm.
d) Dog's head. A S 128. 9.5 cm x 6.5 cm.
e) Four cats in a pillow fight, verse by M G. Artist series, A S. 11.6 cm x 8.3 cm.

*The following cards are by artists unknown, except for two in number 39.*

30. Four cards, a lamb in a woodland scene, bordered by flowers and branches, with verses by F L, S K C on reverse, also used for Easter (see Volume 76, no. 28). Early 1880's. 9.2 cm x 14.3 cm.

31. Three cards, dogs in photographic poses, signed N H. There is a verse by F L on the back of one card. A S. 10.3 cm x 13.7 cm.

32. Three cards, two designs of dogs in horseshoes with forget-me-nots or holly, signed with a monogram, one marked A S 1327. 9.5 cm x 13.3 cm.

33. Two cards, humanised monkeys, one in top hat, one with banjo. A S 1251. 7.7 cm x 11.1 cm.

34. Two cards.
a) Humanised dogs, as a soldier and his lady, A S 2265. 10.5 cm x 14 cm.
b) Frogs in Highland dress, one with bagpipes, one doing a sword dance (no number) c1890. 13.3 cm x 9.1 cm.

35. Three cards, monkeys, one with a group in a forest, A S 251, c1885, and two with two monkeys in comic scenes, in serrated borders, c1890. 15 cm x 8.3 cm, 12 cm x 9 cm, 8.7 cm x 13.5 cm.

36. Three cards. One card has a dog with a basket of flowers, and a verse by S K C, marked A S. Two cards have two dogs, with humorous captions, A S 5048, 5154. Sizes up to 13.4 cm x 10.3 cm.

37. One card, the pet's portrait, a dog with a pink bow. A S ?5417. 12 cm x 16.6 cm.

38. Six miscellaneous humorous cards with cats and dogs, late 1880's, one "after Landseer". Sizes up to 12 cm x 9 cm.

39. Seven cards with cats and dogs, two by Helena Maguire, late 1880's. 8.2 cm x 6.3 cm to 11.2 cm x 8 cm.

40. Two embossed cards, comic scenes with frog on a broomstick, or two mice under mistletoe, with verses on reverse. 1890's. 13.8 cm x 10.5 cm, 13.8 cm x 9.8 cm.

# VOLUME 78:
# RAPHAEL TUCK. BIRDS

**This volume has some 1880 prize designs and prize exhibition cards, some London registered, 1881-1883. The later cards are mid 1880's with a few later, including two marked with the Royal Warrant to Queen Victoria and to King Edward VII and Queen Alexandra.**

1. Three cards by T H Allchin, second prize 1880. These have silver borders, with birds, bees and butterflies, and verses by E H and F L on reverse. 9.5 cm x 15.2 cm.

2/3. Four cards by May S Story, fourth prize 1880, two designs. One card has a bird on a branch of fir, three have butterflies and leafy branches, all with varied greetings and verses by F L, E H, on reverse of two cards. 14.2 cm x 11.8 cm.

4. Two cards, one a prize design by E A Bailey with portrait of an owl, the other a prize exhibition design of an owl on an ivied tower. 10.3 cm x 14 cm, 10.3 cm x 13.5 cm.

5. Two cards, with Lilliputian figures on tree branches, one card with a group of giant robins, the other with owls. These are labelled "Prize Design", but are not listed by Gleeson White. 14.2 cm x 10.2 cm.

6. Four cards, two designs of robins, with three different verses on reverse by F R and F L, who did not perhaps excel in this one
"Tax gatherer of the household crumbs
You darling little peeper
On whose fond breast as Christmas comes
The happy blush grows deeper".
Prize exhibition designs. 9.5 cm x 14 cm.

7. One card, a band of gnomes with a robin. Prize exhibition design. 15.2 cm x 10.7 cm. (This card is illustrated in an article on the Exhibition which appeared in the Magazine of Art, volume 4, 1881).

8/9. Nine cards (two Easter, one birthday), two sizes, five designs of birds' nests and flowers. The large cards have verses by F L, F R and A P on reverse, and are marked prize exhibition. Two of the small cards are marked London registered, one dated 1882 by the sender. 16.7 cm x 11.5 cm, 10 cm x 6.8 cm.

10. Three cards, two with birds' nests and flowers, one with verse by E H on reverse, London registered, one with verse by F L, marked A S. The third card has birds' eggs and daisies, marked prize exhibition. 13.5 cm x 10.2 cm, 11.8 cm x 8.8 cm, 10.3 cm x 6.8 cm.

11. Four cards, two of robins, one of horses in stable, and one of a dog in a mountain scene. Three have verses by F L on reverse, and all are marked prize exhibition. 16.1 cm x 7.7 cm, 7.7 cm x 16.1 cm.

12. Two cards, one of two blue tits on a branch, with verse by F L on reverse, the other an owl in a romantic moonlight setting, with quotations from Shelley and from Gray's Elegy. Both are prize exhibition designs. 8.1 cm x 13.1 cm, 14.1 cm x 9 cm.

13. Two cards, one design of a bird on a flowering branch in Japanese style, one completely unmarked, the other London registered. 13.5 cm x 9 cm.

14. Six embossed cards, four designs of colourful birds in Japanese style. One is dated 1883 by the sender, and three are marked R T London on the front. 10.8 cm x 7.1 cm.

15. Two cards, a dead robin and a dead blue tit "Sweet messenger of calm decay and peace divine", a curious message for Christmas. One only is labelled R T London. 16.4 cm x 11 cm.

16. Three cards, two designs of a robin and a blue tit with nests, and verses by F R on reverse. Marked no. 2005, possibly early 1880's, but the number is difficult to date. 17.7 cm x 8.6 cm.

17. Two cards, country scenes with geese, turkey and a dog, and a verse by F L on reverse. London registered. 14 cm x 10.1 cm.

18. Four cards (one a valentine), three designs of ducks, fowls, and a kitten in baskets. Two are marked London registered. 14.5 cm x 10.5 cm.

19. Seven cards, two larger with ducklings in water, and verse by E H on reverse, A S, and five smaller with three embossed designs of single chicks, London registered. 12.1 cm x 9.1 cm, 5.5 cm x 7.6 cm.

20. Four cards, three with birds' nests, one with a group of birds on a wall, with flowers, leaves and insects. Two have a verse by F R on reverse, and one only is marked London registered. 9.8 cm x 14.4 cm.

21. Five cards, set of four designs with birds in different seasons, and one similar with a bird's nest. Verses on reverse are by F R and E H. London registered. 8.4 cm x 11.3 cm.

22. Two cards, one a flock of robins in a winter scene, the other a parrot on a flowering branch. London registered. 14.2 cm x 10 cm, 9.8 cm x 15 cm.

23. Two cards, wide silver borders, with flowers on a wood grain background and birds peeping through a hole, and verses by F R, S K C, on reverse. A S. 18.2 cm x 11.6 cm.

24. One embossed card, swallows flying round telephone wires, pink flowers beneath. A S. 21.5 cm x 15.5 cm.

25. Six cards (one birthday), four designs of swallows flying over water, with leaves and flowers in foreground. Four of the five larger cards have verses by E H and F R on reverse. A S. 12.2 cm x 9 cm, 10.6 cm x 7.5 cm.

26. Three cards, hens and chickens, verses by E H on reverse. A S. 13.4 cm x 8.5 cm.

27. Four cards, three designs, two sizes, signed A J G, probably Arthur J Gaskin, robins in snow outside mediaeval style windows. The larger cards have verses by H M B, S K C, on reverse, A S, Y series 354,

and the smaller cards are A S 2033.
9.3 cm x 14.5 cm, 6.9 cm x 10.3 cm.

28. Two cards.
a) Robins in flight, in snow, with verse on reverse by Canon Bell, A S 2085.
12.6 cm x 8.5 cm.
b) A robin perching on ivy growing up a wall. A S 2150. 8.6 cm x 13.4 cm.

29. Two cards, one design of birds on fir branches, with verses by H M B, A M H, on reverse. A S 286. 10.8 cm x 13.2 cm.

30. Four cards. Two have a grey border, a flower spray and a robin or a goldfinch perching on a hand, with verses by E H, F L, on reverse. A S. The other two have flying birds in a vignette with flower or grass beside, and verse by E H below, dated by the sender 1885. A S 1283.
8 cm x 12.6 cm, 7.7 cm x 12.6 cm.

31. A folding card, baby birds on flowering branches, with scenes in vignettes outside.
A S. 17.5 cm x 11.7 cm open.

32. Three cards, one with a chick and a frog and a verse by F L on reverse, one with two owls and a verse by F L, both Artist Series, the third owls playing chess, A S. 11 cm x 7.6 cm up to
14.5 cm x 11.1 cm.

33. Three cards.
a) Gulls flying over ship, verse by H M B on reverse. A S 335.
b) Swallow in archway, verse by S K C.
A S 133.
c) Swallows flying, leaves behind, verse by H M B on reverse. A S 144. Sizes up to 10 cm x 13 cm.

34. One card with serrated edge, a snow scene with two chaffinches, and a verse by Lady L H. Art Gem Panels, A S. 1890's.
12.2 cm x 16.2 cm.

35. Three miscellaneous cards.
a) Hen and chicks, with verse by H M B, A S 6266.
b) A birthday card with bird on flowering branch, A S 966.
c) An embossed design of two gilded birds on a nest, and verse by H M B. c1890. Sizes up to 12.7 cm x 9.5 cm.

36. Two cards.
a) Embossed design of two birds on a floral branch. Royal Warrant. c1895.
b) Robins with ivy and forget-me-nots, gilded border. Royal Warrant to King Edward VII. c1902. 11.5 cm x 8 cm.

## VOLUME 79:
## RAPHAEL TUCK. BIRDS

**Most of these cards are signed by the artists, who include R F McIntyre, Giacomelli, Harry Bright, and Helena Maguire. They were published in the mid 1880's, unless otherwise stated.**

*Numbers 1-6 have cards attributed to R F McIntyre.*

1. Two cards, robins with oak leaves or mistletoe, and verses by F R, M Y W on reverse, and signed by a monogram, probably R F McIntyre. A S.
12 cm x 16.5 cm, 16.5 cm x 12 cm.

2. Two similar smaller cards, robins, one with same monogram, the other signed F Mc. A S 1268. 11.8 cm x 8.9 cm.

3. Two cards, signed R F Mc, robins in winter scenes, one with a lost doll, and verses by S K C, H M B, on reverse.
A S 2260. 10 cm x 13.8 cm.

4. Two cards, one signed R F Mc, one R F McIntyre, both birds in snow scenes. One has a verse by H M B on reverse, A S 2056, the other a verse by C H, no visible number, c1890. 8.3 cm x 11 cm, 9.4 cm x 13.4 cm.

5. Two cards, one an owl in a moonlit Gothic ruin, the other with three crows on a snowy branch, with verses by F L on reverse. A S 2132. 9.4 cm x 12.6 cm.

6. Two cards, serrated edges, signed in full, the same design of birds keeping warm by a smoking chimney, with two different verses by H M B on reverse. One is dated 1887 by the sender. A S 422.
11.5 cm x 15.6 cm.

7. Three cards by Harry Bright. Two have a robin and a bullfinch in green circular vignettes, with verses by A L S and S K C on reverse, A S; the third has serrated edges, and a picture of robins in snow, Artist series, A S, c1890. 10.5 cm x 10.5 cm, 16.5 cm x 12 cm.

*Numbers 8-14 have cards signed by H Giacomelli.*

8. Three cards, groups of birds in spring and summer scenes - "Songs without words", "The foraging bird", "The Toilet". London registered, c1882.
17.4 cm x 11.7 cm.

9. One card, a goldfinch, with verse by H M B on reverse. Artist series, A S 255.
9.5 cm x 13.8 cm.

10. Four cards, birds on branches - black cap warbler, waxbill, amaranth, spermestes - with verse by H M B on reverse. Artist series, A S 477.
9.4 cm x 16 cm.

11. One card, a Bogotar finch and an American blue bird. A S 502?
10.7 cm x 18.5 cm.

12. One card, chaffinches on nest, with verse by H M B on reverse. A S 580.
13.7 cm x 22 cm.

13. Two cards, one with two birds on a branch, the other a yellow bird on what appears to be a nest in an inverted fur hat, with verses by H M B and F L on reverse. Artist series, A S 2404. 10.7 cm x 16.6 cm.

14. Four miscellaneous cards.
a) Two birds on a branch, verse by K P beneath. The Mizpah. A S?
b) A bird on a flowering branch, dated by sender 1887. A S 106.
c/d) A parrot and a bullfinch on perches.
A S 2219. Sizes 6.7 cm x 9.5 cm up to 9.3 cm x 13.7 cm.

*Numbers 15-18 have cards by C White.*

15. Three cards, humanised cocks and hens, skating, playing the fiddle, and playing the piano, with verses by F L on reverse. A S 2286. 10.3 cm x 15.2 cm.

16. Three similar, cock and hen riding a tricycle, cocks playing cricket and football. Two are marked A S 2403, one A S 2061.
11 cm x 13.8 cm, 12.3 cm x 9 cm.

17. Two cards.
a) A chaffinch in a winter scene, with verse by F R H. The Mizpah.
b) Two sparrows on a berried branch, with verse by C M beneath, dated by the sender 1889. Mizpah series 120, A S.
10.5 cm x 13.8 cm.

18. Two cards.
a) Goldcrests in a winter scene, with verse by M S H on reverse, A S. 12 cm x 8.3 cm.
b) A sepia design with flying swallow A S 405. 8 cm x 6 cm.

19. One card by F L Fuller, a robin holding an umbrella over another bird. A S?
9.5 cm x 12.7 cm.

*Numbers 20-22 have cards signed by Helena Maguire.*

20. Two cards, serrated edges, grey wash designs, one of a hen and chickens, the other of seagulls on a cliff. Artist series, A S. c1890. 16.3 cm x 12 cm.

21. Two cards, one with parrots and a verse by A A P, the other embossed with a flying dove, and a verse by H M B on reverse. Artist series, A S c1890.
14.3 cm x 11 cm, 15.6 cm x 12.5 cm.

22. A birthday card, a chicken looking at the egg-shell from which it has just emerged, with a verse by H M B above.
A S. c1890. 13 cm x 10.6 cm.

23. A frosted card, by F A R, possibly Frank Arthur Ramsey, an owl on a fence with a lantern and a bunch of keys - "The night watchman". A verse by F L is on the back. A S 498. 16.3 cm x 12.2 cm.

24. Two cards by F A R, groups of storks in sea and mountain scenes, with verses by F L on reverse. A S. 16.5 cm x 11.7 cm.

25. Four cards, signed M H, three designs of birds on tree branches in circular vignettes, with greetings around. A S 1228. 8.5 cm x 8.5 cm.

*Numbers 26-28 have cards signed with a monogram J H or H J, all c1890.*

26. Three cards, one of two goldfinches carrying mistletoe, with verse by E D C below, A S 6254, one of a bluetit eating forsythia flowers, with verse by H M B below, A S, and the third two robins in snow, with an unsigned verse below, A S 6170. Sizes up to 9.8 cm x 13.2 cm.

27. A well designed tinselled card, with a bullfinch flying with a bunch of holly, over a winter scene with a mill in the background. A S. 6363. 9.4 cm x 13 cm.

28. Two embossed cards with serrated edges, both tinselled, with the same group of three robins, the first with an ivy leaf and a verse by C B below, the second with a greeting and a verse by H M B on reverse. 9.2 cm x 12.5 cm, 12 cm x 8.5 cm.

29. Three cards with cut-out edges, a bird with bells and mistletoe, robins by a church, chaffinches on blossom, all A S. Sizes up to 12 cm x 8.8 cm.

30. Four cards, two sizes, three designs of storks on rocks. The two larger are marked A S 1575, with designs on reverse, and the two smaller are A S 115 with verses on reverse by F L. 10.4 cm x 18 cm, 6.6 cm x 11.3 cm.

31. Two cards with robins signed H O C and B C P (untraced). A S 2108, AS. 10 cm x 10 cm, 12 cm x 8.5 cm.

32. Four cards, three designs of peacock feathers and other feathers, with verses by S K C and E C on reverse. One is marked A S 154. 12 cm x 8 cm.

33. Two cards by H O C, birds' feathers, with verses by S K C. A S 185. 10.4 cm x 10.4 cm.

## VOLUMES 80, 81, 82: RAPHAEL TUCK. SCENES

**These volumes contain cards, mostly in large sizes, with town, country, and seaside views, some with background figures. Many have verses or descriptive passages on front or back, and some have scenes in vignettes with flower or leaf decoration.**

## VOLUME 80: RAPHAEL TUCK. CARDS DATED FROM 1880 - EARLY 1890'S, MANY UNSIGNED BY THE ARTIST

1. Two cards, a country scene with farmhouse and geese, and a snow clad countryside with the shadow of the Cross in green. Prize Exhibition series. 15.8 cm x 9.5 cm, 16.2 cm x 11.7 cm.

2. A card with sailing ships in the sunset, and a verse by E H on reverse. Prize Exhibition design. 12.8 cm x 15.8 cm.

3. Four cards, two designs of trees in autumn and winter, with verses by E H and A M B on reverse of three. Prize Exhibition design. 10.3 cm x 14.7 cm.

4. Three cards, two designs of winter scenes with three different verses below in illuminated script. One is marked Prize Exhibition design. 10 cm x 13.3 cm.

5. Two cards. The first has two scenes in vignettes with grasses on a mottled ground, and a verse by E H on reverse. Prize Exhibition design. The second is a lake scene in subdued colours with a trail of flowers and ivy around, Prize Exhibition series. 10.2 cm x 14.7 cm, 16.4 cm x 8.9 cm.

6. Two cards, a farm scene with cows by a river bridge, and sheep on a path by the sea, marked Prize Painter series, probably designed by an unidentified 1880 Prizewinner at a later date. 16.2 cm x 11.1 cm.

7. Four cards, two designs of winter scenes with birds in the snow, and a villager homeward bound with the Christmas goose, both with verses by E H, E on reverse. London registered. 14.2 cm x 9 cm.

8. Four cards, winter scenes in subdued colours on a grey ground. London registered. 13.5 cm x 11 cm.

9. Two cards, one design of forest trees, one with birthday greeting, and an anonymous verse on the back of the other. London registered. 9.7 cm x 13 cm.

10. Two cards, one design of a Norman doorway with "Annus 1883" above, and a verse by E S on the reverse of one card, with no marking. The other has R T & Sons only on the front. 11 cm x 13.6 cm.

*Numbers 11-18 have cards designed by R F McIntyre.*

11/12. Four cards, three designs of villagers gathering Christmas greenery, with verses by F L on reverse. Registered at Stationers' Hall, 27-6-1882. Prize Exhibition design. 16.2 cm x 11.6 cm.

13. Four cards, three with two of the above designs, and verses by F L, F F and E H on reverse, the fourth another design, marked A S 2052. 12 cm x 8.8 cm, 8.6 cm x 11.8 cm.

14. Three cards, winter scenes framing other scenes in vignettes, one with a verse by S K C on reverse. One only is marked A S 250. 12.4 cm x 8.9 cm, 9.2 cm x 14.3 cm.

**79.11**

15. Two cards, winter scenes, the Christmas Carrier, and the Mailcart, with verses by F L on reverse. A S 277. 16 cm x 10 cm.

16. Two cards, both of a countryman and his dog struggling to reach a lighted house through the snow. One has a verse by H M B on reverse, A S 2239, the other is marked A S 505. 10.1 cm x 15 cm, 16.5 cm x 12.1 cm.

17. Two cards, winter scenes, one a farmer with horses, and verse by H M B on reverse, A S 2432, the other Kirkstall Abbey, A S. 11.4 cm x 15.5 cm, 15.8 cm x 10.4 cm.

18. One card, a lake in moonlight, with a text and a verse by F R H above. A.S? 10.8 cm x 13.9 cm.

19. Two cards, signed by L Springett, attractive woodland winter scenes, one with a rabbit, the other with a fox, and verses by H M B on reverse. A S 473. 11.5 cm x 15.2 cm.

20/21. Six cards, signed by E Hay, all of old buildings in Shrewsbury, Shropshire, or Chester. Two have verses by F L, Anon, on reverse, A S 1463, two have a lake scene on reverse, A S, W 1533, one a verse by S K C, A S 1413, and a smaller one is marked A S only. 10.2 cm x 15.1 cm, 11 cm x 16.5 cm, 7.4 cm x 11.1 cm.

22. Two cards, old buildings in Chester. One has a river scene on reverse, A S I 1596, the other a verse by E C, A S I series 464. 11.7 cm x 16.3 cm, 16.3 cm x 11.7 cm.

23. One card, Boston Market, by A Rimmer (one of a set of six, dated 1886, Buday). A S 2340. 11.7 cm x 16 cm.

24. Two cards signed Jessie Chase, Tintern Abbey, with verse by F L on reverse, A S 1491, and Haddon Hall, with verse by E H, A S. 10.3 cm x 13.5 cm, 13.5 cm x 10.3 cm.

25/28. Eight cards, colourful scenes in and around London, possibly by W L Wyllie, with greetings on silver borders, and a descriptive paragraph on reverse. They are numbered in sequence, two A S 412, two A S 413, three A S 414 and one A S 415. 16.5 cm x 10.7 cm.

29/30. A set of four cards, signed Wilmot Pilsbury A R W S, country scenes, probably those titled Spring, Summer, Autumn, Winter, registered at Stationers' Hall 1-6-1885. Verses by F L, M S M, and E M M, on reverse. A S. 16.6 cm x 12 cm.

31/32. Four cards, signed Edwin A Penley, lake and mountain scenes, all titled, numbered A S? 225, A S 2371, dated by sender 1893, A S, with verse by H M B, A S 4018, dated by sender 1888-9. Two have the typical rounded corners of the period c1890, and one has serrated edges. Sizes up to 18 cm x 13.3 cm.

33. Two cards signed C White, the same design of a man and horses before a house, with verses by H M B and S K C, on reverse. A S 2203. One is dated by the sender 1887. 11.5 cm x 14 cm.

34. Two cards on thick board, signed W Gilbert Foster, sea scenes in vignettes with decorative designs of lake and trees around, and verses by E C on reverse. Artist series, A S, U series 520. 10 cm x 17.5 cm.

35. Two cards signed L H White. One shows a windmill in a stormy scene, with a verse by Rev N H on reverse, Artist series, Mizpah. The other is St John's Hospital, Canterbury, with a design on reverse, Artist series, A S 2448. 10.5 cm x 14.4 cm, 15 cm x 10.2 cm.

36. Four cards, signed F F, i.e. Fred Fitch, various winter scenes, numbered A S 2081, A S 116, A S 2337, with verses by H M B, and A S 432. 8.1 cm x 10.2 cm up to 15 cm x 11 cm.

37. An unusual card by C Noakes showing an Eastern scene with mosque, A S 1000. 13.2 cm x 13.2 cm.

## VOLUME 81:
## RAPHAEL TUCK. SCENES, DATED 1885 -EARLY 1890'S, MOST SIGNED BY THE ARTISTS

*Numbers 1-7 have cards designed by Albert Bowers.*

1. Three cards, moonlit country scenes. A S 5206. 13.7 cm x 10.5 cm.

2. Two cards, country scenes, one oval, marked Artist series, A S 627, the other with rounded corners and gilded edges, greetings on reverse, Artist series, A S. 15.7 cm x 11.7 cm, 16.3 cm x 12 cm.

3. Six miscellaneous cards of country scenes with church and cottages, one with verse below by A L S, marked A S, A S 400, A S 211, A S 2313, A S, A S 104. 7.4 cm x 6.5 cm up to 16.3 cm x 11 cm.

4. Two cards, one with serrated edges, a cottage by a lake, with verse below by H M B, A S 461, 10.5 cm x 13.7 cm, and another with a scene in circular vignette and a verse by E F B on reverse. A S 2235. 13.2 cm x 10.45 cm.

5. Two cards, one a pastoral scene with farm and sheep and a verse by H M B on reverse, A S 3436, the other a monochrome picture of a forest with people, and greetings on reverse, Artist series, A S. 15 cm x 10.7 cm, 16.5 cm x 12 cm.

6/7. Four cards, monochrome studies of English country scenes, with serrated edges, and greetings on reverse. Artist series, A S. 16.3 cm x 11.9 cm.

*Numbers 8-18 have cards designed by C Noakes.*

8/9. Four cards, views of Newcastle-on-Tyne, with descriptive paragraphs on reverse. Artist series. 12 cm x 16.5 cm.

10. One card, Old London, The Cock Tavern, with descriptive paragraph on reverse. A S. 11.9 cm x 16.5 cm.

11. Four cards, woodland scenes in vignettes with flower and fern decoration. A S. 11.2 cm x 11.2 cm.

12. Three cards, lake scenes in Gothic style vignettes, with flower and grasses decoration. A S. 9.2 cm x 17.3 cm.

13. Two cards, lake scenes in circular vignettes with trailing leaf decoration, one dated by sender 1886. A S. 9.2 cm x 16.9 cm.

14. Three cards (one birthday), two with lake scenes in rectangular vignettes with tree and grass decoration, and verses below by A M H, A S, 9.4 cm x 14.5 cm, and another folding card with verse inside by H M B, A S 706, 9 cm x 13.6 cm.

15. Three cards, all winter forest scenes. One is a folder with flower designs on the cover, Artist series, the others are marked A S 2019, A S, V series 305. 15.6 cm x 8.7cm closed, 12.1 cm x 6.8 cm, 15.6 cm x 8.7 cm.

16. Two cards, one a river with flowers, and verse above by S K C, A S 467, the other a lake scene in vignette with fern and ivy around, A S, V series 396. 15.1 cm x 10.2 cm, 16.2 cm x 8.2 cm.

17. Two cards, lake scenes in shield shaped vignettes, with leaf and grass decoration, and a ship design on reverse. A S 1559. 11 cm x 16.3 cm.

18. Four cards on thick board with gilt edges, woodland scenes in vignettes in trompe l'oeil style, with holly, rose, ivy, or mistletoe branches around. A S 1462. 10.2 cm x 10.2 cm.

19. Two cards, signed A Wilde Parsons. One shows a windmill in snow with a verse by S K C, on reverse, A S 2430, the other is titled "Thames Barges off Gravesend", and has a picture of birds on reverse, A S. 17.5 cm x 12 cm, 15.6 cm x 12.6 cm.

20. Two cards.
a) A Wilde Parsons, a moonlight scene of a cottage by a stream, with verse by M S H on reverse, Artist series A S, dated by the sender 1891. 14.8 cm x 10.6 cm.
b) E Rowstone, "Ullswater" in moonlight, with verse by S K C on reverse, Artist series, dated by the sender 1887. 13.7 cm x 10.1 cm.

21. Two cards, signed E R, probably E Rowstone, lake scenes in moonlight, with verses on reverse by Burns and Bishop Heber. A S, A series 343. 11 cm x 11 cm.

22. Two cards, signed E R, scenes and figures in snow in oval vignette. A S, A S series 387. 10.3 cm x 15.4 cm, 15.9 cm x 10.3 cm.

23. Four cards, three designs, winter scenes with cottages, A S. These cards are signed by a monogram L W or W L. Other artists with similar monograms are Walter Langley, Linnie Watt, and the Marchioness of Waterford, but this signature differes somewhat from those known to be used by these artists. 9.5 cm x 13.3 cm.

24. Three cards, signed as above, one a sea scene on thick board, A S, one a cottage by a lake in snow, A S 1244, the third a farm by a church, with a scene on reverse, dated by sender 1888, A S 1551. 12.5 cm x 5.6 cm up to 16.3 cm x 11.7 cm.

25. Two cards, sea scenes, signed by M A, one titled "Near Scarborough", with verse on reverse by M S H. The other, with serrated edges, has a verse by H M B on reverse. Both A S. 11.9 cm x 15.8 cm, 14.6 cm x 10.8 cm.

26. Four cards, two with the same design of a forest in snow, A S, and two smaller, one with a forest in snow, the other a hilly scene with a signpost, A S 1225. 15.2 cm x 10.4 cm, 11 cm x 7.6 cm.

27. Two cards by C White, one design of trees by a lake, with a verse below by F R H. A S 16. 9.5 cm x 13.7 cm.

28. Three miscellaneous cards.
a) A houseboat by a lake, with swans, and a verse by E H below. A S 2234.
b) A shepherd with sheep, in snow, verse below by H M B. A S 2238.
c) A stile leading to a farm, with verse below by E H. A S 2267. Sizes up to 10.5 cm x 13.7 cm.

29. Three miscellaneous cards, two of waterfalls, A S 2276 and 2219, the third a church, with a verse by Rev N H, marked The Mizpah, A S 150. Sizes up to 10.5 cm x 13.7 cm.

30. Two cards, monochrome scenes, one a girl in a wood, the other a lake with boats, both with verses by Rev E H B on reverse. The Mizpah, A S 17. 11 cm x 15.8 cm.

31. Five miscellaneous cards, summer and winter scenes, marked A S 2020, A S 2075, A S, Y 1372?, A S, D series 369, A S 213. 10.3 cm x 7.3 cm up to 9.3 cm x 13.7 cm.

# VOLUME 82:
# RAPHAEL TUCK.
# SCENES, INCLUDING REPRODUCTIONS OF OLD MASTERS, SHIPS, SHELLS, AND SCENES IN VIGNETTES WITH FLOWERS AND GREENERY, DATED C1885-1895

1/2. Three cards, reproductions of pictures in the National Gallery by J M W Turner, R A. Two have designs of birds by W N D, on reverse, the third an unsigned verse. A S, I series, nos. 452, 453, 454. 15.9 cm x 12.5 cm.

3. One card, Fish Market on Hastings Beach, after David Cox, in sepia. A S 427. 16.6 cm x 11.5 cm.

4/5. Four cards, by J R J or T R T, fishermen in sea scenes, Morning, Noon, Evening, Night. A S 1529. 15.4 cm x 11.8 cm.

6/7. Five cards, four designs, four birthday, one Christmas, gilt edged cards of sailing ships, with verses by S K C, E H, on reverse. A S 1425. 11 cm x 11 cm.

8. One card, sailing ships on a moonlit sea. A S. 15.2 cm x 9.8 cm.

9. Three cards, moonlight over sea and rocks. One has a verse by the author of John Halifax, Gentleman, on reverse, A S 2231. The others have verses by S K C, E H. A S 1361. 10.2 cm x 15.2 cm, 14.4 cm x 9.5 cm.

10. Three cards, coastal scenes with rocks and cottages, and verses by E C, F L, on reverse. A S 268. 13.5 cm x 9.1 cm.

11. Two cards, shells. A S 1288. 10.5 cm x 10.5 cm.

12. Two cards, moonlight scenes in black and shades of blue green, with verses by S K C and Sigma on reverse. A S 1360. 8.8 cm x 13.5 cm.

13. Two cards, lake and river scenes in rectangular vignettes with holly, on a background forest scene. A S 336. 15.2 cm x 10.2 cm.

14. Two cards, Balmoral Castle and Buckingham Palace, in oval vignettes with holly, on a background forest scene, dated by the senders 1884, 1885. A S. 15.2 cm x 10.2 cm.

15. One card, a river scene in rectangular vignette on a two-tone winter scene background, with a verse by S K C on reverse. A S 1458. 15.2 cm x 10.2 cm.

16. Three cards, two designs, spring and summer scenes in rectangular vignettes with sprays of primroses and roses. A S 1274. 13.8 cm x 8.2 cm.

17. Two cards, wreaths of white flowers around moonlit sea views, the first with a verse by E H on reverse, the second dated by the sender 1884, A S. 10.7 cm x 12.6 cm, 11.7 cm x 13.5 cm.

18. Two cards, each with scenes in three vignettes, and verses by Moore and Robert Burns, numbered A S series 490, A S 2117. 16.6 cm x 11.8 cm, 9.2 cm x 12.4 cm.

19. Four similar cards, one a folder, with verses by G W, Longfellow, Thomas Tusser, 1567, and Anon. Unmarked, but attributed by similarity. 14 cm x 10.5 cm.

20. One card on thick board, a spray of violets across a country scene in sepia, dated by the sender 1883, but no trade mark is visible. 15.5 cm x 12.5 cm.

21. Two cards, signed Bertha Maguire, one a scene in oval vignette with lilies around, dated by the sender 1890, A S 276, the other a moonlit lake with Christmas roses and ivy on horseshoe shaped thick board, A S 2695. 10.3 cm x 14.3 cm, 12.5 cm x 14.3 cm.

22. Two cards.
a) Signed M L Bewley, a path with a stile leading to a church, with a spray of lilies and a verse by H M B. The Mizpah, A S 15. 11 cm x 13.7 cm.
b) A forest scene with Christmas roses and ivy, and a verse by S K C, dated 1888 by the sender. A S 339. 14.9 cm x 10.9 cm.

23. Two cards.
a) Haystacks and a church in rectangular vignette over a spray of fern and harebells, with verse by F L on reverse. A S 28. 9.3 cm x 13.7 cm.

b) A lake and mountain scene in a wreath of spring flowers. A S. 16.5 cm x 11.7 cm.

24. Two cards.
a) Two scenes in vignettes, with flower spray. A S 315. 15 cm x 10.3 cm.
b) "Dear old England" in rectangular vignette, with sprays of flowering thorn on a coloured ground, and a verse by Mrs Hemans on reverse. A S 482. 16.5 cm x 10.9 cm.

25. Two cards.
a) A moonlit country scene, with a spray of ivy. A S 2323. 15.4 cm x 11 cm.
b) A snow scene, with snowdrop spray around. A S 2442. 17.5 cm x 12.3 cm.

26. Two cards, scenes in circular vignettes, verses by H M B, on reverse. A S. 11 cm x 11 cm, 13.6 cm x 11.6 cm.

27. One card on thick board, a cottage and bridge in a vignette with a background lake scene, and verse by Cowper on reverse. A S Christmas series 476. 9.5 cm x 14.5 cm.

28. Two cards.
a) Ships in a circular vignette with flower spray, signed Julian M Price, with verse by H M B on reverse. A S. 10.4 cm x 13.7 cm.
b) A sepia scene in a moon shaped vignette, by A W Head, with a verse by J V. A S. 13 cm x 10.3 cm.

29. Four cards.
a) Country scene in oval vignette on red ground with embossed silver holly leaves, and verse by H M B on reverse. A S. 10.8 cm x 9 cm.
b) Country scene in vignette, with primroses on silver ground. A S. 8.7 cm x 11.5 cm.
c) Country scene in vignette, with ivy sprays on silver ground, and verse by S K C on reverse. A S 150. 12.5 cm x 9.1 cm.
d) Similar, with spray of mistletoe and forget-me-not. A S 2071. 11.5 cm x 8.3 cm.

30. Six cards, five having scenes in vignettes with flower sprays or wreaths, marked A S 114, A S 1242, A S 15?, dated 1885 by the sender, A S only, A S 148 with verse by Cowper on reverse. The sixth card is a winter scene with farmers before a cottage, and a verse by Moore on reverse, A S 172. Sizes up to 10.7 cm x 12.6 cm.

31. Two cards, scenes in vignettes with embossed flower sprays, both marked with the Royal Warrant to H M Queen Victoria, c1895. 8 cm x 11.4 cm.

32. A card in mediaeval style with a red seal and ribbon, and an Olde Englishe greeting, and a seascape in a rectangular vignette. A S. c1890. 13.2 cm x 11.2 cm, and another with landscape and holly, A S 339, 14.8 cm x 10.8 cm.

33/34. Seven cards with ships. 11.2 cm x 6.5 cm up to 10.2 cm x 15.3 cm.

## VOLUMES 83-88: RAPHAEL TUCK. FLOWERS AND FOLIAGE

These six volumes contain cards with flowers, Christmas greenery, and decorative leaf and fern designs. Some cards with butterflies are included.

## VOLUME 83: RAPHAEL TUCK

This includes early cards, Prize Exhibition series, London registered, and Original Design series, many of them embossed, nearly all published about 1880-1883.

1. Four cards with holly and mistletoe, 1880-1895.
a) A birthday card with holly, London registered trade mark c1880. 11.7 cm x 8.7 cm.
b) A holly spray with New Year greetings, A S 122. 11.2 cm x 7.7 cm.
c) New Year greeting picked out in mistletoe berries and forget-me-nots, frosted. A S 2122. 11.7 cm x 8.7 cm.
d) Holly and ivy spray with Christmas greeting, serrated edge, marked with Royal Warrant. c1895. 8.5 cm x 11.7 cm.

2. Six small embossed cards, two with cherubs and flowers marked R T only, late 1870's, the other four marked R T London, c1880. Sizes up to 10.7 cm x 6.5 cm.

3. Five cards with various flower sprays, four marked R T London, c1880, the fifth R T & Sons, London, and dated by the sender 1882. Sizes up to 7.9 cm x 14 cm.

4. Three embossed cards, birthday, with various flower sprays. Prize Exhibition series. 15.2 cm x 9.2 cm.

5. Six cards, four designs of flower sprays with greeting on gilt panel and gilded corners, one marked Prize Exhibition series. 8.8 cm x 12 cm.

6. Five similar cards, four small with three of the above designs and one other, marked A S, and a larger similar card of a different set, unmarked. 6 cm x 8 cm, 9.5 cm x 12 cm.

7. Four cards, three designs of butterflies in circular vignette, with catkins or flowering branches, and verses by F R, E H, on reverse. Two are marked Prize Exhibition series, R T & Sons London, and one is dated by the sender 1881. One is marked "Rock of Ages series no 40", and is dated by the sender 1883. 9 cm x 13.6 cm.

8. Two cards, the same design of butterflies in an oval vignette with grasses, and different greetings in an oval panel. One is marked Prize Exhibition series. 9 cm x 13.6 cm.

9. Three cards, two with mixed flowers on a grey ground, the other an agapanthus plant. Prize Exhibition series. 7 cm x 10.3 cm, 8.2 cm x 12.2 cm.

10. Three cards, two designs of dog roses and anemones on a beige ground. Prize Exhibition series. 8.3 cm x 13.7 cm.

11. Three cards, two designs of wild flowers against a blue sky, with verses by E.H. on the reverse of two cards. One is dated 1882 by the sender. Prize Exhibition series. 8.1 cm x 13 cm.

12. Five miscellaneous cards, various flower sprays on coloured grounds. All Prize Exhibition series. Sizes up to 10.1 cm x 13.3 cm.

*Numbers 13-22 have cards marked R T London, with no trademark, dated c1880-1882.*

13. Three embossed cards, one on a decorative mount, two designs of fuchsia or lilac with a bird. 8.1 cm x 12.6 cm.

14. Two embossed cards, one birthday, the same design of a butterfly on a spray of forget-me-nots and roses, one dated by the sender 1882. 8.4 cm x 15.4 cm.

15. Three embossed cards in trompe l'oeil style, wreaths of roses on a fringed scroll marked like moire silk, in blue or beige. 6.8 cm x 12 cm.

16/17. Seven embossed cards in trompe l'oeil style, four designs of various flowers lying on a background imitating a wooden box lid, complete with grain, knots, and nails. One card is mechanical, with the lid sliding in grooves to reveal the interior, which is another card with a fruit design, one of the set below. Two cards are dated 1881 by the sender. 13.6 cm x 9 cm, 12.6 cm x 8.2 cm.

18. Three cards, trompe l'oeil designs of fruit apparently lying in a wooden box, with verses by F R on the reverse of one, and on the front of two. 13.6 cm x 9 cm.

19. Eight embossed cards (two birthday), various flower sprays on grey ground, one dated 1881 by the sender. 7 cm x 11.3 cm.

20/21. Ten embossed cards, gilt edges, four designs of spring flowers and leaves. Five have texts in panels, and are marked Rock of Ages series no. 35, and five have Christmas or New year greetings. 10.4 cm x 7.2 cm.

22. Two cards with silver borders, moonlight scenes, one with waterlilies and butterfly, the other with Alpine rose. There are verses by E H, H M B, on the backs. 8.5 cm x 12.7 cm.

23. Four embossed cards, with flower sprays on a panelled background, marked R T & Sons only. 8.5 cm x 12 cm.

*Numbers 24-31 have cards marked R T & Sons with the London registered trade mark.*

24. Seven embossed cards, five designs of fans with flower decoration. 8 cm x 4.5 cm.

25/26. Sixteen cards, six designs of flowers in baskets showing a variety of greetings. Four are birthday cards. 10.3 cm x 7 cm.

27. Four embossed cards, two designs of oak leaves or creepers. One only is marked, but they are obviously the same set. 8.2 cm x 11.4 cm.

28. Three cards, a curious combination of flowers, leaves, a butterfly, and insects, with an open pea pod, a piece of apple peel, or a ribbon. One is dated 1882 by the sender. 12.9 cm x 6.6 cm.

29. Six cards in trompe l'oeil style, open books with flowers and greeting verses. Five are embossed, and one is plain, with a text. 9.5 cm x 7.7 cm.

30. Four miscellaneous cards with gilt edges, various flower sprays. 10.4 cm x 7 cm up to 10 cm x 15 cm.

31. Four cards, three designs of sprays of mallow, two with Christmas greetings, two with texts marked Rock of Ages, no. 39. 11.6 cm x 9 cm.

*Numbers 32-34 have the trade mark labelled "Original Design", and are probably about 1882.*

32. Five cards including two different sets. Three cards have alpine flowers growing on a cliff, with verses on the reverse of two by E H, I M E S. One card has a border of branches with forget-me-nots. The other is a folder incorporating two cards from each set, with a verse by F L. 11.5 cm x 7.5 cm, 12.4 cm x 7.5 cm.

33. Two cards, the same design of primroses on a mossy bank, with two different verses, one by Whittier. 15 cm x 11.5 cm.

34. Two cards, forget-me-nots and ivy, and grasses and fern, in wreaths around the greetings. 9 cm x 7.4 cm.

## VOLUME 84: RAPHAEL TUCK. FLOWERS AND FOLIAGE IN POTS AND VASES, FLOWERS WITH MOONLIGHT SCENES, PARALLELOGRAM SHAPES, LARGE CARDS, 1880-1885

1. Three cards, two designs of roses in vases, one a Prize design by Kate Sadler, two London registered with verses by F L, J C, on reverse. 10.2 cm x 15.5 cm, 9 cm x 13.5 cm.

2. Two birthday cards, carnations or begonias in a glass tumbler or jug, with verses by F R on reverse. Prize Exhibition design. 11.7 cm x 15.4 cm.

3. Four cards (one birthday, one valentine), plants in pots, with verses by F L, E H, F R, on the reverse of three cards. Prize Exhibition design. 11 cm x 10.6 cm.

4. Six cards, two embossed with lilies of the valley in pots, London registered, and four with flowers in vases, two marked Prize Exhibition design, and two marked A S 1215. 7 cm x 11 cm, 6.8 cm x 10.3 cm.

5. Three cards. Two are in Chinese style with teapot or plate and decorated frieze below, and a verse by F R on reverse, Prize Exhibition series. The third pictures a vase of snowdrops with a four-fold screen of ship pictures, probably a card, with verse by H M B on reverse, A S 2269. 9 cm x 13.3 cm, 11.2 cm x 13 cm.

6. Two cards on dark backgrounds, sweet peas in a decorated glass beaker, with verse by E H on reverse, dated 1882 by the sender, and phlox and autumn leaves by a crystal ball, both marked "Original design". 11.5 cm x 14 cm, 14 cm x 11.5 cm.

7. Five cards, three designs of flowers in vases, with verses by J C and F R on the backs of two cards, and three different verses by E H on the backs of the same design of roses, with different greetings. London registered. 10.2 cm x 13.7 cm.

8. Three cards, two with sunflower or feathers in a decorated vase beside a plate, marked R T London, the third a curious vase encrusted with flowers on a blue ground with silver decoration and a verse by E H on reverse, trade mark obscured. 10.4 cm x 13.4 cm and 10.4 cm x 15.3 cm.

9. An elaborate card, three vases on a silver background, one with a sunflower, one with tulips on a Japanese style cabinet, and a verse by S K C on reverse. A S. 11.8 cm x 16.5 cm.

10. Three cards, various berries in rustic baskets, marked R T & Sons only. 11.2 cm x 8.5 cm.

11. Two cards, one of flowers in a glass vase, marked R T & Sons, the other a fern in a rustic pot, with verse by S K C on reverse. A S. 10 cm x 13.5 cm, 10.2 cm x 13.5 cm.

12. Four cards, lilies, water lilies, and convolvulus, with butterflies or dragonflies, in moonlight scenes. Two have verses on reverse by E R and J C. London registered. 9.2 cm x 15 cm.

13/15. Eleven cards, flowers in moonlight scenes, growing against fences or trees. There are nine cards in one set with four

designs, showing a variety of greetings, with verses by F R, E H, J M S, A M B, and J V on reverse, one being a folder, all London registered. The other two have verses by E H on reverse, and are marked A S. 9 cm x 13.5 cm, 9.2 cm x 13.8 cm.

16/17. Four cards, two designs of Christmas roses or wild roses on a blue ground with decorated border, and verses by F L and E H on reverse. Prize Exhibition design. 16.1 cm x 11.8 cm.

18. Two cards, holly or mistletoe sprays on a green and gold ground, with verses by F L in a panel. A S. 16 cm x 10 cm.

19. Two cards, blackberries, or snowberries, on a blue ground with wide gilt border, and verses by E H on reverse. A S. 16 cm x 12 cm.

20. One card, a butterfly and a china rose in a leaf shaped vignette, on brown and silver ground. A S. 11.8 cm x 16.4 cm.

21/23. Eleven cards, all parallelogram in shape, including four folders, with various designs of flowers or ferns in coloured borders. One only is marked R T London, no. 1978, but the others, some numbered 1998, 2014, are attributed from the similarity of the designs on reverse, with poems by F R. 13 cm x 8.5 cm, 10 cm x 7 cm, 14 cm x 9.5 cm.

24. Two cards on dark grounds. One is a woodland scene with butterflies, flowers, and hazel nuts, and a verse by E H on reverse, marked Prize Exhibition design. The other, a sunflower and leaves, with a verse by F L on reverse, is London registered. 9 cm x 14 cm, 15.5 cm x 11.6 cm.

25. Two cards, clumps of primroses or violets, with trees behind, backs damaged by Victorian glue used in albums. c1884. 11.8 cm x 16.4 cm.

26. Two cards, dog roses, or apple blossom, with fence behind, and a bird design on reverse. A S. 11.8 cm x 16.4 cm.

27. Two cards, one a mixed bunch of stocks, with a verse by S K C on reverse, the other a wreath of violets, fir, and pussy willow. A S. 11.8 cm x 16.4 cm, 16.4 cm x 11.8 cm.

28. One card, a spray of potentillas with an unsigned verse below, c1885. 11.8 cm x 16.4 cm.

29. Three miscellaneous cards, various flowers on coloured grounds, with verses on reverse by S K C, F R, E H. A S. Sizes up to 11.4 cm x 16 cm.

30. Three cards, two of one set with sprays of daphne or convolvulus, the third a single foxglove, with verse by E H on reverse. A S. 9.4 cm x 17.4 cm, 10.4 cm x 17.8 cm.

31. Two cards, sprays of flowers. The first has a bunch of spring flowers on a black ground, with verse by S K C below, A S 1719. The second has stocks, with brown leaves, on a green ground, and a verse by E H on reverse. A S. 11.6 cm x 15 cm, 11.2 cm x 11.2 cm.

32. Two cards, clematis or buttercup sprays on a beige ground. A S. 15.1 cm x 10.4 cm.

33. Two cards, white flowers and leaves on a pale background, the first with verse by S K C on reverse, A S, the second dated by the sender 1885. 15.1 cm x 10.4 cm.

34. Two cards, the first a rose and forget-me-nots, with verse by E H on reverse, A S, the second lilies and fern, with a ship picture on reverse, marked D series 386.

35. Two cards, the first Christmas roses with foliage, dated by the sender 1885, A S, the second pansies in a crown of thorns, with a verse by S K C on reverse, A S 1498. 11.6 cm x 13.5 cm, 13.5 cm x 11.6 cm.

36. Three cards, flower sprays, the first anemones with verse by S K C on reverse, A S, the second pansies, with verse by "the author of John Halifax, Gentleman", A S 2153, the third Christmas roses, with verse by S K C on reverse, A S 1418. 10.2 cm x 13.7 cm, 8.8 cm x 13.5 cm.

37. Three miscellaneous cards, clematis or geraniums, all A S. Sizes up to 9.2 cm x 19.3 cm.

38. Four cards, butterflies with flowers. The two larger are marked R T & Sons only, the two smaller "Original design". 10.2 cm x 15.2 cm, 7.6 cm x 11.5 cm.

39. Four cards. Two have flower sprays and ferns in a decorative gilded border, with verses by E H, S K C on reverse, A S 1219. The other two have flowers and ferns with greetings in illuminated script. A S. 9.2 cm x 10.9 cm, 8.8 cm x 11.7 cm.

## VOLUME 85: RAPHAEL TUCK. FLOWERS AND FOLIAGE, SOME FOLDING, SOME SIGNED CARDS, 1880-90

*Numbers 1-15 have cards also used in folders. The vast output of this firm is evident here from some cards numbered 2,000 up, which were published about 1882 from the registration mark.*

1. Four cards, two designs of white roses or geraniums on a pink ground, with verse or greeting in a panel or shield. One card is a rare example of a wedding greeting, a four-page folder "Wishing you every Happiness", with the rose design, silver decoration, and a suitable greeting by F R; another is on a silver bordered mount. One

is marked R T London, entered at Stationers' Hall, and this has been traced to 25-4-1879, Thomas Dupuy & Sons. 12.5 cm x 9 cm, 10.5 cm x 7 cm.

2. Two four-page folder cards, green or red outside with gilt decoration, and the same flower card of polyanthus within, with verses by E H, F L. London registered no. 170. 13.2 cm x 9.4 cm.

3/6. Twelve cards (five birthday) including six single cards and six folders with six embossed designs of various flower sprays on a coloured mottled ground. The folders, numbered 2006, have pink, yellow, grey, beige, or blue covers, with four different designs, and cards affixed inside, with verses by H S, F R. London registered. 13 cm x 8.7 cm, 11 cm x 6.5 cm.

7. Two four-page birthday folder cards, blue and beige backgrounds, with flower cards within and verses by F R. Unmarked, numbered 2007, 2008. 13.2 cm x 9.4 cm,13.5 cm x 10.2 cm.

8. Four cards, a four-page Easter folder with a flower card on a blue and gold mount and a verse by F R, with three cards, two designs of geraniums and azaleas from the same set (one birthday). The cards are marked R T London, the folder no. 2008. 13.5 cm x 10.2 cm, 10.1 cm x 6.8 cm.

9/10. Five cards, two four-page folders, showing four flower designs in a blue circular vignette of the same set as the three single cards, with a design of a stork in the sunset on a gold ground inside. London registered. 9.4 cm x 12 cm.

11. Three cards, an elaborate shaped birthday folder, with a primrose and catkin design and a verse by S K C within, dated by the sender 1884. The two single cards are of the same set, the primrose design, and a rose design. A S. 11.2 cm x 7.8 cm closed, 10.2 cm x 7 cm.

12. Two elaborate shaped birthday folders, with floral cards within and verses by E H and S J, with greetings and gilt decorated mounts. R T & Sons, London, Nos. 6014, 6018. 12.8 cm x 9.7 cm closed.

13/14. Six cards, five single cards with three designs of sprays of brown leaves and flowers, and a folder with two of these designs outside and a woodland scene within, with verses by A P. London registered. 9 cm x 13.5 cm.

15. Two birthday cards, a folder with poppies and Christmas roses on the outside, and a single embossed card with the poppy design. The folder has a verse by Cowper within, and another small card. R T London. 14 cm x 6.7 cm.

*Numbers 16-31 have cards signed with the same monogram, M B or B M, untraced. It is tempting to assume that these were by the prolific flower painter, Bertha Maguire, but her usual signature was "Bertha", or her name in full, and neither the lettering nor the style of these cards can be said to resemble her signed pictures. Some unsigned cards in Volume 86 might be by this untraced artist.*

16. Four cards, three designs of autumn leaves by iron railings, beneath stormy skies, with verses by E H on reverse. One card is marked Prize Exhibition series. 9 cm x 13.5 cm.

17. Eight cards, six designs of flowers and foliage. One series of five cards is marked Prize Exhibition series, the other three A S. 10.2 cm x 6.8 cm.

18. Five cards, sprays of daisies, periwinkle, thistle, catkins, and snowy branches, three marked Prize Exhibition series. 10.2 cm x 6.8 cm.

19. Four larger cards, same set as above, using the daisy, thistle and periwinkle designs, two dated by the senders 1881, 1882. London registered. 13.5 cm x 10.2 cm.

20. Three similar birthday cards, two designs, meadow encircled by a wreath of flowers and leaves, and a butterfly with clover and Christmas roses. One has a verse by F R on the back, and two are dated 1884, 1885 by the sender. London registered. 13.5 cm x 10.2 cm.

21. Two four-page folder cards, showing four designs of catkins and spring flowers outside, and winter scenes inside. One has a registration (kite) mark for 18-3-1882, the other is marked A S. 7.8 cm x 14.2 cm closed.

22. Five cards, three of the catkin set above, A S, with two others of mistletoe or firbranches with birds in the snow, and verses by E C and Burns on the reverse. A S. 8.1 cm x 14 cm, 13.6 cm x 9.1 cm.

23. Four cards, three designs in two sizes, white flowers and brown foliage with wide borders. The small cards are A S 1246, the large A S. 11 cm x 7.8 cm, 15.2 cm x 10.3 cm.

24. Two cards, a four-page folder with two designs of trailing plants and gilded brown leaves outside and two designs of grasses within, and a single card with one of the trailing plant designs. London registered. 7.5 cm x 14 cm.

25. A folding birthday card, with verses by F R on the two flaps enclosing a card with wild roses, and a gilded mosaic patterned cover. Marked R T & Sons only. 14 cm x 11 cm closed.

26. Two cards, white flowers and gilded brown leaves. A S 1213. 10.8 cm x 7.4 cm.

27. Two cards, flower with brown gilded leaves, studs in corners, verse by E H on reverse, A S 1349, and a spray of white flowers with gilded leaves, dated by the sender 1884, A S. 11 cm x 11 cm, 13.6 cm x 10.2 cm.

28. Three miscellaneous cards, flower and leaf sprays, one with verse by E H on reverse, A S 1506, one London registered the third A S. 13.5 cm x 10.2 cm, 8.8 cm x 11.8 cm.

29. Two large cards, a sunflower, and a tiger lily with ivy, both A S. 11.8 cm x 16.5 cm.

30. One card, a spray of lilac and narcissi, with a verse by E C below in silver print. A S. 13 cm x 20 cm.

31. A card in the form of a calendar for 1885, with a spray of convolvulus, and the dates on a curved scroll, with Happy New Year greeting below. A S. 9.1 cm x 13.7 cm.

*Numbers 32-37 have cards signed by Bertha Maguire, for comparison with those above.*

32. One card, a spray of Christmas roses, forget-me-nots and ivy, with New Year greeting in silver. A S 409. 13.3 cm x 16 cm.

33. Four cards, two designs of snowdrops or chrysanthemums with brown foliage, framing verses printed in silver. Three are marked A S, D 1474; the fourth, on thicker card, with a verse by E H on the front and by S K C on the back, is marked A S. 10.2 cm x 13.5 cm.

34. Three miscellaneous cards, white flowers with foliage, and verses on the front by C S, S K C, and S K C, marked A S, A S 470, A S 374 respectively. Sizes up to 16.5 cm x 12.5 cm.

35. Two cards, a spray of holly, A S 2101, orchids, with verse by H M B on reverse, A S. 9.8 cm x 13.1 cm.

36. Two cards, flower sprays, A S. c1890. 12 cm x 16.4 cm, 13.6 cm x 11 cm.

37. A large card on thick board, orchids with a verse by H M B below. Indistinct marking, A S 2703? 15 cm x 18.9 cm.

38. Three cards by Kate Sadler, vases with chrysanthemums, Prize Painter series, early 1880's. 10.2 cm x 15 cm.

# VOLUME 86: RAPHAEL TUCK. FLOWERS AND FOLIAGE, INCLUDING ROSES, MISCELLANEOUS COLOURFUL MEDIUM SIZED CARDS, MANY WITH BROWN FOLIAGE WITH GOLD HIGHLIGHTS, DATED 1880 - 1885

1/2. Five cards, with three designs of single roses. Two are birthday folders, with a card on yellow or blue mounts with illuminated decoration, no. 2011, and three are single cards, two having texts. London registered. 14.4 cm x 10 cm closed, 13.4 cm x 8.5 cm.

3. Four cards, three designs of rose sprays, one frosted, on black or coloured ground, one dated 1881 by the sender, two Prize Exhibition design. 9 cm x 14.8 cm.

4/5. Seven cards, four designs of a single rose and buds placed on grass, with verses by J C and F R on reverse, one dated by the sender 1882. Prize Exhibition design. 14 cm x 9.5 cm.

6. A birthday card from the previous set on a fancy blue and gold mount. 17 cm x 12.2 cm.

7. Two cards, one a mixed bunch of roses, the other a rose and a butterfly. Prize Exhibition design. 12.1 cm x 15.3 cm, 13.4 cm x 10.1 cm.

8. Two cards, one design of a spray of white field roses, with silver border and greeting. Prize Exhibition design. 11.5 cm x 13.5 cm.

9. Two cards, one a country scene with a border of pink and red roses, and a verse by E H on reverse, A S, the other pink briar roses on a blue ground, London registered. 9.1 cm x 12.7 cm, 9.5 cm x 15 cm.

10. Three miscellaneous cards, a single rose with a bud, one a valentine marked A S 109, the others embossed, marked R T & Sons, London. Sizes up to 7.6 cm x 12.2 cm.

11. Two embossed cards, a single rose with ferns, foliage and forget-me-nots, on pale blue ground, one marked R T & Sons London, with a verse by F R. 15.5 cm x 11.6 cm.

12. Two cards, one design of white roses with leaves touched with gold, London registered. 14.6 cm x 11 cm.

13. Two cards, a hand with frilled cuff holding moss roses, and a bouquet of red roses. London registered. 9.7 cm x 15.5 cm, 11.7 cm x 15.6 cm.

14. Three cards, gilt borders, rose sprays, one with forget-me-nots. London registered. 4.7 cm x 12.2 cm.

15. Two embossed cards, single roses in a scroll, with wide gilt borders. London registered. 7.5 cm x 11.2 cm.

16. Five miscellaneous cards of roses, one held in a hand, one in a posy, marked respectively A S, R T & Sons, Prize Exhibition series, A S 6032 dated 1886 by the sender, and A S. Sizes up to 12.3 cm x 10.3 cm.

17. Three embossed cards, one Easter, two designs of a single pink rose. A S. 10.3 cm x 7 cm.

18. Two cards, one a pink rose with black berries, dated 1883 by the sender, the other a bunch of yellow roses, signed C E (untraced), both A S. 10 cm x 15.4 cm, 15.2 cm x 10.3 cm.

19. Two cards, a wreath of foliage and fern with a pink or red rose, and verses below by H M B and E C, A S 2141. 9.6 cm x 12.4 cm.

20. Three cards, two designs of laburnum and viburnum or bouvardia, gilt borders. Prize Exhibition series. 10 cm x 13.5 cm.

21. Two cards, a crown of thorns with cydonia or forget-me-nots, one marked Prize Exhibition series. 13.5 cm x 10.2 cm.

22. Four cards, (one Easter), three designs of cornflowers, roses, or chrysanthemum, on a paper with a turned down corner and seal in trompe l'oeil style. London registered. 13.4 cm x 10.2 cm (see Volume 89 no. 23 for set of four).

23/24. Eight cards, two sets of four designs of berries with brown foliage, one set for Christmas, the other for birthdays, one dated 1881 by the sender, three having verses by F R on reverse. London registered. 12.9 cm x 9.9 cm.

25. Three cards, silver borders, roses, Christmas roses, fuchsia with autumn leaves. London registered. 13.4 cm x 10.7 cm.

26/27. Eight cards, three designs of white flowers and green foliage, one design showing five different greetings, one in German. One card was dated 1882 by the sender. London registered. 11.7 cm x 8.9 cm.

28. Three cards, wide gold borders, various flowers with brown foliage touched with gold, and verses on reverse by E H, H S. London registered. 13.5 cm x 9 cm.

29. Four cards, wild flowers and thistles with brown and gold foliage, two dated by the sender 1883, 1885. London registered. 12.5 cm x 8.2 cm.

30. One card, ferns and clover leaves, with verse by E H on reverse. London registered. 10.8 cm x 17.2 cm.

31. Five cards, signed H S, possibly H Sandier. Four cards are London registered and have two designs of ferns in wicker baskets. The fifth has a bunch of brown and green ferns, marked A S, and was dated by the sender 1885. 10.2 cm x 7 cm, 11.7 cm x 8.8 cm.

32. Two cards, one with berries and gilded leaves and grasses and a wide gilt border, the other holly and fern. Both marked R T & Sons, London. 13.5 cm x 10.2 cm, 9 cm x 14.5 cm.

33. Five cards, gilt border, four large and one small, all the same design of Christmas roses and brown gilded leaves. Six different greetings are known on this design. The large cards are London registered, the small A S. 12.9 cm x 9.9 cm, 7.5 cm x 6 cm.

34. Five similar cards, one design of ivy leaves and berries, with red line in border. A S. 12.9 cm x 9.9 cm, 7.5 cm x 6 cm.

35. Two cards, brown foliage with gilt highlights. A S. 9 cm x 13.5 cm.

36. Two cards, daisies, and brown autumn leaves and seed heads. A S? c1884. 15.2 cm x 10.1 cm.

37. One card, thistles with ivy, with verse by F L beneath, dated by the sender 1886. A S 1494. 15.2 cm x 10.1 cm.

# VOLUME 87: RAPHAEL TUCK. FLOWERS AND FOLIAGE, 1880 - EARLY 1890'S

**Most of these cards show the vogue for designs with white flowers and ferns, popular in the 1880's, but giving somewhat colourless effects.**

1. Six cards, (one birthday), four designs of various white flowers with maidenhair fern on a cream ground. Prize Exhibition series. 8.8 cm x 11.8 cm.

2. Three cards, two designs of sprays of forget-me-nots or lilies of the valley with maidenhair fern. One card is a folder with an illuminated design on yellow ground outside, and a verse by F F and the forget-me-not design within; the other two are single cards. Prize Exhibition design. 10 cm x 13.5 cm, 8.8 cm x 11.8 cm.

3. Two cards, one a birthday card with a spray of ferns on a yellow mount with illuminated design on reverse, the other a wreath of fern and lily of the valley on a similar blue mount. London registered. 10.7 cm x 13.5 cm.

4. Two cards, the same design of white azaleas or rhododendrons, one round a birthday greeting in an oval vignette with silver frame, London registered, the other with a verse by E H, A S 1516.
10.3 cm x 15.2 cm, 10.3 cm x 15 cm.

5. Three cards, silver borders, sprays of roses, white azaleas, or Christmas roses, tied with white ribbon, one dated 1883 by the sender. A S. 13.6 cm x 9.1 cm.

6. Three cards, silver borders, two designs of convolvulus and forget-me-nots, and Christmas roses, two having birthday greetings. One card has a verse by E H on reverse, and is marked A S.
10.5 cm x 15.8 cm.

7. Two cards, signed H S, possibly H Sandier. One has daisies and an open book with a text, A S 1410; the other has white jasmine against a blue sky, with a verse by E C on reverse, A S 242.
11.9 cm x 11.9 cm, 11.5 cm x 11.5 cm.

8. Two cards, one a wreath of snowdrops around a winter scene, the other narcissi and maidenhair fern. Both A S.
10.5 cm x 15.4 cm, 16.2 cm x 11 cm.

9. Six cards, four designs of wreaths of spring flowers and leaves around greetings, some in verse. A S.
7.4 cm x 9.1 cm.

10. Two cards, wreaths of white flowers around greetings, one a verse by S K C. A S 1524. 11.1 cm x 11.1 cm.

11. Five miscellaneous cards, four with sprays of white flowers, catkins, forget-me-nots, and leaves. The first was dated 1883 by the sender, marked A S, the second has a verse by S K C on reverse, A S 236, the third a verse by S L on reverse, marked A S, and the fourth is also marked A S. The fifth has violets.
Sizes up to 12.7 cm x 9.4 cm.

12. Four miscellaneous cards, sprays of white flowers, leaves, and fern, two with verses by E C on reverse, all marked A S, series 209, 272, 365, 156.
Sizes up to 10.1 cm x 13.5 cm.

13. Seven miscellaneous cards, sprays of white flowers, forget-me-nots, leaves and fern. Three are signed by H S, possibly H Sandier and marked A S 1243, 1220, ? One is signed K W, A S, another J E and the others are marked A S, A S 108.
Sizes up to 9 cm x 11.8 cm.

*The following cards were probably published c1890, and many are on thick board.*

14. Four cards, thick board, three designs of white flowers and ferns. One has a birthday verse by S Herbert, and an untraced signature, A S 223. The second was dated by the sender 1906, but is

marked A S and was certainly published before 1893. Two of the same design are signed by K W, and one has a verse by J V. A S, D1587.
10 cm x 10 cm up to 10 cm x 13.4 cm.

15. One card with brown border, begonia leaves in plant pot. No mark visible on reverse. 11.7 cm x 11.7 cm.

16. Two cards, sprays of white flowers with leaves or fern. A S?
11.7 cm x 11.7 cm, 12 cm x 12 cm.

17. Two cards, sprays of ivy with violets or narcissi, one signed by E Leistner. A S 447, A S. 9.1 cm x 12.4 cm, 8.3 cm x 11.9 cm.

18. Two cards, one embossed with mistletoe, the other ivy leaves with lilies of the valley, both marked Artist series.
11.1 cm x 14.7 cm, 10.9 cm x 13.8 cm.

19. Two cards on thick board, with floral sprays and unsigned verses, one signed E M (untraced), A S 1538, the other J series 563. 10 cm x 14.9 cm, 12.4 cm x 15.4 cm.

20. Two cards on thick board, one with daisies and bracken in a lake scene, A S 26, the other roses and maiden hair and a flowering branch, A S 2679.
16.7 cm x 9 cm, 16.3 cm x 10.9 cm.

21. Two cards, sprays of gilded leaves with snowdrops or daisies, marked A S 435, A S 2342. 13.2 cm x 10.5 cm, 14.9 cm x 10.1 cm.

22. Two embossed gilded cards, one a bird on a flowering branch, the other daisies. Both A S.
9.5 cm x 12.7 cm, 10.1 cm x 14 cm.

23/24. Nine miscellaneous cards, with sprays or wreaths of various flowers, all with verses on the front by A L S, H M B, M R J, or S K C.
Sizes up to 10.7 cm x 13.2 cm.

25. Two cards.
a) Brown fern and daisies, jewelled. A S. 12 cm x 14.2 cm
b) Waterlilies and reeds by a lake. Art Gem Panel. 11.4 cm x 12.6 cm.

26. Two cards on brightly coloured grounds, one a spray of white flowers and autumn leaves on blue shading to bronze, the other a wreath of snowdrops and ivy on pink, with verses by I E W. Both A S. 10.5 cm x 14.5 cm, 14.5 cm x 10.5 cm.

27. Two similar cards, Christmas roses and forget-me-nots and ivy on pink shading to brown, and ivy with violets on a white shield in a pink shaded background. Both A S. 10.1 cm x 15 cm, 10.4 cm x 13.7 cm.

28. Two cards, with sprays of flowers and ivy or fern on a green shaded ground, one with a verse by M S H on reverse, one signed by Bertha Maguire. A S.
12.7 cm x 16.6 cm, 16.6 cm x 11.9 cm.

29. Three cards in "photographic" style, flower sprays on a cream ground with greetings in gold on a brown border. One card is marked A S 1466 and has a verse by S K C on reverse, but the other two have damaged backs. These are marked with the monogram M B (see Volume 85) so although they appear to be photographs, they bear the hand of an artist.
10.8 cm x 16.5 cm.

30. Two similar cards, flower sprays, one signed M B as above, with verse by M S N and design on reverse, marked A S 820, the other smaller, with a verse by E H on reverse, A S 12??
9.4 cm x 14.5 cm, 6.5 cm x 10.5 cm.

## VOLUME 88: RAPHAEL TUCK. FLOWERS AND FOLIAGE, SMALL CARDS, MISCELLANEOUS LATER CARDS. CORRESPONDENCE STYLE CARDS

**These cards have no particular artistic merit, but are typical examples from the 1880's. Cards with a space left for the name of the recipient or sender, classed as "correspondence style", became popular later in the decade, though few examples have been found for this collection. More elaborate examples may be seen in later volumes.**

1. Six cards with flower sprays or bunches, four embossed, two Rock of Ages series no. 36 with texts, all London registered.
9 cm x 5.4 cm, 4.1 cm x 10 cm,
7.1 cm x 10.7 cm.

2. Seven embossed cards, four on gilt ground with three designs of holly, rose, and strawberry, three gilt edged with flowers and butterflies. All London registered. 4.6 cm x 7.9 cm, 9.3 cm x 5.7 cm.

3. Four cards, various flower sprays on trompe l'oeil style folded paper, one dated 1883 by the sender, London registered. (See Volume 89, no 19, for full set of six designs). 9 cm x 5 cm.

4. Four embossed cards, three designs of roses and daisies. Two identical cards are shown, one marked, one unmarked. London registered. 9 cm x 5.8 cm.

5. Three embossed cards, two designs of flowers, fruits and foliage. Marked R T & Sons only. 8.8 cm x 5.8 cm.

6. Nine miscellaneous small cards with flower sprays, four on a grey ground, A S, two with verses by E H, A S 1201, and three others A S 1200, 103, 100. Sizes up to 8 cm x 6 cm.

7. Six cards with gilt borders. Three have flowers and maidenhair, the other three flower sprays with greetings on gilt panel. All A S. 9.5 cm x 6.6 cm, 10 cm x 7.6 cm.

8. Three cards, one embossed, various flower sprays with greetings or verses, all London registered. 7 cm x 11 cm, 12 cm x 9 cm, 12 cm x 9.5 cm.

9. Five cards, flower sprays, two London registered, two A S, one unmarked. 6.8 cm x 10.1 cm.

10. Four cards, silver borders, three designs of flower wreaths. A S. 9.9 cm x 6.6 cm.

11. Five cards, silver borders, four designs of various flower sprays with greetings or verses, two having turned down corners in trompe l'oeil style. All A S. 7.8 cm x 9.2 cm up to 8 cm x 12 cm.

12. Three cards with gilt borders, one with birthday verse, sprays of white flowers and ferns on background with two colours and turned down corners in trompe l'oeil style. One was dated 1885 by the sender. A S 1283. 11.1 cm x 7.8 cm.

13. Seven cards with flower sprays, four with white flowers, three with roses or forget-me-nots. Four marked A S 102, three R T & Sons only. 9.4 cm x 6.7 cm.

14. Two cards, lilies of the valley or primroses in a background of ferns and leaves. R T & Sons only. 12 cm x 8 cm.

15. Five miscellaneous cards, one with ivy leaves signed T H Allchin, A S, the others various flower sprays, marked A S, A S 162, A S 1248 with a verse by S K C on reverse, A S 1235.  6.9 cm x 10.3 cm up to 11.8 cm x 8.8 cm.

16. Seven miscellaneous cards, flowers and ferns. Two are marked A S 1204, A S 2003, the others A S. 6 cm x 7.8 cm up to 9 cm x 12 cm.

17. Two cards, grey borders, colourful spring flowers, with verses by S K C and E H on reverse. A S 1279. 8.3 cm x 13.3 cm.

18. Five miscellaneous unbordered cards, various flower and leaf sprays, late 1880's. One has a verse by H M B, A S 1230, three are marked A S, one of these dated 1887 by the sender; another has a verse by M S H on reverse, and the fifth is marked A S 121. 6 cm x 8 cm up to 9.2 cm x 12.6 cm.

19. Four miscellaneous cards, one of daisies and holly dated by the sender 1893, and one with a serrated edge, of lilies of the valley with a verse by S K C, both marked A S. The other two are a mixed spray with a pansy and a branch of prunus?, both marked with the Royal Warrant. 6.5 cm x 8.7 cm up to 8.8 cm x 12 cm.

20. Three cards, sprays of spring flowers, two with verses, A S 2094, the other A S 2057. 8.8 cm x 11.8 cm.

21. Six miscellaneous bordered cards, flower sprays, two Artist Series no 136, Two A S, two with Royal Warrant. Sizes up to 8.2 cm x 11 cm.

22. Two cards, flower sprays, reversed to show decorated backs with verses by F L & S K C. A S 1267, 1310. 9.5 cm x 12.6 cm.

*Numbers 23-26 show cards in correspondence style. They have small pictures, with space for names, and simple greetings, and are dated about 1885-90.*

23. Three cards, one with angels and moon, one with a lady in a winter scene, the third a girl by the sea. A S. Sizes up to 11.8 cm x 9.4 cm.

24. Three cards, monochrome pictures of birds on branches, signed J H, C White, and A West, marked A S, A S 543, A S 35 respectively. 12 cm x 8.8 cm.

25. Three cards of animals, a dog, dated by the sender 1888, a sheep, and two cats by Helena Maguire, marked A S 65, A S 75, A S respectively. 12 cm x 9 cm.

26. Four cards, three with flowers, and one of ivy by E Leistner, three marked A S, one of snowdrops marked A S.  Mizpah series 24. Sizes up to 12 cm x 10.2 cm.

## VOLUME 89: RAPHAEL TUCK. FOLDING CARDS, SCREENS, SILK FRINGES, CARDS PRINTED ON SILK

**This volume contains cards in elaborate styles, folding screens using up to eight pictures, folders enclosing cards which were published previously in series as well as silk pictures from earlier publications. The silk fringes, popular in the later 1880's, are reminiscent of the fussy decoration of Victorian drawing rooms.**

1. Triptych card in three pieces, a nativity scene in Gothic style in the centre with angels at the sides. The outside has a scene with a church, and a moveable flap to support it standing up. R T & Sons only. 18 cm x 10.2 cm closed.

2. Three pieces from two similar cards, with a different nativity scene and angels, a cover with Gothic arches, and verses by Bishop Heber. Artist series. 10.2 cm x 17.8 cm, 5.2 cm x 17.8 cm.

3. Three pieces from similar cards, with nativities and angels. Two pieces have greetings on reverse and might have been used as individual cards. 10.2 cm x 18 cm, 5.2 cm x 17.8 cm, 6.7 cm x 12 cm.

4. A three-fold screen with brown border in Gothic style.  There are pictures of old houses by E Hay, scenes inside, narcissi outside. Artist series 1656. 11.5 cm x 20.2 cm.

5. Two cards, by R F McIntyre.  One is a three-fold card with scenes on the Thames outside and an incongruous floral design within with greetings in silver circles; the other is a single birthday card with the same Thames design as the centre piece. A S 599. 15.5 cm x 15.5 cm.

6. A four-fold screen, with a design of orange and yellow berries on one side, and river scenes in vignettes surrounded by leaf sprays on the other side. Prize Competition series. 9.5 cm x 14.3 cm.

7. Two four-fold screens.
a) Trees in winter on one side, with black and gilt borders, and four pictures of various white flowers in oval vignettes on a silver mount on the other side (see Volume 87, no 4), with a poem by E H. A S. Registration mark for 18-3-1882. 11.3 cm x 17.3 cm.
b) Floral sprays on gilt on one side with black and beige borders, and vignettes and scenes by R F McIntyre on the other. Registration mark for 18-3-1882. 9.4 cm x 16.3 cm.

8. Two four-fold screens.
a) Birthday card, four designs of wreaths, signed with B M monogram, around verse by E H, and scenes in silver circles on the other. Artist series, registration mark for 18-3-1882. 7.5 cm x 12.5 cm.
b) Winter scenes on one side with brown and silver borders, flower sprays on the other. Artist series, 1628. Registration mark for 1-12-1882. 5.8 cm x 17 cm.

9. Two four-page folders on pale blue mounts.
a) A sailing ship on a rough sea and a verse by F R within, and an illuminated design of ships outside. R T London, no 1839. 14.2 cm x 11 cm.
b) A ship in moonlight, and a verse by E C inside, with greeting and illuminated design outside. A S 6633. 14 cm x 11.8 cm.

10. Four triptych folders, all with illuminated designs and greetings outside, all London registered, opening to show:-
a) Verse by E H on side panels, and a card with flowers and berries.
b) Versy by F L on side panels, and a Georgian couple with sheep, no 531.
c) Verse by F R on side panels, a card with harebells, no 806.
d) Verse by F R on side panels, a card with winter foliage, no 203. 13.5 cm x 10 cm, 14.2 cm x 11 cm.

11. Four triptych folders, with flowers or grasses outside on gilded panels, opening to show:-
a) "Medway near Aylesford", in circular vignette with flowers. A S 1528.
b) "Thames near Temple", in rectangular vignette with floral branch. A S 1582.
c/d) Scenes on the Thames, with verses by S K C, signed C N, Charles Noakes. Artist series 1634.
Sizes 9 cm x 10 cm, 14.2 cm x 11.7 cm.

12. Three folder cards.
a) In envelope form, gilt and silver borders, with birds and flowers outside and river scenes within. Artist series 435.
8.2 cm x 10.5 cm.
b) Triptych style, a curious combination of brown leaves and Christmas roses, and mermaids on the outside, opening to show a scene with insects and flowers around a log with a door opening to show a fairy within. 13 cm x 10 cm.
c) A four-page folder, a child at a window with snow-laden branches and a robin, opening to show a Dutch canal scene by G B Lefanu and verses by F G. Marked R T & Sons. 11 cm x 15.3 cm.

*The following three cards are the Art Gem Panel series, all with serrated edges, on thick board with greetings in silver, c1890.*

13. An elaborate design of a winter scene with twisted cord around, on a mount with ivy and forget-me-nots, and a metal support at the back, marked London registered. 17.6 cm x 15 cm.

14. An elaborate design of a heron in a water scene, signed L A, with a fan attached edged with twisted cord, dated by the sender 1889. 17.6 cm x 15 cm.

15. Another similar, with flamingo, signed L A. 21.4 cm x 17.4 cm.

*Numbers 16-21 have cards with silk fringes, using up to six single cards in folders with tassels for ease of opening.*

16. Two two-sided cards, one a seaman, by Isa Thompson, with white fringe, the other ferns in baskets by H S, possibly H Sandier, marked R T & Sons, London, with blue fringe.
8 cm x 11 cm, 10.2 cm x 6.9 cm.

17. Two cards, one a four-page valentine with wreaths of spring flowers around messages, and gold fringe, by H S, the other two-sided, with flowers and fern and red fringe and birthday greeting, both marked R T & Sons.
11 cm x 8 cm, 9 cm x 11.8 cm.

18. Two four-page folders, one with white flowers and fern and verses by S K C, and beige fringe, the other with three cards of spring flowers and a silk cover, with

orange fringe. Both marked R T & Sons, the first series 175.
8.2 cm x 11 cm, 6.8 cm x 10.2 cm.

19. A six-sided birthday card using a set of roses, fuchsias, and spring flowers, with yellow fringe and pink tassel. (See Volume 88, no 3). R T & Sons, London. 9 cm x 5 cm.

20. An Easter card with a floral cross, a floral design on reverse, and a white fringe, with the backing card removed. R T & Sons, London. 11.7 cm x 16.4 cm.

21. An Easter card with pansies and a wreath of thorns, with verse by R A H on reverse, with the backing card removed. (See Volume 84, no 35 for the same card with Christmas greeting). R T & Sons. 13.5 cm x 11.7 cm.

*Numbers 22-26 have cards printed on silk, some repeating designs seen in previous volumes.*

22. Two cards, elegant ladies with scenes in heart-shaped vignettes. These give a fourth design for the three cards in Volume 71 no 24. R T & Sons.
10.2 cm x 15 cm.

23. Five miscellaneous cards, one with a scene in a vignette surrounded by a holly wreath, signed with monogram B M (see cards in Volume 85). Three of the other four are marked Prize Exhibition series, the fourth A S, and one of these cards gives a fourth design of violets for the set in Volume 86, no 22.
Sizes up to 15 cm x 10.3 cm.

24. Six flower cards. Three are probably from the same set of flower sprays, one marked Prize Exhibition design. The others are marked A S, one dated 1885 by the sender.
11.2 cm x 9 cm, 6.8 cm x 10.3 cm.

25. Five cards, sprays of white flowers, forget-me-nots, and maidenhair fern, all from designs shown in Volume 87. Sizes up to 10 cm x 12.2 cm.

26. Three cards, one convolvulus signed L S P, one lilies, London registered and one sunflowers with monogram B M (see Volume 85) A S. 9.6 cm x 17 cm, 11.4 cm x 16.4 cm, 11.8 cm x 16.4 cm.

## VOLUME 90: RAPHAEL TUCK. SINGLE SHEET CARDS WITH CUT OUT AND PIERCED BORDERS, SHAPED CARDS, ART NOUVEAU, WITH SCENES AND FLOWERS, DATED 1885 TO1895 EXCEPT FOR A FEW EARLY PRIZE EXHIBITION AND LONDON SERIES

1. Three cards by Albert Bowers, country scenes with cut out edges. Two have

verses by M S H on reverse, Artist series, the third is A S. Sizes up to 12 cm x 15 cm.

2. Four shaped cards by Albert Bowers.
a) Country scene on a palette. Artist series. A S 2334. 13 cm x 9.6 cm.
b) Country scene in sepia set in a circle, with a silver and blue embossed border of the signs of the Zodiac. Dated by the sender 1888. A S. Diameter 12.2 cm.
c) River scene "The Old Ferry Boat", on a boat shaped card. A S. 17.5 cm x 10 cm.
d) Snow scene with cattle, turned down corners. Artist series. A S.
11.5 cm x 8.5 cm.

3. Three cards by Albert Bowers, country scenes in sepia tones with embossed, cut, and pierced borders, and verses by H M B, E N, M R J, on reverse. All Artist series. Sizes up to 15.7 cm x 9.2 cm.

4. Three cards.
a) A snow clad cottage, with pierced lattice work, by L H White. A S 3223.
b) A church with cut out trees and steeple, by C White, with verse by H M B on reverse. Artist series.
c) A cottage in a field, by C Noakes, verse by M R J on reverse. A S.
Sizes up to 11 cm x 14.1 cm.

5. Four cards.
a) Horseshoe, with coach and horses, by George Cruikshank junior. A S.
12 cm x 13 cm.
b) Cattle grazing by a lake, in tambourine, by R F McIntyre. A S. 12.5 cm diameter.
c) Palette, with winter scene by R F McIntyre, and verse by H M B on reverse. A S 452. 11 cm x 15 cm.
d) Two birds on a branch, in tambourine, by Harry Bright. 12.5 cm diameter.

6. Four oval cards.
a) Snow scene, signed W L. A S 1323 A.
b/c) Sea scenes with a flower spray. A S 1317.
d) Snow covered woodland signed E R, possibly E Rawstone. A S. 12 cm x 7.7 cm, 15.5 cm x 9.7 cm.

7. Six shaped cards.
a/b) Sea scenes by T R Kennedy, on a fan shape, and a lifebuoy. A S 228, A S 448.
c/d) Winter scenes on oval palettes. A S 2103, A S 2147.
e) Country scene on a moon shape, by W J Webb. A S.
f) A pastoral scene on a circular mount, with verse by H M B on reverse. A S. Sizes up to 13.5 cm x 13.5 cm.

8. Three cards with cut and embossed borders, a winter scene in sepia with a verse by S K C, a windmill in a vignette with robins and a verse by H M B, and a church tower with bells and a verse, on a blue ground. All A S.
Sizes up to 11 cm x 15.7 cm.

9. Two cards with cut out borders.
a) Holly and a bell, by Bessie Simpson, with a verse by A L S.
b) Holly and a fan, by Agnes Steel, with a Shakespeare quotation. Both A S. 12.6 cm x 11 cm, 16 cm x 10.8 cm.

10. Three cards, cut and pierced borders, with holly, mistletoe, or Christmas roses. All A S (one Art Gem Panel). Sizes up to 13.5 cm x 11 cm.

11. Two cards, cut out borders, one tinselled, with roses and a verse by M R J, the other cornflowers and butterflies with a verse by H M B. A S 6537, A S. 13.3 cm x 9.2 cm, 15 cm x 10.4 cm.

12. Six cards, pierced and cut out borders, with various flowers. Two are in correspondence style, two have verses by M R J and H M B. Two are A S, two Artist series, and two A S 1014, 4206. Sizes up to 12 cm x 8.8 cm.

13. Four cards, flowers. Three have cut and pierced borders (one with feathers), and verses, two anonymous, one by G A F, all A S. The fourth is a rectangular palette with narcissi and fern, A S 2390. Sizes up to 11.3 cm x 13.8 cm.

14. Five elaborate pierced and cut cards with birds.
a) Robins on a fence with appleblossom, embossed. 15 cm x 9 cm.
b/c) Three robins, and three wrens, with a tinselled snowy border, signed B E P dated 1892 by the sender. 11.5 cm x 8.2 cm.
d/e) Swallows and robins in a lake scene with floral borders. All Artist series. 11.7 cm x 9.2 cm.

15. Three cards with cut out white flower borders, two dated 1893 by the sender, A S, the third waterlilies on a blue ground, A S 7216.
12.5 cm x 9 cm, 13.3 cm x 10.2 cm.

16. Two embossed cards with ivy and mistletoe, one with cut out and pierced border and a verse by A O H, the other with cut out panels, dated 1893 by the sender. Both A S, 13.5 cm x 10.5 cm, 13.3 cm x 9.5 cm.

17. Four cards.
a) Oval palette with colours and brushes, and fuchsias, dated 1882 by the sender. Prize Exhibition design, 16 cm x 11.7 cm.
b) Christmas roses on a circular plate, birthday greeting, Prize Exhibition series. Diameter 12 cm.
c) Oval card with autumn leaves and flowers, signed E L, possibly E Leistner. A S 2420. 13 cm x 10.2 cm.
d) Oval birthday card, a flower spray by Bertha Maguire. A S 478.
15.9 cm x 11.7 cm.

18. Four shaped cards with flowers.
a) Silver horseshoe, embossed lilies and forget-me-nots, with a verse by S K C. A S 2113. 8.5 cm x 11 cm.
b) Three vases with daisies, verse by A L S on reverse. A S 6391. 10.1 cm x 12.5 cm.
c) Pansies on a tambourine. A S. 12.5 cm x 12.5 cm.
d) Gloves and roses, with Shakespeare quotation. Artist series. 14 cm x 4.9 cm.

19. Four shaped cards.
a) A horseshoe with lake scene and pansies. A S 4044. 10 cm x 11.5 cm.
b) A sheaf of cards in quodlibet style, with pansies and scenes and a verse by E A L K on reverse. 13.4 cm x 10 cm.
c) An open book in trompe l'oeil style, with violets. Royal Warrant, A S. 13.5 cm x 9 cm.
d) An open envelope with pansies. Royal Warrant, A S. 9.2 cm x 10 cm.

20. Four cards. Three are fan shaped, one red and black with a girl's head in vignette, London registered, one white with ivy, A S, the third brown and silver, Artist series. Radius 8 cm. The fourth is a bell with robins. A S. 11 cm x 11 cm.

*The following cards all have the Royal Warrant, published 1893 on. Some are marked A S, but no numbers are given.*

21. Six embossed cards, with birds, flowers, and scenes in vignettes, (one birthday, Artist series). Five have serrated borders.
Sizes 9.5 cm x 6.5 cm to 9 cm x 12.5 cm.

22. Four cards, pierced, embossed, and cut out borders, two with scenes in vignettes and forget-me-nots, the other two with the same design of scenes in vignettes and roses. 12.5 cm x 9.5 cm, 13.7 cm x 8.5 cm.

23. Six cards, five with pierced embossed borders of flowers around greetings, the sixth a cut out chrysanthemum with Art Nouveau style gilt border around greeting. Sizes 6.5 cm x 7.5 cm to 12.2 cm x 15 cm.

24. Four embossed cards in Art Nouveau style, flowers or scenes in curved and gilded borders.
Sizes up to 12.8 cm x 16.3 cm.

25. Three cards, two with country scenes and a cut out border of roses or pansies, the third an embossed card with roses and forget-me-nots in an elaborate lattice border. 15.3 cm x 11 cm, 11.3 cm x 8 cm.

## VOLUME 91:
## RAPHAEL TUCK. CARDS OF THE LATE 1880'S AND 1890'S, INCLUDING SHAPED AND CUT OUT CARDS WITH ANIMALS AND CHILDREN, OPENING CARDS, ALSO SOME MECHANICAL AND ART NOUVEAU EXAMPLES

1. Four cards in the shape of buckets, by Helena Maguire, with pictures of dogs at the seaside. Artist series, A S 3107.
8.5 cm x 10.3 cm.

2. Four cards by Helena Maguire, three of dogs, donkeys and children, with cut out borders, and one of cats going to bed with candles on a staircase with cut out bannisters. Verses by M G and F L are on the backs of two cards. All A S.
10 cm x 7.5 cm up to 15 cm x 10.4 cm.

3. Eight shaped cards.
a/b) Dogs by Helena Maguire, with verses by F L, H M B, on reverse. A S. 10.7 cm x 7.5 cm.
c/d) Cats by Helena Maguire, on circular boxes. A S 4104. 8.8 cm x 7.3 cm.
e) Two cats in an ark, by Anne Simpson. A S. 10.3 cm x 8.3 cm.
f) Two cats on a chair. A S. 7 cm x 9.7 cm.
g) Two cats on a cotton reel. A S. 9.4 cm x 7 cm.
h) A cat in a cradle. A S. 8 cm x 9.7 cm.

4. Two cards, bulldogs on a leather luggage label, one signed J A Shepherd. A S, A S 4108.
9.2 cm x 19.5 cm, 6.4 cm x 13.5 cm.

5. Five shaped cards.
a) Two robins in a cage, with holly. Artist series. A S 3233. 11.3 cm x 10 cm.
b) Two mice on a log, by I C Vickery, with verse by F L on reverse. A S. 11 cm x 5.2 cm.
c) Birds on a log, by C Noakes. Artist series, A S. 18.5 cm x 5.5 cm.
d) A 4lb weight with robins and holly, and a verse by M R J on reverse. A S. 8.7 cm x 12 cm.
e) Two birds with an umbrella in snow by a fence, by F L Fuller. A S. 8.2 cm x 11.5 cm.

6. Four opening cards.
a) Dogs stealing a goose from a pantry, with the doors opening to show it falling on them. 7.5 cm x 11.3 cm.
b) Two owls in windows, dated 1892 by sender. 11.7 cm x 8.7 cm.
c) Robins by a cottage, in snow. 8 cm x 10 cm.
d) A card opening to show a three-dimensional scene with robins. 9 cm x 7.7 cm. All A S.

7. Two cards with cut out borders, one of two bulldogs on a wall, the other three geese at the Christmas table. Both Royal Warrant. 10.7 cm x 13 cm, 12.7 cm x 8.8 cm.

8. Four cards with animals, opening to show further scenes or greetings, one of a squirrel with a stocking and a verse by H M B, one of a dog beating a drum, one of cats with Big Ben in the background, and one of two cats with a Christmas pudding. All Royal Warrant.
8 cm x 9.8 cm to 8 cm x 13.5 cm.

9. Six shaped cards, one a Scotsman face and back, opening to show a verse by F L, A S. Five are small folder cards, one shaped like a strawberry, with verse by M S H, A S, a box tied with pink ribbon with forget-me-nots inside, A S, a booklet with forget-me-nots, A S 715, a four leaved clover, and a box tied with mauve ribbon with violets inside, Royal Warrant.
5.5 cm x 5.5 cm up to 7.5 cm x 9.5 cm.

10. Seven shaped cards.
a/b) Two battledores with shuttlecocks. A S. 13.5 cm x 5 cm.
c) A shirt front with a "masher" on it. A S. 7.5 cm x 11.8 cm.
d/e) Two cotton reels with buttons, key, and pins, and a verse by F L, probably parts of a folding card. A S. 9 cm x 5.4 cm.
f) A man fending off a bull with an umbrella, by Ellam (see Volume 73, no 24). A S. 9.5 cm x 11.3 cm.
g) A hat with feathers, greeting on reverse. Royal Warrant. 12 cm x 7.5 cm.

11. Three folding cards for children, two in rebus style with pictures for words, Christmas Letter series, another similar with pictures which might have been inspired by the "Boys in a Bedroom" set, in Volume 73, no 2. 9.1 cm x 12.5 cm.

12. Five shaped cards with children, three girls and a snowman by E A Cook, A S, a boy dressed in an eggshell, three children by a wall, A S 9065, a doll and a doll's house by L H White with verse by H M B on reverse, A S, an ark with a picture of a girl pulling a cart with a boy, and a verse by H M B on reverse, A S 3106. 8 cm x 9 cm up to 12.7 cm x 8.6 cm.

13. Four cut-out cards, two of kittens with fans, a boy chef riding on a lobster, and a plump chef with movable head and a verse by F L on reverse. All Royal Warrant. Heights 12 cm to 13.7 cm.

14. A frosted card by C White, a water mill with trees. This has coloured paper in the windows to allow light to shine through, and opens out to stand up, an early well designed version of the "Hold to Light" cards of the 1900's. There is a verse by E N on the back. Artist series. 12 cm x 13.5 cm.

15. Two cards.
a) Interesting topical three piece folder by E A Cook, with three pictures of children in Chinese dress, and a poem on reverse "Their clothes were made by Liberty..." by H M B. This can stand up in triangular prism form. 15 cm x 10 cm closed.
b) An opening card with two children, probably by E A Cook, with a verse by H M B. Both A S. 13.3 cm x 10.5 cm closed.

16. Two mechanical cards, opening to show a monkey pulling a Chinaman's pigtail, and a policeman pulling the ear of a Pierrot. Royal Warrant. 9 cm x 12.4 cm.

17. Two mechanical cards.
a) Santa Claus, opening to show three-dimensional scene. 7.5 cm x 13.5 cm.
b) A card showing three different pictures of a dog, obtained by pulling a tab which moves a series of shutters. Both Royal Warrant. 7 cm x 11 cm.

18. Five cards with children, one a little girl in elaborate dress and hat, the others opening to stand up including a girl on a rocking horse, two of girls drinking cocoa, and a girl and boy at the seaside. All Royal Warrant.
7 cm x 11.3 cm up to 14.5 cm x 12 cm.

19. Three cut-out cards with children in carriages. Two are single cards with greetings; the third is a stand up model with four wheels and two donkeys without greetings, of a type often sent to children at Christmas. Royal Warrant. 13 cm x 8.5 cm, 16 cm x 9.5 cm.

20. Two cards, each of three figures, with movable legs for standing. One is of Santa Claus and two children, the other has three little maids from school in white caps and aprons. Both Royal Warrant.
16.7 cm x 13 cm, 14 cm x 15.5 cm.

21. Cut-out figures of Cinderella and Red Riding Hood, each with two additional pieces to make a stand up scene. Though these have not the appearance of Christmas cards, they have greetings on the back and might have been sent as cards to children. Royal Warrant.
Height 15.2 cm.

22. Four "cards", "Feeding the Birds", similar to above, Mother Hubbard, The Three Kittens (main figures only), and a clown with a hoop. Royal Warrant. Height 12.7 cm to 16 cm.

*The following folder cards have elaborate decoration and fancy borders, some in Art Nouveau style, and all are marked with the Royal Warrant.*

23. Five cards with robins, two having verses by H M B, C B.
7.9 cm x 9 cm up to 14 cm x 9 cm.

24. Five cards, four with children or elegant ladies, and one in plainer style with hunting scenes.
7.5 cm x 7.5 cm up to 12.7 cm x 9 cm.

25. Two cards, each of three plump little girls, and holly, with verses by H M B within. 11.5 cm x 9.3 cm.

26. Six cards with children, two single sheet, four opening, three of these having verses within by H M B.
6.5 cm x 10.5 cm up to 14.5 cm x 10 cm.

27. Six opening cards, with elaborately dressed children, one with a verse within by H M B.
6.3 cm x 9 cm up to 8.7 cm x 12.5 cm.

28. Four opening cards showing the influence of Art Nouveau. Two have a Georgian couple, the others an elegant lady, and all have verses within by H M B. Sizes up to 8.5 cm x 16.5 cm.

29. Three cards, c1900, with elaborate fancy borders. One has a small boy in a frilled suit with a humanised cracker; the other two have Japanese ladies, one with a verse by S K C. Sizes up to 8.2 cm x 13.5 cm.

## VOLUME 92: RAPHAEL TUCK. FOLDING CARDS, 1890-1901, FEATURING FLOWERS AND FOLIAGE WITH AN OCCASIONAL BIRD

**These cards range from the simple folders of 1890 to the elaborate cards decorated with frosting, jewelling, pierced and cut-out borders and lace work. All are embossed, and many have verses in addition to greetings; a few have eight pages, tied with cord or ribbon. They were all manufactured in Saxony or Bavaria, the latter providing some of the better designs.**

*Numbers 1-3 have cards published before 1893.*

1. Eight cards, six in folding envelope style with serrated or cut out borders and verses on two by E N, B S, a folder with birds and a verse by A R, A S 7211, and one with cut out decoration opening to show a verse by H M B, Artist series.
8.3 cm x 5.4 cm to 12 cm x 9.3 cm.

2. Seven cards, with holly or flowers, one with birds. Two are in shaped envelope style, the others are folders with shaped or cut out borders; two have verses by H M B, one has a verse by E W.
Sizes up to 13.4 cm x 7.2 cm.

3. Four cards, one with a bird on a flowering branch, signed C White, with a gold cord holding an inside folder with a verse by F R H. The other three have various pierced and cut designs, and verses on two by E N and H M B.
Sizes up to 8.6 cm x 12 cm.

*The following cards all have the Royal Warrant to Queen Victoria, and were published from 1893 to 1901. Most are marked A S, without numbers.*

4. Six cards, three in envelope style, and three folders, all with designs of holly and mistletoe. Three have verses by G A F and C B. 6.9 cm x 9 cm to 8.7 cm x 11.8 cm.

5. Five cards with various pink flowers and elaborate cut edges. One is frosted, with a ribbon bow holding an opening flap, and two have verses by C B, H M B. 8.5 cm x 11.6 cm up to 14.5 cm x 10 cm.

6. Two cards with cut-out borders, one of violets, one of heather, both with mauve ribbon bows holding opening flaps. One has a verse by H M B. 11 cm x 14 cm, 15.5 cm x 10 cm.

7. Six cards with violets, three having verses by H M B and C B. One card has the greeting "For Christmas and a Golden 1900", and another is a triangular Easter card with a silver cross. 8 cm x 8 cm up to 13.2 cm x 8.3 cm.

8. Four elaborate cut-out cards with violets, one with a verse by H M B. The largest card has opening doors with a Shakespeare quotation inside. 9 cm x 11.5 cm up to 12.5 cm x 16.4 cm.

9. An eight page card with jewelled pansies and violets, framed by silver lattice, with a cord and tassel, and a verse by H M B inside. 11.7 cm x 16.5 cm.

10. Five cards (one birthday), pansies, with elaborate pierced and cut out borders, three with jewelled decoration, one with a verse by H M B. Sizes up to 13.8 cm x 13.5 cm.

11. Six cards with pansies, three having Art Nouveau style borders, the others serrated borders. One has a verse by H M B. Sizes up to 14 cm x 9 cm.

12. Four cards, ivy and forget-me-nots, two with verses by H M B. One has latticed side pieces opening to show a river scene, another has opening panels with lace paper borders. Sizes up to 11 cm x 15 cm.

13. Seven cards, forget-me-nots and foliage. One is jewelled, with eight pages held by a cord with tassels, and a verse by H M B, another has a quotation from Burns. Sizes up to 14 cm x 7.5 cm.

14. Four cards with serrated edges. Two have birds and forget-me-nots, and verses by H M B and E W, the others have insects and flowers and looped forget-me-not edges. 8 cm x 11.8 cm, 11.5 cm x 7.5 cm.

15. Three cards with jewelled decoration on lace paper, one of yellow poppies with verse by H M B, one of ivy with a verse from Longfellow, the third of primroses and forget-me-nots with eight pages held by a cord with tassels, and a verse by C M. 13 cm x 8.5 cm, 8 cm x 14 cm, 10.5 cm x 14 cm.

16. Three elaborate jewelled cards, one with chrysanthemums and horseshoes and a verse by H M B, another with violets and narcissi and a verse by C B, the third with lilies and a verse by CB. 8 cm x 11.5 cm up to 15 cm x 11.8 cm.

17. Five cards of daisies, one with pierced silvered decoration, and a verse by G S, another jewelled, and one with a verse by H M B. 11.5 cm x 6.3 cm up to 10.5 cm x 11.2 cm.

18. Four cards, daisies, one with a verse by E W. Sizes up to 9 cm x 11.4 cm.

19. Four cards with cut-out edges. One has lilac, and a verse by H M B, another green carnations and a verse by C B, the third lilies and a verse by F R H. The fourth card has eight pages tied by ribbon and a verse within by H M B. Sizes up to 10 cm x 16.5 cm.

20. Five cards, three with foliage (one with a verse by H M B), one an open book with forget-me-nots, the fifth hellenium with a blue ribbon and a verse by H M B. 12.5 cm x 6.8 cm to 11.5 cm x 12.5 cm.

21. Three cards with cut-out borders, one of ivy with a verse by H M B, the other two of snowdrops and appleblossom, each with a quotation from Burns. 9.5 cm x 12.2 cm, 9.5 cm x 13 cm.

22. Four cards with tinselled decoration. Two cards, with various flowers and ivy, have eight pages tied with tasselled cord. Two have verses by W H S, the others verses by E W. 12 cm x 7.8 cm up to 14 cm x 9.3 cm.

23. Six cards, various flowers, two with silver decoration, and verses by E W, F L, J L B and a quotation from Longfellow. 8 cm x 11.6 cm to 15.5 cm x 8 cm.

24. Four cards with cut-out edges, various springflowers, and verses by H M B, a quotation from Shakespeare, and "Christians Awake". Sizes up to 9 cm x 14 cm.

25. Four cards, various flowers, cut and pierced borders, one with butterflies, one with birds, and two with scenes in vignettes. One has a verse by H M B. 8 cm x 11.2 cm to 11.2 cm x 15 cm.

26. Seven cards, primroses and various flowers, two with verses by H M B. 5.5 cm x 15 cm to 8 cm x 12.5 cm.

27. Eight cards, various flowers, five with pierced decoration, three with cut out borders. 8 cm x 7 cm to 11.5 cm x 8 cm.

28. Two cards, Diamond Jubilee series, in the shape of a crown, one with rose, thistle and shamrock opening to show a greeting to the Queen, the other a single card with gilt greeting and decoration. These cards are of finer quality and design than many in this volume, and are marked "Made in Bavaria". 12.5 cm x 10.5 cm, 12 cm x 10 cm.

29. Two cards, also made in Bavaria. One has cut-out roses opening to show a greeting, the other is a ship scene marked "Entering the New Century", on an eight page folder tied with a pink ribbon. 10.7 cm x 9.7 cm, 15.5 cm x 10.8 cm.

30. Seven cards, c1900, in styles developed further in the 1900's, with scenes, illuminated script, and white embossed figures, and verses by H M B and E A C P. 11.7 cm x 6.5 cm to 11.7 cm x 9.5 cm.

31. Four birthday cards, pierced and cut decoration and silver frosting, with various flowers. Two have verses by C B and W H S. 9.7 cm x 11.8 cm to 15 cm x 8.5 cm.

32. Five Easter cards, pierced and cut decoration, silver and coloured frosting on various flowers in subdued colours. Two have verses by H M B, one a verse by L H. 11.2 cm x 8 cm to 9.5 cm x 13.4 cm.

33. Four Easter cards, passion flowers and spring flowers, one with a cord tying eight pages, and one with a verse by H M B. 8.8 cm x 11.4 cm to 10 cm x 15 cm.

34. Six cards with pansies in pierced and patterned borders. Sizes up to 9 cm x 14 cm.

## VOLUME 93: RAPHAEL TUCK. A SMALL SELECTION OF EARLY 20TH CENTURY CARDS, WITH THE ROYAL WARRANT TO KING EDWARD AND QUEEN ALEXANDRA

*Numbers 1-16 have folding cards published from 1901-1910, all printed in Germany, most in Bavaria. They have the R T trade mark and usually are labelled Artists series.*

1. An eight page folder tied with ribbon, pansies on a silk mount with gold and silver decoration, and a verse by H M B. 9.2 cm x 15 cm.

2. Two embossed cards, the same design of a Japanese girl, with cut out decoration, and verses by H M B, E H C. 5.6 cm x 16.6 cm.

3. Five embossed cards, (one a single sheet), children in costume. Four have gilt decoration, and one serrated edges, with a verse by H M B on one card. Sizes up to 12 cm x 9 cm.

4. Five embossed cards. Three are eight-page folders with robins or bluetit, tied with ribbon, and verses by H M B, one is a

folder with holly and a verse by C B, and the fifth is a star shape with holly border. 8.7 cm x 9.5 cm to 9 cm x 14.4 cm.

5. Two cards, eight-page folders tied with cord or ribbon, one with an illuminated cover and a verse by H M B, the other with music "The Old Wish" by M A Salmond, words by H M B.
11.6 cm x 15 cm, 14.1 cm x 10 cm.

6. Three cards in illuminated style with nativity scenes, having red, green, or blue borders. One has the Royal Warrant to Queen Victoria but is dated 1902 by the sender. Sizes up to 10.7 cm x 8.5 cm.

7. Three children's cards from a set with a small girl in red with holly, and verses by H M B. 8.5 cm x 11.5 cm.

8. Three children's cards, one of a girl in a hat which moves to reveal a seaside scene, and two cards with wooden dolls and verses within by H M B. Sizes up to 9 cm x 12 cm.

9. Four cards with cats. Two are signed Louis Wain (Artist series), and all have verses within by H M B. Sizes up to 9 cm x 13 cm.

10. Four cards, three with cats, one with dogs, two having verses by H M B. Sizes up to 11 cm x 9.3 cm.

11. A set of four comic characters - The Lady Killer, Two Army cooks with Christmas fare, "Special Scotch", and "Rather Foxy" - two hunting men. 8.8 cm x 12.5 cm.

12. Five humorous cards. Two, with cars shaped like pipes, and a humanised string orchestra, are signed R Warren Vernon, the first with a verse by S K C. The others show Dan Leno as a fireman, a donkey and a scarecrow, and two cocks in morning dress. Sizes up to 12 cm x 9.7 cm.

13. Three cards, one of monks "Laugh & Grow Fat", a Georgian couple with a Christmas hamper and a verse by S K C, and Old Mother Hubbard, with a verse by H M B. Sizes up to 9 cm x 12.7 cm.

14. Two cards, transport. One is an eight-page card tied by a cord, with a train and an aeroplane "speeding a mile a minute", with ivy and forget-me-nots and a verse by W C J inside, the other has a train "to speed my greetings".
9 cm x 12.7 cm, 11.4 cm x 8.3 cm.

15. Seven miscellaneous cards, all eight pages, tied with cord or ribbon, with flowers or scenes. One is a seascape, with a verse by K A B, and one is made of celluloid. 8.3 cm x 5.5 cm to 9 cm x 14 cm.

16. Eight miscellaneous cards, four of flowers, two holly and mistletoe, one a

scene in a vignette, and one an Irish Harp with four leaved shamrock.
10.8 cm x 5 cm to 9 cm x 13.3 cm.

*The remaining cards are examples of postcards, all about 13.8 cm x 9 cm, made before the First World War except for the last two, most of them printed in Germany. The dates given are as the postmarks. Note here that some cards are postmarked 11.45 p.m. on December 24th, obviously in the expectation of arriving on Christmas Day. The numbers of the series give some idea of the vast output of this firm, one of the few to continue into the 20th Century.*

17. Five cards.
a) Boys in the Bedroom" (see Volume 73, no. 2) 1902, Art P C 902.
b) Dogs - Oilette no. 9362, by B Cobb.
c) Clowns - Christmas P C no. 8003, 1906.
d/e) Two of babies, 1905, nos. Christmas P C 8047 and 8256.

18. Four cards.
a) Thistles, 1909, Oilette no. 9612.
b) Santa Claus, Oilette no. C 1062.
c) Santa Claus and child, Christmas P C no. 1822.
d) Santa Claus in balloon, 1906, Oilette no. 8412.

19. Five cards with children. New Year series no. 8392, 1909, Art P C no. C 254, 1907, Christmas series 8341 and 8152, Jolly Years series 605.

20. Four cards.
a) Illuminated, with holly, Christmas series no. 1986, 1911.
b) Angel and child Christmas P C no. 8007.
c) A nativity scene Christmas P C 1763.
d) Two angels, Christmas series no. 8358.

21. Four cards with children.
a) "Our Christmas Market", Rapholette Glosso no. C 3634, 1910.
b/c) Two Oilette series nos. C 3685, (1910) and C 1068.
d) One of the Christmas series no. 8110.

22. Three cards, with a glossy finish, all the Gem Christmas series, with roses, two with verses by S K C and H M B, nos. C 1728, C 1879 (1910), and C 1881 (1910).

23. Four cards. Two winter scenes, both Oilette, no. 9567 (1909), and Christmas P C no. 8623. The other two are dated 1919, made in England, marked Coloured Crayon series nos. C 4081, 6009, the first with a verse by J R L.

24. Four Easter cards. Three are village scenes by W S Coleman, Art Series 1197, perhaps reprinted from earlier designs. The fourth is a scene in North Devon, from Easter Series E1153.

25. Four Easter cards. Two have a rose tree on a background winter scene, Easter Series E1040. The third has snowdrops around a cross with a country scene, postmarked 1907, no. E 113, and the fourth has white lilies, no. E 1037, postmarked 1914.

# THE HILDESHEIMERS - SIEGMUND, ALBERT, AND HILDESHEIMER AND FAULKNER, LATER C W FAULKNER

## SIEGMUND HILDESHEIMER

*Section*
## 10

This firm was originally based in Manchester, and was entered in the local trade directory in 1871. By 1881 it was also working from London and New York, and in this year, which saw the first entry in the Manchester directory relating to the manufacture of Christmas cards, an exhibition was held in St James Hall, London, in connection with a competition for prize money of £2,000. This was judged by G D Leslie, R A, Briton Riviere, R A, and W Hagelberg, and it is interesting to note that early registrations at Stationers' Hall by the firm were entered jointly with Hagelberg. Some of these early cards also appear with Marcus Ward, and it is possible that they were manufactured by Hagelberg and imported by both firms. Siegmund was born in Berlin but became a naturalised British citizen.

The firm employed a number of well known artists, including many women. Their cards used verses, not so many as Raphael Tuck, and few were signed. Cards in later volumes of this collection, filed under subject headings, might have been published by this firm, but positive attribution is difficult, though some unmarked cards are included in volume 104 which the writer would identify as S Hildesheimer products. Buday refers to the "Penny Basket" of 1879, but so far no evidence of this has been found for this collection, and in view of the few cards found dated before 1880, this early "basket" might have been made up from cheap imported and unmarked products. The large number of Stationers' Hall registrations between 1882 and 1885 were mainly for cards of good quality and design, though some of the later ones are inferior both in design and make up. The height of production was reached with the magnificent silvered and frosted items produced between 1882 and 1885, many of which are found in volumes 97, 98, 100, 101. The quality of their embossed cards was unsurpassed.

Production of Christmas cards appears to have diminished during the 1890's, though the firm manufactured postcards into the 20th century. The firm went into voluntary liquidation in 1927. One elaborate mechanical card of distinct Germanic appearance is in volume 15 no. 18. The connection between the three Hildesheimer firms is dealt with in the introduction to Albert Hildesheimer preceding volume 105.

## VOLUME 94: S HILDESHEIMER. CARDS OF CHILDREN AND FAMILY SCENES

This volume has cards which won prizes in the 1881 competition, with others by known artists, all dated in the early 1880's. Most are numbered.

*Numbers 1-3 have cards by Linnie Watt.*

1. Three cards, one printed on silk, children in summer scenes, with verses in a patterned border on reverse. This set won first prize of £150 in the 1881 competition, and was registered at Stationers' Hall 27-2-1882, no. 52. 15 cm x 10.7 cm.

2. Three square cards, the same designs as above cut down to fit in circular vignettes, with gilt corners. Registered at Stationers' Hall 31-3-1883, no. 296. 8.2 cm x 8.2 cm.

3. Six cards, four designs of children at the seaside, a set which won fourth prize. Three square cards have pictures in circular vignettes with gilt corners, and three have pictures in pointed ovals with grey corners. Registered at Stationers' Hall 25-3-1882, 29-3-1883, nos 65, 297. 8.2 cm x 8.2 cm, 5.4 cm x 8.6 cm.

4. Two cards with unsigned verses on reverse.
a) A girl with a doll, seated by an oak chest, by Caroline Toulmin Paterson, a second prize winner of £100. This was one out of three registered at Stationers' Hall 25-3-1882, no. 35.
b) Two children with flowers, artist unknown, in the same size and format. 12.4 cm x 17 cm.

5. Two cards, probably by C T Paterson, maidens in elaborate gowns and bonnets, with verses on reverse. 9.4 cm x 15 cm.

*Numbers 6-8 have cards by Eliza Ann Lemann.*

6. Two cards, one with twelve children representing the months, the other with children gathering apples and holly, third prize of £75. These are two out of three registered at Stationers' Hall 6-4-1882, no. 377. 17.2 cm x 12 cm.

7. Three cards, soulful ladies in long gowns, one holding a baby, with verses on reverse. 8 cm x 15.9 cm.

8. Two cards, a boy and a girl in blue caps in diamond shaped vignettes, with floral designs around. 10 cm x 10 cm.

*Numbers 9-15 have cards by Harry Arnold.*

9/10. Six cards, four designs of Christmas scenes, gathering holly and mistletoe, delivering the Christmas goose, and a stagecoach, two with plain edges, no. 61,

94.26

and four with gilt borders, no. 230. These won a third prize in 1881. 15 cm x 9.7 cm, 13.5 cm x 8.4 cm, 15 cm x 9.5 cm.

11. Five cards, four with family Christmas scenes in a Georgian manor house, and one larger with the family decorating the hall. 7.5 cm x 9.5 cm, 15 cm x 9.5 cm. The nine designs in nos. 9, 10, 11, are from ten registered at Stationers' Hall 8-6-1883.

12. Two cards, summer scenes of children by a river, which won a small prize in 1881. They are two out of three registered at Stationers' Hall 25-3-1882, no. 62. 12 cm x 8.3 cm.

13. Five cards, a set of four with gilt borders around circular vignettes with children in winter scenes, and another of one of these designs in a white border. Registered at Stationers' Hall 21-5-1883. 8.2 cm x 8.2 cm, 10.3 cm x 10.3 cm.

14. Four cards, children in winter scenes, with gilt borders and foliage, one dated 1882 by the sender. No. 16. 15 cm x 10 cm.

15. Two cards, circular vignettes with winter scenes around, one with three children reading, the other with grandfather telling a story to four children. Registered at Stationers Hall 8-6-1883, no. 272. 12 cm x 15 cm.

16. Two cards by George Bishop, prize designs of a boy painting and a girl dancing in dark interior settings, with verses on reverse. These are two out of three designs registered at Stationers' Hall 1-5-1882, no. 43. 10 cm x 15 cm.

17. Two cards, prize designs, well dressed little girls, one with a dog, the other with a goose. These are two out of three designs registered at Stationers' Hall 25-3-1882, by Cel. Dusser, no. 58. Possibly Felix Dussert

who did a large number of cards in the same style for the publisher Augustus Thierry. These can be seen in volume 147. 7.5 cm x 12.5 cm.

18/19. Six cards by Catherine Frances Frere, two prize designs, a boy in a sailor suit by the sea, and a girl in a flowery meadow. Three are folders, three single cards. The two pictures were registered at Stationers' Hall 25-3-1882, and the designs on the outside of the folders, one cliffs and sea, the other a clock, were registered at Stationers' Hall 27-3-1882. 10 cm x 10 cm.

20. A set of four cards by Elizabeth Sutherland Naughton of children's heads, two with little girls in bonnets, a boy in a sailor hat, and a boy in a Scotch bonnet. These won a £20 prize. Registered at Stationers' Hall 25-3-1882, no. 264. 8.5 cm x 8.5 cm.

21. Three cards, prize designs of little girls, head and shoulder, in continental style dress. No. 32. 8.3 cm x 12 cm.

22/23. Five cards by Rebecca Coleman, two designs of girls with flowing hair in spring scenes, in three different formats, two large with verses and design on reverse, no. 41, one small, no. 410, and two others. Registered at Stationers' Hall 18-4-1882. 12.5 cm x 17 cm, 12 cm x 15.4 cm, 8 cm x 10.7 cm.

24. Five cards by Helena Maguire, a set of four designs of children indoors with cats or dogs, and verses on reverse by J E P, A H B, F E E H, and A H C. A smaller card is shown from the same set no. 478, probably published later. Registered at Stationers' Hall 19-4-1883. 13 cm x 10 cm, 9.2 cm x 7.2 cm.

25. Three cards by Helena Maguire, with verse and a design of toys on reverse, showing children in nightgowns with Christmas stockings, one dated 1884 by the sender. No. 431. 9.9 cm x 13 cm.

26. Three colourful cards by Henry Zimmermann, five children in Christmas scenes with toys and crackers. These are three from four designs registered at Stationers' Hall 6-4-1882, no. 26. 15 cm x 10.8 cm.

27. Three cards by Henry Zimmermann, girls in bonnets and frilled dresses, two with dolls, one with holly and mistletoe. These are three from four designs registered at Stationers' Hall 6-4-1882, no. 27. 8.3 cm x 11.9 cm.

28. Three cards by Emily Andrews, maidens in frilled caps, fichus, and aprons, in floral surroundings, with verses on reverse. These are three from four designs registered at Stationers' Hall 1-5-1882, no. 31. 8.3 cm x 12 cm.

29. Three cards, one design of a boy in a blue hat, sitting on a wall with sunflowers below, in two sizes, with a verse and a picture on the back of the large card. This is one of three designs by Frances Anne Hopkins registered at Stationers' Hall 25-5-1883, no. 32. 10.7 cm x 16.2 cm, 9 cm x 12.1 cm.

30. Three cards, two designs of a girl in pink, one with a bowl, one with a cat, in two sizes, with a verse on the back of the larger card. No. 58. 12.5 cm x 17 cm, 8.8 cm x 12 cm.

31. Three cards, one design of a lady a boy and a dog, two cards on a gilt ground, the other on brown, registered at Stationers' Hall 6-4-1882 by Matilda Maria Blake, no. 387. 11 cm x 15.5 cm, 10 cm x 12.6 cm.

32. Two cards on gilt grounds, two designs of ladies, one feeding pigeons, the other with a child and a lamb, registered at Stationers' Hall 6-4-1882 by John Auster Fitzgerald. 12.5 cm x 17 cm.

33. Four cards, three designs of girls, head and shoulders, registered at Stationers' Hall 18-4-1882 by John Eyre. 10 cm x 13 cm, 8.1 cm x 9.8 cm.

34. Five cards by Edwin Gardener, four designs of a boy and girl at the seaside, in circular vignettes on plain white bordered cards with verse or greeting. The set of four designs is made up as a four-page silk fringed folding card, with verses on each page. Registered at Stationers' Hall 13-4-1883. 9.2 cm x 11.8 cm, 9.7 cm x 10 cm.

35/36. Six cards, four designs of children in summer scenes with flowers, one a folder. Three cards have flower designs by Emily Whymper on the reverse, and it is possible that she also designed the children's pictures, but this collection has no other evidence of her designing in this field. The cards are not marked, but have verses printed in typical S Hildesheimer style. 8.3 cm x 12.8 cm.

## VOLUME 95:
## S HILDESHEIMER. CARDS WITH CHILDREN AND FAMILY SCENES, HUMOUR, NEGROES

*Numbers 1-16 have cards signed S Hildesheimer & Co, and were published in the early 1880's.*

1. Two cards, with silver borders, family parties in rectangular vignettes set in winter scenes. 12 cm x 8.3 cm.

2. Three cards with silver borders, children in winter scenes in tinselled vignettes, framed by designs of birds and grasses in silver. No. 492. 10.7 cm x 13.6 cm.

3. Five miscellaneous cards of single children, including a boy with a hoop signed A B, no. 42, and a boy in a long fur coat by Harry Beard with the caption "I am Santa Claus", marked "Copyright 1883". 8.7 cm x 12.4 cm, 8.3 cm x 12 cm.

4. Two cards, babies with flowers or toys, one dated 1885 by the sender. No. 439. 8.3 cm x 12 cm.

5. Two cards. One has a birthday verse and a girl's head encircled by forget-me-nots, probably one out of four registered at Stationers' Hall 6-9-1882, by Caroline Paterson, no. 146. The other has a girl's head in a vignette with pansies around, no. 455. 8.3 cm x 12 cm, 10 cm x 15 cm.

6. One card, a young lady dressed in red, seated beneath a holly bush fixing her skates. No. 448. 12 cm x 15 cm.

7. A large card, a boy in fur hat and collar in a rectangular vignette with a border of owls and the new moon. No. 2027. 15 cm x 18.8 cm.

8. One card, three little girls with a small Christmas tree and a doll. No. 2063. 15 cm x 10.7 cm.

9. Three cards of toys, Punch, a Jack-in-a-box, and a doll. No. 55. 7.5 cm x 7.5 cm.

10. Two small embossed cards, with two children in summer scenes. No. 529. 6.9 cm x 10 cm.

11. Five cards, blue borders, in two sizes, four designs of children playing games with a dog. The larger card is numbered 481. 12.7 cm x 10 cm, 9.7 cm x 7.7 cm.

12. Four cards, three designs of a girl and boy, blowing bubbles, with a Christmas tree, or with mistletoe, by H S T. Nos. 96, 2123. 12.5 cm x 8.6 cm, 12.2 cm x 9 cm.

13. Six cards, four designs of small girls, showing repeats of the same design in different format. Two have a girl with a basket of toys, nos. 409, 2078, one has a basket of holly, no. 448. The other three have little girls with toys, one no. 459. 8.3 cm x 8.3 cm, 7.5 cm x 7.5 cm.

14. Six cards, five designs of children, playing in wicker hampers, or with dogs. Two are numbered 2112, one 194. 8.3 cm x 8.3 cm to 12 cm x 8.5 cm.

15. Four cards, three designs of unprepossessing children on inferior paper. Two show a boy in a sailor suit, one has three children at a party, the fourth has a girl with a cat and kitten. Nos. 489, 499. 10.5 cm x 14.3 cm, 8.2 cm x 12.3 cm.

16. Seven miscellaneous cards, one a baby in a bath, by Helena Maguire, no. 171, a girl and boy in a sailor suit, by E F M, no. 484, two of a baby in a carriage with a dog, no. 456, a girl by the sea, no. 204, and a girl in a swing, no. 444. 9.3 cm x 6.7 cm to 10 cm x 13 cm.

*The following cards are marked S Hildesheimer & Co Limited, and are dated about 1885-90. Many are marked "Made in Germany".*

17/18. A well designed and well printed set of four cards with girls playing in the snow, though they are inadequately clad in short sleeved dresses. No. 534. 11 cm x 16.9 cm.

19. Two cards, a boy playing a violin, no. 328, and a girl in riding habit holding a dog, no. 535. 10.5 cm x 14.3 cm, 10.7 cm x 15 cm.

20. Four cards, two with girls with tennis racquet in one hand and flowers in the other, no. 576, and two with girls out of doors in snowy weather (one with damaged corners), no. 211. 8.7 cm x 13 cm.

21. Four cards, three with little girls sitting on grassy banks, no. 1238, the other a boy in Fauntleroy garb feeding a robin on snow covered steps. 8.3 cm x 11.3 cm, 8.7 cm x 11.3 cm.

22. Three cards, one a girl and a dog indoors, no. 2034, one two boys on a wall dangling a ball before a kitten with two more boys peeping, and a third card with part of this picture and a cut out edge, and a verse by S K C, no. 2304. Sizes 7.7 cm x 10.3 cm. to 10.7 cm x 14.9 cm.

23. Five miscellaneous cards with single children, including one with serrated edges of a little girl out in the snow, no. 2547, and a repeat of a card in no. 18 in a different format. Three smaller cards are numbered 7035, 1213, 3250. 6.4 cm x 9.2 cm to 8.4 cm x 13.5 cm.

24. Two cards, girls and boys in sailor suits at the seaside, no. 1156, 10 cm x 10 cm.

25. Three cards, two sizes, two designs, a scene of a family with children in Stuart times, no. 1022, and a mother and child on

a snowy balcony. 12.8 cm x 16.6 cm, 10 cm x 12.5 cm.

*The following cards have humorous pictures published in the early 1880's, some with negroes.*

26. Two cards by Herbert Sidney, a lady dressing for a ball, and the lady and a gentleman indulging in flirtation observed by disapproving chaperon. Narrative poems are on the reverse. Registered at Stationers' Hall 22-5-1882, no 25. 9.5 cm x 15 cm.

27. Four cards by Louis Edouin Edouard (Manchester), showing a clown, Pierrot, and pantaloon in various comic situations. Registered at Stationers' Hall 25-3-1882. 10.7 cm x 7.5 cm, 9.8 cm x 6.7 cm.

28. Three cards, humanised vegetables in courtship situations, no. 497. 7.5 cm x 10.7 cm.

29. Five cards by Charles Chumleigh, one with two jesters on hobby horses, no. 432, and a set of four comic men in coloured coats and pantaloons on a green background, registered at Stationers' Hall 25-3-1882, no. 87. 12.5 cm x 8.6 cm, 7.4 cm x 10.7 cm.

30. Four cards by Charles Chumleigh, a set of four comic characters, (one trimmed), on an orange background, a cook, a Chinaman, a Harlequin and a boy, registered at Stationers' Hall 31-3-1883, no. 291. 7.4 cm x 10.7 cm.

31. Five cards by Charles Chumleigh, a set of four comic characters on a blue ground, a soldier, a sweep, a servant girl, and a schoolmaster. No. 177. 8.8 cm x 8.8 cm.

32. One card, a negro boy taking an egg from a nest in a flowering tree, no. 302. 9.5 cm x 13.5 cm.

33. Three cards, single negro children, one on a turtle, one with a doll, the third with a drum. No. 469. 7.5 cm x 7.5 cm.

34. Four cards, a set of four negro babies by Harry Beard, one with a dog, one in a bath with a cat, one with a spider, and the fourth eating melon. Registered at Stationers' Hall 4-4-1883, no. 262. 8.2 cm x 11.9 cm.

35. Four cards, two designs in three styles, two boys on a donkey encountering a pig - "A sudden check". Nos. 984, 1216. 13.7 cm x 10.2 cm, 9 cm x 6.5 cm.

36. A rare card, signed Ernest Griset, gentlemen skaters in trouble on the ice, no. 39. 13.9 cm x 9.3 cm.

37. Three cards, hunting and driving scenes. 10 cm x 13 cm.

## VOLUME 96: S HILDESHEIMER. ANIMALS AND BIRDS

*Most of these cards were published in the mid 1880's, and some registrations and artists have been traced. The quality of paper and printing shows deterioration towards the 1890's.*

1. Five cards by Bringhurst B Laurance, monkeys. Two cards show monkeys on a perch and in a cage, and are two out of three which won a fifth prize in the 1881 competition, and were registered at Stationers' Hall 25-3-1882, no. 57. The other three have monkeys sitting on perches, and were registered at Stationers' Hall 19-4-1883, no. 269. 12.5 cm x 8.6 cm, 12 cm x 7.5 cm.

2. Six cards (one birthday), four designs of playful kittens, by Helena Maguire, registered at Stationers' Hall 6-4-1882, no. 75. 10 cm x 6.9 cm. The monogram H J M is traced to her through the registration and descriptions.

3. Three cards, each of two kittens with crackers or holly, by Helena Maguire (unsigned). These are three out of four registered at Stationer's Hall 13-4-1883. 12 cm x 7.5 cm.

4. Three cards, kittens' heads, by Helena Maguire. 7.5 cm x 5.4 cm.

5. Two cards by Helena Maguire, cats with a basket of flowers, no. 2006, and a cat's head with a yellow ribbon and bell, no. 447. 10 cm x 13 cm, 12 cm x 15 cm.

6. Four cards by Edith Carrington, playful kittens, registered at Stationers' Hall 29-3-1883, no. 245. 10 cm x 6.3 cm.

7. Four cards, each with four kittens playing in the snow, no. 503. 13 cm x 10 cm.

8. Five cards, three designs in two sizes of two kittens in a border of flowers, with a verse of greeting, the larger card no. 462, with the designs repeated later in smaller cards, no. 2081, one dated 1886 by the sender. 13 cm x 10 cm, 10.7 cm x 7.5 cm.

9. Two cards, two kittens playing in snow, no. 519. 15.4 cm x 12.3 cm.

10. Two embossed cards, each with two kittens in a bowl or in a slipper, with a verse of greeting. c1890. 10 cm x 7.2 cm.

11. Two cards, one a mastiff's head, no. 435, the other two cats blowing bubbles, no. 2049. 9.5 cm x 13.8 cm, 12,2 cm x 11.5 cm.

12. Four cards, a series entitles "A Farmyard Romance, or the Consequences of Curiosity". This shows a pig investigating a hat with a cockerel inside, and was also issued as a folder, of which

the cover is shown. Early 1880's. 12.5 cm x 8.6 cm.

13. Four cards, incidents in a farmyard with cat, dog, donkey, and pigs. One is dated 1886 by the sender, but the cards were probably published earlier. 11.5 cm x 7.4 cm.

14. Four cards by William Henry Tuck, comic cats dressed in human clothing, registered at Stationers' Hall 19-4-1883, no. 240. 7.5 cm x 10.8 cm.

15. Two cards, one a frog with a bouquet, the other a mouse in a frilled party dress, no. 336. 7.5 cm x 10.2 cm.

16. Six cards, animals in human clothing, a cat with a doll, no. 185, a pig in a smock, no. 2075, a baby elephant with a doll, no. 335, and three dogs, one as a soldier, one a Highlander, and one as Dog Toby, no. 521. 7.7 cm x 7.7 cm, 8.5 cm x 8.5 cm, 8.3 cm x 8.3 cm.

17. Three humorous cards with monkeys, one at table, one with a baby and a Jack-in-a-box, the third with father monkey beating his naughty son with his tail. One is marked Copyright 1884. 8.3 cm x 12 cm.

18. Five miscellaneous cards, two with monkeys, no. 431, one with a monkey teasing a dog no. 2181, one with two cats, no. 2175, and one a man in a nightcap throwing a boot at howling cats, no. 57. Sizes 6.8 cm x 10 cm up to 9.4 cm x 13.2 cm.

19. Three cards, one in correspondence style with two dogs in the corners, no. 577, and two others from the same set reissued later in 1890's. 12.2 cm x 8.8 cm.

20. Three cards by Helena Maguire, cockatoos in tropical surroundings. These are three out of four designs registered at Stationers' Hall 25-3-1882, no. 395. 6.8 cm x 10 cm.

21. Three cards by Emily Whymper, robins and other small birds in winter scenes, registered at Stationers' Hall 25-3-1882, no. 394. 15 cm x 9.5 cm.

22. Two cards by Emily Whymper, chicks in vignettes encircled by violets or snowdrops, with a greeting verse below. These are two out of four designs registered at Stationers' Hall 21-5-1883, no. 243. 10.7 cm x 16.3 cm.

23. Four cards, signed B L, Bringhurst B Laurance, storks on a beige coloured background, no. 446. 7.5 cm x 10.7 cm.

24. Two cards, blue tits in spring, robins in winter, no. 2064. 11.8 cm x 15.8 cm.

25. Two cards, various birds on a branch, with a new moon, and another of owls with a full moon. No. 205. 14.7 cm x 8.5 cm.

26. Four cards, robins in snow, two marked no. 12. 10 cm x 7 cm.

27. Four cards, a set of various birds in circular vignettes, with holly, mistletoe, or roses, one dated 1886 by the sender. No. 2066. 8.3 cm x 8.3 cm.

28. Six cards, swans in circular vignettes with flower decoration, in two sizes, no. 457, 458. 9.9 cm x 9.9 cm, 8.3 cm x 8.3 cm.

29. Three cards with gilt borders, finches, blue tits, and swallows, in flight, no. 430. 7.5 cm x 10.7 cm.

30. A set of four cards telling the story of Robin Redbreast and Jenny Wren, ending in a wedding, no. 20. 12 cm x 8.5 cm.

31. Three cards, serrated borders, robins or blue tits on snowladen branches or flowers, two with a verse by Longfellow on reverse, one with a poem by S K C. c1890. 11.5 cm x 9 cm.

32. Seven miscellaneous cards with birds, including a robin on a basket of holly by Edith Carrington, registered at Stationers' Hall 25-5-1883 no. 251, and a basket of birds eggs by Marian Chase, c1884, with four smaller cards of birds, one of geese. 6.8 cm x 7.5 cm up to 15 cm x 10.7 cm.

## VOLUME 97: S HILDESHEIMER. SCENES, 1883-1890

**Many of these cards show scenes in vignettes with flower or foliage decoration, and those on silver backgrounds, with tinselled decoration giving a frosted appearance, show a high standard of design and production.**

1. Three cards by Marian Chase, with mistletoe, ivy, or rowan, around vignettes of a castle, a windmill, or a seashore, all with frosting on a silver background with a leaf design. These are three out of four cards registered at Stationers' Hall 8-6-1883. 11.7 cm x 15.5 cm.

2/3. Four cards by Marian Chase. Three are from a set with views decorated by rowan, holly, or mistletoe, on a white ground, no. 31. The fourth is a similar card with holly around a river view, no. 29. 15.5 cm x 11.7 cm, 9.5 cm x 13.8 cm.

4. Two frosted cards, one with ivy over a moonlit church, no. 57, the other with frosted branches under a new moon, no. 33. 9.9 cm x 12 cm.

5. Two frosted cards, forest views in vignettes with holly or mistletoe on a silver patterned background, no. 47. 10 cm x 16 cm, 14.8 cm x 10.6 cm.

6. Three frosted cards, mountain scenes in shades of blue, with ivy, blackberry, or catkin sprays, no. 222. 12.2 cm x 13.5 cm.

7. A frosted card, view of Niagara Falls in a circular vignette, with a winter scene below and a silver border, no. 483. 11.4 cm x 18.9 cm. (See Vol. 99 no. 20 for silk fringed card in the same design).

8. Two cards in silver borders, one a forest scene with a silver background dated 1885 by the sender, the other a vignette of the Thames embankment with a border of birds and houses, no. 243. 12.4 cm x 17 cm, 17 cm x 11 cm.

9. Two frosted cards, one with robins in a silver border and a vignette of a snowbound stream, no. 2065, the other two scenes in vignettes with a spray of chrysanthemums on a silver background, no. 481. 12.4 cm x 17 cm.

10. Two cards, silver borders, with frosted scenes of a windmill and a country house in vignettes, no. 484. 12 cm x 18.8 cm.

11. Two cards, sea scenes in vignettes in silver borders, one with birds, the other with roses. Nos. 268, 2012. 12 cm x 12.8 cm, 17 cm x 12.5 cm.

12. Two frosted cards, winter scenes in vignettes, in gold borders, with birds perched on branches, no. 2136 copyright W. 16.3 cm x 10.7 cm.

13. Four cards, all country scenes in winter. Two small frosted cards are numbered 2168, with one dated 1885 by the sender. The other two have the same picture, but one is frosted, no. 79, the other plain, no. 49, the former obviously reissued later in more decorative form. 10.1 cm x 6.8 cm, 13 cm x 10.2 cm.

14. Four cards, a set of designs by Emily Whymper, scenes of a castle with spray of ivy, a ship with oak leaves and acorns, a field of sheep with mistletoe, and a sunset over the sea with mistletoe, registered at Stationers' Hall 25-5-1883. Two of the cards were part of a folder with a verse by Charles Mackay on reverse in an elaborate gilt border, no. 301. 10.7 cm x 15 cm.

15. Three cards from the set in no. 14. One has sheep with mistletoe, in a white border, no. 70, and two others with holly and mistletoe have verses on reverse signed C G and M O, one marked no. 208. So the set was issued in three stages, first with the white border and plain black, with grey border and verses, and again as a folder. 10 cm x 15 cm, 9.3 cm x 14.2 cm.

16. Three cards, two designs by Emily Whymper, with harvest scenes in circular vignettes with grass or flower sprays, two having birthday greetings and one a verse by Dean Alford. These are two designs out

of six registered at Stationers' Hall 29-3-1883, one no. 384. 10.8 cm x 14.9 cm.

17. Three similar cards, cottage scenes in circular vignettes with flowers, and verses below, nos. 422, 2038. 10.6 cm x 16.3 cm, 9.4 cm x 13.7 cm.

18. One card, an easel with a picture of a castle, and flowers on the ground below, by Marian Chase, one out of four registered at Stationers' Hall 15-6-1883. 11.6 cm x 16.3 cm.

19. Two cards, large flower sprays with verses and views of Grasmere or Ullswater in circular vignettes, no. 418? 16.2 cm x 10.5 cm.

20. Two cards, winter scenes of houses in snow in circular vignettes, with ivy or berry sprays, no. 537. 13 cm x 15 cm.

21. Two cards, river scenes in vignettes with violets or pansies, nos. 28, 322. 11.2 cm x 13.2 cm, 12 cm x 13 cm.

22. Two cards, with frosted scenes in rectangular vignettes on a brown and gold background, no. 496. 15.9 cm x 11.9 cm.

23. Two cards, winter scenes in rectangular vignettes, with borders picturing lakes, one signed E I B. No. 263. 12.5 cm x 10 cm.

24. Three cards, scenes in rectangular or circular vignettes, with decorative border. Nos. 1232, 35 copyright A. 11.6 cm x 9.1 cm, 12 cm x 12 cm.

25. Eight small cards, five designs of churches, one by A F Lydon, in circular, star shaped, or cross shaped, vignettes. Late 1880's. 7.8 cm x 7.8 cm.

26. One card, Horton Castle in snow, by L H White. No. 257 copyright I. 11.5 cm x 15.5 cm.

27. Two cards, one with cut out border of owl and ivy over a village with a river in moonlight, on dark blue background, the other on thick card with an owl on ivy. Nos. 1031, 2023. 12 cm x 17, 10.3 cm x 16 cm.

28. Three miscellaneous cards, two with scenes in vignettes, the other a castle by a lake. Nos. 174, 326 copyright I, 440. 7.5 cm x 7.5 cm, 10.7 cm x 7.5 cm, 10.7 cm x 13.9 cm.

29. Three cards, harbour scenes in vignettes with borders showing fishing tackle. Nos. 36, 461. 10.7 cm x 7.5 cm, 12.5 cm x 8.5 cm.

30. One card, prize design of a shell with seaweed, no. 46. 10.7 cm x 15 cm.

31. Two cards, in correspondence style on sepia coloured paper, one with a view of Blenheim and a verse, the other a

cathedral. Nos. 604, 562. c1885.
11.5 cm x 9 cm.

## VOLUME 98:
## S HILDESHEIMER,
## RELIGIOUS CARDS

**These cards were published from
1882 to about 1890, and include a
number of Easter cards, with some
well-designed and lavishly produced
examples on silver backgrounds
with tinselling.**

1. Three cards by Louisa Bewley, scenes of
the Holy Land in semi-circular vignettes,
with flower or foliage sprays, and religious
texts and verses below. These are three out
of six registered at Stationers' Hall
13-4-1883, no. 205. 10.7 cm x 16.4 cm.

2/5. A set of six cards by Louisa Bewley
"Pictures from Palestine", packet no. 643,
complete with envelope with decorative
illuminated cover. These have scenes of the
Holy Land in rectangular vignettes, with
flower sprays or ferns, and texts and
verses below. Registered at Stationers' Hall
25-3-1882. 10.7 cm x 16.4 cm.

6/7. Four cards, three designs signed
L F B, scenes in arched vignettes, with
flower sprays on silver tinselled ground
with frosted leaf pattern. Two identical
cards are marked differently, one
S Hildesheimer, the other Faudel Phillips
& Son, London, no. 9. This set, however,
answers to the description of one by
Louisa Bewley registered at Stationers'
Hall 20-12-1883, by S Hildesheimer, so it
would appear that the other firm was the
retailer. 12.4 cm x 15 cm.

8. Three similar cards with scenes in
circular vignettes, signed L F B (Louisa
Bewley), with sprays of white flowers, one
marked Faudel Phillips as above. No. 34.
11.7 cm x 15.5 cm.

9/10. Five cards, silver borders, three
designs of houses or churches with
Nativity scene in silver star shaped
vignette above. Three sizes, two numbered
2022. 12.5 cm x 17 cm, 8.5 cm x 11.6 cm,
17.6 cm x 12.9 cm.

11. Two cards, church scenes with the Star
of Bethlehem above. No. 2154, copyright
A. 12 cm x 12 cm.

12. One card, a cathedral in a tinselled
diamond shaped vignette, with mountain
scenes around. No. 69, copyright A.
12.2 cm x 13 cm.

13. Two cards, one a winter scene with the
Star of Bethlehem and a text, no. 230, the
other a country house and a church with a
silver cut out border of branches and a
Christmas verse, no. 1009.
15.5 cm x 11 cm, 10.2 cm x 14.5 cm.

14. A card by E F Manning, three angels
with the three crosses of Gethsemane in
the background, no. 671. 12.9 cm x 19 cm.

15. Four cards, one circular, by A F Lydon,
with a Nativity scene, and an angel, no.
540, another an angel in an oval vignette
with a border of lilies, no. 914, and two
cards of the same set with different format.
12.7 cm diameter,
11.2 cm x 15.9 cm, 10 cm x 12.4 cm.

16. An Easter card, with lilies and lilies of
the valley bordering a moonlit sea in
shades of dark blue. No. 2031 copyright T.
12 cm x 18.8 cm.

17. Two cards, scroll shaped in trompe
l'oeil style, with the same design of
shepherds and angels. No. 538.
10.2 cm x 15 cm.

18. Two Easter cards, one a small girl
breaking out of a large egg, no. 150, the
other an angel's head in a silver circle with
passion flowers around, no. 2026.
6.8 cm x 10.2 cm, 16.8 cm x 12.5 cm.

19/20. Two Easter cards, one signed by
Emily Whymper, passion flowers or irises
on a brown background with a text in
gold. 12.7 cm x 20.4 cm, 12.7 cm x 22.4 cm.

21. Three cards by Marian Chase, with
gold crosses and white flowers. Two are
Easter cards with verses, from four
registered at Stationers' Hall 6-9-1882,
no. 153. The third has a Christmas verse by
S K C, and is probably one out of three
registered at Stationers' Hall 20-12-1883,
no. 131. 8.3 cm x 12 cm, 10.3 cm x 15 cm.

22. Four cards (three Easter), a set of four
designs by Marian Chase, rustic crosses
with white flowers and ferns, and religious
verses, one dated Christmas 1882 by the
sender. They were registered at Stationers'
Hall 20-12-1883, illustrating the fact that
registration sometimes occurred after
publication. One is numbered 396.
9.4 cm x 12 cm.

23. Three embossed cards, (one Easter),
rustic crosses entwined with ferns and
clematis or lilies, no. 183.
14.9 cm x 10.8 cm.

24. Six cards, (two Easter), four designs of
gold crosses with white flowers, signed
H M B, no. 391. 6.7 cm x 10.7 cm.

25. Six cards, (five Easter), with silver
borders. Three have gold crosses with
white flowers, no. 463, two have silver
crosses, no. 327, another similar is
numbered 2032. 9 cm x 9 cm,
12.5 cm x 8.5 cm, 12 cm x 6.8 cm.

26. Three Easter cards, one with a bell and
white flowers, one with a cross and shield
and flowers, no. 328, the third a rustic
cross with flowers, ferns, and leaves,

no. 137. 15 cm x 10 cm, 9.4 cm x 13.8 cm,
8.3 cm x 12 cm.

27. Three Easter cards, one with white
flowers against a background of clouds,
no. 669, another an eight-sided star with
lilies of the valley, no. 146, the third a
shield with violets and a silver cross,
no. 151. 12.8 cm x 16.3 cm, 8.8 cm x 8.8 cm,
8.8 cm x 10.5 cm.

28. Four miscellaneous Easter cards with
crosses, flowers, and verses, nos. 155, 165,
653, 658. Sizes up to 10.1 cm x 13 cm.

29. Four miscellaneous cards. One is
circular with Easter greeting and a
shadowy cross with white blossom,
no. 149; another Easter card has a rustic
cross with fern and narcissi, no. 56. The
third card has a spray of white blossom,
signed E C and a Christmas verse, no. 17,
the fourth is a cross with violets and New
Year greeting, no. 153.
Sizes up to 12.5 cm x 9 cm.

*The following cards are not marked
S Hildesheimer, but were probably published
by that firm, 1880-1885.*

30. Three Easter cards with crosses and
white flowers, designed by Fanny Elton
Davies, all with gold borders and verses,
one by Jeremy Taylor.
12.5 cm x 9.3 cm, 9.3 cm x 12.5 cm.

31. Five embossed cards, (three Easter),
four designs of rustic crosses touched with
gold, entwined with passion flowers, lilies,
convolvulus, or narcissi and
forget-me-nots. 6.9 cm x 14.1 cm.

32/33. Five embossed cards, (two Easter),
three designs of rustic crosses with various
white and coloured flowers, and verses
and text below. 18.7 cm x 11.8 cm.

34. Three embossed cards, gilded crosses
with white flowers, verses below.
12.6 cm x 17 cm.

35. Two embossed cards, one a gilded
cross with spring flowers, the other a cross
of fir branches with lilies, one New Year,
one Easter, both with verses.
15 cm x 10.7 cm, 18.7 cm x 12 cm.

36. Six cards, two Christmas, four Easter,
five designs of gilt crosses, white flowers,
and foliage, with appropriate verses
below. 6.2 cm x 12 cm.

37. Two cards, Biblical scenes in vignettes
framed by holly or mistletoe, with text and
verse below. 15 cm x 12 cm.

38. Three Easter cards, gilded crosses with
spring flowers, and one with an anchor
(marked).
7.5 cm x 15 cm, 10.7 cm x 16.5 cm.

39. Five Easter cards, two with hollyhock
or passion flowers on dark grey ground,

three with rustic crosses and spring flowers on light grey ground, all with verses (one by Jeremy Taylor).
7.9 cm x 14.1 cm, 10 cm x 6.8 cm.

40. Four cards, white flowers with gilt crosses. 8.1 cm x 13.8 cm.

# VOLUME 99:
## S HILDESHEIMER. MISCELLANEOUS FANCY CARDS

**These include some cards with crosses, elaborate mounts, folding cards, cut out and shaped examples, some printed on silk or with silk fringe.**

1/2. Sixteen cards with crosses, five designs of roses, pansies, and lilies. There are eight small cards, including four for Easter, two larger marked S Hildesheimer & Co, entered at Stationers' Hall, and six on fancy mounts. These are five designs out of eight registered at Stationers' Hall 17-3-1875, 13-7-1876, with W Hagelberg. Identical scraps appear on some Canton and Marcus Ward cards in volumes 18 and 30. 5.2 cm x 8.3 cm up to 9.5 cm x 12.3 cm.

3. Three cards.
a) A triptych folding card with a house on the front, Santa Claus on the back, and inside a family party with Santa Claus going up and down the stairs.
11.5 cm x 15 cm.
b) The same Santa Claus picture on a single card, no. 491. 11.5 cm x 15 cm.
c) A brown Santa Claus bearing a tree and a basketful of toys, no. 292.
7.2 cm x 11.6 cm.

4. Two folding cards.
a) A tryptych card, brown outside, opening to show verses and illuminated borders on the side flaps and a birds' nest by Emily Whymper inside.
14.4 cm x 11 cm closed.
b) A four-page folder with gilt border on yellow and a seascape outside, opening to show the same border with a Christmas verse on one side and a prize design of flowers and foliage on the other, no. 97. 15.3 cm x 11.7 cm. (See volumes 102, nos. 15, 16, and volume 100, no. 7, for similar designs).

5. Two triptych cards by William Henry Tuck, with party scenes inside, and winter scenes of the house and a skating party outside. The brown backs have adjustable flaps to prop up the cards. Registered at Stationers' Hall 25-5-1883. 15 cm x 12 cm closed.

6. Two cards, one a folding card with an illuminated design outside, and sprays of gentians or sweetpeas with a Christmas verse within. The other is a single similar card with pansies. 8 cm x 17.8 cm

*Numbers 7-19 have shaped cards, dated 1885-1890.*

7. Four octagon-shaped frosted cards, three designs of Durham Cathedral, Corfe Castle, Lincoln Cathedral in a central circle with fold-over edges in trompe l'oeil style, no. 210. 10.5 cm diameter.

8. Four circular cards with scenes in vignettes on mistletoe or winter branches, two dated by the senders 1886, 1888. Nos. 239, 508. 9.7 cm, 11.2 cm diameter.

9. Three cards with churches, one oval no. 211, two circular no. 241, copyright A. 12 cm x 8.8 cm, 13 cm diameter.

10. Two circular cards with silver scalloped borders, views of the Old Palace, Lincoln, framed in trees. 14 cm diameter.

11. Six cards by A F Lydon, two moon shaped with churches, no. 493, four circles on crosses with three views of York, Durham, or Salisbury, no. 499. 13 cm x 5.7 cm, 9.7 cm x 9.7 cm.

12. Three cards by A F Lydon, pictures of Jerusalem, Bethlehem, and Nazareth in crosses with silver borders, no. 501. 13.5 cm x 13.5 cm.

13. Two embossed cards, with lake views touched with silver, and a cut out leaf pattern on two sides, no. 1016. 11.7 cm x 12.5 cm.

14. Two similar, with pictures of churches in snow, and cut out borders of ivy and bells, no. 1024. 13.3 cm x 18 cm.

15. Four cards in trompe l'oeil style. Two are scroll shaped with the same picture of a village church, nos. 510, 580 (the second is a reprint in correspondence style). The other two are like a paper roll with a cut out ivy border in the folds, and village scenes, no. 1260. Two cards are signed Nöel. 14.5 cm x 9 cm, 10 cm x 13 cm.

16. Four similar, in trompe l'oeil style imitating paper rolls, with village scenes. The two larger have cut out holly or ivy borders, no. 1010, the others have robins and a holly or mistletoe branch, no. 1200. 14.3 cm x 11.4 cm, 11.5 cm x 8.6 cm.

17. Three cards, one a scroll with a church and birthday verse, no. 988, the others cut out church scenes with verses by H S H, S K S, on reverse, no. 1355. 8.3 cm x 11.8 cm, 12.3 cm x 9.2 cm.

18. Five shaped cards. Two are hats filled with flowers, no. 487, and three have white flowers, one oval with a silver border, no. 513, two circular in pale blue, no. 2033. 12 cm x 5 cm, 15 cm x 11 cm, 12.5 cm diameter.

19. Three curious monochrome cards shaped like Father Christmas, with

pictures of children on the body, signed E J M, no. 1230. 15.5 cm x 6.8 cm.

*Numbers 20-24 have silk decoration of various kinds, 1885-90.*

20. Very fine two-sided card fringed with blue silk, around frosted views of Niagara Falls in vignettes set in winter scenes, no. 483. (See volume 97 no. 7).
18 cm x 25.7 cm with fringe.

21. Three embossed cards with silk insets, one a little girl no. 12586, one roses in a paper folder, the third violets with a white silk bow, no. 5624.
Sizes up to 8.3 cm x 12.5 cm.

22. Five cards printed on silk, with various flowers, two with verses. One was dated 1885 by the sender, two are numbered 310, 312, the latter identical with a design in volume 100, no. 19, but differently numbered. Sizes up to 14.8 cm x 12.5 cm.

23. Two silk fringed folders, one with white and gold fringe and four pictures of forget-me-nots, the other with blue fringe and four pictures of flowers or berries. 10 cm x 6.9 cm without fringe.

24. One card with brown and gold silk fringe, with flower designs on two sides, one repeating a card in volume 103 no. 18. 10.7 cm x 16.5 cm without fringe.

25. Two folding cards c1890.
a) A frosted card with two-sided flaps of cut out children, opening to show a winter scene. 8.9 cm x 12.9 cm.
b) A folding card, three humanised geese sitting at table, opening to show a verse, no. 2716. 11.5 cm x 6 cm. Both are marked "S Hildesheimer & Co, printed in Germany".

26. Four cards, 1890's, three with serrated edges, one gilded. One opens to reveal a view, no. 2525, another has a jewelled window opening to show a view, no. 2649. The third has dwarfs pulling bell ropes, no. 3255, and the fourth has a bunch of violets, no. 1958.
Sizes up to 13 cm x 8.5 cm.

# VOLUME 100:
## S HILDESHEIMER. FLOWERS & FOLIAGE 1876-1883

**This volume includes prize designs of 1881, and some artists' cards, with flowers and foliage, holly and mistletoe, and a few unusual cards with decorated china.**

1/2. Eighteen small cards, two with texts, one a valentine, and one a birthday greeting. They have six designs of rose, moss rose, carnation, violets, passion flowers, and forget-me-nots, nine on beige grounds (one on a gilt-edged mount), and nine on black backgrounds. The same designs were also issued by Marcus Ward

**101.8**

(see volume 44, nos. 1-5), but they were registered at Stationers' Hall 22-4-1876 by S Hildesheimer, and were probably supplied by Hagelberg to both firms. The unmarked cards might have been issued by either firm, but a representative selection has been included for each.
8.3 cm x 5.5 cm.

3/5. Eleven cards, including two with birthday greetings, six designs of rose, carnations, cornflowers, forget-me-nots, pansies, camellias, three on beige grounds, eight on black backgrounds. These are also found marked Marcus Ward (see volume 45 nos. 1-4), but were registered at Stationers' Hall 22-4-1876 as above.
12.2 cm x 7.2 cm.

6. One embossed card, a fourth prize design by Susan Annie Ashworth, with snowdrops and fern in snow. Registered at Stationers' Hall 25-3-1882, no. 36.
12.5 cm x 17.1 cm.

7. Four gilt-edged cards, prize designs with white flowers and brown foliage, no. 97. 12 cm x 8.4 cm.

8. Triptych folding card, with an illuminated ivy design on the cover and the flaps, which open to show a prize design card of roses and ferns.
13.5 cm x 18.1 cm closed.

9. Two cards, prize designs of a rose on a grey ground, no. 71. 10 cm x 15 cm.

10. Two prize designs, roses.
a) Yellow roses in a paper holder, by M E Duffield, one out of four registered at Stationers' Hall 25-3-1882, no. 45.
16.4 cm x 10.7 cm.
b) Yellow roses on a bordered card, no. 48. 16 cm x 11.8 cm.

11. Two prize designs, roses.
a) Fifth prize design, red roses hanging on a wall on a bordered card, no. 98.
11.4 cm x 16.6 cm.
b) Red roses with an overturned wicker basket, no. 103. 15 cm x 10.7 cm.

12. Two cards by Robert Rayment, prize designs of three jugs and vases, with ferns, two out of three designs registered at Stationers' Hall 25-3-1882, no. 53.
10.7 cm x 15 cm.

13/14. Six cards, with four prize designs by Marie Nussbaum, flowers or holly with the paper torn back in trompe l'oeil style to show mountains, lake, or forest. Two variants are shown, one the same size but embossed, one smaller. Registered at Stationers' Hall 27-3-1882, no. 100.
11.5 cm x 18.4 cm, 10 cm x 15 cm.

15. An embossed card by Fanny Elton Davis, azaleas in a mounted shell, one out of four registered at Stationers' Hall 6-4-1882, no. 54. 9.4 cm x 10.7 cm.

16. Two gilt edged cards by Jessie Chase, snowdrops or forget-me-nots with a piece of a crested letter, registered at Stationers' Hall 4-4-1883, no. 270. 15 cm x 10 cm.

17. Five cards in two sizes, four designs by Edith Carrington of various flowers with a hanging horseshoe, registered at Stationers' Hall 4-4-1883. One small card is numbered 66.
10.7 cm x 15 cm, 7 cm x 10 cm.

18. Two cards by Edith Carrington, ivy or mistletoe sprays on a tinselled silver background, similar to that in cards by other artists. These are two out of three designs registered at Stationers' Hall 13-4-1883, no. 8. 10.5 cm x 7.6 cm.

19. Three cards by Edith Carrington, various flowers with a quill pen, three out of four designs registered at Stationers' Hall 13-4-1883, one no. 290.
15.8 cm x 11.9 cm.

20. An embossed card, prize design by Walter Charles Strong, a "pottle", or wicker holder, with a bunch of red roses, one out of three designs registered at Stationers' Hall 6-4-1882. 12 cm x 18.7 cm.

21. One card, a large shell with white and purple violets and leaves, prize design, no. 50. 15 cm x 12 cm.

22. Three cards by Alice Turner, one a valentine, two designs of heart shaped flower wreaths with a single rose, two out of three designs registered at Stationers' Hall 20-12-1883, no. 331. 8.3 cm x 8.3 cm.

23. Four cards on a tinselled silver background, with holly, oak leaf, flower, or kingfisher, each with suitable verse.
15.2 cm x 8.3 cm.

24. Set of four embossed cards on frosted silver background with leaf pattern, holly, mistletoe, oak, and ivy sprays.
15.2 cm x 9.6 cm.

25. Two cards, a spray of mistletoe or ivy leaves with a background pattern of frosted cobwebs, one numbered 6. These are perhaps two out of four registered 13-4-1883 by Emily Whymper, but positive identification is uncertain from the descriptions in the register.
15.1 cm x 9.4 cm.

26. Three cards, one with a frosted holly branch, no. 74, two silver bordered with frosted mistletoe or berberis, and a verse of greeting, no. 22.
8.5 cm x 8.5 cm, 8.5 cm x 12 cm.

27. Two cards, holly sprays, one on a plain grey card, no. 54, the other a bordered frosted card with spiders' webs, no. 21.
8.7 cm x 12 cm, 13 cm x 8 cm.

28. Four small cards by Marian Chase, ivy, holly, mistletoe, oak, with appropriate verses, three embossed, no. 196, one plain. Probably those registered at Stationers' Hall 29-3-1883. 8.4 cm x 6 cm.

29. Two cards with holly sprays and verses, one with a plain edge, no. 200, the other with a silver border and a verse by F E E H, no. 189.
10.7 cm x 15 cm, 10.7 cm x 16.5cm.

30. A set of four embossed illuminated cards, each with a decorated china bowl and plate, no. 21. 12 cm x 8.3 cm.

31. Five cards, one a birthday card as in no. 30, two of plates as in no. 30, one a teapot with flowers, the fifth a decorated vase and fan. Sizes up to 12 cm x 8.3 cm.

## VOLUME 101: S HILDESHEIMER. CARDS BY MARIAN CHASE & BERTHA MAGUIRE, WITH FLOWERS, FERNS & FOLIAGE

*Numbers 1-19 have cards designed by Marian Chase, dated from 1880-1883. They are usually signed M C, and many have Stationers' Hall registrations, though identification is sometimes uncertain from the descriptions in the register.*

1. Four cards, flowers in paper holders, registered at Stationers' Hall 25-3-1882, no. 73. 10.7 cm x 6.7 cm.

2. Three cards, ferns planted in blue and white china slippers. These are three out of four registered at Stationers' Hall 27-3-1882, no. 95. 6.9 cm x 10 cm.

3. Five cards, two with flowers threaded through palettes, two out of four registered at Stationers' Hall 25-3-1882, no. 110 and three more, two designs, with flowers in blue and white bowls, two out of four

registered at Stationers' Hall 31-3-1883, no. 219. 12 cm x 8.4 cm, 8.4 cm x 8.4 cm.

4. Two embossed cards, one with a bunch of ferns, no. 77, the other ferns growing in a plant pot, one out of four registered at Stationers' Hall 6-4-1882, no. 86. 8.6 cm x 12.5 cm, 8.4 cm x 12 cm.

5/6. Four cards, prize designs, ferns in hanging wire baskets on plain beige cards, registered at Stationers' Hall 6-4-1882, no. 80. 12.5 cm x 17 cm.

7. Seven embossed cards, four designs in two styles and sizes, bunches of ferns. These are four out of six designs registered at Stationers' Hall 27-3-1882. 10 cm x 6.9 cm, 8.4 cm x 6 cm.

8. Five embossed cards, one birthday, four designs of ferns on a beige ground, with verses below, unsigned. 7.8 cm x 14 cm.

9. Three embossed cards, ferns on a white ground, verses below. 15 cm x 10.7 cm.

10. Two embossed cards, ferns and grasses on beige grounds with a verse, unsigned. 8 cm x 14.1 cm.

11. Four miscellaneous cards, ferns, leaves, and ivy, one a birthday card with a cross, one a prize design no. 65, the others nos. 82, 84.
Sizes 10.7 cm x 6.7 cm up to 10 cm x 15 cm.

12. Four cards, chrysanthemums in china bowls, registered at Stationers' Hall 6-4-1882, no. 94. 15 cm x 10.7 cm.

13. Three cards, flowers and ferns with verse. 15 cm x 10.7 cm

14. Two cards, mixed flowers in rustic garden stands, two out of four designs registered at Stationers' Hall 13-4-1883, no. 253. 12.5 cm x 17 cm.

15. One card, lilac in a stone jug, one out of two registered at Stationers' Hall , 19-10-1882, no. 241. 12 cm x 15 cm.

16. One card, creepers trailing from a hanging shell, one out of four registered at Stationers' Hall 13-4-1883. 11.7 cm x 15.8 cm.

17. Four embossed cards, two designs of white flowers and ferns, one birthday, one a valentine, two Easter cards, one dated 1882 by the sender. 12.5 cm x 8.5 cm.

18. Three embossed cards, two designs of white flowers and ferns with verses, two birthday, one a valentine. 10.7 cm x 14.8 cm.

19. Two silver bordered cards, white flower sprays with verse, no. 335. 12.5 cm x 8.5 cm.

*Numbers 20-28 have cards designed by Bertha Maguire. Her cards were signed "Bertha", or B M, or her full name.*

20. Eight cards, six with four designs of flowers in baskets, registered at Stationers' Hall 25-3-1882, no. 74, and two with a single rose, no. 28?, two out of four registered at Stationers' Hall 25-3-1882. 10 cm x 6.8 cm, 9.3 cm x 5.5 cm.

21. Four cards, three designs of flowers with palettes inscribed with greetings, (one on a fancy gilded pink mount), three out of four designs registered at Stationers' Hall 6-4-1882. 10 cm x 6.9 cm, 14 cm x 10.5 cm.

22. Two cards, forget-me-not and lily of the valley sprays on a beige card with verse, two out of four registered at Stationers' Hall 6-4-1882, no. 92. 12.5 cm x 8.5 cm.

23. Two cards.
a) Fern in hanging basket, one out of four registered at Stationers' Hall 6-4-1882, no. 385. 15 cm x 12 cm.
b) Lilies of the valley in a glass tumbler, one out of four registered at Stationers' Hall 13-4-1883, no. 263. 12 cm x 15 cm.

24. Three cards, flowers in hanging cork baskets, three out of four designs registered at Stationers' Hall 6-9-1882, no. 152. 12 cm x 15 cm.

25. One card, white flowers and ferns in a decorated jar, no. 42. 12.4 cm x 17 cm.

26. Three cards, two with roses or violets and ferns, no. 27, the third a later card c1885 with a basket of flowers and a verse by A F Earl. 8.5 cm x 12.5 cm, 10.4 cm x 13.3 cm.

27/28. Four cards, (one birthday), three designs of ferns in earthenware plant pots, c1882. These are signed B M, i.e. Bertha Maguire but not marked S Hildesheimer. Probably published by that firm, though she worked for several other publishers. 11.8 cm x 15.9 cm.

## VOLUME 102: S HILDESHEIMER. CARDS DESIGNED BY EMILY WHYMPER, MAINLY FLOWERS & FOLIAGE, WITH SOME 1881 PRIZE DESIGNS

**The cards are signed E W except where otherwise stated. Few of these cards are marked S Hildesheimer but as Mrs Whymper is not known to have worked for other firms, all the cards in this collection signed by her are included with this publisher's products. They are notable for the large number of designs with grasses and insects, which were surprisingly popular judging by the quantity found in scrap books, perhaps due in part to the appropriate verses linking the summer design to the Christmas**

102.2

**and New Year theme. Many cards are unnumbered, and these were probably published 1880 or earlier.**

1. Three cards, prize designs of flowers and butterflies with trees or lake in circular vignettes, registered at Stationers' Hall 25-3-1882, no. 49. 12.1 cm x 15 cm.

2. Two cards, prize designs of rocks, fishes, and seaweed, two out of four registered at Stationers' Hall 25-3-1882, no. 55. 10 cm x 15 cm.

3/5. Fourteen cards, six designs of butterflies and grasses, two dated 1878 by the sender. There are two complete sets of six, one set embossed, with gilt border, the other plain with white border and verses on the backs, and two spare cards reversed to show the verses, one of which reads:
"Butterflies among the grass
Tell us time doth swiftly pass
Let it wait awhile for me
To wish all Christmas joys to thee"
7.2 cm x 16.6 cm.

6/8. Eleven cards, six designs of insects and flowers on grasses, one set of six embossed with gilt border, and five of a plain edge set with verses on reverse, one on an elaborate pink and gold mount. c1878. 7.2 cm x 16.6 cm, 19.6 cm x 10.2 cm.

9. Six embossed cards, (one birthday), four designs of butterflies and foliage or berries with an appropriate verse below. One card is on a pink and gold mount, and three were dated 1878 by the senders. 6.4 cm x 13.3 cm, 9 cm x 15.9 cm.

10. Four embossed cards, insects and berries or flowers on green mounts, with verses below. c1880. 6.4 cm x 13.3 cm.

**102.15**

11. Three cards, moths on branches on a blue ground, one dated 1879 by the sender. 4.6 cm x 13.3 cm.

12/13. Twelve cards, six designs of insects on grasses, some on a green mount, some on cream, with appropriate verses on reverse:
"As the busy chafer works
In the woods through summer days,
Labour thou through the New Year
That its close may win thee praise."
Two cards are on illuminated mounts, two were dated 1878 by the sender.
4.4 cm x 12.8 cm, 7.1 cm x 15.4 cm.

14. Six cards, fungi and grasses, one dated 1879 by the sender. 5.1 cm x 11.1 cm.

15/16. Eight cards, four designs of birds' nests with eggs, and various flowers. There are two sets in different sizes, with verses on the backs of the larger cards. 14.2 cm x 11 cm, 10 cm x 6.8 cm.

*Numbers 17-21 have cards with dark coloured backgrounds and plain edges, c1880.*

17/18. Six cards, four designs of flower sprays, with verses by J G and F L. 10.9 cm x 14.3 cm.

19. Three cards, heathers, with appropriate verses. 10.9 cm x 14.3 cm.

20. Five cards, two sizes, heathers. These are not signed E W but the designs are repeats of those in no. 19, with appropriate verses. 13.9 cm x 10.3 cm, 7 cm x 10.1 cm.

21. Six cards, heathers, unsigned, but attributed through similarity. 5.5 cm x 12.5 cm.

22. Three cards, wild flower sprays on a grey ground. 7.1 cm x 11.1 cm, 11.1 cm x 7.3 cm.

23/24. Five cards, a set of four gilt edged cards with flower sprays on a black ground, and another of the set on an illuminated mount, c1880. 8.3 cm x 12.7 cm, 11 cm x 15.5 cm.

25/26. Nine cards, four designs of flower sprays on cream or pale green background, showing different captions, one on an illuminated mount, c1878. 11.1 cm x 7.3 cm, 14.2 cm x 10.2 cm.

27/28. Eight cards, (one birthday), five designs of rose sprays on cream or pale green ground, with greetings in gilt, one dated 1878 by the sender. 9.9 cm x 13.2 cm, 8.8 cm x 12.1 cm.

29. Seven cards, repeating four of the above designs, one a birthday card. Two are tinselled, with greetings in red. These might be from eight designs registered at Stationers' Hall 6-4-1882. 7.2 cm x 11 cm.

30/33. Ten cards, (nine embossed), six designs of hanging rose sprays on pale green mounts with verses in gilt. These might be some of the designs registered at Stationers' Hall 25-3-1882, and 6-4-1882, but were probably published earlier. Five have gilt line borders, and some are tinselled. 10.1 cm x 16.7 cm.

34. Four embossed cards repeating four of the above designs, one dated 1880 by the sender. 8 cm x 11.8 cm.

35. Six cards, four designs of rose sprays and grasses, with greetings in gilt, on brown or pale green mount, one tinselled. c1880. 8.3 cm x 13.3 cm.

36. Two smaller embossed cards from the above set. 5.9 cm x 11.2 cm.

37. Six cards, four designs of rose and fern sprays, two being on illuminated mounts. 4.7 cm x 13.4 cm, 8 cm x 16.4 cm.

## VOLUME 103:
## S HILDESHEIMER.
## REMAINING CARDS WITH FLOWERS & FOLIAGE

**Most of these cards are dated from 1881-1886, with a few later ones up to 1892. No artists or Stationers' Hall records have been traced.**

1. Two embossed cards, pink roses on grey ground, no. 60. 12 cm x 8.3 cm.

2. Two embossed cards, pink roses on envelopes tied with white or blue ribbon in trompe l'oeil style. One is marked no. 227, the other has a greeting in German and a message in German from the sender. 13.7 cm x 10.8 cm.

3. One card, a hand in a lace cuff holding a rose over a wall with a garden vase. No. 15. 10.7 cm x 16.5 cm.

4. Three cards, similar to those by Emily Whymper but unsigned, two with hanging rosebuds, no. 88, the third with a spray of rose and ferns, no. 106, all with verses. 6.9 cm x 10 cm, 8.5 cm x 12.5 cm.

5. Three plain edge cards, rose sprays on a cream or pale green ground, nos. 710, 172, 173. 11 cm x 15.4 cm, 15 cm x 10 cm.

6. Four cards. Three are unnumbered, with single roses, two birthday, the third with New Year greeting dated 1882 by the sender. The fourth has a border of roses around a Christmas verse, no. 531. Sizes up to 7.5 cm x 10.8 cm.

7. Three cards, single roses on dark grounds. 8.3 cm x 8.3 cm.

8. A folding card, with a forget-me-not and ivy basket on a pale blue mount with gilt decoration, no. 104. 11.6 cm x 15.2 cm closed.

9. Four cards, one embossed repeat of the above design, no. 76, and three other embossed cards with forget-me-nots and lilies of the valley in wicker baskets, no. 70. 8.4 cm x 12.1 cm, 8.4 cm x 5.5 cm.

10. Five cards. One has a wreath of forget-me-nots around a Christmas verse, no. 415. The four others, with three designs of forget-me-nots and various white flowers, have a greeting verse on a panel with a cut out cord through a hole in trompe l'oeil style, no. 341. Two are valentines, two birthday cards. 12 cm x 12 cm, 9.9 cm x 5.6 cm.

11. Two cards, one with a butterfly and grasses, no. 409, the other with a butterfly hovering over a bunch of forget-me-nots and fern, no. 77. 10.7 cm x 16.4 cm, 16 cm x 12.1 cm.

12. Two cards, flowering branches against a moonlit sky, one dated 1884 by the sender. No. 417. 10.7 cm x 7.5 cm.

13. Three cards, (one birthday), two designs of carnations or nasturtiums, one dated 1882 by the sender. 10 cm x 6.8 cm.

14. Four miscellaneous cards, one with forget-me-nots in a vase, one with snowdrops threaded through paper in trompe l'oeil style, one with flowers and ferns, no. 93, the fourth with begonia leaves and fern, no. 176. Sizes up to 8.5 cm x 12.2 cm.

15. Two cards, autumn leaves on a white ground, both with verses, one signed by L N, no. 209. Two cut out pieces, found in an album with the cards, are included, probably from the other two cards in the set. Album compilers often cut up cards to use as decoration. 11.8 cm x 15.7 cm.

16. Two cards, autumn leaves, with fungi in circular vignettes, possibly by Emily Whymper. One was dated 1881 by the sender. 10.7 cm x 15 cm.

17. One embossed card, a basket with ferns and a trailing plant on a white ground, no. 261. 10 cm x 15 cm.

18. Two cards, one with a bunch of leaves and fern. The other has autumn leaves and berries with spikes of blue flowers. Early 1880's. 11.7 cm x 16 cm, 10.8 cm x 16.5 cm.

19. Three cards on grey or cream ground, with trailing flower sprays and verse. Two are numbered 210 and signed O H C, one 260. 9.3 cm x 13.7 cm.

20. Three cards, sprays of trailing plants with brown leaves, one dated 1887 by the sender. Two are numbered 266. 15 cm x 10 cm.

21. One card, a spray of forget-me-nots and white flowers, perhaps spiraea or meadowsweet. No. 370. 10.7 cm x 15 cm.

22. Three miscellaneous cards, one white flowers and a fan on a silver ground, no. 273, another a wreath of white flowers on silver, no. 516, the third with white flowers and fern in an earthenware bowl and a silver border, no. 208. 12 cm x 12 cm, 10 cm x 10 cm, 13.7 cm x 9.3 cm.

23. Two cards with silver borders, flowers in lacy paper holders with a verse, no. 323. One is a wedding card "Bright blessings on your loves united ...". 12 cm x 15 cm.

24. Two cards, silver borders, with lilac or narcissi around an oval vignette bearing a greeting. One has a birthday verse by E M A G, the other is a "Marriage Congratulation - God bless thee on thy Wedding Day". No. 330. 12 cm x 15 cm.

25. Four miscellaneous birthday cards, with forget-me-nots or white flowers. All have verses, three by H M B, E M A G, J P T, and are numbered 322, 337, 328, 2020. Sizes up to 10.7 cm x 15 cm.

26. Four cards, three designs of flowers in an open packet laced with string in trompe l'oeil style, no. 465. 9 cm x 9 cm.

27. Two cards, anemones or Christmas roses on a panel on cream coloured ground. No. 488. 9 cm x 12 cm.

28. Five miscellaneous cards, four of various leaves and berries, one a white flower on a gilt bordered card with cut out corners, four numbered 195, 283, 1214, 1966.
6.2 cm x 9.4 cm up to 8.9 cm x 12.7 cm.

29. Five cards, two with flowers in satin slippers, no. 61, one of forget-me-nots in a shell, no. 2085, and two with sprays of violets or lily of the valley, no. 29. 15 cm x 7.5 cm, 10.4 cm x 6.6 cm.

30. Eight miscellaneous cards, various flower sprays, three of one set no. 350, the others numbered 14, 18, 45, 64, 68. Sizes 6 cm x 9.4 cm up to 13.4 cm x 8.5 cm.

31. Four cards with flower sprays, two birthday no. 504. Two have a serrated edge, and one of these has a pansy design and a Spanish stamp, dated 1892. 11.7 cm x 7.2 cm, 11.5 cm x 9.2 cm.

32. One card in correspondence style with a bunch of snowdrops and fern, no. 567. 11.5 cm x 9 cm.

## VOLUME 104: S HILDESHEIMER? FLOWERS, FRUIT & FOLIAGE, EARLY 1880'S

**These cards are unsigned and unnumbered, but were perhaps published by S Hildesheimer.**

1/3. Twenty-two cards (one a valentine, one Easter, one birthday), six designs of mixed flower sprays on beige grounds, two on gilded mounts similar to other marked cards. They have greetings, texts, or verses, some signed F E E H, G M T, J G. 9.5 cm x 6.4 cm, 12 cm x 9 cm.

4. Three embossed cards on a grey ground, all with an edelweiss and other flowers, and a Christmas greeting verse. 12.5 cm x 7.5 cm, 7.5 cm x 12.5 cm.

5. Four embossed cards (one Easter), three designs of flowers and branches enclosing pictures of churches, with verses below. 7.9 cm x 11.8 cm.

6. Four embossed cards, three designs of white flower sprays on a bright red ground (one birthday), attributed through the type in which the accompanying verses are printed. 7.9 cm x 13.9 cm.

7. Two embossed cards, baskets of strawberries or red and white currants. 15 cm x 10.6 cm.

8. One embossed card, green leaves and small flowers on a mossy bank. 11.7 cm x 16.2 cm.

9. Four embossed cards on grey ground, fungi, ferns, and flowers. Similar to cards by Emily Whymper. 7 cm x 14.2 cm.

10. Five embossed cards on grey ground, two with sweetpeas or narcissus, three with catkins, cones, or flowering branch. 5.7 cm x 11.9 cm.

11. Four cards, grey ground, sprays of spring flowers and ferns with verse below. 7.9 cm x 13.9 cm.

12. Two similar, with butterflies or insect. 8.3 cm x 12.7 cm.

13. Five miscellaneous similar cards with flowers, including one Easter, one birthday. 4.2 cm x 11 cm up to 8.6 cm x 12.6 cm.

14. Four cards, three designs of roses and fir branch, three with verses below. One card is embossed, and another repeats one design but in a later, probably cheaper format, numbered 89. 10.2 cm x 13.8 cm.

15/16. Four cards, various flower sprays on grey ground, with verse below. 10 cm x 15 cm, 11 cm x 14.2 cm.

17. Three cards, hanging wicker baskets with a variety of colourful summer flowers. 15 cm x 12 cm.

18. Three cards, flowers in glass or china bowls (one trimmed). 15 cm x 10.7 cm.

19/20. Ten embossed cards on grey ground, with six designs of spring flowers and verses below. Five are Easter cards and five birthday. The six designs are used singly on smaller cards or in pairs on larger ones. 12 cm x 10.8 cm, 6 cm x 10.8 cm.

21. Four similar embossed cards, three valentines, one birthday, used as above on two sizes of cards. 9.3 cm x 14.3 cm, 4.7 cm x 14.3 cm.

22. Five cards on grey ground with four designs of flowers and ferns, one on an embossed gilded mount. 5 cm x 9.3 cm, 7.6 cm x 11.8 cm.

23. Four cards, three designs of nasturtiums, fuchsias, convolvulus, with greeting or verses on a coloured banner. 5 cm x 14 cm.

24. Two cards, (one birthday), ferns with cyclamen or lilies, wreathed around verses. 15 cm x 10.7 cm.

25. Six cards, all with verses by F R H, three with bouquets of spring flowers in paper holders, and three with wreaths of forget-me-nots or lilies of the valley. (Similar to cards by Bertha Maguire). 10.2 cm x 6.8 cm.

## THE PUBLISHERS ALBERT HILDESHEIMER, HILDESHEIMER & FAULKNER, & C W FAULKNER

The writer has traced some connection between the three Hildesheimer publishers with the help of Mrs Worth, granddaughter of Albert, and her history of the Hildesheimer - Hildesley family, and from the work of David Taylor of the Manchester Local History Library. He has investigated 19th Century street directories in connection with his 1987 Christmas exhibition of S Hildesheimer material in which cards from the Seddon Collection were shown, and from this it would appear that Albert and Siegmund were connected in some way, as their respective addresses in Manchester, after they had emigrated from Germany, were 6 & 8 Bloom Street. Siegmund as related earlier worked from both Manchester and London, but Albert moved to London in 1875, with an address from 1879 at 41 Jewin Street, which became the headquarters of Hildesheimer & Faulkner when he went into partnership with C W Faulkner in 1881; it would appear that the two were working together before this date as some cards in this collection clearly marked H & F were dated 1879 and 1880 by the senders. The partnership was dissolved in 1893, after which C W Faulkner continued the production of Christmas cards. H & F joined Tuck, Prang, and S Hildesheimer in promoting a prize competition for designers in 1881, confused by some writers with the 1882 competition for decorated albums of H & F cards; a notice of the latter is included in volume 115. The 1881 competition was judged by J E Millais, Marcus Stone, and G A Storey, and the entries were shown in an exhibition at the Suffolk Street Galleries, which was reviewed in the Graphic of August 13, 1881, with a noticeable lack of enthusiasm, stating "Many of the works are meritorious enough.... but they have no pretensions whatever to the title of design". Stationers Hall has a few registrations for Albert Hildesheimer in 1878, some for cards

in this collection, and a few from 1896-1900, and there are a few only for Hildesheimer & Faulkner, none traced to cards here. There are a large number for C W Faulkner from 1893-1900, not traced to the few marked cards in this section. The London directories and the London Gazette also confirm that Albert became Hildesheimer & Faulkner, and it is interesting to note that in 1883 Albert & Siegmund both lived in Oxford Gardens, Notting Hill, at nos. 97 and 87, again indicating some family connection, which so far has not been definitely established.

The earlier Hildesheimer & Faulkner cards are unnumbered, but numbers appear from about 1883, though the sequences are difficult to follow. Many cards have verses, particularly those with religious significance, though they do not appear in such quantity as with Raphael Tuck. Initials of writers can be identified, where known, from the index, but some names which appear infrequently are given in full.

## VOLUME 105: ALBERT HILDESHEIMER

This volume includes all cards signed A H or Albert Hildesheimer, published about 1878-1880.

1. Six cards, four designs of small children playing in snow. Four have gilt backgrounds for the sky, and two repeat designs have gilt patterned borders, but a blue sky. 9.8 cm x 6.4 cm, 11.9 cm x 8.3 cm.

2. Four cards, gilt borders patterned in black, two designs of two children in bed on Christmas morning, and children out-of-doors with a robin. 11.9 cm x 8.3 cm.

3. Eight small cards, five designs with varied captions, of flowers with cherubs or insects on pale green or cream coloured ground, two with embossed borders. They have verses by M F Moss and L M F. 8.3 cm x 5.3 cm, 9.6 cm x 6.3 cm.

4. Five cards, three designs of flower sprays and butterflies, one on black ground. These also appear signed T S, i.e. Thomas Stevens, and examples appear in later sections on flowers and foliage. This might indicate that the cards were made elsewhere for more than one firm. 11.2 cm x 7 cm.

5/6. Seven embossed cards, one black backed, six on pale green or cream ground, with six designs of flowers or strawberries, and verses by H or E Ridley on panels. 12.3 cm x 8.3 cm.

7. Four cards of the same set with greetings instead of verses. 12.3 cm x 8.3 cm.

8. Three cards, two designs of clematis and butterfly, or forget-me-nots, with verses by Agnes R Howell. 9.8 cm x 12.8 cm.

9. Two cards, the same design of a bunch of daisies with a greeting on a gilt scroll, one Christmas, one birthday. 9.8 cm x 12.8 cm.

*Numbers 10-14 have cards which were probably all designed by W J Muckley. Four of the designs, narcissus, hawthorn, snowdrops and yellow holly, waterlilies and forget-me-nots were registered for A Hildesheimer at Stationers' Hall 17-8-1878, with Muckley's name as artist, but the other two, holly and mistletoe, and Christmas roses, are in Muckley's style, and were probably designed by him. The cards are on a black ground with greetings on gilt panels or scrolls, and have verses by Fred E Weatherly on reverse.*

10. Three cards as above, one holly and mistletoe, the other yellow holly and snowdrops. 14.3 cm x 11 cm.

11. Two cards, waterlilies and forget-me-nots, with different verses for Christmas and New Year. 14.3 cm x 11 cm.

12. Three cards, all hawthorn, in two styles, (one birthday). 14.3 cm x 11 cm.

13. Three cards, two narcissus, one Christmas rose, (one birthday). 14.3 cm x 11 cm.

14. Two cards, Christmas rose, with two different Christmas verses. 14.3 cm x 11 cm.

15. Three similar cards, probably designed by Muckley, two designs of chrysanthemums and one of Christmas roses and berries. 14.3 cm x 11 cm.

16. Four cards, three designs, apple blossom and sweet peas, lilies and clematis, passion flowers, with greeting verses on gilt panels by Agnes R Howell and Shirley Wynne. 9.8 cm x 12.8 cm.

17. Three cards, two designs of crocus and snowdrops, holly and mistletoe, one a gilt ground, with verses by Agnes R Howell. 12.8 cm x 9.8 cm.

## VOLUME 106: HILDESHEIMER & FAULKNER. CHILDREN, LADIES, FAMILY SCENES

This volume contains prize designs from the 1881 competition, with other cards from some of the winners.

*Numbers 1-7 have cards designed by Alice Havers, published 1881-1886.*

1. "A Dream of Patience", which won the 1st prize of £250. This example is trimmed,

and is a smaller version of the original folding card, with verses from the Gilbert & Sullivan opera on the back. This card was acclaimed by Gleeson White "If we were asked to name the best English card of the modern style, it would come to mind...". 21.7 cm x 7.3 cm.

2. Two cards, the same design of a lady in yellow sending a letter by a bird, in a decorated gilded border, one dated by the sender 1884. Unnumbered, but Buday gives 490W for this card. 10.4 cm x 16.6 cm.

3. Two cards, naked children on flowering branches, with a bird or insect, no. 491W. 10.4 cm x 16.6 cm.

4. One card, a fairy with birds, in a gilt border. This card is illustrated by Gleeson White as "Fairies in Mid Air". 11.7 cm x 16.7 cm.

5. Three cards, elegant maidens with a cat, dog, or parrot, one marked 662U. 9.3 cm x 16.5 cm.

6. One larger card with the maiden and parrot, no. 661. 13.4 cm x 24.3 cm.

7. One card, a sleeping girl surrounded by a spray of ivy, c1886. 15 cm x 10.8 cm.

*Numbers 8-17 have signed cards by J M Dealy, who won two prizes. These are dated from 1881-1887.*

8. Two cards, both prize designs.
a) A long haired girl with a whip.
b) A group of children sitting on the floor, with two ladies - mothers or teachers? 9 cm x 13.6 cm, 13.6 cm x 9 cm.

9. One card, a lady in a green party dress with a fan. 7.3 cm x 13.2 cm.

10. Five cards.
a) Three cards with two designs of childrens' heads, two in a circular vignette, one on a palette shaped mount, nos. 53B, 52Y.
b) Two designs. "Three little maids from school", three girls in a flowery meadow, in the characteristic attitudes as seen in "The Mikado". One card is rectangular, no. 92F, the other palette shaped, no. 108F. 9.9 cm x 9.9 cm up to 15.5 cm x 10.5 cm.

11/12. Fourteen small cards, from two sets, two designs of single girls with flowers, and four designs of two children on the beach. Six cards are rectangular, with verses, nos. 63z, 65z, and eight are palettes with greetings, no. 106z, 107z. 6.7 cm x 9.7 cm, 6.5 cm x 9.3 cm.

13. Five cards with designs as above, three of the single girls, no. 764B, two of two children on the beach, no. 66 Z, all with verses or quotations below. Sizes up to 9.2 cm x 12.2 cm.

14. Three cards in two sizes, girls carrying babies, nos. 48E, 48D, 661Z. 9.2 cm x 12.7 cm, 7.8 cm x 11 cm.

15. Three cards, one in portrait style of a girl with a wreath on flowing hair, one a girl on a stile, with a verse by S K Cowan, no. 693D, the third a girl with a garland of roses. Sizes up to 10.5 cm x 14.5 cm.

16. Two cards of small girls, one in winter with skates, the other in spring with a basket of eggs, with appropriate Christmas and New Year greetings, and verses on reverse by Thomas Beaumont and Ellin Isabelle Tupper. 8.5 cm x 12 cm.

17. Three cards, Indian children, no. 691F, c1887. 13.5 cm x 11 cm.

18. Two cards, prize design by E Blair Leighton, one of two awarded £75. One card is reversed to show the inscription giving details of the prize with the judges' names. 10.8 cm x 16 cm.

19. Two cards, prize designs.
a) A boy and girl in a garden, possibly by E Manly. 10 cm x 14.5 cm.
b) The head of a lady, possibly by E Folkhard. 10.5 cm x 14 cm.

20. Four cards, prize designs, indoor scenes with small children and large dogs, probably by Helena Maguire, 14.7 cm x 10 cm.

21. Three cards signed Helena Maguire, two designs of well dressed little girls, one skating, one feeding a robin. The third card is reversed to show a verse by S S Wigley. 9.1 cm x 12.2 cm.

22. Two cards, prize designs, groups of villagers in winter snow, possibly by Patty Townshend. 9.7 cm x 15.3 cm, 15.2 cm x 9.7 cm.

23. Three cards, prize designs, one with a girl in party dress coming downstairs, and two others with a boy in winter with holly and a girl in summer with flowers. 9.6 cm x 13.9 cm, 9.9 cm x 14.2 cm.

24. Two cards, prize designs of party scenes with children in Georgian style dress. 16.7 cm x 11.8 cm.

25. Three cards, two prize designs, a small girl by a boat, and a boy in a sailor suit. 10 cm x 12.7 cm.

26. Two cards, prize designs, each with a jester and a minstrel. 9.6 cm x 15.2 cm.

27. Two cards, prize designs, composite cards of nursery rhymes with verses, in Kate Greenaway style. 11 cm x 14.7 cm.

*Numbers 28-32 have cards by Eleanor Manly.*

28/29. Fourteen cards, thirteen designs of children's heads, twelve in two formats of

**106.2**

circular bordered cards, two rectangular. There are no visible numbers, but Buday gives 276, 277 for cards of this description. 8.2 diameter, 6.8 cm x 7.5 cm.

30. Set of four cards, Baby Bell series, small girls in fancy bonnets, no. 319B, c1884. 7.8 cm x 10 cm.

31. Two cards, Grecian style ladies with birds, or by a waterfall, signed E M, perhaps Eleanor Manly, though in contrasting style to those above. 6.5 cm x 14.3 cm.

32. Three cards of girls, one with parasol, one at the piano, the third playing cricket. 7.5 cm x 11.5 cm.

*Numbers 33-36 have cards by Linnie Watt, who won three prizes of £75, £50, £20. The cards in nos. 33 and 34, though not marked as prizewinners, might have had this distinction. It is notable that most of her designs were of summer scenes.*

33. Three cards, two with children on the beach and a bird design on reverse, and a third card a girl on the beach which was part of one of the former pictures, no. 316B. 14.5 cm x 9.5 cm, 9 cm x 11 cm.

34. Two cards, summer scenes with two children on a grassy slope, and verses by A Gill on reverse, one with "Designed by Linnie Watt". 16.5 cm x 11.7 cm.

35. Four cards, each of two children in summer scenes. Two are taken from the pictures in 34 above, and have verses below; the other two have a decorative border. 10.7 cm x 10.2 cm, 10.2 cm x 10.2 cm.

36. Five cards, children in outdoor summer scenes, one dated 1885 by the sender. 11 cm x 8.7 cm.

## VOLUME 107: HILDESHEIMER & FAULKNER. CHILDREN & LADIES, PARTY SCENES

**These cards were published in the early 1880's unless otherwise stated; only a few are numbered.**

1. Five cards, possibly by Albert Ludovici, street arabs, ragged children playing and watching Punch and Judy. 11.4 cm x 7.7 cm, 7.7 cm x 11.4 cm, 14.3 cm x 9.2 cm.

2. Four cards, possibly by Albert Ludovici, three designs of children playing on the ice, one with a policeman in the water. 13.7 cm x 8.5 cm.

3. Three cards, street vendors of violets or chestnuts, and a crossing sweeper, with verses by E Ridley on reverse. 9.2 cm x 13.7 cm.

4. Four cards in two sizes, three designs signed G G K., with verses by E Ridley and S Wynne on the backs of the larger cards. The small card is numbered 388B. 12.8 cm x 9.3 cm, 11.4 cm x 8.5 cm.

5. Three cards, two designs by G G Kilburne of a Georgian ballroom. The third card is a folder with a scrap of a violin on the cover, which opens to show one of the designs with a verse by Rev. J W Myers, B A. c1885. 16.5 cm x 10 cm, 14.3 cm x 8 cm folded.

6. Three cards signed E A L, i.e. Eliza Ann Lemann, children out of doors, with verses on reverse. 8 cm x 12.8 cm.

7. Three cards signed F M, probably Fred Morgan, children in period costume, stealing apples, decorating at Christmas, and with a spilt ink bottle. 7.5 cm x 12.5 cm.

8. Three cards of nursery rhyme characters, Tom Tucker, Jack Horner, the little man with a little gun, perhaps by C Green. 8.6 cm x 12.7 cm.

9. A large gilt-edged card with two girls on a stile, dated 1884 by the sender. 11.3 cm x 17.2 cm.

10. Three cards, two designs, one a boy falling on the ice, the other two children and a snowman, two cards dated 1883 by the sender. 10.2 cm x 13.4 cm.

11. Three cards (one birthday), each with a girl in a silk dress, with puppies, kittens, or a parrot. 11.7 cm x 14.5 cm.

12. Three cards, a boy in a sailor suit with a toy boat, a girl on a swing holding a kitten, and a girl in a garden, one dated 1880 by the sender. 9 cm x 13.7 cm.

13/14. Nine cards, four designs of a little girl in bed with toys or books, three dated 1881 by the senders. 11.3 cm x 7.4 cm.

15. Four cards, each with a girl in an elaborate frilled or tucked dress, one dated 1881 by the sender. 8.3 cm x 13.3 cm.

16. Three cards, one a girl with an umbrella in falling snow, and two cards of another set showing a boy with snowballs, and a girl looking at the snow from a doorway. 10.3 cm x 14.1 cm, 9.1 cm x 13.7 cm.

17. Three cards, two children with a sunflower as parasol, a barefoot girl in the snow, and a girl with a dog by a stairway. 9 cm x 12.2 cm.

18. A set of four cards, children in snow, three with a girl and boy, the fourth with a girl holding a letter and a bunch of holly. There is a Maze puzzle on the back of each card with an appropriate verse. 8.2 cm x 11.5 cm.

19. Three cards, children in summer, one with a boy and girl on a haystack, another with pigeons, and the third of a girl with a skipping rope and a kitten. 9.3 cm x 12.1 cm.

20. Three cards, monochrome designs of elaborately dressed little girls, one indoors and two out of doors. These are signed with a monogram E S. 9 cm x 13.5 cm.

21. Three cards, gilt borders, a sleeping babe, a child in a go-cart, and a girl's head. 13 cm x 9.7 cm, 9.2 cm x 12.1 cm, 10.3 cm x 12.8 cm.

22. Three cards, gilt borders, a child with a doll in a go-cart, a baby sleeping in a wicker cot with a wicker rattle by its side, and a small girl with a doll in a pram. 9 cm x 12.7 cm, 13.3 cm x 10.2 cm.

23. Three seaside scenes, a fisher girl with a background of boats, a girl in a bonnet with a wooden spade, and a small girl swinging. 10.3 cm x 13.7 cm, 9.5 cm x 12.5 cm, 9 cm x 13 cm.

24. Three cards with decorative holly or floral borders, each with a girl in a winter or summer scene. 9.4 cm x 13.3 cm.

25. Three cards, one with a girl on a river bank in a vignette set in a background of cherry blossom, and two designs of a small boy trying to catch birds, with verses by H M B. 11.2 cm x 14.2 cm, 10 cm x 11.5 cm.

26. Four cards, a girl in a bonnet and a pink dress, another in a blue dress against a leafy background, and two more with fancy borders and a girl in a summer scene, these two dated 1882 by the sender. 9.5 cm x 14.4 cm, 8 cm x 12.8 cm, 9 cm x 13.6 cm.

27. Three cards, two designs, one a girl praying by her bedside, another asleep in bed with a kitten on the coverlet. They have verses by F E W on the reverse, and one is dated 1883 by the sender. 14 cm x 9.6 cm.

28. Four cards, two of the same set showing a baby in blue and a little girl in a fur trimmed coat and hat, and two with a baby in a draped cot. 6.4 cm x 10.8 cm, 7.5 cm x 9.5 cm.

29. Six cards, three in each of two sizes, each with two children in Kate Greenaway style dress, one dated 1884 by the sender. 9.7 cm x 8.3 cm, 7.2 cm x 9 cm.

30. A set of four cards of child musicians, boys playing a tuba, a drum, or a flute, and a girl with what appears to be a collecting plate. 8 cm x 11.7 cm.

31. Three cards, children in period party clothes. 8.2 cm x 11.3 cm.

32. Three cards each with three children, looking out of a window, or asleep in bed, no. 349B. 9.2 cm x 12.2 cm, 12.2 cm x 9.2 cm.

33. Two cards, signed G S, i.e. George Sadler, each with a girl in party dress holding flowers in white gloved hands, one dated 1887 by the sender. 10 cm x 12.5 cm.

34. Two cards, a lady in transparent draperies writing or reading a letter, with a small cupid on a pedestal beside her. 10.5 cm x 17 cm.

35. A lady seated, at tea, in a garden with a tennis court in the background, dated 1881 by the sender. 10 cm x 13 cm.

36. Two cards, each with a lady in green carrying holly through the snow, with green border and mistletoe in the corners, c1881. 10.4 cm x 15.7 cm.

37. Two cards (one birthday), ladies in white blouse and feathered hat in an oval vignette with green ferns. One has a verse by Shirley Wynne on the reverse. c1885. 11 cm x 13.6 cm.

38. Three cards, children in Kate Greenaway costume on gilt backgrounds. 13.2 cm x 8.5 cm.

## VOLUME 108: HILDESHEIMER & FAULKNER. LATER CHILDREN'S CARDS

**Most of these were published from 1885-1890, except where otherwise stated, and many were numbered.**

1. Three cards, decorated by sprays of flowers, one a small boy with a kitten in a basket, the other two with girls in

vignettes. Early 1880's. 8.5 cm x 11.7 cm, 6.5 cm x 9.6 cm.

2. Three cards, plump little girls wreathed in spring flowers. These cards are similar to some in an 1880 book of cards published by Falck, this in the John Johnson Collection. Possibly imports common to both. 4.7 cm x 8.2 cm.

3. Three cards, two designs, various pictures of small girls apparently balancing on branches. 7.9 cm x 11.9 cm.

4. Five cards, four designs of small girls out in the snow, one dated 1886 by the sender. No. 309. 7.3 cm x 9.4 cm.

5. Four cards, two with a girl in a garden, and two others with a girl with a muff, or a kitten. Early 1880's. 9.2 cm x 13.5 cm.

6. Two cards, a boy with a large kite and a girl with a huge ball. 11.5 cm x 8.5 cm.

7. One card, an angel leaning over a girl with a basket asleep on a snow covered doorstep. No. 342. 9.9 cm x 13.2 cm.

8. Six cards, five designs of children in summer and winter, by the seaside, feeding hens, gathering leaves, or skating. 9.5 cm x 7.3 cm.

9. Four cards, three designs, one of children saying their prayers, no. 626, the others a girl feeding a calf or reading a book, no. 631. 9.5 cm x 7.3 cm.

10. Two cards, gilt borders, a girl skating, no. 133, and two children in a snow scene with holly and umbrella, no. 132. 9.2 cm x 12.6 cm, 9.8 cm x 13 cm.

11. Three cards, mischievous boys making havoc in their schoolroom, no. 216, 247. 14.4 cm x 9.4 cm, 13.2 cm x 9.9 cm.

12. Four miscellaneous cards.
a) Four boys in a bedroom, no. 317.
b) A procession of children in a lane, no. 206.
c) A boy on a donkey.
d) Three Scottish boys dancing a Highland fling. Sizes up to 13.2 cm x 10.2 cm.

13. Five cards signed M E E, i.e. M E Edwards - children at prayer. Two are rectangular, no. 601, and three palette shaped, nos. 170, 641. 7.4 cm x 10 cm, 8.5 cm x 12 cm.

14/15. Six cards, three designs, one a single child holding flowers, the others with two children, all in white dresses with golden hair. These are taken from photographs by Robert Faulkner, and three are in palette shape, nos. 200, 298, and three rectangular, nos. 280, 283, 564. 10.5 cm x 15.4 cm, 10.8 cm x 16.3 cm, 8 cm x 12 cm.

16. Four cards, two designs, each with a child and a kitten. One is in palette shape, no. 296, the others rectangular, no. 557. 12.5 cm x 9.5 cm, 10 cm x 8.2 cm.

17. Three cards, two designs of an Italian girl with a tambourine, one card with a verse by H M Burnside dated 1889 by the sender. 10.7 cm x 8.7 cm, 6.5 cm x 10 cm.

18. Two cards, signed H S T, a girl hanging out her doll's laundry, and a boy with a banner, no. 305. 9.6 cm x 13.3 cm.

19. Two cards, both with little girls asleep in bed, the first signed Edith Scannell, nos. 145, 81W. 13 cm x 9.4 cm, 15 cm x 11 cm.

20. Three cards, children in nightgowns preparing for bed, no. 310. 9.5 cm x 12.5 cm.

21. Five cards, all signed.
a) A boy in a sailor suit with a dog, by A G King, no. 734. 7.3 cm x 9.5 cm.
b) A little girl with birds, by Emily J Harding, no. 605. 8.1 cm x 11.1 cm.
c) Two children in snow, by H Berkely, no. 214. 8.4 cm x 11.4 cm.
d) A little girl with a kitten, by Emily J Harding, with a verse by S K C, no. 506. 8.8 cm x 13 cm.
e) Another girl with a kitten, by J Clark, with a verse by S K C, no. 1033. 9.5 cm x 12.8 cm.

22. Four cards.
a/b) Two little girls in period dress, with flowers, no. 54Z.
c) A girl with a dog, verse by S K C, no. 674Z.
d) A boy with a dog, verse by S K C, no. 733. Sizes up to 11 cm x 8.3 cm.

23. Three cards, children's heads in vignettes, with flowers. One is by J Clark, no. 1031, the others are numbered 127, 604. 7.3 cm x 9.8 cm up to 11 cm x 15 cm.

24. Two cards, one with three children and a robin on a snowy branch, no. 190, the other two children in a wreath of violets, no. 1255. 11.3 cm x 11 cm, 13.7 cm x 10.7 cm.

25. Four cards, two designs, one a small child riding on a flying goose, the other a girl looking in a mirror with a boy peeping from behind a screen. 13.5 cm x 9 cm.

26. One card, a girl with a plum pudding in a circular vignette, with a floral border. 10.4 cm x 10.4 cm.

27. Five cards, four pen and ink designs in correspondence style with pictures of children. 11.3 cm x 8.8 cm.

28. Five miscellaneous cards with babies. 7.5 cm x 5 cm up to 9.2 cm x 6.8 cm.

29. Seven miscellaneous bordered cards with various pictures of children. 6.4 cm x 9 cm up to 11 cm x 9.4 cm.

30. Two cards, one dated 1896 by the sender, each with four babies sitting on a plank, with a robin, marked C W Faulkner, no. 83. 11 cm x 8.5 cm.

## VOLUME 109: HILDESHEIMER & FAULKNER. RELIGIOUS CARDS

**Most of the cards in this volume have designs of flowers and crosses with suitable verses or texts, and though many are Easter cards, they could have been used for Christmas or New Year with different captions. Only a few cards are numbered, and the majority were published before 1885 unless otherwise stated.**

1. Three cards, Faith, Hope, Charity, with appropriate pictures of children, and descriptive verses by H & E Ridley. 9 cm x 13. 4 cm.

2. Three cards, two sizes, heads of winged cherubs against a blue sky, one dated 1883 by the sender. 9.5 cm x 6.8 cm, 9.5 cm x 13 cm.

3. Three cards, one with two little girls, one with angels in the sky and snowdrops below, the third with bells and white flowers, all with verses or texts, nos. 26 1/4, 573, 592. Late 1880's. Sizes up to 11 cm x 13.3 cm.

4. Four cards, two designs of rustic crosses entwined with lilies or ivy and forget-me-nots. 9.5 cm x 14.3 cm.

5. Four Easter cards, gold crosses with various flowers, and texts. 8.4 cm x 13 cm.

6. Three cards (one Easter), two designs of gold crosses with white flowers, and verses by F E Weatherly or text. 8.4 cm x 13 cm.

7. Four Easter cards, gold crosses with daisies, roses, primroses or violets, and verses on reverse. 10.2 cm x 13.8 cm.

8. Three miscellaneous cards, gold or rustic crosses and flowers, one a Christmas card repeating the daisy design in no. 7. Sizes up to 11 cm x 16.3 cm.

9. Four cards (one Easter), three designs of gold crosses lying on the ground, with flower sprays. 14 cm x 9 cm, 14.3 cm x 9.5 cm.

10. Two Easter cards, silver crosses with spring flowers. 11.2 cm x 14.3 cm.

11. Two Easter cards, wooden crosses on the ground, one with passion flowers and a butterfly, the other with narcissus and ferns. 14.2 cm x 10 cm.

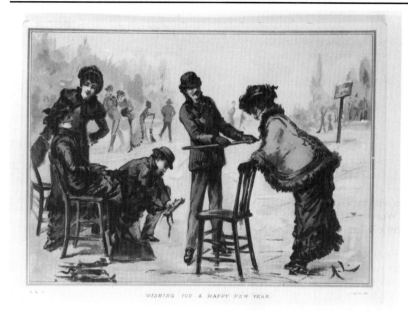

WISHING YOU A HAPPY NEW YEAR.

**110.2**

12. Two Easter cards, gold crosses with flowers, signed by a decorative monogram M E D. This might be M E Duffield, but is unlike her usual signature to the numerous flower cards she designed for Hildesheimer and Faulkner. 8.3 cm x 12.5 cm.

13. Three cards (one Easter), two designs of wooden crosses with passion flowers or white jasmine, one dated 1882 by the sender. 9.2 cm x 15.1 cm.

14. Two Easter cards, flowers and ferns with silver crosses and verses by H M B. 9.8 cm x 15 cm.

15. Two Easter cards, daisies or narcissi on silver crosses with verses by H M B and Needham. They are signed E W, probably E Wilson, and one is dated 1888 by the sender. 10.3 cm x 13.9 cm.

16. Three cards (two Easter), two designs of silver crosses with white flowers at the foot. 9.2 cm x 12.2 cm.

17. Two Easter cards, one with daisies and an ornamental cross, the other, by C Noakes, a star shining on a cross with a wreath of flowers and fern, no. 278. Late 1880's. 6.8 cm x 6.8 cm, 13.9 cm x 11 cm.

18. Five Easter cards, cut out crosses, three with various flowers numbered 118, 489 1/4, the others with flowers or birds on a dark scenic background. Late 1880's. Sizes up to 10.7 cm x 13.6 cm.

19. Two Easter cards, flower wreaths around verses signed H M B, one dated 1882 by the sender. 10.2 cm x 13.4 cm.

20. Three Easter cards, one a flower spray with a quotation from Wordsworth and two smaller with flowers and a cross, nos. 620, 817 1/4. 10 cm x 6.8 cm up to 14.7 cm x 10.2 cm.

21. An elaborate triptych folding card designed by H J Stock, with a picture of the Saviour with children and a long poem by Fred E Weatherley within. There is a red and gold Gothic window design on the flaps outside, and a verse by Clara Thwaites on the back set in a Gothic archway. No. 718, late 1880's. 12 cm x 16 cm closed.

22. A folding Easter card signed A West, robins perched on a gilded crescent moon in a cut-out star, opening to show a country scene of a windmill by a lake. 11.8 cm x 10.8 cm.

## VOLUME 110: HILDESHEIMER & FAULKNER. HUMOROUS CARDS, SPORT, HUNTING, NEGROES, ARMY

**This volume contains a large number of cards by W J Hodgson and some by W L Duffield, husband of M E Duffield. Very few marked cards have been found with negro or army subjects.**

1. Three cards in two styles, by Allan Ludovici, which won a £25 prize in the 1881 competition, probably for a set of four. They caricature the aesthetic movement, and show a lady admiring a tea-pot, a girl gazing soulfully at a Japanese parasol, and a man with a large sunflower. 10.3 cm x 14.3 cm, 8.5 cm x 12.5 cm.

2. Two cards signed A L, 1880, possibly Albert Ludovici, showing family skating scenes. 15.2 cm x 11.1 cm.

3. Three cards, children skating and tobogganing, early 1880's. 13.3 cm x 10.5 cm.

4. Three cards by W L Duffield, two designs of ladies on the river in punts, c1881. 13.7 cm x 9.2 cm.

5. Four cards, three designs with people in boats amid lakeland scenery. There are appropriate poems on the reverse by the author of "John Halifax, Gentleman". Early 1880's. 13.3 cm x 9.7 cm.

6. Four cards by W L Duffield, two from a set showing girls and a boy skating, and two from another set with ladies sliding and snowballing. c1881. 13.3 cm x 8 cm, 12.5 cm x 8.5 cm.

7. Two cards of sporting ladies, one a prize design of a lady in a short skirt with a gun, the other riding in snow with a groom in attendance and a dog. 9 cm x 13.6 cm, 10.7 cm x 14.9 cm.

*Numbers 8-23 have humorous cards by W J Hodgson. These were issued in sets, sometimes as individual cards, also mounted in booklets with the series telling a story, and were published about 1884. Probably a whole set was sent out at one time to a single recipient or perhaps to members of a family, as the cards were usually numbered in sequence and an odd card would not give the whole story. The booklets had greetings on the cover with none on the actual pictures, but individual cards each had a greeting.*

8. A set of four cards with envelope, showing two mischievous boys setting a trap for another. 11 cm x 8.5 cm.

9. Four cards from the series "Hare & Hounds", showing the misadventures of a group of boys out for a run. 11.2 cm x 8 cm.

10. Four cards, pranks in the dormitory, including a midnight feast and a pillow fight. 11.2 cm x 8 cm.

11. Four cards, four boys on a slide encounter a policeman, no. 483B. 11 cm x 8.5 cm.

12. Three cards, possibly from a set of four, two mischievous boys causing trouble with snowballs for a policeman and a farm boy, no. 486B. 11 cm x 8.5 cm.

13. Five cards, four designs of schoolboys playing football or cricket. 11.2 cm x 7.8 cm., 7.8 cm x 11.2 cm.

14. Five cards, possibly from a set of six, showing the unfortunate result of Pothunter and his henchman chasing a hare which proved to be a pet cat. 13.1 cm x 9.2 cm.

15. The Story of a Rustic Courtship. A folder with two cards out of the series of four, showing the green cover, and a single card of the set with a greeting. 13 cm x 9.5 cm.

16. Four cards, telling the story of the lady with a small dog which provokes a very large dog, and ends up being eaten. 13 cm x 9.5 cm.

17. Four cards, showing Old Slocum digging for treasure in his garden, and unearthing a battered doll. 13 cm x 9.5 cm.

18. Four cards "A Story of two determined Characters", a farm boy having trouble with a pig. These have greetings as separate cards, but the series has also been seen in a booklet with greeting on the green cover. 13 cm x 9.5 cm.

19. Four cards, adventures in the hunting field, ending in a fall. 12.4 cm x 10 cm.

20. Four cards, hunting, with the horses refusing to take their fences. These are all dated 1884 in the same hand, so would appear to have been sent as a set. 12 cm x 7.8 cm.

21. Three cards, hunting with problems of broken gates and snow. 9.8 cm x 12.5 cm.

22. Four cards, three with coaches in the snow, no. 693Y, and one with two donkey carts having a race, no. 690Y. 13.2 cm x 9 cm.

23. Four miscellaneous cards, from different series, including a tennis match. Sizes up to 12.5 cm x 10 cm.

*Numbers 24-30 have cards with humorous themes published from 1885-1890.*

24. Three cards.
a) A double-sided card showing a postman putting letters through a door on one side, and the letters falling on a cat inside on the reverse. It is interesting to see that this Victorian door had two separate locks, and a chain. No. 453. 9.7 cm x 15 cm.
b/c) Two cards showing urchins drawing pictures on the wall of a girls' school, and riding on the back of a cab. 10.3 cm x 13.7 cm.

25. Three cards, two designs of barefoot urchins in the snow stretching a rope to trip a policeman, one dated 1887 by the sender. No. 146. 13.3 cm x 9 cm.

26. Three cards, a bucolic couple. Copyright A. 9.3 cm x 12.5 cm.

27. Three cards.
a) Two lovers on a sofa hiding behind a newspaper. No 780. 13 cm x 9.5 cm.
b/c) "Love is blind". Two cards from a set of three showing a couple sitting on a freshly painted bench, and walking away striped in green, with narrative poems by F E W on reverse. No 284. 13.5 cm x 9.5 cm.

28. Four cards.
a/b) The same two sided card in two sizes with different numbers 192, 907, showing an old couple looking out of their bedroom window on one side, with the street musicians being drenched with water on the other. Verses by F E W tell the story. 8 cm x 11.2 cm, 10 cm x 14 cm.
c) A lady and gentleman kissing, with irate father watching at the door, and a verse by F E W. No 835. 10.2 cm x 13.5 cm.
d) Two lovers on a bench, with disapproving parents and laughing small boys looking over the wall, dated 1889 by the sender. No 924. 9.5 cm x 13 cm.

29. Two cards, one with umbrella and bag, the other with pipe, tobacco, and matches, both with appropriate humorous verse by F E Weatherley. Nos 451, 866. 11 cm x 7.7 cm, 11.2 cm x 9.2 cm.

30. Three cards, musical negroes, one with a band of three, no. 324, the other two with fiddle or banjo designed by Frank Feller, no. 656Z. 7.5 cm x 10.4 cm, 7.7 cm x 11 cm.

31. Two cards, "Dragoon", by Frank Feller, in two sizes nos. 654L, 655F, showing a mounted soldier in a winter scene. 13 cm x 17.9 cm, 10.7 cm x 14 cm.

# VOLUME 111: HILDESHEIMER & FAULKNER. ANIMALS

**This volume includes some 1881 prize designs, and a few cards by known artists. They were published in the early 1880's unless otherwise stated.**

1. Set of four cards, three with cats and dogs sitting comfortably in baskets or on tables, and one with a dog out in the snow. One card is dated 1880 by the sender, which is before the official date of the partnership of Hildesheimer & Faulkner. Note that the H & F mark is in a different print from that on later cards. 10.5 cm x 13.8 cm.

2. Three cards, with two designs as in no. 1 above. Two cards are smaller and one of these is dated 1881 by the sender. 10.5 cm x 13.8 cm, 9 cm x 11.9 cm.

3. Two prize designs, one a horse in snow outside a cottage, the other two kittens with a frog. 14.1 cm x 11.8 cm, 14.6 cm x 10.5 cm.

4. Three cards, ponies in the snow, two marked "prize design". 15.5 cm x 8.5 cm.

5. Three cards, various dogs in summer scenes, two marked "prize design". 12.6 cm x 9.8 cm.

6. Two cards, cattle and goats in snow covered fields. 14 cm x 11 cm, 17.9 cm x 14.3 cm.

7. Two cards, donkeys and horses. 15.2 cm x 11.3 cm.

110.28

8. Set of four cards, terriers and spaniels indoors and outdoors. 12.7 cm x 9.6 cm.

9. Two cards, winter scenes with sheep and cattle. 12.7 cm x 9.2 cm.

10. Set of four cards, summer and autumn scenes with cattle, sheep, and harvest, and river and mountain backgrounds. Two cards were dated 1882, 1883, by the senders. 13.2 cm x 9.3 cm.

11. Three cards, two designs of dogs' heads. 9.7 cm x 12.7 cm.

12. Two cards of dogs, one a prize design. 15 cm x 9.5 cm, 13.2 cm x 9.2 cm.

13. Four cards with gilded patterned borders, foxhound puppies in kennel or baskets, signed Valentine T Garland. 11.2 cm x 14.8 cm.

14. Three cards, two designs of dogs heads, one dated 1884 by the sender, perhaps also by VT Garland. 10.7 cm x 15 cm.

15. Five cards by HH Couldery. One is a prize design of two kittens nestling in a ladies hat, with a duplicate reversed to show the award of a £50 prize, by the judges John Everett Millais, GA Storey, and Marcus Stone. There are two smaller cards, one of the same kittens, the other of two puppies, and the fifth card has three kittens playing on a table. 13.7 cm x 11.3 cm, 9.7 cm x 7 cm, 13.7 cm x 10.3 cm.

16. Two cards, cat and dog portraits, probably by H H Couldery, one dated 1883 by the sender. 10.3 cm x 12.8 cm.

17. Two cards, a cat on a cushion, and a bull dog with bandaged head. 12 cm x 14.7 cm.

18/19. Six cards, four designs probably by H H Couldery, mischievous kittens, one dated 1884 by the sender. 16.2 cm x 10.2 cm.

20. Four cards, three designs of musical cats and dogs. 9 cm x 12.7 cm.

21. Two cards, one design of monkeys playing cards, possibly by B B Laurence. 12.4 cm x 8.5 cm.

22/23. Six cards, humanised kittens in childrens' clothes, at school, at play, sitting with mother at the fireside, going upstairs to bed, in bed ill. Three are numbered 203, two 204 (one dated 1890 by sender) and one 839. 13.5 cm x 10.2 cm, 13.6 cm x 10.5 cm.

24. Three miscellaneous cards, one with three cats and a Japanese umbrella, one with two mice carrying an egg, the third a dog's head. Sizes up to 13 cm x 9 cm.

25. One card "A Masher", a dog in top hat, coat and waistcoat with high collar and tie. 10.2 cm x 13.2 cm.

26. Four cards, three designs of mice foraging for food on a table and in a barrel. 10.8 cm x 7.8 cm.

*The following cards were published from the late 1880's to 1893. Many are marked "Designed in England, printed in Germany".*

27. Set of four cards, the adventures of a puppy on ice, ending in immersion, no. 246. 13.2 cm x 9.5 cm.

28. Six miscellaneous cards by Helena Maguire, kittens - one with a dog - nos. 243, 244, 245. Two were dated 1888 by the senders. 8.3 cm x 8.3 cm up to 9.5 cm x 13.2 cm.

29. Four cards by Helena Maguire, a group of kittens, no. 144 and three cards numbered 241 with rows of kittens' heads and dogs' heads, these with verses by S K Cowan. 16.3 cm x 9 cm, 16.3 cm x 8.2 cm.

30. Three cards by Helena Maguire, groups of kittens and puppies, nos. 274, 602. 13 cm x 8.8 cm, 12.5 cm x 8.5 cm.

31. Two cards, kittens at school, signed A M L, probably A M Lockyer. 13.5 cm x 8.1 cm.

32. Three humorous cards, one of dancing pigs by A M Lockyer, no. 235, another of dancing pigs no. 827, and the third with three cat musicians, no. 829. 13.5 cm x 7.8 cm, 11.1 cm x 7.5 cm.

*Numbers 33-35 have cards designed by Beatrix Potter about 1890, some of her earliest published work. They are not signed, but have been authenticated by comparison with the collection of drawings and cards in the*

**111.20**

*possession of the National Trust, which owns Hill Top, Sawrey, her farmhouse in Cumbria, and a large collection of original work.*

33. Two cards, a rabbit postman, and mother rabbit and son, possibly Peter Rabbit or Benjamin Bunny. 9.3 cm x 11.2 cm.

34. One card, badgers at table. 13.2 cm x 8.9 cm.

35. Two shaped cards, mice in a nutshell, one a folder. 10 cm x 8 cm.

36. Three miscellaneous cards, two with kittens at play and at school, no. 202, and one with pigs at school, no. 620. 13.3 cm x 10.2 cm, 16 cm x 9.5 cm.

37. A set of four cards, two with dogs, one in a hat, one with a gun, and two with cats, one with a toy boat, the other with a sword. No. 811. 10 cm x 7.5 cm.

38. Six miscellaneous cards, one a cat no. 327, one a mouse by a candle with a grotesque face no. 337, and four with dogs, nos. 343A, 344Z, 455, 817. 9.3 cm x 6.7 cm up to 9 cm x 13 cm.

## VOLUME 112: HILDESHEIMER & FAULKNER. BIRDS

**This volume shows birds in straightforward and humorous style, with some artists identified. They date from 1881, the prize competition, to the early 1890's.**

*Numbers 1-11 were published in the early 1880's.*

1. Four cards, prize designs by T H Allchin, birds in vignettes with flowers and foliage around. One card has

the notice of the £50 award on the reverse. 11.3 cm x 15 cm.

2. Three cards, prize designs, birds' nests with flowers and foliage. 16.5 cm x 11.5 cm.

3. Five cards, including two prize designs of chaffinches on a pine branch and birds feeding in the snow, with three cards from another set with various birds on branches. 13.2 cm x 9 cm., 13.5 cm x 9 cm.

4. Two cards, birds' nests with flowers, and verses by H M B and Byron on reverse. 13.3 cm x 10.8 cm.

5. Two cards, birds' nests and flowers, and verses by E M M and the "author of Coming thro' the Rye" on reverse. 14.8 cm x 10 cm.

6. Three cards, two sad designs of a dead chaffinch and a bluetit - this peculiar subject appears inappropriate for Christmas and New Year greetings, but is seen in many Victorian albums. 11 cm x 8 cm.

7. Three cards, birds on branches of holly or broom. 10.5 cm x 13.1 cm, 13.1 cm x 10.5 cm.

8. Another card with unlikely subject, robins and wrens inspecting a broken doll lying in the snow. 15 cm x 11 cm.

9. A card showing a baby bird just out of the egg, with three blue eggs still unbroken in the nest. 9 cm x 12 cm.

10. Four cards (two birthday), three designs of birds perching on branches, or in flight. 9.1 cm x 13.5 cm.

11. Three cards, one embossed, with a swallow and forget-me-nots, and two others of birds in the snow with Christmas roses or snowdrops. 8 cm x 12 cm, 7.2 cm x 10.2 cm.

*The remaining cards were published from 1885.*

12. Two cards, one with blue tits on a branch entwined around a verse by M E Hatton, no. 158, the other a robin serenading two birds on a branch with icicles, no. 318. 12 cm x 8.4 cm, 14.4 cm x 10.8 cm.

13. Three cards, two with ducklings, no. 276B, the other a puppy playing with a doll, no. 277B. 13 cm x 9.5 cm.

14. Four cards signed A M Lockyer, three designs of penguins, pelicans, and storks, in procession on the beach. 13.2 cm x 7.7 cm.

15. Two cards signed W Burton, two robins on snowy branches. 11.5 cm x 8.5 cm.

*Numbers 16-22 have cards designed by A West.*

16. Four embossed cards, china plates decorated with flowers and birds, two shaped, no. 94, and two on white mounts, no. 93. 11 cm x 7.6 cm, 9 cm x 9 cm, 13.2 cm x 11 cm.

17. Four cards, robins or tits in winter scenes, two no. 151, two no. 159. 10.2 cm x 8.2 cm, 13.2 cm x 10.5 cm.

18. Five miscellaneous cards, birds in winter scenes, nos. 680Z, 152, 161, 767B. 10.2 cm x 6.4 cm up to 10.2 cm x 12.4 cm.

19. Three cards, sepia designs of birds perched on a fence or on branches. The two smaller cards have verses by S K C. 11.6 cm x 9.1 cm, 11.6 cm x 7.4 cm.

20. Three cards, Mr & Mrs Bird in human dress in comic situations, in the moonlight, at the Zoo, and up in Town, one dated 1890 by the sender. 13.1 cm x 9.1 cm, 11.2 cm x 8.2 cm.

21. Two humorous cards, owls at school, no. 709, Professor Owl with two students, no. 882. 15.8 cm x 8.2 cm, 13.3 cm x 8 cm.

22. Four humorous cards, robins sheltering under a top hat, and bird family activities in the rain and on the ice, one dated 1894, after the partnership had been dissolved; this therefore was published earlier. One of the smaller cards no. 712 has part of the picture on the largest one, no. 710. 10.8 cm x 7.3 cm, 7.8 cm x 11.8 cm, 12 cm x 9.6 cm.

23. Four humorous cards, two with storks on ice, no. 824, and two with robins, in bed on Christmas eve, and eating Christmas dinner. 11.5 cm x 8.3 cm.

24. One card, an owl dressed like an old lady with bonnet, spectacles, and umbrella. 10.3 cm x 17.8 cm.

25. Four cards in correspondence style with space for sender's name, showing birds perched on branches. Sizes up to 11.5 cm x 9.4 cm.

26. Two Easter cards, one star shaped with doves at a window, and verse by J E Cox on reverse, the other with birds perched on branches against a stormy sky. 14.5 cm x 14.5 cm, 10.4 cm x 14 cm.

27. One card, birds in flight over a pool with reeds, no. 823 B. 11 cm x 13.5 cm.

28. Five cards, four with a single coloured feather, the fifth with four feathers. 8 cm x 5 cm, 9.5 cm x 14 cm.

## VOLUME 113: HILDESHEIMER & FAULKNER. SCENES OF COUNTRY & SEASHORE, SOME WITH PEOPLE, ANIMALS, & BIRDS, INCLUDING A FEW PRIZE DESIGNS

*Numbers 1-21 were published from 1881-1885.*

1. Five cards, four designs by A Glendenning, who won a £100 prize in the 1881 competition. They depict country scenes in summer and winter, and some have a flower design on reverse with a notice of the prize award. 12.7 cm x 10.5 cm.

2. Three cards, prize designs, farmyards in winter with sheep, cows, or pigs. 13 cm x 9 cm.

3. One card, prize design, cattle in a country lane, with a leaf design on reverse. 10.9 cm x 15.7 cm.

4. One card, prize design, a lake in spring. 18.5 cm x 11.4 cm.

5. Two cards, country scenes. 16 cm x 9.8 cm, 16 cm x 13.8 cm.

6. Two cards, trees by a river with rocks and waterfall, one dated 1881 by the sender. 10.7 cm x 14.1 cm.

7. Two cards, a farm by a lake, and a sea scene, with rocks, boats, and birds. 13.3 cm x 9 cm.

8. One card, two girls by a country stream, dated 1882 by the sender. 14 cm x 10.8 cm.

9. Set of four cards, seaside scenes with fishermen and boats. 13.5 cm x 9.7 cm.

10. Three cards, from two different sets, with similar lake and mountain scenes, one dated 1883 by the sender. 13.4 cm x 9.6 cm.

11. Three cards, signed C R, lake and mountain scenes with stormy skies. 15 cm x 10.3 cm.

12. Three cards, two designs of churches in winter with people in the precincts. 14 cm x 10 cm.

13. Two cards, winter scenes of farm and river with trees. 9.3 cm x 16 cm.

14. Three cards, two designs, one of a cottage, the other a river with trees, and verses by D E Weatherly and E M M on reverse. 11.2 cm x 12.9 cm, 9.4 cm x 11.5 cm.

15. Three cards, snow covered fields with trees, one with a windmill. 11 cm x 9 cm.

16. Two cards, leafless trees in winter, with verses by Byron & Bryant on reverse, no. 417 F. 14.7 cm x 11 cm.

A happy Christmas to you.

**111.33**

17. Two cards, £50 prize design by H Maurice Page. These have colourful sunset and moonlight scenes in vignettes, bordered by rushes growing from a pond with waterlilies, with silver background. 12.5 cm x 18.4 cm.

18. Two cards by H Maurice Page, winter scenes with people, one in a circular vignette, no. 312 E. 9.4 cm x 13 cm, 12.5 cm x 12.5 cm.

19. Two cards, scenes in vignettes surrounded by holly or mistletoe, one a prize design, the other with a verse by Macdonald. 11 cm x 15.4 cm, 11.8 cm x 15.8 cm.

20. Two smaller cards similar to no. 17. 8.3 cm x 12.6 cm, 10.5 cm x 7 cm.

21. Three cards, various sizes, similar to no. 17, with oak leaves, poppies, or grasses around the vignettes, nos. 663 X, 306 F, 437 W. 10 cm x 16.5 cm, 9.5 cm x 14.2 cm, 11 cm x 16 cm.

*Numbers 22-26 have cards dated 1885-90.*

22. Two cards, one a fishing scene in a decorated embossed border signed with the monogram of Charles Robertson, R W S, the other two people and a dog on a snow covered hill, signed W B, possibly Walter Botham. 11.9 cm x 15.8 cm, 9 cm x 12 cm.

23. Three cards signed Will Anderson, two designs, one of a church and cottage, no. 177, the other a man and a girl outside a cottage, no. 179. Sizes up to 11.5 cm x 16.3 cm.

24. Four cards by Albert Bowers, two of country cottages in autumn, no. 441 I, the other two farm scenes in winter, nos. 269, 858 D. 11.3 cm x 8.2 cm up to 11.1 cm x 15.5 cm.

25. Two cards, vignettes in patterned embossed mounts, one a sea scene, the

other a cornfield at harvest time, no. 135. 15.9 cm x 11.8 cm, 16.4 cm x 11.3 cm.

26. A similar card, a yacht on a lake, no. 205. 11.5 cm x 14.5 cm.

*Numbers 27-30 have nautical scenes.*

27. Two prize designs, yachts at sea, one with a party of people on board. 15.5 cm x 11.2 cm.

28. Four cards, two designs of sailing ships, with nautical verses by F E W on the reverse, c1885. 14.2 cm x 9.2 cm.

29. Two cards, ships at sea, signed C T D, possibly C Davison. c1885. 14 cm x 10.6 cm.

30. Five cards, from two sets, ships approaching harbour, two numbered 651 B with Shakespeare quotations, and three 652 Z with verses by E M M. c1885. 9.4 cm x 12 cm, 8.5 cm x 13.3 cm.

## VOLUME 114: HILDESHEIMER & FAULKNER. SCENES

**Some have vignettes with flowers, and some correspondence style cards, dated from about 1885-1890. Many are signed by the artists.**

1. Three cards by Fred Hines, woodland scenes on thick gilt-edged cards, no. 40. 10.7 cm x 18.1 cm.

2. Two cards by Fred Hines, woodland or church scenes in winter, with verses by H M B, S K C, nos. 214 F, 215 D. 11 cm x 15 cm, 10.5 cm x 14.5 cm.

3. Three cards by Fred Hines, winter scenes, one of Epping Forest no. 233 X, two with vignettes of churches, nos. 251, 861 B. 15.5 cm x 9.4 cm, 9.8 cm x 10 cm, 9.6 cm x 12.3 cm.

4. Two cards, by B D Sigmund, the same design of swans on the Thames near Bray, one with a flower spray, nos. 523, 573. 9.4 cm x 15 cm.

5. Two cards by B D Sigmund, Bray Lock near Dornay, and Windsor, no. 71D. 12.7 cm x 10.3 cm.

6. Three cards by B D Sigmund, houses in vignettes, with flowers. One has a verse by J C Holland on reverse, no. 329 D, the second an elaborate leaf design, and the third is dated 1884 by the sender, no. 460. 14 cm x 10.3 cm, 10.6 cm x 14.5 cm, 8 cm x 11 cm.

7. Four cards by B D Sigmund, two with a church by a stream, Monkey Island no. 770 B, and Lynmouth no. 263 F. 11.7 cm x 9.2 cm, 12.5 cm x 9.5 cm, 11 cm x 15 cm.

115.22

8. Two cards by B D Sigmund, river scenes, one of Lynmouth, nos. 549, 854 D. 10.3 cm x 14 cm, 16.3 cm x 11 cm.

9. Two cards by B D Sigmund, a birthday card showing a view near Bray, no. 545, and Bray Weir no. 759 B. 14.7 cm x 11 cm, 9.1 cm x 12.5 cm.

10. Three bordered cards by F Corbyn Price, winter scenes in vignettes, one with holly no. 293F, the others with berries or acorns no. 302Y with verses on reverse. This artist signed some of these cards in two ways, one with initials F C P, and also with a fancy monogram, occasionally both on the same card. 11.2 cm x 14.7 cm, 9.2 cm x 12.7 cm.

11. Five unbordered cards by F Corbyn Price, country scenes with leafless trees, two no. 751 B, two no. 749 B, and the other dated 1887 by the sender, no. 39 Z. 8.7 cm x 12.3 cm, 8.2 cm x 11.1 cm.

12. Five miscellaneous bordered cards by F Corbyn Price, scenes in vignettes with flowering branches around, some with verses. Nos. 391, 301 D, 337 B, 397 D, 851. Sizes up to 15.8 cm x 11.4 cm.

13. Four cards signed E W, probably E Wilson, one a moonlit winter scene with leaf sprays around, three with summer scenes in vignettes with flowers or birds. Two are numbered 608 (one dated 1887), another 501. 10.7 cm x 14.8 cm, 11.2 cm x 8.1 cm.

14. Three cards signed E Wilson, country scenes. One is of Wargrave, the others have grasses with views of houses in small rectangular vignettes, no. 326 D. 10.1 cm x 13.5 cm.

15. Three miscellaneous cards by E Wilson (one birthday), scenes in vignettes with leaves or flowers, numbered 5 W, 680 I, 30, with verses by Braham, G Herbert, and S K C respectively. 10.7 cm x 16.2 cm, 10.7 cm x 15.2 cm, 10.4 cm x 13.3 cm.

16. One card, sea scene with boats and seagulls at sunset, framing a verse by H M B. 10.9 cm x 15.6 cm.

17. Three cards, one a country scene printed in grey, the others in green and silver, one with a water-mill and a verse by J W Myers BA, no. 240 B, and a church with a verse by J L S, no. 241 B. 13.1 cm x 9.4 cm, 9.5 cm x 12.5 cm.

18. Two cards, winter scenes with church and trees in oval vignettes with plain surround, no. 341 T. 13.8 cm x 10.3 cm.

19. Two cards, summer scenes in circular vignettes with flowers, no. 390 X. 8.7 cm x 15 cm.

20. Two cards, one by S Bowers of the Thames at Mapledurham, no. 219 D, the other a sepia design of cattle in a country scene, no. 690 W. 14.1 cm x 10.8 cm, 16.2 cm x 8.8 cm.

21. A triptych folding card with six different pictures, two of country scenes in vignettes with flower wreaths, no. 448, and four on the side flaps of white flowers, no. 452. 14.2 cm x 10.8 cm folded.

22. Two cards, country scenes in vignettes, no. 852 D, 78 T, one with a verse by S K C. 10.3 cm x 13.8 cm, 16.4 cm x 11.3 cm.

23. Three cards, one a river scene in a vignette, with thistles, and a greeting in a gilt circle, no. 475 W, the other two with berry sprays around country scenes in vignettes, with verses by Moore, no. 633 B. 11 cm x 16 cm, 9.4 cm x 12.7 cm.

24. Two cards, printed in grey, one a cornfield with a verse from W Morris, no. 568, the other a church, no. 516. 9.4 cm x 12.9 cm.

25. Five miscellaneous cards, country or lake scenes in vignettes with leaves or flowers, nos. 420 B, 422 B, 423 B, 449 B, 645 B. Sizes up to 12.9 cm x 10.4 cm.

26. Four miscellaneous cards, two with ships at sea, one numbered 672 B, and two with views of river bridges in vignettes, one with a verse by H M B, the other no. 744 B. 11 cm x 8 cm up to 11.9 cm x 9.5 cm.

27. Six miscellaneous cards with views in circular vignettes of winter scenes. Two are numbered 69 B, two others 444, 604. 8.1 cm x 8.1 cm up to 10.7 cm x 10.7 cm.

28. Six correspondence style cards, with a small scene, greeting, and space for

sender's name, nos. 429, 459 (dated by
sender 1887), 476, 782, 842. 11.5 cm x 9 cm.

29. Five similar cards, nos. 103, 183, 637,
660 (dated 1888), 866. 12.4 cm x 9.3 cm.

## VOLUME 115:
## HILDESHEIMER & FAULKNER.
## FOLDING CARDS, SHAPED
## CARDS

This volume has a variety of cards,
including some well designed
folders, humorous shaped cards with
birds and animals, and folding cards
of the 1890's with a few published
by CW Faulkner after the
partnership was dissolved in 1983.

1. A four-page notice of a competition for
decorated albums of Hildesheimer &
Faulkner cards. This was held in 1882,
with £1,000 in prizes, and the judges were
the artists Mrs William Duffield, Miss
M Ellen Edwards, and Miss Alice Havers.

2/3. Four folding cards, two birthday, two
Christmas, with interesting patterns
outside in pale green and brown. Three
have single flower cards within, and verses
by H M B, H S, E M M, and one has two
flower cards. c1885.
10.2 cm x 14 cm, 11.7 cm x 15.7 cm,
10.3 cm x 12.8 cm, 12.4 cm x 17.2 cm closed.

4/5. A four-fold screen in two pieces, as
found. One side has four pictures of trees
in winter in rectangular vignettes on gilt
ground, and the other side has Christmas
greeting written across four designs of gilt
birds in vignettes on a red-brown ground.
c1885. 11.7 cm x 20 cm closed.

6. Five folding cards, c1885.
a) Yellow cover with a daisy border, and a
sea scene with a wreath of violets and a
verse by Leigh Hunt inside, no. 420 B.
b) A pale green cover with a daisy pattern,
and two cards within with fans and
flowers and verses by Alice Cary and
JC Holland, no. 440 F.
c) A black cover with the same daisy
pattern, and a vignette scene with
cyclamen around and a verse by
Wordsworth within, no. 447 B.
d) A black cover with a leaf spray, and
inside a scene by Fred Hines and a verse
by HMB, dated 1885 by the sender.
No. 561 B.
e) A brown cover with a flowering branch,
and a scene and verses within, no. 859 B.
Sizes up to 10.2 cm x 13.2 cm.

7. Six circular cards (one birthday), with
country scenes and gilt borders, one dated
1881 by the sender. Diameters 12.5 cm,
10 cm, 8.6 cm.

8. Five shaped cards, two large circles
with scenes, one small no. 70 b, one a ship
with a sea scene on the sail no. 206, and the
fifth a lantern opening to show a scene and

**115.21**

a verse within.
Sizes up to 12.5 cm x 13.5 cm.

9. Six shaped cards, two palettes with
scenes no. 111 B, three palettes with scenes,
and greetings on reverse, two numbered
785 D, 59 W, and a bell with a scene,
no. 635. c1885.
Sizes up to 10.5 cm x 16 cm.

The following cards were published from
1885 to 1893.

10. Seven shaped cards, all with scenes or
flowers. Four are battledores, three
numbered 831, 863, 891, one is a heart
dated 1888 by the sender, no. 885, one a
sickle no. 948, and one a hexagon no. 307.
Sizes up to 10.7 cm x 11.5 cm.

11. Four circular cards like plates, two
with flowers superimposed on willow
patterns, the other two plain with flower
sprays and gilt edges (one birthday).
Diameters 13.5 cm, 11.5 cm.

12. Seven miscellaneous folding cards
(one birthday) with scenes within, and
flowers and various verses. Four are
numbered 220, 381, 501, 716.
6 cm x 11.3 cm up to 13.6 cm x 10.4 cm.

13. Seven cards with flowers (two
birthday), one palette shaped, one a folder
with a rose no. 585, and a verse by
FS Hollings, one a folder with daisies by
C Noakes, and four with cut out edges,
two of these numbered 96 and 138.
8 cm x 5.3 cm up to 11.4 cm x 8.8 cm.

14. Six folding cards with spring flowers
and verses, including one by Faith
Quiltern, one no. 34 with pansies dated
1893 by the sender, three others numbered
31, 272, 309.
Sizes 5.1 cm x 7.4 cm to 9.1 cm x 10.8 cm.

15. Six shapd cards with flowers or leaves,
one with cut-out leaf edge dated 1889
no. 296, a cross no. 28, a moon no. 635, two
palettes nos. 35, 538, and a circle no. 256.
Sizes up to 12 cm x 8.5 cm.

16. Six shaped cards with flowers, one an
envelope no. 172, two garden baskets
no. 888, one a wicker basket no. 3, and two
boxes (one with opening lid). All have
greetings on reverse.
Sizes up to 13.5 cm x 11.3 cm.

17. Seven two-sided cards shaped like
leaves, in three different shapes. All have
a flower spray on one side and greetings
on the other.
8 cm x 8.5 cm, 15 cm x 6 cm, 9 cm x 12 cm.

18. Five small shaped and folding cards,
with verses and scenes inside. One is a
Christmas rose no. 310, one a bunch of
primroses no. 706, one a pansy, another a
water lily no. 727, and the fifth a single leaf
no. 929. Sizes up to 11 cm x 6 cm.

19. Four shaped and cut out cards, a
palette with kittens no. 423, a two-sided
cut-out card with puppies no. 933, an
envelope with kittens no. 959, and a group
of kittens by Helena Maguire no. 1018.
Sizes up to 12 cm x 9.7 cm.

20. Six shaped cards.
a) A kitten chasing a mouse hiding in a
jam pot, with descriptive verse by F E W,
no. 859.
b) Three mice eating a cheese, with verse
by F E W on reverse, no. 449.
c/d) A monkey peeping over a slate,
no. 1006.
e) Two reels of cotton, with verse by
F E W on reverse, no. 840.
f) Two pieces of a folder card with a kitten
on a tea-cosy.
Sizes up to 12.5 cm x 9 cm.

21. Seven shaped cards with kittens and puppies, a fan no. 939, a boot no. 909, a cradle no. 938, a box with puppies no. 911, two cards with kittens in a barrel by Helena Maguire no. 905, and one with cats in a basket no. 906.
Sizes up to 12 cm x 9 cm.

22. Eight shaped cards.
a/b) A cat and a dog with a slate, no. 132.
c/d) A puppy peeping through a broken drum, no. 952.
e/f) Kittens and puppies in barrels, no. 913.
g) A cricket bat, opening to show a verse by F E W.
h) A post box, opening to show kittens inside holding letters. The label is a nostalgic reminder of past postal service - "Next collection Christmas morning - Before sunrise, 6 o'clock, 8 o'clock, 12 o'clock". There is a narrative verse on the back.
9 cm x 7.5 cm up to 7 cm x 13.5 cm.

23. Five shaped cards, two palettes with blue tits and birthday greetings by S K C, no. 213, two circular plates with birds, no. 449, and a letter tied with string in trompe l'oeil style with blue tits pecking the seal. Sizes up to 11.2 cm x 9 cm.

24. Seven miscellaneous shaped and folding cards.
a) A pie opening to show blackbirds and a verse by F E W, no. 207.
b/c) Two cards with butterflies and birds, by A West.
d) A birthday card with butterfly, no. 554.
e) An owl, no. 195.
f/g) Boots with tits or chaffinches nesting within, by A West. One is a cut-out shape, no. 92, the other a folder, dated 1890 by the sender. Sizes up to 13.3 cm x 8.7 cm.

25. Seven miscellaneous opening or cut-out cards with birds and various verses, six numbered 155, 290, 560, 560, 552, 746. Sizes up to 12.7 cm x 8.8 cm.

26. Five shaped cards with birds, a cross dated 1889 by the sender, a lifebuoy, two violins, and a fan or battledore with verse by Cecilia Havergal.
Sizes up to 10.7 cm x 13.7 cm.

27. Eight small cards with birds or chicks. Two have birds in hats, dated 1889 by the sender, and another has birds in a pan, no. 90, all three by A West. Four cards have chicks in plant pots, and one has chicks in a basket, dated 1885.
Sizes up to 10 cm x 6.5 cm.

28. Six shaped or folding cards, four of children, three of these numbered 315, 702 D, and 643 D, the last designed by Emily J Harding. The fifth is a folding card with two lovers on a bench, no. 778, with a duplicate single card of the two lovers. Sizes up to 10.5 cm x 11 cm.

29. Six cards with children. Three are folders, two numbered 214, one no. 36 signed Edith Scannell. The remaining three cards are marked C W Faulkner, two no. 72, the other 71.
Sizes up to 7.6 cm x 11 cm.

*The following cards are all C W Faulkner, c1895 to early twentieth century, included here to illustrate changing styles.*

30. Six folding cards (two birthday), five with embossed designs of flowers and scenes and one with dogs. Five are numbered 95, 105, 158, 204, 206 and two have verses by M E Heritage and Marion Wallace. Sizes up to 7.6 cm x 13.7 cm.

31. Six folding cards (four birthday), with cut-out and pierced flower and bird designs, some with verses, four numbered 320, 428, 607, 625.
Sizes up to 14.6 cm x 10 cm.

32. Four folding cards, one with eight dwarfs, another a Highland soldier in snow clutching his bottle of whisky, the third a lace paper frame over a photographic mountain scene, the fourth with embossed flowers.
Sizes up to 14 cm x 11 cm.

33. Five folding cards, designs of people or children in sombre colours, one signed Ethel Parkinson. Early 1900's.
Sizes up to 8.6 cm x 12.6 cm.

34. Four early twentieth century cards, a classical scene, Dutch children, a traditional coaching scene, and the Hunt at the Inn.
5.3 cm x 10.5 cm up to 13.7 cm x 10.2 cm.

## VOLUME 116: HILDESHEIMER & FAULKNER. FLOWERS & FOLIAGE, C1881

**These cards include some 1881 prize designs, and a large number of plain cards with simple flower pictures, mostly of spring flowers and roses with an occasional cyclamen, camellia, or geranium, reminiscent of the early Prang cards. The floral designs on the reverse of some cards were usually line drawings on a green or orange background, also reminiscent of Prang.**

1. A £50 prize card by H W Batley, an interesting illuminated design in the Japanese style, with flowers and birds on leaves. The back has a flower design with a notice of the award. 11.3 cm x 16.6 cm.

2. Three cards, two £50 prize designs by J Edward Barclay, roses and lilac or irises around a country scene in a circular vignette. The third card is reversed to show the award notice. 12 cm x 15 cm.

3. One card, a £75 prize design by W Rathjeans, pansies in a paper folder on a dark ground. 11.5 cm x 14.2 cm.

4. Three prize designs, artists unknown, one with appleblossom against a blue sky, the others with flowers in vases. 9.4 cm x 13 cm, 11 cm x 13.5 cm, 9.8 cm x 14.3 cm.

5. Two cards, prize designs. One is a birthday card with primroses and a verse by H M B on reverse, the other a spray of lilac. 14 cm x 10.1 cm, 12.6 cm x 8.5 cm.

6. One card, signed T H Allchin 1881, a panel with a bee and a butterfly on the left side and an illuminated design with a greeting on the right. 12 cm x 16 cm.

7. Five cards, fans in blue or yellow with gilt, and flowers, birds, and scenes in vignettes, one dated 1882 by the sender. 11.7 cm x 8 cm.

*Numbers 8-29 show unbordered cards with flower sprays, not always well printed, as many of the colours have suffered with age. They are unsigned, but some could have been designed by M E Duffield, whose signed cards are in Volume 117.*

8. Six cards, various flower sprays on a grey ground. 7.6 cm x 9.8 cm.

9. Four cards, various flower sprays on a beige ground, with greetings in red - after Prang? 8.8 cm x 11.8 cm.

10. Six cards, four designs of spring flowers on grey or beige ground, with verses by F R H on reverse. One is dated 1881 by the sender. 7.1 cm x 10.8 cm.

11. Three cards, well printed mixed flower bunches on white ground. 7.5 cm x 11 cm.

12. Six cards, five designs of roses, spring flowers, berries, and grasses, two signed by an unidentified monogram. 8.7 cm x 11.5 cm.

13. Four similar (one birthday), two designs of camellias or roses and ferns. 8.8 cm x 11.8 cm.

14. Three larger cards with camellias or geraniums, on a beige ground. 10.4 cm x 14.4 cm.

15. Four cards, spring flowers lying on the ground, one dated 1880 by the sender and marked H & F, indicating that the firm was operating before the official 1881 date of the partnership. 11.7 cm x 8.8 cm.

16. Six smaller cards, three designs of flower heads on grass. 8.2 cm x 6.2 cm.

17. Six card with flower sprays on grass, in a larger size. 10.6 cm x 7.1 cm.

18. Five cards, four designs with berries or fungi, one dated 1880 by the sender. 11.6 cm x 8.8 cm, 10.6 cm x 7.1 cm.

19. Four cards, flowers in wicker baskets, one dated 1881 by the sender. 12.4 cm x 9 cm.

20. Five cards, four designs of spring flowers and geraniums in wicker baskets. 12.7 cm x 9.6 cm.

21. Three cards, chrysanthemums and geraniums in white bowls, two dated 1881, 1882, by the sender. 14.1 cm x 10.2 cm.

22. Six miscellaneous cards of flower sprays, one with pansies in a decorated bowl. One is by M E Duffield included for comparison - see Volume 117. 6.6 cm x 9 cm up to 12.8 cm x 9.6 cm.

23. Four miscellaneous cards, various flower sprays. 7.1 cm x 11 cm up to 9.9 cm x 13.4 cm.

24. Two cards, both with the same design of wild roses and orchids, date 1881 by the sender. 14 cm x 10.6 cm.

25/26. Twelve cards, seven designs of red, white, or yellow roses, on beige or pale grey ground. 7.3 cm x 11.3 cm.

27. Three larger cards of roses, one of moss roses dated 1881 by the sender. 13 cm x 11 cm, 10.4 cm x 14.3 cm.

28. Three cards, roses and ferns on a grey ground. 11.3 cm x 15.6 cm.

29. Two cards, pink roses, one with a decorated bowl. These are by M E Duffield (see Volume 117). 12.9 cm x 9.6 cm, 17.8 cm x 13.4 cm.

*The following cards have gilt line borders.*

30. Three cards, one embossed, one design of yellow roses on moss, with verses for Christmas or New Year, by F E W. 10 cm x 13.5 cm.

31/32. Four cards, three designs, one of yellow roses, two with roses and a butterfly. 11.5 cm x 15.5 cm.

33/34. Four cards, three designs of pink, red, or yellow roses, one dated 1882, another 1887, but all the same set. 15.5 cm x 11.5 cm.

## VOLUME 117: HILDESHEIMER & FAULKNER. FLOWER CARDS DESIGNED BY WJ MUCKLEY, MRS ME DUFFIELD, KATE SADLER

**These were published in the early 1880's except for no. 32.**

*Numbers 1-7 have colourful well-designed cards by WJ Muckley, most with gilt line borders.*

1. Two cards, geraniums in a glass bowl with a hovering butterfly, and red and white garden daisies in a blue bowl, with a floral design on the reverse of both. 12.8 cm x 18 cm, 18 cm x 12.8 cm.

2. Two cards, pink and white hawthorn in a blue and white bowl with a hovering bee, and flowering cherry in a blue patterned vase with a butterfly, both set against a background of blue sky. Both cards have a floral design on the reverse, and wide white borders. 13.9 cm x 19.2 cm.

3. Three similar cards, two with spring flowers in green vases, the third with white and purple lilac, all with butterflies. 11.6 cm x 17.1 cm.

4. Two similar cards, one with spring flowers in a patterned blue vase with a butterfly, the other with a bee and a butterfly over rhododendrons in a glass vase, both with floral design on reverse. 11.3 cm x 15.8 cm.

5. Two cards, one Christmas roses, the other daisies in a wicker basket, both with a woodland background and a floral design on reverse. 16 cm x 11.2 cm, 18.1 cm x 12.9 cm.

6. Two cards, birds' nests with a butterfly hovering over hawthorn or dogroses, and floral designs on reverse. 16.2 cm x 13.2 cm.

7. Three unsigned cards, probably by Muckley, perhaps published by H & F, colourful bouquets of flowers in blue vases or a German style glass roemer, with verses below. 10.9 cm x 18.6 cm.

*Numbers 8-28 have cards designed by Mrs M E Duffield, all signed M E D, and bordered.*

8. Five cards, the same design of red flowers and white berries in a glass carafe, with different greetings (two birthday). One was dated 1879 by the sender. 13 cm x 10.4 cm, 12 cm x 9.2 cm.

9/10. Four cards, one design of pink roses in a decorated vase, three having different verses on reverse by F E W. Suitable for Christmas or New Year, one dated 1880 by the sender. The fourth has a birthday greeting and a blank back. 14.6 cm x 12 cm.

11/12. Four cards, two designs, one of roses on a mossy bank, the other purple clematis in an overturned basket. There are three different seasonal poems by FEW on the reverse, including one of four stanzas entitled "The Peasant's Christmas Eve". 14.6 cm x 12 cm.

13. Four cards, three designs, two as in no. 11 and 12, and a third of forget-me-nots in a wicker basket. Two are dated 1881 by the sender. 11.7 cm x 9.3 cm.

14. Two cards, two versions of the same design of holly in a wicker basket. 13 cm x 10.4 cm.

15. Four cards, three designs, Christmas roses in a woodland setting, and waterlilies or lilies of the valley in baskets. 13 cm x 10.4 cm.

17. Two cards, one design of pink roses lying on moss, one a birthday card, the other with Christmas greeting and a poem on the reverse by the "Author of John Halifax, Gentleman". 16.9 cm x 13.6 cm.

18. Two similar, yellow roses climbing over a wooden fence, one with Christmas greeting, the other birthday with a poem by the "Author of John Halifax, Gentleman" on reverse. 13.6 cm x 16.9 cm.

19. Two cards, spring flowers in a decorated vase, and blue and white lilac in a white vase, one dated 1881 by the sender. 9.3 cm x 12 cm.

20. Three similar cards in a different format, one with spring flowers as in no. 19, and two others of the same set with flowers in vases. 10.5 cm x 13 cm.

21/22. Four large cards, three designs of roses with other flowers or berries in plain blue or white vases. 13.5 cm x 18.5 cm.

23. Two cards, two more versions of one of the above cards. 11.8 cm x 16.5 cm, 10.2 cm x 13.7 cm.

24. Three cards, red roses in a white vase with a flower design on reverse, and two others of white roses and forget-me-nots in a white vase. 12.8 cm x 17.2 cm, 10.2 cm x 13.5 cm.

25. Two cards, one design of a red and a yellow rose in a glass vase. 13.4 cm x 18.5 cm.

26. Three smaller cards, one another version of no. 25, and two others with white flowers and ferns in a glass vase with berries lying at its foot. 10.2 cm x 13.2 cm, 10.5 cm x 13 cm.

27. Three miscellaneous cards, one with a red rose on the ground, another pink roses in a white bowl, the third snowdrops in a glass tumbler. 13.5 cm x 10.2 cm, 9.7 cm x 14 cm.

28. Five cards in two sizes with three designs of ferns, primroses, and lilies of the valley growing in plant pots. 6.6 cm x 9.5 cm, 10.2 cm x 14.5 cm.

*The following cards were designed by Kate Sadler.*

29. Three cards, £75 prize designs of roses in blue and white Chinese style containers. There is a floral design with notice of the award on reverse. 15.2 cm x 12.5 cm.

30. Two cards, pink roses, red roses, lying on the ground in a woodland setting. 16.7 cm x 13 cm.

31. Two cards, pansies lying on the ground in a woodland setting. 15.1 cm x 11.1 cm.

32. Five later cards, late 1880's, with poor printing, showing roses and azaleas, three with verses by F R H. These are not marked H & F, but are included here for comparison with the good printing of those above.
7.6 cm x 10.5 cm up to 11 cm x 14.6 cm.

## VOLUME 118:
## HILDESHEIMER & FAULKNER. FLOWERS AND FOLIAGE, IN VARIOUS CONTAINERS, AND CARDS WITH HOLLY, MISTLETOE, IVY AND FERNS

**These cards were published in the early 1880's and only four are numbered. Many are signed with monograms but some have not been identified.**

1. Two cards, prize designs, pansies in a Chinese blue and white pot, and roses in a brown vase, both with floral designs on the reverse. 11.3 cm x 14.5 cm.

2. Two cards, prize designs, chrysanthemums in a blue and white pot, and clematis in a brown pot with a birthday greeting and a verse by F F on reverse. 10.5 cm x 12.6 cm.

3. Four cards, various flowers in glass or blue and white china vases, signed O W (untraced). 8.8 cm x 19 cm.

4. Three cards, pansies, roses, or cornflowers in oriental bowls set before decorated plaques in circular vignettes, with an illuminated leaf design in the corners. 12.2 cm x 12.2 cm.

5. Two cards, one design of an oriental style vase, plate, and teapot, set against a background of patterned tiles. 13 cm x 10.8 cm.

6. Two cards, one an oriental style teapot before a Japanese fan with a sprig of holly below, the other pansies in a basket. 11.8 cm x 15.3 cm, 12 cm x 9 cm.

7. Four cards, flowers or berries in ornamental bowls, one a birthday card with a verse by P J T on reverse. 12 cm x 9 cm.

8. Three cards, various spring flowers in patterned vases. 10 cm x 13.7 cm.

9. Two cards, one a Chinese bowl and vase set against a fan, the other a corded bowl with a sprig of holly and tray behind. 10.7 cm x 14 cm.

10. Two cards, one a blue and white Chinese vase with a sunflower, the other white roses in a wineglass with a verse by E I T on reverse, this dated 1883 by the sender. 11.6 cm x 14.8 cm.

11. Three colourful cards with various flowers in glass or china containers against a dark background. 8.7 cm x 13 cm.

12. Six cards, including two designs of daisies and buttercups in earthenware bowl or jug, and two others of an apple, a covered pot and a penknife, and a blue and white jar with an orange and a fork, one dated 1881 by the sender. 11.4 cm x 8.5 cm.

13. Four cards in two sizes, two designs of spring flowers in blue and white bowls, signed with an unidentified monogram, though this might perhaps be interpreted as a variation of M E D, i.e. Mrs M E Duffield, and they certainly echo her style. 9.6 cm x 12.8 cm, 5.8 cm x 7.7 cm.

14. Six cards, four designs of spring flowers in ornamental bowls, one dated 1881 by the sender. 9.9 cm x 7.6 cm.

15. A set of four cards, various flowers in glass or pottery vases, one dated 1882 by the sender. 8 cm x 11.2 cm.

16. Three cards, various flowers in willow pattern vases, one dated 1882 by the sender. 7.5 cm x 10.9 cm.

17. Four cards, three designs of lilies, pansies, or hawthorn, in baskets or bowls in a dark background, one dated 1881 by the sender. 13.8 cm x 8.2 cm.

18. Two cards, one with cornflowers in a cut glass tumbler, the other a birthday card with violets in a white bowl and a floral design on the back.
11 cm x 14 cm, 14 cm x 11 cm.

19. Four miscellaneous cards, two with flowers in blue and white bowl or vase and greetings in a patterned border, one with potentillas in a glass vase, and the fourth with geraniums in a white patterned vase. Sizes up to 11.3 cm x 14.5 cm.

20. Six cards, four signed E Wilson with flowers in tall vases, and two others with snowdrops and hops. 7 cm x 11 cm, 6.5 cm x 9.9 cm, 8.9 cm x 12 cm.

21. Four cards, three designs of ferns in pots. 10 cm x 13.7 cm.

22/23. Eight cards, five designs of holly, mistletoe, ivy, Christmas roses, and snowdrops. 8.4 cm x 12.7 cm.

24. One card, a willow pattern plate festooned with holly. 10.9 cm x 10.9 cm.

25. Three cards, signed by J H, sprays of holly or ivy around panels with Christmas verses by S W or the Author of John Halifax, Gentleman. 10.3 cm x 14 cm.

26. Four cards, hanging bunches of holly, ivy, or mistletoe. 9.7 cm x 14 cm.

27. Three cards with holly or ivy, two with quotations from Burns or Byron, the other dated 1884 by the sender.
9.7 cm x 13.6 cm, 13.5 cm x 9.2 cm.

28. Four cards, sprays of holly, mistletoe, fir, ivy, with verses above by S W. 11.7 cm x 8.8 cm.

29. Three similar, sprays of holly, mistletoe, and ivy, with verses below by S W or H M B. 12.7 cm x 8.4 cm.

30. Four miscellaneous cards with holly and mistletoe, one with a verse by H M B, another signed J H with a verse by A A P, and two numbered 340.
9.1 cm x 6.6 cm, 7.3 cm x 11.6 cm.

31. Four miscellaneous cards with holly, mistletoe, and ivy, one with a verse by H M B, another with a verse by E M M on reverse. Sizes up to 14.3 cm x 10.6 cm.

32. Three cards. Two are curious designs on a pale blue ground, one with a snail on a branch of ivy, the other a festoon of birds' eggs. The third has white berries on an unusual dark red background.
9 cm x 13.5 cm, 6.4 cm x 16.6 cm.

33. Three birthday cards, two from the same set with acorns or nuts, the third a bunch of ferns.
10.7 cm x 11 cm, 8.7 cm x 11.7 cm.

34. Two cards with bunches of ferns, one signed C N, i.e. C Noakes with a pool background, the other with trees and a verse by H M B.
10.4 cm x 12.7 cm, 13.3 cm x 10.7 cm.

35. Four cards, one embossed, three designs of ferns on a grey background, one dated 1883 by the sender. 9 cm x 13.5 cm.

36. Two cards, ferns, with verses by H M B. 9.4 cm x 6.3 cm, 8.7 cm x 12.8 cm.

37. Three cards, ferns on a beige ground. 9 cm x 13.6 cm.

38/39. Five cards, four designs of autumn leaves, berries, and grasses, with verses by H M B. 15 cm x 11 cm.

40. Two cards, fungi and ferns, one dated 1883 by the sender. 7.7 cm x 11.3 cm.

41. Two cards, each of a single autumn leaf lying on grass, with hovering butterflies, c1885, no. 257. 11 cm x 15.5 cm.

## VOLUME 119:
## HILDESHEIMER & FAULKNER.
## FLOWERS & FOLIAGE
## 1880-1885

**Most are bordered, with the flower designs often used for New Year and birthday greetings. Very few are numbered.**

1. Two cards, wreaths of roses with forget-me-nots or lilies of the valley around small vignettes with scenes, and verses by S W. 11.2 cm x 14.5 cm.

2. Three cards, sprays of spring flowers or blackberries around verses by A R H, Astley H Baldwin.
9.9 cm x 13 cm, 10.2 cm x 13.3 cm.

3. Set of four cards, spring flowers or tigerlilies with verses by H M B in panels, one dated 1881 by the sender.
8.7 cm x 12.8 cm.

4. Four cards, (two embossed), with gentians, cyclamen, Christmas roses, or violets and daisies on a dark background, one dated 1881 by the sender.
8.7 cm x 11.6 cm.

5. Four cards, three designs of alpine flowers in oval vignettes, one dated 1881 by the sender. 8.2 cm x 12.6 cm.

6. Two cards, waterlilies in a lake, one with a wooden cross, dated 1881 by the sender, the other with a verse by H M B.
14 cm x 10 cm.

7. Two cards with wide borders, one with white mallow, the other irises, dated 1882 by the sender, with a verse by E M M on reverse.
15.4 cm x 11.1 cm, 11.5 cm x 16.5 cm.

8. Two cards, spring flowers on dark backgrounds framed in wide borders, one with birthday greeting, the other with a poem by E M M on reverse.
11.7 cm x 15 cm.

9. Three cards, dog roses, hawthorn, or forget-me-nots, reflected in a forest pool, one dated 1883 by the sender.
15.1 cm x 11.3 cm.

10. A set of four cards with gilt borders, roses, pansies, forget-me-nots with ferns, one dated 1883 by the sender.
9.6 cm x 14.4 cm.

11. Two cards, harebells or daisies with grasses and a spider's web, with verses by H M B, one dated 1884 by the sender.
10 cm x 15 cm.

12. Two cards, bunches of spring flowers and catkins on a dark background.
11.1 cm x 16.4 cm.

13. Two cards, violets or celandines in vignettes, on a background or catkins or ferns against a blue sky. 10.7 cm x 15 cm.

14. Set of four flower sprays on a beige ground, one dated 1881 by the sender.
8 cm x 12.9 cm.

15. Three cards, sprays of lilac or fruit blossom on a grey ground, two dated 1881 by the sender. 9.9 cm x 12.9 cm.

16. Three birthday cards, spring flowers or dog roses on a beige ground.
7 cm x 13.2 cm.

17. Set of four cards, sprays of roses or spring flowers with verses below by S W. 13.7 cm x 10.2 cm.

18. Four cards, three designs of fuchsias, roses, or forget-me-nots above oval vignettes with verses by S W, two having birthday greetings on gilt grounds.
10.3 cm x 14.7 cm, 10 cm x 14 cm.

19. A similar card with red flowers on a dark background over an oval vignette with verse by A M R. 10.3 cm x 14.7 cm.

20. Three cards signed C N, i.e. C Noakes, two designs of daisies or yellow vetch in oval vignettes, with three different verses by H M B on reverse. 10.2 cm x 12.8 cm.

21. Four cards, from three sets. Two with spring flowers are signed B S, possibly B Simpson, and have a verse by F E W. Another has roses, and the fourth has primroses and a verse by H M B.
10.3 cm x 13.4 cm, 9 cm x 13.4 cm.

22. Four cards, three designs of various flowers growing by a waterfall in circular vignettes, the three larger with verses by E M M on reverse, the small card no. 284.
10.5 cm x 14.3 cm, 9.2 cm x 7 cm.

23. Four miscellaneous cards, one birthday with a wreath of forget-me-nots around a verse by H S, dated 1883 by the sender, another snowdrops and catkins with a verse by Ethel Ridley, and two with spring flowers and greetings below.
10.3 cm x 13.4 cm, 8.7 cm x 11.7 cm.

24. Six cards from three sets. Three are embossed, with a hand holding forget-me-nots and roses, two have flowers against a blue sky with verses below by S W in a gilt panel, and the sixth card has a bouquet of flowers and ferns with a text below. Sizes up to 5.9 cm x 12.6 cm.

25. Four cards, three designs of tulips, forget-me-nots, or convolvulus. They all have verses, for Christmas, Easter, valentine, and birthday. 12.5 cm x 5.7 cm.

26. Five cards (one birthday), four designs of roses, cyclamen, honeysuckle, and appleblossom, with verses by H M B.
11.4 cm x 7.4 cm.

27. Three cards, two designs of butterflies on grasses. 6.5 cm x 12.7 cm.

28. Three cards, one with roses, two with chrysanthemums or hawthorn in shades of russet and green, one dated 1880 by the sender. All have poems by S W.
14.3 cm x 9.6 cm, 7.8 cm x 15.7 cm.

29. Three cards, roses and forget-me-nots with greetings on a panel.
10.2 cm x 5.5 cm.

30. Four miscellaneous cards, sprays of roses, carnations, or geraniums.
12.3 cm x 8.1 cm up to 11 cm x 13.7 cm.

31. Three miscellaneous cards, one with china asters, another with lilac and a verse by H M B, the third cornflowers with a verse by J H Myers BA, dated 1887 by the sender. 9 cm x 13 cm, 9.7 cm x 15.4 cm.

32. Nine small cards, three with pansies or daisies, one dated 1882 by the sender, and six with various spring flowers and ornamental greetings.
Sizes up to 10.2 cm x 6 cm.

33. Nine small cards, six with spring flowers, one having a verse by M Cather, two with butterflies on grasses, and one with two butterflies on nasturtiums with a fan below. Sizes up to 7 cm x 11 cm.

34. Set of four cards, various white flowers and ferns with religious verse by Ernest Power. 11 cm x 13.8 cm.

35. Five cards, two with white flowers and birthday verses, two other birthday cards with spring flowers in vignettes, with a fifth similar card with Christmas greetings, no. 286B.
14.7 cm x 10.2 cm, 11.4 cm x 7.8 cm.

36. Four cards, three designs of various white flowers on beige grounds, one dated 1884 by the sender.
8 cm x 11.6 cm, 9.3 cm x 11.5 cm.

37. Four cards with silver borders in two styles, all white flowers with verses, two signed with monogram J W C, one dated 1882 by the sender.
11.8 cm x 9.8 cm, 14.4 cm x 9.4 cm.

38. Three cards, white and yellow flowers, with verses by H M Burnside.
9 cm x 12.7 cm.

## VOLUME 120: HILDESHEIMER & FAULKNER. FLOWERS & FOLIAGE, LATER CARDS

**These cards were published from about 1884, and most of them are numbered, though the sequence of dates is difficult to define. Rounded corners and borders appear in the later cards. Some are signed by known artists but the designs are of no particular importance or merit. No cards of this type have been found marked C W Faulkner.**

1/2. Six cards in three sizes, various flowers and ferns set around a twisted branch. Three have birthday poems by H M B on reverse, one has Christmas verses by E M M, and one of the two small cards is dated 1884 by the sender.
9.8 cm x 13.5 cm, 10.6 cm x 14.7 cm, 7.2 cm x 10.5 cm.

3. Four cards, three designs, all with verses. Three have daisies or celandines with a circular vignette, no. 377, and the fourth has flowers and fern over a rectangular vignette with a bird, no. 826 D. 9 cm x 13.8 cm.

4. Four cards, leaves and grasses, one a birthday card no. 463 D, the other three with seasonal verses, no. 464 Y.
9.4 cm x 13.5 cm.

5. Four birthday cards, flowers or grasses, two with verses dated 1884 by the sender, and one a basket of primroses signed C N - C Noakes.
9.2 cm x 13.5 cm, 9.2 cm x 14 cm.

6. Four cards (two birthday) various flowers with vignettes, two dated 1883, 1886 by the sender. One signed E W, possibly E Wilson, has a verse by F R H and is marked "Religious Tract Society", H & F no. 820, perhaps a special issue for that organisation.
9.5 cm x 13.2 cm, 8 cm x 13 cm.

7. Three cards, signed C N i.e. C Noakes, flowers and ferns with a fan and verses below, two no. 439 D dated 1884, one no. 443 F. 11 cm x 14 cm, 9.5 cm x 13 cm.

8. Two cards (one birthday), hawthorn or daisies with verses in a panel, one dated 1884 by the sender. 13.2 cm x 10.4 cm.

9. Six miscellaneous cards (two birthday), spring flowers and ferns, some with verses, nos 344, 379, 776, and 603 B dated 1886 by the sender.
Sizes up to 8.1 cm x 11.8 cm.

10. Two cards with roses, wide borders and verses, one no. 673 D signed E W, possibly E Wilson, one no. 674 K signed C N, i.e. C Noakes.
11.6 cm x 16 cm, 13.2 cm x 9.5 cm.

11. Two cards with verses, one china asters, signed E W no. 587 D, the other white flowers and ferns signed C N, no. 572.
11.5 cm x 7.8 cm, 13.3 cm x 10.5 cm.

12. Two cards, one design of buttercups and ferns signed C N, with greetings in a circular vignette. 11 cm x 10.4 cm.

13. Three cards, signed with monogram E W, daisies or buttercups with verse or greeting, one no. 668 D, two no. 842.
13.5 cm x 9.5 cm, 9.3 cm x 11.9 cm.

14. Three cards, roses or forget-me-nots, one with verse by F R H, two embossed with verses by A R H, one dated 1886 by the sender.
12 cm x 7.5 cm, 9.5 cm x 6.1 cm.

15. Four cards, three designs of white flowers and ferns on a shaded background, with poems by H M B. 12.2 cm x 9 cm.

16. Five miscellaneous cards, various flowers and ferns with verses or greetings, one signed E W no. 629 dated 1887 by the sender, two signed C N no. 140, 34, dated 1886 by the sender, another no. 338.
Sizes up to 11.2 cm x 9 cm.

17. Two birthday cards, snowdrops or narcissi with ferns in a rectangular vignette, dated 1888, 1889, by the sender, no. 4D. 10.2 cm x 13.8 cm.

18. Four miscellaneous cards, (two birthday, one valentine), laburnum, forsythia, lily of the valley with bells, dated 1889 by the sender, and wild roses. This card is numbered one though it appears to be a late publication.
Sizes up to 9.4 cm x 12.6 cm.

19. Two cards, one design of Michaelmas daisies on a plain card with rounded corners, no. 777 Z. 13.7 cm x 6.8 cm.

20. Four cards (one birthday). Two have roses in circular vignettes with verses by S K C, no. 33, the others hawthorn or laburnum in circular vignettes with a fence, no. 45 B. 8.7 cm x 12.2 cm.

21. Six cards, with flowers, leaves or ivy. Two have cut out corners, no. 182, three others are numbered 189, 291, 884, and one no. 308 has a Christmas verse by Lady Laura Hampton.
Sizes up to 11.4 cm x 9 cm .

22. Six miscellaneous cards with four designs of spring flowers, three small ones signed C N, the other three with wide borders.
9.4 cm x 6.5 cm up to 9.3 cm x 12 cm.

23. One card with serrated border, a wreath of pansies around a verse by H M B, no. 100, c1890. 10.8 cm x 15.3 cm.

24. Two folding silk fringed cards.
a) A birthday card with four designs of sprays of flowers, and verses, no. 461. 8.5 cm x 11.2 cm.
b) A similar Christmas card, no. 815 Y. 11 cm x 8.8 cm.

# RELIGIOUS CARDS

So far in this catalogue some publishers have been dealt with in individual sections, but for the remainder of the collection to continue in this way would raise problems. In view of the large number of unmarked cards, many of which might, with further study, be allocated to some of the publishers not yet dealt with, it has been thought advisable to continue the sections under subject headings, under which cards definitely attributed will be grouped together under their publishers' names, but will be available for comparison with similar unmarked cards.

It is obvious that a hard and fast line cannot be drawn and that some overlapping will occur. This section includes religious cards up to 1890 with a few oddments in the later1890's. The criterion has been that both picture and sentiments should have religious significance, while including cards with designs of appropriate flowers and birds which adorn the Christian message. Many have crosses, which appear for Christmas, New Year, and birthday as well as for Easter, celebrating the birth of the Saviour while foreshadowing His end. Scenes from the Bible, children at prayer, churches, and reproductions of Old Masters accompany the texts and greetings, and religious poems from the prolific pen of Frances Ridley Havergal frequently appear. Here cards with greetings are listed as such to distinguish them from the text and reward cards, which were however, often used as greetings.

*Section*
*11*

**137.3**

## VOLUME 121:
## RELIGIOUS CARDS,1870-1895

This volume includes greetings cards
and a few French Reward cards in
more elaborate style with lace
border, shaped examples, and some
with cut-out edges. A number of
open-out and stand-up cards of the
1890's are here, many with three
dimensional Nativity scenes. Apart
from a few of the earlier cards, the
publishers are unknown, though
further study might identify some,
perhaps from those firms already
dealt with individually.

*The cards in numbers 1-22 were published in
the early 1870's.*

1. Three cards.
a) A folding card on valentine style lace
paper marked Mossman, with the Lord's
Prayer in an illuminated panel.
12 cm x 18.4 cm.
b) An embossed card marked Mullord,
angels in a gilt border with a verse by
F R H. 11.3 cm x 7.8 cm.
c) A verse by F R H on embossed gilded
paper. 11.2 cm x 7.8 cm.

2. Six embossed cards with various fancy
borders, gilt or coloured, with texts or
religious verses.  5.8 cm x 8.2 cm up to
8 cm x 12 cm.

3. Four cards with gilt and embossed
borders and Christmas verses, three with
coloured scraps. 7.7 cm x 11.7 cm.

4. Seven cards, four designs of gilded
crosses and flowers.  Six have lace borders,
and one is on a gilded embossed card.
6.5 cm x 9.5 cm, 7.8 cm x 11.6 cm.

5. Seven cards, Biblical pictures and texts
or greetings on illuminated lace-edged
cards. 7 cm x 10.7 cm.

6. Eight small cards, crosses with flowers
in five different styles with embossed or
gilded borders. Sizes up to 6.2 cm x 9.7 cm.

7. Four cards, scrap crosses with flowers,
three opening to show texts. One is on a
lace-edged card.  7.3 cm x 11.2 cm.

8. Four similar, on various coloured cards.
One has an opening cross as in no. 7
above, and another a scrap cross with a
tassel and an angel beneath.
Sizes up to 10.2 cm x 13.5 cm.

9. Four miscellaneous cards with crosses.
7.8 cm x 11.8 cm up to 10.7 cm x15.5 cm.

10. Two folding illuminated cards in red
and blue with texts in scrolls, opening out
into a cross shape, one with a circular
print of the Child Jesus.
21.3 cm x 17 cm open.

11. Seven elaborate Easter cards.  Two
have crosses on silver or gilt mounts, one
has an angel, two have eggs lifting to
show verses, and two illuminated cards
with eggs are marked Dean.
Sizes up to 8 cm x 12 cm.

12. A large gilded triptych folding card
with angels and the Madonna and Child
in a gothic style setting, similar to those by
Raphael Tuck but unmarked.
13 cm x 25.5 cm closed.

13. Six cards with scalloped edges and
borders of lilies around prints of angels
and children or Biblical scraps.
8 cm x 12 cm.

14/16. Eighteen cards on elaborate lace,
gilded, or coloured mounts, with prints of
angels and children or Biblical scenes, all
with simple greetings or texts.
7 cm x 10.2 cm up to 8 cm x 12 cm.

17. Four cards, one a sachet with a print of
Christ, two with scraps or crosses on silk
ground, the fourth with flowers lifting to
show small Biblical prints.
8 cm x 11.7 cm up to 9 cm x 13 cm.

18. Six cards with gilt, silver, or coloured
lace borders.  Four have scraps of crosses,
and two have panels opening to show
Nativity scenes. Sizes up to 8 cm x 12 cm.

19. Five cards, four with silver or holly
borders and religious prints.  The fifth is a
folding card in four sections as found in a
scrap book.
7.3 cm x 11 cm, 10 cm x 4.5 cm closed.

20. Four folding cards, three opening to
show scenes from the Bible, the fourth
with flowers and verses by H M B.
6.5 cm x 9 cm up to 13.6 cm x 9.7 cm.

21. Six cards, Bible and Nativity scenes,
three with gilt edges, three with patterned
illuminated borders.
7.7 cm x 11 cm up to 10 cm x 15 cm.

22. Seven cards with various borders,
showing angels and the Child Jesus.
5.4 cm x 9.2 cm up to 10 cm x 13.3 cm.

23. Two folding cards, one a triptych with
picture of Bethlehem, opening to show the
three Kings, the other a winter scene
opening to show a number of small
vignettes of church and Biblical scenes.
15 cm x 12 cm, 12 cm x 15 cm.

24. Three folding cards, two with panels
opening to show angels, the third with a
door opening to reveal a text. 1880's.
7.5 cm x 11.4 cm up to 10.2 cm x 12.8 cm.

25. Three cards, mountain scenes with cut
out borders of Alpine flowers, c1885.
13.2 cm x 10.4 cm.

26. Six cards, shaped like crosses, with
flowers, birds, or Biblical scenes, 1880's.
7:6 cm x 11.6 cm up to 9.7 cm x 14.2 cm.

27. Six cards with angels, five star-shaped,
the sixth a bell, c1890.
6.6 cm x 7.1 cm up to 14 cm x 14 cm.

28. Three folding cards, c1890.
a) A triptych with four pictures of flowers
or crosses on the wings, opening to show a
Nativity scene decorated with dried
grasses. 15 cm x 11 cm.
b) A card on springs opening to show a
Nativity scene in three dimensions with
greeting in German.  It is backed with
transparent blue paper to illuminate the
scene when opened. 8.8 cm x 13.2 cm.
c) A cut-out easel with flowers and text.
9.1 cm x 17.5 cm.

29.  Three cards, opening to show three-
dimensional Nativity scenes, 1890's.
9.5 cm x 14.5 cm, 15.5 cm x 14 cm closed.

30. Two cards.
a) A mechanical card, opening to show a
three-dimensional scene of children and
angels in an arch of flowers, dated 1896 by
the sender. 12.7 cm x 13.8 cm closed.
b) Two angels ringing bells, originally
three dimensional, but found stuck down
in a scrapbook.  11.2 cm x 14 cm.

31. Three cards with children and angels,
two opening to three dimensions, the third
made to stand up with a support.  12 cm x
14 cm, 12.7 cm x 11.2 cm, 9.5 cm x17 cm.

32. Two cards c1890.
a) An elaborate card in the form of gilded
trellised railings, with gates opening to
show an angel on "springs". This card has
some damage, but is included on account
of rarity and its survival over many years
of handling. 12 cm x 16.3 cm.
b) A gilded card in the form of a Gothic
church doorway, opening to show an
angel. 6.8 cm x 15 cm.

33/37. Thirty lace-edged cards showing
Saints and scenes from the Bible. These
were made by a number of French firms,
including Bouasse - Lebel et Fils et Massin,
(Paris), Bonamy (Editeur à Poitiers), Bertin
(Paris), Maison Bassel (Paris). They were
probably given as reward cards to pupils
in Catholic schools or convents, and have
texts in English as well as in French. The
lace paper is of a high standard of
workmanship and design.1870's.
Sizes up to 7.6 cm x 12 cm.

38/42.  Eight large illuminated or
coloured text cards, with well designed
borders around hymns, prayers, or texts.
The edges have been trimmed by scrap
book compilers, so the publishers have not
been identified.
All approximately 14.5 cm x 21 cm.

# VOLUME 122:
# RELIGIOUS CARDS
# PUBLISHED BY CAMPBELL &
# TUDHOPE, GLASGOW

**This firm published mainly religious greeting cards, with text cards and reward of merit cards, combining quotations from the Bible and suitable verses with appropriate pictures; many in this collection have flower and foliage decoration. They are marked with the firm's name in full, or with a monogram, and some have brief greetings, occasionally on the back. None are numbered and precise dating can only be surmised from the senders' inscriptions or the style. Buday records that some cards published by this firm are marked Caswell, but all with that inscription are included in the Caswell volumes. No Stationers' Hall registrations have been found for these cards and no artists are identified.**

1. A cover for "The Bright and Morning Star", twelve Gospel text cards, which has a trade price list inside for texts, Reward cards, and Christmas cards.
13.5 cm x 29 cm open.

2/4. Eighteen cards, eleven designs of various spring flowers entwined with twisted ribbons bearing Christmas texts, some with a robin design on the reverse and a greeting "Compliments of the Season". Four are unmarked, but attributed by similarity. Two were dated 1873, 1875 by the senders.
6.7 cm x 9.9 cm, 9.9 cm x 6.7 cm.

5. Three illuminated cards, with Christmas and New Year poems. 8 cm x 12 cm.

6. Four cards with illuminated borders around Christmas or New Year hymns.
7.7 cm x 11.8 cm, 9 cm x 11.6 cm.

7. Five cards, four designs of open books with texts and flowers, one dated 1875 by the sender, three with Christmas greetings. 11.3 cm x 7.7 cm.

8. Five gilt-backed cards, three designs of flowers or berries, with texts on illuminated panels. 10.6 cm x 6.5 cm.

9. Five cards, flowers, berries, or vine on gilt ground around a panel with Christmas text, and greetings on reverse, one dated 1874 by the sender.
8.9 cm x11.6 cm.

10.Three cards, two with Biblical scenes, one with a knight, and Christmas verses and text on panel. 8.2 cm x 11.8 cm.

11. Four Reward cards, pictures of birds or children with hymns. 7.4 cm x 11 cm.

12. Six cards, birds on branches, around arched panels with texts and verses,

two dated 1875, 1877, by the senders.
9 cm x 11.7 cm.

13/14. Nine cards in two styles, five designs of birds and flowers arranged around a centre panel with text or greetings, one dated 1878 by the sender. Two cards have prayers or texts on the reverse. 6.8 cm x 10.3 cm.

15. Four cards, pictures of birds or an angel on a centre panel, with flowers, texts, and greetings in the border, one dated 1882 by the sender. 9.7 cm x 12.3 cm.

16. One card "To British Sailors on board H M S - ", with picture of a boy in sailor suit in a boat with primroses below.
12 cm x 17.7 cm.

17. Three cards, robins and other birds, with Christmas verses. 7.8 cm x 11.8 cm.

18. Five miscellaneous cards, three with robins, one with children in a circular vignette in an illuminated border, the fifth with holly around a vignette with a winter scene, all with greetings.
Sizes up to 9.7 cm x 13 cm.

19. Five miscellaneous cards with birds, all with Christmas or New Year texts or verses, two dated 1876, 1880 by the sender.
10.1 cm x 7 cm to 7.8 cm x 19.8 cm.

20. Three cards, two designs with sweet peas or irises around Christmas verses in arched panels, one dated 1876 by the sender. 8.7 cm x 12 cm.

21. Four cards on a grey ground in two styles, flowers, berries, foliage and insects around panels or scrolls with texts or verses. 12.5 cm x 9 cm, 12.4 cm x 9.7 cm.

22. Four Reward cards, flowers or berries around gilt-edged panels with texts and Christmas verses, one dated 1877 by the sender. 12.cm x 8.7 cm.

23. Three cards, spring flowers with texts in oval vignettes, and greetings.
10.7 cm x 8.4 cm, 9.3 cm x 7 cm.

24. Four cards in two styles, flowers on a blue ground with texts in panel.
7 cm x10.4 cm.

25. Two cards, flowers and leaves on a white ground with text and greeting.
9.3 cm x 12.9 cm.

26. Four Reward cards, three designs of flowers and butterflies, with verses in arched panels headed Faith, Temperance, Love, Brotherly Kindness, one dated 1880 by the sender. 8.6 cm x 11.9 cm.

27. Seven small cards, three designs of flowers with texts, one with Christmas and three with birthday greetings, one

dated 1881 by the sender.
Sizes up to 5.5 cm x 9.3 cm.

28. Three cards, one design of cherry blossom and fern in green and grey, with text and greeting, two dated 1883, 1884 by the sender. 11.7 cm x 9 cm.

29. Three cards in black and gold, with flowers and a bird, two having scenes in vignettes and greetings.
9.1 cm x 11.7 cm, 7.7 cm x 11.3 cm.

30/31.Twelve miscellaneous cards with texts or verses, one with birthday greeting and six with Christmas or New Year greetings. Sizes up to 11 cm x 13.5 cm.

32. One card, holly and mistletoe with a hand holding a letter bearing a greeting. This was dated 1903 by the sender but was probably published earlier.
13.5 cm x 9.3 cm.

# VOLUME 123:
# RELIGIOUS CARDS,
# CAMPBELL & TUDHOPE
# (Continued).

1. Seven Reward cards with pictures and poems printed in blue, early 1870's.
6.6 cm x 10.2 cm.

2. Nine cards, texts from the Psalms in white panels with spring flowers on gilt grounds, one dated 1876 by the sender.
4.5 cm x 12 cm.

3/4. Four large illuminated text cards, designs of seaweed with Biblical quotations, one dated 1876 by the sender.
12.5 cm x 17.8 cm.

5/6.Five large illuminated text cards, well drawn designs of sprays of spring flowers around oval vignettes with texts, signed with a monogram M T.13.3 cm x18.2 cm.

7/8. Four large illuminated text cards, spring flowers, butterflies, and moths with verses and Biblical quotations.
12 cm x 17.6 cm.

9. Three large text cards, two with trails of flowers and berries, the other with a spray of wheat and blue anemones, one dated 1879 by the sender.
12.5 cm x 16.2 cm, 12.2 cm x 16.2 cm.

10. Three large text cards, two designs of flowers and dragonflies in a brown line border, with texts and verses in panels, one dated 1880 by the sender.
10.7 cm x 17.1 cm.

11. Four illuminated cards with texts and poems, one dated 1883 by the sender.
Sizes up to 8.3 cm x 11.5 cm.

12. Eight white Reward cards, flowers, texts and hymns, one dated 1874 by the sender. 6.6 cm x 10 cm.

13. Seven white cards for religious festivals, Ascension Day, Good Friday, Epiphany, Easter, Christmas, Whit Sunday, with flowers and appropriate texts. 7.7 cm x11.7 cm.

14. Four white Reward cards, flower sprays (one with butterflies), texts and verses, two dated 1874, 1877 by the sender. 8.6 cm x 12 cm.

15. Four grey cards, flower sprays or wreaths around texts or verses. 7.8 cm x11.5 cm.

16. Two white cards, holly and mistletoe or hawthorn with text or verses by Keble. 9.5 cm x 12 cm.

17. Three cards, two designs of spring flowers with text and greeting. 7.9 cm x12 cm.

18. Three cards, Christmas and New Year verses on illuminated panels with snowdrops, roses, or ferns and fungi, dated 1878, 1879, 1880, by the sender. 13.5 cm x 5 cm.

19. Two cards, Christmas texts on a background of ferns or leaves with a butterfly. 12.4 cm x 7.3 cm.

20. Three cards, yellow ground with colourful flower sprays, one with text and twowith verses by F R H, one dated 1880 by the sender.
12.5 cm x 8.2 cm, 15.8 cm x11.2 cm.

21. Two cards with greetings, one with a grapevine, the other with shells, c1880. 6.6 cm x 13.6 cm, 11.3 cm x 7.6 cm.

22. Five cards, four designs of pink and white flowers with autumn leaves, texts, and greetings. 9.4 cm x 13 cm.

23. Seven cards with arched tops, probably for use as bookmarks, flower sprays and texts on grey or beige ground. 4.1 cm x 14.8 cm.

24/25. Eight cards on black backgrounds, seven designs, six of flowers and one of butterflies, with verses or greetings in panels. Three have printed greetings on reverse, and one is dated 1879 by the sender. 10 cm x 12.3 cm, 9.2 cm x 11.4 cm.

26. Four miscellaneous cards, various flowers with texts or verses, one dated 1876 by the sender.
Sizes up to 9.3 cm x 12.8 cm.

27. Six miscellaneous cards as above.  Sizes up to 15.4 cm x 9.4 cm.

28. Three unusual cards, designs of ferns in white on grey ground giving the appearance of stencils, with Christmas texts and verses.
8.2 cm x 20 cm, 9.2 cm x11.8 cm.

# VOLUME 124:
# RELIGIOUS CARDS
# PUBLISHED BY CHARLES
# CASWELL, BIRMINGHAM

**Caswell published chiefly religious cards, predominantly flower designs with texts and verses, and a number of tracts and religious pamphlets. Frances Ridley Havergal signed many of the poems, and Helga von Cramm, who also illustrated Frances's books, designed many of the cards in this collection. They are not numbered, and only one Stationers' Hall registration has been found.  Some of the cards bear a close resemblance to those of S Hildesheimer. They date from the early 1870's to about 1884, with one or two tracts published later.**

1. Five miscellaneous cards with texts, mottoes or verses.  Two have an ivy and berry border and were dated 1873 by the sender.  The verses are signed Mary Douse, B M, L G. Sizes up to 9 cm x 12 cm.

2. Five miscellaneous cards with texts and greetings, four with flower scraps. Early 1870's. Sizes up to 8 cm x 12 cm.

3. Three cards with beige coloured borders and spring flowers, and verses by F R H, E A W. These are three out of eight registered at Stationers' Hall 14-8-1876. 8.2 cm x 11.4 cm.

4. Six text cards with decorative borders and verses by F R H, three with greetings. Sizes up to 11.7 cm x 7.8 cm.

5. Six tract sheets on plain white paper with religious verses by F A W, E A A. These are marked C Caswell, Broad St., Birmingham - 4d per dozen (1⅝ new pence). 10 cm x 15 cm.

6. Three similar on coloured paper, c1890. Sizes up to 13.5 cm x 20.8 cm.

7/9. Sixteen small cards, six designs of coloured spring flowers on a brown background with religious verses or texts, some signed Y E T, E E H. One is a birthday card, the others Christmas or New Year, and they were variously dated by the senders 1877, 1878, 1879, 1880. 11 cm x 7.2 cm.

10. Eight similar cards on grey backgrounds, all with verses by Y E T headed Christmas or New Year. 10.1 cm x 7 cm.

11. Five cards, three designs of flowers on white ground with Christmas or New Year poems signed F R H, Y E T, or G P M. 7.6 cm x 11 cm.

12. Five cards with patterned gilded corners, sprays of flowers or berries with ferns and insects, and verses signed E T and L M L.  Two were dated 1881,1882 by the senders. 7.3 cm x 11.6 cm.

13. Four cards, two with Alpine flowers framing a mountain scene, and two with a Robin perching on a spray of leaves and berries around a winter scene, all with verses, one signed Y E T. 8.2 cm x 12.7 cm.

14. Four cards, wreaths of spring flowers and leaves with butterfly or insect in flight, one verse signed Eva Travers. 8.4 cm x 12.5 cm.

15. Five cards, sprays of flowers or holly with Christmas rose, and poems by H M B, F R H and Bishop Wordsworth, all with Christmas greeting. 7.6 cm x 11.3 cm.

16/17. Nine cards, six designs, colourful flowers with illuminated initials for the verses signed F R H, A C W. There are two colour formats, one with silver border and initials and blue print, the other with gold border and initials and red print. One card appears to be a cover, labelled "12 Scripture Text Cards".  c1880. 9.2 cm x 12.5 cm.

18. Two cards, gilt borders with a panel and a Christmas verse set in borders, one holly and ivy with Shepherds and Angels, the other a yellow flower with a church scene. 12.3 cm x 9.5 cm.

19. Four cards, colourful flower sprays on grey cards with verses by F L, all labelled with their botanical names, one dated 1882 by the sender. 10 cm x 12.6 cm.

20. Two white cards, rose or leaf sprays with brief greetings with illuminated initials, early 1880's. 15.1 cm x 10.7 cm.

21. Two cards, forget-me-nots or violets on a grey ground, with verses by C H and Jetty Vogel. 11.1 cm x 15.1 cm.

22. Two New Year cards, sprays of pink and white flowers, verses signed Jetty Vogel, Marianne Farningham. 12.5 cm x 17 cm, 15 cm x 10.7 cm.

23. Five miscellaneous cards with flowers and texts or religious verses, early1880's. Sizes up to 9.3 cm x 14 cm.

24. Four cards, pale green background, scenes of the Holy Land in vignettes with spring flowers and verses above. 10.7 cm x 13.7 cm.

25. Three cards, scenes of pioneers in the Rocky Mountains, one on a bordered mount and two with gilt borders, these with verses by A S E, M S M, on reverse. The pictures and the religious verses have no obvious relation. 16.5 cm x 12.3 cm, 13.2 cm x 10 cm.

## VOLUME 125: RELIGIOUS CARDS, CASWELL, (Continued)

**All these cards were designed by Helga von Cramm, and feature Alpine flowers and Swiss mountain scenery. Many of the flowers portrayed are labelled with their botanical names.**

1. Six cards, five designs of vignettes with Swiss views, flowers, and religious verses by Achespé and Y E T. 11 cm x 7.3 cm.

2/3. Eight cards, six designs of mountain views and Alpine flowers with verses by F R H, A C W. Four cards were dated 1876, 1878 by the senders. 11 cm x 14.2 cm.

4/5. Eight cards, six designs. Verses by A C W, Achespé, F E E H, have illuminated initials interlaced with flowers and leaves. 8 cm x 14.3 cm.

6/9. Sixteen cards, various sprays of spring flowers, shrubs and holly, with texts or verses by F R H, all with botanical names. Eight are numbered, from two different sets of six, the others are unnumbered; they were dated by the senders from 1877 to 1880. Each design was issued with several different texts or verses - one has been seen with four variants. 14.2 cm x 11 cm.

10. Four cards, Alpine flowers with texts or verses by F R H or Y E T, one dated1877 by the sender, probably designs from a numbered set of six. 10.9 cm x 14.4 cm.

11/12. Eight cards, three designs of flowers probably from a numbered set of six, with verses or texts, one dated 1878 by the sender. Four variants of no. 2, Rosa Alpina, are given. 10.9 cm x 14.4 cm.

13. Four cards, three designs on a dark grey ground of Alpine flowers, with verses by G P M, E M N, F R H, one dated 1878 by the sender.10.9 cm x 14.4 cm.

14. Four cards, colourful sprays of flowers with botanical names, and verses by F R H and Marianne Ferningham. 11.3 cm x 14.4 cm.

15. Three cards, two designs of Alpine flowers with verses by F R H, Y E T, and G M Taylor, one dated 1878 by the sender. Sizes up to 11 cm x 14.2 cm.

16. Four cards, three designs of exotic flowers and fungus, with greetings and verses by F R H, one dated 1882 by the sender. 10.7 cm x 15 cm.

17. Three cards on cream background, colourful flowers, greetings and verses headed "Peace" with illuminated initial, by F R H and C F. 10.7 cm x 15 cm.

**125.21**

18. A triptych folding card with silvered illuminated wings, a picture of Chillon wreathed in roses on the back and a number of texts inside with red, blue, and gold illuminated borders. 13 cm x 17 cm closed.

19. Three cards, two designs of Swiss mountain scenes with Alpine flowers and verses by F R H, one dated 1879 by the sender. 11.3 cm x 14.4 cm.

20. Four cards, Alpine flowers and views of Swiss castle, lake, and mountain views. 14.4 cm x 11.3 cm.

21/22. Four cards (one birthday) three designs with views of Varese, Lake Maggiore, and Alassio framed in flowers. Three have Christmas verses on reverse by H Bonar D D, the birthday card a verse by F R H. 17.7 cm x 13.3 cm.

23. Two cards, Swiss mountain views with simple greetings. 16.4 cm x 10.7 cm.

24. Three cards, birds and nests in mountain or country scenes, with greetings in an illuminated panel. 16.6 cm x 10.3 cm.

25. Two elaborate folding cards with pictures of Lausanne & Chillon within. and verses by E E H with blue and gilt illuminated designs outside. 25.5 cm x 16.4 cm open.

## VOLUME 126: RELIGIOUS CARDS PUBLISHED BY WILLIAM DICKES, THOMAS NELSON & SONS, W A MANSELL

*The cards in numbers 1-15 were printed by Dickes, an early colour printer and designer. About 1850 he took out a licence to work by Baxter's process, but also used chromolithography. He produced many religious cards as well as book illustrations, but the cards here signed by him hardly do justice to the quality of his work. No Stationers' Hall entries have been traced, but the cards appear to be dated about 1870. He was probably responsible for many cards appearing under the imprint of publishers such as the Society for the Promotion of Christian Knowledge and the Religious Tract Society, whose cards can be seen in later volumes in this section.*

1/2. Six cards, butterflies on flowering branches on gilt ground, with panels of religious verses by Henry Vaughan, W Harris, R C Trench, G Herbert, Francis Quarles. 8.9 cm x 12.7 cm.

3/4. Nine cards, various flowers and berries, with texts or verses in rounded panels by S R, A Smith, H Coleridge, R N Milner, G Herbert, A A Proctor, H Alford. 8.7 cm x 12.5 cm.

5. Five cards, flowers on a dark background with simple texts. 9.2 cm x 12.9 cm.

6. Four Reward cards, wreaths of flowers and leaves in shades of pink, green and orange around religious verses. 9.2 cm x 12.9 cm.

7. Five similar cards on a green ground, four headed by a name - Arthur, Christopher, Margaret, Victoria - probably given to a child as named. The fifth card is one of the designs with a birthday verse. 9.2 cm x 13.1 cm.

8/9. Eight text cards, seven with gilded cross entwined with scrolls bearing texts from the Crucifixion. The eighth is an uncut sheet of eight similar small text cards. 8.6 cm x 12.1 cm, 10.1 cm x 9.6 cm.

10. Two large text cards, for Easter Day and New Year's Day, with colourful

borders of Biblical scenes and flowers around panels with hymn or texts. 12.7 cm x16.5 cm.

11/12. Seven text cards, flower borders around shaped panels with texts or verses. 9.5 cm x 12.7 cm.

13. Five cards, birds in woodland scenes with descriptive verses in panels for the robin, bullfinch, titmouse, water wagtail and yellow hammer. 13 cm x 10 cm.

14. Two cards with robin or dog roses and a text with an illuminated capital letter. 10.5 cm x 7.6 cm.

15. Four greeting cards, three with passion flower, pelargoniums or sweet peas, the fourth signed E W, i.e. Emily Whymper, with japonica. 8.3 cm x 4 cm up to 11.5 cm x 7.8 cm.

*The cards in numbers 16-29 were published by Nelson, all Reward of Merit or text cards, some with good early illuminated design. This firm produced many religious cards and some landscapes.*

16/17. Twelve unbordered illuminated cards, with texts in large gilt letters over sprays of flowers, leaves or vines, and a small text below in black print. They are signed Nelson & Sons in a shield, and some were dated 1876, 1877, 1878 by the senders. 11.2 cm x 6.6 cm.

18. Five similar bordered cards, one dated 1881 by the sender.13.1 cm x 7.9 cm.

19. Eight miscellaneous unbordered cards with texts or verses, one with a cross, the others with flower sprays, two dated 1876, 1877 by the senders. Sizes up to 10.8 cm x 6.7 cm.

20/21. Seven cards in two sizes, coloured flowers and Biblical texts. 8.4 cm x12.4 cm, 7.5 cm x 11.2 cm.

22. Six Reward cards with birds and flowers in gilt borders around panels with texts. 9 cm x 13 cm.

23/25. Set of twelve red-bordered picture cards, with packet headed "For families and schools". Each has a domestic or religious steel engraving with a moral precept or verse, headed "The Goodness of God", "The Days of Youth", etc. These have no dates, but could be 1860's or earlier. 8.3 cm x 12.8 cm.

26/28. Twelve similar, with green, blue or yellow borders. 8.3 cm x 12.8 cm.

29. Two similar, one printed in green, the other in purple. 7.7 cm x 12 cm.

*The cards in numbers 30-34 were published by W A Mansell, not to be confused with J Mansell. Although a quantity of Stationers' Hall registrations have been found for this firm, none are for the religious cards here, which were probably issued about 1875.*

30. A very fine text card with gilt cross on a background of roses with an illuminated text. 10.8 cm x 16.6 cm.

31/33. Fourteen cards, various designs of gilded crosses with flowers or leaves and illuminated texts. 4.8 cm x 7 cm up to 7.7 cm x 11.7 cm.

34. Two cards, one a red and gold cross with spring flowers, the other an Easter card with a bouquet of flowers. 10.8 cm x 16.6 cm.

## VOLUME 127: RELIGIOUS CARDS PUBLISHED BY J E HAWKINS

**The cards here show a high standard of design and printing, and some could have come from Dickes. Many have the addresses 70 Welbeck St. W and 12 Paternoster Square, and a few are marked Yapp & Hawkins at the same address, perhaps a partnership, perhaps dissolved later. The pictures are the usual religious subjects of flowers, birds and scenes. All have religious texts or verses, some with greetings, and were issued about 1875 - early 1880's.**

1. Five cards with patterned illuminated borders and New Year greetings, around texts or verses printed in red, blue or gold. Four are dated 1876, 1877, 1878. 11.5 cm x 7.6 cm.

2/3. Seven cards, flowers or leaves on a dark background around scrolls with verses. They are numbered 2, 3, 4, 5, 8, 9, 12, probably from a set of twelve. 12.5 cm x 9.1 cm.

4. Four cards, birds on branches or reeds with berries and flowers around panels with texts or verses, numbered 1, 2, 3, 10, probably from another set of twelve. 12.5 cm x 9.1 cm.

5. Four cards, three numbered 3, 8, 9, lake and river scenes with panels bearing texts. 11.6 cm x 8.2 cm.

6. Three cards, borders of birds on ivy or floral branches around panels with verses, numbered 8, 9, 11, one dated 1876. 12.1 cm x 8.9 cm.

7. Five gilt edged cards, floral borders around panels with texts. 11.6 cm x 8.2 cm.

8. Six similar cards on grey ground, four designs with texts and Christmas or New Year greetings, numbered 2, 3, 4, 6, 12, 12. 11.9 cm x 8.2 cm.

9. Four cards, sloping gilt edged scrolls with texts and colourful mixed flower designs. 12.5 cm x 9.1 cm.

10. Three cards, arched sprays of flowers, grasses and berries with verses and texts, numbered 2, 3, 4, one dated 1875. These cards are marked Yapp & Hawkins. 12.2 cm x 8.9 cm.

11. Four similar cards with gilt line borders, one with holly and ivy. They are numbered 2, 3, 7, 9, and the addresses given are now 36 Baker Street and 12 Paternoster Square. 11.8 cm x 8.2 cm.

12. Three similar cards on a beige ground, numbered 3, 4, 5, one with verse signed M J M. 12.6 cm x 8.9 cm.

13. Two similar New Year cards on a grey ground, one with verse by F R H. 12.7 cm x 9 cm.

14. Three gilt edged cards printed in blue on apricot coloured ground with verses and texts, and flower or leaf sprays around scenes in small shaped vignettes. 12 cm x 8.8 cm.

15. Three gilt edged cards with Christmas and New Year greetings, flower sprays and texts. 12.4 cm x 9 cm.

16.Two similar on apricot coloured ground with flowers and insects. 8.7 cm x12 cm.

17. Two Christmas cards, illuminated texts with initials entwined in vine or snowdrops. 12.5 cm x 10 cm.

18. Two bordered cards printed in orange and grey, ferns and birds' nests with a mountain scene. 8.5 cm x 11.4 cm, 11.4 cm x 8.5 cm.

19. Two cards, one design of ivy and orange blossom with Christmas or New Year greeting and illuminated text. 11.3 cm x 9.6 cm.

20. Three cards with grey borders, spring flowers and illuminated texts and greetings for Christmas, New Year and birthday. 11.1 cm x 14 cm.

21. Two cards for Christmas and New Year, one with ivy spray and a river scene in vignette, the other with illuminated text and flower spray around large initial letter A with a sea view. 11.5 cm x 16.3 cm.

22. One card, two vignettes with a cross and a sinking ship and appropriate verse, marked "Copyright 1881". 12.5 cm x 18.2 cm.

23. One Christmas card, strawberry and periwinkle around a circular vignette with a moonlit mountain scene. 12 cm x 18.5 cm.

24. Two cards with silver borders, one lilies of the valley and a waterfall with New Year greeting, the other a spray of convolvulus with Christmas greeting. 10.7 cm x14 cm, 16 cm x 12 cm.

25/26. Eleven miscellaneous greeting cards, seven with flowers, one with birds, three with scenes in vignettes, dated 1875-1880. 10.3 cm x 8 cm to 10.4 cm x 14 cm.

27/30. Fifteen cards, one only marked with monogram J E H. They are all similar in design and printing, perhaps made by Dickes, and have flowers and berries with butterflies or birds and well printed illuminated texts, eleven with seasonal greetings. They resemble cards marked Mildmay included in vol. 128. Four are dated by the senders 1878, 1879, 1881, 1882. 11.3 cm x 8.6 cm, 9 cm x 12.1 cm.

31. A booklet "Under His Shadow", verse by F R H illustrated with vase of flowers. It is marked "W G Wheeler & Co., successors to J E Hawkins", at the address 17 Paternoster Row, London E C. This has probably some connection with the Wheeler of Mildmay, in volume 128. 13.5 cm x 10 cm.

## VOLUME 128:
## RELIGIOUS CARDS, MILDMAY

**The cards marked Mildmay were probably all published by J G Wheeler, 88 Mildmay Park, London N. Buday lists W H Lever, London, as agent for the Mildmay series, but no evidence of this name has been found in this collection. All the cards have texts, some have greetings, and they were probably published around the middle 1880's. A few similar unmarked cards are included here. No Stationers' Hall registrations have been found.**

1/2. Eight cards, six designs of children in summer scenes, two with Christmas greetings, all marked J G Wheeler, 88 Mildmay Park, London N. 8 cm x 11.6 cm, 11.6 cm x 8 cm.

3. Four cards with beige borders, three designs of children with greetings on reverse. 12.7 cm x 9.7 cm.

4. Three cards, children in circular vignettes, with greetings. 12.7 cm x 9.7 cm, 10 cm x 11 cm.

5. Two cards, mountain views seen through an arch or curtains, with greetings and illuminated texts. 12 cm x 15.4 cm.

6. Two cards, branches with flowers or fir cones in circular or hexagonal vignettes with illuminated texts and greetings. 14.5 cm x 16.5 cm, 14.3 cm x 14.3 cm.

7. Two Christmas cards, floral sprays with butterfly and illuminated texts. 12.2 cm x 15.7 cm.

8. Two cards, each with a single bird, and texts and New Year greeting in gold lettering. 9.5 cm x 13.5 cm.

9/10. Four cards, illuminated texts with various spring flowers marked with botanical names, one marked Mildmay. Three have Christmas greetings, one dated 1885 by the sender, and one is a birthday card. 11.1 cm x 13.7 cm.

11. Two similar cards, with anemones and chrysanthemums. 12 cm x 14.4 cm.

12. Three Christmas or New Year cards printed in red, gold and white on pale blue ground, with flowers and illuminated texts. 8.5 cm x 11.3 cm.

13. Two cards, white flowers and illuminated texts on beige ground, one a birthday card, the other dated 1885 by the sender. 9.1 cm x 12.2 cm.

14. Six cards, flowers or berries with illuminated texts, four having seasonal greetings. One was dated 1885 by the sender. 8.3 cm x 7 cm, 9.9 cm x 7.5 cm.

15. Six miscellaneous cards, two with birds, two with flowers, one with a shepherd and sheep, the sixth a view of Ingatestone, Essex. All have seasonal greetings. 9.3 cm x 7 cm up to 12.5 cm x 8.8 cm.

16. Two cards, flower sprays with illuminated texts and greetings. 11.1 cm x 14.1 cm, 9 cm x 13.2 cm.

17. Three Christmas and New Year cards with beige borders and illuminated texts. Two have branches of cherries or greengages, the third has fungi. One is dated 1886 by the sender. 14.3 cm x 8.5 cm, 8.6 cm x 11.5 cm.

18. Two Christmas cards with illuminated texts, one with sheep in a pastoral scene, the other a view of Mentone. They are marked Mildmay Deaconess, and dated by the senders 1895, 1902, but probably published earlier. 10.5 cm x 7.8 cm, 12.8 cm x 9.7 cm.

*Numbers 19-26 are unmarked, but resemble those above in design and printing.*

19. Four cards with greetings and illuminated texts, children in outdoor scenes. 8.3 cm x 10.8 cm, 9.4 cm x 12.8 cm.

20. Three cards with illuminated texts, two with greetings. One shows the Good Shepherd, another two children by the sea, the third a bunch of roses. Sizes up to 11.7 cm x 9.2 cm.

21. Four cards with illuminated texts. One is a reward card with a bird and a branch of deadly nightshade, one has autumn leaves and berries and a New Year greeting, and two have children and flowers with Christmas greeting. One was dated 1882 by the sender. 9.3 cm x 12.6 cm.

22. Two cards with beige borders, one an open book, the other a view of Bethlehem. 11.8 cm x 9 cm.

23. Two well designed cards with views of Crete and Nauplia, texts in gilt lettering and greetings on reverse. 15 cm x 10.8 cm.

24. Two similar with Scottish views, and texts and verses by B M and George Macdonald on reverse. 16 cm x 11.5 cm.

25. Two cards with Christmas and New Year greetings, illuminated texts, and views of Lucca and Canterbury. 11.5 cm x 16 cm.

26. Three cards with Christmas and New Year greetings, and views of ships, birds and cliffs by the sea, and sheep. One was dated 1889 by the sender. Sizes up to 10.8 cm x 13.2 cm.

27. One card, Motto for 1892, with autumn leaves framing sailing boats on a moonlit sea. This is headed "Ruby Motto no. 29", and marked "printed by Lith Art Anstalt, Munich". The publisher is given as Wheeler, Mildmay Park. 16.2 cm x 11.7 cm.

## VOLUME 129:
## RELIGIOUS CARDS, SIMILAR TO THOSE FROM MILDMAY & HAWKINS

**These cards are unmarked but bear some resemblance to marked cards by Mildmay and Hawkins. They all have illuminated texts, and many have greetings. With a few exceptions, they are dated in the mid 1880's.**

1. Four small cards with flower sprays, three dated 1875, 1876, 1877 by the senders. 7 cm x 9.8 cm.

2. A large card, with two birds on an ivy branch in a gilt edged panel and texts printed in red, gold and blue. 15.6 cm x 22 cm.

3. Three cards, two designs of flowers in blue and gold, one with a butterfly. Two have Christmas greetings and one is a birthday card, dated 1883 by the sender. 8.7 cm x 11.7 cm, 11.7 cm x 8.7 cm.

4. Two similar cards with a cornflower and wheat wreath around an oval panel with illuminated text, one dated 1884 by the sender. 8.9 cm x 11.7 cm.

5. Two Christmas cards, texts in gilt edged panels with spring flowers in a grey border. 9.2 cm x 12.9 cm.

6. Two cards, flowers and butterfly around texts on a plain grey ground. 13.8 cm x 11.2 cm.

7. Two cards, spring flowers or berries and butterfly, one with Christmas greeting. 10.5 cm x 14.8 cm, 10.7 cm x 14.8 cm.

8. Six miscellaneous cards with sprays of flowers, berries or vine. Sizes up to 12 cm x 9 cm.

9. Six greeting cards printed in red and silver with flowers or vine, one dated 1881 by the sender. 9.2 cm x 11.7 cm, 11.7 cm x 9.2 cm.

10. Four greeting cards, three designs, three printed in red, black and gold, one in red and silver. 11.7 cm x 8.9 cm.

11. Two text cards printed in blue and gold, one showing a lake with water lilies, the other two birds. 12 cm x 8.7 cm.

12. Four greeting cards printed in gold and purple, with spring flowers, wheat, grasses and butterflies. 11.5 cm x 8.9 cm, 8.9 cm x 11.5 cm.

13. Four greeting cards, three designs, three printed in red, black and gold, one in red, blue, black and gold, with large decorated initials to texts, one dated 1882 by the sender. 9.2 cm x 11.5 cm.

14. Four miscellaneous cards, two text cards printed in red, black and gold, a New Year card in red and silver, and a Motto 1885 card in red and silver. Sizes up to 13.2 cm x 9.2 cm.

15. Three greeting cards with grey background and scenes in small gilt edged vignettes with flowers printed in white and gold. 9 cm x 11.7 cm.

16. Four greeting cards (one birthday), sprays of spring flowers and leaves. 9.4 cm x 11.7 cm, 11.5 cm x 9.4 cm.

17. Two blue bordered cards showing river scenes with bridge and spring flowers, and texts and greetings in red, blue and gold. 9.5 cm x 12 cm.

18. Three miscellaneous Christmas cards with flower or berry sprays, one dated 1896 by the sender but perhaps published earlier. 11.7 cm x 9 cm up to 14.8 cm x 10.3 cm.

19. Two greeting cards with elaborate illuminated texts, one with autumn leaves, the other with a rose. 11.2 cm x 14.5 cm.

20. Four cards. Three have greetings and banners bearing texts, the fourth shows a ship in a stormy sea with a flag and a distress signal, and the heading "Lord help me". 8.5 cm x 11.4 cm.

21. Three cards in envelope form, monochrome pictures of children, with greetings and text. 13.3 cm x 9.8 cm.

## VOLUME 130: RELIGIOUS CARDS PUBLISHED BY H ROTHE, LONDON

**Most of the cards from this publisher can be classed as religious, though some of the floral cards have no religious texts, but are included here from similarity rather than left to the later section on flowers. The signed cards have H Rothe in full or initials H R, also H R in monogram form, and it appears from this collection that all three signatures are from the same firm. One Stationers' Hall registration has been found, as in nos. 1-6 below. The cards date from about 1877 to 1885.**

1/6. Eighteen cards in two sizes, thirteen designs of flowers and leaves with illuminated initials to texts or quotations from Shakespeare and Milton. Five have Christmas or birthday greetings, and two were dated 1877 by the senders. One sheet has three versions of a design with primroses. Six cards were registered at Stationers' Hall 15-3-1877 by M von Monteuffel, with rose, convolvulus, forget-me-nots, cyclamen, snowdrops and fern, violets and grasses, but only the last two appear here. 8 cm x 19.8 cm, 8 cm x 17.5 cm.

7/9. Nine similar cards with Christmas and New Year verses, five numbered 126, one dated 1879 by the sender. 8 cm x 19.8 cm.

10. Two cards, standing crosses with flowers, in borders with willow or ivy. One has a Christmas verse, the other a poem for Easter. 12.5 cm x 19.1 cm.

11/12. Four cards, three designs of spring flowers with Christmas greeting and text in a border of branches, no. 178. 19.5 cm x 12 cm.

13. A similar card with Christmas greeting and verse. 13.7 cm x 20.5 cm.

14/15. Six cards, four designs of flowers or berries with a butterfly and illuminated initial to verses. Four are Christmas or New Year cards, one Easter, and one has a birthday greeting; two were dated 1879, 1880 by the senders. Four cards are numbered 157, two 156, and they are signed M von M, i.e. Monteuffel. 9.5 cm x 15 cm.

16/17. Four cards, two Easter, two Christmas, gilded crosses festooned with flowers, ferns and ivy. Three have religious verses, two signed J M, M Y W. They are numbered 330, 330, 221, 363. 18.8 cm x 12.4 cm.

18. Two cards, crosses with sprays of flowers and ferns and verses for Easter. Nos. 131, 246. 19.5 cm x 12 cm, 12 cm x 18 cm.

19/20. Two large cards with gilt crosses, one with flowers and a sinking ship in a vignette, the other with a bouquet of roses and lily of the valley and a butterfly. Both have verses by G L A, and are numbered 400, 429. 22.5 cm x 15.8 cm.

21. Three Christmas cards, two with flowers and gilt crosses, no. 416, the third with a Christmas verse by G L A in a border of flowers and leaves, no. 410. 7.9 cm x 19 cm, 11 cm x 15.4 cm.

22. Two cards, one a Christmas card with Christmas roses and tendrils of creeper, the other with a cross and a butterfly festooned with ivy and a birthday verse, both no. 559, dated by the senders 1882, 1889. 11.2 cm x 16.4 cm.

23. Two cards, a birthday card with vine leaves, no. 224, and a Christmas card with azaleas and a border of willow catkins. 11.2 cm x 16.2 cm, 18.7 cm x 12.2 cm.

24. Two Christmas cards, perhaps meant for bookmarks, spring flowers with branches of creeper or ivy, no. 265. 23.7 cm x 5.2 cm.

25. A card printed on silk, repeating the design on the Easter card in no. 10 above, but with Christmas greeting and text. 13.7 cm x 21.3 cm.

26. A card printed on silk, repeating the design in no. 19 above but with a New Year greeting. 26.4 cm x 18.1 cm.

## VOLUME 131: RELIGIOUS CARDS, H ROTHE (Continued) c1880

1. Six cards, four designs of flowers and gilt crosses with pink or silver borders. Five have Christmas greetings, one birthday. 6.6 cm x 10.4 cm.

2. Five cards in two sizes, four Christmas, one Easter. Three have gilt crosses set in flowers, no. 123, and two have the same design of a marbled cross with ferns, forget-me-nots and wild strawberries, no. 289. 6.6 cm x 10.4 cm, 9 cm x 13.5 cm.

3/4. Twenty-nine small text and greeting cards, numbered 116, 135, 182, 173, 258. Twenty-three have gilt crosses and flowers or leaves, five flowers only, and one has a dove with a chalice. 9.2 cm x 3.2 cm, 3.2 cm x 9.2 cm.

5/6. Eight cards, six designs of flowers with illuminated initials to texts or verses. Five have birthday greetings, three are Christmas cards, and one is dated 1878 by the sender. Nos 139, 140. 12 cm x 9.1 cm.

7. Five cards, three designs of spring flowers with illuminated initials to texts and greetings, no. 144. 13 cm x 5.8 cm.

8. Six cards, four Christmas, one birthday, one a text card, with crosses and flowers. Two have illuminated initials, no. 159, and three numbered 318, 360, 413 are small versions of large cards in vol. 130. One card has a text in French. 10.2 cm x 6.5 cm.

9. Three cards with flowers, one a birthday card dated 1880 by the sender, no. 235, and two Easter cards, no. 247. 12 cm x 9.1 cm, 7.7 cm x 11.7 cm.

10. Three cards, one Christmas, two birthday, with flowers and crosses in a panel, and verses by M Y W, nos. 366, 374. 12 cm x 9.1 cm.

11. Four cards, three Christmas, one Easter. Two have spring flowers and ferns in a central panel with verses at the side by M C M, no. 529. The others have blue borders with verses by M Y W framed in spring ferns, signed M H g v M, possibly Monteuffel, no. 370 B. 11.8 cm x 9 cm, 12 cm x 9.6 cm.

12. Five miscellaneous cards with illuminated initials to texts or greetings, one in German, all with flowers, two with butterflies. Three are numbered 206, 206, 132. Sizes 7 cm x 10.3 cm to 12.7 cm x 8.7 cm.

13. Five miscellaneous cards with flowers and crosses, three Christmas and New Year, two Easter, numbered 156, 174, 268, 362, 411. 4.1 cm x 9.5 cm up to 10.3 cm x 16.7 cm.

14. Two Christmas cards. One has a picture of the Ice King and an appropriate verse by G L A, dated 1880 by the sender. The other shows a church belfry with bells, with a verse by M Y W on the back, no. 404. 11 cm x 16.7 cm, 12.7 cm x 9 cm.

15. One card in blue and silver, a starry sky with an angel holding a cross. 10.2 cm x 14.1 cm.

16. Two folder cards. One is a cut out cross with flowers on silver and gilt border, with an Easter verse inside. The other has flowers outside, signed M H g v M - Monteuffel? - and a carol within. 7.5 cm x 10.5 cm, 6.2 cm x 9.2 cm closed.

17. Two folder birthday cards, spring flowers outside on a grey background and texts and verses within. 6.7 cm x 10.4 cm closed.

*The remaining cards have greetings of no particular religious significance, but are included here as they resemble others in this volume.*

18. Three folder cards with flowers outside and verses within, one being in trompe l'oeil style like a book with gilded edges, no. 442. 5.9 cm x 7 cm, 9 cm x 6.5 cm, 7 cm x 10.4 cm closed.

19. Eight cards, five designs with flowers and illuminated initials. Six are numbered 208, and one is signed M v M no 155, with an identical card with greeting in French. Two are dated 1878, 1879 by the senders. 6.9 cm x 9 cm.

20. Five cards, spring flowers or holly sprays around Christmas greetings. Three are numbered 121, and one is signed M h g v M, and numbered 328. 6.2 cm x 9.3 cm.

21. Six cards, probably a set, spring flowers with greetings in scroll or panel, no.122. Two are dated 1877, 1878 by the senders. 12 cm x 7.7 cm.

22. Three cards, spring flowers or berries with illuminated greetings, signed M v M, i.e. Monteuffel, no 128. 11.8 cm x 8.9 cm, 11.8 cm x 8.9 cm.

23. Two cards with birthday or valentine greetings, one design of a cupid in a rose, no. 141. 9.4 cm x 12.5 cm.

24. Three cards, sprays of ferns, grasses and flowers with seasonal greetings, no. 174. 14.3 cm x 6.3 cm.

25. Four cards, three designs of flowering branches over tables set with china or decanters and glasses, with greetings in scrolls, two dated 1880 by the senders. No. 398. 9 cm x 12.8 cm.

26. Five cards, four designs of flowers, holly or heather with illuminated greetings, one dated 1880 by the sender. 5.8 cm x 13 cm.

27. Six cards, flowers on mosaic ground, with greetings for Christmas, New Year, and birthday, one dated 1883 by the sender; two numbered 220, one 148. One card is embossed, an unusual feature for this publisher. 9 cm x 12.2 cm.

28. Four cards signed M H g v M. Two have Christmas greetings, and verses by M Y W in a flag shape surrounded by flowers, one with a moveable flag over this. The third has a bowl of mixed flowers, the fourth has a moonlit lake with water lilies. Nos. 359, 365. 9.7 cm x 7 cm, 12.3 cm x 9.3 cm, 11.8 cm x 9.8 cm.

29. Five cards, three Christmas or New Year, two birthday, with flower sprays, numbers 193, 249, 260. 5.7 cm x 3.8 cm, 12.7 cm x 7.6 cm.

30. A Christmas card with a border of roses and leaves on a frame of branches, with a "scrap" bowl of dried flowers and grasses, no. 449. 11 cm x 16.5 cm.

# VOLUME 132: RELIGIOUS CARDS, VARIOUS PUBLISHERS

**Cards here were published by the Religious Tract Society (R T S), the Society for the Promotion of Christian Knowledge (S P C K), and the Sunday School Union (S S U). They all emphasise the spiritual significance of the Christmas festival with appropriate texts or verses, some with Biblical pictures, many with flower designs. It is doubtful whether the cards were actually printed by these publishers, and many bear the name Riddle & Couchman in addition. Although there are a number of Stationers' Hall entries for this firm, they have not been traced to any of these cards.**

*Numbers 1-31 have cards published by the R T S, signed by the name in full, initials, or a monogram.*

1. Five illuminated Christmas and New Year cards with holly, mistletoe, and Christmas scenes, one dated 1875 by the sender, all marked Riddle & Couchman. 11.5 cm x 7.6 cm, 7.6 cm x 11.5 cm.

2. Three gilt-edged text cards with shells and seaweed, marked Riddle & Couchman, one dated 1879 by the sender. 11.5 cm x 7.8 cm.

3. Two illuminated text cards, Holy Land scenes in vignettes, with spring flowers. 9.5 cm x 13.2 cm.

4. Six miscellaneous cards, including two early reward cards with Kronheim style prints, and four illuminated cards, one dated 1880 by the sender. Sizes up to 11.3 cm x 7.5 cm.

5/6.Six cards with black backgrounds, colourful flowers with texts printed in red in panels, one dated 1877 by the sender. 12.8 cm x 9.4 cm.

7. Six cards, four designs of roses, fuchsias, pansies, convolvulus, with texts printed in gold, one dated 1879 by the sender. These cards also have the signature Dupuy & Sons, a Paris firm. 7 cm x 10.4 cm.

8/10. Twelve Christmas and New Year cards, seven designs of mixed flowers on gilt or pale green ground, with texts in panels and greetings below. Three were dated 1878,1879, 1879 by the senders. 13.5 cm x 7.6 cm.

11/12. Eighteen cards, ten designs of spring flowers, roses, camellias, china asters, on gilt or pale green ground, with texts in panels and greetings below. Two were dated 1878, 1880, by the senders. 9.7 cm x 6.5 cm.

**132.33**

13. Four gilt-edged cards, three with texts and one a birthday card, with texts in panels in floral frames, one dated 1881 by the sender. Two cards have verses on the back by H Bonar, Newton.
8.5 cm x 12.7 cm, 9 cm x 13 cm.

14. Three cards, flowers on gilt ground with texts in scrolls. 7.7 cm x 11 cm.

15. One card, holly and robin framing an Alpine village scene, marked Riddle & Couchman. 10.9 cm x 16.5 cm.

16/17. Four cards marked Riddle & Couchman, various flowers, one with texts in four coloured panels, three with birthday greetings.10.9 cm x 16.5 cm.

18. Two cards with pale blue ground, decorative scrolls with texts framed in flowers. 15.1 cm x 10 cm.

19. Five Christmas or New Year cards, birds in summer or winter scenes with flowers or holly. 11.3 cm x 7.5 cm, 7.5 cm x 11.3 cm.

20. Three text cards, birds with flowers, two on silver ground. 7.1 cm x 10.6 cm.

21. Four greeting cards, two with birds' nests set in spring flowers, the others with nuts and leaves or clover, all with verses in panels. Th. Dupuy, Paris, can be faintly discerned on one card. Two were dated 1879 by the senders. 12.2 cm x 8.8 cm.

22. Five cards on yellow ground, spring flowers and roses with texts in panels and greetings below, one dated 1880 by the sender. 9 cm x 13.6 cm.

23. Six embossed cards, four designs of spring flowers, roses and ferns, with texts in panels, early 1880's. 11 cm x 7 cm.

24. Four embossed cards, two flower designs with texts in panels, two dated 1882, 1885, by the senders. 11 cm x 7 cm.

25. Six miscellaneous gilt-edged cards, five designs with various flowers and texts, early 1880's. Sizes up to 11.4 cm x 8.4 cm.

26. Two text cards, early colour printing with flower borders around texts. 15.3 cm x 10.7 cm.

27. Three cards, for Christmas, New Year and birthday, two designs of dog rose and nasturtium around a panel with verse slotted in to corners in trompe l'oeil style, c1885. 9.9 cm x 14 cm.

28. Three greeting cards, two designs of white flowers and brown leaves with gold highlights, and verses by M E R on reverse, c1885. 13.8 cm x 11.2 cm.

29. Six cards (one probably the cover of the set), four designs of sea, country, or winter scenes with verses by F L, S K C, M K M, Silesius on reverse, c1885.
7.2 cm x10.7 cm.

30. Two cards, silver bells with holly or mistletoe and verses by Dr Mahlenberg or M E Ropes. 9.7 cm x 13 cm.

31. Five miscellaneous cards, three with flowers, one with birds, and a "Search the Scriptures" card. Two are marked Riddle & Couchman, one has a verse by F R H. 10.2 cm x 6.7 cm up to 10 cm x 12.8 cm.

*Numbers 32-36 were published by S P C K. See Volume 141 for some earlier reward cards by this publisher.*

32. Seven gilt-backed cards with flowers and birds. Five have Christmas greetings, two have texts. 11 cm x 7.5 cm, 8.3 cm x 4.7 cm.

33/34. Four illuminated cards, marked C Terry, Lith. These are good designs with nativity scenes on gilt ground, and texts and hymns with elaborate illuminated capital letters. 1870's? 11.1 cm x 15 cm.

35. Three illuminated cards, one Easter with daisies, no. 90, one a Christmas text with hawthorn blossom no. 93, the third a baptism certificate dated 1898, for Edward William Tucker, no. 139. 10 cm x 6.5 cm, 11.7 cm x 8 cm, 11.4 cm x 15.5 cm.

36. Three Christmas cards on pale green ground. Two have flower and leaf sprays, no. 77, the third maidenhair fern with a verse by Keble, no. 98.
9.4 cm x 14.3 cm,13.8 cm x 9.8 cm.

*The following cards were published by the S S U.*

37. Four illuminated text cards, two with Biblical scenes, two with flowers and New Year greeting, all marked Riddle &

Couchman, c1880.
Sizes up to 13.4 cm x 9.4 cm.

38. Four text cards, with flowers, birds, and scenes. One is marked "Sunday School, Battersea, Motto for 1886", another "Baptist Sunday School, Bridge St Chapel, Banbury". Sizes up to 12 cm x 9.2 cm.

## VOLUME 133: RELIGIOUS CARDS FROM VARIOUS PUBLISHERS, INCLUDING SOME OF MANCHESTER INTEREST

1. Six greeting cards, flower and holly sprays, published by Manchester Y M C A. Five are printed in red, black and gold, the sixth has a holly spray with green leaves marked Aikman & Woodhead, litho. c1880. 12 cm x 7.5 cm.

2/4. Seventeen text cards published by Mrs E Grimke, Prestwich, Manchester, designs of birds and sheep printed in red, black and green by E Kaufmann, Baden. Four have texts printed in various foreign languages, and two are dated 1878. 12 cm x 7.5 cm.

5. Two illuminated text cards published by A Stevenson, Edinburgh. 4.5 cm x 9 cm, 11.4 cm x 6.7 cm.

6. Five coloured tracts on cheap paper with three designs of birds and flowers, published by Drummond's Tract Depot, Stirling. Sizes up to 12.4 cm x 9.2 cm.

7. Four cards published or designed by E Vouga, birds, flowers and ships on dark background, two dated 1880, 1884, by the sender. 8.7 cm x 12.5 cm, 12.5 cm x 8.7 cm.

8. Three well printed illuminated cards of the Nativity, printed in Belgium for F Edwards & Co., Brixton. Buday dates this publisher in the 1890's.
8 cm x 12.5 cm, 12 cm x 9 cm.

9. Three similar cards with Biblical scenes, printed in Belgium, one marked "The Art & Book Company, London". Sizes up to 13 cm x 9.5 cm.

10. Five cards marked "The Book Society, London". Three are greeting cards with a picture of St George, two are motto cards for 1894 and 1897.
15 cm x 9.8 cm, 11.2 cm x 9 cm.

11/14. Eight large motto cards published by the Book Society, two for 1887, one 1890, three 1892, one 1897, and one 1898, with various sea and country scenes, some decorated with flowers. The 1898 card has an illuminated initial letter and a serrated edge, and is overprinted with the name of the Zenana Bible and Medical Mission and the Y W C A. Sizes up to 18 cm x 11.4 cm.

15. Two examples of the work of Mrs Georgie C Gaskin for the Leadenhall

Press, showing black and white drawings of angels enclosed in a patterned red border, c1890. 8.5 cm x 12.3 cm, 11.6 cm x 9.2 cm.

16. The first Christmas day, by Wyndham H Hughes, published by Mowbray & Co, Oxford and London. This is a twentieth century repeat of the design first published in 1880. 14.5 cm x 11.4 cm.

17. Three cards published by Mowbray, probably twentieth century. One is a small illuminated card with a verse by A R C, another a folder with illuminated cover and a verse by R B within, the third the Raphael Madonna and Child with a verse by A R C. 11.2 cm x 5.5 cm up to 8.3 cm x 12.7 cm.

18. Two cards, winter scenes with birds and flowers, marked E K. 10 cm x 8 cm, 11 cm x 15.2 cm.

19. One card, Motto for 1894, published by the Scripture Union, with a bunch of narcissi and a text. 12.8 cm x 7.8 cm.

## VOLUME 134: RELIGIOUS CARDS PUBLISHED BY CASTELL BROS., 1880's

The cards here are all, except for the last three numbers, from a set of religious cards titled "The Peniel", probably from Genesis, verse 30 "And Jacob called the name of the place Peniel: for I have seen God face to face and my life is preserved". Many have religious verses by Lucy A Bennett (L A B), and all have seasonal greetings. They have the firm's trademark, a castle, on the back, and all are numbered. Many more cards from this publisher will be seen in later subject sections.

1. A card on thick board designed by F Corbyn Price, a Biblical scene. No. 33. 12.9 cm x 16.5 cm.

2/4. A set of six cards illustrating English Cathedrals, by F Corbyn Price, with verses by E H Bickersteth D D, Bishop of Exeter. No. 54, c1885. 17.2 cm x 12.3 cm.

5/7. A similar set of French and German Cathedrals with verses by Canon Bell, D D. No. 53, c1885.  12.3 cm x 17.2 cm.

8. Two cards, winged cherubs' heads, with verses by L A B. No. 31. 15.5 cm x 11 cm.

9. Two cards, Nativity scenes with texts. No. 35. 15.2 cm x 11.1 cm.

10. Four cards, Biblical scenes with texts. Two are numbered 42, one Packet K, and the fourth is dated 1889 by the sender. Sizes up to 12.4 cm x 13.4 cm.

11. Four cards, Biblical scenes, two dated 1888, 1889.  No. 76. 9 cm x 9.8 cm.

12.  Two cards, the Manger, the three Wise Men, with texts. No. 82. 15 cm x10.6 cm.13. Two cards, Biblical scenes in grey and white, one no. 56, the other signed H D, no. 121 A.  8.7 cm x 13 cm, 12.3 cm x 15.3 cm.

14. Two cards, the Sermon on the Mount, Christ healing the sick, signed A C P, probably Alice Price, with texts and verse by L A B on reverse. No. 88 A. 13.3 cm x 9.2 cm.

15. Four cards in two sizes by Alice Price, monochrome scenes of the Nativity. Nos. 90, 91. 9.1 cm x 9.7 cm, 13.8 cm x 11 cm.

16. One card, an angel by a church window, signed A P and F C P (F Corbyn Price). No. 94 A. 11.8 cm x 15 cm.

17. Another signed A P and F C P, Ruth and Boaz. No. 133 B. 16.4 cm x 14.4 cm.

18. Three cards, flowers and birds with climbing plants, and verses by L A B, one dated 1886 by the sender. No. 16. 9.5 cm x 11 cm.

19. Two cards, sea views glimpsed through arched windows, with verses by F R H. No. 17. 13 cm x 11 cm.

20. Three cards, winter scenes with verses by L A B. No. 40. 9.4 cm x 15 cm.

21. Two cards, stormy skies over river scenes with verses by L A B. No. 41 A. 13 cm x 13 cm.

22. Three cards, monochrome church and country scenes with verses by F R H. No. 43 A. 11 cm x 15.8 cm.

23. Two cards, ships in harbour beneath stormy skies with verses by L A B. No. 55. 11 cm x 15.8 cm.

24. Two cards, a lake and mountain scene with verse by Charles A Fox, no. 87, and a church with verse by L A B, no. 72. 11 cm x 14.2 cm.

25. Two cards, monochrome farm and country winter scenes, one with verse by F R H, no. 83 A, the other with verse by George MacDonald, L L D, no. 84 A. 11.7 cm x 13.5 cm, 11.9 cm x 14.8 cm.

26. Two cards, a church in a circular vignette with verse by Canon Bell, D D, no. 81, and a lake scene with verse by L A B, no. 38. 8.3 cm x 12 cm, 9.2 cm x 12.7 cm.

27. Three cards, summer scenes. The first is signed A L S and has a verse by E H Bickersteth D D, no. 97, and the second has a verse by L A B, no. 109 A. The third is signed Fred Hines, with a verse by F R H,

**134.10**

no. 103 A. 13.6 cm x 10.2 cm, 11.6 cm x 13.2 cm, 13.5 cm x 10.8 cm.

28. Three cards signed C Ryan, one with ivy around a scene of Jerusalem, the others with rose or blackberry and verses by Handley C G Maule M A and L A B. Nos. 19, 65, 74.  Sizes up to 15.5 cm x 11.2 cm.

29. Two cards signed J S Churchill, orchids on a pale blue ground with verses by Canon Bell, D D. No. 92. 12 cm x 15.9 cm.

30. Two cards with verses by L A B, one with lilies, the other with narcissus, marked Packet F. 10.9 cm x 15.6 cm, 12.5 cm x 11.8 cm.

31. Two cards, vignettes with Holy Land scenes and white flowers around, marked Packet C. 9.5 cm x 13.7 cm.

32. Two cards.
a) An eight-page booklet "Wayside Flowers", with texts for each day of the month and sprays of yellow flowers. Marked "Printed in Bavaria". 8 cm x 9.3 cm.
b) Forget-me-nots and ivy with texts. 9.9 cm x 13.9 cm.

## VOLUME 135: RELIGIOUS CARDS FROM VARIOUS PUBLISHERS

These publishers also issued a wide variety of cards which will appear in later sections under subject headings. All are greeting cards, many for Easter, and date from the mid 1880's to early 1890's with some exceptions as stated. Many of the cards were printed in Germany, and some of the publishers' names indicate German origins.

1/2. Five cards published by Eyre & Spottiswoode, an important firm with many more cards in this collection. They have gilded crosses with flowers, birds and texts. Two are numbered 120, two numbered 133 are dated 1878 by the

139

*A happy Christmas.*

**137.14**

sender, and a similar one is numbered 143 E. 7.3 cm x 11.5 cm, 10 cm x 15 cm.

3. Three cards from Eyre & Spottiswoode, gilt crosses and flowers on a dark background, no. 251. 13 cm x 8.4 cm.

4. Two cards published by Charles, Reynolds & Co, convolvulus or laburnum with illuminated texts, probably two out of seven registered at Stationers' Hall by D Guy 8-11-1877. 7.2 cm x 18.2 cm.

*Numbers 5-13 were published by W Hagelberg, some marked Berlin, some London.*

5. Two cards, Nativity scenes with carols on reverse. 15 cm x 11 cm.

6. Four cards, three designs of small angels ringing bells, two numbered 253. 9.5 cm x 9.5 cm.

7. Three Easter cards, winged angels with sea or mountain scenes, two numbered 257, with verses by E E G on reverse. 12.1 cm x 8.8 cm, 9.5 cm x 13 cm.

8. Three shaped cards, one a crescent with a winged cherub, no. 847, and two shaped like a five-point star with Nativity scenes, and a crescent with cherubs, no. 616. 11 cm x 13 cm, 13.5 cm x 13.5 cm.

9. Three shaped Easter cards, a crescent with angels and a cross, no. 40, and two crosses with flowers, one no. 146. 11.8 cm x 5 cm, 7.1 cm x 11 cm.

10. Six cards. Three are small stars with angel or shepherds, and one is an Easter card with a cross on a sea-swept rock and a verse by M S H on reverse, no. 805. Two have angels and a nativity scene with verses by A W B and M S H, nos. 443, 772. Stars 6.5 cm x 6.5 cm, others 7.4 cm x 11.5 cm to 10.6 cm x 14.8 cm.

11. Two large cards with cross and anchor festooned with lilies, passion flowers and forget-me-nots or daisies and wild roses, one Easter, one New Year. These are not marked, but were identified by the writer as two out of four registered at Stationers' Hall by Hermann Beck, 19-10-1882. 10.7 cm x 16.4 cm.

12. Two cards, one with white flowers, and verse by A M Hone on reverse, no. 710, the other abbey ruins with a verse by M S H, no. 2909. 11 cm x 15 cm, 11 cm x 16.4 cm.

13. Four miscellaneous Easter cards with snowdrops and violets and texts or verses. One is a folder with verse by Margaret Haycraft within, no. 903, and another has a cut out silvered edge and a silver cross, no. 298. The two others are numbered 259, 376. Sizes up to 9.4 cm x 12.7 cm.

*Numbers 14-20 were published by J F Schipper & Co, usually with a ship trade mark on reverse or initials J F S.*

14. A large card, woodland scene with flowers and bird's nest, no. 612. 15.7 cm x 24 cm.

15. Two cards with silver borders, flower sprays and hymns, no. 692. 12 cm x 17.5 cm.

16. Four miscellaneous cards with flowers, two with crosses, numbered 172, 561, 586, 874. 6.5 cm x 10.3 cm up to 12.6 cm x 16.2 cm.

17. Three Easter cards, one a wreath of primroses with leaves in the shape of a cross, and two with white flowers and a floral design on reverse, no. 1241. 10.5 cm x 12 cm, 11.8 cm x 8.8 cm.

18. Three Easter cards with white flowers, two having a silver cross, nos. 839, 1251, 1484. Sizes up to 17.7 cm x 11.8 cm.

19. Two cards (one birthday), illuminated texts and scenes in small circular vignettes with rose hips and grasses, signed J E E? No. 1510. 10.7 cm x 14.3 cm.

20. Two cards, one New Year with an angel head no. 1014, the other Easter with cherubs and a silver cross no. 1477. 9.4 cm x 9.4 cm, 10.9 cm x 10.9 cm.

*Numbers 21-25 were published by Ernest Nister & Co, mostly marked London, printed in Bavaria, c1890.*

21. Four cards, two cross shaped with angels, nos. 1278, 970, one with a winter scene no. 977, the fourth the Shepherds seeing the Star. Crosses 8.3 cm x 8.3 cm, others 14 cm x 11.3 cm, 9.8 cm x 13.2 cm.

22. Two cards with angels, nos. 980, 1212. 8.5 cm x 15.2 cm, 17 cm x 12.8 cm.

23. Three cross shaped jewelled Easter cards with passion flowers or lilies, no. 1589. 7.8 cm x 12 cm.

24. Six shaped Easter cards. One has a child in a lily flower, no. 7332, and five are crosses with spring flowers or lilies, nos. 1015, 1027, 1902, 1998, 4580. 1890's. Sizes up to 9.5 cm x 13.7 cm.

25. Two cards published by Wirth Bros & Owen, with tinselled scenes of churches in vignettes and holly and bells. They have verses by Longfellow or Tennyson, and church bells on reverse. No. 230. 11 cm x 11 cm.

26. One card published by Wirth Bros & Owen, a church scene with winged cherubs in the sky above, and verses on the back. No. 373. 10.9 cm x 13.5 cm.

27. One card published by M H Nathan & Co, an angel flying over Bethlehem. 17 cm x 12.5 cm.

*Numbers 28-31 were published by Sockl & Nathan, usually marked S & N. This firm may have some connection with M H Nathan, which further research might establish.*

28. Three cards, one oval, children as angels with wings. 7.1 cm x 10.7 cm up to 12.2 cm x 15.4 cm.

29. Two Easter cards, white doves and leaves in a starlit sky. 11.4 cm x 11.4 cm.

30. Three cards with jewelled marbled crosses, two Easter, one Christmas. 8.2 cm x 11 cm.

31. Two Easter cards with white flowers and elaborate cut out fancy borders, one dated 1889 by the sender. 11 cm x 11 cm, 12.5 cm x 16.3 cm.

32. Three cards published by Bernhard Ollendorff, two designs of angels flying over villages, with three different Christmas verses by E J Pope on reverse. 14.2 cm x 10.7 cm.

33. Three cards from Bernhard Ollendorff. Two are Easter cards in cross shape with a picture of Jerusalem bordered by white flowers, and verses by E I Tupper and H M B on reverse. The other has a wooden cross with flowers and a verse by Cawood. 8.2 cm x 11.4 cm, 10.5 cm x 14.5 cm.

34/35. Four cards published by Philipp Bros, London, all with silver crosses and white flowers, two diamond shaped, two rectangular, one with a verse by F R H. 13.7 cm x 11 cm, 9 cm x 12.3 cm, 12.6 cm x 16.5 cm.

36. Five cards published by Davidson Brothers, three designs of an angel in a silver star looking down on a snow bound church. 9.9 cm x 13 cm.

37. One card published by Obpacher Bros, winged cherubs over Jerusalem.
15.5 cm x 9.7 cm.

38. Two cards. One has two winged angels' heads in the sky over a country scene, the other in similar style has a little girl and her grandfather, head and shoulders. The first card is labelled "Lith Art Anstalt", and might be a product of Obpacher Bros, who according to Buday later became the Artistic Lithographic Company.
16 cm x 12.5 cm, 18 cm x 13.4 cm.

39. Five miscellaneous cards by Obpacher Bros, four with flowers and crosses, nos. 820, 929, 1134, 1538, and one with birds. Four are Easter cards.
7 cm x 10.5 cm up to 9.5 cm x 14 cm.

# VOLUME 136:
# RELIGIOUS CARDS, 1869-1890

**This volume includes early illuminated cards, some with scraps, Nativity and Biblical scenes, scenes with children, all from unidentified publishers except for one card in no. 31. All have seasonal greetings except no. 9.**

1. Three cards with scraps of children and texts or verses, with red or blue hand-coloured borders. These are similar to Canton cards, but unmarked. c1870.
Sizes up to 11.5 cm x 7.5 cm.

2. Eight cards with scalloped borders, and six colourful Biblical scenes in circular vignettes with texts above and hymns below. Two are triptych folding cards with a blue cross and red pattern on the front, and one was dated 1869 by the sender.
6.1 cm x 9.2 cm.

3. Four cards with texts and greetings in gilt pattern borders, c1870. Sizes up to 10.7 cm x 7.6 cm.

4. Three similar with coloured borders, one for the year 1872.
Sizes up to 11.5 cm x 8.9 cm.

5. Six illuminated cards, three designs of flowers and ferns with texts or verses, one dated 1874 by the sender.
Sizes up to 11.2 cm x 7.5 cm.

6/7. Five illuminated cards with Nativity scenes in patterned borders, one dated 1879 by the sender but perhaps published earlier. 12.2 cm x 7.8 cm, 13.7 cm x 8.9 cm.

8. Six illuminated cards, five designs of angels or Nativity scenes, 1870's.
7.7 cm x 11.2 cm.

9. Three text cards with wide gilt borders and Biblical scenes, 1870's.
12.7 cm x 8.9 cm.

10. Three miscellaneous illuminated cards, two with angels and Biblical scenes, the third a Nativity scene with a verse by Meta Going on reverse. The large card was dated 1884 by the sender. 15.3 cm x 10.8 cm, 7 cm x 10.7 cm, 8.6 cm x 9.2 cm.

11. Five cards (one Easter), all with angels, two with crosses, one dated 1871 by the sender. 7 cm x 10 cm, 7.5 cm x 11.2 cm.

12. Three cards, Nativity scenes in illuminated borders, two dated 1879, 1880. 9 cm x 12.8 cm.

13. Five miscellaneous cards with angels or Biblical scenes, one in the shape of a triangle. One card with an angel choir and holly sprays is signed E W, possibly E Wilson. Sizes up to 12.7 cm x 10.6 cm.

14. Four miscellaneous cards with children or Bible scenes.
6.7 cm x 10.4 cm up to 14.7 cm x 9.7 cm.

15. Four miscellaneous cards with scenes of Bethlehem and the Shepherds. One picture of Bethlehem has a verse by J R Macduff on the back. Early 1880's.
11.3 cm x 7.3 cm up to 16.6 cm x 10.8 cm.

16. Three cards, two sepia nativity scenes with embossed gilt borders, the third showing the Shepherds and Bethlehem, with a design on the back resembling those of Prang.
12.5 cm x 8.5 cm, 11.8 cm x 16.3 cm.

17. Three cards, two sepia designs of choirboys, and another in grey of an angel, c1885. 8.7 cm x 12.8 cm, 10.7 cm x 17.5 cm.

18. An elaborate card with patterned border, showing a chorister in yellow surplice before a church organ, c1885.
13.8 cm x 19 cm.

19. A card with silver border, showing shepherds in a silver star superimposed on a winter scene, with a verse by C M on the reverse, early 1880's. 12 cm x 16.7 cm.

20. A card with a holly branch across a winter scene with a church, and winged angels' heads and a star in the sky above, c1885. 10 cm x 13.4 cm.

21. A gilt edged card with a curly haired angel in an oval vignette in a dark border. There is a descriptive poem by C D on the reverse. 13 cm x 17.7 cm.

22. A card showing children in church beneath a banner with a Nativity scene, with a verse by H S Bainbridge on reverse. 10.5 cm x 15.4 cm.

23. Five miscellaneous cards, Biblical scenes and children, c1890. One has a verse by A M H on reverse.
Sizes up to 9.5 cm x 15 cm.

137.21

24. One card, the Virgin Mary and the Child Jesus in a triangular vignette with winged cherubs' heads around and a verse by C M below, dated 1890 by the sender. 13.4 cm x 15.5 cm.

25/26. A set of six cards, scenes of the Holy Land in circular vignettes framed in spring flowers, with texts below, one dated 1882 by the sender. 11 cm x 14.2 cm.

27. Three cards, two being Nativity scenes with the Shepherds and the three Kings, the third a picture of Jerusalem in a convolvulus spray. 8.6 cm x 11.5 cm, 15.7 cm x 10.2 cm.

28. Two cards. One has a Biblical scene with a winged cherub above and a verse by C M below. The other shows the "Approach to Emmaus" in a circular vignette, with text below.
13.5 cm x 16.5 cm, 16.5 cm x 11 cm.

29. Two shaped cards with scenes from the Bible. One is oval with a verse by C H on reverse, the other cirular with a Christmas verse, late 1889's. 11.7 cm x 15 cm, 13.2 cm diameter.

30. Two cards, Biblical scenes with texts, and verses by Hart Milman on reverse.
12.8 cm x 8.2 cm.

31. Two cards, Biblical scenes in sepia. One card is marked H H & Co - probably Hills & Co - an unusual publication for this firm, as other cards found for this collection are in humorous vein. c1890.
11.7 cm x 9.3 cm, 11 cm x 16.5 cm.

138.28

## VOLUME 137:
## RELIGIOUS CARDS WITH ANGELS & CHILDREN, SCENES & FLOWERS

**The publishers of these cards have not been traced. All have greetings, except for a few text cards probably used at Christmas or Easter, and most of them were published around the mid 1880's. Many are Easter cards.**

1. Three Easter cards, winged cherubs with flowers, one embossed with a cross. 7.8 cm x 14.2 cm.

2. An Easter card, a flying angel blowing a trumpet, with a verse on the reverse. 9.1 cm x 12.6 cm.

3. A large elaborate gilt-bordered card with an interesting design of winged cherubs' heads around an open gilded book, in the sky over a village in winter. The back has a spray of lilac with texts in gilded border. 15 cm x 18.7 cm.

4. Six cards, four designs of angels' heads. Two cards are triptych folders with an illuminated design on the outside. 6.7 cm x 6.7 cm, 8 cm x 8 cm closed.

5. Two cards, cherubs' heads in a blue sky with verses by C D on reverse. 14 cm x 10.8 cm.

6. Five text cards with embossed borders, four designs of angels' heads with gilded crowns and wings. One is on a bordered illuminated mount. 10.8 cm x 7 cm, 14 cm x 10.2 cm.

7. Four similar text cards. 8.1 cm x 12.9 cm.

8. Two cards, three angels on a gilt ground with Christmas or New Year verses, one dated 1881 by the sender. 14.1 cm x 8.1 cm.

9. Two Easter cards, three angels in a cloudy sky, with verses by M S H on reverse. 13.1 cm x 9.8 cm.

10. Two cards with winged cherubs' heads, one circular with a verse by M S H, the other rectangular with a verse by F R on reverse. 12.7 cm diameter, 11.7 cm x 16 cm.

11. Two Easter cards with angels, one circular, the other rectangular with a verse on the back. 12.6 cm diameter, 8.5 cm x 14.3 cm.

12. Two cards, an angel with a harp signed H J M, i.e. Helena Maguire, the other an angel flying by a belfry. 10.7 cm x 13.6 cm, 11.7 cm x 16.3 cm.

13. Two cards, angels flying over mountains in a sky with a crescent moon, with verses by C H on reverse. 16 cm x 11.6 cm.

14. Two cards, one an angel's head against a cloudy sky, with a verse by C M on reverse, the other two angels flying over Bethlehem with a starlit sky. 11.7 cm x 16 cm, 16.9 cm x 12.3 cm.

15. Two cards, one with a star-spangled blue border around an angel and a verse by F R H, the other a group of angels in unusual coloured robes against a starry sky. These angels look like children in fancy dress, and might perhaps be reminiscent of the early deaths of many children in Victorian times. 12.3 cm x 15.5 cm, 15.7 cm x 11.2 cm.

16. Four miscellaneous cards of angels. 6.6 cm x 9.8 cm up to 8.4 cm x 15.4 cm.

17. Three cards of angels, one shaped like a cross, with a verse by FRH, one with a verse by Newman, the third with a silver cross. 12.5 cm x 17.2 cm, 9.5 cm x 12.7 cm.

18. Four Easter cards, cut out crosses with angels, one repeating a design in no. 17 above. Sizes up to 8.7 cm x 14.7 cm.

19. Two cards from a set of three with figures representing Faith and Charity, Hope missing, with appropriate verses by Charles J Rowe on reverse, one dated 1885. 7.7 cm x 14.9 cm.

20. An Easter card with three angels around a wooden cross festooned with flowers, signed Robert Dudley, dated 1894 by the sender. This might have been published by Castell, as Dudley worked for them in the 1890's. 10.1 cm x 15 cm.

21. Two cards, three angels ringing church bells with a verse by A M Bode on reverse, and a choirboy in church holding a Bible with a verse by C D on reverse. 8.2 cm x 15.5 cm, 10.9 cm x 16.6 cm.

22. One card, two children singing in church, with a quotation from Frances Ridley Havergal. 12.5 cm x 16 cm.

23. Two cards, pastoral scenes in vignettes, with lilies or passion flowers around and texts and hymns below. 16.4 cm x 10.7 cm.

24. Two cards, wild roses and leaves with country scenes in vignettes and verses by C M. 12.8 cm x 9.5 cm.

25. Two cards, winter scenes in vignettes with swallows flying around and texts below, one dated 1889 by the sender. 9.7 cm x 13.2 cm.

26. Two cards, one with flowers and a summer scene in a vignette with text below, the other a winter scene with a spray of flowers and a verse below by F R H. 11 cm x 15 cm, 11.2 cm x 15.7 cm.

27. Two cards, one design with a wreath of convolvulus around a harvest field, with verses by C H or C M below. 11 cm x 17 cm.

28. Five miscellaneous cards with scenes and flowers. One with a mountain scene, butterflies, and lilies of the valley was dated 1882 by the sender, the others are later 1880's. 9 cm x 6.4 cm up to 15 cm x 11 cm.

29. Four cards, Biblical scenes in diamond vignettes with white flowers and texts. 10.3 cm x 15.7 cm.

## VOLUME 138:
## RELIGIOUS CARDS WITH CROSSES & FLOWERS

**This volume includes cards dated about 1875-1885, most from unidentified publishers, with a few early illuminated examples. All have greetings, many for Easter, and the same design with a cross was often used for both Christmas and Easter.**

1/2. Fifteen cards (two Easter) with crosses and flowers, one marked Sulman, two marked D & S - Dean, c1875. Most of these unmarked cards probably came from these two publishers. Sizes 6.7 cm x 10 cm up to 7.2 cm x 10.4 cm.

3. Five illuminated Easter cards, two embossed, two with angels' heads, all with crosses and flowers, vine, or holly. One was dated 1880 by the sender. 5.6 cm x 7.5 cm up to 6.2 cm x 10.4 cm.

4. Four illuminated Easter cards from one set, gilt crosses with flowers, grasses, or a dove. 6.7 cm x 10.5 cm.

5. Two illuminated Easter cards with crosses, eggs, and flowers. 11 cm x 7.2 cm.

6. Four miscellaneous Easter cards with crosses and flowers, two with eggs, all on

decorated mounts. 6.3 cm x 9.2 cm up to 8.3 cm x 13.3 cm.

7. Seven cards from two sets, all with wooden crosses. The first group has holly and fern on a blue ground, the second has two designs with passion flowers or lilies, two on mounts. One was dated 1881 by the sender. 7 cm x 9.5 cm, 7.5 cm x 11 cm (with mounts).

8. Seven illuminated cards, six designs of flowers, six Easter, one New Year. 9.5 cm x 6.4 cm.

9. Five illuminated well designed Easter cards, various flowers in backgrounds with arches and columns. 7.2 cm x 11 cm.

10. Four Easter Cards, three designs of floral crosses.  6.7 cm x 11.5 cm.

11. Three illuminated cards, one with New Year greeting and crosses, the other two with Easter greeting and small crosses festooned with ivy and fern. 7.5 cm x 11.3 cm, 7.5 cm x 11 cm.

12. Six miscellaneous Easter cards, crosses entwined with flowers. 4.2 cm x 10.5 cm up to 7.2 cm x 11 cm.

13. Five cards, gilt crosses with spring flowers or clematis. 7.5 cm x 10.6 cm.

14. Seven cards (one Easter), four designs of gilt crosses with white flowers, two dated 1883, 1884 by the senders. 7.1 cm x 12 cm.

15. Three cards all with verse by F R H, two with cross and anchor and spring flowers, the other a gilt cross with snowdrops similar to those in no. 14 above. 6.7 cm x 10.3 cm, 8.5 cm x 12.1 cm.

16. Seven cards (three Easter), four designs with silver border, crosses, and a single rose. 7.7 cm x 11.5 cm.

17. Three cards, (two Easter, one New Year). Two are single cards on grey ground with crosses and convolvulus or forget-me-nots, the third is a folder with a white cross on a blue cover and the two designs of the single cards within. One was dated 1880 by the sender. 6.4 cm x 13.3 cm.

18/19. Nine similar cards showing six designs of various crosses with flowers, six for Easter, three Christmas and New Year. Seven are single cards, two are folders with a white cross on a brown cover and two of the single card designs within. 5.6 cm x 11.7 cm.

20. Two gilt-edged cards, gilt crosses with roses and violets or passion flowers. 12 cm x 7.7 cm.

21. Four cards, three designs of illuminated crosses in wreaths of mixed flowers, on a brown ground with a patterned border. 10 cm x 11 cm.

22. Three cards, floral crosses with gilt border on patterned ground. 8.8 cm x 12.4 cm.

23. Two cards, illuminated crosses with flowers and verses by F L, in a decorative gilt border. 14.2 cm x 11 cm.

24. Six cards (three Easter, three Christmas and New Year), illuminated crosses with flowers and verses, one marked 1880 by the sender. 9.5 cm x 12.8 cm.

25. Six cards (two Easter), four designs of floral crosses entwined with other flowers, and with greetings or verses in bordered panels. Two cards are embossed. 8.4 cm x 12 cm.

26. Two embossed gilt-edged cards, wooden crosses entwined with dianthus and harebells or convolvulus, on pale blue background, one dated 1884 by the sender. 9.2 cm x 13.4 cm.

27. Three miscellaneous gilt-edged Easter cards, all with gilt crosses and flowers, one embossed. Early 1880's. 6.5 cm x 14.6 cm up to 14 cm x 8.5 cm.

28. Three miscellaneous embossed gilt-edged cards, all with crosses and flowers. 9.5 cm x 12.4 cm up to 12 cm x 15 cm.

29. Two gilt-edged cards, crosses with various flowers, one with a butterfly and a ribbon bow. 7.4 cm x 16 cm.

30/32. Five large cards (4 Easter, one Christmas), three designs of crosses with mixed flowers. Two are on gilt ground, two on grey, and one is black-backed. c1875? 12.5 cm x 18 cm.

33. Three black-backed cards with floral crosses, the large one Easter, the small ones Christmas. 17 cm x 21.5 cm, 7.3 cm x 10.7 cm.

34. A hand-painted card with passion flowers and scroll around a gilded cross. 13.2 cm x 17.9 cm.

## VOLUME 139: RELIGIOUS CARDS WITH CROSSES & FLOWERS

**These cards date from 1880-1885 with a few from the later years of the decade. All are greeting cards, many for Easter, and the publishers have not been traced.**

1. Two embossed floral crosses with passion flowers or lilies, one Christmas, one Easter. 7.9 cm x 12.5 cm, 10.7 cm x 16.5 cm.

2. Two cards, one Christmas, one Easter, with crosses of brown leaves and white flowers, one dated 1883 by the sender. 10.6 cm x 15.4 cm.

3. Four embossed cards (one Easter), three designs of flowers and leaves with gilt crosses. 9.8 cm x 15.3 cm.

4. Two cards, silver crosses with roses and Christmas verses. 9.8 cm x 15.3 cm.

5. A large Easter card, a decorated gilt cross with convolvulus, and a wide grey border. 12 cm x 18.7 cm.

6. Three cards with gilt crosses, two for Easter with primroses or snowdrops, the third with anemones and a Christmas greeting. 11 cm x 15.6 cm.

7. Two gilt-bordered cards with gilt crosses and white flowers. 13.2 cm x 10.2 cm.

8. Two cards, one with passion flowers on a silver cross and a verse by E J Pope on reverse, the other with clematis on a gilt cross. 16 cm x 10.1 cm, 15.9 cm x 12 cm.

9. Two cards, one Easter, one Christmas, gilt crosses with flowers. 16.2 cm x 12.2 cm., 17 cm x 10.4 cm.

10. Four miscellaneous embossed Easter cards with a variety of crosses and flowers. 10.8 cm x 7.1 cm up to 15.5 cm x 11.8 cm.

11. Four Easter cards, two with spring flowers around gilt crosses, two with gilt borders and gilt crosses in a profusion of white roses or daisies, all c1883. 9.1 cm x 12.6 cm, 9.5 cm x 14.5 cm.

12. Two Easter cards, each with narcissus and a gilt cross, one in an oval vignette, the other on grey ground. 10.8 cm x 16.5 cm, 12.5 cm x 17 cm.

13. Four miscellaneous cards (two Easter), with various crosses and primroses, violets, or cowslips. 8.5 cm x 8.5 cm up to 9.3 cm x 12 cm.

14. Two Easter cards, wooden crosses with flowers and ferns, one dated 1882 by the sender. 8 cm x 14 cm.

15. Four embossed cards, three designs of floral crosses with ferns or grasses. 7.2 cm x 11 cm.

16. Three embossed cards (one birthday), wooden crosses standing in colourful bouquets of flowers and grasses, with verses beneath by C D. 9.8 cm x 12.5 cm.

17. Two large embossed cards of similar design with verses above, one dated 1882 by the sender. 11.6 cm x 15.7 cm.

18. Two cards, crosses lying on the ground, one on a green hillside with Christmas roses, the other with crocuses and snowdrops peeping through the snow, and a robin. 17.2 cm x 11 cm.

19. Three cards with gilt borders, crosses against sombre skies, with white flowers. 12 cm x 15.7 cm.

20. Two cards, one Christmas one Easter, wooden crosses with spring flowers or passion flowers, and verses on reverse. 11.3 cm x 15.8 cm.

21. Three cards, two Easter one Christmas, stone or leaf-covered crosses set in spring flowers and grasses. 8.5 cm x 14.9 cm.

22. Two cards with crosses, one with leaves and flowers, the other with frosted holly and a verse by F R H. 8.5 cm x 13.7 cm, 11.5 cm x 13.5 cm.

23. Two Easter cards, crosses with primroses or pansies and illuminated texts, one dated 1884 by the sender. 9 cm x 13.5 cm.

24. Two Easter cards, wooden crosses entwined with convolvulus or roses. 11.5 cm x 15.7 cm, 16.5 cm x 11.5 cm.

25. Two cards, wooden crosses, one with holly, the other with roses and a butterfly and a verse by Tate. 14.7 cm x 12 cm, 15.3 cm x 12 cm.

26. Three miscellaneous cards with flowers and crosses, two embossed with Christmas and New Year greeting, the third an Easter card with fuchsias. Sizes up to 11 cm x 15.2 cm.

27. Three cards with crosses and flowers, one with Christmas greeting, two Easter with passion flowers. 13.7 cm x 9.2 cm, 16.2 cm x 11 cm, 11 cm x 16.2 cm.

28/29. Ten miscellaneous cards, later 1880's, with various crosses. Three are Easter cards. All have flowers except one which has seaweed around the cross. 10.6 cm x 7.5 cm up to 10 cm x 14 cm.

30. Two Easter cards, silver borders and crosses with white flowers and ferns, two dated 1883, 1884 by the senders. 13.9 cm x 9.7 cm.

31. Five similar smaller cards, three Easter, two Christmas, one dated 1884 by the sender. 11.2 cm x 7.5 cm.

32. A large card with silver border, showing a light shining on a cross on a hillside, with a large spray of lilies below. There is a scene on the reverse. 13.5 cm x 18 cm.

33. Three cards, two Easter, one New Year, silver crosses and white flowers. The large card was dated 1884 by the sender. 12.5 cm x 17 cm, 9.2 cm x 13.7 cm.

34. Two cards, one a silver cross with narcissi, the other a cross made of leaves and small flowers, this dated 1884 by the sender. 11.5 cm x 14.5 cm, 16 cm x 12 cm.

35. One card, a scene set in a cross shaped vignette with hibiscus and grasses. 11.5 cm x 15.5 cm.

36. Two cards, one Easter one Christmas, the same design of a white flower and ferns over an illuminated cross. 11.2 cm x 14 cm.

37. Two Easter cards with silk jewelled flowers, one in the shape of a cross, the other with a white cross and texts. 9.2 cm x 13.4 cm, 9.6 cm x 14 cm.

## VOLUME 140:
## RELIGIOUS CARDS, LATER CARDS WITH CROSSES, OTHERS WITH FLOWERS, BIRDS & ANIMALS

*Numbers 1-13 are cards with crosses, many for Easter, dated from 1885 - early 1890's.*

1. Four cards, marble crosses lying on grass, each with a bunch of spring flowers. 12 cm x 6 cm.

2. A large Easter card with orchids and ferns on a silver cross, and a verse by C M. 13 cm x 18 cm.

3. An Easter card with a sea scene in a cross-shaped vignette, and a lily and seaweed below. There is a brief verse by H M B above. 12 cm x 16.5 cm.

4. Three miscellaneous cards, with flowers and crosses. Two have verses by H M B and F R H. 6.7 cm x 18 cm up to 12.4 cm x 15.6 cm.

5. Three miscellaneous cards, two Easter one Christmas, two with crosses and flowers and cut out edges. The third has a serrated silvered border and was dated 1892 by the sender. Sizes up to 12.7 cm x 9 cm.

6. Five miscellaneous cards, three Easter two Christmas, with silver crosses and spring flowers. 7.4 cm x 11 cm up to 15.2 cm x 10 cm.

7. Seven miscellaneous cards, four Easter, three Christmas and New Year, various flowers with wooden or floral crosses. 6.7 cm up to 8.7 cm x 12 cm.

8. Five miscellaneous cards, three Easter, two Christmas, flowers and crosses, one a smaller version of no. 3 above. Sizes up to 10.2 cm x 13 cm.

9. Four miscellaneous Easter cards, three with crosses and flowers, the fourth with a palm before a sea scene in a vignette and a shadowy cross. 7.7 cm x 11.2 cm up to 10.2 cm x 13.5 cm.

10. Three Easter cards, two with flowers on silver crosses and verses by E E G, the third with a cut out design of doves and bells in a blue border around jewelled

daisies and a verse by F R H. 13 cm x 8.2 cm, 14 cm x 10.4 cm.

11. Three Easter cards, one with a gold cross and flowers in a fancy cut out border, marked Court Greeting Cards. The other two have cut out pierced designs, one of daisies and bells, the other a scene with roses in a cross shaped vignette and a verse below by E E G. 10 cm x 10 cm, 11.6 cm x 7.7 cm, 9.2 cm x 14.8 cm.

12. Two Easter cards with serrated edges, one a silver cross with apple blossom, the other a wreath of fern and violets around a small silver cross. 11 cm x 14.2 cm, 13.5 cm x 13.5 cm (trimmed).

13. Three cards with serrated edges, one with rocks and flowers beneath a moonlit cross, the others with jewelled silver crosses and white flowers and verses by C H and C M. 12 cm x 16 cm, 9 cm x 11.9 cm.

*Numbers 14-24 have cards with flowers and foliage, published in the early 1880's.*

14. Two gilt bordered cards, signed with monogram A W H, forget-me-nots or wood anemones around texts headed "The Rock of our Salvation". 9.5 cm x 13.4 cm.

15. Two cards.
a) Edelweiss with a New Year verse by F R H from "The Ministry of Song". 10.2 cm x 17.3 cm.
b) Passion flowers, with a text in a scroll. 8.8 cm x 12.6 cm.

16. Two gilt-edged cards with pink flowers and texts, one dated 1883 by the sender. 8.3 cm x 12.2 cm.

17. Five small cards (two with text), wreaths of spring flowers around texts and greetings. 11.6 cm x 3.9 cm, 3.9 cm x 11.6 cm.

18. Three gilt-edged cards, illuminated texts and poems by F R H and C H with flower sprays. 10.9 cm x 13.8 cm, 9.8 cm x 13.5 cm.

19. Two cards, the same curious design of spiky seaweed or fern in different formats. 9.7 cm x 12.5 cm, 11.5 cm x 14.4 cm.

20. Three cards with pale blue borders, all with spring flowers, one with a scene in a circular vignette and a verse by W Walsham How, the other two with verses by C M. 9.5 cm x 9.5 cm, 10.2 cm x 7 cm.

21. Four miscellaneous cards, spring flowers and ferns with texts and greetings, one dated 1884 by the sender. 10.3 cm x 7 cm up to 12.8 cm x 9.8 cm.

22. Four miscellaneous Easter cards, three with spring flowers, the fourth with pink flowers and a scroll in Japanese style. Sizes up to 10 cm x 15.3 cm.

23. Three Easter cards, two with lilies and ferns, one with apple blossom. Verses by C H are on the reverse of two cards. 13 cm x 9.4 cm, 11.2 cm x 14.4 cm.

24. Two cards, leaves and flowers, one card with a mountain scene in the background, the other with a country house and a verse by C H. 10.3 cm x 13.5 cm, 10.5 cm x 14.5 cm.

25/26. Seven miscellaneous cards, all with spring flowers or wild roses and various verses or texts. Later 1880's. 7 cm x 10 cm up to 14 cm x 9.9 cm.

27. Two embossed Easter cards, one with lilies of the valley over a gilded I H S, the other with a silver jewelled cross and a verse by F R H, one dated 1891 by the sender. 13 cm x 10 cm, 13 cm x 10.5 cm.

28. Two cards of birds in Baxter type printing, perhaps from Dickes or Kronheim, with gilt borders and greetings and texts in panels c1870. 12.7 cm x 8.4 cm.

29. Four cards in tones of brown with pink or blue, sprays of wild flowers, ferns and berries, with texts. Two cards have a bird in flight, and one was dated 1882 by the sender. 8.9 cm x 11.7 cm.

30. Two Easter cards, one with roses on a gilt border round a lamb holding a banner, and a verse by F L on reverse, the other embossed with blue flowers and a nest with eggs, dated 1883 by the sender. 9 cm x 11.9 cm, 14.2 cm x 10.1 cm.

31. Four miscellaneous cards, three with birds and flowers, one with a birds' nest dated 1883 by the sender. Sizes up to 12.3 cm x 10 cm.

32. Five miscellaneous Easter cards, three with birds and white flowers. One has a cross with white flowers, the fifth has sheep grazing on a hillside with three crosses. Late 1880's. 7.7 cm x 9.2 cm up to 9.6 cm x 13.7 cm.

33. Three cards with serrated or cut out edges, all with flowers and texts, one with a verse by M K M. c1890. Sizes up to 9.7 cm x 12.8 cm.

34. Three Easter cards with flowers, two embossed. The third is a folder card (in two pieces) shaped like a clump of water lilies, with a scene and a verse by Isabella J Postgate within. c1890. 7.7 cm x 8.5 cm up to 14 cm x 11.9 cm.

## VOLUME 141:
## REWARD OF MERIT & TEXT CARDS, 1855 - EARLY 1870's

**The cards in this and in volumes 142-144 are all text cards without greetings, of the kind given to pupils in Sunday Schools, though some have messages indicating that they were sent as gifts to parents, children, or friends. Most of the cards have no publishers' marks, but they would have been made or sold by the firms whose marked cards can be seen in volume 132, and a few signed examples are included here for comparison.**

1. Nine early lithographed hand-coloured Reward cards, two dated by the givers 1858, 1861. 8 cm x 4.1 cm up to 12.7 cm x 7.8 cm.

2. Eight similar, including two printed in red and six hand coloured, one dated 1863. 8.7 cm x 5.7 cm up to 10.3 cm x 6.3 cm.

3. Four Reward cards "for Diligence", with oval hand coloured prints bordered by texts on a patterned gilt background. 6.8 cm x 10.3 cm.

4/5. Ten cards, with embossed gilt patterned borders around attached small domed prints and verses with texts. The prints are in Baxter style and could have been made by the licensees J Mansell or W Dickes. The verses have titles including topics varying from "The Bible", "Christian Friendship", to "Winter" and "The Fly", all with appropriate moral precepts. Two were dated 1856, 1866 by the senders. 7.2 cm x 10.3 cm.

6. Six similar cards with ivy patterned border. 6.2 cm x 9.7 cm.

7. Five cards, embossed gilt scalloped borders, small prints framed in gilt scrolls, and verses with family interest printed in blue. 7.5 cm x 11.7 cm.

8. Three cards, two similar to those in no. 7 above with prints removed, and a third with a gilt-bordered poem "The Bridegroom's Dove" and picture. 7.5 cm x 11.7 cm, 8.7 cm x 13.8 cm.

9/12. Sixteen cards with mauve and white patterned borders. They have attached prints illustrating parables from the New Testament, which are printed on the front of the cards and the back. They are marked S P C K and W Dickes. 7.9 cm x 11.4 cm.

13. Five cards with red and white embossed borders and early prints. Three have parables and are marked S P C K, the other two have poems relating to church going. 8.7 cm x 12.4 cm.

14/15. Eleven cards with ivy patterned pink and white embossed borders, and domed prints in Dickes style with moral verses below. 7.4 cm x 11 cm.

16/17. Eight cards with rose patterned pink or blue embossed borders, framing small prints and moral verses. 8 cm x 12.4 cm.

18. Eight miscellaneous cards with patterned borders in various colours. Two have attached colour prints, six have printed black and white illustrations to the moral verses below. Sizes up to 8.3 cm x 12 cm.

19. Four cards printed in brown with blue or green. Three have patterned borders and pictures with verses below, and the fourth is a "Question and Answer" card with a list of questions on the reverse and spaces for answers. 9.2 cm x 13.7 cm, 10 cm x 13 cm.

20. A card with a picture of Hagar and Ishmael, printed in bright colours with a border of flowers. 10.2 cm x 14.1 cm.

21. Two cards with oval prints of the Nativity and texts printed in Spanish. 15 cm x 10.7 cm.

22. Seven cards with geometric designs in illuminated style, one dated 1868 by the sender. Sizes up to 6.8 cm x 10.1 cm.

23. Three illuminated cards with the "Ten Commandments" written in vignettes with coloured borders. Two are folders, one being in two pieces, and the third is embossed. 6.5 cm x 10 cm, 7.2 cm x 11.3 cm, 7.8 cm x 10.1 cm.

24. Four illuminated cards with texts or verses in panels with coloured borders. One is marked Gall & Inglis and dated 1872 by the sender, who wrote a Christmas greeting on the back, and another was dated 1865 by the sender. Sizes up to 7.4 cm x 11.4 cm

25. Six cards with illuminated initials to the verses and flowers on gilt grounds. 7.4 cm x 11.2 cm, 11.2 cm x 7.4 cm.

26. Five miscellaneous cards with prints of children or family scenes with hymns or texts. 6.7 cm x 10.1 cm up to 13.6 cm x 7.7 cm.

27. Three text cards with black and white small pictures over texts printed in black with red or blue, in matching red or blue borders. 7.2 cm x 10 cm.

28. Two hand-made cards with garlands of flowers and texts. 11.1 cm x 14.6 cm.

29. Five hand-made cards, various decorations with texts or verses. 9.2 cm x 6 cm up to 13.5 cm x 10.5 cm.

## VOLUME 142:
## RELIGIOUS CARDS. REWARD OF MERIT & TEXT CARDS, INCLUDING MANY ILLUMINATED, PUBLISHED IN THE 1870's EXCEPT WHERE OTHERWISE STATED

1. Four cards, texts in panels bordered by flowers with birds or animals and insects

on gilt background, with verses on reverse. 10.9 cm x 7.2 cm, 7.2 cm x 10.9 cm.

2. Four cards with illuminated texts in various shaped panels and flowers in the background. 6.9 cm x 10.6 cm.

3/5. Ten cards, each illustrating a sentence from the Lord's Prayer, perhaps from a set of 12. They have appropriate pictures in vignettes with illuminated flower borders. 8.3 cm x 12.3 cm.

6. A large illuminated card, with a text in a panel in the centre of a design of spring flowers. 17.2 cm x 11 cm.

7. Two similar smaller cards, one dated 1878 by the sender. 8.5 cm x 12.9 cm, 9 cm x 12.6 cm.

8. Eight miscellaneous text cards two of which have black-backgrounds, with various illuminated designs, some with crosses. 6 cm x 9 cm up to 8 cm x 13.6 cm.

9. Two illuminated cards illustrating Charity and Duty, feeding the hungry, going to Church, one with a verse by Eliza Cook. 9.6 cm x 14.6 cm.

10. Three cards with illuminated texts and borders in red, blue, green and gold. 15.9 cm x 12 cm.

11. Four similar cards. 11.5 cm x 9 cm.

12. Five cards with texts in red, blue and gold, or green and purple, and a background flower pattern in gold. 18.9 cm x 7.8 cm, 12 cm x 5.2 cm.

13/14. Four similar larger cards. 21 cm x 10 cm.

15. A card with illuminated text and forget-me-nots. 21.6 cm x 14 cm.

16. A card with text in red, blue and black on a background with a design of shadowy ferns. 15.9 cm x 20.4 cm.

17. Three cards, texts in blue vignettes in gold borders, one with a spray of lilies of the valley. 10.5 cm x 6.7 cm, 11 cm x 14.4 cm.

18. Two cards, illuminated texts framed in harebells or stitchwort. 12.1 cm x 15.8 cm.

19. Six miscellaneous gilt-backed cards with various flowers, two dated 1879,1885. 8.3 cm x 4.8 cm up to 12.4 cm x 7.2 cm.
20. Seven gilt-backed cards, three with scenes of the Holy Land in circular vignettes with flowers, four with various flowers, one dated 1884 by the sender. 7.4 cm x 10.8 cm.

21. Five similar cards with Holy Land scenes on a silver background, early 1880's. 7.4 cm x 10.8 cm.

22. Six cards, scenes from the Gospels against a silver sky background, wtih texts on reverse. 11.7 cm x 8.2 cm.

23. A large tract "A Swarm of Bees without Stings", consisting of 32 Biblical texts beginning with B. 16.4 cm x 22.3 cm.

24. Four cards. Three have texts or verses in ornamental borders, two signed E H Bickersteth, S M B. One of these is marked R J Masters, another Drummond's Tract Depot. The fourth card, a folder headed "New Year's Gifts", is marked S W Partridge and C Caswell. Sizes up to 8.8 cm x 12.5 cm.

25. Six cards. Three have texts, one with a flower and a black border, the other two marked G Morrish, J Smaxted. One is a cross with text and design in green, purple and gold, and two have scenes and flowers printed in blue with illuminated texts. Cross 6.3 cm x 14.5 cm, others up to 7.3 cm x 11.5 cm.

26. Five cards, two with Biblical prints, texts and verses, three with flowers or ferns and texts. Sizes up to 11.1 cm x 7 cm.

27/29. Eight cards, reproductions of Old Masters paintings of Biblical scenes, two by Bernardino di Luini, one by Filippo Lippi, three by Fra Angelico, one by Fra Bartolomeo, and one by Gentile da Fabriano. 12 cm x 16 cm, 16 cm x 12 cm.

## VOLUME 143:
## RELIGIOUS CARDS, TEXT & REWARD CARDS WITH FLOWERS & FOLIAGE, MOTTO CARDS, 1880-1900

*Numbers 1-13 were published in the early 1880's.*

1. Three cards with black backgrounds, one marked Riddle & Couchman. 15.2 cm x 9.2 cm, 14 cm x 10.4 cm, 16 cm x 5.3 cm.

2. A set of six cards, leaves and ferns on a brown background with texts in scrolls. 11.5 cm x 7.4 cm.

3. Two cards, lilies of the valley or convolvulus with insects, each with three texts. 8 cm x 14.4 cm.

4. Five miscellaneous gilt-edged cards, various flowers. 5.5 cm x 7.9 cm up to 12.5 cm x 9.2 cm.

5. Six miscellaneous cards, two gilt-edged, with various flowers. 10.4 cm x 6.5 cm up to 5.5 cm x 15.7 cm.

6. Two cards, spring flowers on a blue background in bouquet form with text on a white card. 11 cm x 14.2 cm, 16.2 cm x 11 cm.

7. Two cards, one design of convolvulus with text in panel. 12.2 cm x 8.3 cm.

8. Three cards, two designs of pansies or pelargoniums and ferns, with text on an open book. 12 cm x 8.8 cm.

9. A set of four bordered cards, pink and white flowers on green background with text below. 16.5 cm x 10 cm.

10. Two cards, sprays of spring flowers, one with a cross, the other with a bird. 14.8 cm x 9 cm, 14.1 cm x 10.8 cm.

11. Two cards, spring flowers on a grey background with text below. 7.5 cm x 13.6 cm

12/13. Thirteen miscellaneous cards, various flowers and ferns, eleven with texts, three with verses. 6.2 cm x 9 cm up to 10.4 cm x 14 cm.

*Numbers 14-23 were published in the later 1880's.*

14. Two cards on thick paper. One has roses, forget-me-nots and ivy on a cut out border resembling wood, with a folding support at the back for standing; the other has various flowers on a cut-out border around an oval vignette with illuminated text, and was dated 1886 by the sender. 11.3 cm x 15.4 cm, 11 cm x 15.3 cm.

15/16. Fifteen miscellaneous text cards with flowers, ferns and grasses. Two have verses. 8.5 cm x 6 cm up to 13.8 cm x 12.1 cm.

17. Four cards with white spring flowers, two in shield shaped vignettes, the others with ivy. 8.2 cm x 12 cm.

18. Six cards, four colourful designs of spring flowers and roses in patterned borders, with texts in panels. 9.1 cm x 12.7 cm.

19. Four miscellaneous cards, texts in panels on blue or brown background with various flowers. Sizes up to 12 cm x 7.9 cm.

20. Four cards, two with scenes in vignettes and flower sprays. The other two have texts in panels, with flowers, and one of these has a view of Hebron below. 7.8 cm x 11.4 cm, 8 cm x 13.3 cm.

21/22. Nine cards "Looking into Jesus", six designs of spring flowers with texts in red or blue. 7.5 cm x 11.7 cm.

23. Three cards, a single moss rose with buds and a spray of spring flowers. 7.7 cm x 12 cm.

24. Four cards, Mottoes for 1879, 1880, 1889, 1890, with texts. The first two, headed "New Hampton Congregational Church", have decorative borders. The third shows a collection of various fruits and is headed "Band of Hope", and marked "printed by Vogelbank & Kaiser, Munich". The fourth card has a wreath of

pink and white flowers and is headed
"Primitive Methodist Connexion".
11.5 cm x 7.6 cm up to 14.8 cm x 12.9 cm.

25. Two cards, one Motto for 1885 with a
verse by G M Taylor, marked 1s 2d per
dozen from G M T, Leamington. The other,
Motto for 1889, has a dove with an
illuminated text in a scroll.
18 cm x 12.5 cm, 18 cm x 12 cm.

26. Two cards, one Motto for 1885 with a
lake scene, the other Motto for 1900 with a
lake and mountain scene and illuminated
text. 13.1 cm x 10.2 cm, 13.1 cm x 9.5 cm.

27. Four miscellaneous cards, colourful
Bible scenes.  10.2 cm x 6.8 cm up to
13 cm x 9.8 cm.

28. Seven miscellaneous cards, four with
birds, one with a child praying, another
with a lighthouse. The seventh card has a
long poem entitled "And a little Child
shall lead them", with a picture of a child
with a lion and lambs. 9.5 cm x 5.7 cm up
to 14 cm x 8.9 cm.

## VOLUME 144:
## RELIGIOUS CARDS. SMALL TEXT & REWARD CARDS, & A FEW LARGE ONES IN PICTURE STYLE

**The small cards here were given as
rewards for attendance and
diligence, and were collected by the
pupils in sets, many of which were
pasted into scrap albums along with
greeting cards. The outsize examples
were often framed to decorate the
walls of Victorian parlours or
bedrooms. The small cards were
probably published in the 1870's, but
the dates are uncertain.**

1. Sixteen small cards in two uncut sheets,
flowers on gilt background with text in
panel, probably issued by Marcus Ward
(see Volume 44). 4.8 cm x 3.3 cm.

2. Twenty-two similar, not identified as
M W, including two uncut sheets of eight.
4.3 cm x 2.8 cm.

3. Fifteen similar with a Greek key pattern
border, including an uncut sheet of six and
two with illuminated texts. 5.5 cm x 3.3 cm.

4. Nineteen cards, including seventeen
small cards with illuminated texts and two
larger with illuminated texts on white
background. 3.7 cm x 2 cm, 8.8 cm x 5 cm.

5. Twenty-one cards from six different sets
with texts and flowers, three marked
Campbell & Tudhope. 3.7 cm x 2.2 cm up
to 6.7 cm x 4.3 cm.

6. Twenty-eight cards, one larger headed
"For Children", with verse in a red
patterned border, and twenty-seven
smaller with flowers, from four different

sets. Larger card 11.3 cm x 7.5 cm, others
3.7 cm x 2.3 cm up to 4.6 cm x 3.3 cm.

7. Thirteen cards from four sets,
illuminated designs with texts. Sizes
4 cm x 2 cm up to 8.4 cm x 4.8 cm.

8. Twenty-one cards from two sets, one set
with flowers and birds' nests, the others
with flowers, birds and butterflies in
patterned border.
4 cm x 3.9 cm, 5.5 cm x 3.7 cm.

9. Thirty-four cards, eighteen designs of
floral geometric patterns in green and
purple around a variety of texts.
3.4 cm x 4.2 cm.

10. Sixteen cards, four with floral
geometric designs around texts in panels.
Twelve are smaller, six printed in red or
blue with patterned border, and six with
floral designs on a mauve background.
5.8 cm x 3.5 cm up to 6.2 cm x 8.7 cm.

11. Twenty-four cards, six geometric
designs in red and blue around a variety of
texts in central vignettes. 4.2 cm x 4.8 cm.

12. Eighteen cards, geometric and scroll
designs in red and green from two
different sets.
5.8 cm x 7.5 cm, 5.1 cm x 5.8 cm.

13. Ten cards, two with verses in floral
border, two with geometric designs and
flowers, and six with flowers and texts on
a cream coloured background, one of these
dated 1879 by the sender. 7 cm x 5.2 cm up
to 6.5 cm x 9.2 cm.

14. Twelve miscellaneous cards, ten with
flowers, two with illuminated texts.
3.3 cm x 2.1 cm up to 10 cm x 3.7 cm.

15. Eleven cards from two sets. Seven have
black and white country and sea scenes,
with verses by E H Bickersteth, Horatius
Bonar D D, W Walsham Howe on reverse;
four are uncut, with scenes of the Holy
Land in vignettes.
8 cm x 5 cm, 6 cm x 4.1 cm.

16. Four cut-out and pierced cards in the
shape of rustic frames threaded with rose
sprays around oval vignettes with texts.
5.7 cm x 8.2 cm.

17. Twenty-three small cards. Thirteen of
one set have the same green printed
picture, perhaps of a missionary, with
different texts, and the other ten have
miscellaneous designs and texts. Set 4.7 cm
x 3.8 cm, others 4.5 cm x 2.5 cm up to
6.3 cm x 4.2 cm.

18. Ten miscellaneous text cards with
flowers.
6.1 cm x 3.7 cm up to 6.1 cm x 8 cm.

19. Nine cards. Four are an uncut set with
flowers, birds and insects, marked
Campbell & Tudhope, and five others have

143.14

birds and scenes.
4.3 cm x 6 cm up to 5.1 cm x 7.8 cm.

20. Three cards or prints on thin paper,
texts in scrolls with ferns and colourful
flowers, one with a cross.
14.5 cm x 15.5 cm.

*The following large cards have texts in gilt and
coloured letters, and were probably published
in the 1890's.*

21/22. Two cards with country scenes and
texts in large gilt letters, one signed S
Bowers.
19.4 cm x 25.4 cm, 20.8 cm x 25.4 cm.

23/24. Two cards with little girls in
country scenes, and texts in coloured
letters. 25.5 cm x 18.9 cm.

25. A card bordered by rustic branches
around roses and lilies of the valley, with
illuminated text in red and gold.
19.4 cm x 25.5 cm.

26/27. Two cards, each with illuminated
text and a bunch of mixed flowers.
19.4 cm x 25.5 cm.

## VOLUME 145:
## RELIGIOUS CARDS. IN MEMORIAM

**Although the cards in these two
volumes are not strictly in the
category of greeting cards, the
sociological material they provide is
the reason for including some
examples in this collection. The use
of verses, especially for the
numerous cards mourning the loss of
children at a too early age, is
interesting, and some early cards
with embossed and cut out designs
illustrate how the valentine makers,**

**145.3**

Wood, Mansell and Windsor, adapted their lace paper works for this purpose. Later cards were simpler with plain black borders, though more elaborate examples with black and silver designs continued well into the 20th century. The cards are nearly all in black and white, sometimes with silver though a few examples have subdued colour. Some Royalty cards are included, some for disasters, and twentieth century examples are given to show the persistence of the Victorian tradition.

1. A large elaborate cut out and embossed card in the shape of a Gothic tomb, in memory of a family of five children. J Mansell, 1850's. 16.7 cm x 23.2 cm.

2. Another large card dated 1886, with a folder card. "In memory of George Drinkwater" flanked by angels with silver wings and cut out decoration in black and silver. 19.8 cm x 23.2 cm.

3. Four cards, embossed and cut out angels and trees with inscriptions on central panels in the style of monuments. One is marked Mansell and dated 1875, two Windsor 1859, 1860, and one Wood 1883. This card is almost identical with one of the Windsor cards, with very slight variations. 11.6 cm x 7.7 cm.

4. Four similar cards marked Wood, dated 1878, 1879, 1880, 1884. 11.6 cm x 7.7 cm.

5. Four cards marked Wood, two unused, two dated 1867, 1878. Two are in lace paper style, two embossed. 11.7 cm x 7.8 cm.

6. Four embossed black-bordered cards, one marked Mansell 1886, two Windsor 1858, 1880, one unmarked dated 1867. All have the names of the departed inscribed on a monument design, three with angels

and two with sorrowing figures. 12.7 cm x 8.8 cm, 11.3 cm x 7.7 cm.

7. Three cards in memory of Princess Alice who died December 14th 1878. One is a letter from Queen Victoria printed on a card edged with a black and white ivy pattern, another has an embossed design of angels with a poem by H B Worth, and the third is a black edged card with an acrostic poem by Mrs Picton. 11.7 cm x 15.2 cm, 11.5 cm x 7.7 cm.

8. Three folder cards in Memoriam for Queen Victoria, Edward VII, and George V, with black and silver borders and portraits of the deceased. 11.5 cm x 7.7 cm, 8 cm x 11.7 cm.

9. Two folder cards for King Edward VII both with portraits and verses. 11.6 cm x 7.7 cm.

10. Four postcards in memory of King Edward VII. Two were published by C W Faulkner, one with a picture of Queen Alexandra and her letter to the nation, the other with portraits of the new King and Queen and King George's message to his people. The other two are cards mourning the King's death with a verse or a hymn, published by Beagles & Philco. 9 cm x 14 cm.

11. Two cards, one an embossed card for the Duke of Wellington, 1852. The other is in Memoriam for the Earl of Beaconsfield appropriately decorated with a wreath of yellow primroses on a blue ground, published by J F Schipper & Co, also used an an Easter card (see volume 135). 11.9 cm x 7.8 cm, 10.5 cm x 12 cm.

12. A disaster card, in memoriam for three crew members of the Southport life boat, drowned June 26th, 1899, in the form of a folder with the story of the tragedy and a poem inside. The proceeds from the sale of the card were given to the widows. 16 cm x 12.7 cm.

13. A card for the Titanic disaster, 1912, with a picture of an iceberg and a poem by W E B. 16.5 cm x 20.5 cm.

14/15. Four folder cards with black and silver borders and a cross and flowers on the outside, with pictures and stories of disasters inside, including the Welsh Pit disaster October 14th 1913, the sinking of the empress of Ireland on May 29th 1914, and the death of John Travers Cornwell at the battle of Jutland, 1916. The fourth card was in memory of The Unknown Warrior, interred at Westminster Abbey November 11th 1920. 11.7 cm x 7.8 cm.

16. Four cards in plainer style with black borders, two folders dated 1878, two single cards dated 1868, 1869, and an envelope with embossed motif. Sizes up to 11.5 cm x 7.7 cm.

17. Five black edged cards, two dated 1874, two 1879, and one dated 1872 with the hymn sung at the funeral of Mrs Dening. 11.3 cm x 7.5 cm, 13.4 cm x 9.4 cm.

18. Four black edged cards, two single sheets with verses dated 1881, 1884, and two folders dated 1884, 1885, and an envelope with embossed motif. 11.5 cm x 7.5 cm.

19. Three cards, two with black and silver edges and motifs on the cover, dated 1884, and one a plain card with verse and an envelope with embossed motif, 1881. 11.5 cm x 8 cm, 11.3 cm x 7.6 cm.

20. Two cards. One is a Catholic card dated 1883, with coloured flowers on a black ground on the front and "Pray for the Soul of Josephine Mary Alice Tuck ..." on the back, with texts. The other, printed in red, black and gold, was dated 1876. 6.8 cm x 10.7 cm, 13.5 cm x 8.5 cm.

21. Three folder cards with black and silver borders, two dated 1887 and 1890 with floral wreaths on the covers, the third dated 1888 with a picture of a church on the back. 11.5 cm x 7.7 cm.

22. Four folder cards, three with black and silver borders, and one with black border, dated 1888, 1888, 1889, 1890. 11.5 cm x 7.8 cm.

## VOLUME 146: RELIGIOUS CARDS. IN MEMORIAM (Continued)

1. Four folding cards, one black backed with envelope, dated 1886, three with black and silver designs dated 1889, 1890, 1894. 11.5 cm x 7.7 cm.

2. Four folding cards. One is black bordered with a decorative "In Memoriam" on the cover, and an interesting verse "Farewell, dear husband, my life is spent ...", dated 1891. Two have

silver borders, dated 1891 and 1895, both marked A S Co - (Artistic Stationery Co Ltd). The fourth card, dated 1898, has a Celtic cross on the cover and is marked M W, included here for comparison, or rather, contrast of design, and it is the only Marcus Ward card of this kind found for the collection. 11.5 cm x 7.7 cm, 7.7 cm x 11.5 cm, 8.1 cm x 10.8 cm.

3. Three folder cards, black and silver borders. One is dated 1895 with a silver border. One is dated 1895 with a silver cross and flowers, one dated 1892, the other incomplete, with an envelope marked Joseph Pike, Undertaker, Hooley Hill, nr Manchester. 11.5 cm x 7.5 cm.

4. Five cards all apparently of the same set, with black and silver borders and flower designs on the covers, dated 1886, 1892, 1893, 1894, 1895. 11.5 cm x 7.5 cm.

5. A large card, in memory of Arthur Joseph Dailly, 1893, with a verse signed Messent, Undertaker, Woolwich set in a Gothic style tomb on a silver background with doves and flower garlands above. 20.6 cm x 25.5 cm.

6. Four folding cards, black and silver borders, with flowers or leaves on the covers, dated 1892, 1894, 1896, 1896. 11.5 cm x 7.8 cm.

7. Four folding cards with flowers on the covers. Three have black and silver borders, the fourth is black, embossed with a gilt flower wreath. Two are dated 1898, two 1899. 11.6 cm x 7.5 cm, 10.5 cm x 8.3 cm.

8. Four folder cards, two black with embossed design and gilt flowers, two black and silver with flowers, dated 1897, 1897, 1898, 1904. 10.5 cm x 8.3 cm, 11 cm x 8 cm, 11.6 cm x 7.5 cm.

9. Four folder cards, all 1902, black and silver borders with flower or ivy decoration. One has a silver panel with a shaded beige border and flowers. 11.5 cm x 7.7 cm.

10. Three folder cards and two envelopes, black and silver borders with spring flowers on the covers. 11.5 cm x 7.7 cm.

11. Four cards, one a single card with an envelope marked "Dear Dad's Deathcard 1906". Two are folders with black and silver designs, dated 1904, 1905, and one is plain white, 1908. 11.5 cm x 7.7 cm.

12. Four folder cards. Two are all black, embossed, with gilt lettering, dated 1904, 1909, one is in memory of a five month old child and has angels on the cover, 1912, and the fourth is for a six month old child who died in 1905 and has forget-me-nots on the cover. Sizes up to 11 cm x 8.8 cm.

13. Five folding cards, four with flower or ivy designs and black and silver borders, one with a silver border and decorated lettering. Three are dated 1909, two 1913. 11.6 cm x 7.8 cm.

14. Three cards "In Sympathy", black and silver embossed designs, unused. Early 1900's? 7.7 cm x 11 cm, 7.5 cm x 11.5 cm.

15. Four bookmarks, printed in black on fringed white silk, dated 1909, 1911, 1917, 1933. Sizes up to 17 cm x 5 cm.

16. Three black-bordered cards, one a folder in memory of a Lance Corporal killed in France in 1917, one a post card (Bamforth) in memory of Lord Kitchener drowned in 1916, and another folder dated 1914 tied with a black cord and tassel. 11.5 cm x 7.7 cm, 14 cm x 8.8 cm, 11.5 cm x 9 cm.

17. Five folder cards with flowers and ivy, four with black and silver borders, one with a black border, dated 1917, 1919, 1919, 1921, 1929. 11.7 cm x 7.7 cm.

18. Six folder cards, three black-bordered, three with black and silver borders, and flowers, ivy, or crosses on the covers. These are dated 1922, 1924, 1931, 1933, 1936, 1948, but have very similar designs to the late Victorian and Edwardian cards. 11.7 cm x 7.7 cm, 12 cm x 7.2 cm.

# CHILDREN, LADIES, FAMILY SCENES, FAIRIES

*Section*
*12*

This section includes cards from publishers not dealt with in full in earlier sections, some of whose cards have already been seen in Section 11, along with unattributed cards in similar styles. Some artists are known, though a number of monograms have not yet been identified. The sequence of cards featuring children now continues from about 1875 to the early 1890's, with the more elaborate shaped, cut-out, and folding cards of the late Victorian and early Edwardian eras appearing in a subsequent section along with other subjects dealt with in a similar way.

The dresses of the children and the costumes of the ladies afford much opportunity for the study of Victorian fashions and the observation of social habits. The elaborately dressed and hatted children on the Victorian beach are in fascinating contrast to the youngsters of today. Most of the children are idealised into rosy-cheeked curly haired little angels, but sometimes a glimpse of naughty small boys snowballing or over-eating can be a refreshing change. The ladies too, were romanticised into beauties in magnificent gowns, but occasionally a fisher girl or cottager appears, or a sportswoman in a costume that could have complicated her activities. Many of the pictures on the cards had little connection with Christmas, though there are a number showing children and families in happy festive scenes. Fairies and elves were often used for greetings, and these are included in this section along with what are described as Flower children, small beings without wings who live in flowers or perch precariously on branches.

**161.2**

*Wishing you every* CHRISTMAS *Blessing!*

**VOLUME 147:
CHILDREN'S CARDS
PUBLISHED BY AUGUSTUS
THIERRY, SOMETIMES
LISTED AS AUGUSTE OR
AUGUSTIN**

**No cards marked with the name of
this firm have been found for this
collection, but most of the cards here
have been positively identified from
Stationers' Hall records, all designed
by Felix Dussert, an artist whose
name has not appeared so far in
greeting card literature. All these
registrations are for Thierry with
Dussert named as artist. A number
of cards for which no registrations
have been traced are included and
attributed to the same artist, and
probably publisher, by the very
characteristic style of children's
figures with bright colours of russet,
green and blue, many on gilt
backgrounds.**

1/2. Sixteen cards, eight designs of a single
boy or girl in winter scenes with gilt or
silver backgrounds, and a variety of
greetings in panels.  Registered at
Stationers' Hall 5-10-1877.  6.6 cm x 10 cm.

3. Six cards, three designs in two styles, of
girls out of doors, with greetings below in
black or in a panel. Three out of four
designs registered at Stationers' Hall
5-10-1877.  7 cm x 10.3 cm.

4. Three blue-bordered cards, quaint chefs
with puddings, geese, or a dog, three out
of four designs registered at Stationers'
Hall 5-10-1877.  7.5 cm x 11.3 cm.

5/6. Sixteen cards, eight designs of a boy
and a girl in brightly coloured clothes out
in the snow. Eight are on grey or pale
green backgrounds, eight on gilt, all with
greetings in black below. Registered at
Stationers' Hall 26-3-1878.
6.8 cm x 10.1 cm.

7. Six cards, five designs of quaint small
boys with insects or geese, five out of six
designs registered at Stationers' Hall
26-3-1878. 13.3 cm x 6.9 cm.

8. Six blue-bordered cards, each with a boy
or girl on a flowering branch on gilt
ground, registered at Stationers' Hall
16-5-1878. One is an advertisement for
Madame Pauline of Regent Circus, with a
long poem on reverse ending
"Where the sweetest of bonnets may daily
be seen
So alluringly fashioned by Madame
Pauline".
11.9 cm x 8.6 cm.

9. Six cards, five designs of small boys
dressed as soldiers, sailors, or policemen,
in various Christmas pursuits. Two cards
are on embossed edge mounts. These are

five from six designs registered at
Stationers' Hall 16-5-1878.
10.3 cm x 7 cm, 11.2 cm x 7.7 cm.

10. Two cards with patterned borders, each
with a girl dreaming of Christmas gifts
and fairies, two out of four registered at
Stationers' Hall 26-3-1878.
8.5 cm x 13.3 cm.

11. Four gilt-backed cards with red or blue
borders, grotesque elves sitting on leaves,
holding toys or puddings. Registered at
Stationers' Hall 14-9-1878.
8.2 cm x 12.4 cm.

12. Three cards. Two with small boys with
a large boot or a watch are from six
registered at Stationers' Hall 19-3-1879, the
third has a boy and girl with a champagne
bottle and is one from four registered at
Stationers' Hall 4-3-1881. 10.3 cm x 7 cm.

13. Seven cards, four designs of a single
boy or girl out in the snow.  Registered at
Stationers' Hall 15-7-1879.
10.1 cm x 6.8 cm.

14. Eight cards, six designs of girls selling
watercress, lemons, violets, flags, flowers,
or fire stove ornaments, on grey
background, registered at Stationers' Hall
17-7-1879.  6.8 cm x 10.1 cm.

15. A similar set of seven cards, five
designs of street boys, sweeping snow or
selling papers or matches. No registration
has been traced. 6.8 cm x 10.1 cm.

16. Eight cards, a delightful set of a baby
girl with toys or pets, in a triangular
vignette bordered by flowers or holly on
gilt background.  One card shows the
child tearing up a scrap album. Registered
at Stationers' Hall 17-7-1879.
10.1 cm x 6.9 cm.

17/18. Sixteen cards, a similar set with
eight designs of a small boy or girl in a
diamond vignette holding labels with
greetings, and flowers, holly and toys in
the corners.  Eight have gilt backed
corners, eight black-backed. No
registration has been found.
6.6 cm x 10.1 cm.

19. Nine cards, including six designs from
the previous set with silver corners, and
three smaller with two of the previous
designs and another of a small boy with a
toy boat. 6.6 cm x 10.1 cm, 4.6 cm x 8.4 cm.

20. Two cards, with different patterned
borders, one design of a girl in Greek dress
with a lily in a pot, one design from four
registered at Stationers' Hall 17-7-1879.
9.2 cm x 19.6 cm, 8.3 cm x 18.3 cm.

21. Two cards, one a folder fringed in red
with four pages, and another single card
repeating one of these designs, which
show a boy and girl on a balcony or with a

parrot and book. They have three designs
out of four registered at Stationers' Hall
2-9-1879. 12 cm x 8.6 cm.

22. Three cards, children in fancy hats in
oval vignette with flowers below, three
from four designs registered at Stationers'
Hall 2-9-1879. 6.8 cm x 10.3 cm.

23. Six gilt-edged cards, five designs of
single children in summer pursuits. Four
of these were registered at Stationers' Hall
28-4-1880. 6.5 cm x 13.3 cm.

24/25. Seven cards, four with girls and
boys in summer pursuits, three in winter.
These are seven from eight designs
registered at Stationers' Hall 4-3-1881.
13.5 cm x 6.7 cm, 6.7 cm x 13.5 cm.

26. Three similar cards, two with girls in
summer scenes. The third is a folder in
two pieces with a boy reading, and a verse
by T E M, with illuminated design on the
cover. 13.4 cm x 6.7 cm, 16.5 cm x 9.3 cm.

27. Five gilt-backed cards with small boys
dressed as soldiers, perhaps caricaturing
the activities of the British Army, five
designs from eight registered at Stationers'
Hall 28-4-1880. 10.1 cm x 6.7 cm.

28. Two cards, gilt patterned borders, one
a lady and child in elaborate pink and
white dresses, the other a youth and
maiden plucking the petals from a daisy.
The latter card is one from three registered
at Stationers' Hall 23-9-1880, but the two
cards are obviously from the same set.
8.4 cm x 18.3 cm.

29. Two similar cards, registrations not
found, with patterned gilt borders, each of
a youth and maiden beneath a flowering
tree.  8.6 cm x 15.7 cm.

30. Three gilt-edged cards with a picture of
a small girl emerging from an egg, on a
background of flowers.  One is a folder in
two pieces, with a verse by T E M and
illuminated border and cover.  These are
three from four designs registered at
Stationers' Hall 23-9-1880.
16.5 cm x 9.3 cm, 13.4 cm x 6.9 cm.

*Registrations for the following cards have not
been found, but they are included here from
similarity.*

31. Three gilt-edged cards, maidens in
Italian style dress, with birds in summer
scenes. 6.8 cm x 13.6 cm.

32. Three similar, in semi circular
vignettes, with illuminated corners.
13.2 cm x 8.6 cm.

33. Four gilt-edged cards, three designs of
a small girl in an egg, a wooden box, or a
basket, all with flowers above.
7.1 cm x 15.2 cm.

34. Five gilt-edged cards, three with two designs of a small girl and a dog, the others with a small boy or girl with flowers or chicks, all with a spray of flowers and a seasonal verse below. 7.1 cm x 15.2 cm, 6.9 cm x 13.7 cm.

35. Two cards, wide borders, well dressed young ladies with flowers. 8.7 cm x 14 cm.

36. Two cards with girls, one with a parasol in summer, one with an umbrella in winter. 8 cm x 17.2 cm.

37. Two cards with girls, one with a bird, one with a lamb, both with verses. 8.2 cm x 14.8 cm

38. One card, a small girl in a gilt vignette, with a blackberry branch, and a cat below licking up spilt milk. 8 cm x 12.2 cm.

39/40. Twelve cards, six designs of girls in fancy costume, five with robins or a cat, one out of doors in snow. Seven have white borders, five are unbordered. 7 cm x 10.4 cm, 6.5 cm x 10 cm.

41. Four miscellaneous cards, two with girls in Neapolitan(?) costume, two with small children and robins. 6.8 cm x 10.4 cm.

## VOLUME 148: CARDS OF CHILDREN - SOME PUBLISHERS

The cards in this volume are marked with publishers' names or trademarks. They include two cards of children published by Jonathan King, the well known manufacturer who amassed a famous collection of cards and associated material. A number are from Eyre & Spottiswoode, and a few are from Ernest Falck, Thomas Stevens, S J Saunders, H Rothe, Parkins & Gotto, Marion, and Rimmel.

1. Two gilt-bordered cards marked J King, oval prints of small boy or girl lifting to show a New Year greeting. 9.2 cm x 12 cm.

*Numbers 2 - 27 were published by Eyre & Spottiswoode, marked with full name, E & S, or a trademark, published in the 1880's.*

2. Four cards, a girl or boy with a verse by F E E H, a spray of flowers, and illuminated medallions in two corners. No. 204. 9 cm x 12.8 cm, 12.8 cm x 9 cm.

3. One card, a boy and girl in a woodland setting with a verse by A C and a wild strawberry spray. 10.8 cm x 14.8 cm.

4/5. Five cards, four designs of summer and winter scenes with boys and girls at play. Three have red backgrounds, two blue, with verses by Eden Hooper in scrolls. 12.3 cm x 8.6 cm.

6. Three cards, by Linnie Watt, summer scenes with a single boy or girl in a circular vignette, with a design and a greeting on reverse, marked with the shield trademark. No. 444. 11.2 cm x 11.4 cm.

7. Three cards, probably by Linnie Watt, children in summer scenes by a river or at the seaside. Two are numbered 456, and the third is identified from a similar border and verse by Louis Novra on reverse. 12.4 cm x 10.3 cm, 12.4 cm x 10.1 cm.

8. Two cards, girls in frilled dresses, one with a cat, the other with flowers. No. 391. 10.8 cm x 15 cm.

9. Five cards with two styles of patterned borders, three with two children, no.132, the others with girls in Greenaway style dresses, no. 276. 9.5 cm x 10 cm, 10.7 cm x 11.5 cm.

10/11. Four gilt-bordered cards by Harry Arnold, groups of children in various winter pursuits, no. 266. 15.5 cm x 11 cm.

12. Two cards signed J M R, one with two children outside a church door, the other a small girl by a cottage door. No. 242. 8.6 cm x 13 cm.

13. Four cards. Three have three pictures in each of a child in mischief and suffering retribution, with narrative verses by Eden Hooper on reverse, no. 303. The fourth repeats two of the pictures on one card, no. 129. 14.5 cm x 9.2 cm, 10 cm x 9 cm.

14. Five gilt-edged cards, sailor boys and young fishermen, with verse below, no. 244.  8.7 cm x 12.3 cm, 12.3 cm x 8.7 cm.

15. Two cards repeating two of the above designs in a different format, one unmarked, the other with the shield tradesmark, thus confirming this as Eyre & Spottiswoode; the E & S on the device is not very clear. No.158. 7.8 cm x 11.5 cm.

16. Three cards with illuminated patterned borders, a girl in a cornfield, a boy fishing, and a boy putting on skates. These are not marked, but are attributed from the border style and the similarity of the script in the greetings to that in other E & S cards. 15.5 cm x 9.4 cm.

17. Four cards, a girl playing Blind Man's Buff, a couple in Greenaway style costume, two girls picking flowers, a boy playing football, nos. 311, 349, 203, 311. Sizes up to 10.6 cm x 14.5 cm.

18. Three gilt-bordered cards, a girl with a hoop dated 1887 by the sender, and two seaside views, no. 236. 13.4 cm x 17.2 cm, 13.8 cm x 10.4 cm.

19. Three cards, two designs of girls, one picking apples, the other seated on a tree trunk, no. 362. 7.4 cm x 10.2 cm.

20. One card, "Roasting the Ox", with villagers awaiting the feast in the grounds of the manor house, dated 1883 by the sender. There is a verse by Eden Hooper on reverse. 19.2 cm x 12.1 cm.

21. Two gilt-edged cards, one a child's head in a circular vignette, with honeysuckle, no. 384, the other a girl's head in a plumed hat in a circular vignette in a green border, no. 618. 9 cm x 13 cm, 16 cm x 17.3 cm.

22. Two cards, nursery rhymes, three vignettes with pictures of Little Bo-Peep or Jack and Jill, in a green and white ornamental border, with verses on the back. No.395. 15.2 cm x 9.7 cm.

23. Four cards, two of boys, one in winter, one in summer, no. 332, and two of small children in night attire draped in shawls or curtains with somewhat coy verses beneath, no. 352. 8.1 cm x 11.6 cm, 10.2 cm x 13.5 cm.

24. Two cards, one a mother and child in snow, no. 202, the other a small child in a large hat with a toy horse, no. 161. 7.7 cm x 11.3 cm, 7.7 cm x 11.1 cm.

25. Three cards with decorative borders, each with a young lady, one in a rose garden, one by a cornfield, the third holding a robin, with verses below, (one trimmed). No. 426.  9 cm x 15.2 cm.

26. Two cards, patterned gilt borders, a lady and children in classical dress and setting, no. 612. 14.9 cm x 10.3 cm.

27. Three cards, one with two children in Georgian dress carrying a basket of flowers, no. 325, the others with a boy and girl perching on sprays of wallflower or narcissus, no. 382. 13.7 cm x 10.4 cm, 13.2 cm x 9.6 cm.

28. Three cards, published by Ernest Falck, two embossed designs of a boy with a butterfly net and a girl by the sea.  These have been identified from an 1880 trade list of Jonathan King in the John Johnson collection, but no marked cards have been found for this publisher. 6 cm x 11.4 cm.

29. Three folding cards published by Falck. They have Christmas scenes inside, with holly and appropriate verses, and flowers in a holly border on the cover. These are not marked, but are three out of four registered at Stationers' Hall 26-5-1879. 10.9 cm x 6.4 cm.

30. Six cards marked Thomas Stevens, five designs of children playing or reading, c1880. 7.6 cm x 11.3 cm.

153

31. Six cards published by S J Saunders & Co, each of a girl and boy with holly or mistletoe, and narrative verses on the back.  8.9 cm x 11.6 cm.

32. Four cards published by S J Saunders, each with a girl and boy investigating a Christmas hamper.12.7 cm x 9.5 cm.

33. Eleven cards, including three folders, using six designs of children and two of flowers, with verses on the backs, published by S J Saunders. 6.2 cm x 9.5 cm.

34/35. Three cards published by H Rothe (one birthday), head and shoulder portraits of little girls, nos. 329, 535, 535. c1885. 12.5 cm x 16.5 cm.

36. Five miscellaneous cards published by H Rothe, three with two children, two with girls, nos. 142, 171, 171, 459, 469. 9.7 cm x 6.6 cm up to 8.3 cm x 13.3 cm.

37. Two cards published by Parkins & Gotto, one of a girl and boy skating, the other with people outside a church, c1880 by the style.  6.3 cm x 10.5 cm, 6.2 cm x 11 cm.

38. Two cards, Parkins & Gotto. These are trade cards with advertisements for this firm, which sold a variety of goods including ornamental articles for the writing table, albums, bags, boxes, wallets etc, but not, according to the lengthy lists on one card, greeting cards. One card is a triptych folder with the skating picture in no. 37 on the front, and pictures of the goods inside, with a list of articles for sale, and the heading "Parkins & Gotto, Fancy Goods Warehouse, 27 & 28 Oxford St. London, by special appointment to H.R.H. The Princess of Wales". The second card is the centre portion of another similar trade card.
8.8 cm x 13.5 cm folded, 8.5 cm x 10.8 cm.

39. Six cards, three designs in two styles of a boy and girl at the seaside, marked Ben George, London. They answer precisely to the description of cards registered at Stationers' Hall 7-11-1878 by Parkins & Gotto, artist Miss M Webb. Ben George is not listed in Buday's appendix of publishers.
8.4 cm x 10 cm, 7.9 cm x 11.3 cm.

40. Four cards of children marked Marion & Co, two in Greenaway style, one in mediaeval costume, the fourth with two little girls playing at soldiers.
Sizes up to 11 cm x 9.5 cm.

41. Four cards from the perfumery firm, Eugen Rimmel, London-Paris. One has a girl's head encircled by flowers, another has a figure in an illuminated border, both with an early small circular seal on reverse. The third has a child printed in blue, and the fourth has two little girls on a seesaw. Sizes up to 7 cm x 10.6 cm.

## VOLUME 149: CHILDREN'S CARDS - MORE PUBLISHERS

**The cards here are marked with publishers' names or trademarks, and are dated from about 1885-1890.**

*Numbers 1-6 were published by Castell Bros, and show two trademarks, a castle, or a double knot of ribbon with bows. Most are marked "printed in Bavaria", and some are numbered.*

1. Three cards signed L L - Lizzie Lawson - children reading, with a holly branch above, and a verse by Lucy A Bennett. No. 32, Peniel.  15.3 cm x 16 cm.

2. Two cards, signed L L, both with two children in church, and a verse by Lucy A Bennett. No. 77, Peniel. 11 cm x 15 cm.

3. Three cards, two with a girl in a mob cap, no. 134A, and a barefoot girl with pigeons, all with verses by Lucy A Bennett. 10.8 cm x 14 cm, 11 cm x 13.5 cm.

4. Four miscellaneous cards, unnumbered, all printed in Bavaria, with children by the sea or with flowers.
7.5 cm x 8.4 cm up to12.9 cm x 9.9 cm.

5. One card, a child with a basket of holly in a winter scene, with a robin.
12.2 cm x 14.3 cm.

6. One card, a child dressed as a postman with a sack of letters.  10.3 cm x 15 cm.

*Numbers 7-15 were published by W Hagelberg, some marked Berlin.*

7. Two cards, a house in winter with a vignette of two girls decorating a room within, dated 1887 by the sender, no. 124, and a little girl in bed with a doll, no. 79.
13.2 cm x 13.3 cm, 10 cm x 13.3 cm.

8. Four cards, each with two children in summer scenes. Two are birthday cards with folded corners in trompe l'oeil fashion and verses by S K C, no. 441. The others have Christmas greetings, no. 38.
9.7 cm x 13 cm, 9.9 cm x 13 cm.

9. One card, Father Christmas in a brown cloak giving presents to two children in an outdoor winter scene, no. 420.
10.7 cm x 15 cm.

10. Five cards (one birthday), with little girls, head and shoulders, in frilled caps. Four are signed by Emily J Harding, two of these oval, no. 620, and two others have verses by M S H, no. 419.  The fifth card is numbered 395.
Sizes up to 10 cm x 13.2 cm.

11. Nine small shaped cards with children in summer scenes, three being birthday cards. Two are fans, no. 146, five are shields including two by E J Harding, one dated 1888 by the sender, one is a star with

an angel, no. 142?, and one is diamond shaped, no.49. 4.5 cm x 6.5 cm up to 8.5 cm x 14.8 cm.

12. Two cards with the same design of a curly headed girl with a brown hooded Santa Claus, one with a verse beneath, no. 412, the other two overlapping rectangles with an embossed daisy spray and a verse by E E Griffin on the back.
12.9 cm x 8.3 cm, 13.3 cm x 10 cm.

13. Four cards, summer scenes. Two have four or five small girls sitting on a fence, one dated 1887 by the sender, no. 539, the others have three girls - triplets? - in identical beribboned dresses, one dated 1891, no. 1125.  12.5 cm x 8.5 cm, 8.3 cm x 12.7 cm.

14. Four miscellaneous cards, children in summer, one dated 1886 by the sender, no. 47, and two others numbered 109, 386. Two cards have verses by A M Hone on reverse.  10.7 cm x 8.5 cm up to 9.8 cm x 13 cm.

15. Four miscellaneous cards.  One has a girl in a tam-o-shanter and a verse by M S H, no. 105, another has a fairy on a flower and a verse by E E G, no. 267, the third has three girls with greenery, no. 467.  The fourth has a small girl with curly hair and a verse by E E G on the reverse. 6.8 cm x 9.4 cm up to 13.1 cm x 9.8 cm.

*Numbers 16-19 were published by Ernest Nister, with a trademark of a palette with a child's head, and most are marked "Printed in Bavaria".*

16. Three cards, one a girl holding an envelope with a picture inside, no. 765, and two of children's faces in flowers, and verses by Ellis Walton, no. 839.
12.1 cm x 16.3 cm, 11.5 cm x 7.8 cm.

17. Three cards, one with two children making shadow pictures on the wall, and a verse by Edwin Waugh, another a little girl with a parrot, both no. 836. The third has two children a baby in a cart pulled by a collie dog, no. 1090.
12.1 cm x 10.2 cm,12.4 cm x 10.4 cm.

18. Six miscellaneous cards, five of children in various activities, one of a girl and boy in Georgian dress, nos. 1572, 1572, 1057, 716, 807, 1089.
8.4 cm x 4.8 cm up to 8.8 cm x 11.3 cm.

19. Three cards in correspondence style with greetings in verse.  One has an applied "scrap" of two little girls with real white ribbon bows. Two are numbered 733, 842. 11.5 cm x 9 cm.

*Numbers 20-21 were published by J F Schipper & Co., with the ship trademark.*

20. One card, a small Cupid, in a cart like a pig, with four attendants, and a festoon of holly above. No. 832. 11.8 cm x 17.5 cm.

21. Two cards, a girl with holly in snow, and a verse by S K C on reverse, no. 1300, and a girl in a mob cap with fichu, no. 629. 11 cm x 15.3 cm, 9.7 cm x 15 cm.

*Numbers 22-25 were published by Wirth Bros. & Owen.*

22. Four cards. Two are circular, one with two boys using a basket as a protection against the snow, the other two girls with an umbrella, both no. 2310. The other two show young ladies enjoying a snowball fight, and have a verse by E H C and a picture of a church on reverse, no. 271. 10.7 cm diameter, 11.8 cm x 16.5 cm.

23. Three cards, two with a boy or a girl in a circular vignette, marked Wirth Bros & Owen, New York, dated 1885 by the sender, and another two girls feeding birds, with a verse by E H C on reverse, no. 239.  9.3 cm x 10 cm, 11 cm x 13.5 cm.

24. A large frosted card, two girls in a sleigh drawn by a goat, dated 1884 by the sender. 18.7 cm x 12 cm.

*Numbers 25-29 were published by Bernhard Ollendorff.*

25. Four cards, one with a boy and a rabbit, another with a girl and a cat, both in oval vignettes, with verses by Lewis Novra on the backs. The other two have a boy with skates, and a girl with a doll and a basket of holly, with verses by M S Mae Ritchie on the backs. 9.9 cm x 12.4 cm, 9.5 cm x 13.2 cm.

26. Three cards, one in grey and white showing children falling off chairs after drawing high up on the wall, the other two with children out of doors with snow and holly and a verse by Nora Manning on the back. 11.7 cm x 8.8 cm, 12.2 cm x 10.2 cm.

27. Four miscellaneous cards, three with children, head and shoulders, the fourth with two street boys and a quotation from Bleak House. 11.2 cm x 6.8 cm up to 10 cm x 11.2 cm.

28. Six cards, three with heads of children in circular vignettes, one a boy in a fur hat, and two a boy or a girl in a snow shower with a dog. 6.2 cm x 9.3 cm up to 7.4 cm x 10.8 cm.

29. Four cards, three designs of young ladies in culinary pursuits, Dorothy making a pudding, Mabel cooking a goose, and Mollie with Christmas pies. Narrative verses and winter scenes are on the backs of the cards. 13.3 cm x 12 cm.

*Numbers 30-32 were published by Obpacher Bros., most of the cards showing rather quaint children.*

30. Four cards, three designs of small children in summer scenes, no. 693. One

duplicate is marked J F S & Co. 8.8 cm x 13 cm.

31. Two cards, a girl and boy making a snowman, no. 917, and a boy with a dog, no.570. 10 cm x 15.2 cm, 13 cm x 9 cm.

32. Three cards, a child with a doll and pram, no. 821, a boy in Georgian dress, no. 954, and a boy and girl in two hanging sabots, no. 1141. 8.6 cm x 13 cm, 6.5 cm x 15.5 cm.

*Numbers 33-36 were published by M H Nathan & Co.*

33/34. Four cards, three designs of girls, two by the sea, one in a garden, with poems on reverse by C D. 11.8 cm x 15.9 cm.

35. Two cards, children on rocks or in a boat, with narrative poems by C D on reverse. 14.9 cm x 11.8 cm.

36. Two cards, a girl picking flowers, dated 1888 by the sender, and a girl in a hammock, with a verse by Byron. 11.9 cm x 15.9 cm, 15.6 cm x 11.6 cm.

37. Three birthday cards published by Albert Marx, each with a small boy and a cat or a dog, one dated 1886 by the sender. 7.4 cm x 11.2 cm.

38. Two cards published by Philipp Bros, a boy or girl in a circular vignette, with autumn leaves and forget-me-nots. 12.5 cm x 8.1 cm.

39. Three cards from Philipp Bros, a girl and a cat, a boy and a cat, a boy with a rabbit. 7.6 cm x 10.5 cm.

## VOLUME 150: CHILDREN, SMALL CARDS, 1875 - EARLY 1880's

**No publishers have been traced for these cards, though the first three sets have initials, either publishers or distributors.**

1. Six cards from two sets, children as street vendors, with a gilt background. Four have greetings in white panels, one marked J C & S, probably the firm listed by Buday as J C & S L. 6.6 cm x 10 cm, 6.7 cm x 10.4 cm.

2.    Three cards, one with two children in a boat, the other two marked J G M (untraced), one a boy punting, the other two children hanging up a sheet bearing a greeting.  9.9 cm x 6 cm, 10.5 cm x 6.8 cm.

3. Three cards, naked small boys, with greetings on an egg or panels on a black background, marked J B B & Co (untraced).  One was dated 1883 by the sender. 10.8 cm x 6.3 cm.

4/5. Eight gilt-edged cards, four designs of children in winter or summer scenes, with ribbon initials to verses by J G, two dated 1878 by the sender. These have a resemblance to Marcus Ward cards, but are not marked. 12.3 cm x 8.3 cm.

6. Four embossed cards, each with two children in summer and a verse, one a folder with gilt cover. 8.7 cm x 5.5 cm.

7. Four blue-bordered cards (one birthday), three designs of two children in European costume and setting. 10.1 cm x 6.8 cm.

8. Five cards, children in various activities, including a sailor boy and a boy on a rocking horse, one dated 1878 by the sender. 6.5 cm x 9.8 cm.

9. Five cards, quaint small figures with pudding, goose, turkey or donkey, with flowers and holly and greeting in a scroll. 6.6 cm x 9.5 cm.

10. Five cards, one frosted, four designs each with two children before a poster with seasonal greetings, two dated 1878, 1879 by the senders. 6.3 cm x 9.5 cm.

11. Five cards of one set with pink and blue border. Three have children with holly and mistletoe, one a robin sheltering in a hat, and the fifth a flaming plum pudding with a number of small flags floating in an Arctic sea. 6.4 cm x 9.5 cm.

12. Three cards with brown background, a boy and girl out in the snow, skating or dancing. 6.4 cm x 9.6 cm.

13. Three cards, black figures of two children on a gilt background dancing or playing games. 10.1 cm x 7.2 cm.

14. Eight cards, six with gilt serrated borders showing a contrast of street vendors and well-to-do children, and two with gilt embossed borders and a boot-black or a crossing sweeper. One was dated 1876 by the sender. 7.2 cm x 10.2 cm, 6.7 cm x 9.6 cm.

15. Six cards from two sets, four with gilt borders, two with pink borders, picturing children with animals, and one curious scene of a small knight giving a bouquet to a juvenile nun. 7 cm x 10 cm.

16. Seven similar cards, six with blue-patterned borders and five designs of children in various outdoor activities (one a valentine).  The seventh has a red patterned border around a girl with a cat and kittens.  7 cm x 10 cm, 7.4 cm x 10 cm.

17. Six cards, wide gilt borders, four designs of children, three in summer with flowers, one in winter with holly. 7.7 cm x 10.9 cm.

18. Four cards, blue borders, three designs of boys playing in the street, signed Ludovici. 7 cm x 10.2 cm.

19. Four cards, one with a greeting in French, two designs of boys in Little Lord Fauntleroy style dress, and one of a girl with rabbits.  6.7 cm x 9.6 cm.

20. A set of four gilt-edged cards, marked no. 58, a boy with holly, a boy with a model boat, a girl skating, and a child with a dog, decorated with berried branches, one dated 1880 by the sender. 8 cm x 12.4 cm.

21. Nine miscellaneous smaller cards of children in three styles, four repeating three of the designs in no. 20 above. 6.5 cm x 9 cm up to 7.8 cm x 12 cm.

22. Four cards. Two have gilt borders, one a birthday card with two children and a dove, and a verse by E I T on reverse, the other two children with toys in the nursery. Two have gilt patterned borders with quaint children skating, or paying a visit. 11.6 cm x 7.5 cm, 11.7 cm x 8.3 cm.

23. Six cards (one frosted), five designs of children in winter with robins, framed in holly or evergreens. 7 cm x 9.7 cm.

24. Six cards, three with two children in winter snow, three with two children in summer with verses on reverse. 6 cm x 8.7 cm, 5.6 cm x 9 cm.

25. Six cards, each with a plump rosy cheeked child, four in winter with robins and holly and two in summer with flowers. The backs have a variety of verses signed E H B, M H O, E K W, F E E H. 6.3 cm x 9.5 cm.

26/27. Eleven cards, six designs of a boy or girl with mistletoe, flowers, doll, or letter. Six cards have gilt backgrounds, five black, and one was dated 1879 by the sender.  6.9 cm x 10.8 cm.

28. Seven gilt-edged cards, six designs of a boy or girl, two indoors, four out in the snow, one dated 1883 by the sender. 7.3 cm x 11.3 cm.

29. Four cards, children in Christmas activities, skating, sweeping snow, making the pudding, hanging the mistletoe. 6.7 cm x 10.5 cm.

30. Six miscellaneous cards with children. 5.5 cm x 8.4 up to 7 cm x 10.5 cm.

31. Two embossed cards, small boys as tailor and customer, and another eating his Christmas dinner, one dated 1879 by the sender. 7 cm x 10.8 cm, 11 cm x 6.5 cm.

## VOLUME 151:
## CHILDREN, SMALL CARDS, INCLUDING SOME FRENCH PUBLISHERS & CARDS IN THE FRENCH STYLE

1. Five cards, published by Aubry, Paris, three with children and animals, one with a Christmas tree, and one a child painting. Two were dated 1881 by the senders. Sizes up to 7.3 cm x 11.5 cm.

2. Five cards, published by J Bognard, Paris, four designs of quaint children as street vendors, and one from the same set showing a man with the head of a bird. 6.7 cm x 10.3 cm.

3. Six trade cards with greetings published by Vallet Minot & Co., Paris, with pictures of children in hats on gilt, blue or red background with gilt and floral border. They have Cash's 1882 calendar on the back. 8.8 cm x 11.8 cm.

4. Four cards, signed V M, i.e. Vallet Minot, children singing or at play, with gilt background. 11 cm x 7.6 cm.

5. Five cards, one with pierrots signed F Appel, Paris, two with an undeciphered monogram with children in summer scenes, and two others with pierrots, unsigned. Sizes up to 13.5 cm x 7.5 cm.

6. Five gilt-bordered cards, each with a small boy and girl in peasant costume, doing the laundry, pressing grapes, reading, shooting, and playing by a pool. 8.3 cm x 6 cm, 6 cm x 8.3 cm, 9.7 cm x 7 cm.

7. Seven similar unbordered cards, one repeating a design from no. 6 above. 6.7 cm x 9.2 cm.

8. Seven cards from three sets, two with two children, robin, and holly, and five with children at play. Sizes up to 10.6 cm x 7.2 cm.

9. Three cards, one with a trumpeter and girl in mediaeval dress.  The other two are curious designs, one of small people carrying a fairy in a large flower, the other a juvenile financier and a girl apparently counting the money bags. 10.7 cm x 6.8 cm, 10.2 cm x 6.8 cm.

10. Six cards, three with a girl carrying flowers or a letter, three with a boy as cook, soldier, or musician. There are appropriate verses by J G on reverse. 7.3 cm x 11 cm.

11/12. Eight cards on black backgrounds with gilt borders, six designs of small children with toys or animals, some in fancy costume. The greetings are incorporated into the designs, on shaped panels, boxes, or a silver plate. 7.3 cm x 11 cm.

13. Three similar gilt-bordered cards on grey background, with greetings on a fountain, a scroll, or an open umbrella. 7.3 cm x 11 cm.

14. Six white-bordered cards, small children in costume, at play, fishing, or making music. 11 cm x 7.3 cm.

15. Six similar cards, children in summer scenes with flowers. 11 cm x 7.3 cm.

16/17. Ten cards on black backgrounds, seven designs of one or two children in three styles of gilt-patterned border. One design is a post boy with a letter and parcel, and two of the cards are embossed prints without greetings. 7.4 cm x 11 cm, 5 cm x 7.5 cm.

18. Seven gilt-edged cards in similar style, five street vendors, two children with sweetmeats, one dated 1880 by the sender. 5 cm x 8 cm.

19. Four embossed cards, single children in winter scenes on a brown background. 5.8 cm x 8.7 cm.

20. Seven cards on black backgrounds, five designs in two styles of two children in elaborate dress. 7.4 cm x 10.4 cm, 6.3 cm x 9.5 cm.

21. Six cards on gilt backgrounds, three designs of a small boy with an outsize rabbit, cat, or bird, one dated 1879 by the sender. 10.7 cm x 6.8 cm.

22. Nine cards, five designs of children in period dress printed in blue on gilt. Two are trade cards for F Preston, Fancy Drapery.  9.4 cm x 6.8 cm.

23. Four miscellaneous cards, children in period costume, one on a silver background.  Sizes up to 10.9 cm x 7.8 cm.

24. Four cards, quaint children on a mauve background with greeting in a white panel. 9.8 cm x 6.8 cm.

25. Three cards, two with girls opening a door, one with a boy and girl under the mistletoe, set in shaped vignettes in a gilt border. 7.3 cm x 10.8 cm.

26. Two cards, a girl skipping, and a girl with a plant in a pot, both on gilt background.  6.6 cm x 10.8 cm.

27. Five cards (two trimmed), four designs of small cooks at work in a castle kitchen. 11.7 cm x 8 cm.

28. Two gilt-edged cards, a country house park with a boy and a deer, and a boy pushing a handcart. 112. cm x 7.5 cm.

29. Six cards from three sets, five designs. Two have children with their Christmas dinner, one has little maids doing the laundry, and two have children with

ducks or pheasants.
Sizes up to 10.5 cm x 7.1 cm.

30. Eight miscellaneous cards, children in various pursuits, with dogs or birds, making the pudding, or out-of-doors. Two cards have boys in Georgian dress. Sizes up to 7 cm x 10.3 cm.

31. Three cards, girls seated on a holly branch or flower in a circular gilt vignette. 7.5 cm x 10.6 cm.

32. Four miscellaneous cards on gilt backgrounds with children, one Red Riding Hood. Sizes up to 8.3 cm x 12 cm.

33. Five cards with gilt-patterned borders and attached prints of pierrots, a jockey, or children out-of-doors. 13 cm x 9.3 cm, 9.3 cm x 13 cm.

34. Five cards, each a boy messenger with flowers, the two larger having verses on the back. 7.3 cm x 10.2 cm, 8.6 cm x 11.8 cm.

35. Three cards with no greeting, children in the snow with robin and holly. 7.5 cm x 11.5 cm.

## VOLUME 152:
## CHILDREN IN CHRISTMAS & WINTER SCENES, 1880-1885

**These cards are unmarked except for one published by Davidson Bros, no. 32, and no artists are positively identified. A number of cards have narrative verses. They show an interesting variety of party and outdoor clothes of the period, contrasting with those of the less well-endowed who occasionally appear.**

1.Four cards, three designs of children with a Christmas tree or out in the snow with robins, in circular vignettes with flower and holly borders. They have verses by E I T on reverse, and one was dated 1880 by the sender. 7.8 cm x 12 cm.

2. Two cards with holly borders, one a family scene with a mistletoe kiss, the other boys unpacking a Christmas hamper. 14 cm x 10.5 cm.

3. Three cards, each with a small girl in party dress in a black border with holly and flowers. 8 cm x 12.3 cm.

4. Three cards with coloured patterned borders, children reading or playing, one dated 1879 by the sender. 13.2 cm x 10.2 cm.

5. Three cards, groups of children playing, and carrying a decorative Christmas greeting. 14.2 cm x 7 cm.

6. Four cards, children dreaming of Christmas presents, one a poor child

asleep on a doorstep. There are verses beneath, with a signature Da, which might refer to verse, picture or publisher, but is so far untraced. 11.9 cm x 7.7 cm.

7. Three cards, little girls in bed playing with dolls, with verses by E Ridley on reverse. 14.7 cm x 10.3 cm.

8. Two cards, small girls in white nightgowns with a sprig of holly or mistletoe, one with a verse by Lewis Novra. 10.2 cm x 13 cm.

9. Four cards, children in bed dreaming of fairies bringing presents, three with verses by Ernest Sigourney on reverse. 8.9 cm x 15.3 cm, 12 cm x 8.5 cm.

10. Two cards, one a girl awakening to see her Christmas presents, with a poem on reverse, the other with two girls in bed looking at the snow falling outside. 6.8 cm x 11.3 cm, 15.3 cm x 10.7 cm.

11. Two cards, Father Christmas giving a doll's house to a girl, and a rocking horse to a boy. 10.2 cm x 13 cm.

12. Three cards, two with children and a Christmas tree and toys, the other an old man with a fir tree, in circular vignettes set in a winter scene. 11 cm x 10.8 cm.

13. Five cards, brown borders, children in seasonal activities with a Christmas tree and holly, and feeding birds, one dated 1881 by the sender. 8.5 cm x 12.3 cm.

14. Four cards, scenes of family life at Christmas. 6.5 cm x 10.7 cm.

15. Two cards, party time, a girl and boy under the mistletoe, and a boy asking a girl to dance, with a narrative verse on the back by E Ridley. 9.8 cm x 13.9 cm, 13.8 cm x 10.6 cm.

16. Two cards. One has children's faces in a bunch of mistletoe and a verse by Shirley Wynne on reverse. The other shows two children pulling a cracker, with a monogram J M R, perhaps J McL. Ralston. 12.3 cm x 16.7 cm, 11 cm x 14.7 cm.

17. Two cards, children playing at soldiers, a boy blowing a horn, one dated 1881 by the sender. 8.5 cm x 12.5 cm.

18/19. Four large cards, a girl in a party dress in the doorway, another in a fur trimmed coat with a muff, a third out in the snow with a cat and a basket of holly, and a boy carrying mistletoe and a Christmas tree. 11.1 cm x 17 cm.

20. Three cards, each showing the same two little girls, reading, looking out at the snow and on a doorstep paying a visit. Each has a narrative verse on the back. 8.5 cm x 11.1 cm, 11.1 cm x 8.5 cm.

21. Two cards, a boy in Fauntleroy costume, a girl in a party dress, each with a letter, and narrative verses by Shirley Wynne on reverse. 8.3 cm x 11.4 cm.

22. Four gilt-edged cards, each with a seated girl, two with dolls in a panelled room, one on a four-poster bed trying on jewels, the fourth in school uniform with a slate. 9 cm x 12.5 cm.

23. One card, two girls looking at the Evening Star, with a verse by Johnston Beall on reverse. 11 cm x 15.2 cm.

24. Two gilt-edged cards, a boy in snow, a girl with a present, each with a verse by F E E H on reverse. 12.5 cm x 15.8 cm.

25. Two cards, a girl in Georgian dress in church, dated 1883 by the sender, and a boy in Stuart costume with a dish of fruit, framed in a decorative gilt and coloured border. 11.5 cm x 15.5 cm, 9.5 cm x 14.5 cm.

26. Three cards, two designs, one a girl skating, the other a girl in a velvet dress holding up an elaborate jelly in Mrs Beeton style. There are three different verses on the backs of the cards. 9.2 cm x 15 cm.

27. Three gilt-edged cards, children in snow, a boy with a letter, dated 1882, a girl with early snowdrops, and a larger card with a girl snowballing. 8.4 cm x 14.9 cm,10.2 cm x 15.2 cm.

28. Two cards, red, green and gilt borders, children playing in snow. 13.7 cm x 8.8 cm.

29. Three miscellaneous cards, girls in snow, one with a verse by S S Wigley. Sizes up to 9 cm x 12.7 cm.

30. Six cards, three designs in three styles with three children, in snow with the Christmas goose, looking at cards in a shop window, and sitting on a bench. Sizes up to 13.6 cm x 8.7 cm.

31. Two cards, a family with children walking in the snow and three boys snowballing an old lady. 11.5 cm x 7.5 cm.

32. Three cards, each with a boy or girl in snow, one marked Davidson Bros. 7.7 cm x 11.8 cm, 7.7 cm x 11.5 cm.

33. Four cards, three designs of warmly clad girls skating or gathering holly. 8.5 cm x 12 cm.

34. Four cards, children out of doors. Two are from the same set, one a summer scene with donkeys, the other a snowball fight. The third has children by a farm gate, the fourth has a boy carrying a large pie, dated 1882 by the sender. Sizes up to 14.3 cm x 10.7 cm.

35. Three cards with groups of children, tobogganing on a hillside, or coming home from school. 12 cm x 8 cm up to 13 cm x 9.5 cm.

36. Three miscellaneous cards, Red Riding Hood, a girl and a cat under an umbrella, a girl in church. Sizes up to 8.5 cm x 12 cm.

37. Four miscellaneous cards, three with children in snow. The fourth has a family party skating with a wind sail, which has a Canadian rather than a British appearance. Sizes up to 15.3 cm x 11 cm.

38. Two cards, one with three children opening a hamper, the other with two little girls in frilled bonnets in snow with churchgoers in a circular vignette. 10.1 cm x 15.6 cm, 11 cm x 15.6 cm.

## VOLUME 153: CHILDREN IN SUMMER SCENES, 1880-1885

**No publishers are positively identified here, and four cards only are signed by the artist. Many of the cards have narrative verses which elucidate the connection between the unseasonal picture and the Christmas greeting.**

1. Six gilt-edged cards, four with a boy or girl at play and verses on reverse, two with a boy playing a trumpet or carrying a basket of grapes. 7.3 cm x 11.1 cm, 6.5 cm x 11 cm.

2. Two cards, children by a pool, or with a cat. 12.8 cm x 8.3 cm.

3. Four cards, three designs of a single child in a country scene, one with a verse by M H N. 8.5 cm x 11.5 cm.

4. Four cards, summer scenes with children on the beach or by a river. 11.5 cm x 8.5 cm.

5. One card, a girl in white fichu picking grapes, dated 1882 by the sender. 9.8 cm x 13 cm

6. One card, a girl in a hat and a white fichu carrying a basket of primroses, with a verse by Ouseley on reverse. 10.1 cm x 14 cm.

7. Two cards, one three children with a toy boat, the other a girl with a basket of speckled eggs. 9 cm x 12 cm, 10.7 cm x 15 cm.

8. Three cards, one with a girl in a flower-filled meadow with a sunshade, the two others with small girls in mob caps, one with a doll, the other with cats. All have verses on reverse. 8.9 cm x 11.8 cm, 8.4 cm x 12.5 cm.

9. One card, a rosy-cheeked girl in a hat with roses, in a border of colourful leaves. 11.2 cm x 11.2 cm.

10. One card, a girl fishing from stepping stones in a river, with a narrative poem on reverse. 9.5 cm x 14.1 cm.

11. Two cards, one a girl and boy with flowers and a watering can, the other a child and its elder sister playing in a meadow. 10 cm x 13.4 cm., 13.9 cm x 11 cm.

12. Three miscellaneous gilt-bordered cards, three children on a hillside with a verse by A L C, two children by a cottage and a greeting with illuminated initial, and a girl picking cherries, with a verse by M E Ropes on reverse. 12.7 cm x 9.7 cm to 9.3 cm x 18 cm.

13. Two cards, brown borders, each with a boy and girl in a garden, with verses by L N on reverse. 9 cm x 13.5 cm.

14. Two gilt-bordered birthday cards, each with a small girl in a white dress with red or blue sash, one smelling roses, the other watching goldfish. 15 cm x 10.7 cm.

15. Four cards, three designs, a girl and a duck, a boy and a frog, and a boy in sailor suit, all with verses and the signature Da. 9.5 cm x 13.6 cm.

16. Four cards, three designs, a girl skipping, swinging, or playing with a ball, signed G S, possibly George Sadler. 7.9 cm x 13 cm.

17. Three cards, a girl with a dog, a boy and a deer, and a boy on a gate. 10.7 cm x 7.6 cm.

18. Three miscellaneous cards, children roller-skating with a verse by L N on reverse, two little girls swinging with a verse by C D on reverse, and three girls playing croquet. Sizes up to 13 cm x 9.6 cm.

19. Three embossed birthday cards, a girl swinging, another carrying a basket of flowers, and a daughter giving a bouquet to her mother. 8.2 cm x 11.5 cm, 7.2 cm x 11 cm.

20. Two cards, two children with a deer, and a girl by a lake waving to a yacht. 7.5 cm x 10.7 cm, 9.7 cm x 13.2 cm.

21. Two cards, three children in the sunset, one with a doll, and three boys fishing. 12.5 cm x 11 cm, 13.5 cm x 10.7 cm.

22. Three cards, two designs of children's games, Kiss-in-the-Ring and Blind Man's Buff. One card has a poem on the back. 15.5 cm x 11.8 cm.

23. One card, marked W & Co, two children walking by a lake with a basket of

apples, perhaps from the tree in the picture. 10.7 cm x 15 cm.

24/25. Seven cards, four designs in two styles of children at play. The larger gilt-edged cards have verses on the back by F Ernest Power. 10.2 cm x 13.5 cm, 7.5 cm x 10.9 cm.

26. One large card, three children playing with a swing and hoops. 12.7 cm x 17 cm.

27. Two cards, children on a seesaw, with a poem by C D on the reverse, and a boy and girl with two cats. 9 cm x 15.8 cm, 9.5 cm x 13.6 cm.

28. Three cards in parallelogram shape, two designs of barefoot small children fishing or watching birds and water-lilies. One card has a silver background and was dated 1883 by the sender. 13 cm x 9 cm.

29. Four cards, a girl or boy in a circular or rectangular vignette set in a summer scene with farm and lake. The seasonal greetings are on the backs. 18 cm x 7.8 cm.

30. Four cards (one birthday), each with a girl and boy, in party dress in two cards and peasant style costume in the other two. 8.4 cm x 12.7 cm.

31. Six miscellaneous cards, two with little girls and dolls, the others children in country scenes. 10 cm x 7.9 cm up to 13 cm x 9.4 cm

32. Three cards, two children at a window. One card is a trade card, for Charles Baker, Boy's Clothing, and it is interesting to see that overcoats are on sale from 3/11- 19/11 i.e. 20 pence to £1. Early 1880's. 12.5 cm x 7.5 cm.

33. Five cards, four designs with groups of children, three including a boy in a top hat and Eton suit. The fifth larger card is a repeat of one design. 8.6 cm x 6 cm, 13 cm x 8 cm.

34. Two cards, a barelegged small boy in a woodland setting, with a toy lamb or painting an album, one dated 1880 by the sender. 10.5 cm x 15.8 cm.

## VOLUME 154: CHILDREN AT THE SEASIDE, BOYS, SILHOUETTES, AND MONOCHROME DESIGNS

**Seaside scenes were also used as Christmas greeting, many with narrative verses, and those in numbers 1-13 were published about 1885-90, by unidentified firms.**

1. One card, a small boy sitting on a rock, with sea and seagulls behind. 11 cm x 15.3 cm.

2. Four cards, three designs of children playing on the beach with a verse on the

front and a narrative poem by Charles J Rowe on the back. 13.2 cm x 7.9 cm.

3. Two cards, a boy and a girl in blue jersey and red cap on a rocky beach. 9.7 cm x 13.1 cm.

4. Four cards with brown border, each with a girl playing on the beach, all wearing hats. 9 cm x 14.7 cm, 8 cm x 13.2 cm.

5. Four gilt-bordered cards, three designs in two sizes, elegantly dressed girls sitting by a breakwater. 12.8 cm x 8.4 cm, 10.9 cm x 7.7 cm.

6. Three miscellaneous cards, one marked W C S & C L G, another with a verse by C D on reverse, all three showing children playing by the sea. Sizes up to 12.8 cm x 9.6 cm.

7. Four cards, three designs, two gilt-edged, two with yellow border, one dated 1886 by the sender, all showing children building sand castles. 10.7 cm x 7 cm, 12 cm x 8.3 cm.

8. Five miscellaneous cards, two with the same design of children making sandpies in different format, the other three similar designs in different sizes with a girl in a vignette set in a seascape. 6.3 cm x 8.6 cm up to 10.4 cm x 14 cm.

9. Two cards, a mother and children on the beach, one dated 1888 by the sender. 12.8 cm x 9.9 cm.

10. Four cards, two from the same set with a fisher girl or boy, one dated 1890 by the sender, one a girl with a creel of fish with boats in the background, the fourth a girl with a basket of shrimps. Sizes up to 9.7 cm x 12.8 cm.

11. Three cards, two in two sizes with the same scene of children in a boat, one with a net, the other children in a sandcastle with a verse by H M B. 12.5 cm x 9.9 cm, 14.8 cm x 10.9 cm.

12. Four cards from two sets, children in the sea or on the beach, c1890. 10.9 cm x 7.9 cm, 15 cm x 8.9 cm.

13. One card, a fisher girl by a boat, with a verse by H M Burnside. 11.8 cm x 16.2 cm.

*Numbers 14-27 have cards probably from sets featuring boys, published in the 1880's.*

14. One card, a boy fishing while eating, with a narrative verse "A good bite" by L N on reverse. 11.8 cm x 14.2 cm.

15. One card, the head of a fisher boy on a background of thistles and a sea scene, with a verse by F M on reverse. 16.9 cm x 12 cm.

16. One card, a boy playing a pipe sitting on a bed with a patchwork cover, and an interesting narrative poem by C D on reverse. 14 cm x 11.1 cm.

17. Two cards, one design of a boy in a blue cap and suit in an oval vignette with different borders and verses. 11.3 cm x 16.5 cm.

18. Three miscellaneous cards, two a boy in a sailor suit, the third a youthful sailor on board ship, one dated 1884 by the sender. Sizes approximately 9 cm x 11.3 cm.

19. Four cards, three designs of boys skating, with appropriate verses by S S Wigley on reverse. 7 cm x 10.4 cm.

20. Three cards, one a boy feeding robins, and two boy minstrels in oval vignettes with holly or ivy. 7.3 cm x 10.7 cm, 6.5 cm x 10.2 cm.

21. One card, a picture frame with two boys in a snowball fight. 11.3 cm x 14.5 cm.

22. Two cards, a small boy in girlish dress with a large dog, and a boy in a velvet suit carrying a tray of letters. 11 cm x 15.9 cm, 9.8 cm x 14 cm.

23. Three miscellaneous cards, two with boys skating, the third a boy writing "Merry Christmas" on a wall. 8.7 cm x 13 cm up to 10.1 cm x 15.4 cm.

24. Two cards, one a boy in an elegant red suit feeding robins, with verse by Eden Hooper on reverse, the other a boy sailing a toy boat. 8.2 cm x 11.3 cm.

25. Five cards from two sets, all with boys in sailor suits by the sea, late 1880's. 7.1 cm x 10.3 cm, 7.6 cm x 11.5 cm.

26. Four miscellaneous cards, boys with dogs or a horse. One card with a boy writing on the wall has a story on the back. Sizes up to 10 cm x 13.5 cm.

27. Four miscellaneous cards, showing boys in a variety of costumes. Sizes up to 7.2 cm x 11.5 cm.

*The following cards are silhouettes or monochrome designs, dated 1880-90. Only one publisher is known for no. 28.*

28. Two cards, published by W A Mansell, black silhouettes of children playing. 8.2 cm x 10.6 cm, 10.2 cm x 7.8 cm.

29. Three cards, two designs with silhouettes on different coloured backgrounds, one children making free with the Christmas fare, the other a girl on a horse. Two are dated 1880, 1881. 12.4 cm x 8.2 cm.

30. Three cards, silhouettes of children playing or reading, in a rectangular

vignette set in a border of leaves and berries. One was dated 1882 by the sender. 12 cm x 9.7 cm.

31. Two cards printed in sepia, one a small girl sitting in a meadow, signed J W, the other four children with a Christmas verse below. 9 cm x 12 cm, 15.3 cm x 11.7 cm.

32. Three cards, printed in sepia, a girl or a boy in 18th century dress. 7.5 cm x 12 cm.

33. Six cards printed in sepia, from two sets, small children in summer and winter activities, dressed in Kate Greenaway style. 9.8 cm x 7.4 cm, 7.6 cm x 10.5 cm.

34. Two cards printed in sepia, girls in summer scenes with flowers. 9 cm x 12 cm, 13.7 cm x 9.7 cm.

35. Four miscellaneous cards, three printed in blue, black, or grey, small people in costume. The fourth is embossed and has two small girls sitting by a tree. Sizes up to 9.2 cm x 9.1 cm.

36. Two cards on thick paper, unprepossessing small girls, one swinging, one with a sun shade. They are signed with a monogram, possibly J V F C. c1890. 10.4 cm x 12.8 cm.

37. One card on thick board, two smiling girls head and shoulders, one in a lace bonnet and collar, signed H J. 15.6 cm x 12.5 cm.

38. Two cards on thick board, each a girl head and shoulders, one signed A E Hart. 9.5 cm x 9.5 cm, 10.7 cm x 10.7 cm.

## VOLUME 155:
## CHILDREN WITH ANIMALS & BIRDS, KATE GREENAWAY STYLE, QUAINT CHILDREN

*Numbers 1-21 have children with animals and birds, published from 1880-1885 with one or two exceptions as noted.*

1. An interesting card showing a small child with a cat. The railings behind and the clothes are adorned with coloured frosting. 9 cm x 12 cm.

2. Three embossed gilt-edged cards, each a small boy with a turkey, ducks, geese, or chickens, one dated 1880 by the sender. 12.5 cm x 10.3 cm.

3/4. Four large cards, two designs of a girl with dogs, their kennels decorated with holly or mistletoe. They have four different greetings and four narrative poems on reverse. 16.1 cm x 14.2 cm.

5. Three cards, two designs of a small girl at table with the meal shared by a dog, and unsigned poems on the reverse. 12 cm x 16 cm.

6. A triptych folding card using one of the above designs, with verses and illuminated designs on wings and cover, perhaps published by S J Saunders or S Hildesheimer. 12 cm x 16 cm closed.

7. Three gilt-bordered cards, small children with dog, cat, or toys. 14 cm x 10.2 cm.

8. Two cards with patterned gilt borders, one a little girl with a cat and a doll, the other in a triptych folder showing a boy with a goat.
10.6 cm x 13.4 cm., 15.3 cm x 11 cm.

9/10. Five cards (three birthday), three designs of a boy or youth with a dog. Each has a different apt Shakespeare quotation on the front and a narrative verse on the back. 15.5 cm x 11.5 cm.

11. Four embossed cards, three designs of a girl or boy carrying a bouquet with a large dog or a pony. 9.2 cm x 15 cm.

12. Two embossed cards, a boy in Highland dress with a crossbow and an animal which might be a dog or a deer, and a birthday card with a girl and birds and a verse by T E M.
15 cm x 9.2 cm, 13 cm x 10.5 cm.

13. Three cards, two with little girls and chickens, the third a girl and a dog, both carrying baskets in a snowstorm.
10.3 cm x 14 cm.

14. Two cards (one birthday), each with two children and a dog. 9.2 cm x 10.2 cm.

15. Five cards with coloured borders, three with children and parrots, and two with a lady and a sheepdog, all from the same set. One was dated 1880 by the sender.
11.7 cm x 7.5 cm.

16. Two cards, a girl feeding chickens and a girl feeding a turkey, the latter with a verse by M S Mac Ritchie on reverse.
10.5 cm x 15.4 cm, 9 cm x 13 cm.

17/18. Nine miscellaneous cards, single children with dogs, cats, pigeons, or a large beetle, later 1880s.
6.8 cm x 10.8 cm up to 13.2 cm x 9.5 cm.

19. Three cards, including two larger embossed scenes of a girl with a calf and a boy with goats, each with a verse by Jonathan Beall. The third card is a repeat of the boy and goat with a verse by M E R. Later 1880's.
15.6 cm x 11 cm, 11.2 cm x 7.8 cm.

20. Four cards, three designs of a girl or boy playing with a dog indoors, c1890.
9.5 cm x 13.5 cm.

21. A card showing a barefoot boy feeding rabbits, with a descriptive verse by C D on reverse. 10.3 cm x 15 cm.

*Numbers 22-29 show children dressed in Kate Greenaway style by unknown artists, probably published about 1885.*

22. Five cards, four designs from a set of six of nursery rhymes and poems without greetings, with a smaller card repeating one of those. These have often been taken as Kate Greenaway products, but two are signed A R.
8.5 cm x 12.5 cm, 7.5 cm x 10.8 cm.

23. Three valentine cards, a youthful couple in affectionate confabulation.
10.5 cm x 7.9 cm.

24. Seven cards, illustrating six nursery rhymes printed on the reverse.
6.9 cm x 10.3 cm.

25. Four cards, three with children on ponies or donkey, and one a girl with a deer.11.6 cm x 8.7 cm.

26. Two cards, each with an older girl and a child in summer scenes.
12.2 cm x 12.6 cm.

27. Four cards from two sets, two with girls in country scenes, two with girl and boy and a large spray of flowers.
9.8 cm x 7.1 cm, 12.5 cm x 8.6 cm.

28. Four cards, children picking flowers, playing croquet, rowing in a tub, and bringing home the Christmas tree.
Sizes up to 12.1 cm x 8 cm.

29. Four cards, two with a small girl with a doll or getting water from a well, and two with small boys, one with a kite, one with a hoop, in curious summer scenes with a fan or a large shell.
9 cm x 13 cm, 12.6 cm x 9.2 cm.

*The following cards show children best described as quaint.*

30. Four cards, children in the snow, three with little girls wearing large bonnets, one dated 1881 by the sender. 8.1 cm x 12.2 cm.

31. Five cards (one trimmed), four designs of youthful figures in various costumes. Sizes up to 9 cm x 11.6 cm.

32. Three cards, one a small boy in a smock carrying a lily and a letter, the other two girls with fantastic beribboned hats out in the snow, with verses by Charles J Rowe on reverse.
8.7 cm x 13.3 cm, 8.3 cm x 13 cm.

33. Three miscellaneous cards, two with a girl and boy perched on a flowering branch, the third two small people followed by a cat.
12 cm x 8.5 cm up to 16 cm x 13 cm.

34/35. Seven miscellaneous cards, including two boys on a fan, and a child in an ulster with two cats dated 1891.
7.5 cm x 11.5 cm up to 14 cm x 7.8 cm.

# VOLUME 156: CHILDREN WITH FLOWERS & FOLIAGE

**These cards have floral decoration as an integral part of the design, as well as the traditional seasonal holly, mistletoe, and ivy. An occasional mother or sister appears with the children. The publishers are unknown except for cards in numbers 23 and 36, included here for comparison. They were issued from about 1877 to the early 1880's.**

1. Four cards, three designs of a girl in an oval vignette with flowers or holly on a gilt background. 9.9 cm x 6.6 cm.

2. Four cards, three with children in a rectangular vignette with holly or flowers on a gilt border, one dated 1877 by the sender, and one with a pink border and a baby in a white dress with roses.
6.7 cm x 10.6 cm, 10.6 cm x 6.7 cm, 5.5 cm x 8.6 cm.

3. Seven cards from two sets. Four have three designs of a child's head in an elaborate bordered vignette with greeting in a scroll bordered by spring flowers and roses; three have a patterned border and two children in a wreath of flowers and leaves, one with verses by E E R, one dated 1878 by the sender.
10.5 cm x 6.3 cm, 11.5 cm x 6.8 cm.

4. Six gilt-edged cards (two birthday), four designs of a child in a decorative oval frame with a greeting in a panel bordered by flowers. 10.7 cm x 7 cm.

5. Three cards, heads of mediaeval people at Gothic style windows framed in ivy, two with verses by Fannie Rochat (sometimes signed Fanny).
9.5 cm x 6.5 cm.

**157.16**

6. Four cards, three with a girl or boy in a doorway with flower garlands above or below, one with two children under a floral wreath. Sizes up to 7.5 cm x 11.2 cm.

7. Seven cards. Three have small boys carrying bouquets, with a verse below, and four are prints from a similar set. 6.5 cm x 10.5 cm, 5 cm x 8 cm.

8. Six gilt-edged cards, four designs of small folk in fancy costume carrying bouquets. 6.5 cm x 10.5 cm.

9. Six cards, two with patterned coloured borders and boy or girl holding bouquet, one a boy with a very large bouquet, and three with serrated edges, two of boys carrying a box with a posy and one a girl with music. Sizes up to 6.8 cm x 10 cm.

10/11. Seven gilt-edged cards, four designs of pretty maidens with flowers, and verses by F L, one dated 1878 by the sender. One card is on a patterned illuminated mount. 7.7 cm x 14.1 cm, 10.7 cm x 17 cm.

12. Three cards, children picking cherries, with flowers, robins, and tits, and at a window framed in ivy looking at pigeons, all with descriptive verses in panels. 13.3 cm x 10.2 cm.

13. Three cards by the same artist as in no. 12. Two are folders with floralilluminated covers, one a valentine with children by a cottage door, the other two children by a tree with a Christmas greeting verse; the third is a small card with two children and a dog. 8.3 cm x 12.7 cm, 11 cm x 7.1 cm (closed), 11 cm x 7.3 cm.

14. Three cards, girls in frilled dresses, standing by large scrolls with verses by Hood or H Constable, wreathed in flowers. 9.5 cm x 12.7 cm.

15. Three cards (one birthday), two designs of a girl and boy with roses or primroses. 9.1 cm x 13 cm.

16. Two birthday cards, a girl and boy in a semi-circular vignette, with an illuminated initial to the greeting verse by Eden Hooper and flowers at the side. 9.5 cm x 15.5 cm.

17. Two cards, a small boy holding up a large basket of flowers dated 1882 by the sender, and a boy's head in a circular vignette with a Christmas message in a panel framed in spring flowers. 9.9 cm x 14.6 cm, 9.3 cm x 13 cm.

18. Three cards, two with two children in a leafy bower and verses by M E Ropes on reverse, the third a girl in a wreath of flowers with a verse on a scroll below. 8.5 cm x 15.6 cm, 8.5 cm x 16 cm.

19. Two cards, each with a boy and a girl in an oval vignette with flowers and

leaves, one in a summer scene, the other with a rocking horse in the nursery. 7 cm x 13.3 cm.

20. Two gilt-edged cards, with flower garlands, one with two girls, the other with one girl and a verse by L M L. 9 cm x 13.7 cm.

21. Two cards, a winter scene with a girl gathering firewood in a garland of holly and Christmas roses, and a summer scene with a girl picking flowers in a garland of spring blossoms. 13 cm x 9.5 cm.

22. Two cards, blue and gilt patterned borders, a boy or girl in an oval vignette adorned with flower bouquets, dated 1880, 1883 by the senders. 15.5 cm x 9.6 cm.

23. Four cards published by S J Saunders, a child's head in a diamond vignette with a spray of spring flowers, and a seasonal verse, set in a gilt-patterned border. 15 cm x 9.4 cm.

24. Two cards, a child with swallows and poppies, and two children with a floral spray and a verse by E I T in a scroll. 11 cm x 15.3 cm, 10 cm x 16.7 cm.

25. Three gilt-edged cards, each with a girl's head set in a bunch of flowers. 11.2 cm x 7.5 cm.

26. Four cards (one birthday), two designs of a girl with birds and a boy with a bee set in a wreath of flowers and grasses. 17.3 cm x 9 cm.

27. Two embossed cards, a girl and a Christmas verse in a circlet of grasses and flowers, and a boy at a window with greeting framed in foliage. 8.2 cm x 11.5 cm, 11.5 cm x 7.4 cm.

28. Two gilt-bordered embossed cards, a boy's head encircled by flowers and leaves, one with a verse by L M L. 7.7 cm x 14.1 cm.

29. Five cards from two sets. Two have the same design of a girl holding a basket of flowers on her head, one with a lace border. Three have groups of children with wreaths and bouquets, and verses on reverse. 7.3 cm x 11.2 cm, 8 cm x 11.8 cm.

30. Four embossed cards on dark grey backgrounds. Two show a girl and boy in party dress with roses or a bouquet. Two repeat two of the designs in no. 29 with the same verses on the back. 8.6 cm x 12.5 cm, 8 cm x 11.8 cm.

31. Two cards, one design of a boy's head in a circular vignette, set in a paper nailed to a piece of wood drawn in trompe l'oeil style. 10.2 cm x 14 cm.

32. Three cards, two designs of a mother and baby, and a lady in a frilled cap, in

rectangular vignettes set in spring or winter scenes with celandines or Christmas roses.10.2 cm x 13.2 cm.

33. Four cards, three of children holding flowers at windows framed in leaves. The fourth card has a gilt border with a girl writing a letter, and a verse by Fanny Rochat on the back. (This name sometimes appears as Fannie). 8.8 cm x 12 cm, 7 cm x 10.4 cm.

34. A large card, a small boy asleep, with pigeons and a large spray of periwinkle and auricula. 18.2 cm x 12.6 cm.

35. Three cards, girl's heads in bonnets with roses or almond blossom. Two of the cards in different sizes have the same design reversed, and the same verse by Lewis Novra on the back. 8 cm x 10.3 cm up to 9.3 cm x 13.7 cm.

36. Four miscellaneous embossed cards, children with bouquets or under flowering trees. One with a child carrying an outsize bouquet was published by Falck and is in the Jonathan King stock book of 1880 at the John Johnson Collection. Sizes up to 8 cm x 12.2 cm.

37. Five miscellaneous cards, children with bouquets or wreaths. 6.5 cm x 9.5 cm up to 8.9 cm x 12.1 cm.

## VOLUME 157: CHILDREN WITH FLOWERS & FOLIAGE, (Continued)

**No publishers or artists are known. These cards were issued from about 1884 to the early 1890's.**

1. Three cards, girls holding daisies, lilies, or roses, each flower repeated in the border design. 7.3 cm x 11 cm.

2. Three cards, one embossed, with a baby in a cradle wreathed in flowers, the other two a baby in a lacy folder in a bunch of mixed flowers. 12.5 cm x 9.5 cm, 12 cm x 8.4 cm.

3. Three cards, two with a small girl and large lilies or sunflowers and a verse by C D on reverse, the third a small boy and girl beneath giant sunflowers. 9 cm x 14.8 cm, 7 cm x 13.5 cm.

4. Five embossed cards from two sets. Two have a boy on a stile and a girl by a gate with flowers and foilage. Three have babies sitting on a hillside, holding flowers or leaves. 8 cm x 12.5 cm, 7 cm x 11.6 cm.

5. Two birthday cards, small girls sitting on grass with a large spray of hawthorn or violets, dated 1884 by the sender. 10 cm x 10.3 cm.

6. Four small cards, small folk making music, one on flower bells, the other three framed in holly. 4.8 cm x 7.5 cm.

161

7. Four cards, small girls, three with flowers or berries, one with holly, perhaps meant for spring, summer, autumn, winter. 6.2 cm x 9.7 cm.

8. Seven cards with black backgrounds, four designs of small children with large flowers, one on a gilt-patterned mount. 5 cm x 7.4 cm, 7 cm x 9.8 cm.

9. Four cards from two sets. Two have a girl amongst cornfield or summer flowers, and two have a boy and girl amongst summer flowers each with the same verse by Lewis Novra. 8.2 cm x 12.1 cm, 8.7 cm x 13 cm.

10. Four cards, three designs of little girls with fan, cat, or pigeons. Two identical cards show difference in colour printing. 8.1 cm x 11.7 cm.

11. Four cards, two with a girl and boy perched on a rose or a poppy, one with Red Riding Hood in a vignette bordered by narcissi and leaves, the fourth with two children and flowers by a scroll with greeting. Sizes up to 8.5 cm x 12 cm.

12. Five cards, four birthday one New Year, four designs of a girl's head and shoulders with wreath, garland, or grasses. 9.4 cm x 12.5 cm.

13. One card, a child looking through a stone peephole, with a verse by C D and a border of forget-me-nots. 11.5 cm x 15.3 cm.

14. Two similar, with small boys, and trails of ivy or creeper around. 9.5 cm x 14.4 cm.

15. Three cards, a boy or girl in an oval vignette wreathed in flowers. 8.3 cm x 12.7 cm.

16. Three cards, two designs of a baby in a rectangular vignette in a border of flowers with a butterfly or blue tits. 9.5 cm x 14.6 cm.

17. Three cards, a girl with lilies and a basket of flowers, another with roses, and "Goldilocks" in a floral necklet with verse on reverse by Shirley Wynne. 10 cm x 13.8 cm, 10.4 cm x 14.3 cm, 11.6 cm x 13.5 cm.

18. A large card, the head of a girl, with a border of daisies, grasses and ivy, and a rose design on reverse. 14 cm x 19.5 cm.

19. Four miscellaneous cards, girls in frilled dresses in rectangular vignettes set in decorative flower borders. Sizes up to 9.7 cm x 14 cm.

20. Two cards, a girl in a party dress holding a bouquet and a banner with greeting, with a verse by Astley H Baldwin on reverse, and another head and shoulders in a floral summer scene. 8.5 cm x 12.8 cm, 15 cm x 15 cm.

21. Three cards, each with a girl in a frilled bonnet and collar in a diamond vignette with flowers in each corner. 11.2 cm x 11 cm.

22. Four miscellaneous cards, three a girl, one a boy, in vignettes in floral or leafy borders, one with a verse by F R P, another with a verse on reverse by A C. Sizes up to 11 cm x 13.8 cm.

23. Six miscellaneous cards, various children in floral settings. Sizes up to 8.5 cm x 12 cm.

24. Two cards, each the head of a girl in a garland of flowers. 11.2 cm x 15.3 cm, 11.5 cm x 16 cm.

25. Another similar, with a young lady in a blue dress. 8.7 cm x 13.5 cm.

26. One card, a small girl in a frilled dress and hat with a feather, with a Christmas verse and decorative foliage. 8.3 cm x 15 cm.

27. One card, a girl with a bird, set in a wreath of wild roses. 11.1 cm x 15 cm.

28/29. Four cards (one birthday), three designs of girl and boy in Stuart costume or party dress, standing on a spray of cherry blossom, roses, or orange blossom. 11.8 cm x 15.9 cm.

30. One card, two small girls in a meadow with a decorative blue and silver flower spray around them. 14.1 cm x 11 cm.

31. One card, a girl in a circular vignette framed in snowdrops and willow catkins. 9.8 cm x 14.4 cm.

32. A large card, a girl and boy playing cats' cradle in a rectangular vignette framed in pansies and grasses. 13.5 cm x 19 cm.

33. Four cards from two sets. Two show a boy or girl in Stuart costume, in a floral border. The others have a boy with roses or a girl with forget-me-nots in typical 1890's costume, in a brown and white border in Art Nouveau style. 8.4 cm x 13.2 cm, 8.7 cm x 13.8 cm.

34. Three cards, one a girl with a ball in a border embossed with a tree design. Two have the same design of a girl with a garland, with a gilt embossed rose design in two different borders. 1890's. 9.8 cm x 14.4 cm, 9.8 cm x 14.1 cm.

35. A large card, a lady with hen and chickens and a large superimposed embossed rose. 14.1 cm x 19 cm.

36. Three cards, each showing the head of a girl set in a crescent moon decorated with white spring flowers, one dated 1891 by the sender. 8.8 cm x 8.8 cm.

37. Three cards, each with a child in a hanging basket of ferns, with a verse of greeting. Late 1880's. 9.1 cm x 12.6 cm, 7.5 cm x 11.5 cm.

## VOLUME 158: CHILDREN, BORDERED CARDS IN SMALLER SIZES

**These cards show children in all seasons and in many activities, a few from the early 1880's but many published later. Their costumes provide interesting sidelights on fashions for Victorian children.**

*Numbers 1-8 were published in the early 1880's.*

1. A set of four cards, signed P T, probably Patty Townshend, showing groups of village children in summer and winter scenes, with narrative poems on reverse. 12.5 cm x 8.6 cm.

2. Two cards, a girl in a hat or a bonnet on a gilt background in a patterned border, with a verse by Lewis Novra on reverse. 10.7 cm x 10.7 cm.

3. Two gilt-edged cards, a boy with a toy boat, a girl and a doll. 7.8 cm x 11.2 cm.

4. Three cards, each a girl with a fan in party or fancy dress. 6.5 cm x 11.7 cm.

5. Two cards, two little girls at bedtime, and a small girl asleep with her head on a table. 9.5 cm x 13.5 cm, 12.9 cm x 11.1 cm.

6. Two cards, a small girl with a doll, and another with sweets in a large paper holder. 7 cm x 10.3 cm.

7. Three cards, each with two children holding fruit, flowers, or toys, set in a patterned border, one dated 1883 by the sender. 8.5 cm x 8.7 cm.

8. Four miscellaneous cards, winter scenes with children. One was dated 1888 by the sender but may have been published earlier. 8.8 cm x 8.8 cm up to 11 cm x 13.4 cm.

*Numbers 9-31 were published in the later 1880's.*

9. Two gilt-edged cards, a small girl in an elegant blue gown, and a girl holding kittens in a basket, this with a verse by E J Pope on reverse, dated 1887 by the sender. 8.1 cm x 12.8 cm.

10. Five cards, three designs in two styles, a boy with a goose or holly, and two children gathering firewood. 9 cm x 9 cm, 6.9 cm x 10.3 cm.

11. Six cards, each with one or two girls and boys in winter scenes, from three different sets. 8.2 cm x 8.2 cm up to 9 cm x 9 cm.

12. Three cards, each showing a child sitting on a trunk or hamper waiting for an approaching train. 9.6 cm x 12.8 cm.

13. Three miscellaneous cards, each of two children in a winter scene or in party dress, one with a verse by E S.
Sizes up to 13.3 cm x 11 cm.

14. Five cards in similar style, four designs of two or three well dressed children leaning over a snow-covered wall.  One card repeats a design from no. 13 but with a different unsigned greeting.
9.3 cm x 6.2 cm up to 10.3 cm x 14.5 cm.

15. Five cards from two sets, each a child with flowers, robin, cat, butterfly, or toy, two dated 1886 and 1888 by the senders.
12 cm x 8.9 cm, 7.5 cm x 10.6 cm.

16. Five miscellaneous cards, children outdoors in all seasons, two with interesting border trompe l'oeil treatment.
9 cm x 9 cm up to 10.3 cm x 14.2 cm.

17. Three cards. Two are valentines, one with a boy giving a letter to a girl, the other a girl posting a letter. The third card has three children on the ice with a Christmas greeting.
7.1 cm x 10.5 cm, 6.6 cm x 10 cm.

18. Four cards, three from one set showing a girl or boy holding flowers or a letter, the fourth a plump child with an elaborate frilled collar. 7.8 cm x 11.8 cm.

19. Four cards, a girl with a sickle, another with a rake, and two cards with boys.
7 cm x 10.3 cm.

20. Three miscellaneous cards, each with a small girl in winter or summer, two with verses by H M Burnside, the other with a poem by Margaret Haycraft.
Sizes up to 11 cm x 11 cm.

21. Four cards, three from one set with two designs of a girl in summer, the fourth in similar style with two children and a dog.
8.5 cm x 12 cm, 6.7 cm x 10.5 cm.

22. Five cards from two sets, three with a girl or boy out-of-doors, two with little girls in elaborate bonnets. 7.4 cm x 10 cm.

23. Four miscellaneous cards including one with two children skating, a girl with a hoop, and two others with girls, one in summer, one in winter.
Sizes up to 8.7 cm x 11.9 cm.

24. Four cards, three with children playing in snow, the other with three children holding a Christmas cake with a Santa Claus on top. Sizes up to 8 cm x 10.8 cm.

25. Four cards, each showing a boy and girl at a party.
6.7 cm x 10.2 cm up to 8.5 cm x 12 cm.

26. Four miscellaneous cards, each with a girl in party dress.
6.1 cm x 10 cm up to 8.4 cm x 12 cm.

27. Six miscellaneous cards with children in various activities with pets or at play.
8 cm x 8.6 cm up to 8.8 cm x 11.5 cm.

28. Two blue-bordered cards, small figures carrying placards with Christmas messages. 6 cm x 10.9 cm, 10.9 cm x 6 cm.

29. Three blue-bordered cards, each with two children playing in the snow or with hoops. 9.7 cm x 6.8 cm.

30. Three grey-bordered cards, one a small boy with a rabbit, and two with the same design of a girl in red and blue showing two variants of printing.
10 cm x 13 cm, 7.4 cm x 10.4 cm.

31. Six miscellaneous cards with various coloured borders, showing children in various activities and including a baby in an elaborate frilled bonnet.
10.4 cm x 7 cm up to 9 cm x 13 cm.

*Numbers 32-35 have a number of small cards difficult to date which are included here together for comparison of styles.*

32. Ten cards, nine designs of a single child. Sizes up to 6 cm x 9 cm.

33. Eight cards, children in summer or winter. Three with yellow borders are from the same set, one dated 1884 by the sender. Sizes up to 6.8 cm x 10 cm.

34. Nine colourful cards including six from one set probably all by the same artist. Sizes up to 5.9 cm x 8.8 cm.

35. Seven miscellaneous cards, including one with a small girl on a sealed envelope in trompe l'oeil style.
5 cm x 7.5 cm up to 10.6 cm x 7.7 cm.

36. Two cards, the same design of a small girl on her knees before a kitten peeping over a chair. The first card was probably issued in the late 1880's, and the second is a postcard, an interesting early specimen with space only for address and none for correspondence.
9 cm x 6.5 cm, 13.9 cm x 9 cm.

## VOLUME 159: CHILDREN, UNBORDERED CARDS, MOST IN SMALL TO MEDIUM SIZES

**Most of these cards were published in the later 1880's and early 90's, with a few exceptions as listed, and many have rounded corners and serrated edges. A few cards were signed by the artists, but except for no. 19, the publishers are unknown.**

1. Nine embossed cards, showing a child peeping through a hole in a paper screen, from three different sets, all with verses. Two were dated 1881, 1883 by the senders. 9.4 cm x 12.6 cm, 10 cm x 13.3 cm, 5 cm x 7.5 cm.

2. Eight cards from two sets. Five have a boy or girl head and shoulders, three dated 1882 by the senders. Two cards have a girl with a tennis racquet, and another a boy with a hoe and a watering can, dated 1883. 5.3 cm x 8 cm, 6 cm x 9.6 cm.

3. Five miscellaneous cards, each a child with a dog, a doll, or in the garden, two with poems. Sizes up to 9.8 cm x 13 cm.

4. Three cards, warmly dressed children with matching hat and socks, carrying a Christmas tree in a snowstorm, with verses on reverse by M M and the Hon M E L.
7.3 cm x 11.2 cm.

5. Four frosted cards from two sets. Two have a girl with a dog or under a rose bush, and two have two children playing in the snow.
8.9 cm x 12.4 cm, 9.3 cm x 13 cm.

6. Four cards of an interesting topical set. Two show sister meeting brother coming home from the sea or college, and two show a boy pulling two children in a large go-cart. 10.7 cm x 12.5 cm.

7. Three cards, two with two children by a fence, one signed E J Manning, and a third with a boy and girl by a river.
Sizes up to 10 cm x 15 cm.

8. Four miscellaneous cards, children dancing, hanging stockings, in school, with a cat. Two cards have verses by E J Pope and Coombes Davies on reverse.
Sizes up to 14.3 cm x 10.5 cm.

9. Four cards, children in night attire opening Christmas stockings, at play, at window with a robin, one with a verse by J H Goring on reverse.
Sizes up to 13 cm x 10 cm.

10. Two cards, a girl and boy on a wicker chair, a girl dancing and a boy playing a violin. 10.5 cm x 15.2 cm, 12.5 cm x 10 cm.

11. Six cards, three with babies, three with children in summer scenes, one with a poem by J E Whitby.
8 cm x 8.5 cm up to 10.3 cm x 13.3 cm.

12. Four miscellaneous cards, three with girls in elaborate bonnets, one with a boy and a satchet of apples signed Adams. Two cards have a verse by S K C and one was dated 1889 by the sender.
Sizes up to 9.2 cm x 12 cm.

13. Four cards, three designs of a girl leaning on a fence or a baby by the sea, each with a poem by H M Burnside. The fourth card is a black and white repeat of one 0..design.
10 cm x 13 cm, 13 cm x 10 cm.

14. Three miscellaneous cards, girls in winter, feeding a robin, sledging, or bringing home the holly.
Sizes up to 11.1 cm x 12.5 cm.

15. Two cards, a schoolroom with three dunces in striped suits signed E A Cook, and a boy pulling a handcart.
13.2 cm x 10.4 cm, 14.5 cm x 10.5 cm.

16. Four cards, three with children in summer, the fourth two children bringing home the holly, with a verse by Elizabeth Love on reverse.
Sizes up to 8.9 cm x 12.2 cm.

17. Seven cards, including three from one set and two from another showing children with toys, another with a boy on a donkey, and the seventh a little girl feeding her doll.
6.6 cm x 9.8 cm up to 7.8 cm x 11.8 cm.

18. Six cards, five designs of children in sailor suits or hats and a girl in a tam'o'shanter.
6.8 cm x 8.4 cm up to 6.1 cm x 10.8 cm.

19. Three cards, each with a girl and flowers.  Two are marked M Priester's Continental Printing Co., the third T S, which is probably Thomas Stevens.
7.6 cm x 11.2 cm, 7.3 cm x 11.2 cm.

20. Four cards, one with children in Georgian dress dated 1894 by the sender, one with a girl and a wooden toy horse, and two the same design of three children leaning on a wall with different verses for the Christmas and New Year greetings.
10 cm x 7.5 cm up to 12.5 cm x 8.7 cm.

21. Two cards, summer scenes, a girl feeding birds and three children wading in the sea, the first with a poem by Lewis Novra on reverse.
9.5 cm x 12.5 cm, 13.2 cm x 10 cm.

22. Three cards, summer scenes with a single child, each with an interesting decorative cut out border.
Sizes up to 9 cm x 14 cm.

23. Two cards, a girl in a fur-edged tippet and bonnet, and five children at a party.
10 cm x 12.5 cm, 11 cm x 11.3 cm.

24. Three cards, each with a girl at one side and the greeting or verse occupying most of the space, one dated 1888 by the sender.
Sizes up to 11.7 cm x 9.4 cm.

25. Six cards from two sets. Three show children in pinafores holding toys or sweets; the other three have two designs of a little girl at bedtime with her doll, one dated 1888 by the sender.
6.1 cm x 9 cm, 8.8 cm x 10.1 cm.

26. Seven miscellaneous cards (one birthday), children in spring, in winter, at parties, or with grandfather.
6.3 cm x 9 cm up to 12.3 cm x 8.9 cm.

27. Six miscellaneous cards, children with toys or in fancy dress.
6.6 cm x 10.6 cm up to 8.5 cm x 10.5 cm.

28. Seven miscellaneous cards with children.
5.9 cm x 6.7 cm up to 8.1 cm x 11 cm.

*Numbers 29-36 have serrated edges.*

29. Two cards, a girl and boy by the sea, with a verse by Elizabeth Love, and a girl sitting on a cliff, signed E A L - Eliza Anne Lemann. 13 cm x 10.2 cm.

30/31. Seven cards, each with two children in spring or winter, signed E D L (untraced). 10 cm x 13 cm, 12.7 cm x 10 cm.

32. Four cards, two winter scenes with a little girl, the other two summer scenes with two girls. 10.2 cm x 13 cm.

33. Three cards, two designs, two boys in caps and overcoats, and a girl in an attractive fur-trimmed hat and coat holding mistletoe over a dog.
8.3 cm x 10.7 cm.

34. Four miscellaneous cards, a girl holding puppies in her skirt, another feeding robins, a boy on a rocking horse, and a boy and girl in party dress. Two have verses on reverse, one by E J P.
8.7 cm x 12 cm, 10 cm x 13 cm.

35. Two cards, five children with a large Christmas cake, and four girls skating, entitled "Four little Skateresses" (plain edged). 14 cm x 10.3 cm, 14.1 cm x 9.5 cm.

36. Seven miscellaneous cards, children in winter or spring, with a parrot, dancing, or in party dress.
6 cm x 10 cm up to 12.2 cm x 8.7 cm.

37/38. Nine cards with patterned embossed borders,1890's, including one with a frosted scrap of an angel.
9.5 cm x 7.5 cm up to 9 cm x 11.6 cm.

39. Two cards, each with a girl in costume as a cat or a hen.  7.5 cm x 11.2 cm.

## VOLUME 160: CHILDREN, LARGER CARDS, SOME WITH BABIES

**These cards show children in all seasons. No artists or publishers have been traced, but most were published from 1885 to early 1890's, with a few exceptions as noted.**

1. One card, a golden haired girl in a blue cloak, with a verse signed J M E S on reverse, dated 1882 by the sender.
9.8 cm x 14.5 cm.

2. Two cards, girls with flowing hair, both dated 1890 by the senders but perhaps published earlier. 10.7 cm x 14.1 cm.

3. Four miscellaneous cards (one birthday), head and shoulder pictures of rosy cheeked children, one dated 1892 with a verse by Johnston Beall. Sizes up to 10.2 cm x 13.2 cm.

4. Three similar, one marked copyright D with a poem by C D on reverse. Sizes up to 10.5 cm x 14.7 cm.

5. Three cards, two designs of winsome curly haired girls, one holding flowers, the other a kitten.  One is large, with a verse below, the other two are small cards from the same set of designs. 12.5 cm x 17 cm, 7.5 cm x 9.2 cm.

6. Two cards, babies in white lace-trimmed frocks. 13.8 cm x 18.6 cm.

7. Two cards, a boy or girl in a rural scene in an oval vignette with decorated border and nursery rhyme verse in a scroll, one dated 1884 by the sender. 10.8 cm x 14 cm.

8. Two cards, each two children singing carols, with a verse by M S H.
10 cm x 13.1 cm.

9. One card, a girl with a large snowball in a border of oak leaves with a verse by A H B.  11.6 cm x 16 cm.

10. One card, two girls in embroidered dresses in Stuart mode, dressing a doll.
12.4 cm x 17 cm.

11. One card, a girl playing pipes in a background of iris and wisteria, with a poem "Sweet Music" by Lewis Novra on reverse.  11.5 cm x 16.7 cm.

12. Four cards of different sizes in similar format, each with a girl in a summer scene.
7.5 cm x 11 cm up to 10.8 cm x 16.4 cm.

13. An unusual card showing a small girl pulling a paper cover from a large portrait of a lady in a pink bonnet, with two similar from the same set made up as a fringed card. 10.5 cm x 15.5 cm.

14. Two cards, three young people skating, a boy gathering firewood with a poem by C D on reverse, both in decorative borders.
8.7 cm x 13.2 cm, 9.2 cm x 12.9 cm.

15. Four cards with green borders, two showing a girl dancing, one a little girl riding a goose, the fourth a basket of flowers in a similar format, probably from the same mixed set.
7.3 cm x 14 cm, 10 cm x 13.4 cm.

16. Two cards, two children in the rain with an umbrella and a dog, and three children skating, both dated 1887 by the senders. 12.6 cm x 17.2 cm.

17. Two cards, a girl serving tea to her dolls, and another holding a doll, both with a verse below by A I G.
10.5 cm x 14.9 cm.

18. Two cards, children in the snow, one with a poem by C D on reverse. 9.8 cm x 14.6 cm, 10.2 cm x 15.5 cm.

19. One card, a girl in a plumed hat on a rustic seat. 11 cm x 16 cm.

20. One card, a girl in fur-trimmed coat and feathered hat. 10.2 cm x 14.4 cm.

21. Four cards, two with children dancing round a large snowball or skating, and two with a girl and a doll sitting on a chair. 10.7 cm x 13.8 cm.

22. Two cards, one a girl getting water from a fountain, the other (from the same set) with two angels, both having verses below by S K Cowan. 10 cm x 15 cm.

23. One card, two little girls in sunbonnets sitting on a fence, marked by an undeciphered publisher's monogram. 10.6 cm x 13.7 cm.

24. Four gilt-bordered cards printed in soft shades of yellow and green, picturing a bare legged small boy on a grassy bank with a kitten or butterfly, one dated 1885 by the sender. 10 cm x 13.5 cm.

25. Three similar cards from a different set, two repeating designs from no. 24. 10 cm x 13.2 cm.

26. Two cards, each with a baby holding a canary in an oval vignette. 10.8 cm x 14.4 cm.

27. Two cards, one design of a bare-legged child sitting on a cliff, in two different styles. 8.5 cm x 11 cm, 11.4 cm x 14.3 cm.

28. Two cards, one design of a girl in a pink frock climbing on a rock, in two different styles. 11.3 cm x 14.2 cm.

29. Two cards, one design of two children in bed, with different style printing for greeting. 10.2 cm x 15.3 cm.

30. Two cards, a girl and a dog on a tree trunk by a lake, dated 1893 by the sender, and a girl with a cat and kitten on a grassy bank. 14 cm x 10.7 cm, 15.8 cm x 11.2 cm.

31. Two cards, children pulling a cracker, and boys and girls dancing under mistletoe. 13.5 cm x 9.5 cm, 13.8 cm x 10 cm.

32. A card with an interesting pierced and embossed border in orange and cream colours, showing a girl in an elaborate dress and hat and a boy in a sailor suit at the seaside. 13 cm x 12.4 cm.

33. Seven cards, one with a baby in a basket looking at a cat, and six small cards with four designs of a baby in a cradle or a bath. 11 cm x 14.7 cm, 9.2 cm x 6 cm.

34. Five miscellaneous cards, babies' heads. Sizes up to 7 cm x 11 cm.

35. Three cards, two with barefoot babies, one a small boy in a frilled frock. Sizes up to 13.5 cm x 10 cm.

36. Three cards, babies with comic expressions, one in a top-hat, one in spectacles, one with a pipe. 8.7 cm x 12.7 cm.

## VOLUME 161: CHILDREN, TAKEN FROM PHOTOGRAPHS, c1890

**These cards are from photographs coloured by hand, and then reproduced usually on thick board. The same pink spot can be seen on the cheeks of the children, many of whom are posed in somewhat arch attitudes in their elders' clothes or spectacles, with an occasional cart drawn by a goat and an interesting trio of boys on penny farthing bicycles scaled down to size. Some of these cards are signed Davidson Bros., and it is likely that many of the unsigned ones were published by that firm (a few appear in the Raphael Tuck section, volume 71). Most of the cards measure about 11 cm x 16 cm, and any significant variation from this is given.**

1. Four children and a Christmas tree.

2. Five children asleep in bed with a collection of wooden dolls.

3. Two cards, children in a cart drawn by a goat, with a background that gives the appearance of a photographer's studio setting, and a poem by G W on reverse.

4. Two cards, one repeating one of the pictures in no. 3 in a different format with poems on reverse, the other two children with a boat.

*Numbers 5-11 are marked Davidson Bros.*

5. Three cards, each with a single girl or boy in an oval vignette, with greeting on a blue border, and poems on reverse. One was dated 1885 by the sender.

6. Two cards, each with a small girl and boy, with poems on reverse by A M H and S K C.

7. Three cards, two showing children playing in a large hamper, the other a little maid in cap and apron with a tea set, all with poems by A M H on reverse.

8. Three cards, each a small girl in frilled cap and spectacles, with poems on reverse by S K C and Moore.

9. Three cards, a girl with a battledore and shuttlecock, another with a Japanese

parasol, and a boy in a velvet suit with small brother on his shoulders, with verses by H M B or A M H on reverse.

10. Two cards, a trio of penny-farthing cyclists. The same boys appear in each picture, in the same costumes, but the colours are different. Poems on the reverse are by S K C.

11. One card, a lady in apron and frilled cap, fishing.

12. Two cards, a boy or a girl with a wooden spade in a seaside background, with poems on reverse by F R H or Lord Byron.

13. Two cards, one with two little girls in elaborate dresses and bonnets and lace trimmed drawers, the other two children in night attire.

14. Two cards, a boy dressed as a barrister, three girls pulling crackers.

15. Two cards, a girl with a doll in a garden, two children in white dresses sitting on a fur rug.

16. Two cards, a sailor boy sitting on a mast, and a little girl with a slate.

17. One card repeating the little girl with a slate, this time with a greeting on the slate.

18. Two cards, each showing a girl in a fur coat in falling snow.

19. Two smaller cards, a girl with holly in snow, a boy in a sailor suit on a chair sledge, one dated 1890 by the sender. 9 cm x 13.7 cm.

20. Two cards printed in sepia only, one showing two little boys in lace dresses and frilly knickers, the other a girl and boy.

21. Three cards, two with a girl and boy in an obvious studio setting. The third card is smaller, with five children preparing for bed. 7.5 cm x 11.7 cm.

22. Three cards, two designs, one a small girl in a lace dress with a basket of flowers, the other a boy with a model ship.

23. Two cards, a girl in a feathered hat with a basket of apples, and another in warm coat with muff in a winter background.

24. Two cards, a fisherwoman and her child, and a Highlander performing a sword dance, with poems by Burns on reverse.

25. Two cards, boys in sailor suits with a seaside background and unsigned poems on reverse.

26. Two cards, one with two children as Darby and Joan, the other a little girl in bed.

27/28. Five cards with shaped and cut out edges, three with warmly clad children in falling snow, two with a girl or a boy dressed up in grandparents' outfits.

29/30. Four cards, children in peasant costume in a cut-out foliage border.

31. One card, a boy in a top hat in a square vignette in a cut out border of branches. 12 cm x 12 cm.

32. Seven small cards, (one birthday) four designs of a small child in a large basket, in two styles. 7.1 cm x 10.7 cm.

33. Four miscellaneous cards, each with a single child. Sizes up to 9 cm x 13.5 cm.

34. Three miscellaneous cards, two with three children, the other with one child. Sizes up to 13 cm x 8.5 cm.

35. Four smaller cards, a boot black, a boy on a swing, a boy in a judge's wig, and a girl in a white dress and bonnet. Sizes up to 10 cm x 13.4 cm.

36. A folding card with three pictures of children (one repeating a design in no. 35) set on a easel. 19 cm x 10 cm folded.

## VOLUME 162: LADIES

**These cards show ladies and girls in portrait style, in costume and classical draperies, with a few sportswomen and some belles of the 90's. They display little of the Christmas spirit, and continue the styles set by the prize competitions and the Raphael Tuck Royal Academy Series. A few cards are marked by their publishers and one or two artists' signatures appear.**

*Numbers 1-25 were published about 1880-1885.*

1. Three cards (two birthday), young ladies in feathered bonnets shown head and shoulders, published by J F Schipper, perhaps designed by G D Leslie. Nos. 594, 595, 595. 12.3 cm x 15.5 cm.

2. Two cards, published by J F Schipper, ladies head and shoulders, one in an oval frame with a pansy design and a greeting on reverse, no. 836, the other with flowing golden hair and a verse on reverse, no.148. 13.7 cm x 16.8 cm, 13.8 cm x 12.7 cm.

3. One card, published by Eyre & Spottiswoode, a lady in a muslin dress and a bonnet sitting on a garden seat, with a poem by Lewis Novra on reverse. 13.2 cm x 17 cm.

4. Two cards, ladies with fans, one in party dress, the other in a blue cloak dated 1885 by the sender. 11.5 cm x 15.3 cm.

5. One card, head of a young girl in frilled cap and fichu. 11.8 cm x 17.5 cm.

6. Two cards, a lady in a garden, with a poem by F L on reverse, dated 1882 by the sender, and two ladies and a child in a garden with cherry trees and a descriptive poem on reverse. 14.5 cm x 11.2 cm, 17 cm x 12.5 cm.

7. One card, a lady with an umbrella walking in snow, with a border of mistletoe. 9.6 cm x 15.5 cm.

8. One card, a lady mountaineer balancing on a rock, in somewhat unsuitable costume. 8.4 cm x 15 cm.

9. One card published by W A Mansell, a lady skating, signed with a monogram T L or L T. This has been submitted to various experts for identification, but so far is elusive. More cards by this artist appear in volume 164. 10.4 cm x 18 cm.

10. A birthday card, an elegant lady in a green dress carrying a red cloak and a bunch of mistletoe. 9.8 cm x 16.3 cm.

11. One card, a lady in a frilled dress and jacket holding a large walking stick. 10.8 cm x 18.2 cm.

12. Another with a lady in a Georgian style dress holding roses, in a blue and gold background. 9.3 cm x 13.8 cm.

13. Two cards, young ladies in long dresses and bonnets with trees behind and a greeting verse on reverse. 6.8 cm x 18.8 cm.

14. Five miscellaneous cards showing ladies in a variety of elegant costumes. 10 cm x 7.5 cm up to 10 cm x 13.2 cm.

15. Two cards, ladies with parasols, in a boat or by the sea, with verses by C D or A Gill on reverse. 13.6 cm x 8.9 cm, 17.6 cm x 11.1 cm.

16. Three cards (one birthday), ladies in classical robes against a background of flowers, two having a patterned back with a greeting. 9 cm x 15 cm.

17. Two cards, each showing a maiden in classical dress feeding birds, with verse by E J P on reverse. 9.9 cm x 13.2 cm.

18. Four cards from one set, three with a lady in classical dress in appropriate setting, the fourth a Victorian girl picking apples, all with a Christmas poem in a panel. 9.3 cm x 13.2 cm.

19. Two cards, one design of a Roman matron and child on a marble bench, in two styles. 8.8 cm x 13 cm, 7 cm x 9.7 cm.

20. Two cards, each showing a lady in flowing draperies, one with a child. 11 cm x 14.8 cm, 10 cm x 15.5 cm.

21. Three miscellaneous cards, maidens in classical dress, one with a large red figure vase incongruously filled with Victorian flowers. Sizes up to 10.4 cm x 13.8 cm.

22. Two cards with illuminated patterned borders, a lady in a yellow robe, and another with a lamb. 10.4 cm x 14.8 cm, 8.8 cm x 14.3 cm.

23. Two cards, each with a lady in flowing draperies perched precariously on a tree

**162.9**

**161.28**

branch or a bundle of reeds.
10.6 cm x 16.7 cm.

24. Three cards, two with a maiden in classical dress, the third with a lady by a lake. 7.6 cm x 13.7 cm, 6.9 cm x 14.8 cm.

25. Six cards, brown and gold ladies' heads in profile against a yellow background, in two sizes, signed by an untraced monogram. 12 cm x 15 cm, 6.6 cm x 10.7 cm.

*Numbers 26-31 were published from 1885-1890.*

26. Two cards, a lady with a dove, another with a sheaf of corn and a sickle. 9 cm x 13 cm.

27. Three miscellaneous cards, each with a lady and flowers or birds. Sizes up to 8.5 cm x 14.5 cm.

28/29. Seven cards, four designs in three different styles of a single lady with a flowering branch or berries. Six have poems by H M B or Cowper. 10 cm x 13 cm, 11.7 cm x 14.7 cm.

30. Three cards, lovely ladies with flowers in their hair, perhaps taken from photographs. 10.7 cm x 16.5 cm.

31. An elegant card c1890, a lady in transparent draperies holding a palm, in a rectangular vignette with silver embossed floral decoration, perhaps designed by E J Harding. 13 cm x 19 cm.

32/33. Four cards by Edward T Reed, ladies of the gay 90's, two black and white, two coloured. Three ladies have cupids in attendance on their means of transport - a sledge, a bicycle, and a small carriage. The fourth is a ballet dancer holding a lantern marked "98". 11.7 cm x 15.9 cm. Buday lists this artist as working for Marcus Ward.

34/35. Four cards in similar style, each with a lady head and shoulders in an elaborate hat or hairstyle, two in black and white, two coloured, perhaps designed by Creswell Woollett. 12 cm x 16 cm.

36. Two elegant silk cards, designed by F Sargent, each with two ladies in classical robes, in mounts with an embossed silver flower and a scroll with a caption by Charlotte Murray or J Sterling. 12.4 cm x 15.5 cm.

## VOLUME 163: FAMILY SCENES

**This volume contains cards designed by Birket Foster, scenes with mothers and children, and some valentines, with Christmas family parties contrasting with the less**

163.3

**fortunate earning their daily bread in the winter streets. They were published 1880-1885.**

1. Two cards designed by Birket Foster, signed with the monogram B F, bucolic scenes entitled "Going to Market", and "Water Lilies", with a poem by Cowper on the reverse of one card. 16 cm x 11.8 cm.

2. Two cards by Birket Foster, seaside scenes, entitled "On the sea shore", and "The way down the cliff". 18.5 cm x 11.8 cm.

3. Two cards by Birket Foster, two designs of children with decorative gilt border. These six cards have no publisher's mark, but Buday lists Birket Foster as having designed for Hildesheimer & Faulkner.

4/9. Eleven cards, labelled "After Birket Foster", published by C P McQueen, London, signed with monogram B F. They are black and white with the appearance of etching, and have four different styles of gilt patterned borders around scenes with village women and children. The cards have pencilled numbers on the backs ranging from 20-38 and might be part of a larger set. 15.6 cm x 19.5 cm.

10. Two cards, good quality genre pictures, a mother reading a letter from her son, and another watching over her baby in its cradle. One was dated 1882 by the sender, and there are narrative poems on the reverse of both cards. 12.5 cm x 17 cm.

11. One card, a mother and two children, with a poem "Maternal bliss" on reverse. 13 cm x 10.1 cm.

12/13. Four gilt-edged cards, summer scenes with a mother and child in Kate Greenaway style dress picking fruit. 8.5 cm x 17.6 cm.

14. Four cards, three designs of a mother and child on gilt backgrounds, with a greeting verse in a panel, one dated 1881 by the sender. 8 cm x 11 cm, 7.3 cm x 11.5 cm.

15. Two cards, two children with a Christmas tree, a mother and child on a balcony, both on gilt ground with greeting in panel. 8.4 cm x 11.5 cm, 8.9 cm x 12.2 cm.

16. Two cards, a mother and children in winter scenes. 7.7 cm x 12.2 cm, 10.7 cm x 15.2 cm.

17. Two cards, Christmas parties, with elegantly costumed ladies, gentlemen, and children, and a narrative poem "Our first dance together ..." on the reverse of one card. 17.2 cm x 13.5 cm.

18. One card showing two villagers with their dog bringing home the holly, dated 1883 by the sender, with a poem by E J P on reverse. 18.3 cm x 13.3 cm.

19. One card, a Victorian family taking a Christmas walk in the park. 19 cm x12.7 cm.

20. Three cards, two showing a "crocodile" of girls from the Ladies Seminary taking a walk by the sea, shepherded by bespectacled schoolmistress. The third card (trimmed) has a group of boys in Eton suits doffing their top hats perhaps to the girls.16.5 cm x 11.6 cm.

21. A card with silver border signed J M L R, a man and woman skating, dated1884 by the sender.11.2 cm x 14.5 cm.

22. A card with a gilt patterned border showing a mother and two children being welcomed by grandfather, in a panelled hall.18.4 cm x 11.3 cm.

**163.20**

23. One card, "A Christmas rescue", showing a lifeboatman with a rescued child, with a verse by M G Watkins M A on the reverse. 13 cm x 16.5 cm.

24. Four cards depicting the winter activities of the less fortunate, boys clearing snow, street vendors, fetching water from the pump, street musicians. Two cards were dated 1878, 1879 by the senders. 12.6 cm x 9 cm.

25. Two cards, a boy and girl roasting chestnuts, and a barefoot couple selling fruit. 13.9 cm x 10.5 cm.

26. Three cards, a crossing sweeper, a paper boy, and a flower seller, all in winter snow. 7.2 cm x 12 cm, 9 cm x 12 cm.

27, Two cards, a mother and two children in the snow, and two street musicians, late 1880's. 9.2 cm x 12 cm.

28. Three embossed valentine cards, each with a boy and girl in Kate Greenaway style costume, one dated 1882 by the sender. 9.4 cm x 14.7 cm.

29. Two valentine cards, a boy and girl in a summer scene. 10.5 cm x 15.9 cm.

30. Two cards, a man and woman in a circular vignette with floral decoration, drawn in the style of Felix Dussert (see volume 147).
7.8 cm x 12.2 cm, 9.5 cm x 13 cm.

31. Three blue-bordered valentine cards, each with a man or woman poised on a flower trying to entrap an outsize butterfly or dragonfly. 9.5 cm x 12.7 cm.

32. Two cards (one birthday), signed H A, a woman with a sheaf of corn, and a shepherd in the snow, with a poem by E C M on the back of one card.
9.3 cm x 15.6 cm.

33. One card, a rustic couple sitting on a tree trunk. The back has a ship with the mark A1, possibly a trade mark.
11 cm x 13.8 cm.

## VOLUME 164:
## FAIRIES, ELVES, AND FLOWER CHILDREN

**This volume and the next depict a variety of fairy folk, including some small children precariously balanced on flowers and branches. Some Easter cards, with eggs, are included, presented in secular vein. A few cards are marked with their publishers' names, and one or two are signed by the artists. Most were published in the early 1880's with a few otherwise as noted.**

1. Five cards from a set, including two designs of small elves inadequately clad for the surrounding winter snow, one of holly, and another with robins, one dated 1874 by the sender. 9.4 cm x 6.5 cm.

2. Seven gilt-backed cards from three sets with fairies and elves, two dated 1872, 1879 by the senders. 10 cm x 6.5 cm up to 12.4 cm x 7.8 cm.

3. Eight gilt edged cards from three sets, four with elves wheeling barrows full of flowers, three with two designs of an elf riding on a grasshopper, and one with three elves making music, in a background of roses. c1875. 4.6 cm x 8.1 cm, 11.2 cm x 7.1 cm.

4. Three gilt-edged cards, two designs of a small fairy with a garland of flowers breaking through a paper screen, with Christmas verse by T E M below.
7.4 cm x 14.1 cm.

5. Thirteen small cards published by E Bollans, seven designs of small elves with flower decorated heart, anchor, or open book, or with a bouquet or garland. Five have valentine greetings, and one is on a green folder. 8.4 cm x 5.7 cm.

6. Five cards, four illustrating various means of transport for fairy folk - riding on a fish, a crab, or a bird, or on a lily leaf drawn by a duck. The fifth card shows a dead hare.11.5 cm x 7.1 cm.

7. A birthday card, a small jockey riding a frog. 13.5 cm x 9 cm.

8. Four miscellaneous cards, small elves or fairies with a scroll or an egg, carrying a large placard with a greeting, or emerging from an open envelope. 10.5 cm x 6.9 cm up to 13.5 cm x 7.9 cm.

9. A forest scene with elves riding on a stag, in an illuminated patterned border. 15.4 cm x 13.2 cm.

10. A card with two fairies perched on an elaborate carved scroll border with flowers. 10.4 cm x 13.3 cm.

11. Two embossed cards, each with a group of cherubs represented as a carving on stone, with a border of spring flowers, one with birthday greeting.
12.4 cm x 8.2 cm.

12. Three cards in black and white, with elves in cap and jerkin. 8.5 cm x 12.2 cm.

*Numbers 13-16 are signed with the monogram T L or L T, all showing plump rosy cheeked fairy children or elves.*

13. Three cards printed in sepia, a fairy on a sledge, another on a tree, and an elf with a fishing net. 7.3 cm x 11 cm.

14. Three cards published by W A Mansell, with fairies in a spider's web, sailing in a shell, or sitting on a rock by the sea. One card has an invitiation on the back for an exhibition by W A Mansell, at 271-3 Oxford St, London, of cards "by all the principal makers, including De La Rue, Goodall, Eyre & Spottiswoode, Hildesheimer & Faulkner, Prang, S Hildesheimer, Marcus Ward, Rothe, Tuck & Son's Prize Cards, etc". This would date the cards in the early 1880's, perhaps 1882. 12.7 cm x 12.7 cm.

15. Two cards, small fairies as the King and Queen of Hearts, one dated 1881 by the sender. 8.9 cm x 11.7 cm.

16. Three miscellaneous cards, a sepia picture of a small girl, two mermaids enticing the sailors on a passing ship, and a number of elfin jockeys riding bats. 11.5 cm x 7.5 cm up to 16.5 cm x 11.7 cm.

17. Two cards, naked cherubs, making music or having a mock sword fight, one dated 1883 by the sender.15.5 cm x 12 cm.

18. Five cards in two sizes, three designs of elves perched on trees or in a bird's nest, one dated 1885 by the sender. Narrative poems by C D are on the backs of the larger cards.
10 cm x 14.5 cm, 7.5 cm x 10.3 cm.

19. Four cards, three designs of fairy transport, by train, donkey cart, or Royal Mail. 8.6 cm x 13.7 cm.

20. Three elegant cards with gilt-patterned borders, each with a fairy in flight, somewhat in the style of W S Coleman, one dated 1887 by the sender.
11.9 cm x 14.9 cm.

21. Four miscellaneous cards (one a valentine), with Cupid, fairies and elves, one signed E A L, i.e. Eliza Ann Lemann. Sizes up to 8.2 cm x 12 cm.

22. Three miscellaneous cards, fairy children in flowery settings or in a bird's nest. Sizes up to 13 cm x 9.6 cm.

23. Two cards, a fairy holding a bunch of mistletoe swinging from a church bell, and another holding forget-me-nots flying over a river. 8.5 cm x 13.8 cm, 14 cm x10 cm.

24. Five cards, four designs of little girls wearing a cap made of a pansy, daisy, rose, or nasturtium, each with a poem on reverse. 8 cm x 11.8 cm.

25. Two cards, elves pulling a cracker, or carrying a pudding. These are from a set of six with similar Christmas themes, but the other four have eluded this collection.13.9cm x 11.2 cm.

26. Four cards, three designs with a fairy looking through a torn paper screen at a village scene. Two of the cards are later editions, perhaps American.
7.2 cm x 12.1 cm.

27. Two cards, flower fairies, carnation and fuchsia. 5 cm x 9.4 cm.

28. Six miscellaneous cards, four designs of fairies riding on birds or butterflies, and one of three children playing with a tortoise.
8.5 cm x 6.7 cm up to 12.7 cm x 9 cm.

29. Three gilt-bordered cards, one design of a baby inside a large egg, used for Easter, Christmas, and birthday greeting, one dated 1882 by the sender.
14.2 cm x10.3 cm.

30. Two embossed valentine cards, a fairy breaking out of a large egg in a nest surrounded by spring flowers (also seen as Easter cards). 9.4 cm x 12.7 cm.

31. Two cards without greeting, a small fairy with a large rabbit and a basket of coloured eggs. 8.4 cm x 13 cm.

**164.14**

32. Two cards, one Easter, one New Year, small elves taking eggs from a bird's nest. 10.7 cm x 7 cm.

33. Two embossed Easter cards, a boy riding a bicycle with eggs instead of wheels, and children painting large eggs. 7.5 cm x 12 cm, 15.1 cm x 10.7 cm.

34. Six miscellaneous cards with elves and fairies. 6.5 cm x 9.3 cm up to 10 cm x 14 cm.

## VOLUME 165:
## FAIRIES, ELVES, & FLOWER CHILDREN, LARGER CARDS

1/2. Four cards published by Bollen & Tidswell, water nymphs, floating on a lily leaf, swinging from a tree, or basking amidst flowers, with verses on reverse. c1880. 15.6 cm x 12 cm.

3. Two cards published by H Rothe, both showing three fairies in flight, bearing roses or a Christmas tree, both with poems on reverse, the first Shakespeare's "Where the bee sucks ...". No. 326.
17.9 cm x 12.5 cm.

4/5. Eight cards published by H Rothe, (two birthday, one with name day greeting in Italian). They have four designs of small fairies with flowers and foliage, and similar cards with birds and a rose, no. 149; two were dated 1878, 1879 by the senders. One was priced 4d.
9.4 cm x 12.5 cm.

6. Four cards published by H Rothe, a gnome in brown cap and jerkin, with holly, mistletoe, ivy, or lime, nos. 229, 273, one with a greeting on reverse. The verse on one card says "See how Father Christmas lingers, Dropping ice from all his fingers", linking this brown-clad figure with the earlier tradition of a brown robe for Santa Claus. 9.6 cm x 12.5 cm.

7. Three cards published by Obpacher Bros., showing dwarfs, riding on a stork, with a large walking stick, or with a

bouquet of flowers, nos. 1183, 1188, 376, the latter with an undeciphered monogram. 9 cm x 12 cm, 9.2 cm x 12.2 cm.

8. Three cards published by J F Schipper, small fairies in mediaeval costume as knight and lady, no. 593, one dated 1882 by the sender. 9.6 cm x 15.8 cm.

9. Two cards published by Eyre & Spottiswoode, monochrome designs of small elves in jester's costume, with a Christmas verse below, one dated 1884 by the sender. 9.5 cm x 13.6 cm.

10. Two cards, each with a bird in flight holding a boy on a trapeze or a girl standing on a ribbon loop in its beak, with a trademark W W - A S Co, probably the Artistic Stationery Co. 10.5 cm x 14.5 cm.

11/12. Three cards signed Höppner. Two have fairy figures, perhaps Oberon & Titania, in bowers of daisies or lilac; the third has fairies guarding a sleeping child, in a border of Christmas roses, all with a poem and two-tone design on reverse. Nos. 144-1, 2, 4. 13.4 cm x 16.3 cm.

13/14. Four cards signed Höppner, or with monogram. Three have fairies feeding robins in the snow, or with spring flowers, nos. 63 - 1, 2, 3. The fourth shows a Christmas child with a tree and toys knocking at a cottage door, no. 54 - 2. All have narrative poems on reverse.
12 cm x 16 cm.

15. One card, two fairies with roses. 10.3 cm x 16 cm.

16. One card, a fairy in a garland of roses, forget-me-nots, and foliage.
9.7 cm x14.7 cm.

17. Three embossed cards, a boy and girl holding a large daisy, lily, or rose, in a border of flowers and butterflies.
9.6 cm x 14.5 cm.

**165.17**

**165.20**

38. Two cards, a small fairy perched on a branch, and another flying after a butterfly, one dated 1892 by the sender. 11 cm x 15.3 cm.

18. One card, a fairy in flight beneath a tree mallow. 12 cm x 16.5 cm.

19. Two cards, one with fairies and butterflies on flowers and grasses and a verse by Eden Hooper, the other a plump cherub sitting on a rose. 10.7 cm x 15 cm, 10.3 cm x 15.4 cm.

20. An interesting embossed card showing a lady in white draperies riding on a fish, in attractive blue, green, and gold colours, marked "Water", probably one of a series. 10.7 cm x 15 cm.

21. Three cards, water sprites in large shells or floating on a water lily, with verses on the backs of two cards. 15.7 cm x 11.8 cm.

22. Two cards, with loving greetings, each showing a water baby with a large shell. 15 cm x 10.7 cm.

23/24. Seven cards, including two with birthday greeting and one with a name day greeting in Italian, four designs of water nymphs and fairies with flower decoration. There are poems on the backs of four cards signed W or H F. 10 cm x 12.8 cm.

25. Two cards, fairies in a sea-shell boat, one with a poem by L N "The Barque of Hope" on reverse. 10.2 cm x 13.4 cm.

26. Two cards, elves skating or sailing in nutshells, one dated 1880 by the sender. 10.1 cm x 13.6 cm.

27. Two embossed cards, small children in a bird's nest. 8.6 cm x 12.7 cm.

28. Two cards, small children swinging and climbing on flowers, one dated 1879 by the sender. 8.6 cm x 13.3 cm.

29. A card with a child's head peeping out from a paper folder of lilies, dated 1882 by the sender. 10.8 cm x 14.9 cm.

30. A curious embossed card showing a marble statue of a Cupid with a bunch of forget-me-nots. 9 cm x 15.1 cm.

31. Two cards, one a fairy playing a violin seated on a branch of apple blossom in a semi-circular vignette bordered with holly garlands. The other shows a small child peeping out of a decorated china jug, with an explanatory verse by G A "I am not a Chinee ..." on reverse. 14 cm x 10 cm, 14.5 cm x 14.5 cm.

32. Three miscellaneous cards, fairies with flowers or by the sea listening to a shell, two with descriptive verses by Eden Hooper or E J M. Sizes up to 10.3 cm x 15.2 cm.

33. Two cards, elegant fairies reclining on cushions in a classical setting. 16 cm x11 cm.

34. Two cards, each with an angel child's head peeping out from a flowering tree, with a verse by L N, one dated 1887 by the sender. 10.5 cm x 14 cm.

35. Four cards in two sizes, three designs of a fur-clad angel boy with a vase of holly or mistletoe, one with a greeting in German. The larger cards have verses by C D on reverse. Late 1880's. 11 cm x 15.6 cm, 7.4 cm x 10.4 cm.

36. Three cards, each with a child in winter clothes wearing angel's wings, with verses by H M B. Late 1880's. 7.8 cm x 11.8 cm.

37. Four cards, fairy children with flowers, one with a verse by Johnston Beall, c1890. 7 cm x 9 cm, 7.9 cm x 11.1 cm.

# SECTION THIRTEEN

The seven volumes of Section 13 contain such a variety of subjects that a suitable title has eluded the writer. The cards range through many festive, social, and recreational activities, and observe some of the fads and foibles of Victorian society, as well as giving a glamourised and sometimes comic view of the soldiers and sailors who protected Victoria's growing Colonial Empire. Father Christmas is here, and the good old times of earlier centuries, as well as the seasonal delights of pantomime, circus, and Harlequinade. Hunting, shooting, and fishing activities are featured, often in humorous vein, and the Victorian passion for Japanese art was reflected in the cards.

Contact with the New World may have encouraged the frequent appearance of "negroes", the terminology commonly used to describe black people at that time. In case these cards might arouse cries of racism, it must be observed that soldiers, policemen, followers of the hunt and other worthy British citizens were as much the butt of greeting card humour as the "negroes". Fashions of the 1880's afford interesting comparisons with those of today, particularly those of cyclists, tennis players, and swimmers. A few topical and political cards, and some with music, appear in volume 172. Five cards satirizing the aesthetic movement are included at the end of this volume, with figures deriving from Gilbert & Sullivan's "Patience" and perhaps from Oscar Wilde.

**172.3**

## VOLUME 166: FESTIVE SCENES, WITH FATHER CHRISTMAS, CLOWNS, PANTOMIMES, AND SEASONAL FARE

These cards show Santa Claus in red, brown, or blue costume, some perhaps going back to the old style Lord of Misrule. Clowns and pantaloons appear in mishaps with policemen, Father Time sends out the Old Year and welcomes the New, and some cards show seasonal food and drink. Most were published in the earlier 1880's with a few exceptions as noted; some artists and publishers are named.

1. Eight small cards with embossed scalloped edges, showing five versions of Father Christmas with one of Red Riding Hood and one of a clown from the same set, c1870. 6 cm x 9 cm, 6.2 cm x 9.7 cm.

2. Three cards, Father Christmas, in a balloon dropping presents, with two children beneath an arch of holly, and in a blue robe with a humanised turkey, pudding, and goose, c1870. 6 cm x 9.1 cm, 6.7 cm x 10 cm.

3. Five cards, four of Father Christmas in a wreath of holly or ivy, the fifth an unusual card of Mother Christmas dressed in a gown with panniers and a pointed hat, in a border with toys and holly. Early 1870's. 6.9 cm x 9.5 cm up to 8.8 cm x 13.7 cm.

4. Two cards, transport for Christmas, one published by Eyre & Spottiswoode, with "King Christmas" in a red robe riding on a goat, the other with Father Christmas in a sleigh, designed by Linley Sambourne. 8.1 cm x 12.4 cm, 11.7 cm x 8.6 cm.

5. Three cards designed by W Claudius published by Birn Bros, showing a brown-garbed Santa Claus cutting a Christmas tree, sorting toys, and delivering parcels carried on a goat. 8.8 cm x 14 cm.

6. Three cards with a brown Santa Claus, Red Riding Hood, or a couple riding in a sleigh, all in romantic woodland settings, with descriptive poems by E J P on reverse. 8.9 cm x 13.3 cm.

7. Three cards, Santa Claus with tree and sack of presents, a couple riding in a sleigh to a country house, and a mother and two children going to church. 7 cm x 10.8 cm.

8. Five miscellaneous cards with a variety of Father Christmas figures, one dated 1887. One card with a Christmas King figure riding on a turkey in a mediaeval setting is marked Raphael Thomson & Co, London, a publisher dated by Buday as operating from 1860-70. 9 cm x 6.2 cm up to 9 cm x 13.7 cm.

9. Two cards, each with a Father Christmas figure and a child in circular vignettes. The first, in a blue cloak and gown, has a verse "Old Christmas comes" by F P, and is dated 1890, the other is in a brown cloak and hood. 9.9 cm x 13.6 cm, 13.6 cm x 9.9 cm.

10. A tinselled card, a red-robed Father Christmas head and shoulders, with the rising sun behind. 11.4 cm x 14.9 cm.

11. A four-page folder card, opening to show a poem by Eden Hooper in a holly border. The front has Santa Claus in brown with a group of children in antique dress, and the back shows the Old Year being dismissed by the New, as a young boy carried on the shoulder of January, with the figure of Hope leading a procession of the months. 13.2 cm x 16 cm.

12. Two cards. One repeats the New Year picture from no. 11 above, with a descriptive poem by Frederick Langbridge on the back; the other shows the young New Year of 1885 emerging from a grandfather clock. 13.2 cm x 16 cm, 10.2 cm x 16 cm.

13. One card, Father Time sitting on a globe holding an hour glass, watching the departure of the Old Year and the arrival of the New. 9.9 cm x 14.5 cm.

14. Three miscellaneous New Year cards, one with a mother and child and a poem "New Year Bells", another with Father Time giving a greeting to a little girl, and the third with the New Year in the guise of a maiden in a sailor style dress and hat alighting from the boat of Father Time. 7.6 cm x 12.8 cm, 9 cm x 11.8 cm

15. Three cards, marked M Chatterton & Co, London. They have pictures on both sides of Santa Claus or pantomime scenes, and might have been from booklets sent as trade greeting cards. 1870's. 7.3 cm x 10.5 cm.

16. Two cards, each with a clown skating and a pantaloon in trouble. 11.2 cm x 8.4 cm.

17. Two cards, a clown with a pig, and a pantaloon holding a Christmas pudding. 8.8 cm x 12.5 cm.

18. Three cards, showing the misadventures of a clown, a pantaloon, a policeman, and a baby. 9 cm x 12.1 cm.

19. Two cards, two clowns and a turkey, and a clown talking to a countryman with a cow, published by J F Schipper, no. 618. 14.9 cm x 9.6 cm.

20. Two cards, a clown training circus dogs signed A Ludovici Junior and a pantaloon drinking a pot of bitter, with a long poem on reverse. 13 cm x 10 cm, 9.4 cm x 15 cm.

**166.12**

21. Two cards, mediaeval scenes, one with a jester entertaining at a feast dated 1880 by the sender, the other a jester teasing a man in the stocks, with a verse by M E Ropes on reverse. 12.7 cm x 8.2 cm, 10.5 cm x 13.4 cm.

22. Four cards, two showing circus performers with tiger and elephant or dogs, and two with a jester or a lady skating. 7.4 cm x 10.1 cm, 7.6 cm x 11 cm.

23. Two gilt-bordered cards, black silhouettes with monkey artists or circus performers. 15 cm x 11.5 cm.

24. A card published by H Rothe, with dancing children and a youthful jester in classical style dress. 12.1 cm x 8 cm.

25. Five miscellaneous cards with clowns, pantaloons and policemen, one published by Eyre & Spottiswoode. Sizes up to 8.4 cm x 12.7 cm.

26. Four cards, three designs of clown, pantaloon, and policeman, pictured as on a stage with footlights. Three of the cards have advertisements for A Brooks, Les Modes Francaises, 125-7 Westminster Bridge Road, London S E, and are marked Rolls & Kelly, Printers, London. 12.4 cm x 8.7 cm.

27. Two cards, Punch & Judy. One is a folder which can stand up like a tent showing pictures of Punch, Judy, the baby, and Dog Toby; the other is a small card with Punch and Judy. 6 cm x 14.5 cm closed, 6 cm x 6 cm.

28. A view of St Paul's Cathedral with a man carrying sandwich boards with the message "Go and see the Christmas Pantomime, plenty of fun". 8.2 cm x 12.8 cm.

29. Two cards, signed M L, "Young Falstaff", "Little Dogberry", with appropriate captions below. 8.5 cm x 12 cm.

**166.17**

30. A card published by H Rothe, no. 290, with a panel of seasonal food and drink and a long poem starting "Join, friends! A toast ...". 10.2 cm x 15.3 cm.

31. Two pieces of a folder card published by Eyre & Spottiswoode, no. 5018, with an illuminated design on the cover, and a poem "A Carol for a Jolly Wassail Bowl" with a picture of singers and a country house on the inside. 7.9 cm x 13.3 cm.

32. Six gilt-backed cards with Father Christmas, Harlequin and Columbine, dancers at a ball, and humanised turkey, pudding etc.
9.5 cm x 6.5 cm, 6.5 cm x 9.5 cm.

33. Two cards, musicians in the winter snow, and people buying their Christmas goose at a market stall. 10.9 cm x 16.2 cm.

34. Three cards, a Christmas pudding with a slice cut revealing a charm, with appropriate verse telling the recipient's future on the back. 10.7 cm x 7.6 cm.

35. One card, a lady's hand holding a glass of champagne. 6.6 cm x 9.6 cm.

36. Two cards, glass jars with sweets and sugar sticks. 6.6 cm x 9.6 cm.

37. Two cards, a monk taking home the Christmas fare, and a group of carol singers outside a manor house.
8.4 cm x 11.6 cm, 9 cm x 14.5 cm.

# VOLUME 167:
# THE GOOD OLD TIMES

**The nostalgic return to earlier times is featured here, together with an occasional Victorian scene in a set. Some are signed by the artists or publishers.**

*Numbers 1-3 were published by Eyre & Spottiswoode.*

1. Two cards, a mediaeval scene, and a Victorian banquet, with Christmas verses above. 11 cm x 7.8 cm.

2. Two cards (one birthday), no. 334, one design of ladies and gentlemen in Stuart dress, one dated 1884.
10.3 cm x 13 cm.

3. Three cards, no. 344, a Georgian gentleman, at table, knocking at a door, or admiring a lady's portrait.
8.7 cm x 13.4 cm.

4/5. Four cards published by the Artistic Stationery Co., dancers through the ages - two Greek maidens, a couple in mediaeval dress, two Eastern damsels, and a Georgian couple. 11 cm x 15.7 cm.

6. A triptych folder card with blue and gold illuminated design on the outside and the wings, with the card from no. 5 of Eastern damsels inside, unmarked, but presumably the same publishers.
13 cm x 16 cm closed.

7. Two cards, a couple in mediaeval dress, marked A S Co. and dated 1884 by the sender, and another with a mediaeval maiden and a nest of blue tits.
11.9 cm x 14.9 cm, 9.4 cm x 14.5 cm.

8. Four cards, two festive Elizabethan scenes, one a Queen and a page in a circular vignette with patterned illuminated border, the fourth an early Victorian coach and passengers arriving at the Old Bell Tavern. Early 1870's. Sizes up to 11.4 cm x 8 cm.

9. One card showing a knight at a mediaeval tournament receiving the accolade from the Queen of Beauty.
12.8 cm x 16 cm.

10. Two cards with blue and gold patterned border, one with mediaeval minstrels, the other with soldiers, both with appropriate Shakespeare quotations. 14.9 cm x 9.7 cm.

11. Four cards, three designs of two figures in period costume with a Christmas verse below, one on a patterned mount. Three cards have a long Christmas poem on reverse. 5.7 cm x 11 cm, 8 cm x 14.3 cm.

12. Two cards. One shows a King and Queen and courtiers in playing card style costume, with a descriptive verse on

reverse; the other is a black and white picture of an Elizabethan man holding a banner marked 1884, and has a scroll printed "With best wishes from the Mayor and Mayoress, December 31st 1883", and a coat of arms above.
13.2 cm x 10 cm, 13.2 cm x 10.3 cm.

13. Six gilt-backed cards with mediaeval figures from three different sets, one dated 1880 by the sender. 10.5 cm x 8 cm, 6.2 cm x 9 cm, 10.3 cm x 6.7 cm.

14. Four cards, two from the same set with a knight and lady or a Georgian couple in oval vignettes with a verse below. The third card has a knight in armour and a lady, and the fourth, published by H Rothe and signed J P or P J has two lovers in mediaeval costume. 7.9 cm x 12 cm up to 9.8 cm x 14.2 cm.

15/16. Two folding cards signed D Knowles, published by Wirth Bros & Owen. The first, no. 284, has four pictures of the life of Shakespeare; the second is a triptych, no. 285, with pictures of soberly dressed 17th century churchgoers and Shakespeare quotations. Both are printed in blue-black with beige borders.
11.8 cm x 13.2 cm, 12 cm x 13.2 cm, closed.

17/18. Six gilt-edged cards, ladies and gentlemen of the Stuart period in romantic situations, or in a garden with flowers or a curious collection of still life. They have verses or greetings in panels or scrolls.
11 cm x 17 cm, 9.5 cm x 12.6 cm.

19. Three similar smaller cards, two designs of a Georgian couple and a boy or girl presenting a nosegay, with verses on reverse, one signed F Thomson.
7 cm x 11 cm.

20. Three cards, two designs of a lady and gentleman in Georgian dress.
11.7 cm x 15.8 cm.

21. Four cards, two designs, a Stuart party with ladies dancing beneath an arch of swords held by the gentlemen, and a Georgian ball with a lady playing a spinet. 15.8 cm x 11.4 cm.

22. Two cards by G G Kilburne, Georgian card parties, entitled "What shall I play?" and "A game of chance".
14.5 cm x 10.8 cm.

23. Three cards of a set, one called "Tale of Life by the Yule Log", an elderly Georgian couple, "Tale of Love by the Yule Log", a young Regency couple, and "A Fairy Tale by the Yule Log" told to Victorian children. The monogram bears some resemblance to that of Millais. There are narrative verses by A Colville on reverse.
17.5 cm x 12.7 cm.

24. Four cards, boys in Elizabethan costume with a Christmas pudding or a

turkey, and boys and girls in Georgian dress dancing or kissing under mistletoe, with descriptive verses by C J Rowe on reverse. 8.9 cm x 11.4 cm.

25. Three miscellaneous cards, with a Georgian beau or Regency couple, one with a poem by H M B on reverse. Sizes up to 14.3 cm x 9 cm.

26. Two curious cards with a couple in Kate Greenaway style costume, with the titles in reversed print - "Going to Church", or "Ye peacocks". One was dated 1881 by the sender. 7.1 cm x 10.7 cm.

27. Two cards, each with a child by a giant open book with a greeting on one page and a Georgian couple on the other. 13.4 cm x 10.7 cm.

28. Three cards, two with elegant ladies, the third with a Georgian couple in a garden setting, one dated 1880 by the sender, with verses by D A. 10 cm x 15.6 cm.

29. Two gilt-edged cards of the Regency period, a man carving a heart on a tree and a lady reading a letter. 7.2 cm x 14.7 cm.

30. Four cards, each with two men and two women in Regency dress, indoors at a party or outside in the snow. 10.7 cm x 7.6 cm.

31. One card, a man and woman in 17th century Quaker style costume, with a verse below about "this piouse paire". 9.1 cm x 13.5 cm.

32. Two cards, an old lady or gentleman, head and shoulders, in bonnet and ruff Elizabethan style, with a Shakespeare quotation below. 10.5 cm x 10.5 cm.

33. One card, a London Mail Coach, with passengers inside and out. 14.5 cm x 12 cm.

34. A set of four cards showing a village couple and their Christmas feast - preparation, cooking, eating, and resting afterwards, with visions of fairy guests. They have decorative holly borders with descriptive verses, and two have what appears to be the original marked price of 2d - two old pence. 12.3 cm x 10.2 cm.

35. Two cards with patterned borders, one a procession of villagers with garlands, the other a country girl in a woodland scene. 16 cm x 9.2 cm, 18 cm x 7.6 cm.

36. Six miscellaneous cards, ladies and gentlemen in costumes of various periods. Sizes up to 8.6 cm x 12.3 cm.

37. Two cards from Thomas Stevens, a Georgian shepherdess and footman. 11.7 cm x 7.2 cm.

## VOLUME 168: SCOTTISH & IRISH GREETINGS, NURSERY RHYMES, CHRISTMAS SCENES, DOCUMENTARY CARDS

**Many cards with Scottish scenes were intended for New Year greetings, with captions such as a "gude" or a "guid" New Year. A few cards featuring nursery rhyme and fairy tale characters are included, and some Christmas scenes. A number of cards made in imitation of ancient documents, with much use of "Ye Olde" and "Right Joyouse Yule Tyde", appeared about 1885. Some cards are marked with the publisher's or artist's name, including the Irish firm of F Guy, Cork. The cards were published in the earlier 1880's except where otherwise stated.**

1. An illuminated card, clasped hands with Scottish greeting, 1870's. 6.2 cm x 9.5 cm.

2. Four gilt-edged cards, Scottish family scenes showing people at work and at play. 7.7 cm x 12.8 cm, 12.8 cm x 7.7 cm.

3. Five similar, featuring Scotch bonnets and tartans. Sizes up to 8.3 cm x 12.5 cm.

4. A large card, with skaters on St Margaret's Loch in a vignette on a background view of Edinburgh. There is a poem by Lewis Novra on the back, "A Scotch Greeting", of eleven lines, of which five are identical with lines from Burns' "Auld Lang Syne". 18 cm x 14 cm.

5. Two cards, a lady spinning, and three Scotsmen on the ice, both in a decorative holly border. 10.7 cm x 7.6 cm.

6. Two cards, elderly Scotsmen, one in snow dated 1882 by the sender, the other indoors with a dog. 10.2 cm x 12.2 cm.

7. Three cards, a shepherd, a Scot with bagpipes, and two men out shooting, late 1880's. 8.6 cm x 12.5 cm, 9.5 cm x 12.3 cm.

8. Four Irish cards published by F Guy, Cork. One is a map of Ireland with the coats of arms of the four provinces, another black-backed with clasped hands in a floral wreath, the third a bard with a harp, the fourth a sea view with a robin and holly. 12.4 cm x 7.2 cm.

9. Four gilt-edged cards, Irish humour, published by Charles, Reynolds & Co. Two show the New and the Old Year as young and old men, another a Scot and an Irishman drinking, the fourth an Irishman on a donkey, all with descriptive verses in panels. 8.7 cm x 12.9 cm, 12.9 cm x 8.7 cm.

168.3

10. One card, an Irish couple dancing, published by J F Schipper. 11.5 cm x 15 cm.

11. Five small cards, Old Mother Hubbard, Old King Cole, Cinderella, Puss in Boots, Red Riding Hood, 1870's. Sizes up to 6.3 cm x 9.2 cm.

12. One card, Old Mother Goose in flight, published by Raphael Thomson & Co, London, c1870. 7.8 cm x 11.3 cm.

13. Three cards of a set, with the Nursery Rhymes of Sing a Song of Sixpence, Hey Diddle Diddle, and Old Mother Hubbard, adapted for Christmas greeting verses. 12.3 cm x 8.2 cm.

14. A gilt-bordered card "Little Red Riding Hood wishes you a Merry Christmas". 12.2 cm x 15.5 cm.

15. Two cards, Cinderella, Little Miss Muffet. 11.2 cm x 16.3 cm, 9.6 cm x 14.9 cm.

16. Three cards, snowmen, two with a robin, one holding an umbrella against the rain. 6.9 cm x 11.5 cm.

17. Two cards, published by Eyre & Spottiswoode, no. 737, both showing an old lady in the sky plucking feathers from a bird which fall as snow over the village. 11 cm x 15 cm.

18. Two cards, one design of a church in winter with holly and mistletoe and choirboys in a vignette, one with Christmas greeting, one New Year. They have a design of an old church on the back, with a Christmas or New Year verse. 14 cm x 19.5 cm.

19. Four cards, winter scenes in a vignette, with illuminated border and greetings, and holly, mistletoe, or roses in the corners. 6.4 cm x 12.6 cm.

20. Four cards, churchgoers at Christmas time, with verses on reverse. 10 cm x 13.9 cm.

21. Two cards with illuminated borders, one Whitnash Church, Leamington, the other a horse drawn sleigh taking people to a party. 15.3 cm x 11.3 cm, 15 cm x 11.7 cm.

22. Three cards in document style, one with a lady's head in a vignette published by Castell Bros, the other two with a red seal, c1885. Sizes up to 15.3 cm x 11.5 cm.

23. Two cards with seals. One is printed in black and red and marked 1884, with an untraced publisher's monogram; the other is a hand made copy signed A F. 16.3 cm x 13.3 cm.

24. Two cards, one printed in red and black with a gold fleur-de-lys and a red seal, the other a town crier and a greeting in red beginning "Oyez ... ". 11.7 cm x 17.5 cm, 15.1 cm x 13.1 cm.

25. An interesting folder card with a seal and yellow ribbon, dated New Yere 1885, with words for Wolcum Yol, a Christmas carol from the Sloane manuscript, no. 2593, and the words and music of the most ancient English song with musical notes extant, c1226, inside. This was designed and published by Masters Matthews & Hodgson, late of the Royal College of Arms, Heraldic Artists & Genealogists, 113 Regent St and 21 Poland St, London W. 23.5 cm x 14 cm.

26. Another in document style printed in red and blue from "Ye King of Ye Yule Tide" with appropriate heraldic arms of gander, sirloin and pudding, and a decorative border. 21.5 cm x 16.1 cm.

27. A greeting in document form promising the visit of Christmas on December 25th, with a seal and yellow ribbon. 24 cm x 27.5 cm.

28. Two cards in mediaeval style, from G Falkner & Sons, Manchester. 11.7 cm x 16.4 cm, 15 cm x 11 cm.

# VOLUME 169:
# THE SPORTING LIFE

**In the 1880's there was a demand for cards reflecting the sender's, and perhaps the recipient's, recreational activities. Here can be seen bicycles of the penny-farthing style, tennis, swimming, skating, fishing, boating, driving, hunting, and field sports. Most of the cards were issued in the later 1880's, with a few exceptions as listed. Some publishers and an occasional artist appear.**

1. Three cards, two with two boys with penny-farthing bicycles, and a card with two girls in a tricycle with double pedals, published by Davidson Bros, one marked 1885 by the sender. 8.4 cm x 13 cm.

2. Three cards, a sweep, a paper boy, and a negro with banjo, all riding penny-farthing bicycles. 8 cm x 12.4 cm.

3. Two cards, one published by H Rothe with two boys in uniform riding penny-farthing bicycles, another with a boy mounting a similar bicycle, dated 1887 and 1883 by the senders. 15.3 cm x 10.2 cm, 9.3 cm x 13.5 cm.

4. Three cards, tennis players, the ladies in long dresses and hats, the men in white flannels and caps. One card with serrated edges was published in the 1890's. 12.3 cm x 8.8 cm, 15 cm x 6.6 cm, 8.7 cm x 12 cm.

5. Two cards, one design of boys swimming, in two sizes, displaying a blue striped bathing costume, c1890. 6.7 cm x 9.7 cm, 8 cm x 11.5 cm.

6. Four miscellaneous cards, three with people skating, the fourth published by H Rothe with a pair of skates lying beside a frozen lake. 10 cm x 6.8 cm up to 12.7 cm x 9 cm.

7. Two cards. One shows two sporting gentlemen fishing from a small boat, signed F C P, i.e. F Corbyn Price, and published by M H Nathan & Co. The other has two working fishermen setting off from harbour with their nets. 14.4 cm x 10.9 cm, 15 cm x 11 cm.

8. Set of four cards, boats on a lake, two with a lady and gentleman, one with a boy fishing, the fourth a mother rowing with her small son. 15.5 cm x 9.1 cm.

9. Three cards, fishing, two with anglers on a river bank, the third with a man and woman fishing from a punt, all with a fish and a net in the border and verses by S K C on reverse. c1890. 11.1 cm x 15 cm.

10. A card signed Harrison Weir, a horse drawn sledge in a winter landscape, with a descriptive poem by G N L on reverse. 16.1 cm x 11 cm.

11. Four cards c1881, three designs of horse-drawn carts, with descriptive poems on reverse. The fourth card is a later version of one design. 12 cm x 8.3 cm.

12. Three miscellaneous cards. Two have coaches drawn by four horses, the third shows a rider greeting a lady by a gate, dated 1888 by the sender. Sizes up to 11.5 cm x 8 cm.

13. Two cards, steeplechasing, entitled "Down in the Lane", "The Finish", published by J F Schipper, No. 730. 14.8 cm x 9.9 cm.

14. Two cards, one a steeplechase rider, the other a polo match. 11.5 cm x 11.5 cm, 14.7 cm x 9.6 cm.

15. Three cards, hunting scenes, "Going to Cover", "The Find", "The Finish", with narrative verses on reverse. 15.1 cm x 10.1 cm.

16. Two cards, hunting scenes, the Meet, and the Kill, with poems by L N and a design on reverse. c1881. 14.8 cm x 11 cm.

17. Two cards, the huntsman with a hound, and two riders returning home after the hunt. 21 cm x 10.8 cm.

18. Two cards, hunting scenes, jumping the brook, finding a gap, one dated 1884 by the sender. 14 cm x 7.8 cm.

19. Two cards, hunting scenes, one showing the kill with hounds and huntsman, the other printed in sepia with a blue and gold border showing a rider jumping a brook with onlookers cheering. 9.5 cm x 19.2 cm, 13.7 cm x 10.7 cm.

20. Three cards in quodlibet form, with vignettes relating to hunting or fishing, two with narrative poems on reverse. The third is from a set of four used also as a silk fringed folder (see Volume 197). 9 cm x 14.4 cm, 8.5 cm x 14 cm.

21. Three miscellaneous cards, hunting scenes, one in a horseshoe vignette dated 1883 by the sender, another dated 1881, the third a horse and rider in a circular vignette, dated 1884. Sizes up to 11.5 cm x 14.4 cm.

22. Three cards published by W Hagelberg, steeplechasing. 11.4 cm x 8.4 cm.

23. Four miscellaneous cards showing mishaps and excitement on the hunting field, one with a fallen rider and an elegant lady in blue riding dress and tall hat with veil signed by Phiz (Hablot K Browne). The print on this card is similar to that used by Prang, and it may have been published by that firm or Ackermann (see volume 64). 12 cm x 8.3 cm up to 14 cm x 9.6 cm.

24. Two cards, a horse throwing its rider, with a decorative bunch of flowers and foliage. 11.7 cm x 7.7 cm.

25. Five cards, hunting scenes, two embossed with a lady and gentleman and a verse by L N, two of single riders, the fifth a folder opening to show a casualty thrown into a brook. 13.3 cm x 6.4 cm, 6.5 cm x 9.7 cm, 11.4 cm x 7.4 cm.

26. Four miscellaneous cards, two with ladies on horseback, two with hunting gentlemen. Sizes up to 10 cm x 13.4 cm.

27. Four cards, scenes in semi-circular vignettes with motifs of hound, fox, whip and cap, or horn, in a corner above. Three have hunting scenes, one shows a coach and horses at an inn. 13.2 cm x 9.9 cm, 13.5 cm x 9 cm.

28. Three humorous cards with miniature hunting men in pink coats and top hats sitting on a giant whip or horn, with a descriptive verse, one dated 1891 by the sender. 13 cm x 9.5 cm.

29. Three miscellaneous cards, hunting men, one being the first of a series called "O'Flanagan's Mare".
Sizes up to 13.3 cm x 11 cm.

30. Five cards, ladies and gentlemen at the hunt, three designs in two styles.
10 cm x 7.3 cm, 9.9 cm x 6.8 cm.

31. Three cards on thick paper with cut-out edges, showing embossed pictures of horse, fox, or hounds, published by H H & Co. Could this be Hamilton Hills & Co or Hills & Co? The three names are listed separately by Buday. c1890. Sizes up to 11 cm x 14.4 cm.

32. Five miscellaneous cards, four with various hunting scenes c1890, the fifth

showing The Oaks, 1901. This is signed somewhat indistinctly, perhaps by Fred Mason. Sizes up to 9 cm x 13 cm.

33/34. Fourteen small cards, variously dated 1880, 1881, 1882, showing black and white engravings of field sports, signed T S Jones. Sizes up to 11.3 cm x 7.4 cm.

35. Three miscellaneous cards, racing scenes, one signed J A Davis. The large card, a racecourse, was published by J F Schipper, no. 763.
8.2 cm x 5 cm up to 17.5 cm x 12 cm.

# VOLUME 170:
# SOLDIERS & SAILORS

**Colourful uniforms provided inspiration for Christmas cards of the army and navy, and no doubt Victorian pride in the Colonial Empire encouraged their production. Some publishers and artists are named, and most of the cards appeared in the later 1880's and early 1890's, with an occasional interesting reference to the Boer War.**

1. A card designed by Harry Payne and published by M H Nathan, showing a Guards Officer and batmen, titled "I'm going on furlough". 11.4 cm x 15.2 cm.

2. Two cards by Harry Payne published by M H Nathan, one design of a soldier in khaki uniform on patrol abroad, perhaps in Egypt. 9.7 cm x 13.4 cm, 8 cm x 10.6 cm.

3. Two cards, one by Harry Payne, the Gordon Highlanders' Band o' Pipers, the other by R Simkin, the Princess Louise's Argyll & Sutherland Highlanders. 11.2 cm x 8.1 cm, 14.9 cm x 11.3 cm.

4. Two cards by R Simkin, the fifth Royal Irish Lancers, and Drums and Fifes of the Grenadier Guards. 10.7 cm x 15.2 cm, 14.5 cm x 11.5 cm.

5. A card showing a less colourful version of Christmas at home, Coldstream Guards in dark overcoats changing guard in a snowstorm, with an appropriate poem on reverse. 10.4 cm x 14.2 cm.

6. A card with a Chelsea Pensioner drinking a New Year toast, with descriptive poem by S K Cowan on reverse. 10.8 cm x 13.9 cm.

7. Two cards, Highland soldiers, with rifles. 9.8 cm x 13.2 cm, 11 cm x 15 cm.

8. Two cards, Guards and Highlanders, with descriptive poems by Coombes Davies on reverse. 12.3 cm x 9 cm.

9. Two cards published by Bernhard Ollendorff, with a picture of a Grenadier of the 26th Cameronian Foot, 1761. One is a single card, the other a four-page folder with a design on the cover and the Grenadier picture and a verse by R P Scott inside. This is also marked "sold by E C Osborne & Co, Birmingham".
9.4 cm x 13.8 cm.

10. A humorous folder card featuring the Boer War. On the outside a soldier is seen carrying a boar's head, labelled "Boer's head á la khaki", and a boy with a dish of oranges, labelled "Dessert - l'Orange, á la Free State". The card opens to show the British lion roaring at the Dutch boar, and a soldier with the Union flag and the British lion at ease on the map of the Orange Free State and Transvaal, with a poem citing Kipling's "Absent-minded Beggar". 11 cm x 14.4 cm closed.

11. A card with a soldier's hat marked C I V (City Imperial Volunteer), with an apt greeting with large capital letters "Comrade I wish Very many Merry Christmases to you". 8.2 cm x 9.8 cm.

12. Two cards, soldiers on foreign soil, one showing pig sticking, perhaps in India, the other with a soldier and a mule on transport service, this published by Hagelberg.
14.2 cm x 14.2 cm, 15 cm x 10.7 cm.

13. Two cards, later 1890's. One shows General Lord Kitchener on horseback, the other shows red-coated soldiers pitching camp. 8.7 cm x 13.4 cm, 15 cm x 10.8 cm.

14. Four miscellaneous cards with soldiers on horseback, one a folder, another in correspondence style with a space for the sender's name. Sizes up to 12 cm x 9 cm.

15. Four humorous cards of soldiers, titled Meeting, Parting, Length, and Breadth, one dated 1884 by the sender. 7.3 cm x 11 cm.

16. Two humorous cards showing soldiers caught smoking by the Sergeant-Major. 12.2 cm x 8.3 cm.

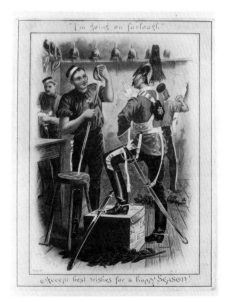

170.1

170.6

17. Eight cards, Christmas time in the army, showing soldiers with a turkey, a pudding, the Yule log, a robin etc, and going on leave. 7 cm x 10.3 cm.

18. Two humorous cards. One has a soldier and a sailor seated on a bench playing a trombone and a violin. The other is a Highlander with a moveable head. 9.5 cm x 13 cm, 9.8 cm x 13.8 cm.

19. Three cards, signed with an untraced monogram, possibly E W. Two are single cards, with soldiers or sailors carrying a Christmas pudding. The third is a folder with the soldier picture and another of a boy on a fence outside, opening to show music for a song "Our Soldiers' Christmas", with words by Lewis Novra. 9.2 cm x 12.2 cm.

20. Five miscellaneous humorous cards, four with soldiers, one with sailors and their Christmas dinner. Sizes up to 9 cm x 12 cm.

21/22. Four well drawn cards of young and old sailors, with narrative poems on reverse about the little middy, the lookout, the old sailor, and Jack Tar. 10.7 cm x 15 cm.

23. Three cards, "Christmas series of England's Defenders Past and Present, chromolithographed from water-colour drawings by Harry Arnold", with appropriate greetings by Eden Hooper. They show sailors manning a gun, or an old sailor with a boy pointing to ancient ships in a harbour. The third card is another card repeating the second design. 13 cm x 10.1 cm, 15.3 cm x 11.5 cm.

24. Two cards from a humorous series "The Tar and a Christmas pudding" showing a sailor on sentry duty looking longingly at a pudding on a nearby window sill. There are descriptive poems by Lewis Novra on reverse. 9.5 cm x 10.1 cm.

25. Three miscellaneous cards with sailors, an officer on deck, a rating doing a hornpipe, and sailors rowing a boat to shore. 7.1 cm x 9 cm, 10.5 cm x 14.7 cm, 13.5 cm x 11.1 cm.

26. Three cards. One shows a group of marines manning a gun; the two others, from another set, show young sailors on duty on board ship. 13.1 cm x 10.7 cm, 7.2 cm x 11.1 cm.

27. A card in correspondence style with space for the names of sender and recipient "To Audrey from her Father, Christmas 1892". It has the coat-of-arms of H M S Anson, and the picture of a black bear marked H & S. 9.4 cm x 13 cm.

## VOLUME 171: "NEGROES", JAPANESE, & OTHERS

**Negroes appeared often as minstrels, dressed in elaborate long-tailed coats, fancy waistcoats, and top hats, as well as in family scenes. Japanese figures were often translated into Western style Christmas situations. One or two publishers are named, and one artist. The cards were published about 1880-1885 unless otherwise stated.**

1. Six cards, printed in red, black and purple, three designs of negro minstrels and one of a couple about to cut into a Christmas pudding with an apprehensive face, one dated 1875 by the sender. One card is on a scallop-edged mount. 10 cm x 6.9 cm, 6.9 cm x 10 cm.

2. Four cards, showing a negress doing her shopping, and a dog stealing her sausages, in oval vignettes on a gilt background, c1875. 7.4 cm x 10 cm.

3. Two gilt-bordered cards, very thin negro minstrels, one sitting on his hat, signed with a monogram C R. There are poems on the back, one called "The Darkie's Wish". 9.2 cm x 13.2 cm.

4. Four cards, three designs in two sizes, negroes in various comic situations. 8.7 cm x 13 cm, 7.5 cm x 11.4 cm.

5. Six cards, signed Ellam, five designs of negroes, three of minstrels on the ice, two of a negress in a sedan chair. One card is a later badly printed copy of one design, another is a trade card for E Peyralbe, Bruxelles, printed in French. 7.7 cm x 11.5 cm.

6. Five cards, negro minstrels, with bones, violin, tambourine, or banjos. Each has a verse by S K Cowan. 7.8 cm x 12 cm.

7. Four cards from two sets, negro minstrels. 8 cm x 12 cm, 6.1 cm x 11.1 cm.

8. Five cards, negro minstrels, including three from one set. 6.4 cm x 9.7 cm up to 8.2 cm x 12.7 cm.

9. Four cards printed in soft colours with pale blue borders, negro minstrels, with punning captions by S K C. 7 cm x 10 cm.

10. One card, a negro boy and girl "The course of true love never did run smooth", with a dog running away after taking a bite at the boy. 10.2 cm x 13.3 cm.

11. Three cards, elderly negroes, Sally at the window, Aunt Chloe with the baby, Uncle Sam reading the paper, with descriptive verses. 7.5 cm x 12 cm.

12/13. Eight cards, from a series of six, in two styles, showing Black Sam playing

tricks on the cook, and the cook's retaliation, with descriptive verses below. 7.5 cm x 10.7 cm, 6.4 cm x 10.9 cm.

14. Two humorous cards, c1890, negroes in kilt or striped trousers being photographed. 14 cm x 10.6 cm.

15. Three miscellaneous cards, negroes, one falling off a penny-farthing bicycle, another with two acrobats, the third with two soldiers in Highland dress. Late 1880's. 9.5 cm x 13 cm, 10.7 cm x 14 cm.

16. Two cards, negroes, a minstrel, and a soldier in Highland dress being chased by a dog. Late 1880's. 9.3 cm x 12.5 cm, 10.6 cm x 13.8 cm.

17. Two cards c1890, one of four black children carrying a curious collection of objects - a small crocodile, a melon, a tortoise, a tusk. The other shows a negro lying in a tub and is marked T B & Co, London. 11.3 cm x 8.7 cm, 8.7 cm x 11.3 cm.

18/19. Ten miscellaneous cards, negroes, including a shaped card with children in bed, and one published by Castell Bros. titled "Old Folks at Home". 1885-90. 5.9 cm x 7.6 cm up to 9.2 cm x 12.5 cm.

20. A card published by Gibbs, Shallard & Co, Australia, picturing an Australian aborigine policeman, with a border of flowers, and a verse headed "Jacky's own story". On the back of the card a letter from the sender about the subject could certainly be described as racist, but may give a fair idea of the attitude c1880 of the white settler to the native. 10.2 cm x 14 cm.

21. A set of four cards with black backgrounds, c1880, each with a different patterned border. They show Japanese figures in Western Christmas situations, singing carols, kissing beneath the mistletoe, boiling the Christmas pudding, and plucking feathers in the sky which turn to snowflakes. 7.5 cm x 11.3 cm.

22. Five cards from a set, Japanese figures in garden settings on gilt ground, with greetings on lanterns, umbrella, or vase, one dated 1878 by the sender. 7 cm x 10.5 cm.

23. A set of four gilt-backed cards, Japanese figures in Christmas situations, dancing, drinking, eating Christmas pudding, or greeting Father Christmas and the New Year. Late 1870's. 10.5 cm x 7 cm.

24. Three cards, Japanese ladies and gentlemen in various situations, with descriptive poems on reverse, one dated 1881 by the sender. 11 cm x 7.3 cm.

25. Five miscellaneous cards, c1880, all with Japanese figures. One has the Yin Yang symbol on a decorative background, and another has three figures studying

177

books with Japanese maxims on reverse.
10.3 cm x 6.3 cm up to 9.2 cm x 18.2 cm.

26. Six small cards in Japanese style with birds, flowers, and figures. 9.5 cm x 4.3 cm.

27. Four cards, small figures in Japanese or Chinese dress, playing or juggling.
9 cm x 6.3 cm.

28. Two embossed cards, children in Japanese dress lying on a large leaf.
12.4 cm x 8.5 cm.

29. A card printed in silver, showing the Ship of Fortune as described in a Japanese legend. "The picture when placed under the pillow on New Year's Eve is said to secure lucky dreams". c1885.
11.4 cm x 15 cm.

30. Six miscellaneous cards with Japanese figures. Three have black backgrounds, one is a silhouette marked M H dep, and another is in correspondence form with space for the names of sender and recipient. 1880's. 8.9 cm x 6.2 cm up to 11.5 cm x 9 cm.

31. Six miscellaneous cards, Japanese figures, flowers, or scene, 1890's.
8.3 cm x 4.7 cm up to 7.8 cm x 11.5 cm.

32. Two unusual cards. One has two small Japanese figures poking an umbrella through an egg, the other has a juggler balancing an egg from which appears a black head smoking a pipe. 7.3 cm x 11 cm.

33. Two cards (one birthday), an Italian shepherd and a peasant girl in traditional dress, and an Eastern potentate being fanned by an attendant maiden.
7.5 cm x 12 cm.

34. Two cards with gilt patterned borders, oriental scenes.  9 cm x 12.4 cm.

35. Three cards, showing Eastern ladies in luxurious surroundings, one card on a patterned mount. Two cards have poems on reverse.
11 cm x 7.3 cm, 14.2 cm x 10.3 cm.

## VOLUME 172:
## TOPICAL & MUSICAL CARDS, WITH SOME MISCELLANEOUS EXAMPLES

The few topical and political cards in the collection are included here, with some musical subjects. The remaining miscellaneous cards cannot be fitted in to any special subject category. A few publishers are identified, and there are some artists' monograms. The cards are dated in the 1880's with a few exceptions as noted.

1. The Prince of Wales, c1875, in uniform on a scallop-edged card. 6.1 cm x 9 cm.

2. Two cards, Gladstone and Irish Home Rule. One is a cartoon with a poem, published by H S C & Co. London, and signed Eustace 1887. The other has a long poem by T Brown flanked by borders with pictures of Gladstone, the Irish harp, and the rose, thistle and shamrock national flowers, marked Kilburn Lith. Nottm, with flowers in a vase on the other side.
16.2 cm x 10.6 cm, 11.3 cm x 14.7 cm.

3. One card, showing John Bright's head breaking through a paper with Reform Club heading and "A Bright Ornament at the foot, and a fishing rod and basket labelled "from Rochdale to Inverness".
11.8 cm x 16.7 cm.

4. One card entitled "The Benefits of the Age - the Phonograph". This shows four men drinking champagne in an office, with one holding the mouthpiece of the instrument talking to his wife, "Shall be late home, dear, heavy mail tonight".
c1890. 11 cm x 15 cm.

5. Two cards featuring ladies from Gilbert & Sullivan's "Mikado", "We're very wide awake to-night, the Moon & I", and "Three Little Maids from School".
10.8 cm x 16.6 cm.

6. A Salvation Army man playing a concertina, with poem "Who killed the cow? I with my row ...". 11 cm x 14.6 cm.

7. Three cards, Indian scenes. These may have been inspired by Queen Victoria's proclamation as Empress of India, 1877, or more likely, by the Colonial and Indian Exhibition of 1886. 10.6 cm x 14.3 cm.

8/9. Four cards, scenes from the Colonial and Indian Exhibition of 1886, each with the Ode written by Lord Tennyson for the occasion on reverse. It is interesting to see that each verse ends with the words "Britons hold your own".
15.2 cm x 11.5 cm.

10. A birthday card, with "Colonial and Indian Exhibition, London, 1886" at the foot, and a vignette with "the Gardens and Prince Albert Monument" set in a Montreal scene. This was published by S & N (Sockl & Nathan). 11.5 cm x 14.6 cm.

11. Two cards, cartoons signed A B picturing a Miss Olga Brandon and a Mrs J H Riddell, each with a verse by F L. These might, from the tone of the poem, have some reference to a cause celebre.
12.7 cm x 10.5 cm, 13 cm x 10.5 cm.

12. Four cards with gilded scalloped edges, illuminated borders, and a small attached scrap over a Christmas carol with music, or a greeting. This set illustrates the problems of cataloguing, as two of these cards might have been put in the Religious section. c1875. 8 cm x 12 cm.

13. Two cards, small vignettes with figures, and a Christmas hymn or carol with music, in a holly border, c1875.
12.2 cm x 6.6 cm.

14. Presentation Music for Christmas and New Year, with a Father Christmas scrap and space for the name of sender and recipient. This contains a song "Hail Christmas" with words by J N Cooper, music by John H L Glover, and was published by Bertini, Seymour & Co, 40 Poland St, London. 18 cm x 25.6 cm.

15. One card, with "While Shepherds Watched" in bold gilt letters over a bar of music, and a poem by Mrs Hemans on reverse. 15.1 cm x 11.2 cm.

16. An interesting four-page folder card, in memory of Mendelssohn. There is a design of various musical instruments in a wreath of flowers on the cover, and another wreath with his birth and death dates and the titles of some of his works on a ribbon wreath; inside there is a portrait in a wreath of spring flowers and a scroll with music of the War March of the Priests from Athalie. c1880? 11.2 cm x 13.5 cm closed.

17. Two cards, a violin leaning against a chair with a poem by F L on reverse, and another with a violin and bow published by Smily & Co, dated 1888 by the sender.
7.5 cm x 14 cm, 11.4 cm x 8.8 cm.

18. Two embossed cards, each with a bunch of coins including a shilling and a threepenny piece dated 1882.
6.7 cm x 10.2 cm.

19. Two cards published by Davidson Bros, one with a candle and a box of cigars, another with several tankards, a box of matches, and a scroll, in a border of vine leaves. 12.9 cm x 8.1 cm.

20. Two cards, a decorated china teapot and a jar on patterned backgrounds.
10.1 cm x 10.1 cm.

21. Two cards, one the Heavens on Christmas Night, with silver stars and a comet, another with snow falling from a moonlit sky on to the globe of the world.
12.7 cm x 11 cm, 10.2 cm x 6.7 cm.

22. Two gilt-bordered cards, silhouette profile of a lady or a gentlemen in an oval vignette, tied up like a parcel with a pencil slotted through the cord. 6.9 cm x 9.9 cm.

23. Five cards, four designs showing palettes or paint boxes and brushes, three with small cards, specimens of the artists' work. 12.2 cm x 9.2 cm.

24/25. Five cards, without greetings, with figures of men or women holding large flowers, satirizing the aesthetic movements of the 1880's, probably inspired by Gilbert & Sullivan's opera "Patience" and perhaps lampooning Oscar Wilde. 8.7 cm x 14.4 cm, 10 cm x 15.9 cm.

# HUMOUR

This section has no monopoly of humour, much of which has already appeared with early cards and with the publishers dealt with fully in previous sections. The cards here have themes which can be taken as comic or satirical, from publishers who specialise in such, of whom Alfred Gray and Angus Thomas are the most prominent, and from firms, some of whose cards have already appeared under subject headings, with similar unattributed cards. There are some from 1875-80, but most were published from 1880-1900, with a few from the 20th century.

Some cards still dwell on the popular theme of fun and problems with the humanised Christmas dinner, but the stock comic situations now involve courting couples, father and baby, boys at war with policemen, animals bringing chaos to their owners, elderly gentlemen losing their balance and their dignity on the ice, aesthetes held up to ridicule, and the "mashers" of the 90's and early 1900's. The "sentiments" on the cards of the 90's became punning variations on the illustrations, which extend, as Gleeson White said, to "facsimiles of coins, corkscrews, razors, or hairpins, for the sake of a punning legend underneath ... and to imitations of unlovely objects, luggage labels, cork soles, slices of blankets or bacon ... and other horrors, to accompany a message of goodwill to their friends". Perhaps this was the usual commercial response to popular demand.

The situations on the cards are mostly concerned with people and the objects criticised above, but the robins of Robert Dudley's cards for Castell Bros. have been included here with a range of his work. More humour with animals and birds appears in the succeeding sections, 15 and 16.

Section
14

173.3

## VOLUME 173:
## HUMOUR. CARDS
## PUBLISHED BY ALFRED GRAY

**These cards were printed from pen and ink drawings, usually with gold borders, and were published in the early 1880's. Alfred Gray himself designed a number of the cards, and others were by W G Baxter. Many lampooned the politics, fads, and foibles of the age, in particular the aesthetic and artistic movements. A similar set by A Page, publisher unknown, is included at the end.**

1. Four cards by W G Baxter caricaturing the Egyptian campaigns of 1881-2, entitled Kassassin - Heroic charge of the Guards, Admiral Seymour's ultimatum and Arabi's defiance, Lord Charles Beresford's Little Game, Bombardment of Alexandria and evacuation by Arabi. 16.2 cm x 8.7 cm.

*Numbers 2-15 were designed by Alfred Gray.*

2/3. Four interesting political cartoons, with red border and greetings in antique style, in which many leading politicians can be identified. A typical title is "Westminster Minstrelsie, a Glee in Foure Parties". 20.5 cm x 13.4 cm.

4. Five cards from two sets, lampooning the aesthetic and artistic movements of the 1880's. The ladies and gentlemen depicted have clothes as seen in "Patience", decorated with sunflowers and peacock feathers. 8 cm x 13.5 cm.

5. Two cards featuring Kate Greenaway style children in a background of sunflowers, carrying feathers and large flowers or Japanese fans and sunshades, with a humorous verse below, a clever combination caricaturing two rather different Victorian enthusiasms in the same picture. 19.2 cm x 10.2 cm.

6. Two cards, mothers and children in Kate Greenaway style outfits taking a walk. 15.4 cm x 10 cm.

7. Two cards, ladies in elegant coats and bonnets, one under a mistletoe twig, the other by a tree branch with robins. 9.6 cm x 14.2 cm.

8. Four cards, family scenes - dancing, skating, at table, two dated 1880, 1881. 11.6 cm x 9.3 cm.

9. Two cards, fairy lovers under a mushroom being teased by mischievous goblins, and two childish sweethearts with irate father and mother approaching. 15.1 cm x 11.2 cm.

10. Three valentines with fairies, one with a robin postman. 15.4 cm x 11.5 cm, 15.7 cm x 11.7 cm.

11. Six cards, the story of a Rugby football match, showing the game, the casualties, and a player being tossed in a blanket. 11.8 cm x 9.4 cm.

12. Three cards, one a farmer and a scarecrow, another the Colonel greeting friends on a walk with dogs, the third a repeat in different format of one design in no. 11. 14.4 cm x 11 cm, 11.8 cm x 9.4 cm.

13. Three cards, a Georgian scene of a lady with two beaux, and two smaller cards showing a mother and children out walking in snow or rain. 11.2 cm x 15.3 cm, 9.7 cm x 10 cm.

14. Two cards, policemen in trouble with a small dog. 12.1 cm x 10 cm.

15. Two cards, a lady walking a dog with an admirer watching, and an old woman in a snowstorm accompanied by a duck and family, a pig, a goat and a dog. This has been coloured by hand. 9 cm x 11.5 cm, 14.4 cm x 11.2 cm.

16. Two four-page folder cards with illuminated designs of birds and flowers on three sides. One has an attached picture of geraniums and berries hand painted on celluloid, but the picture is missing from the other. These are not strictly speaking humorous cards, but are included here as products of Alfred Gray. 11.6 cm x 11.6 cm, 13.3 cm x 16.2 cm.

*Numbers 17-24 were designed by W G Baxter.*

17. Two cards, a farmer with a pitchfork and "Happy Christmas" on his overalls, and a man rising from a bench with Merry Christmas in wet paint transferred in reverse to his coat, one dated 1881 by the sender. 9.7 cm x 12.2 cm.

18. A convict on a treadmill, "Such is Life", dated 1881 by the sender. 9.2 cm x 12.7 cm.

19. Two small cards, silhouettes of policeman and Punchinello, and children with a Punch and Judy show, one dated 1883 by the sender. 6 cm x 8.7 cm, 8.7 cm x 6 cm.

20. Five valentine cards from two sets, caricatures of loving couples, with verses from Tennyson, Thomas Moore, Burns, and Shelley. 9.7 cm x 9.7 cm, 9 cm x 11.7 cm.

21. Two valentine cards, one "To my Romeo" - an actor on a stage, the other two lovers and chaperon crossing a river on stepping stones, this with a quotation from the Hon. Mrs Norton. 8.5 cm x 14 cm, 13.2 cm x 11.3 cm.

22. Two cards, one with mischievous boys and an old man with a telescope on the edge of a cliff, the other a skating party with ladies admiring the curate executing a figure 1883. 14.7 cm x 10.9 cm.

23. Three coloured cards from a set of four, showing small urchins and their dog playing tricks on a policeman, one dated 1887 by the sender. 11.5 cm x 15.3 cm.

24. "The Nile Expedition", no. 2 of the series, Gordon in sight, the famous relief campaign somewhat cruelly caricatured. 17.8 cm x 11.4 cm.

25. Two cards. One has two men on a boat with greetings on the sail and flag, by W G Baxter. The other, a valentine designed by Harry Furniss, has a young lady and her lover with father apparently asking his intentions. 14.2 cm x 11 cm, 13.6 cm x 11 cm.

26. Three cards, pen and ink drawings similar to those in no. 4 by Alfred Gray, one signed Page, one A P. A P is listed by Buday as having designed for Schipper and H & F. One is dated 1881 by the sender. 7.5 cm x 12.1 cm.

## VOLUME 174:
## HUMOUR. VARIOUS
## PUBLISHERS

**This volume has cards from known publishers, some of whose cards have already appeared in sections 11 and 12. The well known artist and illustrator, Robert Dudley, designed many cards for Castell Bros, and his humorous cards for that firm, of people, birds, and the personified Christmas dinner, appear here.**

1. Three cards published by Ernest Falck, two designs of a winter landscape concealing a Father Christmas face, with caption on reverse "In this landscape you can trace a jolly Father Christmas face", registered at Stationers' Hall 19-5-1879. The third card is on a silver-bordered mount, and opens to show another card with a small boy wreathed in flowers. This card is one of a set, volume 19 no. 1, listed as published by Canton from similarity of design and technique, and the silver-bordered mount was also used by J Mansell, so the folder could have been a made-up card from products of different publishers. 11.4 cm x 7.2 cm, 12 cm x 8 cm.

*Numbers 2-11 were published by Castell Bros. and designed by Robert Dudley, dated in the late 1880's or early 1890's.*

2. Five cards no. 500, a set of four designs showing the Christmas activities of humanised robins including "Robin the Mail", a popular card showing Robin Redbreast as a highwayman being shot by policeman Sparrow. The fifth card, no. 520, is a later reprint of one design, marked "printed in Bavaria". 11.6 cm x 9 cm.

3. Two cards from set no. 501, showing owls at table, and birds as carol singers. 11.6 cm x 9 cm.

4. Three cards from set no. 502, with turkeys dressed as Shakespearean characters seen in scenes from Macbeth, Othello, and Hamlet. 11.6 cm x 9 cm.

5. Three cards from set no. 503 with birds as fairy tale and nursery rhyme characters, in scenes from Cinderella, Red Riding Hood, and Little Jack Horner. 11.6 cm x 9 cm.

6. Set of four cards, no. 504, "The Whirligig of Time", showing Father Time in various scenes - Greeting Time, Present Time, Playing Time, Coming Time. These cards were issued in packs of a dozen in boxes with an appropriate picture on the lid. 11.6 cm x 9 cm.

7. Three cards from set no. 505, various scenes with Father Christmas in different guises, as St Anthony resisting the temptation of a Christmas dinner, as Friar Tuck with Robin Hood, and as Old King Cole with three bird fiddlers. 11.6 cm x 9 cm.

8. One card with owls as country gentlemen meeting on a walk in the snow, no. 526, printed in Bavaria. 9.5 cm x 14.1 cm.

9. Two cards, family scenes with humanised robins, nos. 525, 622, printed in Bavaria. 14 cm x 9.4 cm, 14.4 cm x 9.2 cm.

10. Four embossed folding cards with serrated edges (two with covers only), owls dressed as admiral, general, barrister, or bishop, 1890's. 8.8 cm x 11.6 cm.

11. Four similar with robins as choristers, holding music. 9.5 cm x 11.8 cm.

12. Three miscellaneous cards published by Castell Bros. One has a clock with a punning verse below, another signed E T Reed shows an apprehensive group on a seaside switchback, the third has three Irish folk with a verse by Lever. All were printed in Bavaria, late 1880's. 7.4 cm x 13.5 cm, 13.5 cm x 11 cm, 12.1 cm x 10.4 cm.

13. "A Page of Christmas confessions", published by Castell Bros, a folder card showing favourite motto, occupation, flower, dish etc. 10.2 cm x 12.5 cm closed.

14. Three cards published by H Rothe, vegetables in human guise, one as a cook, and two as "mashers". c1880. no. 361. 11.6 cm x 8.9 cm.

15. Three miscellaneous cards published by H Rothe, a cock in man's clothing, a personified bottle, sirloin, and Christmas pudding dancing on a plate, and a goblin attacking a fish with a spear, nos. 433, 334, 375. Sizes up to 13 cm x 9 cm.

16/17. Six cards, comic Christmas scenes showing waits, mishaps to the Christmas dinner, and naughty boys snowballing unwary victims. These are marked B Bros, probably Baddeley. 12.7 cm x 12.3 cm.

*Numbers 18-20 were published by W Hagelberg in the late 1880's.*

18. Four cards, two showing a curate knocked down by a tobogganning boy, another with an inebriated farmer talking to a scarecrow, the fourth a disappointed Scotsman before a shut-up inn, nos. 90, 269. Two have narrative verses by E E Griffin. 7.5 cm x 10.7 cm, 8.3 cm x 12.8 cm.

19. Four miscellaneous cards, a muffin man, the Modern Troubadour with a tuba, dated 1890 by the sender with a verse by E E G on reverse, (numbers indistinct), a postman falling on a slide, no. 102, and Bumble the Beadle, no. 225. Sizes up to 8.3 cm x 12 cm.

20. Three cards showing the same design used differently. The first has four policemen leaning over a garden wall with a verse by E E Griffin "A maid was in the garden", with their back views on the back of the card, no. 757. The other two cards show the front and the back views of three of the policemen with descriptive poems by E E G on reverse, no. 758. 13.2 cm x 9.6 cm, 9.4 cm x 11.2 cm.

21. Three cards published by Ernest Nister, with embossed borders, c1890. One shows a country gentleman in a railway carriage looking apprehensively at an approaching mother with a crying child, another has two cricketers chasing a dog with their ball in its mouth, and the third shows an irate farmer demanding compensation from a sportsman for a slaughtered duck. Nos. 2455, 1476, 2455. 10.1 cm x 12.3 cm, 12.3 cm x 10.1 cm.

22. Three miscellaneous cards published by M H Nathan & Co., an artist painting a bull's portrait, a young archer, and a Scot with bagpipes. All approximately 8.2 cm x 12 cm.

23. Two cards, one marked J F S (Schipper), a wooden board or slate. One has a pencil drawing of a boy with a sunflower in Greenaway costume, labelled "Like K Greenery". The other has children's drawings mixed up with sums. 10.5 cm x 13 cm, 13.3 cm x 10.5 cm.

24. Three similar cards, slates with sums and drawings, one marked J F S. 9.6 cm x 12 cm.

25. One card, a policeman retrieving his helmet (probably one of a set involving naughty boys), published by Davidson Bros., designed by W Ellam. 10.1 cm x 13.7 cm.

26. Two cards published by Misch & Stock, with carriages, cab and farm cart racing in the snow. They have appropriate quotations from Dickens on reverse. 12.2 cm x 8.2 cm.

27. A card printed from an ink drawing in red and black, showing the good things of life in red and the bad in black. This was published by M & Co (Mowbray?), and designed by J B C. 12.8 cm x 9 cm.

## VOLUME 175: HUMOUR. CARDS FROM UNKNOWN PUBLISHERS FROM 1875-1890

*Numbers 1-6 were published 1875-80.*

1. Three cards with scalloped embossed edges. One shows a man with a bouquet of flowers for the New Year. Two have attached opening book covers, "The Whole Duty of Man", and "The Woman in White", with appropriate comic pictures within. 7 cm x 10.3 cm, 6.6 cm x 9.5 cm.

**174.20**

2. Three cards printed in red and black, one showing a humanised sirloin, the others with a goose attacking a man and a pudding hitting a clown. 10 cm x 5.8 cm.

3. Two cards, the cook frightening a boy stealing jam from the larder, and a farmer's boy with the ghost of his donkey. 9 cm x 7.3 cm, 10 cm x 10 cm.

4. A set of four cards signed F W or E W, three showing comic figures in a balloon, a boat, or sitting on a fence, the fourth with Father Christmas. 6.7 cm x 9.3 cm.

5. Six embossed cards, five from one set of street vendors, policeman and sandwich man, with a similar card from another set. 6.5 cm x 10.1 cm, 7 cm x 12.5 cm.

6. Three miscellaneous cards, the humanised Christmas dinner, one entitled "Songs Without Words" showing a pig playing the piano. Sizes up to 11.2 cm x 7.6 cm.

*Numbers 7-14 were published in the early 1880's.*

7. Five cards, four designs, two with children and an elephant, and two with a donkey running away with its rider. 9.8 cm x 8 cm.

8. Five cards from a set of six with orange borders, showing a dancing bear, mischievous boys, skaters, and a gentleman with a drink at a bar. (The missing card has bicycles, much sought after by collectors, and has eluded this collection). 7.1 cm x 10.3 cm.

9. Two cards, humorous pictures with a red pillar box, headed "Just caught the post". 9.4 cm x 13.4 cm.

10. A set of four cards, showing the tribulations of a gentleman in the snow at Christmas time. 7.3 cm x 11.3 cm.

11. Four cards, various Christmas scenes, the arrival of the turkey, delivery of a hamper, small boy snowballing policeman, and boy waits arousing an irate old man. 7.3 cm x 11.3 cm.

12. Two cards, a fiddler playing and children dancing, and a gentleman in evening dress playing a drum with a country boy playing a fiddle, singed E W or F W. There are narrative poems by Lewis Novra on reverse. 9.3 cm x 13 cm.

13. Four cards, a sportsman accidentally shooting a pig, an old lady in a cart with animals, and two country scenes with horse and cart or donkey, one signed C White. Sizes up to 14 cm x 10.9 cm.

14. Three cards, boys tying a firework to a policeman's coat, an old man falling through the ice, and a dentist extracting a

tooth assisted by a boy pulling his coat tails. 10.7 cm x 8.9 cm.

*Numbers 15-33 were published from 1885-90.*

15. Two cards showing a lady and gentleman watching a race from a bench, which broke and landed them on the ground. These cards have an interesting silk finish. 10.5 cm x 13.7 cm.

16. Two cards showing loving couples with sardonic captions. The first had two donkeys in the background, "Two more not far off", the second, with geese, is marked "Any amount of us". 11 cm x 14 cm.

17. Three cards, well dressed men and women on a switchback, a barrister with lady client, and a "Masher" for sale. 14.2 cm x 10.7 cm, 13 cm x 10 cm.

18. A card with seventeen men's faces grouped around a billiard table, some of which might be identifiied as contemporary portraits. There is a verse by J H Goring on the reverse with many punning allusions to billiards. 11.4 cm x 14 cm.

19. Three cards, comic figures representing England, Scotland, and Ireland. 8.2 cm x 11 cm.

20. Four cards, "mashers" through the ages, from Elizabethan times to the present. 8.1 cm x 12 cm.

*Note: The definition of "masher", a word not often encountered in the 1980's though in common use in the 1880's and 90's, is: - "A fop posing as a lady killer".*

21. A shaped card, showing a gentleman in a striped costume diving from a bathing machine into a group of ladies being "ducked" by the attendant. 12.3 cm x 8.4 cm with a triangular addition.

22. Three miscellaneous cards, a boy barrister, Mr Pickwick, and an aesthetic young man with lilies and sunflower dated 1887 by the sender. Sizes up to 8.4 cm x 12 cm.

23. Three cards, policemen, one with mistletoe and two having problems with a clown or small boys. Sizes up to 10.5 cm x 14.1 cm.

24/25. Eight miscellaneous cards, including skaters, a policeman and his sweetheart, a family scene at bathtime, boys snowballing an old lady, and men in trouble with animals or fish. 7 cm x 9.5 cm up to 13 cm x 9.5 cm.

26. Four miscellaneous cards, a footman playing the piano before an admiring maidservant, a dog tearing a boy's coat tails, a gentleman with a Christmas

hamper, and a hairdresser with a bald customer and a verse by R P Scott on reverse. Sizes up to 9.3 cm x 12.4 cm.

27. Three cards, slates with humorous drawings and greetings. 7.8 cm x 11 cm.

28. Four cards signed E C M, from pen and ink sketches, people in difficulties, a rider about to go over a cliff, unhappy folk on board ship in a rough sea, an invalid with his feet in mustard and water, and a mischievous dog. 12.4 cm x 8.8 cm.

29. Two similar cards, one of an old man by E C M, another a man posting greetings on a wall. 8.8 cm x 12.4 cm, 11.4 cm x 9.3 cm.

30. Two cards, gentlemen in trouble, one clinging to a punt pole, the other being thrown out by irate father. 10.2 cm x 15.1 cm, 10.5 cm x 14.1 cm.

31. Four miscellaneous cards, a snowman and a scarecrow dancing, a cook offering a tit-bit to the Man in the Moon, an oval card with goats and a man with a face like a goat, and a card with Humpty-Dumpty-like figures riding on pigs, by Maud Goodwin. Sizes up to 14.3 cm x 9 cm.

32. Four cards or prints, a bird dressed as a "masher" making unwelcome advances to ladies, printed in red and gold. 7.4 cm x 11.2 cm.

33. Three cards, "mashers". Two are gilt-edged with comic characters in eccentric clothes; the third has two gentlemen in top hats and frock coats saying "How d'ye do". 7.5 cm x 10.5 cm, 9.1 cm x 13 cm.

34/35. Four cards signed W A H, which might be the artist or the writer of the accompanying comic verses. Three have topical interest, showing Nelson's column, a real match and a verse about "strikers", and a bunch of bills and a verse about Jubilee Year. The fourth has a Christmas hamper. 9 cm x 11.6 cm, 11.6 cm x 9 cm.

36. Three cards, from pen and ink sketches. One is a curious drawing showing skeletons, date uncertain. The other two have motor-cars, one with an apt quotation from Macbeth, perhaps published c1900. 15 cm x 10.8 cm, 11.2 cm x 8.8 cm.

37. A card in the form of a letter enclosing a free ticket for the "Happy Time Line" for 1888-89. 18 cm x 11.3 cm.

## VOLUME 176: HUMOUR. CARDS PUBLISHED BY JONATHAN KING & ANGUS THOMAS

These cards appeared in the late 1890's or early 1900's. Most are adorned by coloured scraps, and have appropriate verses making full use of puns to illustrate the pictures and give a Christmas message.

1. Two cards published by Jonathan King. One is perhaps a valentine in reverse, with a real hook and two eyes, and the verse "you'll take your (hook) if you are wise, or my brother will give you (two black eyes)". The other, marked 1897, has an embossed sovereign and florin, both incorporated into the punning verse.
8.3 cm x 8.3 cm, 13.5 cm x 8 cm.

*Numbers 2-22 were published by Angus Thomas.*

2. A blue-bordered card with a coloured scrap of King Edward VII and a verse below about "King Edward, Britain's pride", an exception without puns. It is numbered 375, which gives some clue to the dates of the other cards, filed roughly in order of number, as this was probably issued in 1901 or 1902. 10 cm x 13 cm.

3. Four cards, with coloured scraps of a nurse with triplets, a door mat marked "Welcome", an inebriated man in a horse trough, and two lovers wrapped in a shawl. Three are numbered 19, 19, 20.
Sizes up to 11 cm x 10 cm.

4. A folder card with a scrap of a small Cupid - "With sweet wishes for a Kissmassy Kissmas". No. 45.
9.3 cm x 13.3 cm.

5. Three folder cards, with scraps of a lady at a piano, a train "My Festive Train of Thought", and a husband and wife with Christmas goodies, all having other scraps and verses within. Nos. 82, 62, 121.
Sizes up to 14 cm x 9 cm.

6. Four cards, a stammering man, a sideboard with two mugs, a pipe and tobacco, and a rail ticket "Railway of Life, from Heart to Heart". Three are numbered 15, 119, 128, and the fourth is a postcard from the Popular Series.
Sizes up to 14 cm x 9 cm.

7. Four cards. Two are unnumbered with a rail ticket or a dice. The third has a flap opening to show two lovers kissing, no. 67, and the fourth has a target, no. 17.
Sizes up to 13 cm x 8 cm.

8. Four cards, one with a lady on a bicycle, no. 212, another with a man in his underwear beneath a hallstand with his clothes, no. 103. The other two are folders, one with a couple by the fireside, the other with two lovers kissing, nos. 41, 22.
Sizes up to 12.6 cm x 9 cm.

9. Four cards, all with scraps of loving couples in humorous situations, two numbered 200, 324.
Sizes up to 9.5 cm x 12 cm.

10. Four cards. One has a tennis racquet - "At every ball may you be courted ...", another shows a goose and Father Christmas holding a line full of Christmas fare - "A line of good cheer", and a third

has a fabric ivy leaf ..."Turn this new leaf o'er", no. 150. The fourth card, perhaps the prize specimen in this volume, has a pair of pink paper bloomers, with the caption "Wishing you a warm and comfy Christmas and a bloomer-ing fine New Year", no. 227.
11.5 cm x 9 cm, 9 cm x 11.5 cm.

11. Four unnumbered cards. One has a pair of bellows, another a pipe, glass, and cards. The third has a Union Flag with the caption "England expects every man to do his Duty and Pay, Pay, Pay!" The fourth is a surprisingly tasteful card with a bird and two lines of the "Auld Lang Syne" music embossed in gold, with acceptable puns "I send you Bars of Gold and Notes as well ...". 9 cm x 11.5 cm.

12. Four cards, three with a variety of scraps, a cradle, a clock, a silver tea-pot with a cheque for ?5,000 a year. The fourth has two opening flaps labelled History, Herstory, with appropriate scraps beneath, no. 209. Sizes up to 13 cm x 9.8 cm.

13. Four cards with serrated edges. Three are unnumbered, with a tram ticket punched at "Merry Christmas to Happy New Year", a cup of tea, and a man in a chair. The fourth has a set of three decanters with comic heads as stoppers, no. 285 - "Hoping that your Christmas spirits won't be diluted with care's cold water". 10.2 cm x 11 cm, 8.4 cm x 12.9 cm.

14. Three cards, a pot of jam and a spoon, a girl alarmed by a mouse which "ran up the clock of her pretty red sock", no. 218, and a man and woman with umbrellas, no. 154.
8.9 cm x 11.5 cm, 8 cm x 14 cm,
11.7 cm x 10.3 cm.

15. Four cards, a bull tossing a man, a girl turning a somersault, a man with a Christmas pudding, and another falling from steps, nos. 334, 342, 373, 369.
Sizes up to 8.8 cm x 12.8 cm.

16. Six cards, five with serrated edges. Two are folders, with a pudding or a sirloin, three have turned down corners, with umbrella, lady, or hand, the sixth has a tartan ribbon. Two are numbered 344, 463. Sizes up to 10.5 cm x 7.5 cm.

17. Four cards with serrated edges, and scraps of a gallows, a hand with cigarette no. 483, a hand and an eye, and a soldier in khaki with the Union Flag.
7.7 cm x 11 cm up to 9.8 cm x 13 cm.

18. Four cards, three with scraps of shamrock and a green coat, a pair of trousers, and an anvil. The fourth is a folder with a donkey and a devil ... "I'm just in the Nick of time ...", no. 534.
Sizes up to 14.4 cm x 10 cm.

19. Four cards. Two are octagonal with serrated edges and scraps of a pan and a pudding, or a chair, knife and fork and plate. The third has a dress shirt. The fourth achieves the nadir of bad taste with a man hunting a flea in his bed ... "With Hearty Wishes that you'll catch the Flea-ting pleasures of a merry Christmas ..." No. 564. Sizes up to 13 cm x 10 cm.

20. Two cards. One has a Jack-in-the-Box with a pleasant verse and no puns, and is a postcard with a trademark on the reverse side for the address. The other shows the bare shoulders of a pretty girl ... "She wore a wreath of roses", but on lifting the flap "and her other clothes of course". No. 549.
14 cm x 8.7 cm, 7.6 cm x 12.1 cm.

21. Four cards with various scraps, a man with a trunk, herrings (3d lb) and sprats, lipsalve (for a sweet, sweet Kissmas), and a gouty foot in a bandage. Nos. 343, 489, 524, 756. Sizes up to 8 cm x 12.7 cm.

176.17

176.15

22. Three cards from a set, with scraps of a fiddle, a carrot and a turnip, and a man falling off a bicycle, one dated 1901 by the sender, another numbered 790.
8.3 cm x 13 cm.

*Numbers 23-29 are similar in style, but unmarked.*

23. Four cards with fancy edges.
a) A cook, whose apron lifts to show a bottle of gin.
b) A folding card with an embossed picture of a shirt on the front, with the man inside behind a towel on which is written a verse of greeting.
c) An embossed picture of a lifebuoy - "Hoping you will always go Swimmingly ..."
d) A folding card with a scrap of half an apple and a punning verse inside.
Sizes up to 9 cm x 12 cm.

24. Two cards with scraps. One has a purse, with a pound of sausages inside. The other has a meat safe - "You'll find herein a little Fish, and just a little Pastry ..." The "pastry" is a young lady labelled "Sweet little tart", hardly in the best of taste, but perhaps acceptable to the recipient as the card is marked "To George, from Henry".
9 cm x 13.3 cm., 13.3 cm x 9 cm.

25. Two cards. One has an attached button ... "Who does not care a ...". The other has a lace trimmed nightcap hiding a glass of good cheer.
14.2 cm x 11.2 cm, 13 cm x 9.7 cm.

26. A card with a scrap of Father Christmas drinking a toast and a verse ending "But 'mid the Feasting have a care Remember! You've a liver". 9 cm x 13.7 cm.

27. Two cards, a barrister drinking the Christmas spirit while sitting on a case, and a lady in bloomers riding a bicycle ... "Don't forget the A-tyre".
8.1 cm x 12.7 cm, 12.2 cm x 8 cm.

28. Four cards, photograph of a turkey, a case of cigars, twin high chairs "May each Christmas double your joys ...", and a gilded knocker and letterbox, all used to illustrate punning verses.
7.5 cm x 12.5 cm up to 10 cm x 14 cm.

29. Four cards, two with a chair "Best wishes for a chairful Christmas". The third has a scrap of a spoon, lifting to show a message, the fourth opens to show a three-dimensional scene of armchairs around a table with drinks and cigars.
12.5 cm x 7.8 cm up to 15 cm x 7.9 cm.

30. Two cards in the shape of luggage labels, one with a negro mother and baby in a tub, marked Dennison's novelty, the other a turkey in top hat holding a bottle, marked with Angus Thomas's trademark.
15 cm x 7.2 cm.

## VOLUME 177:
## HUMOUR.  MORE CARDS OF THE 1890's & 1900's

**Most of these cards were published in the late 1890's and early 1900's, though a few very similar ones were dated by the senders well into the 20th century. Some are marked with the publishers' names or initials, including a number by Hills & Co, H H & Co, and E H. As all these firms have cards marked "Unique series", it is possible that they are the same, but definite evidence of this is not available. They continue the Angus Thomas style of pictures inspiring punning verses, with a few cards in the rebus tradition.**

1. Two cards, marked H H & Co, a soldier "battalions of joy", and a train, with eight lines of verse each with reference to a railway term. 12.2 cm x 10.2 cm.

2. Four cards, H H & Co. Three are from the Unique series, one a verse, another a bunch of keys, the third a nail - "May this small token nail our friendship more firmly together". The fourth card has a stamp, cut out in the shape of a well "A well-centred stamp".
Sizes up to 12.2 cm x 10 cm.

3. Two cards, H H & Co, each with a hand of cards.  13.4 cm x 10.5 cm.

4. Two cards, H H & Co, a "masher", and a barometer with appropriate verse featuring the weather.
9.8 cm x 13.8 cm, 14.2 cm x 10.4 cm.

5. Two cards. One is marked Hills & Co with a musical greeting printed in silver "May all your Christmas joys be on the Higher scale!" The other has a minstrel, with the words and music of a musical roundelaye by Anne Thiballier, marked H H & Co.
8.7 cm x 11.4 cm, 13.2 cm x 10.5 cm.

6. Four cards, Hills & Co, two with a silver crown piece, and two others from the Unique series, one with a bee and a letter B ... "May your Christmas B a happy one", the other with firetongs dated 1893 by the sender. Sizes up to 13.2 cm x 10.8 cm.

*Numbers 7-12 are marked with publishers' initials which have not been positively identified.*

7. Three cards. Two are marked E H, one with a cape and a pile of bills, the other a desk with school books. The third card is a folder, marked D & Co, with an embossed donkey on the cover and a verse within.
9 cm x 11.5 cm, 11.5 cm x 9 cm.

8. Four cards, one marked E H, matches by Bryant & May, a hammer and tongs, an anchor and a lifebuoy, and a bed, probably

all from the same publisher.
12.2 cm x 9 cm.

9. Three cards marked B & S, the Old Yule Log, a spinning top, and a money bag hanging from a gallows.
Sizes up to 15 cm x 11.5 cm.

10. Two cards, each with a magnet, one marked B & S - "May you be the centre of attraction".
9 cm x 13.4 cm, 13.4 cm x 10.5 cm.

11. Four embossed cards, H S C & Co, printed in red, black, and gold, with a pillar box, sealing wax, a candle, and a warming pan. 12.5 cm x 10.8 cm.

12. Two cards, one marked M J B, with a whip. The other has a fig leaf "Out of old Adam's book", and is marked Merry Andrew Series no. 11, M K & Co, and dated 1934 by the sender, though it is similar in style to the earlier cards. M K might be the Max Kracke listed by Buday.
12.6 cm x 10 cm.

13, Five cards, four designs of Scotsmen riding a bicycle, playing the bagpipes, in a wheelbarrow, or falling in the snow, all with a poem by J G F on the front or back. One was dated 1895 by the sender.
9.5 cm x 15 cm, 11.4 cm x 9.5 cm.

14. Two cards, one with a trouser press, the other with a Christmas pudding.
10 cm x 15.8 cm, 13.2 cm x 9.8 cm.

15. Four miscellaneous cards, three with a bag of shellfish, a hand, or a bloater. The fourth has an umbrella "A souvenir of the longest reign", perhaps made in 1897 for the Diamond Jubilee.
Sizes up to 10 cm x 15 cm.

16. Five cards with serrated edges, four from one set with a funnel, a kipper, a bundle of firewood, or a bag of "humanised" potatoes. The fifth has four stick-like men carrying Christmas puddings on their heads.
12.4 cm x 8.5 cm, 9 cm x 11.7 cm.

17. Four cards in rebus style. Two are folders with verses inside by Constance H Dubois; the third is embossed with a serrated edge, the fourth is gilt-edged and tinselled.
7.8 cm x 11.2 cm, 11.5 cm x 9.2 cm.

18. Four rebus cards, two with an illuminated initial letter, two others with serrated edges, one dated 1894 by the sender. 12.2 cm x 8.8 cm, 12.4 cm x 10 cm.

19. Three rebus cards with serrated edges. 11.5 cm x 8.8 cm.

20. Two cards. One is a rebus with a clever verse giving variations on bread in words and pictures. The other is a complicated poem with pictures of various relations "If your Grandmother's Aunt was your

Uncle's Mamma"... with eight lines of this ending "Who would you be?"
9 cm x 11.5 cm, 11.3 cm x 8.6 cm.

21. Four embossed cards, silver scissors, a knife, fork, and spoon, a golden tap pouring out money, and two walking sticks - "You stick to me and I'll stick to you", dated 1894. 11.2 cm x 8.7 cm up to 13.5 cm x 10.2 cm.

22. Four trick cards.
a) A real needle threaded with wool ..."I'm darned if I don't wish you a Happy Christmas".
b) An elastic band "May it bind us closer yet".
c) A poker hand, four aces and a ten, opening to show a warning to the gambler and his wife's arm wielding a rolling pin.
d) A folder of brown paper with a knot of string "I'm sending you the paper and the string", but no present, marked Alpha series, London. 9 cm x 12 cm, 10 cm x 9.2 cm, 7.7 cm x 14.3 cm.

23. Four cards, serrated edges.
a) An applied furry monkey with a feather on a match-stick pole "May you poll many votes for a Merry Christmas ..." and ... "Fortune's Monkey Tricks ...".
9.5 cm x 13.5 cm.
b) Two potatoes ... "I suppose, as a spectater, you'll see the jokes, as there are so many Eyes about" ... 12.3 cm x 7.5 cm.
c) A watch with a bag of money, and eight lines of verse each with a punning reference to the watch. 9.5 cm x 13.5 cm.
d) A ticket to the World's End, dated 25-12-99. 11.8 cm x 9.2 cm.

24. Five cards, one with a brush, another with chestnuts. Three others with serrated edges have a box of vestas (matches), three chairs - three cheers for Christmas, and a briefcase. The latter was dated 1928 by the sender but is in 1900 style.
9.7 cm x 7 cm up to 11.5 cm x 9 cm.

25. Two cards in the form of cheques. One is dated Christmas, 1898, and says "Pay ... 1,000 hearty greetings", with a good luck excise stamp. The other is dated 24-12-32, and says "Pay ... 365 Good Wishes for 52 weeks Happiness", and is marked "Alpha Publishing Co, Ltd, printed in England".
19.8 cm x 8.5 cm, 18 cm x 9 cm.

26. Four folding cards, early 1900's, a collar and can, boys snowballing a donkey, a pipe and matches, dated 1900-1901, and a fourth with scraps of pills, money, and a baby, labelled health, wealth, and bliss.
10.5 cm x 6.2 cm up to 11.4 cm x 9.8 cm.

27. Four cards, early 20th century, a father in dressing gown and smoking cap with his baby, a boy fishing, a lady putting her feet into a hot bath, and a desk. The latter is the excuse for the caption "May you have a Christmas of the finest desk-cription" and a punning verse within.
Sizes up to 9.8 cm x 12.3 cm.

# VOLUME 178:
# HUMOUR, MECHANICAL & FOLDING CARDS

**This volume includes some ingenious opening and mechanical cards of the 1890s, and folding cards, some 20th century. These continue in the Angus Thomas tradition of verses with punning allusions to the picture or scrap. Some have not been precisely dated.**

1. Six cards which open lifting a leg or arm of the figure in the picture. Two, published by Houghton, Blackpool, printed in Germany, have Scotsmen displaying what was worn beneath the kilt, with quotations from Burns. Another has a housemaid on a ladder showing her frilly petticoats, and the fourth has a similar young lady with the caption "May Christmas be a jolly time for a regular high kicker". The fifth has two dancers doing a can-can, and the sixth in more sober vein has a soldier lifting his arm in salute, with a verse by J H Goring.
5.5 cm x 11.9 cm to 8 cm x 11.5 cm closed.

2. Three cards, each with four joined figures, which stand up when opened out. One has sandwichmen, another midshipmen, and the third, with sailors, is marked M W (Marcus Ward).
4.8 cm x 14 cm, 5 cm x 13.5 cm, 4.8 cm x 12.7 cm closed.

3. Two cards.
a) A lady and two gentlemen in evening dress. When the flap is pulled down the gentlemen shake hands. 12.2 cm x 10.7 cm.
b) Three negro minstrels sitting on a wall, ingeniously weighted so that they move when the card is opened and stood up.
14 cm x 15 cm.

4. The Salvation Army, a very rare card with eight cut-out figures, mounted on springs to make a three-dimensional display. Printed in Bavaria.
16.3 cm x 12.5 cm.

5. A card published by Ernest Nister with an embossed ivy patterned border. When the tab is pulled, the picture, with an ingenious shutter arrangement, changes from a goose to a turkey. No. 2013, printed in Bavaria. 11.5 cm x 14.7 cm.

6. Four cards, two designs of a Scotsman in kilt and bonnet, c1895. One card has a giant hand which lifts to show a space for the sender's name, and two others have giant feet. All have verses by J G F.
8.7 cm x 12.9 cm.

7. Three folder cards.
a) A scrap of a flying machine, lifting to show a heap of Victorian coins.
9.8 cm x 12.9 cm.
b/c) Two cards with military allusions, one showing an arm with stripes "Promotion-for you", the other a Victoria Cross "Hoping this will be a Prize Medal Christmas". 8.7 cm x 11.7 cm.

*Numbers 8-14 are folders, early 20th century, many with cord or ribbon bows characteristic of the period.*

8. Four cards, three with a key, a donkey, and a safe, with the usual punning verses, one signed H J R. The fourth card has a case with six cards inside, each having a suitable reply for a lady to make to a too-persistent swain.
Sizes up to 10.7 cm x 15 cm.

9. Six cards, all with scraps, a ball of string revealing money when pulled, an oyster

**178.5**

**178.5**

hiding a baby, two hands, a fire escape, two inebriated gentlemen, and a collection of coins dated 1905 by the sender. Sizes up to 12.2 cm x 10 cm.

10. Six cards with scraps, a nightdress case, a cashbox, an egg, a dustpan and brush, a gas meter lifting to show a courting couple, and a camera with its black cloth lifting to show another couple upside down. 10.3 cm x 10 cm to 14 cm x 8 cm.

11. Four cards, three with scraps of a key, a couple in the snow, and a cracker lifting to show twin babies. The fourth shows the back of a conductor "Hoping there will BEAT-TIME for you to come and see me this Christmas ...".
Sizes up to 13.5 cm x 10.2 cm.

12. Four cards, three with pictures of a beer-barrel, a nightshirt, and roller skates. The fourth is an ingenious scrap of a three-tier cake which pulls out to show a baby. Sizes up to 10 cm x 13.2 cm.

13. Four cards with ribbon bows, a bunch of silver keys, a man clinging to a lamp post, a pair of breeches, and a patch. 12.2 cm x 10.1 cm.

14. Four similar, three with a bell, a nightshirt and a bed, and a bar of music "He's a jolly good fellow". The fourth card has a notice "The New Act, Babies minded here, please take a ticket". There were Acts in 1904 and 1908 for the protection of children, and this card might have some connection with one of them.
10.1 cm x 12.2 cm.

15. Two mechanical cards.
a) A negress pulling a negro's nose. When the card is opened, the nose is extended - dated 1912 by the sender.
b) A similar card with a postman delivering letters to a lady.
13.3 cm x 8.3 cm.

16/17. Seven cards, four signed Donald McGill, c1920. These are in the form of letter cards, and show scenes of jollity and the Christmas spirit, liquid and otherwise. Frank Staff, in "The Picture Postcard and its Origins", says of this artist "...he in the early years of this century quickly became known for his comic postcards which, although never downright obscene, sometimes had a suggestive sense of vulgarity about them which ... typifies an aspect of English life and humour", a fitting comment which could well apply to many of the cards in the last three volumes.
8.9 cm x 14.4 cm, 14.4 cm x 8.9 cm.

# ANIMAL CARDS

As in the previous subject sections, cards from known publishers and some artists have been filed in Volumes 179 & 180, with the remaining four volumes containing cards of unidentified origin. With the exception of Hagelberg & Schipper and the publishers previously dealt with in detail, few animal cards are marked, though some might be assigned from similarity. A few cards are signed by artists, and Helena Maguire's name appears on some cards; narrative verses appear on front and back, the names of Lewis Novra and E E Griffin frequently occurring, and on cards of the later 1880's and early 1890's puns are often seen. A few cards with frogs are included. More examples with animals will be seen in the later sections with shaped, cut-out, and folding cards.

*Section*

*15*

179.8

# VOLUME 179: ANIMAL CARDS FROM KNOWN PUBLISHERS.

*Numbers 1-3 were published by Eyre and Spottiswoode.*

1. Two cards, sunset and moonlight forest scenes with deer, in gilt-patterned yellow borders, no. 234, early 1880's.
14 cm x 9.7 cm.

2. Two cards, cats in gentlemen's clothes, one raising a top hat, the other smoking a pipe, no. 206. 8.8 cm x 13.5 cm.

3. Two cards, two pigs with a firework, marked no. 2 and no. 3, series 729, probably from a set of three, one dated 1887 by the sender. 10.8 cm x 7.7 cm.

4. Three humorous cards published by Castell Bros. Two show dogs in human clothing. The third card is signed R D, i.e. Robert Dudley, with three pigs in children's clothes eating from a plate on a table, no. 524. 10.1 cm x 7 cm up to 12.6 cm x 9 cm.

*Numbers 5-16 were published by W Hagelberg from late 1880's-1895, numbered with some marked "Berlin", which might account for some inconsistence in the sequence of numbers (compare nos. 8 & 11), and a consequent difficulty in precise dating. Many have verses by E E Griffin.*

5. Four cards, kittens and puppies at play, one unnumbered with a verse by "Elbetee" on reverse, two no. 121, the fourth with verses by E E G on reverse, no. 211 Berlin.
10.7 cm x 7.5 cm up to 12.7 cm x 8.3 cm.

6. Four cards. One is in trompe l'oeil style no. 415 Berlin, with two apparently superimposed cards with dogs chasing a hedgehog. The three others have the same design of two collie dogs in two formats, one no. 122 Berlin. 13 cm x 9.5 cm, 9.9 cm x 6.3 cm, 9.3 cm x 12.7 cm.

7. Three cards, frogs. Two show four frogs playing guitars, or bathing, no. 105 Berlin. The third has three frogs in a rowing boat, with a descriptive verse by E E G on reverse, no. 278 Berlin. 10.8 cm x 7.6 cm, 12.8 cm x 8.3 cm.

8. Three cards, monkeys. Two have one design of three monkeys singing, no. 223. The third shows four monkeys on a wall each holding a letter X, M, A, S, with their tails arranged to show 1891, with a verse by E E G on reverse, no. 120 Berlin.
12.5 cm x 8.5 cm, 11.2 cm x 7.4 cm.

9. Four cards, three with four hares, cats, or dogs riding penny-farthing bicycles, the fourth with four monkeys in top hats, no.s. 287, 51, 51, 212. One has a verse by E E G. Sizes about 12 cm x 8 cm.

**179.12**

10. Three cards, two designs, one with four bulldogs in top-hats smoking cigars, the other with four bulldogs in spectacles reading newspapers, both with verses by E E G. No. 316 Berlin. 12.7 cm x 9.4 cm.

11. Five cards, four designs of kittens and puppies at play. Two are signed by Helena Maguire, no. 385 Berlin, with verse by E E G on reverse, and one has a verse by "Nemo" on reverse, no. 327. The two others have the same design of a kitten up a tree, one dated 1887 by the senders, no. 222. Sizes up to 12.7 cm x 9.4 cm.

12. Two cards, a bulldog in cap, collar, and tie, smoking a pipe, no. 439 Berlin, and a retriever, no. 565 Berlin, both with verses by E E G.
10 cm x 13.3 cm, 9.5 cm x 13.8 cm.

13. Two cards, five bulldogs in front of their kennels, no. 756 Berlin, and a collie with two pups under the mistletoe, no. 569 Berlin. 12.8 cm x 9.5 cm, 13.2 cm x 10 cm.

14. Five unnumbered cards from two sets. Two cards show a dog or a cat holding a banner. Three cards have two designs of five well dressed dogs or cats out walking. 7.4 cm x 11.2 cm, 12.8 cm x 8.3 cm.

15. One card, five dogs rowing a boat, with verse by "Nemo" on reverse.
15 cm x 11 cm.

16. Six miscellaneous cards, four with decorative borders, and verses by E E G on two cards and by A W B on one. Five are numbered 124, 157, 291, 317, 383. Sizes up to 8.3 cm x 12.9 cm.

*Numbers 17-22 were published by J F Schipper in the early 1880's, all in humorous vein.*

17. A gilt-bordered card with a bull in man's clothing feasting on oysters, no. 655. 9.7 cm x 12.5 cm.

18. Two cards, a cats' dinner party held in a barn, and an old lady throwing water over a cats' musical party on her roof, no. 797. 16 cm x 10.5 cm.

19. Three cards, the hunt - monkeys riding on dogs, no. 1048. 15 cm x 10 cm.

20. Two cards, probably from a set of four, no. 1132, one dated 1884 by the sender. These show smartly dressed dogs sitting round a banqueting table, and the party chasing away an intruding cat with sad results to their clothes. 16 cm x 10.5 cm.

21/22. Four cards, monkeys in human attire, at a banquet, playing Blind Man's Buff, dancing, and going home after the party. 16 cm x 10.2 cm.

23/24. Ten miscellaneous cards published by Ernest Nister, printed in Bavaria in the 1890's, with cats, dogs, a rabbit, a monkey band, dog and cat protest meetings etc. One was dated 1896, another no. 1053 was dated 1893, the others were numbered 803, 827, 1565, 1521, 4709, 2504, 1116. 9.6 cm x 7.8 cm up to 9.3 cm x 11.7 cm.

*Numbers 25-27 were published by Wirth Bros & Owen in the late 1880's.*

25. Two cards, two cats playing with a sewing machine or dipping into the contents of a cruet, no. 212. 11.8 cm x 8.2 cm.

26. Five cards marked Wirth Brothers, kittens and puppies at play, three numbered 319, 327, 382, ano.ther dated 1887 by the sender. Sizes up to 9.4 cm x 13 cm.

27. Two silver-bordered cards, mice with a Christmas tree or mistletoe. 12 cm x 9.4 cm.

*Numbers 28-30 were published by Bernhard Ollendorff, about 1885.*

28. Three cards, monkeys, one with playing cards, ano.ther combing its hair by a looking glass, the third playing with a doll. This gave rise to the verse by Lewis Novra on the back beginning "A monkey and nursing its dolly. The picture's absurd, I admit But nursing each trouble's a folly To my mind, as great ev'ry bit ..." Perhaps a prize example of "sentiments" justifying the picture. 9 cm x 11.8 cm.

29. Five cards, a set of four designs of various small dogs - holding a straw hat, eating dinner with napkin round neck, under a sunshade, and wearing a counsel's wig, one dated 1885 by the sender. Four cards are unmarked, but a fifth duplicate is marked, thus illustrating the difficulty of identifying publishers. 7.6 cm x 10.7 cm.

30. Three cards, a donkey carrying a load of holly and mistletoe through the snow, and two others with a kitten making havoc

with a sewing basket or a watering can.
12.5 cm x 9.7 cm, 7.8 cm x 11.1 cm.

31. One card published by Campbell &
Tudhope, a squirrel in a circular vignette
surrounded by trails of ivy leaves. This,
unlike the bulk of this publisher's output,
has no religious message or significance.
10.8 cm x 7.4 cm.

## VOLUME 180:
## ANIMAL CARDS, MORE
## PUBLISHERS & SOME
## ARTISTS

1. Five cards. Three, published by Birn
Bros., have a cat, squirrel or rabbit, with a
basket of fruit and flowers. The other two
are gilt-edged, with one design of a rabbit
and a basket of roses, perhaps from the
same publisher. Late 1870's.
11 cm x 6.9 cm, 11.8 cm x 8.8 cm.

*Numbers 2-5 were published by Davidson Bros
in the late 1880's.*

2. Two cards, puppies by a lake, cats on a
roof, signed H J M - Helena Maguire - both
dated 1887 by the senders.
14.3 cm x 11.5 cm, 15.4 cm x 11.5 cm.

3. A black and white snow scene with
sheep signed T K, and a verse by
S K Cowan. 8.4 cm x 13.2 cm.

4/5. Four cards in photographic style,
showing cats and dogs on a cushion with
the same cup and medicine bottle in each
picture. 10.8 cm x 16.5 cm,
16.5 cm x 10.8 cm.

*Numbers 6-12 are from various publishers,
dated in the late 1880's.*

6. Three cards from M H Nathan & Co,
frogs in human situations, one fishing,
another walking, and a doctor and patient.
10.2 cm x 13.4 cm.

7. Three cards marked S & N (Sockl &
Nathan), two designs of mother cat and
kittens engaged in roasting a turkey or
taking medicine, one dated 1886 by the
sender. 11.4 cm x 8.9 cm.

8. An embossed card printed in sepia
marked Lith. Art Anstalt,Munich, three
kittens looking over a fence, no. 2059.
9 cm x 9 cm.

9. Two orange bordered birthday cards by
Obpacher Bros, no. 772, each of a mouse
leaning on a rustic fence. 9.1 cm x 13.5 cm.

10. Three cards published by Philipp Bros,
a rabbit in cap and tie, a cat dressed as an
opera singer, and a dog as the "Masher
King". 9.2 cm x 9.2 cm, 8.8 cm x 12.2 cm.

11. Four cards from Meissner & Buch,
Leipzig. Two have the same picture of a
monkey band, one with a verse by F E
referring to the band of Godfrey Strauss.

"BLIND - MAN'S BUFF."

I WISH YOU A HAPPY CHRISTMAS.

179.21

The third has two dogs by a wall, and the
fourth has a pierced design with a dog,
with a verse by J J S. 9.7 cm x 6.2 cm up to
9.5 cm x 10.8 cm.

12. Five cards, one published by Alfred
Lea with a monkey artist painting the
portrait of a dog. Four other cards have
similar designs of the heads of cats or
dogs, but one is marked Alfred Lea and
another S & N.
11 cm x 8.5 cm, 10.2 cm x 6.7 cm.

*Numbers 13-24 are signed by known artists,
but in most cases the publishers are unknown.*

13. Two folding humorous cards by Ernest
Griset, c1880.
a) The cover has a black and white picture
of a fox's head, and opens to show its
encounters with a crow, geese, and a
rabbit. 8.9 cm x 11.1 cm.
b) A six-page folder with comic pictures of
elephants and giraffes on the outside,
opening to show three scenes of the
encounter of a sailor with a bear at the
North Pole, marked S J S - S J Saunders &
Co. 9.4 cm x 12.8 cm.

14/16. Eight humorous cards from pen
and ink drawings by Myra Howard
Meyrick, showing pigs in human
situations, one with two pigs as Romeo &
Juliet, two dated 1878, 1879 by the senders.
One card, a musical party, might be one
registered at Stationers' Hall 13-3-1882 by
W A Mansell, and the other cards might
have been published by this firm.
12 cm x 9 cm, 9 cm x 12 cm, 15.7 cm x
12 cm.

17/18. Five cards from pen and ink
drawings, four designs of cats and dogs,
one dated 1880 by the sender. Two are
signed by H H Couldery, and the others
are similar.
12 cm x 9.5 cm, 9.2 cm x 12.3 cm.

19. Two cards, one with a donkey in black
and white, and another marked Harding,
48 Piccadilly W., with a cat and dogs by
the fire.

*Numbers 20-24 were designed by Helena
Maguire, in the late 1880's.*

20. One card, cats with a Christmas tree,
and a greeting in German.
14.5 cm x 11.3 cm.

21. Two cards, the same design of a
donkey in winter in two sizes with
different greetings. 7.6 cm x 9.8 cm,
10.8 cm x 13.7 cm.

22. Four cards from two sets. Two show
kittens and puppies at play, the others
have puppies playing by a river, these
perhaps published by Davidson Bros.
12 cm x 8.5 cm, 11.8 cm x 9.4 cm.

23. Two cards, cats' heads on a horseshoe,
and two cats walking paw in paw under a
sunshade.
11.6 cm x 15.4 cm, 10.3 cm x 14.4 cm.

24. Four cards, two with two kittens, the
others with dogs in the sea. Sizes up to
9.2 cm x 12.5 cm.

25. Three cards, a fox riding a bicycle
signed R André, two cats by a window,
signed M S, and two sheep in snow, signed
A T, c1885. 8.5 cm x 8.5 cm,
8.3 cm x 11.8 cm, 11.7 cm x 9.1 cm.

*Numbers 26-28 are in photographic style.*

26. Two cards published by William Luks,
dated 1880, 1881. One is of two cats under
mistletoe, probably china figures. The
other is a frog carrying a stalk of grass, and
though this is in the same photographic
style it is difficult to see how this could be

produced, except from a drawing.
10.7 cm x 16.7 cm, 6.5 cm x 10.2 cm.

27/28. Four cards, three designs of cats and dogs, with verses by Moore, Marianne Farningham, and W H Drummond, on reverse.
10.5 cm x 16.3 cm, 16.3 cm x 10.7 cm.

## VOLUME 181: ANIMALS, SMALLER CARDS UP TO 1885

These cards are in small to medium sizes from untraced publishers, though some might be attributed from similarity. They are dated from about 1875-1885, and a few are signed by artists' monograms.

1. Three scallop-edged cards, two designs of a donkey and a terrier, both carrying a greeting, c1875, perhaps Sulman?
9 cm x 6.2 cm.

2. Eight cards, plain edges. Three of one set have two designs of a mouse riding on a lobster, and three pet dogs. Another set with three cards has a deer, a stag, or a dog. Another card has a frog and an otter(?) holding a greeting, and the eighth card repeats the dog design in no. 1 above.
c1875. 8 cm x 4 cm up to 9.7 cm x 5.3 cm.

3. Seven cards in two styles, three gilt-bordered, with five designs of a rabbit, deer, stag, or dogs, in a leafy background with a greeting in a bordered panel. One was dated 1880 by the sender.
10.4 cm x 6.4 cm.

4. Eight cards, embossed with gilt borders. Seven of a set have five designs of dogs' heads holding greetings in mouth, and a similar card from another set has a dog in a cap. One is on a mount with patterned border. c1880. 8 cm x 4.7 cm, 5 cm x 8 cm, 10.7 cm x 7.9 cm.

5. Six cards, four designs of mischievous puppies or kittens, one on a scallop-edged mount, c1880.
8.5 cm x 5.2 cm, 9.7 cm x 6.2 cm.

*Numbers 6-27 were published in the early 1880's.*

6. Four cards, one birthday. Two from the same set have a squirrel or hare in a circular vignette with roses or pansies. The third has a monkey in coat and spectacles, and the fourth has a terrier in a circular vignette with a butterfly and forget-me-nots, signed B D, which might be artist or publisher, and a verse by Hume on reverse. Sizes approximately 12 cm x 9 cm.

7. Two black-backed cards, sheep or goats in a pastoral scene, with a Christmas verse in a panel. 12.8 cm x 8.8 cm.

8. Three cards from a set, a squirrel with blackberries, lambs with hawthorn, and a kingfisher with roses. 11.8 cm x 8.1 cm.

9. Three cards, one design of a squirrel on a flowering almond tree, with three different illuminated greetings on scrolls.
12.2 cm x 9.4 cm.

10. Three cards, a rabbit, fox, or dog, holding a card with greeting in their paws.
7.2 cm x 10.8 cm.

11. Three embossed cards with a dog or cat peeping through torn paper, and a verse below. 8.4 cm x 12 cm.

12. Five embossed cards showing the back of an envelope with monkey and dog, kittens, or cat and dog breaking the seal, one dated 1883 by the sender. (See volume 197 no. 18).
11.2 cm x 6.9 cm, 9.7 cm x 6.8 cm.

13. Two cards with kittens or a puppy in an open umbrella, one with another kitten stalking a hen and chickens.
12 cm x 8.9 cm.

14. Three gilt-bordered cards. One has a dog holding a bunch of roses. Two from another set have a sleeping dog, and a fox trying to catch a duck, both with a holly garland. 12.7 cm x 8 cm, 13 cm x 8.6 cm.

15. Three cards, two designs, an owl in a tree with a mouse below, and a fox stalking a rabbit, all with Christmas verses.
6.8 cm x 16.5 cm.

16. Five cards, a set of four designs of a dog holding a card with a greeting and a flower. 10.7 cm x 7.5 cm.

17. Three miscellaneous cards, two with horses, one a cat with primroses.
Sizes up to 7.5 cm x 11 cm.

18. Four embossed cards on a pale green background, three designs, a kitten teasing a parrot, two kittens in a basket, three pups in a hamper, all with sprays of flowers and leaves. 15.5 cm x 6.9 cm.

19. Five cards, a set of four designs of mischievous puppies, and a folding card using one of the set with a Christmas poem by A H B and illuminated border and cover designs. One was dated 1882 by the sender. 10.5 cm x 7.4 cm, 13.1 cm x 10 cm.

20. One card, a spaniel with a blue bow, and a Christmas verse. 7.6 cm x 11 cm.

21. Three gilt-bordered cards, an owl, a rabbit, and a squirrel, on grey backgrounds.
8.2 cm x 10.7 cm, 10.7 cm x 8.2 cm.

22. Three cards, two designs of rabbits in two sizes.
12.2 cm x 8.2 cm, 8.4 cm x 5.5 cm.

23. Two cards, a donkey in the snow, "Poor thing!", and two collie dogs pulling a sleigh filled with holly.
9.5 cm x 6.7 cm, 11.5 cm x 8.8 cm.

24. Three cards, a shepherd and a dog rescuing a sheep caught in a blizzard, and a spring and winter scene with deer or stags.
12 cm x 7.5 cm up to 14.6 cm x 9.5 cm.

25. Two gilt-edged cards, mice looking through paper torn in trompe l'oeil style.
10.4 cm x 7 cm.

26. Three cards, one a cat in a cigar box, and two from another set with a dog by a door and pigeons by a dove cote, both with a Christmas verse in a panel.
13 cm x 7.5 cm, 13.2 cm x 9 cm.

27. Two cards, the head of a deer or a donkey, with flowers. 8.8 cm x 11.1 cm.

*Numbers 28-34 were published c1885.*

28. Three gilt-edged cards, puppies or kittens on steps or a chair, with a bunch of mistletoe, and verses by Frederick Langbridge and H S Bainbridge on panels.
8.2 cm x 10 cm.

29. Three cards, kittens in boxes with straw, labelled "passenger train", "with care", or "this side up". Verses by Horace Lennard are on the reverse.
13 cm x 10.1 cm.

30/31. Nine cards from similar series, some gilt-edged, with six designs of kittens or dogs, usually in mischief. One card is a folder with blue and gilt cover and border, using two of the pictures of dogs. Two are dated 1884 by the sender, one 1885.
10.4 cm x 7.2 cm, 10.1 cm x 6.8 cm, folder 13.5 cm x 9.3 cm.

32. Four miscellaneous gilt-edged cards, three designs of kittens, one with a poem by S Herbert.
10.2 cm x 6.7 cm up to 12.2 cm x 8.2 cm.

33. Six cards. Three are from a set of playful kittens, another has a white kitten trying to write after spilling the ink, one has a terrier looking at a mouse, the sixth has a pug with a candle.
10.1 cm x 6.2 cm up to 10.5 cm x 7 cm.

34. Seven cards, five designs in two styles of heads of cats or dogs framed in flowers.
7.2 cm x 10 cm.

35. Five cards, frogs, two gilt bordered dated 1878 by the sender.
9.1 cm x 5.5 cm up to 9.9 cm x 7 cm.

36. Three cards with frogs, a family sitting on a bench, bathing in human fashion, and one in a carriage drawn by insects, with descriptive verses, c1880. 11.5 cm x 7.7 cm.

37. Four miscellaneous cards, a rabbit, frogs, squirrel, and some unidentified water denizens. Sizes up to 13.5 cm x 9 cm.

## VOLUME 182:
## ANIMALS, LARGER CARDS

**These cards were published in the early 1880's with a few exceptions as noted, and no publishers have been traced. Some cards are signed by the artist, including monograms, and most of them are in large sizes.**

1. Three gilt-bordered cards with cats and dogs, signed H H Couldery. There is another signature, Seitz Wandsbeck(?) on the cards. One was dated 1878 by the sender. 13.2 cm x 10.1 cm.

2. Two blue-bordered cards, a kitten or a lamb in an oval vignette with a floral background, one dated 1879 by the sender. 8.5 cm x 13.2 cm.

3. Three cards, two with cats, chasing a mouse or by a chair indoors. The third is from another set and shows a tabby cat sitting by a fender. All have narrative poems on reverse. 8.6 cm x 12.5 cm, 14.5 cm x 10.5 cm.

4. Two cards with patterned gilt borders, marked "Friendship" and "Danger", with a cat and dog by the fire, and a cat looking at birds in a cage. Both have narrative poems by F Ernest Power on reverse. 11.8 cm x 15.3 cm.

5. Two cards with household pets sitting by the fire, one with a pug dog, the other with cats. Both have verses by Fannie Rochat on reverse. 16.5 cm x 11.6 cm.

6. Two cards with patterned gilt borders, both picturing bull mastiffs or pugs. 12.7 cm x 16 cm, 17 cm x 13 cm.

7. Three cards, two designs, one a dog in the snow and a cat on a window sill, the other a cat licking a cooking pot, both with verses by F Ernest Power on reverse. 11.5 cm x 15.7 cm.

8/9. A set of four cards with various dogs, outside the door in the snow, under the mistletoe, or by the fireside, with a verse of greeting below. 10.7 cm x 15.1 cm.

10. Two cards. One has a gilt pattered border and two pet dogs lying on a coat and gloves, dated 1879 by the sender. The other has a dog on a chair with a cat below, dated 1882 by the sender. 9.7 cm x 12.8 cm, 14.6 cm x 10.5 cm.

11. A set of four cards, well drawn pictures of wild horses in mountain scenery, two with verses by R D on reverse. 14.7 cm x 11.6 cm.

**182.11**

12. Three cards, sheep and cattle in winter and spring, with verses on the backs by F E E H, Table Book, Washington Irving and Adams. 16 cm x 12 cm.

13. Two cards, bisons in snow, two ponies on a hillside dated 1881 by the sender. 15 cm x 10.8 cm, 15.2 cm x 12.3 cm.

14. Two cards. One has a King Charles spaniel at a window and a poem by Shirley Wynne on reverse; the other has a dog watching by an injured or dead sheep in snow. 18 cm x 12.9 cm, 17.7 cm x 13.6 cm.

15. Three gilt-bordered cards, a cow in winter, two donkeys by a holly bush, and a dog watching by a dead sheep in snow, all with a verse below and a poem by E J P on reverse. They are signed T G C. 9.1 cm x 13.7 cm.

16. Five cards, three designs of rabbits, squirrels, or guinea-pigs, with greetings on scrolls, showing three varieties of greeting on one design. 9 cm x 13.4 cm.

17. Three cards of a set with different patterned gilded borders, with rabbits, lamb, or kitten on a scroll in a background imitating wood, two dated 1882. 9.9 cm x 13.3 cm.

18. Three cards, gun dogs, two with dead hares. One has a verse by E H on reverse, another was dated 1882 by the sender. 10.4 cm x 13.4 cm, 12.2 cm x 9.4 cm.

19/20. Nine cards in two sizes, four designs of gun dogs retrieving dead birds or hares, signed C H W. The larger cards have somewhat unfeeling verses on the backs, signed R D. 12.6 cm x 10 cm, 10.7 cm x 7.4 cm.

21. Four cards, two designs of winter scenes with deer, and verses by Fred E Weatherly on reverse. 13.6 cm x 9.6 cm.

22. Two cards, farm scenes with animals. 13 cm x 10 cm.

23. Two cards, dogs in falling snow with holly or mistletoe, one with a poem on reverse. 13.5 cm x 10.1 cm.

24. Two cards, illustrating fables of La Fontaine, "The Two Goats", and "The Lion and the Rat". 9.7 cm x 14.7 cm.

25. A card with two spaniels, each with a coloured bow, signed W A G. The monogram resembles that of William Hamilton Gibson. 10.5 cm x 12.5 cm.

26. Two gilt-bordered cards, a donkey and calf in a background of flowers and grass, and a terrier holding a basket of forget-me-nots, with a verse on reverse. 13.3 cm x 16.3 cm, 12.5 cm x 16.5 cm.

27. An embossed card with two dogs in a kennel decorated by a garland of flowers. 11.5 cm x 15.7 cm.

*The following cards were published after 1885.*

28. Three miscellaneous cards. One has a dog and a wooden horse, and a narrative poem by Leonard Whitby on reverse, another has puppies on a window sill and a verse by Lewis No.vra on reverse, and the third has kittens on a doorstep. All approximately 14 cm x 10 cm.

29. Two cards, one with greyhounds racing over a hillside, another a kitten with mistletoe and a poem by Fanny Forrester on reverse. 13.5 cm x 10.8 cm, 15.6 cm x 12.2 cm.

30. Two cards, each with two kittens and a butterfly in a bunch of holly or violets. 15.7 cm x 11.6 cm.

31. Three miscellaneous cards, a pug in a frilled collar, a spaniel with a basket of flowers, and a terrier puppy with a sprig

JUMBO AND ALICE UNITED, *They wish you a Bright New Year ;*

**183.5**

of mistletoe. 10 cm x 10 cm,
10.4 cm x 15.3 cm, 9 cm x 11.7 cm.

32. Two cards, four pugs with a sprig of
holly, and four kittens with a spray of
white flowers, both with a verse of
greeting. 11.9 cm x 15.4 cm.

33. Two cards, one design of the head of a
kitten, by H H Couldery.
12.7 cm x 16.5 cm.

34. Two cards, one design of a pug dog
with a pile of Christmas cards, with two
different styles of greeting below. This is
signed E B S M, i.e. E B S Montefiore, listed
by Buday as designing for S Hildesheimer
1881. One card however is dated 1911 by
the sender, but it does not appear to be a
later reprint. 10 cm x 13.3 cm.

## VOLUME 183:
## ANIMAL HUMOUR FROM
## UNTRACED PUBLISHERS

**The humour here derives mainly
from the animals appearing in
human dress and human situations,
with monkeys up to mischievous
tricks and pigs appearing about 1890.
Many of the verses make use of
puns.**

*Numbers 1-12 were published in the early
1880's.*

1. Six cards, five designs with mice, dogs,
cats, frogs, and foxes in 18th century
clothes, one dated 1880 by the sender.
6.7 cm x 10.1 cm.

2. Six grey-bordered cards with dogs, cats,
monkeys, mice, a tortoise, and birds, in
comic situations, with greetings and title
printed in red. They are signed B, probably
the artist (not identified). 12.8 cm x 9 cm.

3. An unmarked card, showing a
bloodhound casting a shadow on the wall

very like Sherlock Holmes. This card is
illustrated by Buday as an 1881 product of
S Hildesheimer from a set of four.
10.7 cm x 7.4 cm.

4. Four cards, three designs probably from
one set, dogs pulling knitting to pieces,
another chasing birds, and a heron after a
frog, two dated 1880, 1882 by the sender.
13.3 cm x 7.4 cm.

5. Three cards, an elephant family out
walking, father elephant sitting in a chair
gazing at a sunflower, and a circus
elephant smoking a pipe and holding a
tankard. They are printed in tones of black
and grey with the exception of the yellow
sunflower. 14.4 cm x 10.2 cm.

6. Two cards, one design in two sizes, four
dogs in human clothing walking on hind
legs. 13.4 cm x 8.4 cm, 15 cm x 6.2 cm.

7. Three cards, cats and dogs in human
clothing, at a banquet, walking on the roof,
and the cat family greeting a mouse as
guest. 11.6 cm x 7.6 cm.

8. Two cards, a ram lecturing to an
audience of sheep, and a dog holding forth
to a group of dogs, all in evening dress.
13.5 cm x 9.4 cm.

9. Two cards, cats dressed as humans, one
a nursemaid wheeling a kitten in a go-
cart, the other a policeman talking to a
maidservant. 8.8 cm x 13 cm.

10. Two gilt-edged cards, bullmastiffs, one
in a smoking cap reading a newspaper, the
other with a basket of flowers, both on a
fluffy white rug. There is a descriptive
verse below by S K C. 9.6 cm x 13.3 cm.

11. Four cards, a hare dressed as a masher,
a cat as a herald, a rabbit as a country
gentleman, and another cat as a flower
seller, all with a verse below by S K C.
7 cm x 10.2 cm.

12. Three cards, dogs dressed as pantaloon,
harlequin, or clown. 7.3 cm x 10.3 cm.

*Numbers 13-25 were published from 1885-
1895.*

13. Two cards, a frog dressed as a lady
with a guitar, and a dog and cat as Spanish
Dancers, the first with a verse by R P Scott
on reverse.
9.2 cm x 14 cm, 11.5 cm x 8.6 cm.

14. Three miscellaneous cards, a cat as a
ballet dancer, a boar in evening dress, and
another cat as a minstrel, "An a-mewsing
time may New Year be And never bring a
cat-astrophe".
Sizes all approximately 7.7 cm x 11.5 cm.

15. Three cards, dogs, one dressed as a girl
with a battledore and shuttlecock, ano.ther
as a drummer boy, the third in a sailor suit
with bucket and spade. 7.9 cm x 12 cm.

16. Four cards, three designs, monkeys
reading a book (in two sizes), rabbits
having their hair cut, and dogs dancing.
13 cm x 11 cm, 10.4 cm x 7.9 cm.

17. One card, five monkeys writing a
greeting on a wall, with a verse on reverse.
14.7 cm x 11 cm.

18. Two cards, monkeys, one with a
policeman chasing a clown, the other a
teacher in a schoolroom lecturing on the
Darwin theory, signed A V P.
8.8 cm x 12.5 cm, 10 cm x 13.4 cm.

19. Six miscellaneous cards of monkeys,
including two from one set showing them
teasing a cat or a dog.
9.8 cm x 6.2 cm up to 11.7 cm x 8.5 cm.

20. Two cards, pigs, one a school cricket
match with the ball hitting the headmaster,
the other a dormitory fight disturbed by
the teacher's arrival. 10.8 cm x 14 cm.

21. Two cards, pigs, a schoolboy doing
sums on a slate, and mother pig going to
market, one dated 1891 by the sender.
9 cm x 12.4 cm.

22. Two cards, a pig in a green coat, and
schoolboy piglets in mischief while their
teacher's back is turned.
10 cm x 10 cm, 11.2 cm x 10.5 cm.

23. A tinselled card, donkeys "kicking and
prancing in a Christmas dance".
14 cm x 10.8 cm.

24. Four miscellaneous cards, cats playing
in a baby carriage, cats fraternising with
robins in the snow, and two versions of a
card showing a party of dogs with brush,
comb and mirror.
Sizes up to 13 cm x 10 cm.

25. Two cards showing a party of cats at
Christmas time, one with Christmas
decorations, the other with Japanese

lanterns, both with a narrative punning verse by J H Goring on reverse. 13.4 cm x 10.6 cm.

*The following cards were published in the early 1890's.*

26. Two cards with a cat photographer, and narrative verses by Lewis Novra on reverse. 13.4 cm x 10.6 cm.

27. Four miscellaneous cards, a cat in a handbag, mice eating a cheese, a procession of musical cats, and a dog in a sporting suit catching butterflies dated 1890 by the sender, with a verse by Lewis Novra on reverse.
Sizes up to 14.1 cm x 10.5 cm.

28. Three cards, cats, one with mother cat cooking dinner for her kittens, another with three cats cooking mice, the third a birthday card with a cat chasing a mouse. Sizes up to 12.6 cm x 9.8 cm.

29. One card, two rabbits in a hip bath. 10.4 cm x 13.3 cm.

30. A set of four cards with serrated edges, three with animals and birds dressed in clothes in human situations, on bicycles, with a milk cart, and taking pigs to market. The fourth has a small girl feeding ducks. 10.3 cm x 7.6 cm.

31. Two cards with a turned down corner, four pigs in bibs licking spoons, and four cats with bouquets. 11.7 cm x 9.1 cm.

32. Six miscellaneous cards, including two of a set with a fox playing golf and a dog with a gun, a puppy dressed in a girl's clothes with a hoop, five kittens in milk cans, three puppies tearing a doll to pieces, and three cats skating.
7.5 cm x 9.8 cm up to 14.7 cm x 6.8 cm.

33. Five miscellaneous cards with serrated edges, with cats, monkeys, and squirrels riding bicycles, one dated 1895 by the sender.
9.2 cm x 6.5 cm up to 13 cm x 8.7 cm.

## VOLUME 184:
## ANIMAL CARDS PUBLISHED FROM 1885 - EARLY 1890's

**These cards are not marked, with one exception, but some might be attributed from resemblance to similar cards from known publishers.**

1. Six gilt-edged cards, four designs in two sizes of cats on the water in a basin, a pan, on a raft, or rowing a tub, with six different verses by S Herbert.
13 cm x 9.2 cm, 10 cm x 7.2 cm.

2. Five cards from three sets, one with three dogs in an oval vignette, two with a cat looking at a dog at a window, and a dog looking at a cat, and two with a dog in a circular vignette and a cat below. One was dated 1885 by the sender. Sizes up to 8.3 cm x 12 cm.

3. Two cards, kittens at school, having a geography lesson or doing sums. 15.4 cm x 11.8 cm.

4. Three cards from two sets, two with a kitten playing with knitting, and a dog pulling a toy to pieces, the third with two dogs and a letter.
11.5 cm x 8.3 cm, 11.2 cm x 7.5 cm.

5. Two cards, four squirrels sitting on a horn, and four cats on a pipe, with verse by Lewis Novra on reverse "Wishing you a purr-fectly Happy Christmas".
13.4 cm x 9 cm.

6. Two cards, dog portraits, a spaniel and a collie. 10 cm x 10 cm, 9.8 cm x 11.2 cm.

7. Three cards, one with eight dogs in a row dated 1887 by the sender, and two others with the same design of two dogs begging, with the same verse of greeting adapted for both Christmas and New Year. 9.5 cm x 9.5 cm, 8.8 cm x 12.9 cm.

8. Three cards from two sets, one with five kittens' heads peeping over a curious arrangement of folded paper. The other two are embossed, each with three dog's heads in vignettes. 11.8 cm x 9 cm.

9. Six miscellaneous cards of cats and dogs, including two from one set with four heads of kittens or puppies peeping over a wall. Sizes up to 8.2 cm x 11.2 cm.

10. Two cards each with two kittens, in a hammock, or with a sprig of holly and mistletoe.
10.3 cm x 12.2 cm, 14.1 cm x 9 cm.

11/12. Four cards, each with seven heads of cats, dogs, monkeys, or rabbits, the greeting in each case beginning "Our wish", "Our greeting", "Our message", "Our petition". One was dated 1889 by the sender. 11.5 cm x 11.5 cm.

13. Four cards, three designs in two styles with a mischievous kitten upsetting flowers or ink or tearing cards, one dated 1887 by the sender.
9.7 cm x 7.5 cm, 8.7 cm x 5.9 cm.

14. Five cards, including two from one set with a fox or deer, and three others with cat or dogs.
7.5 cm x 7.3 cm up to 11 cm x 7.4 cm.

*Numbers 15-27 were probably published in the early 1890's.*

15. Two cards, kittens, one wrapped in a shawl, the other with a large sash. 7.6 cm x 10.8 cm.

16. Two cards, each with kittens in a basket. 13.3 cm x 10.6 cm.

183.13

17. Four cards from two sets, two with one design of a puppy looking at its reflection in the water, two with kittens playing by the sea, or looking at a frog. 8.8 cm x 12 cm, 9 cm x 12.8 cm.

18. Three cards, cats, in a sinking boat, at a picnic, and frolicking in and out of three pieces of oriental china. One was dated 1893 by the sender. 15.5 cm x 11 cm.

19. A set of four tinselled cards, kittens playing in the snow, with greetings in gilt script. 14.5 cm x 9.7 cm.

20. Six cards from three sets. Three have the head of a dog and a cat, two have a cat up a tree and two cats at a window. The sixth has a cat in a boot. 7.2 cm x 7.2 cm, 10 cm x 8.9 cm, 6.5 cm x 10.8 cm.

21. Seven cards, five designs of cats and dogs. Two of the cards have the same design of three dogs, one marked S Hildesheimer, included to illustrate the problems of attributing unmarked cards. A third, with two cats on a tree branch, is probably also S Hildesheimer but has no mark or greeting (see Volume 96). The other four cards show kittens at play or at school. Sizes up to 10.3 cm x 7 cm.

22. Ten miscellaneous small cards, nine designs of cats and dogs.
5 cm x 6.8 cm up to 10.2 cm x 6.6 cm.

23. Four miscellaneous cards, dogs, including one with serrated edge and a cut out picture of two dogs.
Sizes up to 8.8 cm x 13 cm.

24. Two curious cards in trompe l'oeil style
showing a sewn-up parcel or sack and a
cat with a lantern watching a mouse
nibbling its way out. 10.7 cm x 7.6 cm.

25. A card with two puppies in a vignette
with edges imitating torn brown paper.
12 cm x 9.2 cm.

26. Three embossed cards with mice,
donkeys, or a minstrel cat, on a cream
background.
7.6 cm x 11.2 cm up to 10 cm x 13 cm.

27. Five miscellaneous cards, with cats,
dogs, rabbits, and a horse.
5.5 cm x 8.1 cm up to 13.8 cm x 9.9 cm.

# BIRDS AND INSECTS, 1870-1890

Birds were a popular greeting card subject, the robin with its Christmas associations taking first place in winter scenes, accompanied by verses often linking its winter needs with those of the human hungry and homeless. Tits, swallows and doves follow closely in popularity, with the bullfinch's bright colours often appearing. Complete identification has not been attempted, but enough names are given to show the range of varieties used. Some drawings were stylised, many in Oriental fashion, and tropical birds and some beyond identification even by the experts consulted appear, often with incongruous backgrounds. Many have spring and summer flowers in contrast to the snow and ice of the robin, but though these would be more appropriate for birthday, valentine, or Easter cards, they often have Christmas and New Year greetings. Publishers and artists appear in Volumes 185 and 186, and some monograms in later volumes. Volume 194 contains cards with butterflies and other insects. A few cards have their scientific names appended to the designs, but on the whole these cards are somewhat glamourised representations, with the robin more red and the blue tit more blue than ever seen in the garden.

*Section*
*16*

189.23

## VOLUME 185: BIRDS, CARDS FROM KNOWN PUBLISHERS

**Volumes 185 and 186 contain cards of birds from known publishers and artists, and include, as in the previous subject sections, products of firms not dealt with in the volumes dealing with individual publishers.**

*Numbers 1 and 2 were published by Falck, and were identified from Jonathan King's trade list of 1880 in the John Johnson Collection.*

1. Three embossed cards, two designs of birds with a basket of fruit in an oval vignette on a gilt ground with leaves, from a set of four selling at 8/- per gross. 10 cm x 7.6 cm.

2. Two cards, a blue tit in flight, and a goldfinch on its nest, both with a floral background, from a set of four. 17.8 cm x 8.8 cm.

*Numbers 3-10 were published by Eyre & Spottiswoode, early 1880's.*

3. Six cards, four designs of various birds peeping through torn paper, each with a flower, mistletoe, or insect. No. 102. 7.8 cm x 11.5 cm.

4. Five cards, three designs repeating the birds in no. 3 but peeping through fans or a leaf. One has a greeting in German. No. 137. 7.8 cm x 11.5 cm.

5. Four cards, three designs of various birds on berried branches. Three are unmarked, but were identified from the fourth marked card repeating one design on a different mount, no. 233. 10.2 cm x 14.2 cm, 9.4 cm x 13.5 cm.

6. One card, two greenfinches by a lake, no. 333. 9.5 cm x 13 cm.

7. Three cards, various birds on flowers or foliage, with verses by Milton or Eden Hooper, in a patterned border, no. 301. One was dated 1881 by the sender. 12 cm x 7.5 cm.

8. Three cards, each with two birds on fruit bushes, blue tits, bullfinches, goldfinches, two dated 1886 by the senders. No. 336. 9.5 cm x 15.7 cm.

9. Two gilt-bordered cards, swans on a lake, no. 403. 13 cm x 11.2 cm.

10. Three cards, two designs of a stork or flamingo against a wall background with Egyptian hieroglyphics. 14.1 cm x 11.4 cm.

*Numbers 11-14 were published by Thomas Stevens.*

11. Six embossed cards, four designs of exotic birds in Chinese style on various coloured backgrounds, with verse or greetings in a panel, late 1870's. 10.9 cm x 6.9 cm.

12/13. Ten cards (three birthday), birds on a floral background, in three different colours, six designs with verse of greetings in a panel. One card is on a scallop-edged mount and two were dated 1878, 1879 by the senders. 10.9 cm x 7 cm, 12.5 cm x 8.5 cm.

14. One card, robins flying over cliffs by the sea, marked T S, no. 651. 8.7 cm x 13.1 cm.

15. Five cards published by Terry, Stoneman & Co, marked on reverse "Congratulation Cards". They show brightly coloured foreign birds, and three have birthday greetings. 11.7 cm x 7.6 cm.

16. Five cards marked C R & Co, i.e. Charles, Reynolds & Co, with various garden birds on a floral background and a verse of greeting. These are five out of six registered at Stationers' Hall 4-6-1878. 8.8 cm x 13.1 cm.

17. Two cards marked A S Co, i.e. Artistic Stationery Co., showing birds in flight, nos. 430, 434. 7.7 cm x 17.2 cm, 11 cm x 17.2 cm.

18/19. Five cards published by Bollin & Tidswell, four designs of garden birds perching on branches, on background patterns in blue and white, registered at Stationers' Hall 8-7- 1880 by Henry John Smith. 10.4 cm x 16.5 cm.

20. Two cards published by Castell Bros, signed H Binbeck, robins in winter and spring, no. 57, c1885. 15.7 cm x 11 cm.

21. Two cards, Castell Bros., each with three chicks or ducklings perching on a table, c1890. 14.5 cm x 7.8 cm.

*Numbers 22-25 were published by Obpacher Bros.*

22. Three cards, swallows, on a nest, feeding their young, and perching on telegraph wires, one dated 1883 by the sender. No. 819. 11 cm x 15.8 cm.

23. Two cards, swallows flying over sea, no. 1516, and domestic fowls in a farmyard, no. 886. 13.9 cm x 10.8 cm, 15 cm x 10.8 cm.

24. A card on thick board with a humming bird on a rose bush. 11.7 cm x 18.5 cm.

25. A card with a peacock and a child holding a large feather. 13.3 cm x 10 cm.

26. Two cards published by E Rimmel, robins in winter scenes, with gilt border. One card has an advertisement on reverse for C E Tregoning's, Truro, confectioners' novelties for the season 1875-6. 6.6 cm x 10.3 cm

## VOLUME 186: BIRDS, CARDS FROM KNOWN ARTISTS & PUBLISHERS

1. Four cards designed by Harrison Weir, c1880, published by Bernhard Ollendorff, three designs of winter scenes with robins, and descriptive verses by E J Pope on reverse. 9.6 cm x 13.3 cm.

*Numbers 2-9 were designed by Harry Bright for various publishers in the 1880's.*

2. Two cards published by J B B & Co, winter scenes with robins, bullfinch, and blue tits. 11.5 cm x 16.5 cm.

3. Four cards in two sizes, two designs of robins with snow and holly and descriptive verse, one dated 1880 by the sender. 11 cm x 14.3 cm, 8.7 cm x 10.8 cm.

4. Four cards c1880, three designs of robins, bullfinch, or blue tits with holly and mistletoe and verses by Fred E Weatherly. 10 cm x 12.5 cm.

5/6. Five cards, four designs, four cards with robins or bullfinches in two sizes and another of a winter scene with robins and a blackbird. One was dated 1887 by the sender. 12.5 cm x 16.5 cm, 8 cm x 10.2 cm, 10.3 cm x 14.5 cm.

7. Six cards in three sizes, four designs of snow scenes with various birds. 7.5 cm x 11.8 cm, 6.2 cm x 8.8 cm, 5 cm x 8 cm.

8/9. Three cards published by Wirth Bros. & Owen c1885. One shows robins on a snow-covered branch, no. 281, the others have snow scenes with bullfinches in

185.8

flight, nos. 232, 273. 13.2 cm x 19 cm, 11 cm x 13.7 cm, 16.5 cm x 11.9 cm.

10. Two cards, one a pen and ink drawing of wrens in winter, signed H B, probably Harry Bright, with a poem by M E M. The other has a sea scene with gulls, signed R F McIntyre.
11.4 cm x 14 cm, 12 cm x 16.5 cm.

11. One card, a gaggle of geese, signed W Hengerson.  8.8 cm x 11.3 cm.

12. Three cards signed H W C, with robins and mistletoe, ivy, or snowdrops, and verses by E J P on reverse. 7 cm x 10.5 cm.

13. Two cards signed H W C, robins or blackbirds with nests, and verses by E J P on reverse. 12.4 cm x 15.3 cm. H W C is listed by Buday as working on cards in 1880.

14. Three cards signed C White, two snow scenes with robins, the third a swallow in flight. Verses by A F E and S Herbert are on the backs. 10.6 cm x 13.4 cm.

15. Two cards published by Ollendorff c1885, robins in snow by a letter box or a window, with verse below by A H B.
9.3 cm x 13 cm.

16. Three cards published by Ollendorff, a birthday card with cut-out doves on a wall, another with swans on a lake, the third a swallow carrying a letter.
Sizes up to 11.8 cm x 7.8 cm.

*Numbers 17-19 were published by Davidson Bros. in the later 1880's.*

17. Three cards, owls in moonlight scenes, signed A F Lydon.
14.5 cm x 10.5 cm, 10.5 cm x 14.5 cm.

18. Two cards in correspondence style, signed A F Lydon, owls or robins in winter scenes. 9.3 cm x 11.4 cm.

19. Three cards, swallows dated 1885 by the sender, parrots on a silver background dated 1886 by the sender, and a group of blue tits perched on a branch, with a verse by Charlotte Murray on reverse.
8.8 cm x 8.8 cm, 11 cm x 9.7 cm, 14 cm x 10.6 cm.

20/21. Two tinselled cards published by Wirth Bros. & Owen, showing snow scenes with birds.
12.6 cm x 20 cm, 9.4 cm x 15 cm.

*Numbers 22-27 were published by W Hagelberg, 1885-90.*

22. Two humorous cards, a bird orchestra with audience seated in chairs, and a reception with birds in evening dress, both with verses by E E Griffin on reverse, no. 219. 12.9 cm x 8.3 cm.

23. Three cards, two designs of swallows or sparrows in flight, no. 310.
11.9 cm x 8.3 cm.

24. Five miscellaneous cards, swans, doves, pigeon, greenfinch?, robins, in spring scenes, the first four numbered 52, 277, 211, 118. Sizes up to 11.5 cm x 9.2 cm.

25. Three cards, owls in moonlight scenes, one octagonal no. 229, another no. 317. The third card is a folder opening to show a picture of bells and a verse by J W Myers B A. Sizes up to 13 cm x 8.2 cm.

26. Six cards, three from one set with two designs of swallows in flight and an appropriate verse, no. 727. Two from another set have sparrows or martins with spring blossom, no. 265, and the sixth has birds on a flowering tree. 10.7 cm x 7.6 cm, 12 cm x 8.3 cm, 7.5 cm x 11.2 cm.

27. Three cards with coloured borders, various birds in winter or with flowers, nos. 108, 702, 802.
Sizes up to 9.5 cm x 11.8 cm.

28. Four cards published by Ernest Nister. Three are dated about 1890, one with a robin no. 1069, another a family of cock, hen, and chicks with umbrellas, no. 704, the third a robin in snow hoping for crumbs. The fourth card has an owl with a slate and was dated 1889 by the sender. Sizes up to 10.3 cm x 10.8 cm.

29. Two cards published by J F Schipper & Co., humming birds or swallows with flowers and a small cupid or scenes in the background, c1885, nos. 652, 1098.
9.3 cm x 12.8 cm, 13 cm x 9.8 cm.

30. A card published by Schipper, signed R J Mackay, with a robin on oak leaves, no. 1508. 13 cm x 11.3 cm.

## VOLUME 187: CARDS WITH ROBINS & OTHER BIRDS, MOST IN WINTER SCENES

*Numbers 1-25 were published before 1885. Two cards only are signed.*

1. Three scallop-edged cards, robins and blue tits with holly, mistletoe, and ivy, and greeting verses in scrolls, one dated 1872 by the sender. 13.4 cm x 7.5 cm.

2. Two cards, robin with holly, and a martin with flowers, c1875.
11.2 cm x 7.5 cm.

3. Seven miscellaneous cards c1875, all with robins. One is a folder with music of a Christmas carol inside and spring flowers on the cover, and another single card repeats part of this design.
Sizes up to 6 cm x 10.3 cm.

4. Seven cards c1875, a set of six with robins, one repeated on a decorated mount. 8.3 cm x 4.7 cm, 11.7 cm x 8 cm.

5/6. Eight cards c1880, three designs of robins with holly, flowers, or ivy, on varied backgrounds of gold, silver, black, or cream, with a greeting verse on a scroll. 11.5 cm x 7.5 cm.

7. Four cards, winter scenes, two with robins, two with blue tits.
5 cm x 11.4 cm, 10.1 cm x 6.8 cm.

8. Four cards from two sets. Two have the same picture of bullfinches in flight; the others have wrens or bullfinches with nests. (These are the closest approximations for not very accurate ornithological drawings).
10.7 cm x 7.5 cm, 11.9 cm x 7.4 cm.

9. Two cards, each with two intertwined fans decorated with birds and winter scenes, one with a robin, the other with deer. One was dated 1880 by the sender.
11.6 cm x 15.4 cm.

10. Four miscellaneous cards, robins or goldfinches with holly or greenery.
4.5 cm x 8 cm to 11 cm x 7.2 cm.

11. Five embossed cards with icicles on a grey background and various birds, with a greeting or a verse by Ada.
7.7 cm x 14.2 cm.

12. Two embossed cards, each with a bird perched on a fence festooned with autumn leaves, flowers, and berries. Traces of an early snowfall can be seen.
8.7 cm x 13.2 cm.

13. A well designed seasonal card with a robin, holly touched with snow, and a greeting by Eden Hooper in a gilt-edged scroll. 10.3 cm x 18.5 cm.

14. Four cards, two designs probably from a set of three, in two sizes, telling the tale of the robins party. No. 1 - the invitation, and no. 3 - robins and blue tits enjoying the feast - are here, with narrative verses by Lewis Novra on reverse. One was dated 1882 by the sender.
10.9 cm x 8.7 cm, 14.2 cm x 11 cm.

15. Two cards, a robin with holly and a poem by C D on reverse, and robins on a wall with ivy.
8.5 cm x 13.9 cm, 13 cm x 10.1 cm.

16. Two embossed cards, winter scenes with robins.
9.3 cm x 12.5 cm, 10 cm x 10.5 cm.

17. Three cards, two from a set with robins in winter scenes, the third a bullfinch in a snow covered landscape.
7.7 cm x 11 cm, 9.3 cm x 13.2 cm.

18. Three cards, robins in human clothing as street sweeper, musician, or sandwich man. 7.2 cm x 10.7 cm.

19. Two cards, each with two robins or tits on a tree, with verse below. 9 cm x 13.2 cm.

20. Two large cards, winter scenes with holly, mistletoe, and a robin, and verses signed Da or J L E E. 13.2 cm x 20.2 cm.

21. An embossed card, a robin in a wreath of spring flowers on a grey background. 9.9 cm x 13.5 cm.

22. A large card, winter scene of lake and mountains with bullfinches. 13.8 cm x 20 cm.

23. Two cards, a bullfinch on a holly branch with a winter scene in a circular vignette, and two robins with holly and Christmas roses. 11.5 cm x 15.3 cm, 16.2 cm x 11.8 cm.

24. A winter scene with a blackbird and mistletoe. 11 cm x 16 cm.

25. Four cards, winter scenes in circular vignettes with robins on bare branches or with holly or snowdrops, two dated 1884, 1885, by the senders. 7.2 cm x 10.6 cm.

26. Four miscellaneous cards, robins in winter scenes or with flowers or mistletoe. Sizes up to 9.5 cm x 13.2 cm.

*The following cards were published from 1885 on.*

27. Eight miscellaneous cards, all with robins in spring or winter scenes, one signed A F Lydon. 5 cm x 7.4 cm to 13.5 cm x 9 cm.

28. Two cards, one design of a robin and bullfinches in a winter scene with holly and mistletoe. 15.1 cm x 11 cm.

29. Four small cards, winter scenes with country houses, woods, and robins. 8.7 cm x 5 cm.

30. Four cards, three from a set showing a robin investigating an overturned plant pot, the fourth a robin delivering a letter, signed with a monogram J H. 7.6 cm x 7.6 cm, 9.3 cm x 7.1 cm.

31. Seven cards with serrated edges, some embossed and tinselled, showing robins and blue tits. 9.4 cm x 6.6 cm to 9.2 cm x 11.2 cm.

32. Four cards, each with a small embossed robin and a greeting in gilt letters, one in correspondence style. Sizes up to 11.5 cm x 9.2 cm.

# VOLUME 188:
# BIRDS, CARDS IN SMALLER SIZES

**These cards were published in the early 1880's except where otherwise stated.**

1. Four cards on various coloured backgrounds, each with a colourful bird perched on a twig or leaves, perhaps published by Sulman, c1875. 8.2 cm x 5.4 cm, 9.4 cm x 6.3 cm.

2. Three cards, two designs of exotic long-tailed birds and flowers, one dated 1877 by the sender. 6.5 cm x 9.2 cm.

3. Four cards (one birthday), three designs of blue tits and martin with strawberries, roses, or nuts. 11.7 cm x 7.6 cm, 7 cm x 10.5 cm.

4. Six cards, three designs in shades of brown, gold and orange, showing a parrot on a balcony, and a skylark and a lapwing with chicks. 10.5 cm x 7.3 cm.

5. Three miscellaneous cards, colourful birds on brown or black backgrounds. Sizes up to 12.5 cm x 8 cm.

6. Seven miscellaneous cards, four designs with robins and blue tits on a floral background. Two were dated 1878, 1880 by the senders and six are embossed. 7.8 cm x 4.5 cm.

7. Five cards, three designs of various birds with nests or boxes, and greetings or a verse by Ada in panels. One was dated 1879 by the sender. 10.2 cm x 6.5 cm.

8. Five cards, four designs of various birds with nests and flowers or holly on a pale blue background and a scroll below with verses signed by H L N, F O or D g. 5.6 cm x 9.1 cm.

9. Five cards, four designs of various birds in floral settings, two with nest boxes, framed in green or brown borders. 11 cm x 6.7 cm.

10. Six cards (1 birthday), five designs with a peacock, ducks, and various garden birds, with floral borders or backgrounds, one dated 1878 by the sender. 6.8 cm x 9.6 cm.

11. Six cards on brown or blue background, various colourful birds with floral sprays. 6.3 cm x 9.5 cm, 9.5 cm x 6.3 cm.

12/13. Nine bordered cards c1878, seven designs of various birds on gilt, black, or grey ground, with sprays of flowers or leaves and greetings in a panel with Japanese style border. 11 cm x 7.4 cm.

14. Seven similar unbordered cards on green or cream ground with six designs of birds with flowers. 10.5 cm x 6.9 cm.

15. Three cards, single birds with a leafy background and a greeting verse in a shield-shaped panel. 10.7 cm x 7.5 cm.

16. Four cards from two sets, two with single birds on a gilt background and a verse in a panel, and two with a border of twigs showing a kingfisher and a robin in flight. 11.3 cm x 8 cm, 12.2 cm x 9.2 cm.

17. Two valentine cards, robin or skylark on floral background. 10.6 cm x 6.4 cm.

18. Three cards, garden scenes with flowers or berries and robin, blue tit, or sparrow, one dated 1880 by the sender. 7.3 cm x 11 cm.

19. Three cards, each with two colourful birds on a floral background. 11 cm x 7.3 cm.

20. Eight miscellaneous small cards, seven designs, each with a single bird in a floral background, 1880-85. Sizes up to 10.8 cm x 8.8 cm.

21. Seven miscellaneous cards, all with white doves and flowers. 6.8 cm x 5 cm up to 11.8 cm x 7.7 cm.

22. Three cards, two designs of a white dove against a starry sky, with a verse below by H M Burnside. 9 cm x 9 cm.

23. Five cards, four designs of a single bird in a woodland setting. 7.6 cm x 10.9 cm.

24. Seven embossed cards, five designs of robins, wren, martin, and nightingale, two tinselled. 7.6 cm x 10.9 cm.

25. Nine miscellaneous small cards, various birds in winter scenes or with flowers, 1880's. 7.7 cm x 4.8 cm up to 10.6 cm x 6.7 cm.

*The following cards have single birds in portrait style, and are rather larger than the previous ones.*

26/28. Nine cards (one birthday), four designs of a robin and three colourful foreign birds, on grey or gilt backgrounds. One with a printed verse was found in U S A, and another is on an elaborate white embossed mount. Late 1870's. 8.3 cm x 12.7 cm, 15.3 cm x 19.2 cm.

29. Four cards, one design of a bullfinch on green, grey, yellow or gilt mounts, one dated 1887 by the sender. 12 cm x 6.8 cm.

30. Six similar cards, two designs of a yellow wagtail and an unidentified blue bird, on mounts in four colours, one dated 1878. 12 cm x 6.8 cm.

31. Four similar, one design of a nightingale on mounts in four colours. 6.8 cm x 12 cm.

32. Five similar cards, four designs of a robin, parrot, and two foreign birds. 12 cm x 6.8 cm.

33. Four cards, two designs of stylised birds on brown or gilt background, probably based on woodpeckers. 12 cm x 6.8 cm.

34. Two embossed cards, cockatoos or birds of paradise. 7 cm x 15.3 cm.

## VOLUME 189:
## BIRDS, GILDED & EMBOSSED CARDS WITH FLOWERS & FOLIAGE

**These cards were published in the early 1880's unless otherwise stated.**

1. Five cards, c1875, a set of four embossed scallop-edged cards with small birds, flowers and holly, festive fare and presents. The fifth card is larger with a peacock and a number of antique vases, a helmet, and a spear. 9 cm x 5.4 cm, 13.4 cm x 8.2 cm.

2. Three gilt-edged birthday cards, a robin with holly, and two brightly coloured red and blue birds with flowers, all with verses in bordered panels. One was dated 1878 by the sender. 10.4 cm x 6.4 cm.

3. Four cards c1875 with patterned gilt edges, a robin, nightingale, thrush, and two yellow doves on nest, all with wreaths of flowers and foliage. 7.6 cm x 10.6 cm.

4. Four miscellaneous gilt-backed cards, various birds on flowering branches, two with scenes in vignettes. 9.3 cm x 6.3 cm up to 11.3 cm x 7.4 cm.

5. Two embossed cards in Japanese style (one trimmed), with birds in a floral border. 12.2 cm x 6.8 cm.

6. Five cards, three designs of stylised birds in floral or leafy setting with gilt, black, or silver borders, one dated 1878 by the sender. 6.8 cm x 11.9 cm.

7. Four gilt-backed cards, colourful exotic birds with flowers and foliage. 10.7 cm x 6.7 cm, 7 cm x 11.1 cm.

8. Three bordered cards (one birthday), a lyre bird, peacock, or kingfisher in an oval vignette on a floral patterned gilt or blue background, two dated 1880, 1883 by the senders. 11.3 cm x 7.4 cm.

9. Three cards (one birthday), scenes with ducks, swans, and kingfishers on gilt background with verses in panel, one dated 1880 by the sender. 8.5 cm x 12.2 cm.

10. Five embossed cards with patterned gilt borders (one birthday), robins, swallows, goldfinches and bullfinch with a variety of flowers, two dated 1880 by the senders. Each has a long narrative poem by Astley H Baldwin. 9 cm x 13.2 cm.

11. Four similar cards with various birds and unsigned poems. 8.6 cm x 12.3 cm.

12. Three cards, one with a verse in a panel, a flower spray and two pigeons. The other two have flying swallows and blue tits on a leaf and berry background with a greeting verse in a panel, and were dated 1879, 1880, by the senders. 8 cm x 12.2 cm.

13. Three embossed cards, one design of a tropical bird with flowers, a pineapple, and a butterfly. 7.7 cm x 11.9 cm.

14. Two cards, blue tits and swallows with a basket of fruit or in a woodland scene, set in a border of leaves. 9 cm x 12.1 cm.

15. Two gilt-edged cards, a swallow flying through an arch of flowers, and a robin in a riverside setting, with greeting verses in panels. 7.5 cm x 11.2 cm.

16. Two cards with elaborate patterned border around a sparrow in a circular vignette. 9.2 cm x 9.2 cm.

17/18. Ten miscellaneous cards (two birthday) with gilt border or background, each with colourful birds and fruit, flowers, or mistletoe. Sizes up to 9 cm x 13 cm.

19. Three gilt-bordered cards, two designs of a bullfinch on a blackberry bush and a blue tit on roses, with a verse by S C H on a scroll. 9.5 cm x 13.1 cm.

20. Three gilt-bordered cards, scenes with birds in floral borders. 8 cm x 12 cm.

21. Four miscellaneous cards, various birds with flowers. 6 cm x 8.8 cm up to 7.3 cm x 17 cm.

22. Four cards from two sets. Two have parrots or a canary with their cage. The others have a patterned border and a swallow flying over a woodland scene with flowers, and verses by MER on reverse. 7 cm x 15.3 cm, 7.4 cm x 14.3 cm.

23. Three elaborate cards, birds in a circular vignette set in a Japanese style background. These are probably those registered at Stationers' Hall by F Belbeder for the publishers Smith, Val Rosa & Co., 12-5-1881. 13 cm x 9.2 cm.

24. Three cards, each with a bird on a brown diagonal band over spring flowers, and a religious verse on the back. 10.3 cm x 15 cm.

25. A gilt-bordered embossed card with a blue tit on a berried branch. 10 cm 15.3 cm.

26. A large gilt-edged embossed card, a white dove holding a rose and a parcel flying over a country scene, with greeting on a gilded weather vane. 19 cm x 14 cm.

27. Four gilt-edged embossed cards (one birthday), three designs of colourful stylised birds perched on branches, with verse in panel. 13.1 cm x 8.2 cm.

28. Two cards, one with tropical birds in a circular vignette with flowers, on a green scroll in a gilt background, the other canaries with roses, c1885. 10 cm x 14.5 cm, 9.6 cm x 14.2 cm.

29. Three miscellaneous cards, birds with flowers, one on a gilt cross. Sizes up to 13 cm x 10 cm.

30. Three cards, robins, goldfinch, and chaffinches on nests in a silver horseshoe, later 1880's. 8 cm x 11 cm.

31. Two embossed cards on thick board, tropical birds on gilded branches in Japanese style. These are stamped "Howlett" perhaps the retailer, but they have the appearance of late De La Rue cards, c1890. 11.8 cm x 11 cm.

## VOLUME 190:
## BIRDS WITH FLOWERS & FOLIAGE

**These cards, while similar to those in Volume 189, are not so lavishly embellished with gilt decoration. They were published in the early 1880's except where otherwise stated.**

1. Four cards, three designs of robins, swallows, and doves, with flowers on a decorative border framing a verse. Two were dated 1878 by the senders. 8.1 cm x 14 cm.

2. One card, a blue tit by a lake with irises and bulrushes. 6.3 cm x 16 cm.

3. One card, blue tits sheltering beneath flower-decked branches, dated 1880 by the sender. 10.3 cm x 14.9 cm.

4. Two birthday cards, doves with roses or carnations and a birthday verse. 11.6 cm x 15.5 cm.

5. Three cards, one a folder with two pictures of birds in floral settings on the cover opening to show a poem by Fannie Rochat, and two single cards with the same bird designs. 8.7 cm x 11.3 cm.

6. Two cards, robins or goldfinches perched on trees, with Christmas roses or autumn flowers below. 9 cm x 13.4 cm.

7. Two cards, blue tits on blackberries, crested tits? on a branch. 7.8 cm x 12.3 cm.

8. Two cards, tropical bird with a bowl of forget-me-nots, 14.8 cm x 12 cm, and

another with two birds on foliage, dated 1882 by the sender. 9.5 cm x 15.7 cm.

9. Two cards with ferns in a scroll, and a white dove or two robins on branches below. 9.8 cm x 13.7 cm.

10. Eight embossed cards with small birds and flower garlands. Seven have four designs on different shades of background with greeting or verse, and the other is triangular in shape. 5.1 cm x 12 cm, 14 cm x 10.2 cm x 10.2 cm.

11. Four cards (one birthday), three designs of birds and flowers in Japanese style. 7.9 cm x 13 cm.

12. Two cards, tropical birds with a butterfly. 9.5 cm x 9.5 cm.

13. Six embossed cards, three designs of robin, nightingale, or white dove each carrying a garland of flowers. 11 cm x 7.1 cm.

14. Two cards, pigeons on a roof or balcony with flowers. 14.3 cm x 9.5 cm.

15. Three miscellaneous cards, blue tits with nasturtiums, sparrows and nest and goldfinches with nest on hawthorn, one dated 1881. 10 cm x 15 cm, 13.1 cm x 8.3 cm, 11.8 cm x 7.8 cm.

16. Three miscellaneous cards (two embossed), tropical birds with lakeland scenes and verses or text in panels. 12 cm x 8.9 cm, 10.8 cm x 7 cm, 9.8 cm x 7.5 cm.

17. Five embossed cards with various birds in woodland scenes or perched on flowers. Sizes up to 11.6 x 7.5 cm.

18. Four miscellaneous embossed cards, colourful birds with flowers and foliage, two with nests. 7 cm x 11 cm up to 8.4 cm x 14.5 cm.

19. Four cards (three embossed), three designs of robins and blue tits in flight over flowers and grasses, one dated 1883 by the sender. 6.9 cm x 15.2 cm.

20/21. Seven cards, probably all from one set, three designs with birds and one with a cat, in a bordered rectangular or oval vignette framed in flowers, with greeting or verse in a scroll or panel below. 8.6 cm x 12.2 cm.

22. Two cards, a martin flying over a lake with waterlilies and blackberries, and an approximation to bullfinches on a hawthorn bush. 18.3 cm x 12.3 cm, 15.5 cm x 11.2 cm.

23. Four miscellaneous embossed cards with birds and flowers, one perhaps a golden oriole. 7.5 cm x 13.4 cm up to 11.9 cm x 15.6 cm.

24. Two gilt bordered cards, a parrot with flowering cactus, and flamingoes in a lake, this dated 1883 by the sender. 9.9 cm x 15 cm, 13.5 cm x 8.5 cm.

25. Two cards in Japanese style, one with birds on a flowering tree, the other a heron in a lake with water plants. These are signed with a monogram F D (untraced). 9.7 cm x 15 cm.

26. Two cards, a humming bird in flight, with a verse by C D on reverse, and an unidentified bird in reeds. 10.7 cm x 15.3 cm.

*The following cards were published from 1885-90.*

27. One card, a sparrow with a pink and blue butterfly in its beak, matching the background of dog roses and blue sky. The "Peace, Love, and Plenty" of the verse by L M L ignores the plight of the butterfly. The monogram C D F has not been traced. 10.5 cm x 14.9 cm.

28. One card, an exotic bird on roses, with trees and lake below. 11.7 cm x 15.7 cm.

29. Five miscellaneous cards, various birds with flowers, two with winter scenes in vignettes. Sizes up to 13 cm x 8.4 cm.

30. Four cards from two sets. Two are valentines and have a martin or dove bearing flowers with a greeting on a scroll; the others have a swallow or blue tit perched on a rose. 11.2 cm x 7 cm, 12.2 cm x 8.1 cm.

31. Two cards, each with a colourful bird perched on a rose and an incongruous winter scene in the background. One was dated 1891 by the sender. 10.2 cm x 15.5 cm.

32. Three cards from a set, birds or a butterfly with ivy, autumn leaves, or roses. 14.8 cm x 9 cm.

## VOLUME 191: BIRDS. SOME CHRISTMAS CASUALTIES, PARROTS, OWLS, STORKS, SWANS, AND BIRDS IN COUNTRY SCENES

**These cards were published in the early 1880's, with exceptions as stated.**

1. Five cards with gilt or floral borders, showing dead grouse, pheasants, and duck awaiting the pot. One larger card was dated 1879 by the sender, and three smaller ones are from one set. 8.5 cm x 12 cm, 11.7 cm x 8.6 cm, 7 cm x 9.9 cm.

2. Four cards. Two show turkey or ducks hung with a bunch of holly and mistletoe, and the third has two grouse or ptarmigan hung on a wooden wall, in monochrome.

The fourth card shows a bird caught in a trap, with the verse "Unlike poor birdie, caught in a trap, may the New Year bring you no mishap!" a distasteful card to send or receive. 10 cm x 15 cm, 7.7 cm x 11.4 cm, 12 cm x 7.9 cm.

3. Three similar, with grouse, pheasant, or duck hung from a nail in a wooden wall, greeting below. 8 cm x 12.4 cm.

4. Four miscellaneous cards, parrots and cockatoos, late 1870's. 7.4 cm x 5.3 cm up to 9.8 cm x 15 cm.

5. One card, two blue birds on a matching nest set in a scroll, with a verse below "These lovely birds of rainbow hue...". 9 cm x 12.2 cm.

6. Two cards, one a parrot's head with a verse by S K C, and another with three colourful birds perched on a rose, and a gilt border. 13.6 cm x 9.3 cm, 15.7 cm x 10.2 cm.

7. Two large cards, a parrot and a cockatoo perched on branches. 16.9 cm x 12.5 cm.

8. A set of four cards, each with an owl perched on a signpost, a clock, or a branch, set against a moonlit starry sky, with humorous captions. 6.8 cm x 10 cm.

9. Four cards, three designs of owls against a starlit sky, one carrying a letter with greeting. 8.6 cm x 12.5 cm.

10. Two cards with silver borders, signed A M D, showing musical owls in "A Moonlight Sonata" and "A Quartette". There is a verse by Lewis Novra on the reverse of one, probably originally on the other, damaged by Victorian glue. 10 cm x 13.2 cm.

11. One card, a choir of owls under a crescent moon, dated 1888 by the sender. 11.9 cm x 16.2 cm.

**191.9**

12. Two humorous cards, owls skating, with descriptive verse below, and two owls in hats perched on a branch smoking and drinking, later 1880's.
11.8 cm x 9 cm, 14 cm x 10.6 cm.

13. Three cards, two designs of storks, under mistletoe or with bouquet of flowers. 8.6 cm x 12.3 cm.

14. A birthday card in Japanese style showing a crane with flowers by a river.
13.2 cm x 10.2 cm.

15. Four cards, storks with babies. These show the storks perhaps delivering the babies to hopeful parents, by penny-farthing bicycle, in boxes, or by balloon, and getting supplies by fishing in the river.
9.5 cm x 6.7 cm, 11.5 cm x 7.8 cm.

16. Four cards, two designs in two styles of swans or ducks on a lake.
11 cm x 13.8 cm, 8.8 cm x 12.3 cm.

17. Three cards, lake scenes with swans, two with verses by Samuel K Cowan.
14.5 cm x 10.4 cm, 14.5 cm x 10 cm.

18. Two cards, swans. One in monochrome has an interesting poem "King Christmas" by A G on reverse.
9 cm x 12.7 cm, 8.8 cm x 13 cm.

19. Two cards from a set of woodland scenes, one with a deer, butterfly, and flowers, the other with a duck on a pond and a dragonfly above. 9 cm x 11.6 cm.

20. Two curious cards, one with a stork, and a hare eating carrots, the other a chameleon with a bird, butterfly and dragonfly. They have a narrative verse on a diagonal band. 7.4 cm x 11 cm.

21. Three cards, two embossed sea scenes with birds, and a woodland scene with birds in flight.
12 cm x 5.4 cm, 17 cm x 6.8 cm.

22. Three cards, sea scenes with swallows, terns, or fulmars. 10 cm x 15 cm.

23. Five miscellaneous cards, birds in winter or summer and a sea scene.
5.7 cm x 7.8 cm up to 9 cm x 13.4 cm.

24. One card, ravens on a branch, with a country scene in a circular vignette.
10.5 cm x 14.3 cm.

25. Two cards, a martin flying over sea carrying a Christmas greeting in its beak, and swallows on reeds in a country scene.
12.2 cm x 9.3 cm, 11.8 cm x 14.7 cm.

26. Three miscellaneous cards, various birds in flight over sea or river. Sizes up to 14.5 cm x 10.2 cm.

27. Three cards c1890.
a) A bird, labelled "Oriolus Bengalensis" with an Indian lotus and an appropriate

backwater scene in a vignette.
10.2 cm x 14.4 cm.
b) Swallows flying over bulrushes, red border, greeting on gilt panel.
9.3 cm x14.7 cm.
c) Two magpies in a country scene.
9.2 cm x 13.2 cm.

## VOLUME 192: BIRDS, MORE CARDS FROM 1880-1890

**This volume includes some larger cards from 1880-85, with later cards up to 1890 in varied styles.**

*Numbers 1-9 were published in the early 1880's.*

1. Two cards, martins flying over cliffs, and kingfishers by a stream.
10.9 cm x 14.7 cm.

2. Four cards, a robin on holly, a goldfinch on ivy, a nightingale on lilac, and a martin on a rose bush. 9.9 cm x 14.3 cm.

3. Three cards, martins, flying over sea, with roses or apple blossom, one dated 1883 by the sender. 11 cm x 15.7 cm.

4. Two cards, goldfinches, nightingales, with nests. 11.4 cm x 14 cm.

5. One card, a grey wagtail with nest by a stream. 12.3 cm x 17.6 cm.

6. Two cards, a skylark, and a martin in flight over countryside. 18 cm x 10.3 cm.

7. One card, a small parakeet(?) perching on a branch. 12 cm x 15.8 cm.

8. An embossed card, baby swallows in nest. 12 cm x 15 cm.

9. Two cards, chicks holding a letter in their beaks, with verses below by

Marianne Farningham and Moore.
9.4 cm x 11.4 cm.

*Numbers 10-18 were published c1885.*

10. Two cards, mallards, by a stone arch or by a lake. 10.8 cm x 13 cm,
13.2 cm x 9.8 cm.

11. Two cards, winter scenes with robin or bullfinch, one with a verse by E Love, the other with a poem by M S Haycraft on reverse. 9.7 cm x 13 cm, 10 cm x 14.1 cm.

12. A set of four tinselled cards, robins, tits and bullfinches sheltering from the snow under umbrellas, in a pan or an old hat.
9.9 cm x 13 cm.

13. Two cards, owls perched on a ledge with a verse below by E E Griffin, and doves on a window sill with a verse by Nemo. 8.6 cm x 12.5 cm.

14. Two cards, winter scenes with various birds flying or roosting on branches, with verses by Charlotte Murray and Cecilia Havergal. 12.5 cm x 9.5 cm.

15. Two cards, one a pen and ink drawing with a winter scene and a nightingale, the other swallows flying over the sea, this with cut-out edge.
9 cm x 11.7 cm, 10.8 cm x 15.4 cm.

16. Four miscellaneous cards, with robins, finches, thrush, and other birds. One card shows musical blue tits playing in a brass band.
11.7 cm x 8 cm up to 12.9 cm x 9.7 cm.

17. Two cards, magpies with a descriptive punning verse, and chaffinches? flying over a church steeple, with a verse by Charlotte Murray on reverse.
14 cm x 10.8 cm.

18. Two cards, baby birds drinking water from a shell, and two chaffinches in a

192.28

**193.10**

winter scene.
13.5 cm x 11 cm, 15.8 cm x 12 cm.

*The following cards were published from 1885-90.*

19/20. Ten miscellaneous cards, nine designs of various birds in spring and winter scenes.
9.5 cm x 5.5 cm up to 12.5 cm x 9.5 cm.

21. Three cards, two designs of musical sparrows in two styles playing the drums and blowing a horn.
10.1 cm x 7.7 cm, 10.8 cm x 8.5 cm.

22. Four cards, various birds perched on flowering branches or reeds.
6 cm x 9.7 cm up to 8.6 cm x 13.1 cm.

23. Two cards, lake scenes with birds on branches.  12.7 cm x 10.2 cm.

24. Four miscellaneous cards, various birds, including flamingoes, and blue tits with a violin.
11.7 cm x 9.2 cm up to 15.5 cm x 10.1 cm.

25. One card on thick board with serrated edge, birds in a tree, with a verse by Samuel K Cowan printed in silver, c1890.
13.6 cm x 14.5 cm.

26. Two cards, c1890.
a) Robins in a vignette bordered by a silver jewelled tree, with a verse by E E Griffin on reverse.
b) Goldfinches flying over a field in an oval vignette in a background with a country scene, and a verse by Ernest Sigourney on reverse.
13.2 cm x 11.2 cm, 15.1 cm x 10.9 cm.

27. Two cards with robins, tits, and goldfinches on a holly branch or with flowers, and a verse by S K Cowan, on a silver background. 11.9 cm x 8.8 cm.

28. Three cards c1890.
a) A moorland scene in a butterfly-shaped vignette on embossed green background.
b) Swans in a shell-shaped vignette on a shaded red and gold background.
c) Robins in a fan-shaped vignette on a shaded red and gold background. The first has a verse by H M Burnside on reverse, and there are traces of similar ones on the backs of the other two. 13.9 cm x 10.7 cm.

29. Four miscellaneous embossed cards, c1890, small birds, three with flowers, the fourth with a tinselled crescent moon. All approximately 13 cm x 9.2 cm.

30. Six miscellaneous cards, one with greeting in French.
7 cm x 7 cm up to 11.5 cm x 7.8 cm.

31. One card in triangular shape, thick board, with martins flying over countryside, c1890.
13.8 cm x 10.5 cm x 10.5 cm,

32. Four cards in photographic style, hand-coloured, robins with flowers. One was published by Marion, two by William Luks, 1880's. 6.5 cm x 10.2 cm,
10.8 cm x 16.7 cm, 16.5 cm x 10.8 cm.

33. Two cards in photographic style, a dove carrying a bouquet of flowers, with a verse by Mrs Hemans on reverse, and bullfinches in the snow, 1880's.
16.5 cm x 10.8 cm.

## VOLUME 193:
## BIRDS. CHICKS, DUCKS, FARMYARD SCENES, NESTS AND EGGS

It might be expected that baby chicks and birds' eggs and nests would appear on Easter and birthday cards, but they were also used to greet Christmas and New Year as the cards included here demonstrate. The

same design, as has already been shown in previous volumes, was often used for Christmas, New Year, Easter, and birthday greetings, and even for valentines.

1. Six black background cards c1875 showing chicks just out of the egg at play with frogs or mice. Three cards marked Sulman are included here for comparison, and the cards in numbers 1-4 might have all been published by Sulman.
9.4 cm x 6 cm, 8.7 cm x 5.3 cm.

2. Nine similar smaller cards, six designs (repeating one from no. 1) of chicks just out of the egg. Four cards are on gilt-bordered mounts. 7.8 cm x 3.6 cm, mounts up to 11.3 cm x 7.6 cm.

3. Nine cards on gilt, green, or brown background, two designs of chicks or mallards showing variations of colour, size, and captions. Three were dated 1877, 1878, 1879.
10.8 cm x 6.7 cm, 8.3 cm x 5.3 cm.

4. Seven cards, five designs with chicks, mice, and frogs on blue, beige, or black backgrounds, c1875. 9.5 cm x 6.3 cm.

5. Three cards, hens, mallard, pheasant on black or beige background.
12.3 cm x 8.8 cm, 13.3 cm x 6.7 cm.

6. One black background card with a cock and a duck, on a patterned green and gold mount similar to those used by Eyre & Spottiswoode. 11.2 cm x 7.2 cm.

7. Five embossed cards(one birthday), four designs of a fox with chicks, a dog and birds, and ducklings with a hen or a frog, one dated 1879 by the sender.
11.9 cm x 9 cm.

8. Four embossed cards, three designs with three chicks just out of the egg, three with verses, one with greeting. 10.6 cm x 6.7 cm.

*Numbers 9-20 were published in the early 1880's.*

9. Three cards, a stream in springtime with a swan, mallards, or a hen and ducklings.
15.2 cm x 11.2 cm.

10. Two embossed cards with gilt and blue patterned borders, a cock and hen with chicks, ducks with ducklings.
13.4 cm x 9.4 cm.

11. Four embossed cards (one birthday), two designs of chicks with a basket of eggs, another with rabbits and flowers, on beige, blue, or grey backgrounds.
12.8 cm x 9.2 cm.

12. Four miscellaneous cards, domestic fowls and chicks in farmyard settings.
Sizes up to 13.4 cm x 10 cm.

13. Two cards, a newly hatched chick encountering a snail or looking at itself in a broken mirror. 11.7 cm x 9 cm.

14. Three miscellaneous cards, two of cocks, one marked H R 258, the third a cock with two hens. Sizes approximately 12.5 cm x 8 cm.

15. Six cards, turkeys, with greetings. 11.2 cm x 6.7 cm.

16. Three embossed cards, repeating two of the turkey designs in no. 15, but with verses, one signed Fannie Rochat. One card was dated 1882 by the sender. 11.2 cm x 6.7 cm.

17. One card, a well-drawn picture of three mallards in reeds, with a verse by Ernest Sigourney on reverse. 15.2 cm x 12.8 cm.

18. Two cards with wide gilt borders, showing a group of chicks' or ducklings' heads, one dated 1885 by the sender. 10.7 cm x 13.5 cm.

19. Two cards, baby chicks on a table with blue and white china, eating shrimps or cress. There is a narrative verse signed G N L on the reverse of one, with similar traces of a poem on the damaged back of the second card. 15.4 cm x 11.9 cm.

20. Two cards, baby chicks, one signed with the monogram J T. 8.5 cm x 13.6 cm, 9.3 cm x 13 cm.

*The following cards were published in the 1890's.*

21. Four miscellaneous cards with baby chicks, two with punning verses, one with a lobster, another signed O & G E. 5.8 cm x 5 cm up to 12.9 cm x 10.2 cm.

22. One card with turkeys and a seasonal verse -"He grows as plump as he is able That he may grace your Christmas table". Dated 1893 by the sender. 14 cm x 9.4 cm.

23. Two humorous cards, a cockerel bowling a hoop, and two ducklings, dressed as boys, skating. 10.7 cm x 7 cm, 12 cm x 10 cm.

24. Five cards on a cream coloured embossed background, four designs of baby chicks and ducklings. 8.8 cm x 8.8 cm up to 14.8 cm x 11.5 cm.

*The following cards show birds' nests, eggs and feathers.*

25. Two cards, nests with eggs, one of a whitethroat with red currants, and a hedge sparrow's nest with wallflowers. One was dated 1881 by the sender and both have long unsigned poems on reverse. 17 cm x 12.5 cm.

26. Two cards, nests with eggs, flowers and ferns in circular vignettes in a black border, one dated 1881 by the sender. 9.5 cm x 10.3 cm.

27. An Easter card, a large egg with spring flowers and leaves, and a cupid with an egg on reverse. This is marked White, Stokes, & Allen, copyright 1883. 13.3 cm x 17.7 cm.

28. Two embossed Easter cards, one with a basket of eggs by a gate, the other an egg shell with a bouquet of flowers, c1885. 9.2 cm x 12.8 cm, 15.5 cm x 12.8 cm.

29. Six cards, four designs of birds' eggs, lying on moss or grass and feathers, four with birthday, two with Easter greetings. 9.8 cm x 6.8 cm.

30. Four Easter cards, three with birds' eggs in a nest, the fourth an egg with a snowdrop, this dated 1883 by the sender. 10.7 cm x 6.7 cm, 9.1 cm x 5.7 cm.

31. Four cards, all Christmas or New Year. Two have baskets of birds' eggs against a crimson curtain, the third a basket of hens' eggs in a fuchsia bush, the fourth a bird's nest with eggs on spring flowers. 11.3 cm x 8.4 cm, 14.2 cm x 10.2 cm, 12.8 cm x 9.2 cm.

## VOLUME 194: BUTTERFLIES & OTHER INSECTS

**A popular greeting card subject was butterflies. The examples here are where the insect is the main theme of the design, though flowers play an important role as well. The Peacock, Red Admiral, and Swallowtail butterflies appear most often, but others seen include the Brimstone, Painted Lady, Orange Tip, Comma, and various Whites and Blues, as well as a number of stylised versions. Dragonflies and damselflies are also seen, and a few cards feature beetles, flies, and other insects.**

*Nos. 1-5 were published by Eyre & Spottiswoode c1880.*

1. Five cards, butterflies on leaves or grass, from two sets nos. 112, 131. 11 cm x 8.7 cm, 7.9 cm x 12 cm.

2. Three cards, butterflies on a flower or catkins and a dragonfly on a water lily, on blue background, no. 203. 13.6 cm x 7.8 cm.

3. Four cards, three designs of butterflies or bee on leaves, no. 207. 8.5 cm x 14 cm.

4. Three cards, butterflies, insects, and frogs in lake and woodland settings, with gilt patterned borders, no. 254. One was dated 1879 by the sender. 10.1 cm x 14.1 cm.

5. Three cards, butterflies on blackberries or flowers in a circular red-bordered vignette, with a greeting verse by F E E H in a gilt-edged panel. No. 314. 14.2 cm x 10.3 cm.

*Numbers 6-24 were published from 1879-1885.*

6. Four cards, butterflies and flowers, three with a Christmas poem. Three were dated 1879, 1880, 1883 by the senders. 7.3 cm x 11 cm.

7. Four cards, one with dragonflies, three with two designs of butterflies, one marked Terry Stoneman & Co. Sizes up to 7 cm x 11 cm.

8. Five cards (one a valentine), various moths and butterflies on grey ground with verse in panel. 11 cm x 5.6 cm.

9. Six cards from three sets, various designs of butterflies on flowers or in country scenes. 9.3 cm x 5.6 cm, 9 cm x 5.3 cm, 11.2 cm x 7.7 cm.

10. Five cards, butterflies and moths on a large leaf with flowers or fruit on grey background. 9.5 cm x 6.5 cm.

11. Four cards, stylised butterflies with flowers and grasses on grey background. 7 cm x 16.2 cm.

12. Three cards, two designs, one dragonflies on a lake, the other a butterfly with primroses. 13.6 cm x 8.1 cm.

13. Five gilt-backed cards, butterflies and dragonflies with flowers or over water. They have greetings in English and titles in French. 10 cm x 6.5 cm.

14. Four cards, butterflies in flight, and dragonflies, beetles, wasps, and flies on large leaves. 10.8 cm x 7.5 cm.

15. Four cards. Two with gilt borders have dragonflies and a fly over a lake, one has a beetle and dragonfly on a white scroll, and the fourth has a butterfly hovering over a pond with frogs. Sizes up to 10.9 cm x 7.4 cm.

16. Five well designed embossed cards (one birthday), with two designs of a dragonfly and two of a butterfly with various flowers. The wings extend over the edges of the cards, giving a cut-out finish. 5.8 cm x 11.8 cm.

17. Four cards from two sets, butterflies with flowers, two with verses. 11.7 cm x 8.9 cm, 12.5 cm x 8.6 cm.

18. Four cards with butterflies and flowers or grasses. 5.3 cm x 7.3 cm up to 13 cm x 9.5 cm.

19. Two cards, a butterfly with hawthorn, and another with a snail and harebells. The

first card has a poem by Shirley Wynne on reverse. 14.3 cm x 10.5 cm.

20. Two gilt-edged cards, butterflies harnessed to a letter with a greeting, on a green background with flowers. 9.3 cm x 13.9 cm.

21. Three embossed cards, one Christmas, two birthday, with butterflies and flowers beside a lake. All have verses by E J P or S Ph A. 11 cm x 14.5 cm.

22. Three cards on a grey background, moths and various insects hovering over flowers, with a verse of greeting. 10.5 cm x 13 cm.

23. Three cards, each with a single butterfly on grass, on plain cream-coloured background with illuminated greeting, marked "Design 1". 7.7 cm x 10 cm.

24. Three embossed cards on pale blue backgrounds, butterflies on flowers, leaves, and berries. Sizes up to 14 cm x 9.8 cm.

25. Three cards, butterflies on flowers or fruit, c1890. 10 cm x 17.2 cm, 10.6 cm x 14.6 cm, 14.6 cm x 11.2 cm.

26. Two birthday cards with serrated edges, spring flowers with hovering butterflies, and verses by M S H on reverse. 9.9 cm x 13.2 cm.

27. A card on thick paper, various brightly coloured stylised butterflies on a brown background, with a verse by Cecilia Havergal on reverse. c1890. 15.9 cm x 11.6 cm.

28. Two cards, one with butterflies against a blue sky, the other embossed with flowers and stylised butterflies, c1890. 7 cm x 11 cm, 11.7 cm x 9.6 cm.

29. Four amusing cards, c1880, showing stag beetles with holly or mistletoe, dancing with a frog, or carrying a hamper of Christmas fare. 8.8 cm x 5.1 cm.

30. Three similar, showing a stag beetle with a telescope, another in a race with a snail, and a grasshopper riding on a moth, one dated 1880 by the sender. 11.8 cm x 5.5 cm.

31. Two cards, early 1880's.
a) A four-page folder, with four designs of moths and beetles around lighted candles, a bottle, a cup of cocoa, or a sugar cone. 8.3 cm x 13.3 cm folded.
b) A similar single card with two ground beetles (?) and a butterfly, under a crescent moon.  8.6 cm x 12.6 cm.

32. Three cards, various insects seated at a dinner table, playing cards, or making music, one dated 1883 by the sender. 10.1 cm x 22.3 cm.

194.32

# MISCELLANY

This section groups cards using silks, lace and feathers for decoration and construction, many made by French publishers, and a number of the silk fringed cards from English firms such as Thomas Stevens. Plainer cards from foreign publishers are included with some from English firms bearing greetings in foreign languages, made for export. One volume has cards from Canadian and Australian publishers which reflect the national pastimes and natural surroundings of those countries, with some from the United States including copies of English cards seen elsewhere in this collection. Advertising and postal cards appear in volume 201, and there are three volumes of personal greetings and hand-coloured and handmade cards.

Section
*17*

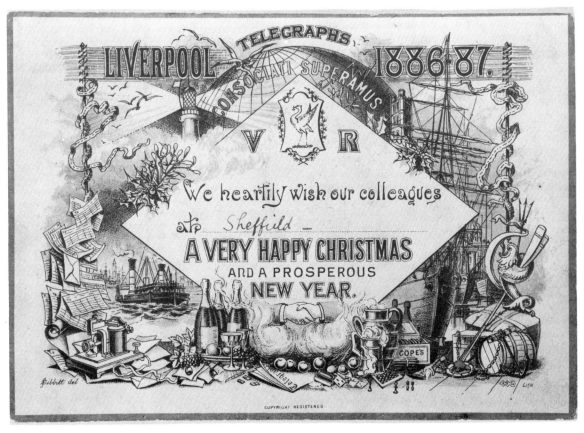

**201.27**

## VOLUME 195: FRENCH AND ENGLISH DECORATED CARDS

The French publishers made a large number of cards lavishly decorated with silk and mother-of-pearl, often mounted on rice paper edged with paper lace. This collection contains a number of these cards in reasonable condition. Their fragile nature resulted in few surviving for a hundred years without damage and removal from scrap books often resulted in collapse. The firm of Marion,based in both Paris and London, acted as agent for many of the French manufacturers, and this name often appears on their cards, as well as alone, perhaps on cards made by Marion. A number of Stationers' Hall registrations have been found for Marion, but none appear to apply to cards in this volume.

**195.5**

*Numbers 1-4 were published by Aubry, Paris, most of them numbered, indicating a very large production, these dated about 1875-1880. Some have greetings in French, some in English.*

1. A large card, mother-of-pearl tulip flowers applied to a card printed with forget-me-nots and grasses, series 316 no.1. 11.5 cm x 17.6 cm.

2. Four cards, three with printed silk flowers, one with moveable scraps, mounted on flower prints. Two are numbered series 348, one 286 no.4, and one is also marked Marion & Co., London. Sizes up to 8.8 cm x 12.8 cm.

3. Six cards. Three have silk flowers, one has a floral scrap on a cross, series 339 no. 4, one has a silk dog, and the other has a ˙ basket with silk flowers and dried grasses. 6.7 cm x 10.1 cm to 8.2 cm x 13 cm.

4. Six cards. Two have mother-of-pearl flowers on rice paper, no.18 and series 224 no.32, one has a flower scrap on a print with lace paper edge; three small cards have flowers and crosses edged with paper lace. 7.3 cm x 11.5 cm, 4.5 cm x 6.7 cm, 5.5 cm x 8 cm, 2.8 cm x 4.6 cm.

*Numbers 5-8 are from Paris firms who appear to be connected, some also marked Marion, dated 1875-1880.*

5. Seven lace-edged cards with silk scraps of robins, flowers, and holly on rice paper. Five are larger, with the same border, two marked G N Brevete SDGB and one marked De L et G N Brevete SDGB. Two smaller cards with a different patterned border are also De L et G N Brevete SDGB. 7.3 cm x 10.8 cm, 6.3 cm x 8.5 cm.

6. Seven cards. Five have the same border as five cards in no.5 above, with silk flowers, holly, and robins, and two are marked G N, two De L et G N, and one N. Genoux. A larger card with a different border is marked De L et G N and Marion, London, and a small plain-edged card is marked De Labarrie et N. Genoux. 7.3 cm x 10.8 cm, 9.5 cm x 14 cm, 5.5 cm x 8.7 cm.

7. Eight cards, seven with silk flowers and birds on rice paper, one with machine embroidered flowers on black silk, all with plain borders. Two are marked Marion, two N. Genoux and two G N and Marion. 5.7 cm x 8.5 cm up to 7.8 cm x 11 cm.

8. Six cards, silk flowers, birds, holly, or vine on plain-edged cards, one with a cross. Three are marked G N and Marion, two Marion, and one N. Genoux. 6.2 cm x 9.4 cm up to 11.3 cm x 16.4 cm.

9. Five cards, four with silk flowers on rice paper, one with leaves of mother-of- pearl, all marked Me (Madame), Lafon, Editeur, Paris. 5.5 cm x 8 cm up to 8.2 cm x 11.9 cm.

10. Eight unmarked cards, all with silk or mother-of-pearl flowers and birds on rice paper, two lace edged, two with crosses. 5.5 cm x 8.7 cm up to 8 cm x 11.3 cm.

11. A card marked E. Rimmel, London, with silk flowers and holly on a cross on rice paper in a plain border. Rimmel had Paris connections, but the cards and trade lists found for this collection appear to be based on London. Possibly this card was made for Rimmel in Paris. 11.2 cm x 16 cm.

12. Four small cards on pale brown lace paper mounts. Three have oval prints, and the fourth with painted flowers on rice paper is marked J Bazire, 43B Malegherbes, Paris. 5.2 cm x 8 cm.

*The following cards were made in England and are examples of the use of silk and embroidery for cards, from 1875 to the early 1880's,*

*continuing from earlier cards of this kind in volume 13.*

13. Four cards :
a/b) The same design of machine embroidered holly and mistletoe on silk ovals, on different fancy mounts. 8.4 cm x 12 cm, 7.8 cm x 11.6 cm.
c) A painted holly spray on rice paper with silver lace border on a lace edged mount. 7.5 cm x 11 cm.
d) A triptych folder with illuminated gilt pattern cover and support for standing, opening to show a machine embroidered flower spray on black silk and a poem, signed T.S. copyright, probably Thomas Stevens, who specialised in this type of embroidery for bookmarks and cards. 12.8 cm x 8.9 cm.

14. Six cards, three with scraps, three with painted pictures, all on silk with various patterned gilded mounts. One has a greeting in German. All about 8 cm x 12 cm.

15. Six cards. Four have scraps and flowers printed on silk with three different gilded lace borders. Another has a wreath of flowers printed on silk with a silver lace border, and the sixth is a folder with a flower scrap on a white and silver lace cover opening to show a Christmas greeting printed on silk. 6.7 cm x 10 cm up to 11 cm x 12.9 cm.

16. A large "card" with a wreath of pansies printed on ivory silk, around a handwritten New Year greeting for 1880. 18.7 cm x 25.3 cm.

17. A card with a handworked border of pink and brown silk, and a wreath of leaves and flowers around a Christmas poem, with trademark for 29-1-1883. 12 cm x 16.7 cm.

18. A card with paper lace border framing a machine embroidered picture with red flowers and ferns. 14.6 cm x 10.2 cm.

19. A silk card printed with two girls' heads draped in a veil set against a blue sky with clouds. 15.4 cm x 16 cm.

20. A card with a moss rose and bud, the flower, bud and leaves made of silk. 11.3 cm x 16 cm.

## VOLUME 196: CARDS FROM FRENCH PUBLISHERS, AND OTHERS WITH GREETINGS IN FRENCH

A number of cards in plainer style from Aubry and a few from other French publishers are here, issued about 1875-1880, with greetings in both French and English. A few cards from English publishers with French greetings are included, some sent from France, but others used in England. The French publishers had

English agents to market their cards in this country and it would be interesting to have evidence to show if English cards were marketed in any quantity abroad.

*Numbers 1-16 were published by Aubry, some marked Marion. Most were numbered, either in series or with a single figure, and nearly all were found in English albums.*

1/3. Three large cards with gilt crosses wreathed in flowers, and greetings in English, series 232 nos.23,25,25, one dated 1875 by the sender. 14.6 cm x 22.5 cm.

4. Two cards, flowers and crosses with English greetings, series 268 no.2, 360 no.4. 11.6 cm x 16.6 cm, 10 cm x 15 cm.

5. Four cards, flowers and crosses, two with birds, English greetings. Series 325 nos. 2, 4, 7, 340 no. 16. 8 cm x 12.7 cm, 7.6 cm x 11.3 cm.

6. Six cards, flowers and crosses, one with birds. Three have French greetings, series 185 nos. 150, 153, 190, the others English greetings, series 185 nos. 105, 150, 151. 7 cm x 11 cm.

7. Eleven smaller cards from several sets, all with flowers and crosses, five with English, six with French greetings. Three are also marked Marion, London. 3 cm x 4.8 cm up to 5.5 cm x 8.7 cm.

8. Three miscellaneous cards, flowers and crosses. One has birds, another has vignettes with holy symbols originally covered with moveable flowers, series 286 no. 2, and the third has a bunch of cornfield blossoms, series 320 no. 7 and was dated 1877 by the sender. 7.4 cm x 11.8 cm, 7 cm x 11 cm.

9. Six cards with birds and flowers or holly, all with English captions. Two are from series 305, one series 185 no. 84, the others are numbered 15, 32, 58?, the last four marked also Marion & Co., London. 5.4 cm x 8 cm up to 7.7 cm x 11.5 cm.

10. Five cards, birds and flowers, one small gilt-edged card numbered 44, one other series 185 no. 31. 5.4 cm x 9 cm, 7 cm x 11 cm.

11. Two cards. One has a bunch of white flowers and forget-me-nots, series 316 no. 10. The other has a wreath of cornfield flowers around an English greeting, and is marked Raphael Tuck, London, indicating that this firm may have acted as an agent for Aubry's cards in England. 11.5 cm x 17.7 cm, 11.5 cm x 16.5 cm.

12/13. Eight cards, with seven designs of colourful flower bouquets, two with French greetings and six with English, the same design appearing with both languages. Series 185, nos. 86, 120, 141, series 187 nos. 25, 27, and no. 139, one

unnumbered. 7 cm x 11 cm, 7.5 cm x 11.8 cm.

14. Eleven cards, all with flowers. Ten cards in three sizes are small, including two headed "Langage des Fleurs". The other is larger, gilt-backed, also "Langage des Fleurs", with a spray of purple flowers titled Belle de Jour. 3.1 cm x 4.7 cm up to 7.6 cm x 11.9 cm.

15. Six miscellaneous cards with flowers, five designs, series 358 no. 4, 213 nos. 56, 57, 339 no. 36, 210 no. 10, and no. 98. 5.4 cm x 7.8 cm up to 10.8 cm x 7.3 cm.

16. Four cards, two designs of a bouquet of roses and forget-me-nots with a feather bearing English greetings, three embossed, two tinselled. One card only is marked, series 387, but the others are attributed from similarity. 11 cm x 6.5 cm.

*Numbers 17-21 were published by Marion, most being marked both Paris and London, all with English greetings.*

17. Four cards with decorated crosses and flowers or holly. Two have advertisements on the back for Nesterton's Library, "Novelties from Paris & Vienna", no. 18. The others are numbered 15, 42. 7.3 cm x 11.8 cm.

18. Three cards, two with flowers, one marked 9, the third with a branch of cherries and leaves. Sizes up to 8 cm x 10.3 cm.

19. Three cards, two with flower designs printed on silk, signed M & Co, another with a border of flowers painted on silk. 16.3 cm x 10.7 cm, 7.7 cm x 11.1 cm.

20. One card, repeating one design in no. 19 on plain card with greeting in gilt letters. 16.5 cm x 10.9 cm.

21. Four cards, white flowers and green leaves on pale blue background with greeting in gilt letters and gilt or silver border. 14.7 cm x 9.5 cm.

22. Six miscellaneous cards published by Bonamy, Paris. Three have two designs with flowers and crosses, nos. 121, 124, and three have flowers, nos. 92, 104, 312. 4.7 cm x 7.2 cm up to 7 cm x 11 cm.

23. Three cards published by Baillard, Paris, bunches of flowers on a leafy background, one dated 1879 by the sender. 6.5 cm x 10.3 cm.

24. Seven miscellaneous cards, all with flowers, one with a cross, others with birds, butterflies, or dog. Two were published by Blot, one marked with name of London agent W H Rice Cooke, Regent St. Four are marked Bouasse, one Wentzel, all Paris. 5.3 cm x 8.3 cm up to 7.5 cm x 11.5 cm.

25. Nine miscellaneous cards. Three with flowers and crosses are signed with a monogram J T or T J (see Volume 151, no. 5). Three more with crosses are marked L Turgis and Benziger Frères, two others Villemuir and Leroy, all Paris, and one is from L Eudes, Tours. 4.4 cm x 6.5 cm up to 6.2 cm x 9.7 cm.

26. A large gilt-edged card with meadow flowers and a butterfly and a castle in the distance, and an advertisement for the Galèries Sedanaises, Sedan, on the back. 11.8 cm x 17.5 cm.

*The following unmarked cards have greetings or verses in French, but were probably all from English publishers.*

27. Eight cards, including three with scraps of children or cherubs, three from one set with wreaths of flowers and leaves, and two with flowers around a panel with greeting, 1875-80. 8.8 cm x 5.8 cm up to 7 cm x 11 cm.

28. Seven cards with flowers, two with crosses, two embossed, on grey or beige backgrounds. 10 cm x 6.8 cm up to 8.6 cm x 13.1 cm.

29. Seven miscellaneous cards with flowers, c1880. 4 cm x 9 cm up to 11 cm x 7.2 cm.

30. Six miscellaneous cards, birds and flowers, late 1880's. 8 cm x 6 cm up to 11.1 cm x 8 cm.

31. Four cards, two folding with birds or roses, one with a flower bouquet and an open envelope, the fourth with a spray of forget-me-nots postmarked Versailles 1887. Sizes up to 11.6 cm x 8.6 cm.

## VOLUME 197: FRINGED & PADDED CARDS FROM ENGLISH PUBLISHERS

**Thomas Stevens of Coventry is renowned for the production of silk bookmarks, but he also published many greeting cards, some using machine embroidery. Cards with silk and lace fringes became popular in the mid 1880's, and were made by many publishers, sometimes using sets of four or six cards as booklets, furnished with tassel or ribbon for ease of opening. Measurements are given with fringe, closed.**

*Numbers 1-4 were made by Thomas Stevens.*

1. A handsome four-page birthday folder with a triangular set of flower pictures, fringed in orange silk with tassel, in its original wrapper labelled "Post Protector, registered at Stationers' Hall". 16 cm x 13 cm x 13 cm, wrapper 12.6 cm x 17.4 cm.

2. Two cards.
a) A white silk padded cushion with cards of flower pictures on the front and back, and white fringe and cord for hanging. No. 604.
b) A four-page folder with white flowers and autumn leaves and valentine greetings, cream coloured fringe and tassel. No. 605.
8 cm x 9.5 cm, 13.2 cm x 10 cm.

3. A four-page folder with mauve knotted fringe, each page having a view of Stratford-on-Avon in a circular vignette, with a spray of wild flowers. No. 654.
9.5 cm x 15 cm.

4. A four-page folder with corded fringe, birds flying over water, each page having a seasonal verse. No. 651. 9.5 cm x 14.5 cm.

5. Two four-page folders published by Eyre & Spottiswoode.
a) Four designs of spring flowers with seasonal verses by F E E H and a pink and red fringe and orange tassels.
b) Four designs of garden flowers with fringe. 8.7 cm x 13.8 cm, 12.7 cm x 11.5 cm.

6. Two cards.
a) A two-sided card by Marion Chase, published by S Hildesheimer, with blue fringe.
b) A four-page folder marked S J S & Co, i.e. S J Saunders with four designs of spring flowers in baskets and yellow fringe with ribbon for opening.
12.7 cm x 9.2 cm, 11.2 cm x 9.5 cm.

7/8. Two two-sided cards, Wirth Bros. & Owen, with four tinselled pictures of romantic winter scenes and knotted looped cream or blue fringes.
12 cm x 21 cm.

9. A four-page valentine folder with blue knotted fringe and tassels, and four designs of roses and a silver patterned horseshoe. 15.7 cm x 18.5 cm.

10. A large two-sided card marked J H 1883, with a cream looped and knotted fringe, and two designs of a young lady with pansies. This might be of transatlantic origin. 17.6 cm x 23 cm.

11. Two cards.
a) A four-page folder with orange and yellow fringe and red tassel, and four designs of winter scenes in small vignettes with flowers and leaves, M H Nathan & Co.
b) A two-sided card with white fringe and two tinselled robin designs by Harrison Weir. 13 cm x 14.2 cm, 12 cm x 16 cm.

12. A six-page folder with orange fringe, three angel figures representing Faith, Hope, and Charity, and descriptive verses on the other three pages by Charles J. Rowe. (See volume 137 No.19 for two single cards of this set.) 9 cm x 18 cm.

13. Two two-sided cards.
a) A small girl with a doll, a boy with rabbits and a robin, with a red fringe.
b) Small girls in heart shaped vignettes, one framed in yellow roses, the other in pansies, with a knotted pale pink fringe.
12.5 cm x 14.5 cm, 13 cm x 16.5 cm.

14. A four-page birthday card fringed in red, with four designs of small girl with flower garlands, and verses signed H A L and I H L and yellow tassels.
8.5 cm x 17 cm.

15. Two cards.
a) A four-page card with a set of military bands, Gordon Highlanders, Royal Horse Guards, 11th Hussars, and Coldstream Guards, fringed in cream with a grey tassel.
b) A four-page folder with a brown fringe showing Harlequin and Columbine on the outside and poems inside, inaccessible due to the pages being stuck together.
13.3 cm x 10.5 cm, 11 cm x 17.5 cm.

16. A four-page card with a looped cream fringe, showing heads of cats in bonnets with verses by A B below. 12.3 cm x 17 cm.

17. A four-page folder fringed in white and purple with orange tassels, each page in quodlibet style with pictures of hunting, shooting, and sailing and a golden horseshoe. (A single card of this set is in volume 169 no.20.) 10 cm x 16.5 cm.

18. Two four-page folders.
a) A birthday card with brown and gold fringe and pictures of birds and animals.
b) Four designs of animals breaking out of a sealed envelope, fringed in purple. (Two cards of this set are in volume 181, no.12).
12 cm x 9.5 cm, 11 cm x 9.5 cm.

19. A four-page folder with blue fringe, heads of cats and dogs in oval vignettes.
9 cm x 13 cm.

20. An elaborate four-page folder with gold fringe and white tassel. It has four pictures of country scenes on embossed cards with silver patterned lace border.
19.2 cm x 14 cm.

21. A padded card with a pocket and pictures of country scenes with flowers, and a gold fringe. A cord for hanging the card is attached to a blue brocaded triangular top. 14 cm x 25 cm.

22. Two cards, both with gold fringe.
a) Two sides, one ruched in pink and red around a print of a handshake, the other with a country scene and forget-me-nots.
b) A four-page folder with red velvet cover and greeting on a diagonal pink silk band, and three designs of ivy and berries with verses by J L Wharton.
14.5 cm x 10.5 cm, 11.5 cm x 9.5 cm.

23. Two cards.
a) A four-page folder with white fringe and tassel, the cover padded with white silk and a flower scrap, and three pictures of castles or sea.
b) A plain card with a picture of a country scene mounted on pale green silk.
9.4 cm x 8.5 cm, 10.7 cm x 16.7 cm.

24. A four-page folder fringed in pink with the designs of lakeside scenes signed C R.
16 cm x 13 cm.

25. A two-sided card fringed in pale blue, Niagara Falls on one side, the Mirror Lake, California, on reverse. 20.6 cm x 15.3 cm.

26. A four-page folder fringed in pale blue with three scenes of sea or river in vignettes shaped like a shell, lifebuoy, or ship's wheel, and a poem by Lewis Novra on the fourth side which has a silver lace border and a white tassel.
12.2 cm x 16.8 cm.

27. Two four-page folders.
a) Four winter scenes in circular vignettes with a pale blue fringe.
b) Four well-drawn scenes, probably the English Lake District, with blue fringe and tassel. 7.4 cm x 9 cm, 15.8 cm x 11.5 cm.

28. Two cards.
a) A fan with rose design and gold fringe and red tassel.
b) A gilded easel with a picture which opens to show birthday greetings and four small prints, mounted on a padded card covered in blue silk.
15.5 cm x 8 cm, 7 cm x 12 cm.

29. Two cards.
a) A fan fringed in gold with embossed designs of flowers and birds in Japanese style on both sides.
b) An oval palette with a hand-painted flower spray, and a white fringe.
15 cm x 10.5 cm, 10.5 cm x 14 cm.

30. A four-page folder with black and gold fringe and ribbon for opening. The outside has two embossed cards with roses, Christmas roses, evergreens and Christmas verses, and inside are two cards with flowering holly or pink blossom.
12.5 cm x 16.8 cm.

31. Two four-page folders, one with gilt crosses and white flowers and a white and gold fringe, the other with gilt crosses and flower garlands.
8.5 cm x 13.5 cm, 9 cm x 15 cm.

32. A four-page folder with orange fringe and white tassel, and two designs of anchors and two of crosses, all covered in ferns and spring flowers. 11 cm x 16.5 cm.

33. Two four-page folders.
a) Four designs of various red flowers with red fringe and orange tassels.
b) Four embossed designs of bunches of mixed flowers, with red fringe and white ribbon. 8.7 cm x 12.8 cm, 9.8 cm x 14 cm.

34. Two four-page folders.
a) Four embossed designs of various flowers with Christmas verses in panels, fringed in blue with white tassels.
b) Four embossed designs of a single rose on an envelope, with pale green fringe and blue tassels.
8.7 cm x 12.5 cm, 14 cm x 10.4 cm.

35. Two four-page folders, each with four designs of various flowers and leaves, one with white and gold fringe, the other pink and white.
10.5 cm x 8.5 cm, 9 cm x 10.2 cm.

36. Two two-sided cards with flowers in vases, and looped fringes of white and yellow respectively.
11 cm x 14.5 cm, 11.8 cm x 16 cm.

37. Two four-page folders fringed in blue, each with four designs of scenes in circular vignettes with flowers. One has poems by Frances Ridley Havergal.
8.8 cm x 13.7 cm, 9.6 cm x 14.5 cm.

38. A four-page folder with pictures of roses, berries, and spring flowers, and purple and white fringe with orange tassels. 9.9 cm x 14.2 cm.

39. Two cards.
a) A six-page folder fringed in purple and white, with four designs of autumn fruits and white flowers.
b) A four-page folder with cream knotted fringe and spring flowers in oval frames.12.2 cm x 15.3 cm, 9.5 cm x 15.3 cm.

40. Two single cards.
a) Two pictures of spring flowers and grasses, with verses by Cecilia Havergal and pink fringe.
b) An embossed design of roses and lilies of the valley with a multicolour fringe in blue, black, green, and white.
13 cm x 11.6 cm, 16 cm x 13 cm.

41. A large card with looped white fringe and two designs of pansies.
19.5 cm x 14.2 cm.

42. An interesting card with a country scene wreathed in speedwell flowers and a frilled/lace border, mounted on a padded white silk base with a silk flower scrap.
14 cm x 19.5 cm.

## VOLUME 198:
## CARDS WITH SILK AND FEATHERS FROM ENGLISH PUBLISHERS

**By about 1885, silk was used as part of the design, being inserted to form an embossed part of costume, flowers, or birds. Feathers and mother-of-pearl were also used as decoration, and the printing on silk, already seen in earlier cards, was continued into the 1890's. Some of these cards may have been made**

**abroad, but all the publishers mentioned here had premises in London. Some cards with machine embroidery are included.**

*Numbers 1-16 have silk inserts, dated 1885-90.*

1. Two cards.
a) A yellowhammer, with silk breast and flowers.
b) A procession of six girls in a field, probably by J M Dealy, perhaps published by Hildesheimer and Faulkner but unmarked.
7.4 cm x 10.7 cm, 12 cm x 8.3 cm.

2. Four cards, published by Bernhard Ollendorff, three designs of boy or girls with animals, teaching them to play the piano, read a book, or write a letter. Two cards have silk inserts, and the two plain ones have narrative poems by R P Scott on reverse. 10.1 cm x 13 cm.

3. Three cards from two sets with children, partly dressed in silk.
10.2 cm x 13 cm., 9.2 cm x 13 cm.

4. Two cards, a footman with bouquet, in a pink silk coat, and a little girl in silk dress and stockings carrying a bouquet of silk flowers, with a greeting in German.
7.1 cm x 10.4 cm, 7.8 cm x 11.7 cm.

5. A birthday card, c. 1890, with a scrap of a girl and boy in silk costume on thick brown board. 10.8 cm x 16.5 cm.

6. Three cards of a set, published by Ollendorff, garlands with silk blossoms around seasonal verses, one dated 1885.
12 cm x 8.4 cm.

7. Two cards, Ollendorff, a red silk poppy, and a birthday card with silk roses and leaves, No.8477.
7 cm x 11.2 cm, 11.2 cm x 7.2 cm.

8. A card published by W Hagelberg, with white silk flowers and a verse by A M Hone, dated 1890 by the sender. This card is marked "Berlin", but the firm had a London office by 1885. 11 cm x 15 cm.

9. Six miscellaneous cards.
a) Mother-of-pearl flowers and leaves in a diamond vignette, with illuminated corner decoration. 9 cm x 11.4 cm.
b) A small oval card with a mother-of-pearl butterfly. 8 cm x 5.6 cm.
c) Birds on a rustic border around white silk flowers. 11 cm x 12.5 cm.
d/e) Two birthday cards with silk flowers. 10.3 cm x 7.5 cm, 9.8 cm x 6.8 cm.
f) A circular card with silk forget-me-nots and a patent device for standing, registered in U.S.A. in 1887, also in England and Germany, by Hagelberg.
10.8 cm diameter.

10. Four cards.
a) A fan with silk flowers and feather fringe. 13 cm x 9.3 cm.

198.19

b) Silk flowers on a cut-out border, with a New Year verse. 12.5 cm x 10 cm.
c) A white silk dove with a pansy in its beak. 11 cm x 6.5 cm.
d) Another silk dove with silk flowers. 11 cm x 7 cm.

11. Four cards (three birthday), all with silk forget-me-nots, two with verses.
10.7 cm x 7.5 cm up to 9.2 cm x 13.5 cm.

12. Two cards, silk flowers on a background of leaves, one with a birthday greeting on reverse, c1890.
13 cm x 10.2 cm, 14 cm x 9.2 cm.

13. Two cards, one with a red silk rose, the other with a basket of flowers, some of silk, c1890.
10.5 cm x 16.4 cm, 13.7 cm x 10.1 cm.

14. Six miscellaneous cards with silk flowers, one with a hand in a silk sleeve holding a rose dated 1885 by the sender, another a pink rose with a French greeting.
9 cm x 6.5 cm up to 9.2 cm x 13 cm.

15. A card with silk flowers and velvet leaves, c1890. 9.8 cm x 14.2 cm.

16. Four cards (one birthday), three with various silk flowers and verses, another with silk pansies dated 1890 by the sender. Sizes up to 12.5 cm x 10 cm.

17. Three cards with machine embroidered pictures in vignettes, one a ship in a star, another flowers in a shield, the third a sea scene with castle and ship in a parallelogram, late 1880's.
8.5 cm x 9 cm up to 12.9 cm x 9.4 cm.

*Numbers 18 - 25 are printed on silk.*

18. Three cards, two with an illuminated capital letter to a verse signed F E E H, and a flower spray, in a blue border. The third has embossed flowers and a greeting

printed on silk.
8.3 cm x 12.2 cm, 12.3 cm x 8.1 cm.

19. A silk card with a Welsh boy and girl dancing, and a Welsh caption, with the Prince of Wales' feathers.
11.5 cm x 14.8 cm.

20. Two silk cards with winter scenes, one marked Wirth Bros. & Owen, the other with a verse by E H C on reverse.
10.8 cm x 13.4 cm, 11.8 cm x 16.4 cm.

21. Three silk cards, all with flowers, one marked J.F. Schipper No. 838, the other two probably H Rothe, one with German greeting.
11.9 cm x 9 cm up to 15.6 cm x 10.4 cm.

22. A silk card, an angel head in an oval vignette with yellow daisies below, dated 1891 by the sender, marked Schipper.
11.2 cm x 15.7 cm.

23. Four silk cards, two with flowers and crosses, two with flower sprays.
7 cm x 13.3 cm up to 8 cm x 18 cm.

24. A gilt-edged card with moss roses on cream silk.  12.2 cm x 17.5 cm.

25. Three birthday cards with scenes on silk inserted into shaped vignettes, one with a cut-out owl let into the border.
11 cm x 6.5 cm up to 12.5 cm x 8.5 cm.

26. A card with a feather flower and butterfly.  12.3 cm x 9.1 cm.

## VOLUME 199:
## CARDS WITH FOREIGN LANGUAGE GREETINGS

**These cards have greetings in Russian, German, Italian, or Spanish, but many of them were made by English manufacturers, some of these designs being duplicated with English greetings in other volumes of this collection.**

1. Two cards from Russia. One has silk flower inserts similar to those in volume 198. The other has a postman with a letter, a winter scene with a sleigh, and six stamps dated 1879.
11.4 cm x 6.8 cm, 11.3 cm x 8.4 cm.

*Numbers 2 - 15 have greetings in German.*

2. Six small cards with flowers or scenes, one dated 1862 by the sender, the others c1870.
8.9 cm x 5.1 cm up to 10.7 cm x 7.2 cm.

3. Two cards, gilded fancy borders, one with a small angel, the other with two children and a giant bouquet, both dated 1879 by the senders.
7 cm x 10.3 cm, 10.8 cm x 7.4 cm.

4. Five miscellaneous cards with flowers. Two have silk insets, one a white dove, the other flowers.
8.7 cm x 5.6 cm up to 15.5 cm x 11.6 cm.

5. Seven miscellaneous cards with flowers, one from the same set as two cards with French greetings in volume 196 No.24.
6.8 cm x 5.1 cm up to 6.3 cm x 13.4 cm.

6. Five cards with flowers and ferns, two from S Hildesheimer, two from S J Saunders, the fifth Thomas Stevens, early 1880's. 14 cm x 8 cm, 10.1 cm x 6.7 cm, 10.5 cm x 6.5 cm.

7. Five cards with flowers c 1880. Four are signed G O, listed by Buday as publishing cards with both English and German greetings. One is signed M Hg v M, probably Monteuffel, who designed cards for H Rothe (see volume 130).
6.3 cm x 9.2 cm up to 8.6 cm x 13.7cm.

8. Four cards with flowers and ferns.
7.5 cm x 9.6 cm up to 9.8 cm x 12.9 cm.

9. Two cards, a small boy with a bouquet, and another with a giant quill pen marked G O, c1885.
7.7 cm x 11.1 cm, 13.2 cm x 10.1 cm.

10. Four cards, two with winter scenes, another with two children, the fourth with a female figure holding a crown printed in gold. Late 1880's.
7.1 cm x 9.5 cm up to 11.5 cm x 14.2 cm.

11/12. Nine cards dated from 1889 to 1896, one with an embossed village scene on a plain white card, six with flowers and greetings printed in gold, another with a small tinselled fairy, and one with a winter scene over a silk flower and a greeting in silver. 10 cm x 6.2 cm up to 14 cm x 9 cm.

13. Three cards, two with roses (one on a cross), the third a guitar over a black and white scene marked Lith. Art Anstalt, Munchen. 9.8 cm x 11.1 cm, 15.3 cm x 12 cm, 9.4 cm x 12.9 cm.

14. Five cards, one with four cats holding banners, a silk-fringed flower card, a small card with a rose scrap, and two fancy folding cards of the 1890's.
8.8 cm x 4.6 cm up to 10 cm x 13.2 cm.

15. Four cards, 1890's, two with angels , one with birds and leaves, the fourth a folding card with four-leaved clovers or shamrock.
6.6 cm x 9.7 cm up to 9.4 cm x 12.7 cm.

*Numbers 16-20 have greetings in Italian, with one card, as noted, in Spanish.*

16. Six small cards, 1870's, one with flowers, two with birds, two with dogs, the sixth with three demons holding a banner with greeting.
9 cm x 5.3 cm up to 6 cm x 9.8 cm.

17. Six cards, 1880's, two with children, one a view of Rome, one a dwarf with pansies, another an artist on a palette. The sixth card has a spray of moss roses in the same design as one with German greeting in No.3 above.
6 cm x 9.4 cm up to 8.3 cm x 11.4 cm.

18. Eight miscellaneous cards with flowers, probably made in England, early 1880's, one with a greeting in Spanish.
7.7 cm x 5.6 cm up to 9.1 cm x 13.6 cm.

19. Five cards with flowers, 1880's, one published by Raphael Tuck, another by Hildesheimer and Faulkner.
11.4 cm x 7.5 cm up to 13.5 cm x 10.1 cm.

20. Three cards, one a scene in a circular vignette with birds and flowers, another two cats in a railway carriage, the third a view of the Forum at Rome, marked Marcucci, Via Condotti 72.
10.1 cm x 13.4cm, 10.2 cm x 7.8 cm, 11.4 cm x 6.5 cm.

## VOLUME 200:
## CARDS FROM U.S.A., CANADA, AUSTRALIA, THE FAR EAST, WITH GREETINGS IN ENGLISH

*Numbers 1-12 are from the United States of America, dated 1880-90. Some were designed there, but numbers 6-12 have designs copied from English cards, seen elsewhere in this collection, and some of these may have been pirated designs. Most of them were found in the States by the writer.*

1. Seven trade cards c1880 with flowers, probably published by Prang. Three are from the Boston store of W H Hislop & Co., sent with a greeting, and two have black background advertisements for Mme Demorest, of Paris and New York. The sixth is from the American Baptist Publication Society, New York, and the seventh is a centennial calendar for 1876 with greeting for Dundas Dick & Co. Sizes up to 12.8 cm x 7.7 cm.

2. Three cards, one a Reward of Merit with flowers and a lakeland scene designed by Frank Vernon, New York. Two have roses, and are sample copies from David C. Cook, Chicago. Late 1880's.
11.6 cm x 7.3 cm, 12 cm x 8.4 cm.

3. Three cards, all probably made in England for the American market. One has small children holding a banner, another has flowers around a gilt scroll, both being trade cards for the Philadelphia store of John Wanamaker. The third has a girl in a garland of flowers and advertises "The Fair", Seneca Falls, New York.
9.5 cm x 6.4 cm. up to 12.4 cm x 7.3 cm.

4. A sample folder showing five visiting or greeting cards with coloured scraps of a hand holding flowers, some also with

birds, from Tuttle Brothers, Totoket, Connecticut, with more designs printed on reverse, prices from 10 cents to 50 cents per dozen. c1890. Sizes up to 10 cm x 5.5 cm.

5. Twelve examples of similar cards with various borders. Sizes up to 10 cm x 5.2 cm.

6. Two cards.
a) A copy of a De La Rue card by W S Coleman, a girl in scanty costume with a cat, the background altered slightly from the original. This is marked Bufford, Boston and New York. See Volume 55, no. 26, for the original.
b) A copy of a De La Rue card by Rebecca Coleman, a girl in a hat, marked copyright. See Volume 55, no. 14, for original.
10.1 cm x 15.5 cm, 10.6 cm x11.6 cm.

7. Three cards with yellow borders.
a) A dove on a cross, with flowers.
b/c) Two cards of girls with wings, from the same set as a card by W S Coleman published by Tuck in volume 68, no. 10. 11.6 cm x 10.6 cm.

8. Two cards.
a) An angel scattering roses
b) A girl on a stool talking to a boy on a garden wall. This is an enlarged copy of a card in volume 106 No.19 published by Hildesheimer and Faulkner, perhaps designed by E Manly. The two cards have similar coloured borders and are marked "copyright". 11.6 cm x 17.7 cm.

9. Two cards showing girls in antique costume and sandals, one tending flowers, one feeding a robin, advertising the Metropolitan Life Insurance Company of New York, with full details of their business on reverse. These were by Felix Dussert, registered at Stationers' Hall 17-7-1879 (see volume 147, no. 20). 6.9 cm x 16.1 cm.

10. Four trade cards for Mrs. J S Mills, dealer, Stone Store, Venice, New York, showing birds, two overprinted Christmas, or 4th July. One card, robins with a broken doll in snow, is a copy of a Hildesheimer and Faulkner card with an altered background in volume 112 no. 8. 11.7 cm x 7.1 cm.

11. Two cards.
a) A small girl dressed as a nasturtium with a flower cap, a copy of one in volume 164 no. 24, crudely printed with added spectacles to make a trade-card for Jas. A. Horne, Dover, N H, dealer in jewellery and spectacles, etc. 7.4 cm x 11.5 cm.
b) A birthday card with a girl in a convolvulus wreath, a poor copy of one in volume 157 no. 12, marked copyright. 11.1 cm x 17 cm.

12. Two cards, each with two small girls in nightgowns with a doll, in a circular

**200.13**

vignette. These are exact copies of English prints of better quality. 11.6 cm x 13.5 cm.

*Numbers 13-21 are from Canadian publishers, all with seasonal winter views, early 1880's.*

13/14. Eight cards marked G & W Clarke, Montreal. Six show winter sports, one a lumber shanty, and the other has maple leaves and a heraldic shield. 13.7 cm x 8.5cm.

15. Four cards marked William J Clarke, Montreal, showing aspects of life in Canada - a lumber shanty, making maple syrup, cutting ice, and a train crossing the St. Laurence in winter. 14.5 cm x 10 cm.

16. Four cards, James Campbell & Son, two of Niagara Falls in winter, two of winter sports. Three were dated 1881, 1882, 1883 by the senders, and one was from Toronto. 15.5 cm x 9 cm.

17. Three cards, Rolph, Smith & Co., Toronto, a harbour scene with ships, snow shoes with maple leaves, people skating, the last two inscribed on reverse "Entered according to Act of Parliament of Canada in the year 1881 by Rolph, Smith & Co. in the Office of the Ministry of Agriculture." 16 cm x 9.9 cm, 12.5 cm x 8.3 cm, 13.6 cm x 17.8 cm.

18. Three cards, Rolph, Smith & Co., all entered as above. One is a Canadian winter scene marked 1st Prize, F M Bell Smith, another shows the St. Laurence at Quebec, marked James Weston, prize. The third has maple leaves and snowshoes with a heraldic shield. 18.5 cm x 10.5 cm, 17.4 cm x 10.3 cm, 10.2 cm x 17.1 cm.

19. Two cards, a girl tobogganing, published by Bennet & Co., Montreal, and another with young Canadians at winter sports. 9.9 cm x 15.5 cm, 10.5 cm 16.5 cm.

20. Four cards, J T Henderson, Montreal, the Burland Lith. Co., showing Canadian

winter scenes, including one of Market Day before Christmas. 17.4 cm x 7.6 cm.

21. Two cards, a horse-drawn sleigh, and a lake with an Indian wigwam, unsigned but probably Canadian. 13.4 cm x 8.3 cm, 15.5 cm x 9 cm.

*Numbers 22-29 were made in Australia in the early 1880's, featuring kangaroos, native flowers and shells.*

22. Two cards, one with birds, the other berries and leaves, both prize designs published by John Sands and marked with an apt hourglass trademark. Each has an appropriate verse on reverse, signed Veni or Rev. C W Roberts. 12.1 cm x 16.9 cm.

23. A card with blue and gold border, showing kangaroos in a vignette with a patterned surround. 9 cm x 18.4 cm.

24. Three cards, native flowers and leaves with verses in oval vignettes, one dated 1883 by the sender. The botanical and common names of the flowers are given on reverse, with the caption "Copyright - printed in Sydney by Gibbs, Shallard, & Co." 12.1 cm x 15.7 cm.

25. Two cards, Gibbs, Shallard & Co., with flowers, and verses by H M Burnside. 12.7 cm x 16.4 cm.

26. Another Gibbs Shallard card with a vase of flowers and shells. 13.1 cm x 11 cm.

27. Three humorous cards with kangaroos in human dress, prospecting, having a boat race with a beaver, and on honeymoon, the first two marked Gibbs Shallard. 13.2 cm x 10.8 cm, 14.2.cm x 10.9 cm, 9.7 cm x 12 cm.

28. A fringed card from Gibbs Shallard, with flowers and a kangaroo on one side and an aborigine policeman on reverse (see volume 171 no. 20). 14.5 cm x 10.7 cm without fringe.

29. A card showing a harbour view, published by Gibbs Shallard, signed J G H, with a Christmas poem by Mrs. E Wolstenholme writing of the difference between the English traditional Christmas and that of Australia. 17.2 cm x 11.8 cm.

30. A card with roses and a large shell, with the caption "A Christmas greeting from over the sea", perhaps Australian. 19.3 cm x 12.8 cm.

31. Three cards, two from Japan, one from Singapore, probably 20th century but added here for interest. The Japanese cards are on paper with a silk finish and have attractive designs of birds, flowers, and scenery, and the Singapore card has an inserted piece of blue embroidered silk. 7.5 cm x 10.6 cm, 22 cm x 11.2 cm, 8.8 cm x 11.2 cm.

32/33. Eight cards from India, printed in Calcutta, showing scenes of Indian life with English titles and rather faint seasonal greetings. 12.2 cm x 7 cm.

## VOLUME 201: ADVERTISING AND POSTAL CARDS

The cards here, with a few exceptions as stated, were greetings cards for Christmas and New Year sent by tradesmen to customers, most published in the 1880's. Some calendars with greetings are included. Few sets of such cards have been found and publishers' imprints are rarely seen, but the random collection here shows the wide use of greetings cards for publicity and gives an interesting sidelight on Victorian prices. The designs rarely bear any relation to the products advertised.

The postal cards include envelopes with imitation postmarks, some stamps, mock telegrams, allusions to the postman's lot, and two Post Office Savings Bank greetings.

1. An illuminated trade card, 1860's, from Drulin, Lithographic Artist and Printer, Kentish Town. This has no greeting but is included as a fine example of this period. 10.7 cm x 7 cm.

2. A black-backed card with an angel and flowers, published by Kronheim, London and Manchester, with information on reverse about the Royal Insurance Co., Liverpool and London. 15.1 cm x 10 cm.

3. Five cards, including a set of four designs of a young lady with a rose, published by S J Saunders. Three have calendars on reverse for 1880 advertising the Liquor Tea Co., Tower Hill, London,

and two are greeting cards, included to complete the set. 7 cm x 10.6 cm.

4. Six cards. Two are text cards from the magazine "Sunday at Home", another has a Christmas verse in an illuminated border of holly, from "Leisure Hour", and three have two designs of Red Riding Hood or Father Christmas with a Christmas or New Year verse, from "Little Folks". All have details of the contents of the magazines on reverse. 8.2 cm x 13 cm, 12.5 cm x 8.2 cm, 12 cm x 6.5 cm.

5. Five cards, 1880's. Four are from dealers in Christmas and and New Year cards, including one from T H Ponting & Co., Westbourne Grove, with a message on reverse "No lady should buy Christmas or New Year cards without first seeing T H Ponting & Co.'s astonishing collection", priced from 2¾d per dozen to 1d each. The fifth card is an advertisement for Raphael Tuck with a sunset scene in a palette and a calendar for 1887 on reverse, overprinted with "T L Kelly's Book Department, Milwaukee, Wis.", giving some evidence that Tuck's cards were sold through agents in the United States, as well as being pirated as in volume 200. 8.2 cm x 5.3 cm up to 14.5 cm x 9.7 cm.

6. Five cards, Stacy & Cook's special Christmas cards, including two large scenes, two small cards with scenes in vignettes and flowers, and a cat with a puppy. This firm, of London and Bristol, must have been a dealer selling cards from 1s 3d (6 new pence) per gross to 12/- per gross for a card designed by Albert Bowers. 9.1 cm x 6.3 cm up to 12.2 cm x 17.2 cm.

7. Three cards.
a) A lady with a parrot, from J Cuthbertson & Co., 44 Brompton Road, London S.W., price 1d a dozen.
b/c) Two small cards with verse by Fanny Rochat and a child's head in a garland, from Thomas J Hooper, Knightsbridge, London, sold at 1s 9d per gross in 1880 and 1881. 12.4 cm x 8 cm, 7.3 cm x 4.5 cm.

8. Six cards with flowers, from dealers in Christmas novelties and presents. One has a list of jewellery prices on reverse, including gold brooches for 4/- (20 pence), another folder published by H Rothe was from Mrs. Dent, Books and Stationery, Southport, with an interesting shell design and a calendar for 1881 on reverse. 8 cm x 7cm up to 15.1 cm x 7.3 cm.

9. Four cards. Two with figures on a palette shape are from Cash's woven names, 6s 6d per gross, without greeting but probably also used as cards. The other two have flowers in illuminated borders, from the Alexandria Drapery Co., Clifton, and two are further designs from a part set in volume 138 no. 9. 7 cm x 10.4 cm, 9.3 cm x 11.1 cm.

10. A Raphael Tuck card by W J Wiegand, small children clearing snow, from C E Tregoning, Truro, Wedding Cakes etc. (See volume 72, no. 20 for another card from this set.) 11 cm x 11 cm.

11. Five cards, all with calendars on reverse.
a) 1877, from the Theatre Royal, Drury Lane, printed by Montague, Chatterton & Co. (See also Volumes 8 no. 6, 166 no. 15)
b) 1878, John Clark Junior and Co., Glasgow, with a small figure but no greeting.
c) 1881, David Dennis, Grocer, Birmingham, with roses.
d) 1882, R S Aitken, Draper, Chesham, with a romantic scene.
e) 1879-80, John Piggott, Cheapside, "My Hatter, My Tailor", with an interesting cartoon of Gladstone and Disraeli before the shop, signed Faustin (Belbedir?) Sizes up to 7.1 cm x 10 cm.

12. Four cards advertising theatres at Christmas, a ship from the New Theatre Royal, Sheffield, flowers from the Mechanics Institute, New Swindon, 1882, a winter scene from the Prince of Wales Theatre, Greenwich, 1887, and a young man and woman in a circular vignette, probably by Felix Dussert, from the Middlesex Music Hall, Drury Lane, 1892. 11 cm x 7.6 cm up to 9.6 cm x 13.1 cm.

13. Two cards, one scene set in a garland of ivy with silver bells, from T Cheshire of Whittlesea, Draper, the other a squirrel from T L Mumford, Hosier & Glover, of Regent Street and Burlington Arcade (see volume 181 no. 9 for a similar card.) 12.4 cm x 10.8 cm, 13.4 cm x 9.4 cm.

14. Two cards, Alfred Lea, Albion Street, Leeds, Jewellery and Fancy Goods. One has two boys playing with tops and advertisement on reverse, the other shows children playing on the ice with Christmas greeting only. 13.5 cm x 9.4 cm, 10.1 cm x 13.5 cm.

15. Three cards with flowers or holly from E Lacy & Co., Whitechapel Road, London E, manufacturer of a Gout and Rheumatism mixture, with testimonials on reverse dated 1872, 1875 from satisfied users. 14.1 cm x 8.1 cm.

16. Seven cards.
a) Boys in snow by W J Hodgson for Hildesheimer & Faulkner (see volume 110 no. 8 for complete set), sent by Wells & Co., 39 South Audley Street, London W, moneylenders.
b) A black and white design of bells and flowers marked Wirth Bros., from W E Ganney, Dental Surgeon, London.
c) A floral cross, a sixth design for those published by S Hildesheimer in volume 99 no. 1, from John Peck, Draper, Liverpool. The four others have floral designs from E Orgel, Furniture (a room for £5), W Davis, Picture Framer, Birmingham,

John Whiting, Machines, Woodford (1876), and a Scottish Accident Insurance Co. agent.
5.2 cm x 8.3 cm up to 11.1 cm x 10.9 cm.

17. Six cards, including three with children from McEwan, Grocer, Cheshunt, William Murton, Grocer, Faversham, and the Central Restaurant, London, for Gentlemen only. Two cards with Chinese figures were from Henry Gleave's New Galleries, New Oxford Street, London, and the sixth showing a boy stealing a pig is marked Joseph Crowther, Provision Merchant. These three have no greeting.
9.5 cm x 6.8 cm up to 7.4 cm x 11 cm.

18. Five cards. Three have flowers with clasped hands or a dove, and have on reverse "If you want your boys to look well, go to the Yorkshire Clothing Co." The fourth has a bunch of asters, from J Lingard, Hatter, Nottingham, and the fifth has a scene with flowers from the Boot Repairing Co., 180 Union Street, Oldham.
10.7 cm x 7 cm up to 9.5 cm x 13 cm.

19. Six cards with children and flowers from various tailors, hatters, cleaners, and Bazaars, in London and the North.
6.2 cm x 9.7 cm up to 11.5 cm x 7.4 cm.

20. Five cards with flowers. Two from Goode, Gainsford & Co. of London, S E, are designs by Emily Whymper for S Hildesheimer (see volume 102 no. 25 for set). One from Popham, Radford & Co. of Plymouth, selling Wools for autumn and winter, 1883, was published by Eyre & Spottiswoode. Two others were from John Noble of Manchester, Manufacturer, with different designs but with the same advertisement on reverse headed "Christmas Boxes - the best Christmas present for a poor family is a pair of blankets or Heavy Bolton sheets." The price of Witney blankets, length 2½ yards, is given as 10s 10d for the best quality pair.
11 cm x 6.2 cm up to 8.4 cm up to 12.1 cm.

21. Five cards with flower designs, extolling the virtues of paraffin oil at 7d per gallon from the Red House, Doncaster, Loproso Cocoa from Thomas Ditton, tea from Cooper, Cooper & Co., London, Noble whiskey (with an 1885 calendar on a card published by H Rothe), and the Indo-China Tea Association, Ltd. The Tea-Totalers Song, on the reverse of the last card, contrasts strongly with the exhortation on the previous card to "Drink Noble Whiskey every day in the year."
9 cm x 7.1 cm up to 10.7 cm x 16.5 cm.

22. Four cards with children. Two have winter scenes, from Great Western Stores, London W, marked Christmas 1889, the other two were from Clark & Co. Anchor threads, Paisley, and Bettesworth, Confectioners, London.
Sizes up to 8.2 cm x 11 cm.

201.23

*The following cards have postal interest.*

23. Two cards.
a) The Postman's respectful Compliments of the Season, a long poem on green paper with a picture of the postman knocking at the door - "Wet or dry he daily trudges, and his labour never grudges."... This may have been handed hopefully to householders in the 1860's.
7.2 cm x 11.4 cm.
b) A card imitating an envelope with 1890 postmark and seal, and a picture of a postman. 13.7 cm x 10.2 cm.

24. An envelope folder decorated with holly and ivy, with imitation postmark December 25, 1881, and the card enclosed, a design of daisies and grasses.
8.9 cm x 11.8 cm.

25. Four cards.
a) A door with letters in the letter box, published by H Rothe, no. 467.
8.6 cm x 15 cm.
b) A blotter with a pen, letter and stamped envelope, published by J F Schipper, no.1058. 8.5 cm x 11.3 cm.
c) A card edged with pansies, around an envelope with an imitation postmark, published by Raphael Tuck, A S no. 1038.
11.5 cm x 10 cm.
d) A card with flowers, a letter, and a stamped envelope, signed J C.
14.7 cm x 10 cm.

26. Four cards
a) A French card with an elegant lady holding a post card, with 1886 Paris postmark attached on reverse.
7 cm x 11.3 cm.
b) A small card with a seal, and its envelope, with original stamp and postmark 1885. 10 cm x 7.7 cm.
c) A card with fuchsias, and an imitation London postmark. 12.1 cm x 9 cm.
d) A small folder card in the form of a

registered letter with Edward VII stamp, and verse within. 7.2 cm x 4.2 cm.

27. A card printed in sepia, from Liverpool Telegraphs 1886-7 to colleagues in Sheffield, with an interesting mixture of designs showing ships, telegraph material, and festive fare. It is signed Sibbitt del., and A S Co. Lith. (Artistic Stationery Company). Samuel Sibbitt registered a number of designs at Stationers' Hall for the A S Co., but the entry for this one has not been seen. 16.5 cm x 11.8 cm.

28. A New Year Telegram, with a 25-word message as greeting, and decorations of holly and mistletoe and festive fare.
20.5 cm x 13 cm.

29. Five cards with animals, four in the form of envelopes with imitation postmarks, one published by S Hildesheimer. The fifth card is a small postcard.
10.4 cm x 6.8 cm up to 11.9 cm x 8.7 cm.

30. Two 20th century folder cards issued by the Post Office Savings Bank, one dated 1906. One has two pictures of "Our Neighbourhood Long Ago", the other two pictures of "Our Neighbourhood", all scenes of London. Each has in addition two designs signed R T H, with a note on one "Designed and drawn by Officers of the Post Office Savings Bank."
12.9 cm x 16.6 cm., 12.5 cm x 16 cm.

## VOLUME 202:
## CARDS COLOURED BY HAND

**These cards fall into two classes, those supplied already coloured by publishers or with designs ready for colouring by the purchasers, and cards individually designed for special recipients. It is not easy to decide who coloured the publisher's cards. Some cards have a list of colours to be used on the card, and**

perhaps these were issued penny plain rather than twopence coloured. A few cards with pressed flowers are included here.

1. Two cards, published by Halford Bros., designed by E Warwick, with sprays of holly and Christmas roses or spring flowers, mid 1870's. 9.1 cm x 13.4 cm.

2. Six similar smaller cards with flowers and holly, one dated 1876 by the sender. Two cards have 1. Green 2. Red 3. Blue, printed below - instructions to the professional artist or to the purchaser? Sizes up to 6.9 cm x 10.8 cm.

3. Three similar unmarked cards with good designs of robins and holly. 6.9 cm x 10.6 cm, 8.3 cm x 12.1 cm.

4. Two cards, one with holly and mistletoe marked Walker & Pierce, the other with holly, ivy, and china asters marked Stannard & Son, London, late 1870's. 10.7 cm x 6.7 cm, 18.3 cm x 13.5 cm.

5. Five cards with flowers, four with texts. Two are marked Halford Bros., two Stannard & Son, and one unmarked was dated 1877 by the sender. 10.7 cm x 6.7 cm up to 12.1 cm x 9.3 cm.

6. One card with serrated gilded edge, H H & Co. Unique Series, a robin on a branch with rose hips. 10.5 cm x 14 cm.

7. Two cards, H H & Co., well painted winter scenes, one with gilded and serrated edge, the other silvered. 11.3 cm x 11.3 cm, 10 cm x 13.2 cm.

8. A similar card, unmarked, with pansies and fern. 10.5 cm x 15.2 cm.

9. A black-backed card with holly and a white rose. 6 cm x 10.3 cm.

10. Two cards, a robin with roses, dated by the sender 1877, and a bluebird with flowers, dated by the French sender 1879. These cards and numbers 11 and 12 were probably made in France, and some have French captions. The flowers resemble the silk flowers seen on Aubry cards in volume 195.
9 cm x 13.3 cm, 11 cm x 16.7 cm.

11. Seven smaller cards (one birthday), with flower sprays, two dated by the senders 1875, 1878.
9.2 cm x 5.9 cm up to 7 cm x 11.3 cm.

12. Four cards (two birthday), spring flowers and roses with greetings on scrolls, one dated 1877 by the sender.
11.3 cm x 7.5 cm.

13. One card, a spray of mixed flowers and berries, with a handwritten inscription to "Father", dated 1879 by the sender, typical

of the drawings found in Victorian albums. 13.9 cm x 17.8 cm.

14. Three cards, garlands of flowers and leaves. 11.4 cm x 15.6 cm.

15. Two Easter cards, a cross with a white rose, and another with ivy.
11.4 cm x 15.6 cm.

16. Four cards, three with flower sprays, one with a cross and violets.
Sizes up to 9.2 cm x 12.5 cm.

17. Three cards, flowers with greetings in scrolls or panel.
12 cm x 7.2 cm, 10.8 cm x 15.2 cm.

18. Five cards (two birthday), two with birds, one with flowers and butterflies, one with a cross and a flower garland, the fifth with violets.
6.2 cm x 12.3 cm up to 9.6 cm x 12.8 cm.

*Numbers 19 - 25 were probably drawn by the senders.*

19. Five cards, four with flowers, the fifth with a pleasing design of a robin with a garland of colourful flowers.
5.8 cm x 10.3 cm up to 8 cm x 11.5 cm.

20. Three cards, one with a design of various fruits, another blackberries, the third flowers. 11.4 cm x 15.3 cm, 13.5 cm x 10.2 cm, 11.5cm x 7.6 cm.

21. Four cards with birds.
7.8 cm x 11.2 cm up to 11.4 cm x 15 cm.

22. Two cards, a Christmas card with white daisies and a birthday card with narcissi. 10.5 cm x 16.5 cm, 8.3 cm x 18 cm.

23. Two cards, a valentine with white dog roses, and a Christmas card with a flower spray around a ship in a circular vignette.
10.7 cm x 16.5 cm, 10.5 cm x 16.5 cm.

24. Four cards, two with snowdrops, one with mistletoe, the fourth with butterflies and grasses. Sizes up to 11.6 cm x 9 cm.

25. A card with cut out china asters on pale green paper and an attached seasonal greeting. 13 cm x 17.3 cm.

26/27. Seven cards with pressed leaves and flowers of indifferent artistic merit, one with a printed greeting probably professionally made.
10.5 cm x 6 cm up to 10 cm x 15 cm.

## VOLUME 203: PERSONAL GREETING CARDS, 1873-1910

These include cards specially designed and printed for the senders, in monochrome with one exception, and a few handmade examples, some with Manchester

interest. The standardised personal greeting cards from publishers are in a later volume in Section 20.

1/2. Seven cards, specially designed and printed for the Goodman family, in sepia, blue, or black. Six are dated 1873, 1875, 1876, 1877-8, 1879, 1883, and two are signed H W L and G H Birch. They all have the names of members of the family bordered with Nativity and geometric designs.
10 cm x 12.7 cm up to 12.8 cm x 20.4 cm.

3. Two cards, a drawing of a horse and its rider outside a house in winter snow, and a Norwegian river scene signed Ethel, 1883, perhaps the Ethel Stone of nos. 4 and 5. 12.6 cm x 9 cm, 13.3 cm x 10.8 cm.

4. Two pen and ink drawings, Kirkstall, Yorkshire, and a ruined abbey, signed respectively Ethel, 1883 copied, and E M Stone, the second with the caption "Christmas greetings from all at the Grange". 18 cm x 11.9 cm, 17.7 cm x 15 cm.

5. Two cards, a hand-drawn pen and ink winter scene, from Ethel 1881, and a printed view of the Grange, Erdington, signed Ethel Mary Stone, with the caption "Christmas Greetings from all at the Grange", Erdington 1883.
16.6 cm x 11 cm, 18.2 cm x 12.6 cm.

6/7. Two "cards", printed on thin rice paper in black, with decorative holly, ivy and mistletoe borders around greetings from "Mr & Mrs J B Stone and family, the Grange, Erdington." 1881, 1884.
30.5 cm x 21 cm, 27.7 cm x 19.3 cm.

8. Two black and white designs with the appearance of etchings, a church by a river, and a country mansion in snow.
17.7 cm x 12.6 cm, 17.5 cm x 13 cm.

9. A card printed in black on green paper for Christmas 1884, with a picture and poem, "The Old Water Mill", both signed J B, from Mr & Mrs John Bragg.
25.2 cm x 11 cm.

10. Two cards printed in black from E & F G Jackson, the first for 1883 illustrating "God Rest Ye, Merry Gentlemen", the other for 1884 with a Christmas verse and a Christmas figure, holly and angels.
13.2 cm x 20.5 cm, 13.3 cm x 21 cm.

11. A card with a page boy in green and purple Georgian costume, printed in sepia for Mrs Clegg, Broomhurst, Werneth, 1885.
12 cm x 18.5 cm.

12. Two cards, the same design showing the original draft and the print from it for a greeting from Sydney H Morgan, Prestwich, Manchester, showing a boy lying on a beach watching a ship, perhaps 1890's or later. 20 cm x 14.1 cm.

13. Two folder cards.
a) A pen and ink drawing of a judge with a quotation from the Merchant of Venice, signed H C B., and a greeting from H Clifford Bowling. 10.7 cm x 9.1 cm.
b) A house by the river with a poem "Lays of a L#, Venice, an owl on a branch, and a thatched hut with a Christmas verse, signed Walker. 13.1 cm x 8.6 cm, 9.5 cm x 14.9 cm.

14. Three personal cards.
a) Dr & Mrs Ford Anderson, a mediaeval style greeting for 1885 printed in red, with a black seal. 12.5 cm x 9.2 cm.
b) A pen and ink drawing of Father Time for 1898-9, from John Skeaping, 173 Upper Parliament Street, Liverpool. 15.3 cm x 11.5 cm.
c) A card printed for Professor & Mrs Sylvanus P Thompson of West Hampstead, Christmas 1893, a well-designed woodcut with a border of leaf and heraldic designs around the greeting. 13 cm x 15.2 cm.

15. An eight-page folder card printed in green by G Falkner & Sons, Manchester and London, from T C W Crook, the Woodlands, Pleasington, with four designs of a girl, owls, and children signed by him and dated 1898. 12.6 cm x 17.7 cm.

16. Two cards.
a) A greeting for New Year, 1906, printed in dark red with an Art Nouveau design of doves and leaves, from Mr & Mrs H Bloomfield Bane, the Red House, 142A Islington, Liverpool, signed H B B. 11.5 cm x 15.2 cm.
b) A folder card from Edmund H New, Evesham, with a picture of Broad Gate, Ludlow, signed E H N, 1902, printed in black. 8.5 cm x 14.8 cm.

17. A four-page folder card from Sir Edwin & Lady Burning-Lawrence, Ascot, Berks, dated Christmas 1910 - New Year 1911, printed in brown, with a holly border incorporating the rose, thistle, and shamrock, around verses and greetings. One of these begins "King Edward's dead" ... another "God Bless King George" ..., an interesting combination of seasonal greetings with patriotism. 12 cm x 16.5 cm.

18. Three handmade cards, a drawing in blue of the Rialto, Venice, an owl on a branch, and a thatched hut with a Christmas verse, signed Walker. 13.1 cm x 8.6 cm, 9.5 cm x 14.9 cm.

19. Five cards, a pen and ink drawing of a Viking ship signed M M C, from Maude M Crewe, a winter scene, two cards with churches in vignettes, and a birthday card with frolicking pigs, dated 1887. 9.2 cm x 6 cm up to 15 cm x 9.5 cm.

20. Five cards, pen and ink sketches, two with flowers, one with an owl, another with a screen, two men with cats and a dog, the fifth a maidservant cleaning shoes. 9.5 cm x 6.2 cm up to 9.3 cm x 15 cm.

21. A card, no greeting, with a girl's head in a bonnet, framed in a diamond shaped border with twelve heads of men and women. 11.5 cm x 15.2 cm.

# VOLUME 204: HANDMADE CARDS, LATE 1880's AND EARLY 1890's

**This volume shows cards designed and coloured by the senders for individual recipients, with a number painted on celluloid or ivorine, some of which may have been handmade for the publishers. The artistic standard here is not very high, except for number 1.**

1. Three birthday cards by the Woodward sisters, sent to members of their family, c1890.
a) A lady at a window, by Alice Bolingbroke Woodward, 12.7 cm x 12.7 cm.
b) A peasant girl with a bird by E C (Nellie) Woodward. 8.3 cm x 13 cm.
c) A milkmaid with a pail by Gertrude M Bradley, nee Woodward. 7.5 cm x 11.4 cm.

*Numbers 2-13 were drawn and coloured by the senders, some perhaps inspired by publishers' cards.*

2. Five cards, a small boy with a tray of loaves, a couple on a sofa behind a newspaper, a fox and a goose with a tray of Christmas fare, a bottle and glasses, and a man holding a bouquet for his lady love with a donkey nibbling the flowers. 5 cm x 8.7 cm up to 10.7 cm x 14.3 cm.

3/4. Three cards of children, two inspired by Kate Greenaway. 11.3 cm x 15.4 cm, 10.2 cm x 12.4 cm, 18.2 cm x 11.7 cm.

5. Five cards, a mother and baby, a lake with stepping stones, dwarfs on a wall, rabbits, hounds chasing a fox. 6.2 cm x 9 cm up to 11.5 cm x 8.8 cm.

6. Two cards, a lady and gentleman hunting, and a gun with a grouse and a salmon and descriptive poem on reverse. 10.7 cm x 13.8 cm, 16.4 cm x 10.7 cm.
7. Two cards, girls in Kate Greenaway costume, with a flowering branch. 10.7 cm x 19.4 cm.

8. Two cards, a woodland scene dated 1877, and another with a ship in a vignette and an owl. 10.4 cm x 15.3 cm, 12 cm x 15.5 cm.

9. Six cards with various scenes, four with sailing ships, one a house in Lowestoft, another a lakeside village with mountains behind. 10 cm x 6 cm up to 11.4 cm x 8.9 cm.

10. Two cards, a well drawn scene with sailing ships, and a church by a lake. 10.6 cm x 6.5 cm, 14.4 cm x 11 cm.

11. Three cards with birds. Sizes up to 13.5 cm x 10.4 cm.

12. Five cards, one with flowers, one with a bee, a folding card opening to show Roman ruins, and a boy with a bundle. The fifth card has a coloured geometric border and a touching verse ending "To dear old dad from his daughters three." 6.5 cm x 10 cm up to 14 cm x 7.6 cm.

13. A picture of the Old Year "As Ye Yeare Fades", in grey wash on thick white card. 11.7 cm x 15.5 cm.

*The following cards are on celluloid, some perhaps as issued by publishers, but others may have been painted by the senders.*

14. Three cards, one with pansies marked T B & Co., the two smaller with blackberries or leaves. 10.5 cm x 15 cm, 4.6 cm x 11.9 cm, 4.8 cm x 8.5 cm.

15. Two cards with fancy borders, a Scotsman skating, and sailing ships. 8.7 cm x 11.3 cm, 8.6 cm x 10.7 cm.

16. Three cards, probably professionally designed, two with sailing ships on cream card mounts, the third a waterfall. They all have embossed printed greetings with gilt letters. 10.1 cm x 14 cm, 6.4 cm x 11.2 cm.

17. Two cards, a winter village scene, and a spray of flowers and fern, both on cream card mounts. 14 cm x 10.6 cm, 14.6 cm x 9.7 cm.

18. Six cards (one birthday), all with flowers. Four have greetings in gilt letters. 6.8 cm x 4.7 cm up to 9 cm x 11.3 cm.

19. Four cards, Santa Claus, sent from Versailles 1885, the others with robin, holly and mistletoe, and forget-me-nots, all rather crudely drawn. 6.8 cm x 10 cm.

20. Four cards, a house on a hill, a rider on a white horse, and two with roses. 7.5 cm x 11 cm, 6.2 cm x 9.4 cm.

21. Five cards with flowers, including two with greetings in French, sent from France. 7.3 cm x 3.7 cm up to 8 cm x 11.2 cm.

22. Three cards, a spray of painted flowers with the music of "Hark the Herald Angels sing" printed in gold, and two others with flowers. 17.5 cm x 12 cm, 8.9 cm x 10.4 cm, 7.3 cm x 10.8 cm.

23. Three cards, one painted roses on a card marked J W & Co, dated 1882, another with Christmas roses, a third with a winter scene. 10.5 cm x 14.8 cm,

# SCENES, PUBLISHED FROM THE LATE 1870's TO ABOUT 1890

*Section*

*18*

Winter and summer views appear here, many in vignettes framed in holly, foliage, or flowers. Churches, usually in winter moonlight, are often pictured, along with mountains, pastoral country views, and lakes, rivers and waterfalls, with an occasional town or village street. Many are drawn from the artist's imagination but a few are inspired by actual places. Sailing ships, at sea and in harbour, were popular subjects, an occasional steamship appearing.

Cards from known publishers are filed in volumes 205-208, with some cards signed by artists; a few untraced monograms can be seen. The flower decorations are not always suited to the scenes they accompany, roses often being drawn with winter scenes, but the spring flowers can be accepted as signifying wishes for happiness in the New Year.

A HAPPY NEW YEAR TO YOU!

209.4

217

## VOLUME 205:
## SCENES, SOME IN VIGNETTES, PUBLISHED BY EYRE & SPOTTISWOODE AND W HAGELBERG

*Numbers 1-11 were published by Eyre & Spottiswoode in the early 1880's, and show a high standard of design and production.*

1. Three cards, lake and mountain scenes in oval vignettes with heather or Christmas roses, and text in panel, no. 136. 7.9 cm x 11 cm.

2. Three cards, Irish lake and mountain scenes in oval vignettes with flower garlands, no. 232.
9.5 cm x 12 cm, 12 cm x 9.5 cm.

3. Three cards, two with mountain scenes and Alpine flowers, no. 213, the other with a mountain scene as in no. 1 above in an oval vignette framed in ferns, no. 236.
8.9 cm x 14 cm, 12 cm x 9 cm.

4. Three cards, two with scenes on a circular fan with handle, one dated 1882, the other with a scene and flowers on two similar fans, no. 308.
9 cm x 11.7 cm, 12 cm x 9.9 cm.

5. Two cards in quodlibet style with cat or dog, moonlight scenes, and birds, on a panel pinned to a wooden frame in trompe l'oeil effect. No. 306. 9.7 cm x 14.4 cm.

6. Three cards, two designs of white flowers around vignettes with winter scenes in pen and ink style, two with verses, one by Lewis Novra. No. 310.
14.8 cm x 9.5 cm.

7. Three cards, sailing ships in circular or square vignettes on a background of shells and seaweed, no. 412.
11.4 cm x 15.7 cm, 15.7 cm x 11.4cm.

8. Two cards, a Christmas scene with two girls decorating the dining room in a vignette with holly background, no. 454, and a waterfall, no. 424.
14.4 cm x 10.5 cm, 11cm x 14.7 cm.

9. Three cards printed in shades of brown and blue, showing winter on a farm. Each has two pictures of winter scenes and farm activities, with a Christmas poem signed L N in a panel. No. 653. 12 cm x 16.5 cm.

10. Three cards, showing ancient buildings or sailing boats in palette shaped vignettes with flowering branches. 10.7 cm x 14 cm.

11. Two cards, each with a forest in a circular vignette with a wallflower or hyacinths, one a birthday card, no. 612. 16.5 cm x 14.5 cm.

*The following cards were published by W Hagelberg, c1885-90, many printed in Berlin. With a few exceptions, they were printed in pale colours on plain white mounts.*

12. Two cards, winter scenes with churches in semi-circular vignettes, no. 23.
15 cm x 12 cm.

13. Three cards, ships in harbour no. 288, a church at sunset no. 63, and a woodland scene with a house in a circular vignette. Sizes up to 13 cm x 9.9 cm.

14. Three small cards, country scenes at sunset, no. 53. 9.2 cm x 6.5 cm.

15. Three cards, village scenes and flowers set on a silver circle, one dated 1887 by the sender. No. 85. 9.2 cm x 12.3 cm.

16. Four cards. Two signed L D, i.e. Lucien Davis have moonlit country houses in winter snow, no. 417. The others (one birthday) have monochrome river scenes in moonlight, no. 226.
13.1 cm x 9.8 cm, 8 cm x 10.9 cm.

17/18. Seven miscellaneous cards with various winter scenes, nos.10, 54, 113, 128, 43, 64, 101.
11.2 cm x 7.4 cm up to 10.8 cm x 15 cm.

19. Two cards, river scenes with floral decoration, no. 18 dated 1886 by the sender, no. 438 dated 1888.
11.7 cm x 15.7 cm, 13.2 cm x 9.9 cm.

20. Four cards, winter scenes. Two have large overprinted crescent moons, no. 321, and two are signed L D, nos. 421, 534.
9.4 cm x 12.8 cm, 9.8 cm x 12.9 cm.

21/22. Seven miscellaneous cards with various winter scenes, one a stormy sea, another showing a windmill, with serrated edges. Nos. 431, 328 (dated 1889), 29, 119, 625, 1203, 116.
8.4 cm x 12 cm up to 17.5 cm x 10.7 cm.

23. Two cards, a church at nightfall with a verse by S K Cowan MA, and a waterfall

with flowers and a verse by J W Myers, BA. These appear to be from the same set but are numbered 86 (dated 1887 by the sender) and 628. 10.5 cm x 14.9 cm.

24. Two cards, sea and mountain scenes with overprinted crescent moon, and the same verse by M S H on both. One is numbered 623, the other is signed L D. 11 cm x 14.9 cm, 14.9 cm x 11 cm.

25. Two cards. One has a river scene in a rectangular vignette with a background of a lake with swans and a girl's head above, no. 50. The other has a girl picking flowers in a circular vignette, dated 1886 by the sender, no. 215.
13.4 cm x 18 cm, 14.9 cm x 10.7 cm.

26. Two cards, a scene with ship and lighthouse in a sail-shaped vignette, and HMS Victory in Portsmouth harbour. 9.4 cm x 9.4 cm, 11 cm x 11 cm.

27. Two cards, village scenes in shades of brown and grey, one no. 721, the other with a verse by E H Griffin on reverse. 13.1 cm x 9.9 cm, 15 cm x 11 cm.

28. Three cards, colourful scenes of sailing ships, no. 437. 13.2 cm x 9.9 cm.

29. Two cards, sailing ships, with quotations from Spenser and Shakespeare, a ship design on the reverse of one, and poems by M S H. No. 468. 10.9 cm x 15 cm.

30. Three cards with scenes or birds in vignettes with gilt or silver patterned coloured borders, no. 78. 11.3 cm x 7.3 cm.

31. Two similar cards with scenes in circular or rectangular vignettes and birds in the borders, one dated 1890 by the sender with a verse by E E G.
8.3 cm x 12.9 cm, 13.3 cm x 10 cm.

32. Three cards, yachts on a lake, bordered by embossed silver leaves, with poems signed F on reverse. 14.7 cm x 7.2 cm.

## VOLUME 206:
## SCENES FROM VARIOUS PUBLISHERS, c1885-90

**Cards from Castell Bros., Wirth Bros. & Owen, Sockl & Nathan, and M H Nathan & Co. appear here.**

*Numbers 1-6 were published by Castell Bros.*

1. One card, a lake with large waterlilies, the Peniel series, no. 20. 14.7 cm x 10.6 cm.

2. Two cards, the Thames near Pangbourne no. 101A, and a church in moonlight, no. 141A, both Peniel.
13.5 cm x 11 cm, 14.5 cm x 10.8 cm.

3. Three cards signed F Corbyn Price, Magdalen College Oxford, Oriel College and Merton Tower, and Ely, nos. 136B,

205.9

118A, 124, all Peniel. 10.5 cm x 13.9 cm, 11.5 cm x 8.3 cm.

4. Three miscellaneous cards, all sea scenes, two unnumbered. The third is in a vignette wreathed in ivy leaves, no. 57, Peniel. 7.3 cm x 8.4 cm, 9.3 cm x 11.2 cm, 16.6 cm x 10.7 cm.

5. Two tinselled cards, winter scenes in vignettes with birds in a silver border, one dated 1886 by the sender, no. 2065. One of these cards appears in volume 97 no. 9 marked S Hildesheimer, also no. 2065, leading to speculation about the original manufacturer. 12.5 cm x 17 cm.

6. Two similar cards, one design with scenes in two small vignettes and Christmas roses in the silver border, no. 481, one dated 1887 by the sender. 12.5 cm x 17 cm.

*Numbers 7-23 were published by Wirth Bros. & Owen.*

7. Four frosted cards, printed in grey and brown, with two designs of deer in a forest and a mediaeval town in circular vignettes, in three sizes. One card has a poem by E H C on reverse, another was numbered 186. 7.2 cm x 9.5 cm, 9.5 cm x 11.9 cm, 11.9 cm x 15.8 cm.

8. Three cards, two designs of woodland in winter, no. 201, with a picture of bells and a descriptive poem by E H C on reverse. 10 cm x 10 cm.

9. Three cards, winter scenes in vignettes, all with a picture of bells and the same poem by E H C on reverse. Nos. 200, 238, 256. 11 cm x 13.5 cm, 10.5 cm x 13 cm.

10. Five frosted cards, winter scenes, with flowers or thistles. The large card, no. 250, has bells and another poem on this theme by E H C. 11 cm x 8.5 cm, 9.3 cm x 10.1 cm, 12 cm x 12 cm.

11. Two tinselled cards, village scenes in winter, nos. 259 and 272, the latter with a picture of a church and another bell poem by E H C on reverse. 16.5 cm x 11.9 cm.

12. Four frosted cards, two designs of Niagara Falls in two styles, and a country scene in a circular vignette in gilded border. A further poem about bells by E H C appears on the reverse of one card. 9.7 cm x 15.2 cm, 8.2 cm x 11.9 cm, 12.4 cm x 11.5 cm.

13. Three cards, moonlit winter scenes, nos. 190, 341, 1884. The first card has yet another bell poem by E H C. 9.4 cm x 7.4 cm, 11.4 cm x 9 cm, 13 cm x 9.3 cm.

14. A card printed in shades of brown, with the moon rising over a village in a circular vignette bordered by a tree with three owls, and a further three-stanza bell poem by E H C on reverse. No. 279. 13.2 cm x 17 cm.

15. An attractive tinselled card with a farm in a rectangular vignette, bordered by holly and ivy on a silver background. 18.5 cm x 12.8 cm.

16. One card, a moonlit sea in a rectangular vignette with Christmas roses and fir branches in a grey border. 11.9 cm x 18.6 cm.

17. Two cards, a church in a circular vignette, and a ship beneath a stormy sky bordered by seaweed, both marked New York. 9.4 cm x 10cm, 12 cm x 12 cm.

18. Four miscellaneous cards, country scenes in vignettes, with flowers, grasses, or foliage. Two are numbered 213, 251, and two are marked New York. 11.8 cm x 9.3 cm up to 11 cm x 13.6 cm.

19. Three cards, country scenes in winter. One is numbered 218, another dated 1884 by the sender, and the third is marked Wirth Bros., printed in Leipzig. Sizes up to 9.5 cm x 13.2 cm.

20. Six miscellaneous cards with country scenes, four in vignettes, all marked Wirth Bros., four numbered 264, 302, 311, 370. One card shows the picture on a pair of bellows, with tongs and shovel behind, with the caption "Happiness be your Fireside Companion." 7.2 cm x 9.5 cm up to 13.5 cm x 10.8 cm.

21. Three cards, church and country views in circular vignettes, decorated with holly, leaves, or flowers, one no. 455 with a birthday poem on reverse by E H C. All are marked Wirth Bros. 7.7 cm x 9.4 cm, 9.2 cm x 10.4 cm.

22. Two cards, the moon rising over a river, and swallows flying over a mediaeval town, the latter with a birthday greeting from Shakespeare. 15.1 cm x 9.4 cm, 11.9 cm x 16.4 cm.

23. A folding card with the Star of Bethlehem shining on a tinselled woodland scene within and flowers on the outside, marked Wirth Bros. 12 cm x 14.6 cm closed.

*Numbers 24-28 were published by Sockl and Nathan.*

24. Four frosted cards, three designs of rocks and waterfalls with snow and ice, in two sizes, one dated 1886 by the sender. 13 cm x 17 cm, 8.3 cm x 11 cm.

25. Two cards showing Medmenham and Dryburgh Abbeys in vignettes framed in leaves, with verses by Charlotte Murray. 12.6 cm x 10.2 cm.

26. Two cards, scenes in vignettes in the form of hanging calendars, with snowdrops or mistletoe, and verses below by Charlotte Murray. 9 cm x 12.8 cm.

27. Two cards, one with a country scene in a vignette with flowers above and a poem by Alice C Wilkinson. The other has ships in a vignette above a scene with flying seagulls. 14.6 cm x 11.5 cm, 9.9 cm x 15 cm.

28. Three cards, two with a star shining on a circular vignette with church and village, the third with three scenes in vignettes bordered by mistletoe, dated 1886 by the sender. Sizes up to 10 cm x 14 cm.

*Numbers 29,30 were published by M H Nathan & Co.*

29. Two interesting nocturnal sea pictures in wide borders, signed, but undeciphered, nos. 104B, 113. 10.1 cm x 10.1 cm, 11 cm x 13.6 cm.

30. Five miscellaneous cards, three with country scenes in vignettes, one a seascape with boats. The fifth has a pleasing design of boats and seaweed in shades of brown and russet, with a quotation from Wordsworth, no. 1113. 10 cm x 8.5 cm up to 14.2 cm x 10.2 cm.

## VOLUME 207: SCENES FROM THE PUBLISHERS ALBERT MARX AND DAVIDSON BROS., WITH OTHER CARDS DESIGNED BY ALBERT BOWERS

**Albert Bowers worked for several publishers including Raphael Tuck and Hildesheimer & Faulkner, and some of his cards have been seen in previous sections. A number are included here from unidentified**

206.12

publishers as well as those from Marx and Davidson.

*Numbers 1-4 were published by Albert Marx, London, c1885.*

1. Two cards by Albert Bowers, a farmhouse in snow, and another titled "The Woodman's Return." 17.3 cm x 12.2 cm.

2. A frosted card by Albert Bowers, a woman gathering wood in the forest. 16.5 cm x 12.7 cm.

3. Two unsigned cards by Albert Bowers, repeating the design in no. 2 and "The Woodman's Return" from no.1, in different format. 13.5 cm x 12.1 cm.

4. A card with a country farmhouse in spring, and a New Year poem by A H B on reverse. 15.8 cm x 11.6 cm.

*Numbers 5-12 were published by Davidson Bros. in the later 1880's.*

5. Two cards by Albert Bowers, one design showing a train in a winter landscape, with two different poems by H M Burnside on reverse. 16.4 cm x 11.3 cm.

6. Two cards by Albert Bowers, winter scenes, gipsies following their caravan, and a punt by a river bridge. 18 cm x 10.8 cm, 17.7 cm x 10.8 cm.

7. Three cards, a river scene signed F E B? with a verse by H M Burnside on reverse and another with a coastal steamship. The third card has a country scene in a vignette and a verse by S K Cowan, MA. 16.4 cm x 8 cm, 14.6 cm x 10.5 cm.

8. Two grey-bordered frosted cards with cottages in winter, and verses by S K Cowan on reverse. 10.6 cm x 14.5 cm.

9. Two cards, one embossed with an Italianate mansion in a vignette bordered by spring flowers, signed Davidson Bros., Manchester. The other has a waterfall in an arched vignette with forget-me-nots, and a verse by Eliza Cook. 11 cm x 14.9 cm, 10.4 cm x 14.5 cm.

10. A single card with view of a continental town with river, sailing ships, and swans. 10.5 cm x 14.4 cm.

11. Three miscellaneous cards, winter scenes, a timbered house signed Albert Bowers, a farm on silver background, and a cottage by a river in a circular vignette marked Wolff Davidson. 13.6 cm x 10.5 cm, 10.1 cm x 13.5 cm, 8.6 cm x 8.6 cm.

12. Three cards (two birthday), scenes in vignettes with background flowers, one with a verse by H M Burnside. Sizes up to 11.5 cm x 15.2 cm.

*Numbers 13-23 were designed by Albert Bowers, in the late 1880's, for unnamed publishers.*

13. Two cards, pictures of a farm and a village in winter with poems by F R Havergal in panels. 11.5 cm x 15.7 cm.

14. An attractive card with people in sledges on a hillside near their village, and a Christmas poem by Cecilia Havergal on reverse. 17.1 cm x 10.8 cm.

15. Two cards, Ifield Sussex, and East Grinstead, in winter snow, one dated 1889 by the sender. 11.6 cm x 15.4 cm.

16. Two cards showing the Thames in flood, near Windsor in the morning and by Eton in the evening. 15.4 cm x 11.6 cm.

17. Two cards, the Bridge of Clunie in winter, and a farm in snow, both with greetings printed in silver. 17.2 cm x 12.2 cm, 16 cm x 11.6 cm.

18. Two cards, one design of a timbered farmhouse in snow with different styles of greeting in silver. One has a poem by Mrs Hemans on reverse. 15.4 cm x 11.6 cm.

19. Two cards, a village in a snowstorm, and a snow-covered farmyard. 15.4 cm x 11.6 cm.

20. Three cards, country scenes with farms or cottages, one titled "Farm House in Herts." 13.5 cm x 10.2 cm.

21. Three cards, two designs showing contrasts, one with a cottage in summer and in winter, the other with a houseboat on a calm river and a storm at sea. They have a poem by H M Burnside and two by Moore in panels, and one was dated 1889 by the sender. 10.9 cm x 13.9 cm.

22. Three miscellaneous cards, Stirling Castle, Crawley, and a cottage in snow. 17.3 cm x 12.2 cm, 10.2 cm x 13.4 cm, 7.5 cm x 10 cm.

23. Four cards, three of old cottages in black and white, the fourth a repeat of one design with colours and birds, signed AB, probably Albert Bowers. They have poems on reverse, three by Elizabeth Love, one by S K Cowan MA. 9 cm x 12.3 cm, 9 cm x 12.8 cm.

24. An interesting card signed S Bowers, rowing boats by a lock on the Thames near Windsor with an apt quotation from Wordsworth on reverse. 16.4 cm x 11.3 cm.

## VOLUME 208: SCENES, VARIOUS PUBLISHERS

**All the remaining cards from known publishers are included here, dated**

in the late 1880's except where otherwise stated. Many were printed in Germany.

*Numbers 1-8 were published by J F Schipper & Co.*

1. One card, a copy of J M W Turner's "Fighting Temeraire", copied by G Clements, dated 1885 by the sender. 14.3 cm x 11.2 cm.

2. Three cards, river scenes with birds seen through an open wooden door with a hanging horseshoe and flowers and a hovering bee or butterfly. 9.7 cm x 14.7 cm.

3. Two cards, scenes in circular vignettes, one a birthday card with foxgloves and a signpost, no. 684, the other with bougainvillea no. 687. 9.7 cm x 12.6 cm, 12 cm x 16.4 cm.

4. Two cards with the same design of a river in winter with birds and fir branches, no. 690. 12 cm x 16.5 cm.

5. Four miscellaneous cards, three scenes in vignettes with flowers, the fourth a picture on an easel, nos. 622, 622, 615, 864. 7 cm x 9.8 cm up to 10.5 cm x 13.1 cm.

6. A birthday card, a ruined castle with lake and swans, no. 1053. 16.3 cm x 10.6 cm.

7. A folding card made up of two sea and river scenes in circular vignettes with a silver border on blue and silver background, and verses by S K C, no. 1271. A third design from this set is in no. 8. 14.7 cm x 12.2 cm folded.

8. Two cards with ships in vignettes, one circular with a silver border on a blue and silver background, the other a small rectangle in a large shell with seaweed, nos. 1271, 1489. The first has a poem on reverse signed S K C. 14.7 cm x 12.2 cm, 15.3 cm x 11.3 cm.

*Numbers 9-11 were published by Thomas Stevens.*

9/10. Eight cards, gilded borders with red line, four designs of a ship in rough sea, a sailing ship at sunset, a farmer with horses and plough, and a church, showing different greetings and eight poems by Ada. Early 1880's. 13.2 cm x 8.8 cm.

11. Five miscellaneous cards marked T S, two with winter scenes, one a windmill, one a lake with a large rose, the fifth a winter scene in oval vignette with holly and birds. 7.4 cm x 11 cm up to 8.5 cm x 13 cm.

12/14. Six cards (one birthday) published by Nelson & Co., scenes of Derwentwater, Buttermere, three views of Edinburgh, and Dumbarton Castle, in rectangular vignettes with five designs of various flowers in the wide gilt borders and decorated backs. Early 1880's. 15.5 cm x 11 cm, one 17 cm x 12.6 cm.

*Numbers 15-19 were published by Bernhard Ollendorff, c1885.*

15. Two cards, sailing ships and a steamship approaching harbour, in large oval vignettes. One card has a gilded design on reverse with ships in four small circular vignettes. 14.8 cm x 12 cm.

16. Three cards, one with Haddon Hall in snow in a rectangular vignette with mistletoe, and a poem by Charlotte Murray on reverse, dated 1884 by the sender. Two smaller cards have country scenes in oval vignettes, both with periwinkle or forget-me-not. 12 cm x 17.1 cm, 7.8 cm x 11.8 cm.

17. Two cards, the same design of London Bridge in a vignette with snowdrops. One card has silk flowers, the other has a poem by M S Haycraft in a fan on reverse. 11 cm x 12.8 cm.

18. Two cards, a snow scene with a ship in a circular vignette with mistletoe, and a sailing ship in a rectangular vignette with roses and forget-me-nots. 10.9 cm x 8.5 cm, 9.4 cm x 13 cm.

19. Seven small cards, five with winter scenes in circular vignettes bordered by flowers or leaves, two with winter scenes in wide borders. 6.7 cm x 6.7 cm, 8.2 cm x 5.7 cm.

20. Two cards, marked S J S & Co., i.e. S J Saunders, a small card with a ship, and a lake and mountain scene on pale blue ground. This card is from the same set as two cards in volume 113 no. 6 published by Hildesheimer & Faulkner, and these must have been supplied to both publishers by another firm. 9.3 cm x 6.6 cm, 10.7 cm x 14 cm.

21/22. Six cards published by Philipp Bros. These have scenes in horseshoe shaped vignettes and verses by Eliza Cook, another has a farmhouse in snow and a verse by Cowper. Two have scenes in vignettes bordered by flowers, and the sixth is a winter scene on paper with a trompe l'oeil torn effect, those three with verses by S K Cowan MA and Frances Ridley Havergal. 9 cm x 12.2 cm up to 11.5 cm x 14.9 cm.

23. Three cards (two birthday), river and seaside scenes published by H Rothe, one dated 1879 by the sender. 9.5 cm x 12.4 cm.

24. Three miscellaneous cards published by Obpacher Bros., a forest scene in a vignette with roses and decorative gilt border, no. 932, trees by the sea, no. 913, and a winter scene with church, no. 1570. 10 cm x 14.5 cm, 9 cm x 14.2 cm, 11 cm x 15 cm.

25. Two gilt bordered cards printed in brown and grey, people going to church, and gathering wood, one dated 1886 by the sender. These are marked M L J & Co., probably M L Jonas, have verses by Ada on reverse, and are signed G Fraipunt(?) 8.5 cm x 15 cm.

26/27. Five cards, published by M Priester's Continental Printing Co., scenes in vignettes, three with flowers, one with birds. They are numbered 70, 155, 205, 161, 202 prefixed by the French word "serie", so perhaps the firm was based in France. 8.5 cm x 11.4 cm up to 10.6 cm x 15.9 cm.

28. Four cards, Meissner & Buch, various scenes, all with verses, two signed M S H, S K Cowan MA. 11 cm x 8 cm up to 15.6 cm x 11 cm.

29. Four cards, two winter scenes from Charles, Reynolds & Co. printed in sepia, two with scenes in vignettes and flowers or leaves, one marked L S, the other J Brady & Co. London N. 8.8 cm x 12.8 cm, 12.6 cm x 9.1 cm, 14.5 cm x 10.6 cm.

30. One card, Misch & Stock. a seascape with verse by H S Bainbridge on reverse. 12.7 cm x 9.4 cm.

## VOLUME 209: BORDERED SCENES

**No publishers have been identified but a few cards were signed by the artists; they were published in the early 1880's with a few exceptions as noted.**

1. A view of Windermere set in a border imitating grained wood, with a poem by Fanny Rochat on reverse. 15.1 cm x 8.9 cm.

2/3. Five gilt-edged cards, Scottish views, with Old Songs and poems by Dunlop, Wordsworth, Burns, Scott on reverse, one dated 1879 by the sender. 14.1 cm x 10.1 cm, 10.1 cm x 14.1 cm.

4. Two unusual cards, London scenes of Holborn Viaduct and Westminster, one with scissors, the other with a brush. The first has a poem by Eden Hooper on reverse. 15.3 cm x 10.4 cm.

5. Three cards, views of Snowdon, Killarney, and Windermere, with verses signed Anon, Alford, and N Holt on reverse. 14.3 cm x 9.3 cm.

6. Three cards, views of the Watch Oak, Leominster, Kenilworth Castle, and Whitnash Church, Leamington, all with poems on reverse by E J Pope. 13.6 cm x 9 cm.

7. A card showing Niagara Falls in winter in green and black tones, with a descriptive verse by E H C on reverse. Later 1880's. 15.5 cm x 11 cm.

8. Two forest scenes signed H Krabbe, showing autumn colour. 11.1 cm x 14 cm, 14 cm x 11.1 cm.

9. Two cards, one of Westminster Abbey in snow, signed A F Lydon. The other shows cattle by a river, on thick card with a scalloped border, signed FCP, ie F Corbyn Price, with a poem by Tennyson on reverse, c1890. 13.5 cm x 11 cm, 17.8 cm x 12.4 cm.

10. Two unusual cards showing the Charing Cross Hotel and the National Gallery, made with large orange coloured scraps with cut-out windows on thick white card, and shadowy trees behind, c1890. 16 cm x 10.8 cm.

11. Two cards with Baxter type prints, one a country inn on an embossed scallop-edged mount, the other Kew gardens on a mount with gilt-patterned border, 1870's. 14 cm x 10 cm, 14 cm x 11 cm.

12. Two cards with woodland scenes in spring and autumn. 12.8 cm x 18.9 cm.

13. Two cards, country scenes with haystacks and geese, and verses by Frederick Langbridge and Lavinia M Lancaster on reverse. 15.5 cm x 11 cm.

14. A card with a river in springtime and two people in a punt, with appropriate sentiment "Joyous as spring may the season be to you." 18.6 cm x 12.4 cm.

15. One card, illegibly signed, a farmer ploughing, with a rainbow in the sky, dated 1882 by the sender. A poem by Eden Hooper is on the back. 12.5 cm x 15.9 cm.

16. Two cards, a farm in winter, and cattle by a river bridge, both with mountain backgrounds. 17.5 cm x 12 cm.

17. Two cards, a farmer with a cow, and another taking home the Yule log from a snow-covered forest, dated 1883 by the sender. 15.3 cm x 11.7 cm, 16.5 cm x 12.2 cm.

18. Two cards, country scenes, one with children by a stile dated 1884 by the sender, the other a lane with hills in the background. 10.6 cm x 14.5 cm, 15.7 cm x 10.9 cm.

19. Two cards, a shepherd and dog with sheep in a country lane, and a man fishing from a river bridge. 10.9 cm x 16 cm, 10 cm x 15.8 cm.

20. Two cards, winter snow, one with people walking home through the woods, the other a flock of sheep and a farmer with horses and cart. 15.2 cm x 10.5 cm.

21. One card, a snowbound village. 17 cm x 11 cm.

22. Three miscellaneous cards, winter scenes. Sizes up to 13.6 cm x 11.2 cm.

23. Three miscellaneous cards, trees in winter. Sizes up to 16 cm x 12 cm.

24. Three cards, two gilt-edged showing a river bridge or a timbered farmhouse, with a verse by A Gill, the other a girl in a lane beside a country cottage.
10.6 cm x 13.8 cm, 10 cm x 13 cm.

25. Four miscellaneous cards with patterned borders, two with lake scenes, two with people in winter and autumn scenes. Sizes up to 12 cm x 10.6 cm.

26. Three miscellaneous gilt-edged cards, country scenes with trees.
11.3 cm x 7.7 cm up to 10.8 cm x 16 cm.

27. Three cards, two designs showing a ruined arch and a Gothic style doorway, one repeat design embossed.
9.3 cm x 13.5 cm.

28. Three cards, silver borders, winter scenes with trees and cottages.
10.9 cm x 14.2 cm.

29. Two cards in monochrome, a country scene with oak leaves, and a mansion with statues along the drive, signed G S.
18.4 cm x 12.2 cm, 19.3 cm x 14.4 cm.

30. Two black-edged cards, a country mansion in moonlight with carol singers, and a mother and child going to church, both with quotations from Longfellow.
10.7 cm x 16.5 cm.

31. Two similar cards with country scenes and quotations from Shakespeare.
10.6 cm x 16.3 cm.

32. Two similar smaller cards showing a farm and a lake scene. 13 cm x 8 cm.

33. Three cards, grey borders, one showing a blacksmith's forge, two smaller with a snow-covered cottage, both tinselled.
13.8 cm x 16.9 cm, 12.1 cm x 9.1 cm.

34. Four miscellaneous cards, winter scenes with trees and cottages. Sizes up to 10 cm x 13.3 cm.

35. Two cards, grey borders, winter scenes, one with a serrated border and a poem by E E Griffin on reverse.
8.7 cm x 13 cm, 15.4 cm x 11 cm.

## VOLUME 210.
## SCENES, 1884-90

**Most of these cards are unbordered, many printed on thick paper in the later 1880's. A few are signed by artists but the publishers have not been traced. They are less colourful than the earlier cards, many being printed in soft shades of brown,**

**blue, and green, with a few in monochrome.**

1. Two cards, a view of the Cathedral gateway, Canterbury, signed W H S T, with a verse by Eliza Cook on reverse, and another of the Houses of Parliament.
15.5 cm x 11.3 cm, 16.4 cm x 11.1 cm.

2. Three cards, Beccles, signed P R, a country scene signed F C P and a village in snow signed Wilfred Ball with a poem by Frances Ridley Havergal. 11 cm x 8.8 cm, 13.4 cm x 10.8 cm, 16.2 cm x 11.5 cm.

3. Two cards, both views of Kenilworth Castle, the smaller with a verse by Arthur Steine on reverse. 10 cm x 7.5 cm, 16.4 cm x 11.4 cm.

4. A set of four cards signed O H C, country scenes in winter snow, with poems on reverse. 13.8 cm x 10.8 cm.

5. Six cards, all named cathedrals or churches from two sets, two signed A F Lydon. 10 cm x 12.6 cm, 10.8 cm x 8 cm.

6/7. A set of four cards, country scenes with farm activities, with texts and religious verses by Nicolai, Dix, Walsham How, and H Downton on reverse.
16.3 cm x 12.1 cm.

8. Three cards, country scenes in black and white, two with verses by H M Burnside on reverse. 12.2 cm x 8.8 cm.

9. Three cards, one a farm, two with people going to church and poem below by E Love. 9.7 cm x 13 cm.

10. Four cards with serrated edges, country scenes, three in winter, one in spring.
13 cm x 10.2 cm.

11. One card, sea and rocks beneath a colourful sky. 12.3 cm x 15 cm.

12/14. Seven cards, four designs of lakes with various water birds. Two have black borders, three are plain, and two are folders with silver borders and ornamental covers, with poems by Frances Ridley Havergal. All have quotations from Shakespeare, and one was dated 1884 by the sender. 16.3 cm x 11.7 cm, 14.7 cm x 10.5 cm, 15.5 cm x 11.3 cm.

15. Four cards, lake, sea, and country scenes with Shakespeare quotations.
11 cm x 13.7 cm.

16. Three cards, country scenes with villagers, one with scalloped edge. Sizes up to 13.2 cm x 9.7 cm.

17. Three cards (one birthday), two designs with summer scenes showing a weir, and a church seen through an arch.
18.4 cm x 11.8 cm, 16.3 cm x 11 cm, 11.2 cm x 8 cm.

18. Three miscellaneous cards, moonlight scenes with church, lake, or castle. Sizes up to 14.2 cm x 10.4 cm.

19. Three cards, a church in winter, a market town with church, and an arched doorway opening to show a village street, with verses by S K Cowan or Frances Ridley Havergal. 10.7 cm x 14 cm, 10.8 cm x 10.8 cm, 10.7 cm x 14 cm.

20. Three cards, country views with lake and trees. 10.7 cm x 15 cm.

21. Two cards, a river scene signed A W B dated 1889 by the sender, with a verse signed E C W B, and a farm in winter.
13.2 cm x 11.3 cm, 15 cm x 11 cm.

22. Three cards, monochrome, Durham Cathedral, a country scene with snow, and a rocky beach. 9.7 cm x 14.3 cm, 11.3 cm x 8.4 cm, 12.8 cm x 8.5 cm.

23. Two cards, a lake scene with a poem by M E R, dated 1889 by the sender, and a pastoral scene with cattle.
15 cm x 11 cm, 15.6 cm x 11.2 cm.

24. Two cards, trees in winter, the same poem serving for two different pictures.
8.9 cm x 12.2 cm.

25. Four miscellaneous bordered cards, with trees, churches, or cottage.
8.8 cm x 12.5 cm up to 9.9 cm x 15.1 cm.

26. Two cards printed in shades of blue and brown, one design of a house by a waterfall in two formats. 11.4 cm x 14.2 cm, 13 cm x 10 cm.

27. Three miscellaneous cards, lake scenes, one printed in sepia with a verse by S K Cowan on reverse, the others with verses by Johnston Beall and Frances Ridley Havergal.
Sizes approximately 14 cm x 11 cm.

28 Four miscellaneous cards, cottages in summer or winter.
6.4 cm x 10 cm up to 15.7 cm x 11.7 cm.

29. Six miscellaneous cards, scenes with churches, lakes, trees, and cottages.
7.9 cm x 10.2 cm up to 9.6 cm x 14.6 cm.

30. Two cards, a ruined castle in moonlight with an owl on a curved branch dated 1886 by the sender, and a house in snow with birds above.
13.4 cm x 9.9 cm, 15.7 cm x 10.6 cm.

31. Six miscellaneous cards with churches, one a smaller version of the first card in no.30. Sizes up to 9.6 cm x 11.6 cm.

32. Five cards from two sets in similar style. Three have quotations from Coleridge and Longfellow, one dated 1886 by the sender.
7 cm x 10.7 cm, 13 cm x 8.9 cm.

33. Seven miscellaneous cards with various country scenes. Three have verses, two by William Morris, one by A L Salmon. Sizes up to 10.1 cm x 11 cm.

34. Two cards with cut-out edges, a sea scene dated 1888 by the sender with a verse by S K Cowan, and a birthday card with a moonlit country scene, c1890. 10.5 cm x 14 cm, 13 cm x 9.5 cm.

35. Two frosted cards, a cave with icicles, and a frozen waterfall in a cut-out border, c1890. 15 cm x 12.5 cm, 17 cm x 14 cm.

36. Five miscellaneous cards with serrated edges, country scenes. Sizes up to 9.2 cm x 12 cm.

## VOLUME 211:
## SCENES WITH SHIPS, SEA,
## SHELLS AND SEAWEED, 1880's

**These cards include straightforward seascapes with ships, cliffs and beaches, with a number in vignettes unsuitably decorated with flowers, though seaweed and shells were also used as embellishments. A few cards with shells and fishes are included here, as the small number of these in this collection does not justify a separate volume.**

1. Two cards, Sunrise on the Maas, Holland, and a Dutch Galliott off Beachy Head, both with sea poems on reverse. 16 cm x 11.9 cm.

2. Two cards, a ship in full sail, entitled "Noon", probably one of a set, and another with boats in Littlehampton Harbour. 13.2 cm x 16.4 cm, 11.9 cm x 16 cm.

3/4. Six cards, four designs of sailing boats in coastal waters in two formats, one dated 1884 by the sender. 10.9 cm x 7.5 cm, 14.4 cm x 10.7 cm.

5. Seven gilt-edged cards. Four larger cards have two designs of a sailing ship and an unusual steamer with sails, with verses by Fannie Rochat on reverse, one dated 1881 by the sender. Three smaller cards have sailing ships. 11.3 cm x 8 cm, 8.2 cm x 5.7 cm.

6. Two cards, a sailing boat with passengers beneath a moonlit sky, and another in black and white. 9.3 cm x 14.6 cm, 17.9 cm x 12.8 cm.

7. Two cards, each with sailing ships in vignettes, one bordered by shells and seaweed. 13.7 cm x 10.2 cm, 15.3 cm x 10.4 cm.

8. A triptych folder card with a picture of a ship in a stormy sea and rescuers on shore, and elaborate illuminated design on wings and cover. 13 cm x 16 cm closed.

211.15

9. Three cards, two designs, one in two styles, one a fishing boat, the other a lighthouse beneath a stormy sky, each with a poem by Ada. 16.8 cm x 11.3 cm, 16 cm x 10.5 cm.

10. Four miscellaneous cards with sailing ships. (See Volume 210 nos. 5 and 12 for two similar cards used as trade cards). Sizes up to 14.5 cm x 9.5 cm.

11. Two cards, sailing ships, one a birthday card with verse by S K Cowan, the other with a poem on reverse. 13 cm x 8 cm, 13.7 cm x 9.7 cm.

12. Three cards, sailing ships, one with a verse by Eliza Simmonds. The other two are birthday cards with quotations from Wordsworth on reverse. 9.7 cm x 13.9 cm, 9.2 cm x 12.9 cm.

13. Two cards, sailing ships, one with a verse by E E Griffin on reverse. 10.7 cm x 13.7 cm, 10.5 cm x 15.6 cm.

14. Five small cards from two sets, sailing ships. 6.7 cm x 9.7 cm, 9.7 cm x 7.3 cm.

15. Five cards, scenes with rocks and ships in circular or rectangular vignettes. One with blue border is marked W Hagelberg, included here for comparison. 7.4 cm x 7.4 cm up to 9 cm x 12.2 cm.

16. Five miscellaneous cards, four with sailing ships, one opening to show a steamship. The fifth card shows a stormy sea and people on the beach pulling in salvage. 9.3 cm x 6.5 cm up to 13.4 cm x 9.4 cm.

17. Two cards, sailing ships in moonlight, decorated with flower garlands, with verses on reverse. 11.2 cm x 15.3 cm.

18. Two cards, one design with a curious mixture of sailing ships in moonlight, three mice in a bowl, in a border of leaves and a red rose. 11.4 cm x 15.9 cm.

19. Two cards, sailing ships of continental appearance in rectangular vignettes in a decorated circle, one with a red rose, the other with pelargoniums. 13.2 cm x 8.5 cm.

20. Five miscellaneous cards, sailing ships in vignettes with various flowers or grasses. Sizes up to 9.1 cm x 12 7 cm.

21. Two cards, sea scenes in vignettes with apple blossom or forget-me-nots in border. 15.2 cm x 10.2 cm, 16.1 cm x 10.2 cm.

22. Five miscellaneous cards, sea scenes and sailing ships in vignettes, three bordered by forget-me-nots, one by shells and seaweed. Sizes up to 11.4 xm x 8.7 cm.

23. Two cards, vignettes with boats in harbour or at sea, bordered by white flowers, one dated 1886 by the sender. 14.4 cm x 9.4 cm, 14.4 cm x 11.3 cm.

24. A triptych folder card with a coastal scene and a poem by Frances Ridley Havergal within, and an unusual design of a belt and buckle on the cover. 12.7 cm x 11 cm closed.

25. Two cards, a harbour scene with a boat in a sail-shaped vignette, and sailing ships in a vignette with an anchor and seaweed. 11.1 cm x 14.2 cm, 15 cm x 11 cm.

26. Three miscellaneous cards, sailing ships and fishing boats with borders of seaweed and shells. 9.5 cm x 12.9 cm, 10.2 cm x 13.4 cm, 12.6 cm x 17 cm.

27. Four cards, one design of a boat and lobster pots on a beach, with a seaweed border, in three formats, one dated 1883 by the sender. 11.3 cm x 9.1 cm, 13.1 cm x 10.1 cm, 13.8 cm x 11 cm.

28. A large card with a view of the sea at Scarborough, and a vignette surrounded by seaweed showing Scarborough castle, with a poem on reverse signed L N. 13.3 cm x 18 cm.

29. Three cards, shells and seaweed on black or green background, with shell scrap which lifts to show greeting. 10.9 cm x 6.9 cm.

30. Three cards, two with shells and seaweed and a verse by Eden Hooper. The third card has a ship at sea with a border of flowers, shells, and seaweed, and an identical card with variant greeting is part of a set included in section 19 on flowers. 7.6 cm x 11.5 cm.

31. Two cards, interesting designs of life in ocean depths with fish, seaweed, and shells, in a seaweed border, one dated 1883 by the sender. 15.3 cm x 11.4 cm.

BIRTHDAY

*In every nook a message see
And give my card a smile for me!*

**211.31**

32. Three cards. Two marked V O W have shells and seaweed around a panel with greeting. The third has a sunset over sea and a border with a vase, plate, cup and saucer with eggs, set in a background of shells and seaweed. 12.2 cm x 8 cm, 14 cm x 8.5 cm.

33. A set of four cards with shells and seaweed and verses by Shirley Wynne or A M R, published by Hildesheimer & Faulkner, but included here for comparison with similar cards. 11.7 cm x 9 cm.

34. Four miscellaneous cards, shells and seaweed, one with a bird flying over a tropical scene. Sizes up to 9.5 cm x 14.4 cm.

35. Three cards. One has a ship printed on silk in the shape of a scallop, with a border of seaweed; the second has fine seaweed mounted on a gilt-edged card. The third card, dated 1884, has shells and seaweed and a birthday greeting by Eden Hooper. 8.4 cm x 12.4 cm, 9 cm x 12.7 cm, 8.5 cm x 12.2 cm.

## VOLUME 212:
## SCENES WITH SEASONAL
## DECORATION, 1880's

**Holly, mistletoe, ivy, berries, and greenery embellish these cards, most of the scenes being in vignettes.**

1. A card with a winter scene in a circular vignette in a border of holly on a thorny branch, with a verse below by S K Cowan. 11.8 cm x 15.6 cm.

2. An embossed card, a village in winter with a Christmas verse below in a border of holly, mistletoe and Christmas roses. 9.7 cm x 9.7 cm.

3. Three cards, winter scenes with timbered cottages, set in a silver border

with rose hips, one dated 1886 by the sender. 10.6 cm x 14.2 cm.

4. Two cards, a coastal scene with holly and a timbered house with peacock feathers. 11.6 cm x 9.2 cm.

5. Four miscellaneous cards, various scenes bordered by holly, mistletoe, and oak leaves, one dated 1886 by the sender. Sizes up to 10.2 cm x 13 cm.

6. Four cards, one design of a water mill by a river bridge. Two cards show the scene in winter, with a holly spray and a quotation from Tennyson; the others show it in summer, with dog roses and a quotation from Shakespeare. One was dated 1885 by the sender and two have black borders. 9.5 cm x 13.2 cm, 10 cm x 15.7 cm.

7. Three cards, one a birthday card with three pictures of Bolton Abbey and neighbourhood, wreathed in ivy, with a quotation from Longfellow. The other two have churches, Stoke Poges in a mistletoe border, and Bray in a border of ivy. 10.1 cm x 14.8 cm, 12.5 cm x 9.2 cm.

8. Four cards from two sets, winter scenes in vignettes with holly, mistletoe, or autumn leaves. 9 cm x 13 cm, 9.9 cm x 13.9 cm.

9. Two cards, winter scenes in vignettes, one with holly, the other with ivy. 11.2 cm x 15.2 cm, 10.6 cm x 14.5 cm.

10. One card, people going to evening church, in a circular vignette with holly and fir in a gilt border. 15 cm x 15 cm.

11. Four cards, winter scenes bordered by mistletoe or a branch. Two have verses by Eden Hooper, and one has a poem by Moore on reverse. Sizes up to 13.5 cm x 9.5 cm.

12. Two cards, a lake in winter with bare trees, holly sprays below, and a birthday verse. 10.2 cm x 14.5 cm.

13. Four embossed cards, summer and winter scenes in rectangular vignettes bordered by various leaves, fruit, and flowers. 10.2 cm x 14.2 cm.

14. Three cards, two designs of winter scenes with holly or ivy. The third card is a folder on blue paper with gilt decoration and a verse by A A Proctor, with the holly card mounted within. 6 cm x 9.4 cm, 8.2 cm x 12 cm closed.

15. A folder card imitating an open book in trompe l'oeil style. The cover has winter pictures in brown on blue, with more pictures and a Christmas verse with holly decoration inside. 11.7 cm x 13.3 cm closed.

16. Five miscellaneous cards, winter scenes with holly, ivy, or mistletoe. 6.6 cm x 8.7 cm up to 14 cm x 10.4 cm.

17. A set of four cards, winter scenes, three in mountain country, in circular vignettes bordered by holly, ivy or spring flowers. 11.6 cm x 11.6 cm.

18. Two cards, rivers in spring with church or castle and ferns in a grey border. They have poems on reverse and one was dated 1883 by the sender. 10.4 cm x 15 cm.

19. Two cards, winter scenes in rectangular vignettes, one with autumn leaves in a cream coloured border, the other with ivy on a gilt border, dated 1882 and 1883 by the senders. 11 cm x 15.3 cm, 11 cm x 15.6 cm.

20. Three miscellaneous cards, winter scenes in vignettes bordered by ivy or blackberry. Sizes up to 8 cm x 12.2 cm.

21. Four cards (two birthday) two designs with winter scenes bordered by branches, and verses by Frances Ridley Havergal below, all in silver borders. 9 cm x 12.3 cm.

22. Five cards. A set of four has winter scenes in oval vignettes bordered by thistles, berries, and grasses. The fifth card is a larger gilt-edged version of one design. 11.1 cm x 8 cm, 15.7 cm x 11.1 cm.

23. Two cards, the cromlech Kit's Coty, and a church, both with ivy. 10.5 cm x 13.4 cm, 13.3 cm x 10.8 cm.

24. Four frosted cards with country scenes in winter. Two are in palette shaped vignettes set in a rustic frame; the others have borders of branches with ivy. 9.4 cm x 13 cm, 10 cm x 13.5 cm.

25. Three cards, winter scenes in leaf-shaped vignettes, one on a silver background, another with a poem on reverse. Sizes up to 12 cm x 9.1 cm.

26. Two cards printed in sepia, country scenes in borders of oak leaves or ivy, some embossed with silver. They have Christmas poems by Charlotte Murray. 14 cm x 11 cm.

27. Two cards, winter scenes with a church and trees in vignettes wreathed in ivy. 13.5 cm x 10.2 cm, 10.6 cm x 13.8 cm.

28. Four cards, scenes in small vignettes with various leaves. Two have greetings on a silver panel. Sizes up to 12 cm x 9 cm.

29. Two cards with serrated edges, King's College Chapel, Cambridge, and St. Paul's Cathedral, in arched vignettes with holly or ivy above, one signed W H S T. 11.8 cm x 8.7 cm.

30. Five cards, c1890, winter scenes in vignettes with holly, mistletoe, or ferns. Sizes up to 13.3 cm x 10 cm.

31. Three cards, two designs of trees and a lake in winter, with a pink or blue branch with leaves in a gilt border. Two have quotations from Shelley. c1885. 7.5 cm x 11.5 cm.

32. Two cards, cottages in woodland in rectangular vignettes in gilt borders with birds on branches, c1885. 8.8 cm x 12.9 cm.

33. A card with a farmhouse in a vignette resembling torn paper, in a shaded border with birds and a tree bough. c1890. 10.9 cm x 14.9 cm.

34. Four cards, various scenes in vignettes, late 1880's. Two have silver borders with ivy or reeds, two have blue borders with branches or leaves. 10.3 cm x 10.3 cm, 8 cm x 11.7 cm.

## VOLUME 213: SCENES IN VIGNETTES, AND PHOTOGRAPHS

**Some vignettes are on a plain background, others are in patterned borders, a few with leaf decoration. A few cards are marked but the publishers have not been traced.**

*Numbers 1-17 were issued in the later 1880's.*

1. Three cards showing springtime in the country with water mill, river, cottages and cattle, in oval vignettes, with verses below from Goldsmith, Epes Sargent, and a text from the Psalms. 10 cm x 12.5 cm.

2. Two cards, oval vignettes, one with a village scene, the other a castle on a hill, this with a verse by S K Cowan. 15.7 cm x 11.2 cm, 16 cm x 12.4 cm.

3. Two cards, a river in moonlight with Christmas poem below, and a bridge over a stream. 11.4 cm x 14.6 cm, 14.6 cm x 10.1 cm.

4. Two cards, country scenes with church or cottage, and Christmas poems below by M E Ropes. 11 cm x 15.3 cm.

5. Two cards, a field in winter, a cottage by a stream in moonlight, both in decorative borders. 11.2 cm x 14.4 cm, 9.6 cm x 15.3 cm.

6. Three cards, country scenes with hills or river in circular vignettes in patterned borders. The two larger cards have silver borders, and poems on reverse. 11 cm x 11 cm, 9.3 cm x 9.3 cm.

7. Two cards. One has a silver border and country scenes in four moonshaped vignettes on a pink background, the other has a view of lake and mountains in a circular vignette on blue ground with a silver patterned border, dated 1887, 1886 by the senders. 10.2 cm x 10.2 cm, 12.8 cm x 10.5 cm.

8. Three cards, winter scenes in circular vignettes on plain background, one with a verse by S K Cowan. Sizes up to 11.4 cm x 11.4 cm.

9. Three miscellaneous cards, winter scenes of forest, moonlit lake, and waterfall, the first with a verse by G N L on reverse. Sizes up to 10 cm x 13 cm.

10. Four miscellaneous cards, springtime views with trees in various shaped vignettes. Sizes up to 13.1 cm x 10.7 cm.

11. Two unusual cards, one design of a country sunset in a fan shaped vignette, with two different poems on reverse by Charlotte Murray. 8.2 cm x 16.3 cm.

12. Four cards, two gilt-bordered with country sunset scenes in semi-circular vignettes, and two others with a winter and a summer scene in rectangular vignettes. Sizes up to 11.6 cm x 9.2 cm.

13. Six cards, winter scenes in oval vignettes on plain backgrounds. Sizes up to 9 cm x 11 cm.

14. Five cards. Two have summer country views on fan-shaped vignettes with verses by Frances Ridley Havergal below. The other three have winter scenes with leaf-patterned borders. 7.5 cm x 7.5 cm up to 13.7 cm x 8.4 cm.

15. Two cards showing rivers with trees and a sluice gate. 10.9 cm x 14 cm.

16. Four miscellaneous cards, showing meadows, a river, a church in winter and a moonlit windmill, the latter with a poem below signed A H B. 7.1 cm x 10.5 cm up to 10.7 cm x 14.5 cm.

17. A card with trees on a snow-covered hillside in a horseshoe vignette, dated 1888 by the sender. 13.6 cm x 16.6 cm.

*Numbers 18-25 were published c1890.*

18. Three cards. Two have the same design of a river in moonlight with birds above, and a verse below for Christmas or New Year. The third has a cottage by a river in a palette, with gilt embossed brushes through the hole. 9.9 cm x 9.9 cm, 12.8 cm x 10 cm.

19. Two embossed cards, a church printed in sepia with a border of gilded bells, and a pastoral scene with cattle by a river in a decorated border. 13.5 cm x 10.8 cm, 15 cm x 11 cm.

20. Two cards, a church in snow, and a castle in moonlight, both with floral patterned borders. 12.8 cm x 9.5 cm, 15.8 cm x 11.2 cm.

21. Four miscellaneous cards, winter scenes in vignettes shaped like a shield, a star, a square or rectangle, one with gilt greeting, two with gilt decoration, the fourth with silver-patterned background. Sizes up to 12.6 cm x 9.8 cm.

22. Six miscellaneous cards, various scenes in vignettes on embossed background, one with gilt decoration. Sizes up to 8.8 cm x 11.8 cm.

23. Two cards, country scenes with a church spire in the same patterned border, one gilt, one silver. 11.2 cm x 9.5 cm, 9.9 cm x 11.4 cm.

24. Two birthday cards, scenes in open fans on a blue background, one with a poem by H M Burnside dated 1891 by the sender. 14 cm x 10.8 cm, 15 cm x 10.5 cm.

25. Two cards, country scenes in gilt-edged fan-shaped vignettes. 8 cm x 11.8 cm, 13.5 cm x 10.1 cm.

*Numbers 26-33 have attached photographic prints published about 1890.*

26. Two birthday cards. One has a small faded photograph of a country lane, and the music of Auld Lang Syne printed in gold on brown; the other is hand-coloured and shows a village street through a lych gate. 14.5 cm x 10.4 cm, 16.5 cm x 10.5 cm.

27. Two cards, one Patterdale Church, Cumbria, with a verse by S C Hall below. The other is titled "The Brook" and signed Harvey Barton, who might be either publisher or photographer, and has the familiar poem by Tennyson and an old Carol printed in gold on yellow ground. 10.8 cm x 16.3 cm, 16.4 cm x 11 cm.

28. Four cards, various pictures of country scenes or houses, one with black border. 11.3 cm x 7.5 cm up to 14.2 cm x 10.3 cm.

29. A birthday card, the entrance to Bolton Woods, with verse below signed S A W. 10.9 cm x 16.3 cm.

30. A four-page folder birthday card, with a picture of trees, "The Three Sisters, near Rydal Mount, Westmorland", "photographed from nature by Payne Jennings." This is mounted on pale blue ground, with a blue and gold border pattern and cover design. 11.9 cm x 15.9 cm.

31. Two four-page folders, by Payne Jennings, with pink or blue covers, and pictures of Ullswater or Dublin Bay. The greeting verses are printed in red. 11.4 cm x 9.3 cm.

32. Two four-page folders, pale blue with gilt patterned borders and bird and holly designs on the covers, with pictures of a wood or a stormy sea. 13 cm x 10.8 cm.

33. Two four-page folders, one Mentmore Towers dated 1893, the other a seaside town marked F F & Co. 11.1 cm x 9 cm, 12 cm x 7.8 cm.

## VOLUME 214: SCENES, LARGE CARDS WITH FLOWER DECORATIONS

**The scenes are usually in vignettes with backgrounds embellished by flowers, not always suited to the picture's theme. They were published from 1879 to the late 1880's.**

1. A gilt-edged card dated 1879 by the sender, with a romantic vista of a river with castles on the hillsides. A bunch of cornflowers and anemones decorates the white panel with Christmas greeting. 9.5 cm x 16.1 cm.

2. A gilt-edged card with a mediaeval town by a river in the background and heathers, ferns and a butterfly in a gilt-edged border. (Another of this set is in volume 196, no.24 with a French advertisement on reverse.) 12 cm x 17.5 cm.

3. A gilt-edged card with a picture of the Swallow Falls, Bettws-y-Coed, in an oval vignette, on a background scene with Welsh figures and flowers. There is a poem "Welsh Greeting" signed L N on the back. 12 cm x 16 cm.

4. Two cards, lake scenes with waterlilies and bulrushes, and a 24-line poem on reverse. 10.7 cm x 16.5 cm.

5. Two cards, an autumn scene in a vignette on a background of blackberries and autumn leaves and Christmas greeting, and a spring scene with background of spring flowers and New Year greeting. The same poem by Fanny Rochat is on both backs. 10 cm x 13.5 cm.

6. Two cards, castle towers in daytime and moonlight each with a colourful spray of

red and white flowers, and a poem by A M B on the reverse. 9.5 cm x 14 cm.

7. Two cards, rectangular vignettes, one showing harvesters with cornflowers behind, the other a small girl picking primroses in a wood, with ivy and primroses behind. 11.6 cm x 15.8 cm.

8. Two cards, winter scenes in mountain country, in a grey border with pink and white flowers. One has a German greeting, the other has a poem by A Norton on reverse. 11.1 cm x 15.8 cm.

9. A card with an autumnal country scene in an oval vignette on a background with blackberries, signed with a monogram E S or S E (untraced). There is a Christmas poem on the back. 12.2 cm x 17 cm.

10. Two cards with views of Florence, set in garlands of flowers and grasses, marked Ruby Series. 10.8 cm x 14.6 cm.

11. Two cards, winter scenes in rectangular vignettes with sprays of ivy and chrysanthemums. 9.9 cm x 14.4 cm, 11.2 cm x 15.8 cm.

12. A card with a monochrome design of trees and a waterfall, and red primulas below. 10.8 cm x 15.7 cm.

13. Two cards, scenes in rectangular vignettes printed in blue, one of "Palmyras in the Godavery" with trees and a tiger, the other trees and mountains with a narcissus in the background. 11.9 cm x 16 cm, 12 cm x 15.4 cm.

14. Two cards, each with a ruined archway and flowers below, one set in a silver border with a text in red. 10.1 cm x 14.2 cm, 10.9 cm x 15.8 cm.

*Numbers 15-18 have a monogram BB or perhaps ORB, probably the artist. Though it has been attributed sometimes to Birn Bros, it is unusual for publishers to sign in this way. More cards with this signature can be seen in Section 19, Volume 220.*

15. Four cards, three designs of winter scenes of castle or farm, in rectangular vignettes with spring flowers, holly, and catkins at the side. One is marked Religious Tract Society, but probably not made by them. All have a text and a poem on reverse. 9.7 cm x 14 cm.

16. A large card, a country house in winter snow, with fir and snowdrops in the grey border. There is a poem by Sabina on reverse and a monochrome design of a ship and a waterfall. 13 cm x 19.2 cm.

17. A similar card with a forest scene and a spray of roses, and a picture of a girl with flowers on reverse. 13.8 cm x 19.5 cm.

18. Three cards, one a farmhouse with daisies and forget-me-nots, and two with

lakes in moonlight, one with irises, the other with harebells, this with Easter greeting. 15.5 cm x 11 cm, 9.7 cm x 14 cm.

19. A card with a cottage and trees, and a border of apple blossom. This is signed by a monogram BM or MB, also seen on a number of cards from Raphael Tuck in volume 85. 14 cm x 19.5 cm.

20. Two cards, a moonlit lake with a daisy chain border, and a farm in a diamond vignette with forget-me-nots. 9.8 cm x 13.6 cm, 12.1 cm x 13 cm.

21. Three miscellaneous cards, villagers gathering wood, harvesters in a border of cornflowers and barley, and an easel with a picture of two girls in a woodland scene with violets and catkins. 8.4 cm x 13 cm, 9.7 cm x 13.9 cm, 10.5 cm x 16.2 cm.

22. Two cards, a village scene in a rectangular vignette with cornflowers, and a landscape in a triangular vignette bordered by thorny branches. 11.3 cm x 15.2 cm, 12 cm x 15 cm.

23. Two cards, one dated 1883 with a mountain vista in a frame of convolvulus with birds. The other has what appears to be a museum or exhibition hall, perhaps the 1886 Colonial and Indian exhibition, in a border of orchids. 12 cm x 14.5 cm, 11.7 cm x 15.2 cm.

24. Two cards, illustrations to the classics in circular vignettes, Bleak House, and The Mill on the Floss, with roses and forget-me-nots in the background and verses below signed G A. 10.9 cm x 14.5 cm.

25. Two cards. One has a monochrome view of a lake and countryside in a large letter X, forming the first letter of the greeting with "mas" below. The other has a seascape with a floral bouquet behind. 11.7 cm x 15.5 cm, 10.5 cm x 14.5 cm.

26. Two cards, scenes in small vignettes, one with a background of berries and autumn leaves, the other with roses. 11.3 cm x 15.5 cm, 9.7 cm x 15 cm.

27. Two cards, moonlight scenes in small vignettes bordered with flowers, one dated 1886 by the sender with a poem by Frances Ridley Havergal. 11.1 cm x 17 cm, 15.5 cm x 9.4 cm.

28. A card with two vignettes, a forest glade and a lake with waterlilies, on a gilt background. 10.8 cm x 16.5 cm.

29. Two cards, a snow covered wall and gate behind a bunch of Christmas roses and snowdrops with a verse by C D on reverse, and a moonlit lake in an oval vignette with roses. 13 cm x 10 cm, 14.5 cm x 9.6 cm.

30. Three cards, two winter scenes in vignettes with flowers. The third card is a

Biblical scene in a diamond vignette, with a Christmas poem by Frances Ridley Havergal. (The complete set of four is in volume 137 no.4, with texts). Sizes up to 11.8 cm x 15.2 cm.

31. Two cards, a seaside view with anemones, and a winter scene with a church and Christmas roses and ivy. 13.9 cm x 10.6 cm, 15 cm x 12 cm.

32. Two cards on thick paper, a birthday card with a country scene on a silver disc and pink flowers, and a winter scene with a snow-covered road and a quotation from Southey, dated 1886, 1887 by the senders. 12.5 cm x 15.7 cm, 16.5 cm x 11.5 cm.

33. Two cards, a cottage in a vignette with a tennis racquet and dog roses and a verse by S K Cowan, and another with two crossed fans, one with deer, one with birds. 11.6 cm x 15.3 cm, 11.5 cm x 15.4 cm.

## VOLUME 215:
## SCENES IN VIGNETTES WITH FLOWERS AND FOLIAGE

**The publishers and artists of these cards, dated from 1879 to about 1890, have not been traced. They resemble those in volume 214 but are smaller in size. A few miscellaneous cards are included.**

1/2. Seven cards, four designs with various scenes and flowers or holly, and greetings with illuminated capital letter in panels signed Da, RHS, H, EER. One card on a decorative mount was dated 1879 by the sender. 7.6 cm x 11.6 cm, 7.6 cm x 13 cm, 11.5 cm x 15.3 cm.

*Numbers 3-20 were published c1880-1885.*

3. Two cards, an open book with a lake scene and flowers on a gilt background, and a country scene in a gilt frame with flowers and a Christmas verse signed TEM. 14.3 cm x 8.5 cm, 17.6 cm x 8.7 cm.

4. A set of four embossed cards in quodlibet style, each with four Swiss views and Alpine flowers. 13.5 cm x 9 cm.

5. Three cards, two with trees in a vignette in a decorative blue border with pink flowers, the third a birthday card with a country scene in an oval vignette with a border of flowers. 8 cm x 14.4 cm, 10 cm x 15.1 cm.

6. Three cards, two designs of lake and waterfall in circular vignettes bordered by forget-me-nots or grasses. One card is on a gilt-patterned mount, and they have three different poems, two by Burns, one by Grahame. 6.9 cm x 13.5 cm, 9 cm x 15.8 cm.

7. Three cards. One has a sea and mountain view in a border of passion flowers with a verse signed A H B, another

is a birthday card with a vignette over a cross with flowers and a verse by H M Burnside, the third has a country scene in a star-shaped vignette with pink flowers and a New Year greeting signed J P. 12.5 cm x 8.3 cm, 10 cm x 10 cm.

8. Two cards, winter scenes in oval vignettes in floral patterned borders. 9.2 cm x 12.8 cm.

9. Three cards, country scenes in rectangular vignettes with spring flowers. Two have a design with insects and japonica on reverse. 8 cm x 12 cm.

10. Two cards, winter scenes in rectangular vignettes, with flowers, fruit, or leaves in a grey border. 13.4 cm x 8 cm.

11. Three cards, two designs, lake scenes in oval vignettes with daisies or cornflowers. One is on a mount with patterned border, which has a gilded design of a stork in Japanese style on reverse. 8 cm x 11.6 cm, 10.5 cm x 14.7 cm.

12. Two cards, country scenes in oval vignettes set in wreaths of spring flowers, with poems by Thring on reverse. 8.4 cm x 12.2 cm.

13/15. Twelve cards, each with a country or mountain scene in a vignette with flowers or leaves. 7.6 cm x 10.7 cm up to 7.8 cm x 12.2 cm.

16. A folding card with scenes in circular vignettes and patterned borders in shades of blue, brown, and green. 16.1 cm x 12.9 cm.

17. A folding card with a scene in a circular vignette and a Christmas verse by Frances Ridley Havergal inside and elaborate illuminated designs with daisies and butterflies on the outside. 12 cm x 12 cm closed.

18. A card with triangular flaps each with a scene in a small circular vignette folding over a lake scene and pansies, with a holly design and a greeting on the cover. 12.4 cm x 9.3 cm closed.

19. An unusual three-fold card with black cover, opening to show a paint box with a greeting and a country scene. 7.8 cm x 11.1 cm closed.

*Numbers 20-36 were published c1885-1890.*

20. Three cards, moonlight scenes in rectangular vignettes with daisies, poppies, or pansies on the cream-coloured background. 8.8 cm x 8.8 cm.

21. Four cards (one birthday), each with a scene in a small vignette bordered by branches with flowers or leaves. Two have verses by Frances Ridley Havergal, and one has a verse by Moore. 8.5 cm x 10 cm up to 9.2 cm x 13 cm.

22. Three cards with scenes in vignettes bordered by flowers. One has a verse by Eliza Cook, another has a further scene in a vignette with leaves on reverse dated 1887 by the sender, the third was dated 1886 by the sender. Sizes up to 10 cm x 13 cm.

23. Three cards, scenes in vignettes with white flowers. Two have verses signed H S B. 11.3 cm x 13.2 cm, 9.9 cm x 12.9 cm.

24. Two cards, lake views in triangular vignettes with spring flowers and greeting verse. 10 cm x 14 cm.

25. Three cards, various scenes in gilt-edged vignettes with white flowers. Sizes up to 13.7 cm x 11.2 cm.

26. Two cards, one with pink convolvulus reflected in a lake, the other a moonlit sea with pink roses and a poem by C H Spurgeon. 14 cm x 11 cm, 14 cm x 10.7 cm.

27. Two cards, one design of a sunset over a lake and mountains, with heather and narcissus. There are two different poems by Fanny Rochat on reverse. 14 cm x 10.4 cm.

28. Three miscellaneous cards, various country scenes in vignettes, one with wisteria on a gold border and a poem by Eden Hooper on reverse, another with a poem by S K Cowan on reverse, the third with strawberries on a metallic border. Sizes up to 10.5 cm x 12.7 cm.

29. Five miscellaneous cards with various scenes in vignettes, three with flowers, one with birds. Sizes up to 12 cm x 8.3 cm.

30. Two gilt-edged cards with well-drawn winter scenes, and greeting verses in panels. 13.9 cm x 10.6 cm.

31. Three miscellaneous cards, the Priory at Dover, roofs and a church tower, and a birthday card with a Gothic arch and a verse by Eden Hooper on reverse. Sizes up to 12 cm x 15.3 cm.

32. Two cards, lighted churches in moonlight, with orange borders. 8.8 cm x 8.8 cm.

33. Two cards from pen and ink sketches, Impington Hall Cambridge, and a forest with a blasted oak and a poem by L Novra on reverse. 11.5 cm x 8.8 cm, 14 cm x 14 cm.

34. A card with a country scene in an oval vignette covered by net, in a floral border. 8.3 cm x 12.3 cm.

35/36. Three cards printed on thick blue paper, showing churches in the winter night, one dated 1889 by the sender. Sizes up to 11.6 cm x 15.5 cm.

## VOLUME 216:
## SCENES, SOME IN VIGNETTES WITH FLOWERS AND FOLIAGE, AND A NUMBER OF SMALL CARDS

*Numbers 1-24 have scenes in vignettes with flower and foliage decoration, published c1885-1890.*

1. Four cards, two blue-bordered with winter scenes and berries, and two others with a winter and a lake scene with flowers and leaves.
Sizes up to 10.1 cm x 13.5 cm.

2. Two cards, scenes in small vignettes on silver background with white flowers.
13.9 cm x 9.6 cm, 14.3 cm x 9.9 cm.

3/4/5. Twelve miscellaneous cards, spring or winter scenes in various shaped vignettes with spring flowers or roses.
Sizes up to 10.4 cm x 13.9 cm.

6. Two cards, one frosted with a church in winter and autumn leaves and berries, another a winter mountain scene with pink erica. 13.3 cm x 10.7 cm, 14.7 cm x 8.8 cm.

7. Four cards, three with silver borders, various scenes with spring flowers.
Sizes up to 9.5 cm x 13.5 cm.

8/9. Seven cards, country scenes with spring flowers.
Sizes up to 12.7 cm x 9.7 cm.

10. Three cards, lake or sea views with spring flowers. One card has a misprint "wisches" for "wishes", perhaps indicating printing in Germany. 13.9 cm x 10.2 cm.

11. Two cards, a mountain view in a gilt horseshoe with lilies or roses, and a winter scene with daisies.
10.6 cm x 14 cm, 14.6 cm x 10.5 cm.

12. Two birthday cards, a lake with daisies and a verse by Frances Ridley Havergal, and a waterfall with celandines, dated 1888 by the sender.
10.7 cm x 13.6 cm, 10.5 cm x 14 cm.

13. Two cards, each with a country scene with a spray of roses above, and verses by Charlotte Murray and Mrs Hemans.
10.8 cm x 14.3 cm.

14. Two cards, a sea view and a canal with a windmill, each framed in white roses, with greeting verse below.
11.1 cm x 15.7 cm, 10.3 cm x 14.5 cm.

15. Two cards, one with two scenes in vignettes and a flower spray, the other a river bridge in moonlight framed in a silver crescent, this with a verse by the Rev. J R Macduff, DD, dated 1890 by the sender.
11.7 cm x 14.4 cm, 11.9 cm x 14.4 cm.

16. Two cards, country scenes on shaded backgrounds, framed in flowers or grasses, with verses by S K Cowan on reverse.
11.5 cm x 15 cm.

17. Two cards, both with a large spray of roses on a background of a lake and country view. 12.5 cm x 16.8 cm.

18. Two cards, lakeside views printed in blue in oval vignettes, with large sprays of roses and spring flowers. 15 cm x 12 cm.

19. Three cards, each with two rectangular vignettes, one with spring flowers, the other with a country scene, placed crosswise. One was dated 1892 by the sender. 12.1 cm x 12.3 cm.

20. Two cards, one with a view of Bournemouth and a blackberry spray, and a verse by Frances Ridley Havergal on reverse, the other a river scene with a large yellow rose above. 10.4 cm x 15.5 cm, 12.4 cm x 14.6 cm.

21. Six cards, various scenes with spring flowers, two with verses signed JPT, A A Proctor.
7.5 cm x 9.5 cm up to 13.1 cm x 10.3 cm.

22. Five cards, scenes in vignettes with roses.
9.2 cm x 6.3 cm up to 10.2 cm x 12.7 cm.

23/24. Ten cards, scenes in various shaped vignettes with spring flowers and leaves, or roses.
7.1 cm x 10.5 cm up to 10 cm x 12.9 cm.

*The following small cards have scenes, a few in vignettes with flowers, and were published in the 1880's except for no.25.*

25. Four small cards, scenes with the appearance of lithographs, dated 1877 by the senders. 6.1 cm x 10.1 cm.

26. Seven cards from four sets, winter or summer scenes, one signed Edwin A Penley. Sizes up to 9.2 cm x 6.6 cm.

27. Six miscellaneous bordered cards, winter scenes from different sets.
12.1 cm x 8.1 cm.

28. Nine cards from five sets, winter scenes.
6.7 cm x 4.8 cm 7 up to 9.4 cm x 7.3 cm.

29. Nine miscellaneous cards, winter scenes (three in vignettes).
6.6 cm x 6.6 cm up to 7.5 cm x 10 cm.

30. Six miscellaneous bordered cards, including four winter scenes with churches, a mountain view, and one with tropical vegetation.
Sizes up to 11.1 cm x 8.3 cm.

31. Seven miscellaneous bordered cards, winter scenes with houses and churches or woodland.
4.7 cm x 6.5 cm up to 7.3 cm x 10.2 cm.

32. Six miscellaneous cards, one gilt-edged with a coastal panorama, one with a lake, and four winter scenes.
Sizes up to 11.4 cm x 7.5 cm.

33. Seven miscellaneous cards, various scenes including windmills and a waterfall, three in vignettes with flowers.
5.2 cm x 9.9 cm up to 6.7 cm x 9.9 cm.

**215.4**

A HAPPY SEASON!

Merrily, merrily, to and fro,
Under the holly and mistletoe,
Tripping it lightly, we come and go,
While music sounds, and our spirits flow,
Our hearts a-tune and our cheeks aglow,
With mirth which CHRISTMAS alone can show.
Dear, dear old CHRISTMAS! come ever so!

62.25

Wishing you
A Happy New Year!

Merry Christmas!

62.13

CHRISTMAS comes! While you are sleeping,
In the holy Angels' keeping,
He around your bed is creeping,
And within the curtains peeping,
Leaving for all good girls and boys
Such merry games, and pretty toys.

A MERRY CHRISTMAS!

"Come what come may,
Time and the hour runs through
the roughest day."

1878

**56.1**

**158.10**

**158.10**

May you have a very happy NEW YEAR

A JOYOUS
CHRISTMAS
AND
A HAPPY NEW YEAR.

**56.1**

Oh! may this Happy Christmas, be
A time replete with joy for thee.

**152.18**

May peace and love and hope and glee,
Hang radiant on thy Christmas-tree.

**152.19**

"A PENNY A BUNCH."

*With my best wishes for the coming year.*

107.3

WISHING YOU A BRIGHT AND HAPPY CHRISTMAS.

152.7

MY LOVE I SEND THEE WITH MY CHRISTMAS GREETING.

56.25

RING OUT THE OLD YEAR RING IN THE NEW
WITH BLOSSOMS AND GARLANDS OF GLADNESS FOR YOU!

152.9

"SPARE A COPPER SIR."

WISHING YOU A HAPPY CHRISTMAS.

107.3

A CHRISTMAS GREETING WITH LOVE.

152.7

Hark ! the waits, with cheerful rhyme,
Welcome in bright Christmas time.

When the old lady who sits high and dry,
Picks the white feathers, Christmas is nigh.

The kiss of sweet reluctance now,
Is heard beneath thy mystic bough,
Oh, Mistletoe.

Peace and Plenty, Love and Mirth,
To old and young, throughout the earth.

Music hath charms, and so have I: and so
A doubly-charming Christmas may you know!

Samuel K: Cowan M.A.

"A thing of beauty is a joy for ever":
So-gaze on me, and be unhappy-never!

Samuel K: Cowan M.A.

171.5

May the New Year sparkle with delight and happiness for you.

Dat's de way to wish you
de
Season's Compliments

74.1

**Christmas Fun**

THE BEST WISHES OF THE SEASON.

55.33

THE COMPLIMENTS OF THE SEASON.

55.33

WISHING YOU A merry CHRISTMAS

With best wishes of a happy NEW YEAR

W.F. YEAMES. 1881.

W.F. YEAMES. 1881.

68.1

Cards designed by WS Coleman and WF Yeames

A happy
Christ-
mas.

With best
Christmas wishes.

A New Year laden        with Happiness.

A happy Christmas
to you.

Elegance from Raphael Tuck

117.3 &middot;WITH&middot;BEST&middot;WISHES&middot;FOR&middot;THE&middot;NEW&middot;YEAR&middot; &middot;With best wishes for a Happy Christmas&middot;

MAY CHRISTMAS BE BRIGHT AND HAPPY. NEW YEAR GREETING — JOY, PEACE, AND LOVE.

00.14

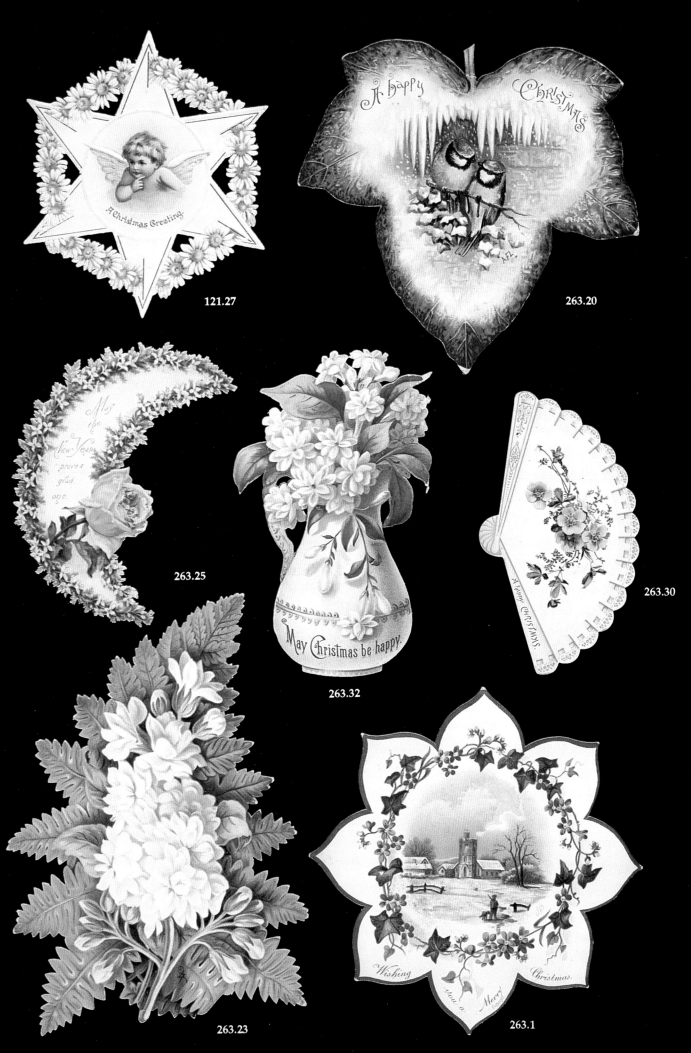

121.27

263.20

263.25

263.30

263.32

263.23

263.1

Shapes , c1890

TAKE FRIENDSHIP'S TOLL—A HEARTY CHRISTMAS GREETING.

**169.11**

MAY YOU A BRIGHT NEW YEAR ENJOY.

**169.4**

A MERRY CHRISTMAS AND A HAPPY YEAR.

Wishing you a very happy Christmas.

**169.26**

**174.13**

"GOING TO COVER"—Get forrard Rambler! Get forrard !!

MAY THIS GLAD SEASON BRING THEE SWEET CONTENT.

**169.15**

WISHING YOU MANY HAPPY RETURNS.

**169.3**

Here's to wish you good speed and the HIGHEST of GEAR.

R. Warren Vernon

93.12

RATHER FOXEY this Season eh!

93.11

I can't help it don't you know!

THE LADY KILLER

93.11

A LIVING PICTURE.

YVETTE GUILBERT

Linger Longer Loo.

Jolly Christmas Greetings

73.26

17th LANCERS.

S'Death or Glory!

A merry Christmas to you my Boy.

73.27

**Topical Humour from Raphael Tuck, 1890's**

New Year Greetings.

MARDALE HEAD
WESTMORLAND

RAPHAEL TUCK & SONS.    COPYRIGHT.

80.31

A Thames Flood. Eton. Evening.    Alb Bowers.

With the Compliments of the Season.

207.16

L.B.

Christmas greeting.
wishing · you · every · happiness.

205.16

The Castle Newcastle on Tyne.    C.Nostas.

81.9

Magdalen College
from
St John Baptist Quad.

Wishing
you
a very happy New Year.

206.3

265.5

260.11

260.11

262.12

261.21

259.12

Folding and cut-out cards 1890's

260.26

260.26

My Deputation – a
United Band – bring
with them Hearty Greetings
and Good Wishes.

178.4

**Song and Dance**

91.20

262.3

260.28

91.20

Cut-out cards for children

NIAGARA IN WINTER

THE HORSE SHOE FALL

Wishing
YOU
A VERY
Happy Christmas.

Fringed and tinselled two-sided card with pictures of Niagara Falls published by S Hildesheimer

# FLOWERS, FRUIT, AND FOLIAGE

*Section*
*19*

This very large section includes Christmas evergreens along with floral subjects, and fruits and berries. There are a few cards from the 1870's and the early 1890's but the majority here are from the 1880's. The earlier cards used flowers as models for formal designs and patterns, but these gave way in the 1880's to straightforward portraits, though an occasional stylised design, sometimes in Japanese form, appeared. As before in the subject sections those publishers not dealt with more fully in sections 1-10 are grouped together in volumes, though a few cards from known publishers are included in later volumes for comparison with the large number of unmarked cards. Floral subjects have not yet been discussed in great detail in Christmas card literature, perhaps because their use appears inappropriate, but they were certainly very popular in Victorian times, not only for birthday and valentine cards but also for Christmas, New Year, and Easter, the same design being used for several purposes with a suitable variation of sentiment. The sentiment, indeed, often justified the picture.

"Spring beauties, autumn glories, we have seen you go
Now old Christmas hides the blossoms with a robe of snow."

"May heartsease ever with you go
And make your whole life bright."

"Sweet flowers to winter homes may bring
A grateful sense of joyful spring."

These and many other similar verses as well as quotations from the poets were sometimes incorporated in the design and occasionally appeared on the reverse.

There have been considerable problems in sorting and filing this section. After allowing for publishers, holly and mistletoe, with three volumes for the rose, the most popular flower, arrangement has been made with consideration for date and style, but inevitably some cards could be dealt with in several ways. While space does not allow for all the flowers depicted to be named, enough have been identified to give some idea of the vast range of subjects, though an analysis of the ferns and leaves has not been attempted - maidenhair fern was most commonly used. Familiar names are generally given though some species are named where this appears more suitable. Illustration generally appears to be scientifically accurate, but some artistic licence has crept in here and there.

## VOLUME 217
## CARDS PUBLISHED BY EYRE AND SPOTTISWOODE WITH FLOWERS, FRUIT, AND FOLIAGE

The two volumes of cards from this publisher continue the high quality of design and workmanship shown in previous subject sections. Most of them are numbered and marked with trade mark, full name, or initials. One numbered 206 was dated 1879 by the sender, another numbered 438 was dated 1882, which gives some guidance for the time of publication, and all the cards in this volume were probably issued by 1885.

1. Seven cards, one with holly and mistletoe on a black background, the others with various flowers on gilt and illuminated backgrounds, nos.113, 114, 123, 333 (this dated 1883 by the sender). 11.6 cm x 7.2 cm up 7.5 cm x 13.5cm.

2. Four cards with decorative initial letters to verses signed E H, A T, J L E Freeman, S C Hall. One large card, no. 206, with a background of spring flowers and berries, was dated 1879 by the sender; the three others, no. 90, have spring flowers and holly beneath the gilded initial letter. 20 cm x 12.5cm, 9.6 cm x 6.1 cm.

3. Three cards, with illuminated initial letter to text or verse and a bouquet of spring flowers, no.102 C. 8 cm x 20 cm.

4. Two similar cards, each with a verse by Milton or Cowper accompanied by a picture of the poet set in to the illuminated initial letter. These are marked "Entered at Stationers' Hall", but the registration has not been traced. 8 cm x 20 cm.

5. Five similar smaller cards with quotations from Shakespeare, and his portrait set in to the initial letter. 12 cm x 9.4 cm.

6. Three cards with Christmas verses. Two have spring flowers on a yellow background, no.152, and the third has a patterned illuminated background, no.188. 9 cm x 12.5 cm, 10 cm x 15 cm.

7. A large card showing a blue and white bowl holding the Christmas punch, on an illuminated background with holly and mistletoe, no. 4312. 20 cm x 13.7 cm.

8. Four cards, with trees, ferns, berries and birds in various background scenes. Three are numbered 103, one dated 1878 by the sender. 7.8 cm x 19.8 cm.

9. Three cards, berries, mistletoe, or willow catkins on a pale blue background with a butterfly, one dated 1881 by the sender. No. 216. 8 cm x 14.5 cm.

10. Three cards with spring flowers. One has a greeting in a panel, no. 209; the other two have verses by F E E H or Eden Hooper, no. 258. 14.2 cm x 9 cm, 15.2 cm x 10 cm.

11. Three cards on pale blue background, one with holly, no. 342, and two with spring flowers, no. 223. 10 cm x 12.6 cm.

12. Three gilt-edged cards, two with cydonia or appleblossom, no. 237, the third white peonies, no. 244. 14.7 cm x 9.8 cm, 13.1 cm x 9.8 cm.

13. Four cards, two birthday, two Easter, three designs of pansies, chrysanthemums, or bindweed, all white, in a decorative patterned border. No. 309. 10 cm x 15 cm.

14. Three cards, meadow flowers and butterflies wth blue sky beyond. No. 332. 8.8 cm 16.4 cm.

15. A card with a bird's nest and spring flowers in a semi circular lunette with Gothic style tracery above. No. 210. 17.5 cm x 11.5 cm.

16. Two cards. One has wood anemones with a verse by F E E H, dated 1883 by the sender, no. 472. The other has magnolia and forget-me-nots, no. 303. 11.5 cm x 16 cm, 16.7 cm x 11.5 cm.

17. One card with strawberry and red and white currant fruits framing a Christmas verse by Eden Hooper, no 224. 10.7 cm x 14 cm.

18. Three cards, camellia, hyacinth, anemones, nos. 335, 385, 380, the first dated 1886 by the sender. 14.3 cm x 11.6 cm, 9.3 cm x 15.2 cm, 9.1 cm x 14.2 cm.

19. Two silver-bordered cards, sweet williams, carnations, no. 365. 9.3 cm x 15.5 cm.

20. Two gilt-edged cards, blue and white campanula or bindweed framing seasonal greeting, one dated 1882 by the sender. No. 373. 10 cm x 15 cm.

21. Three cards.
a) An unusual picture of the South American climber, Mandevilla Splendens, no. 374. 13 cm x 105 cm.
b) A plant pot with pink azalea, overturned, no. 425 14.2 cm x 10.8 cm.
c) Pink hawthorn, no. 367.

22. Two cards, thistles or red berries in a gold and silver patterned border, with verses by J W, one dated 1884 by the sender. No. 386. 10.5 cm x 10 cm, 10 cm x 14.7 cm.

23/25 Eight cards, all with leaves or ferns on a pale green background, curious subjects for festive greetings. One also has a pot with a white flower, and two have

shells. Nos. 328, 329, 375, 404, 453. 13 cm x 11 cm up to 16 cm x 12 cm.

26. Three gilt-edged cards, garden flowers on grey background, one with birthday greeting. One was dated 1886 by the sender. No. 401. 11.6 cm x 16.2 cm.

27. Two cards, Guernsey lily with fern, and a tropical yellow flower, unidentified, with bamboo-like stem. Nos. 417, 409. 16.4 cm x 11.2 cm.

28. One card, lungwort and primroses in a grey border, no. 427. 12.7 x 12.7 cm.

29. Two cards, tropical flowers in a blue and white vase or a silver goblet, nos. 428, 430, one dated 1883 by the sender. 10.4 cm x 15 cm.

30. Two cards, narcissi or hawthorn in a blue and yellow patterned border, no. 432. 12.8 cm x 17.9 cm.

31. Two cards (one birthday), dog roses or hawthorn in a woodland setting. One was dated 1882 by the sender and has an inappropriate poem from Scott "Ancient Christmas" telling of the onslaught of the "savage Danish horde". No. 438. 14 cm x11.5 cm.

32. Three cards, two designs of spring flowers in two styles of border, one with birthday greeting. No. 439. 16.4 cm x 10.3 cm,17. 5 cm x 11.5 cm.

33. Two cards. One with pink and gold border is probably the Chilean Bellflower, no. 602. The other, in a green border, is an orchid (odontoglossam Citrosmum) on pale green background, no. 407. 12.2 cm x 17.4 cm, 10 cm x 16 cm.

34. A large card with a butterfly hovering over white pelargonium, no. 637. 15 cm x 19.7 cm.

35. A gilt-edged card in quodlibet style with pictures of various spring flowers, ferns, and corn. No. 639. 16 cm x 12 cm.

36. Two cards with roses, one silver-edged on a blue ground, the other gilt-edged with butterflies. No. 645. 9.8 cm x 15.4 cm, 15.5 cm x 12 cm.

37. Two cards, one with violets and bindweed, the other with sandwort(?) framing a Christmas poem by Eden Hooper. 10.4 cm x 13.5 cm, 13.8 cm x 10.4 cm.

38. Three cards in photographic style, the large one with a verse by F E E H. 10.9 cm x 16.2 cm, 6.5 cm x 10.5 cm.

217.7

## VOLUME 218.
## FLOWERS, FRUIT, FOLIAGE, CARDS PUBLISHED BY EYRE AND SPOTTISWOODE

**Most of these cards are small in size, and were published from the late 1870's to early 1880's.**

1. Five cards, three designs of spring flowers and roses with stones below. No. 95. 9.8 cm x 6 cm.
2. Four cards, roses and spring flowers against a shadowy background, one with a bird. No. 99. 5.3 cm x 8 cm.

3. Two silver-bordered cards with grasses and violets or red campion, nos. 102, 102a. 11.5 cm x 8.5 cm.

4. Five cards, four designs of flowers and berries in a rustic border, no. 103. 11.2 cm x 6.7 cm.

5. Four cards with holly, ivy, spring flowers, and ferns, with a verse of greeting, one dated 1878 by the sender. No. 104. 12.7 cm x 8.2 cm, 8.2 x 12.7

6. Five cards, four designs of flower garlands on a plain background with text, verse, or greeting. Two cards with the same design are numbered 96 and 104, but are quite different from those in no.5 above. 8.7 cm x 7.5 cm, 7.5 cm x 11. 7 cm.

7. Two cards, spring flowers and grasses, also no. 104, but different from nos. 5 and 6 above. 6 cm x 12.5 cm.

8. Five cards with gilt patterned borders, four designs of wild flowers on green or cream background, with greeting in panel, one dated 1881 by the sender. No. 108. 9.5 cm x 9.5 cm.

9. Three cards, two designs of spring flowers and passion flowers in rustic border. Two more dated 1881 and one is marked with publisher's name and numbered 109. 11.9 cm x 7.2 cm.

10/11. Ten cards, eight designs of spring and garden flowers on grey background, in two styles, with greeting in a panel or on a small ribbon bow. Three were dated 1878 by the sender. No. 111. 7.2 cm x 11.4 cm.

12. Three cards, birds hovering over garden flowers, with greeting on scroll. No. 112. 11.2 cm x 8.2 cm.

13. Five cards, panels with anemones, poppies, speedwell, heather, or buttercup, in two styles, one marked 1881. Nos. 118, 213. 6.8 cm x 11.7 cm, 7.6 cm x 11.7 cm.

14. Four blue-bordered cards, three designs with wild flowers, no. 124. 8.5 cm x 12 cm.

15. Six cards from two sets using similar designs with berries, spring flowers, acorns, and foliage decorating the gilt initial to seasonal verses by Eden Hooper, J L F Freeman, and H Warren K L. Two have gilt borders, and four have scallop edges and are numbered 211. 8.5 cm x 7cm, 12.5 cm x 7.7 cm.

16. Two cards with spring flowers, ferns, and grasses, and gilt initials to verses by J L E Freeman. No. 231. 11.2 cm x 8 cm.

17. Three cards, each with a child in a scenic background framed in a wreath of strawberries, cyclamen, or spring flowers, two dated 1879 by the senders. No. 222. 11 cm x 7.6 cm.

18. Six cards, with verses by S C Hall, E H W, Goldsmith, or Shakespeare, and birds or butterflies on garlands of spring or Alpine flowers, three no. 153, one no. 453, two no. 253 dated 1883 by the sender. Sizes approximately 8 cm x 11.3 cm.

19. Seven scallop-edged cards with spring flowers or heather, all in similar format but numbered 201, 231, 322, 331. 7 cm x 10.7 cm.

20. Two grey-bordered cards with mimulus or rudbeckia, and a greeting verse by F E E H, no. 236. 13 cm x 9.1 cm.

21. Two cards, each with a single rose in a gilt-patterned border, no. 243. 12.2 cm x 9.3 cm.

22. Two cards, corn flowers or field roses in a circular vignette in a patterned blue border, no. 246. 11.5 cm x 11.5 cm.

23. Two cards, red campion and grasses, ox-eye daisies with ivy, in pink borders. No. 269. 8.7 cm x 14. 2 cm, 14.2 cm x 8.7 cm.

24. Two cards, roses or primulas with cupids in a grey background and a verse by Eden Hooper. No. 302. 14 cm x 8.5 cm.

25. Four gilt-edged cards, three designs of spring flowers and berries, two with dragon flies, one dated 1881 by the sender. No. 311. 9 cm x 12.8 cm.

26. Three cards, a dragonfly on berries (as in no. 25), bees on heather, a butterfly on blackberries. No. 343. 8.5 cm x 11.7 cm.

27. Three gilt-edged cards with roses. One is octagonal, no. 310. The others have New Year or birthday verses by Eden Hooper, the latter dated 1883 by the sender who wrote an acrostic to the recipient, Mary Shaw, on the back. No. 339. 9.4 cm x 12.9 cm, 10 cm x 13.1 cm.

28. Two blue-bordered cards with white flowers and ferns on blue background, no. 328. 12.4 cm x 9.5 cm.

29. Two cards, trailing leaves with flowers or berries and a bee or butterfly embossed in gold on a cream coloured background, one with birthday greeting. No. 341. 6.3 cm x 11.6 cm.

30. Three cards, greetings or texts in panel over sprays of harebells, hawthorn, or daphne, one dated 1881 by the sender. No 361. 11.5 cm x 7.6 cm.

31. Four miscellaneous wide-bordered cards, with holly, spring flowers, clematis, cydonia. Nos. 318, 230, 261, 317. Sizes up to 10 cm x 13. 6 cm.

32. Three miscellaneous cards with daffodils, berberis, or white clematis, nos. 69, 72, 234. 10.3 cm x 15 cm, 9.1 cm x 13 cm, 11 cm x 8.7 cm.

33. Three cards, two with moss roses no. 133, the third with a fading rose on a grassy bank, no. 953. 7.6 cm x 10. 5 cm, 13.2 cm x 10 cm.

34/35. Eleven miscellaneous cards with various flowers, nos. 125, 162, 179, 262, 277, 288, 321, 401, 416. 11.2 cm x 6.3 cm up to 11 cm x 14.8 cm.

36. One card with larkspur in a gilt-patterned border, with a picture of birds printed in silver on reverse, no. 086. 13.5 cm x 9.9 cm.

37. Five cards, three designs of violets, poppies, carnations, no 085. 9.7 cm x 6.5 cm.

38. Five cards with texts, one Easter with catkins and violets, no. 281, two small cards with holly or poppies, another with berries and spring flowers, the fifth with spring flowers, no. 132. 5 cm x 16.5 cm, 3 cm x 9 cm, 11.8 cm x 9 cm, 12.4 cm x 9cm.

39. Seven miscellaneous cards with flowers or ferns, nos. 91, 97, 110, 122, 160, 081, 093. 9.2 cm x 6.5 cm up to 12.1 x 8.2 cm.

(It is difficult fitting in those numbers beginning with 0 to the dating sequence - they could be a later series.)

## VOLUME 219. CARDS PUBLISHED BY THOMAS STEVENS AND TERRY, STONEMAN & CO, WITH FLOWERS, FRUIT AND FOLIAGE

**Cards signed T S were probably published by Thomas Stevens, though the similarity of initials, and sometimes of style, might lead to some doubt. Thomas Stevens published many well designed cards, mostly with floral subjects, in addition to the well known machine embroidery for bookmarks, and the silk motifs and fringes for cards already seen in volumes 13 and 197. Some of the cards here also have other publishers' names, indicating that these designs could have been obtained by several publishers from another source. All these cards except no. 34 are attributed to Stevens, with qualification as above, and were published in the late 1870's to the early 1880's with a few exceptions as noted.**

1. Seven cards (two birthday), four designs of spring flowers and roses, with greetings or texts, one dated 1877 by the sender. The colour printing is similar in style to that of W Dickes. 10.7 cm x 6.5 cm.

2/4. Thirty three small cards with eight designs of spring flowers, heather, and roses, with greetings in scrolls; variously dated 1877, 1878, 1879, by the senders. One is on a decorative silver-bordered mount, ten are on black and nine on gilt backgrounds. Some cards are marked T S but two identical cards are marked J Mansell and B Sulman, indicating that these cards may have been supplied by another maker to all three firms. 8.3 cm x 4.7 cm

5. Nine cards, including seven on gilt background, with five designs of roses, asters, forget-me-nots, blackberries, holly and mistletoe, two with a robin or a squirrel, one dated 1879 by the sender. 5.7 cm x 8.8 cm.

6. Six cards on black ground. Four have designs as in no 5, two have a greeting in a panel over strawberries or roses. 5.7 cm x 8.8 cm, 10.7 cm x 6.4 cm.

7/9. Fourteen embossed cards, six designs of spring flowers, heather, or roses, on a blue or cream background, with greeting or text in a scroll. Two were dated 1879, 1881, by the senders. 10.8 cm x 7.1 cm.

10. Six cards (one birthday, one valentine) wtih the same design of violets, snowdrops, and ferns, showing variation of colour printing and greeting. One card is marked T S, another J Mansell - perhaps supplied to both firms from a third source. 10.9 cm x 6.4 cm.

11. Five embossed cards (three birthday), three designs of roses, forget-me-nots, convolvulus, in a decorative border with flowers or berries. 12.2 cm x 7.8 cm, 13.1 cm x 9.3 cm.

12/14. Fifteen embossed cards (five birthday), nine designs of roses, forget-me-nots, poppies, cornflowers, carnations, with various greetings, three dated 1880 by the senders. Seven cards are on four varieties of decorative mounts. 11 cm x 7 cm, 12.5 cm x 8.5 cm, 12.8 cm 8.7 cm.

15. Three gilt-bordered cards with flower bouquets tied in blue ribbon, with poetic greeting, one birthday, one valentine, one New Year. 8.3 cm x 14.3 cm.

16. Four cards, colourful garlands of various flowers on blue or cream background. 6.2 cm x 12.4 cm.

17/19. Thirteen cards, four designs of mixed flower sprays on four background colours, with various greetings, verses, and texts, one dated 1879 by the sender. 7 cm x 16.2 cm.

20/21. Eleven cards, six designs of mixed flowers and a butterfly on three background colours with verses or greetings. These are marked T S but the designs are identical with those marked A Hildesheimer in Volume 105, no. 4, and J Mansell, Volume 23 no. 22. 11.2 cm x 7 cm, 10.8 cm x 6.3 cm.

22. Six cards. Four have black backgrounds with the same design of lilies of the valley with various greetings. Two are embossed with spring flowers, unmarked, but included here from the similarity of lettering. 10.8 cm x 6.4 cm.

23/24. Twelve cards, with six designs of spring flowers around panels with greetings. One is on a decorative gilt-bordered mount, and four have small Cupid figures in one corner. 9.6 cm x 5.7 cm, 10.5 cm x 6.4 cm.

25/26. Fifteen cards (three birthday), six designs of spring flowers, five with a pink ribbon bow, on beige, pink, or green mounts. They have verse or greeting in a panel; one is frosted, and one was dated 1879 by the sender. 10.5 cm x 6.4 cm.

27. Four similar larger cards on beige backgrounds, unmarked, one dated 1877 by the sender. 14.1 cm x 8.3 cm.

28. Eight cards, a mixed set with flowers, birds, strawberries, Red Riding Hood and the Babes in the wood. 9.3 cm x 6.4 cm.

29. Two folding cards with flowers within and gilt patterned covers.
6.2 cm x 9.5 cm, 9.1 cm x 13.2 cm folded.

30. Eight cards from two sets. Four have two designs of roses and forget-me-nots with a greeting on a panel; the others have three designs of flowers printed in sepia and a greeting on a panel. Two were dated 1877, 1878 by the senders. Sizes about 9.3 cm x 5.8 cm.

31. Six cards, including three from a set with trails of flowers printed in pink or blue on beige or pale blue. One has ivy with berries, another dicentra, and the sixth is triangular with white lilies and ferns (see volume 197 no.1 for another card of this set with silk fringe). 5.5 cm x 9.2 cm, 8.1 cm x 12.8 cm, 13 x 10.8 cm x 10.8 cm.

32. Six miscellaneous cards with spring flowers, heather, roses, Christmas roses. Five are numbered, 616, 617 dated 1886 by the senders, 01 dated 1885, and 618, 638, indicating the probability that numbering of Stevens cards began about 1885.
9 cm x 6 cm up to 12 cm x 9 cm.

33. Four cards, with forget-me-nots, cyclamen, ivy, and ferns, nos. 606, 617, 632, 673. 7 cm x 7 cm up to 9.5 cm x 13.6 cm.

34. Three cards, pink and white flowers on beige background with greeting in decorative scroll, marked Terry, Stoneman & Co., one on a decorative mount.
10.6 cm x 7 cm, 14 cm x 10.1 cm.

## VOLUME 220.
## FLOWERS, FRUIT, AND FOLIAGE FROM VARIOUS PUBLISHERS

These cards were published by
S J Saunders & Co. and Charles, Reynolds & Co., with others marked E Vouga and by the monogram B B. They dated from 1877 to the 1890's, with the majority in the early 1880's.

*Numbers 1-7 were published by S J Saunders & Co.*

1. Seven embossed cards, four designs of roses and a flower garland, six framing verses by E L T or S Ph A, one with a girl's head over New Year greeting, one dated 1881 by the sender. These are not marked, but attributed from an identical marked trade card in volume 201, no. 3. One verse is signed S Ph A, listed by Buday as a publisher, but it would appear from this and other evidence that these initials belong to a writer.
6.7 cm x 10.2 cm, 7.1 cm x 10.6 cm.

2/3. Eleven cards (three birthday), four designs of spring flowers in baskets, three

embossed, variously dated 1880, 1881 by the senders. One is on a gilt-patterned mount, and two are folders with decorative borders and covers. These are unmarked, but attributed from a marked fringed folding card in volume 197, no. 6.
10.1 cm x 7 cm, 12.5 cm x 9.3 cm, 12.1 cm x 9 cm (closed).

4. Two embossed cards, waterlilies and spring flowers, both dated 1880 by the senders. 11 cm x 7.5 cm.

5. Three cards, two being folders with flower pictures inside and gilt decoration and a verse by Astley H Baldwin on the covers. The third card is a small repeat of part of one of these flower designs.
11.8 cm x 5.2 cm closed, 5.2 cm x 11.8 cm.

6. Six cards, three designs of fern and white lilies, with verse below, including a birthday and an Easter card, one dated 1881 by the sender. 12.1 cm x 9.3 cm.

7. Three cards, two with roses dated 1882 by the sender, another with daisies on thick paper, dated 1894 by the sender.
8.8 cm x 12.3 cm, 14.5 cm x 12 cm.

*Numbers 8 and 9 were published by Charles, Reynolds & Co.*

8. Four colourful cards with roses and spring flowers in a gilt-patterned border, one dated 1879 by the sender. They were registered at Stationers' Hall 19-6-1877, but no artist was named. 13.7 cm x 10 cm.

9. Four cards in three varieties of gilt border, with various fruits, grasses, and butterflies. These are four designs from twelve registered at Stationers' Hall 31-5-1879 by Douglas Guy.
8.3 cm x 16.6 cm, 8.8 cm x 14.7 cm.

*Numbers 10-17 are signed with a monogram, possibly B B, perhaps the artist. Similar cards with scenes and flowers are in Volume 214.*

10. Four gilt-bordered cards with various colours of anemones, all with birthday greeting, and a monochrome design of cherubs' heads on reverse.
9.4 cm x 15. 2 cm.

11. Four cards in two sizes, three designs of roses or heather pinned in a bordered cloth or paper in trompe l'oeil style, with Christmas verses on the two large cards.
11 cm x 17.1 cm, 10.7 cm x 6.6 cm.

12. Two cards, one design of a wreath of roses and ivy on pale blue background, with birthday greeting or New Year verses, the latter embossed. They were dated 1884, 1885, by the sender.
10 cm x 13 cm.

13. Two cards, violets or lilies of the valley in a rustic barrow. 17.6 cm x 13.1 cm.

220.1

14. Two cards, garlands of roses and lilies of the valley or chamomile on pale blue background, with monochrome design and verse by Sabina on reverse.
12.8 cm x 16.5 cm

15/16. Two large cards, one with ox-eye daisies and corn marigolds and fern by a stream, dated 1891 by the sender, the other with roses, both with monochrome design of a girl in a garden on reverse.
13.9 cm x 23.5 cm.

17. Three miscellaneous cards, geranium and ivy with a horseshoe, orange lilies and a butterfly, and a red rose, the two latter dated 1883 by the senders. Sizes up to 10.1 cm x 16.1 cm.

*Numbers 18-22 are signed E Vouga. Several cards have the French "deposé" instead of copyright, so it is likely that these cards originated from a French firm, but further evidence is needed.*

18/20. Eleven cards (three birthday), eight designs with lilies, poppies, roses, woodland flowers, some with birds or butterflies, one on a lace-edged mount.
8.7 cm x 12.5 cm, 12.3 cm x 17 cm.

21. Two similar cards with sprays of white flowers and fir or leaves. 12.6 cm x 9 cm.

22. A large card with forget-me-nots.
12.3 cm x 20 cm.

23. Four cards. Three are marked Osborne, New St. two of these with strawberries, the other forget-me-nots and ivy and a Gothic arch. The fourth card has alpine flowers in a mountain scene and is marked W M Thompson, 20 Cockspur St., Pall Mall London. Perhaps both these firms were retailers. Vouga, Osborne and Thompson

233

are not listed by Buday. 8.2 cm x 5 cm,
9.1 cm x 12 cm, 10.7 cm x 16 cm.

24. Four cards marked E Rimmel,
Perfumer, perhaps once part of a booklet.
6.6 cm x 9.2 cm

## VOLUME 221.
## CARDS PUBLISHED BY
## CASTELL BROS.,
## W HAGELBERG, J F SCHIPPER,
## 1880'S, WITH FLOWERS, FRUIT
## AND FOLIAGE

*Numbers 1-3 were published by Castell Bros.
c1885.*

1. Two cards signed R J Mackay, white
orchids, with poems by Fannie Rochat.
No. 64, the Peniel. 15.3 cm x 10.1 cm.

2. Two cards, roses on gilt-edged paper,
with poem signed C E J. No. 68, the Peniel.
12 cm x 11 cm.

3. Four miscellaneous cards, lilies of the
valley, forget-me-nots no. 62, waterlilies
no. 67, and a boat-load of globe flowers.
5.4 cm x 6.5 cm up to 17.6 cm x 8 cm.

*Numbers 4-11 were published by W Hagelberg,
c. 1885-1890*

4. Five miscellaneous cards, forget-me-nots
no. 13, oak leaf no. 1134, both on gilt
background, an ivy leaf no 31, a birthday
card with cherry blossom and a verse by
M S H on reverse, no. 445, and an
unnumbered card with dog roses.
9.8 cm x 7.5 cm up to 9.4 cm x 12.7 cm.

5. Four miscellaneous cards with roses,
daisies, forget-me-nots, three numbered 35
(dated 1887), 65, 126 (Berlin).
10.7 cm x 7.5 cm up to 10 cm x 13.1 cm.

6. Four miscellaneous cards in subdued
colours, various flowers with greeting or
verse, three numbered 126, 205, 342.
Sizes up to 8.3 cm x 12.4 cm.

7. Three cards with pansies and auriculas
in shades of maroon and yellow, one
no. 109 dated 1885 by the sender, another
no. 209.
8.3 cm x 12 cm up to 10.6 cm x 14.8 cm.

8. A card with serrated border, pansies by
a lake, with a verse by M S H and a
monochrome design of a ship on reverse.
No. 451. 11 cm x 14.9 cm.

9. Three cards, two with roses or forget-
me-nots and verses below, no. 205, another
with daisies and a cross and an Easter
verse below, no. 207. 8.3 cm x 12.8 cm.

10. Two cards with roses, under a Japanese
parasol or in an overturned boat, the first
with verse by A M Hone on reverse, no.
483. 10.9 cm x 13.7 cm, 14.9 cm x 10.6 cm.

11. Six miscellaneous cards with flowers or
autumn leaves, unmarked but probably
Hagelberg. Sizes up to 11.3 cm x 7.3 cm.

*Numbers 12-28 were published by J F Schipper
in the 1880's. No. 691 was dated 1883 by the
sender and the numbers appear to be in date
sequence.*

12. Four cards with spring flowers, nos.
551, 551, 555, 732.
10.5 cm x 7 cm up to 9.5 cm x 12.6 cm.

13. Two cards, each with an anchor by a
stream with flowers and a butterfly or
insect, no. 553. 10.8 cm x 14.3 cm.

14. A card with roses in an ornamental
border, no. 610. 11.6 cm x 17.7 cm.

15. Two cards, grasses in terracotta
handled vases with spring flowers and
bird or butterfly decoration. No. 685.
12 cm x 16.3 cm.

16. A set of four cards with spring flowers
in tall pottery vases, no. 683.
8.4 cm x 12.7 cm.

17. Four cards, two with white flowers in
glass tumblers, no. 992, the others with
mixed flowers in vases, no. 605.
9 cm x 12 cm, 9.1 cm x 12.3 cm.

18. Two cards, white flowers with leaves
and ferns, nos. 602, 838.
11.9 cm x 17 cm, 15.3 cm x 10.6 cm.

19. Two cards, Christmas roses with ferns
or berries and verses below by F E E H,
no. 678. 12.2 cm x 19.5 cm.

20. Three birthday cards with various
flowers, two with roses. Nos. 691, dated
1883 by the sender, 674, 737.
9 cm x 13 cm up to 12 cm x 17.5 cm.

21. Three cards, two with white flowers
and brown leaves, no. 623, the third with
phlox, dated 1885 by the sender, no. 1065.
14.2 cm x 10.8 cm, 13.2 cm x 9.9 cm.

22. Two cards, a birthday card with
Christmas roses, no. 840, and a Christmas
card with cyclamen and a large shell,
no. 695. 17.9 cm x 12 cm, 18.8 cm x 12.2 cm.

23. Two cards with pansies, one birthday,
nos. 601, 1238.
9.7 cm x 11.5 cm, 10.8 cm x 14.4 cm.

24. Three cards, white phlox, violets and
primroses with a moonlit sky, nos. 1066,
1066, 999.
9.8 cm x 15.4 cm, 9.8 cm x 15.8 cm.

25. Two cards, roses and fern with
birthday greeting no. 796, lilies and
convolvulus with New Year verse by
S K C, dated 1887 by the sender, no. 1282.
17 cm x 10.7 cm, 17.4 cm x 11.9 cm.

26. Four cards on gilt-edged board with
various white flowers and ivy or fern, one
with a cross. All have the same
monochrome fuchsia design on reverse,
and one is signed R J Mackay. Nos. 1085,
1086, 1089, 1090. 10 cm x 12.9 cm.

27. Three cards on thick board with
various spring flowers, one Easter, one
birthday, the third a valentine. Nos. 995,
1103, 1358. Sizes up to 14.2 cm x 11 cm.

28. Three cards, one silver-bordered with
snowdrops, another white jasmine in a
silver horseshoe, the third a cactus flower
with a tropical bird, the first two
numbered1233, 1455.
7.1 cm x 10.3 cm up to 9.5 cm x 10.9 cm.

## VOLUME 222.
## FLOWERS, FRUIT, AND
## FOLIAGE FROM SEVERAL
## PUBLISHERS, 1880'S.

*Numbers 1-8 were published by Obpacher
Bros., mid 1880's.*

1. Two cards, geraniums and London pride
no. 542, and rowan with berries,
apparently from the same set. The second
card however is faintly marked H Rothe,
no. 443, so it is possible that these cards
were supplied from a third source.
10.4 cm x 13.8 cm.

2. A card with nasturtiums growing round
a rustic border framing a quotation from
Shelley's "Love's Philosophy". No. 642.
13.4 cm x 14.5 cm.

3. Three miscellaneous cards with various
flowrs, a valentine no. 564, a birthday card
no. 561, and New Year card with verse
signed F G, no. 721.
Sizes up to 12.7 cm x 8.7 cm.

4. A card with spring flowers arranged on
a rustic cross, dated 1883 by the sender,
no. 713. 12 cm x 17.6 cm.

5. Two cards, pottery jugs with daisies and
forget-me-nots against patterned curtains,
with a verse above. No. 743.
11.4 x 17.8 cm.

6. A large gilt-edged card with a wreath of
roses, dated 1885 by the sender, no. 773,
19.2 cm x 13.6 cm.

7. Two cards, one with a bunch of roses
and a patterned folder, no. 906, the other
with a New Year greeting framed in alpine
flowers, no. 644.
10.4 cm x 15.4 cm, 11.4 cm x 15.7 cm.

8. Two cards, signed AH, double cherry
blossom, roses and lilac, on a grey
background with greeting in silver.
No. 1185. 14.9 cm x 10.4 cm.

*Numbers 9 and 10 were published by Wirth
Bros. & Owen, c1885.*

**223.1**

9. Four miscellaneous cards, three frosted, one with holly and Christmas roses, the others with spring flowers. All have a poem on reverse by EHC about Christmas bells. Nos. 184, 185, 204, 264.
7.3 cm x 9.5 cm up to 11.9 cm x 16.7 cm.

10. Two cards, snowdrops, holly and apple blossom. 8.3 cm x 12.2 cm, 9.3 cm x 12 cm.

*Numbers 11-14 were published by Davidson Bros. in the later 1880's.*

11. Three cards, two with roses, one with snowdrops and forget-me-nots, both with a verse of greeting. 11.3 cm x 7.3 cm.

12. Two cards with silver edges and greeting, various spring flowers and ferns, and verses by Cecilia Havergal.
15.4 cm x 15.4 cm.

13. Three valentine cards, all with white spring flowers, one with verse by AGA, two with Shakespeare quotations.
Sizes up to 10.6 cm x 14.7 cm.

14. Three miscellaneous cards (two birthday), with various flowers, and verses by Charlotte Murray, S K Cowan, or Lewis Novra. One with a wreath of harebells is signed Wolff Davidson.
Sizes up to 11.6 cm x 15.2 cm.

*Numbers 15-16 were published by Bernhard Ollendorff, later 1880's.*

15. Two cards, moss roses with a poem by Charlotte Murray on reverse, and pansies with verses by J S H Horton.
12.4 cm x 9.8 cm, 11.9 cm x 16.8 cm.

16. Five miscellaneous cards with roses or spring flowers and verses or greeting.
9.6 cm x 6.9 cm up to 13.5 cm x 9.5 cm.

*Numbers 17-20 were published by Philipp Bros, later 1880's.*

17. A birthday card with silver border and a verse by S K Cowan on a hanging banner with roses. 10.2 cm x 13.5 cm.

18. Three cards, one with a bunch of violets and a rose lying on a silver card with a verse by Frances Ridley Havergal below. The other two have the same design of dog roses with Christmas or New Year greeting in a rustic bordered vignette and the same verse for each by S K Cowan.
14.3 cm x 10.7 cm, 9.9 cm x 12 cm.

19. Two cards, forget-me-nots and pansy with a birthday verse by H M Burnside, field roses with verse by S K Cowan.
11.6 cm x 14.7 cm.

20. Two cards, lilies of the valley and ivy in an oval frame with a verse from Tennyson below, and white jasmine and fern in a pointed window with verse by Frances Ridley Havergal.
11.5 cm x 15 cm, 14.4 cm x 11.5 cm.

*Numbers 21-23 were published by Sockl and Nathan, later 1880's.*

21. Three cards, one with lilies of the valley and an ivy leaf in a serrated border with verse by Charlotte Murray. Two have roses against a moonlit sky, with verses by Alice C Wilkinson.
10.2 cm x 15.2 cm, 12.8 x 8.7 cm.

22. Six cards, three with various flowers and verses by I L W, S K Cowan, H M Burnside. The other three have roses, two repeating the designs in no. 21 in different format.
7.5 cm x 7.5 cm up to 10 cm x 12.9 cm.

23. Three miscellaneous cards with lilies and chrysanthemums, one with a verse by Margaret S Haycraft.
Sizes up to 12.5 cm x 16.9 cm.

24. A card published by M H Nathan & Co., roses with a Union Jack and a patriotic verse by C D. The drawing is signed by a monogram J C or T C? 13.5 cm x 10.2 cm.

25/26. Seven cards published by Meissner & Buch, Leipzig, late 1880's, with various well drawn designs of spring flowers, some with verses by J B, Frances Ridley Havergal, Charlotte Murray.
7 cm x 11.1 cm up to 10.8 cm x 15.7 cm.

27. Three miscellaneous cards (one birthday), published by Albert Marx, various spring flowers, two with verses by A H B and Hemans. The third card with a wreath of forget-me-nots in blue and silver might be a wedding or silver wedding greeting.
9.5 cm x 9.5 cm up to 11.4 cm x 15.8 cm.

28. Three gilt-edged cards published by I Spargoe, signed F D, with brown leaves and ferns and thistles on a cream background, with seasonal poems on reverse. 17.8 cm x 10.7 cm.

29. Two cards, A S Co. (Artistic Stationery), pink roses on mosaic background, no. 602, shamrock and grasses in a mountain scene, no. 835.
9.7 cm x 1.4 cm, 10.7 cm x 13.7 cm.

30. A card marked A O L, no. 265, spring flowers with verse on a scroll.
11.3 cm x 14.3 cm.

31. A large card marked W & Co., with a dragon fly on gladioli flowers.
14.5 cm x 19.5 cm.

32. Three cards, two with red berries and white flowers on a golden anchor with verse by H M Burnside, the third with leaves and berries on a pink ground. These are marked Reed, 282 Regent Street, printed in Germany.
13.6 cm x 16.6 cm, 14 cm x 10.5 cm.

33. Nine cards. Seven were published or sold by Alfred Lea and have five designs of spring flowers. Two are marked L S, and have sprays of harebells and heather. Late 1880's.
6.7 cm x 6.7 cm up to 9 cm x 13.7 cm.

34. Two cards, one a blue periwinkle with a verse marked T B & Co., who published in 1880's. The other has a branch of berries and leaves and is marked M Priester's Continental Printing Co., series no. 221.
9.1 cm x 6 cm, 12.4 cm 8.9 cm.

223.10

## VOLUME 223.
## FLOWER CARDS
## ASSOCIATED WITH ERNEST
## FALCK & CO., JONATHAN
## KING, E RIMMEL, AND
## SIMILAR, C1880

A number of these cards are marked "Rights reserved", including some in a set one of which is marked Rimmel (nos. 13/14). This however is not adequate evidence to attribute all such cards to Rimmel in view of the complications already seen with the same design marked with more than one publisher's name.These cards are grouped together on account of similarity of style and a certain elegance of production, and perhaps more evidence will emerge of their provenance. They were issued around 1880, and it is likely that more could be traced to Falck & King.

1. Nine embossed cards, six designs of small winged figures with a profusion of flowers. These could be from Ernest Falck & Co., as they resemble cards in the Jonathan King album no. 207 (dated 1880, in the John Johnson collection), supplied to King by Falck. One was dated 1880 by the sender.  8.6 cm x 5.3 cm.

2. Four embossed cards, garlands of spring flowers and roses, two with a butterfly. These are similar to cards from Falck seen in the 1880 Jonathan King album. 8 cm x 13.9 cm.

3. Eight cards (five embossed), with seven designs of spring flowers tied with a pink or blue ribbon. They have greetings in verse and one differs slightly with a greeting in a panel.  4.7 cm x 8.4 cm.

4/5. Eight embossed gilt-bordered cards, four designs of roses, spring and alpine flowers, tied with pink or blue ribbon, with seven different greetings. One was dated 1878 by the sender. 8.3 cm x 14.8 cm.

6. Three cards marked "rights reserved", a four page folder and two single cards with flower garlands, one with a butterfly. The folder has a gold and sepia design in Japanese style on the outside. 6.4 cm x 9.5 cm, 5.8 cm x 9 cm.

7. Seven embossed cards, "rights reserved" with spring flowers and roses. Four have greetings on gilt-edged scrolls and hovering insects; three have posies and a box of jewels with greeting in a panel, and two of these are on coloured mounts. 16.7 cm x 6.6 cm, 11 cm x 5.6 cm, 10 cm x 6.7 cm.

8. Two similar larger cards, "rights reserved", with spring flowers and grasses, butterflies and insects, and greetings in panels. 16.7 cm x 6.6 cm, 22.3 cm x 8.8 cm.

9/10. Two similar large cards with birthday greetings in elaborate panels and a variety of flowers including cornflowers and fuchsia. 27.6 cm x 10.4 cm.

11. Five embossed cards, "rights reserved", four on coloured mounts, with four designs of roses, camellias, lilac, spring flowers, ivy and fern, one dated 1879 by the sender. They have poetic greetings with illuminated initial letters. 11.7 cm x 7.6 cm, 10.4 cm x 6.3 cm.

12. Three embossed cards, flowers, ferns, and shells, on coloured mounts. 11.7 cm x 7.6 cm.

13/14. Eight embossed cards, "rights reserved", five designs with roses, forget-me-nots, cherry blossom, myrtle(?), two dated 1879 by the senders. One card is stamped E Rimmel. 11.5 cm x 7 cm.

15. Six embossed cards, five designs with roses. camellias, lilies, spring flowers in gilt border on green or cream mount. One card from a different set is marked "rights reserved", and three were dated 1879 and 1880 by the senders. 7.7 cm x 12.5 cm, 8.4 cm x 14.5 cm.

16. Three embossed cards, "rights reserved", with bunches of roses, forget-me-nots,cornfield flowers, and seasonal verses. 7.7 cm x 14.1 cm.

17/18. Six embossed cards, "rights reserved", three designs of camellias, Christmas roses, peonies, and spring flowers, with seasonal poems on gilded banners or scrolls. One was dated 1881 by the sender. 8.5 cm x 15.9 cm.

19. Four embossed cards, "rights reserved", three designs of holly, oak and acacia, the leaves touched with snow. They have Christmas verses on gilded scrolls. 8.5 cm x 15.9 cm.

20. Eight embossed cards, "rights reserved", in three styles of patterned borders, five designs of trails of roses and spring flowers with holly, ivy, or vine, and greetings in verse. 5.3 cm x 12 cm.

21. Four embossed cards, "rights reserved", three designs of fans, one in cut-out form. All are decorated with roses and forget-me-nots; one has a peacock feather border, another lace, the third white plumes. One was dated 1879 by the sender. 12.7 cm x 7.7 cm, 11.3 cm x 6.5 cm.

## VOLUME 224.
## FLOWERS, FRUIT AND FOLIAGE, SIMILAR CARDS TO THOSE IN VOLUME 223

**Some of these elegant cards may have been published by Jonathan King or Falck, but none are marked. They all date from about 1880 or a little earlier.**

1. Four cards with gilt line borders, three designs of garlands or roses and spring flowers around greeting verses, one dated 1878 by the sender. 8.2 cm x 14 cm.

2. Three embossed cards with gilt line borders (two birthday), two designs of wreaths of lilies, roses and spring flowers. Two have verses signed Da, H L N. 8.3 cm x 12 cm.

3. Five cards, gilt line borders, four designs of sprays of roses, china asters and a variety of spring and summer flowers, one dated 1877 by the sender. 7.8 cm x 14.3 cm.

4/5. Eight gilt-bordered cards from two sets. Six have four designs with roses, camellias, and lilies of the valley tied with ribbon bows, and verses, four birthday. The other two have camellias and china asters with a Christmas verse. 8.3 cm x 14.7 cm, 8 cm x 14.2 cm.

6/7. Six similar larger cards with flower bouquets, three tied with ribbon bows. 11.4 cm x 15.1 cm.

8. Four embossed cards, three designs, each with a child's head, one with fruit and autumn leaves, another with sheaves of corn and flowers, the third with holly, a robin, and more flowers. One was dated 1880 by the sender. 7.9 cm x 12.5 cm.

9. Six embossed cards (one birthday), four designs of a hand holding a rose and spring flowers, with verses, two signed Fannie Rochat. 7.9 cm x 12.5 cm.

10. Two embossed cards, small winged cherubs with a bird's nest and a garland of flowers, one dated 1881 by the sender. 12.5 cm x 6.3 cm.

11. Two embossed gilt-bordered cards, with garlands of mixed flowers around a mountain scene and a New Year verse. 8.2 cm x 17.5 cm.

12. Three cards, small winged cherubs with spring flowers, water lilies, shells and aquatic plants, or poppies and morning glory, and Christmas verses signed R H S. 8.2 cm x 19.5 cm.

13. Two cards, flowers of the cornfield around a vignette with Windsor Castle, and poppies with wild flowers and a verse by Eden Hooper. 14 cm x 10.1 cm, 15.9 cm x 10 cm.

14. Three gilt-bordered cards. One has two small fairies nestling in a bunch of roses; the others have a girl or boy holding a branch of mixed flowers or roses. 10 cm x 15.1 cm, 7.6 cm x 19.3 cm.

15. Two gilt-bordered cards, each with a winged cherub holding a cornucopia of flowers, with valentine or New Year verse signed E T or E E R. 8.8 cm x 17.4 cm.

16. Two embossed gilt-bordered birthday cards, a lady playing a lute in a garland of holly, and another with a harp in a garland of poppies. 8.5 cm x 14.4 cm.

17. Four embossed cards, one a valentine, one birthday, three designs with roses, narcissi, dicentra, fuchsia, and verses of greeting in decorative lettering. One card is frosted. 8.1 cm x 17.3 cm.

18. Three similar cards, all birthday. 8.1 cm x 17 cm.

19. Two embossed cards with spring flowers in decorative vases, one a valentine with a verse signed E J P, the other with a Christmas poem by H F. 8.7 cm x 17.4 cm.

20. Two cards, one with roses and fern, the other with holly, snowdrops and violets dated 1879 by the sender. Both have the same decorative gilded border and a seasonal verse. 15.5 cm x 11.5 cm.

21. Four cards, flower sprays with azaleas, roses, thistles, poppies, cornflowers, lilac, etc., dated 1879 by the sender. 10.1 cm x 16.5 cm.

22. Two large embossed cards with roses and forget-me-nots and seasonal verses. 11.2 cm x 15.8 cm.

23. Three embossed cards with dark borders and a variety of flowers arranged in crescent shape around seasonal verses. 11.2 cm x 15.2 cm.

## VOLUME 225.
## FLOWERS, FRUIT, FOLIAGE, SMALL CARDS

**These cards were published about 1880; a few are marked, and grouped with similar unmarked cards. Most measure about 11 cms x 6.5 cms, and sizes are omitted except for significant variation from this figure.**

1/3. Fourteen embossed cards with patterned white borders, one marked S J S (S J Saunders). There are nine designs of roses, poppies, azaleas, and spring flowers, on sepia or shaded blue and grey backgrounds, with a greeting or verse in a white panel.

4/5. Thirteen embossed cards, white embossed borders, with four designs of roses, violets, forget-me-nots, lilies of the valley, and greetings or verses in panels or scrolls. Four are on silver backgrounds with verses by Eden Hooper, and three cards are smaller, 9.2 cm x 5.5 cm.

6. Three cards, one signed E B & Co. (Bollans), one design of camellias and forget-me-nots with greeting in scroll. One card is on a mount with gilt-patterned border.

7. Six embossed cards, three designs with wild roses or cornfield flowers, one marked D W (untraced).

8. Five embossed cards, one marked D W, two designs, one with roses on an open book, the other with poppies and cornflowers by a rock, all on a blue shaded background.

9. Nine embossed cards from two sets. Five have four designs of roses or lilac tied with pink or blue ribbon, one dated 1879 by the sender; four have roses or spring flowers with greeting on a white leaf. Sizes 9 cm x 5.9 cm, 8.2 cm x 4.8 cm.

10. Six embossed cards. Two have the same design of a butterfly on pink roses tied with a blue bow, one with valentine greeting. Four are smaller, each with a butterfly on spring flowers, 7.9 cm x 4.5 cm.

11. Four embossed cards, three designs with camellias, roses, forget-me-nots, and greeting on panels or scrolls. One is frosted, and has a valentine greeting.

12. Nine cards from three sets, two designs with roses, five with violets or lilies of the valley. Two are smaller, 9 cm x 5.3 cm, and two were dated 1877, 1880 by the senders.

13. Four cards with lilies, tulips, and other spring flowers. These are similar to cards attributed to Marcus Ward (see volume 45 nos. 19/22), but are included here for comparison.

14. Four cards, three designs of camellias, forget-me-nots, lilies of the valley, with greetings on bordered scrolls, one dated 1879 by the sender. 12 cm x 7 cm.

15. Three miscellaneous embossed cards, with roses, bindweed, forget-me-nots, and grasses.

16. Three embossed birthday cards with roses, one with forget-me-nots.

17. Five cards, four designs of roses and spring flowers, with greetings in panels.

18. Two embossed cards, carnations or fuchsias, one dated 1881 by the sender.

19. Four cards from two sets, various pink and white flowers. The two larger cards

have verses by Cecilia Havergal and measure 12 cm x 7.8 cm.

20. Three embossed cards, rose sprays on a blue and cream mosaic background, two dated 1880, 1882 by the senders.

21. Four embossed cards (three birthday), three designs with roses or forget-me-nots, three on a background imitating wood grain, one on plain pink background.

22. Four embossed cards, two designs of pansies or lilies of the valley and forget-me-nots on a grey mosaic background.

23. Five embossed cards, four designs of musical instruments with roses, fuchsias, pansies, tulips, daisies. One card is on a gilt-bordered mount.

24. Five embossed cards with patterned gilt borders, with roses, carnations, poppies, cornflowers, and daisies, two with birds. All have greetings in white panels.

25. Four gilt-edged cards. Two have roses and forget-me-nots, one with a cross, the other with flowers in an open box. The other two have a butterfly on a diagonal gilt-bordered band with greeting, and passion flowers with a variety of spring blossoms. 12 cm x 8.3 cm.

26. Four embossed gilt-edged cards from two sets. Two have roses or lilac with a bird flying to its nest, and are shaped like parallelograms with a turned down corner. The others have convolvulus or iris with spring flowers, and are larger, 14 cm x 7.8 cm, one dated 1880 by the sender.

27. Six embossed colourful cards with four designs of roses or pansies with fuchsias and heathers. 11.5 cm x 7.4 cm.

28. Four miscellaneous embossed cards, water lilies with a dragonfly, passion flowers on a cross, roses with a horseshoe, and violets and spring flowers with a bird's nest.

## VOLUME 226.
## FLOWERS, FRUIT, EARLY CARDS, MANY ON BLACK OR GILT BACKGROUND

**This volume includes a few marked cards, grouped as before with similar unmarked examples. The same design was used on black, gilt, or various coloured backgrounds. Most are small, dated in the late 1870's, with one early set from 1871.**

1/4. Twenty one cards, published by Adam & Co., Newcastle, in two sizes, with six designs in the larger size and four in the smaller of spring flowers and roses. They have greetings in white panels on backgrounds of black, gilt, brown, blue,

pink, and green, and resemble Prang's cards in style. Late 1870's. 9.3 cm x 5.6 cm, 13.6 x 7.7 cm.

5/6. Fifteen cards in two sizes, one on a coloured mount, four with texts. There are twelve designs with a variety of flowers, six with a butterfly, and the backgrounds are black, blue, grey, or beige. Late 1870's. 9.6 cm x 5.1 cm, 13.5 cm x 6.5 cm.

7. Eight cards, four designs with colourful flower borders around panels with verses, some with illuminated initial letters, on dark blue backgrounds with patterned gilt borders. Two were dated 1871, 1872 by the senders. 8.7 cm x 6 cm.

8/11. Thirty cards, six designs with roses, fuchsia, and spring flowers. Six have gilt backgrounds, nine black, and fifteen beige. There are eighteen different verses or greetings in white panels with flower or leaf borders, including a birthday verse and three valentine verses, and one was dated 1877 by the sender. 9.5 cm x 6.3 cm.

12. Two large black background cards with elegant designs of roses or lilies with spring flowers, and greeting or text in gilt lettering on a white scroll. 21.5 cm x 7.4 cm.

13. Six black background cards (one birthday), four designs with various colourful spring flowers, and greetings on white panels, three dated 1876, 1877, 1879 by the senders. 9.5 cm x 6.3 cm.

14. Nine similar cards (one birthday), six on black backgrounds. Four have greetings on bordered scrolls, five on panels, and one was dated 1877 by the sender. 10cm x 6 cm.

15. Three cards, two designs with roses and spring flowers, one with black background, two with grey. Each has a poem by S C H in a scallop-edged panel, and one was dated 1877 by the sender. 12.1 cm x 7.2 cm.

16. Seven cards with various flowers and ferns or ivy, one on black background, another on an embossed mount, all with verses or greetings in elaborate gilt-edged illuminated scrolls. 10.3 cm x 6.3 cm, 12.2 cm x 8 cm.

17. Nine cards (four birthday), seven on black backgrounds, with seven designs of roses and spring flowers from several sets. All have greetings in white panels. 10.1 cm x 6.4 cm.

18/19. Thirteen cards from three sets with greetings on white bordered scrolls, and nine designs with one or two flower fairies or cupids and wreaths of roses, convolvulus, camellias, forget-me-nots, snowdrops, azaleas, narcissi, buttercup etc. They have black, green or cream-coloured backgrounds, and two were dated 1878 by

the senders. Six are valentines and two have birthday greetings. 10.7 cm 6.8 cm.

20. Four cards with a Christmas scene or flower garlands on plain black backgrounds. 11 cm x 6.6 cm.

21. Three cards, illuminated stylised designs of holly, oak, and violets with autumn leaves, on plain black backgrounds with verses by S C H or R C W in gilt-edged panels. 10.5 cm x 6.8 cm.

22. Six cards (four on black backgrounds, one on a gilt-edge mount), with four designs. Three have poppies, carnations, or roses. The fourth design is probably from the old style "hyacinth orientalis", now superseded in gardens by the modern large-flowered varieties. 10.6 cm x 7.7 cm, 11.3 cm x 8.1 cm.

23. Six miscellaneous black background cards with formal flower designs, two dated 1876, 1878 by the senders. Sizes up to 11.5 cm x 5 cm.

24. Seven cards from four sets, including two on brown backgrounds, one for Easter with passion flowers, the other a valentine with crocuses. Holly, hawthorn, and spring flowers adorn the other five black background cards. 9.3 cm x 5 cm up to 13.2 cm x 6.3 cm.

25. Five cards, four with formal designs of roses, fuchsia, snowdrops, heather, on black backgrounds, the fifth card having a pool with acquatic plants. The small card with heather is marked W Dickes on the back. 8.5 cm x 4 cm up to 15 cm x 7.3 cm.

26. Five cards, one design of holly and blackberries with a greeting on a miniature stamped postcard, one dated 1879 by the sender. Three cards have black backgrounds, all with different greetings, one is on gilt, the other on grey. 12 cm x 8 cm.

27. Four cards on gilt backgrounds, three designs, one holly and nasturtiums, another a robin with asters and a greeting on an open book, the third seaweed and a turtle with a greeting on a shell. One was dated 1879 by the sender. 12.3 cm x 8.4 cm.

28. Four cards with pansies, forget-me-nots, poppies, cornflowers, and daisies on gilt backgrounds, and greetings on white panels. 11.5 cm x 6.7 cm.

29. Four cards (two valentines, one birthday), with roses, convolvulus, hibiscus, forget-me-nots, daisies, on gilt backgrounds, and greetings or verse on white panels. One is marked M & Co., Marion? 11 cm x 7.4 cm.

30. Two cards, tulips or acorns on gilt background, with blank space for personal greeting. 12 cm x 7.2 cm.

31. Eight miscellaneous cards with various flowers and holly on gilt background and greetings in panels. One has a strawberry plant with a pastoral scene in a vignette.
7.7 cm x 4.5 cm to 11.9 cm x 7.8 cm.

32/33. Ten cards, five on black backgrounds, two on gilt, with four designs of flowers on a scenic background - poppies and cornflowers by a cornfield, roses and forget-me-nots with a pastoral scene, hawthorn with birds by a lake, violets and crysanthemums with a winter scene. One was dated 1880 by the sender.
11.1 cm x 7.6 cm.

34. Four cards, black backgrounds, a fairy with carnations dated 1880 by the sender, a bowl and fan with spring flowers, and two cards with pansies and other flowers in a style similar to that of Prang.
10 cm x 6.5 cm up to 14.5 cm x 6.5 cm.

## VOLUME 227.
## FLOWERS, FRUIT, AND FOLIAGE, MORE SMALL EARLY CARDS

**These were published from about 1876-1880, on various coloured backgrounds, some black. A few cards have cupids or cherubs and insects with the flowers, and two cards have publisher's initials.**

1. Three cards with floral sprays and greetings on white panels, one on a green mount, one dated 1876 by the sender.
12 cm x 5.5 cm, 14 cm x 17.5 cm.

2. Eight cards, including two valentines, four designs of spring flowers with greetings on ribbon panels, one marked "published by H W Wickins, 18 Monkwell Street, London EC" another dated 1877 by the sender. Wickins is not listed by Buday.
9.5 cm x 5.9 cm.

3. Nine cards on blue or fawn backgrounds. Seven from one set have four designs of flower bouquets in wicket baskets. Two are embossed, with one design of roses and spring flowers in a decorative illuminated panel. Two were dated 1878, 1879, by the senders.
9.3 cm x 6.3 cm.

4. Seven cards (one birthday), three designs of mixed flowers, two with a bird or dragonfly. The third design of poppies and cornflowers appears in three sizes.
8.2 cm x 5 cm up to 10 cm x 6.6 cm.

5. Nine cards from three sets, on blue or grey background, with eight designs of flower wreaths or sprays, some with pink or blue ribbon, around greetings on white panels, six with ornate gilded borders.
8.8 cm x 5 cm up to 9.7 cm x 6 cm.

6/8. Twenty seven embossed cards from several sets probably all made by the same firm, including nine on black backgrounds,

five birthday and one valentine. There are five designs with wreaths of mixed flowers, and nine designs with spring flowers, roses, heather, geranium and sweet william. One was dated Christmas 1879, another New Year 1880, by the senders. 8.7 cm x 5.9 cm.

9. Nine embossed cards (one birthday), five designs of roses, heather, pansies, carnations, Christmas roses, on blue or cream backgrounds with greetings on white panels, perhaps from two sets. One was dated 1880 by the sender.
7.8 cm x 4.5 cm.

10. Twelve cards from three sets, eight designs of ferns and flowers, with greetings on decorative panels or scrolls, one dated 1880 by the sender.
8 cm x 4 cm up to 8.5 cm x 5.4 cm.

11. Four embossed cards on brown backgrounds, three designs of roses and forget-me-nots, one with greeting on a palette, another on music for a lyre, the third written by a hand holding a pen on a white card. One was dated 1879 by the sender. 10.6 cm x 6.4 cm.

12. Nine cards, all with birthday greetings on white panels, with seven designs of roses, camellias, pansies, grape vine, or strawberries, on blue or beige backgrounds. 10.3 cm x 6.3 cm.

13/14. Twelve embossed cards, six with black, six with grey backgrounds, nine designs of roses, camellias, and spring flowers, with greetings on white panels (one in German). 10.6 cm x 6.2 cm.

15. Four cards, three embossed one plain, one design of violets and lilies of the valley on blue or cream background, with a greeting verse on a postcard, one dated 1880 by the sender. 10.6 cm x 6.4 cm.

16. Two embossed cards, one design of a swallow with pink roses. 10.3 cm x 6.8 cm.

17. Two embossed cards, one with waterlilies and forget-me-nots and greetings on a shell with ladybirds, the other with lilies of the valley and forget-me-nots and butterflies and greetings on a bordered panel. 10.3 cm x 6.8 cm.

18. Eight miscellaneous embossed cards with various flowers, six with greetings on decorative panels. Three were dated 1880, 1881, 1884, by the senders. 8 cm x 4.5 cm up to 10.9 cm x 6.5 cm.

19. Seven small embossed cards on blue or cream ground, five designs of flower sprays or wreaths, with greetings on scrolls or panels, two for birthday. 8.6 cm x 5.3 cm.

20. Five small cards in subdued colours with four designs of wild flowers, foliage, and insects. 8.4 cm x 5.5 cm.

21. Six cards, five designs of tulips, cyclamen, roses and other spring flowers, on shaded brown background with greetings in decorative scrolls.
10.3 cm x 6.7 cm.

22. Two colourful cards with formal flower designs in a central panel and in the corners, with greetings on four separate scrolls. 11 cm x 6.5 cm.

23/24. Fourteen miscellaneous cards (one a folder), on beige or green backgrounds, with thirteen designs of a variety of flower sprays and wreaths and verses or greetings in panels.
7 cm x 4.5 cm up to 10.2 cm x 6.4 cm.

25. Nine cards, beige backgrounds, two with birthday greetings. Five have a figure of a girl or boy, four have a cupid in an oval vignette, all with greetings in decorative scrolls with flowers and leaves. 10.5 cm x 6.7 cm.

26. Five cards, four designs with winged cherubs and flowers, one dated 1884 by the sender. Two have verses by Fannie Rochat. All approximately 10.9 cm x 6.7 cm.

27. Two cards, each with a cupid standing by a panel with greeting and flowers, probably used as valentines.
10.8 cm x 7 cm.

28. Six embossed cards, each with a winged cherub and garlands of flowers or ferns, two with verses signed S H or F E E H. One card dated 1879 by the sender is marked S J S & Co. i.e. S J Saunders. Sizes up to 12.1 cm x 8.2 cm.

## VOLUME 228.
## FLOWERS, FRUIT, AND FOLIAGE, VERY SMALL CARDS

**These were published from the later 1870's to early 1880's with a few of later date. Most are simple designs of sprays of flowers with a verse or greeting. Some cards have decorative leaves, perhaps inspired by begonia or coleus.**

1. Five cards on black backgrounds, with illuminated floral designs. Four have greetings in gilt letters on white scrolls, and the fifth is on a mount with patterned border and has a greeting in red letters. c1875. 9.5 cm x 4.2 cm, 12.7 cm x 7.4 cm (mount).

2. Nine cards on grey backgrounds, with six designs of floral sprays and seasonal greetings in white letters. One is on a decorative mount.
9.5 cm x 4.3 cm, 12.7 cm x 7.5 cm (mount).

3. Nine cards from three sets, with six designs of autumn leaves or holly and mistletoe, one dated 1878 by the sender.

228.1

Six cards have a butterfly or dragonfly. 6.8 cm x 4 cm up to 8.6 cm x 5.5 cm.

4. Seven cards (two birthday), four designs of flower sprays on grey backgrounds, one on a mount with illuminated border. One card was dated 1879 by the sender. 8.3 cm x 4.7 cm, 11 cm x 7.3 cm (mount).

5. Seven cards, including a valentine and two birthday greetings. There are five variations on one design of lilies of the valley and forget-me-nots, and two others with roses and forget-me-nots. One was dated 1879 by the sender. 9 cm x 5.8 cm.

6/8. Twenty five cards, six designs of a lily, crocuses, fuchsia, camellia, rose, and philadelphus (an unusual six-petalled variety), on blue or cream backgrounds, including some texts, birthday, and valentine greetings. Five cards are on decorative bordered mounts. Late 1870's. 8.3 cm x 4.7 cm, 11 cm x 7.1 cm (mount).

9. Five embossed cards, four designs of mixed flower sprays on grey backgrounds, with a hovering insect or a snail, one dated 1880 by the senders. 8.3 cm x 4.8 cm.

10. Nine cards (one birthday), five designs of various flowers including heather and dicentra. Three are on decorative mounts and two were dated 1880 by the senders. 8 cm x 5 cm, 9.5 cm x 6.3 cm (mount).

11. Nine cards from four sets, seven designs with sprays of roses or spring flowers, one dated 1881 by the sender. 8 cm x 4 cm up to 9 cm x 5.5 cm.

12. Seven cards. Four on a cream background have small sprays of spring flowers or waterlilies with greeting and text. Three on a grey background have the same design of lilies of the valley with Christmas verse, text, or loving greeting on white bordered panels. 8 cm x 4 cm, 8.8 cm x 5.8 cm.

13. Three embossed cards, two designs of floral bouquets with a seasonal couplet signed G A. One is on a gilt-patterned mount. 9.2 cm x 5.4 cm, 12.5 cm x 9 cm (mount).

14. Two embossed cards with patterned borders, one a basket of fruit, the other flowers with three birds eggs. 7.5 cm x 6 cm.

15. Sixteen embossed cards with gilt border, twelve designs of decorative leaves and small flower sprays, with greetings or verse in white panels. Three cards are marked "Rights reserved" and one has a greeting in Welsh. 8.1 cm x 5 cm.

16. Seven embossed cards. Three have a spray of roses with greeting in verse. The other four have three designs of a palette with grapes, a lute with poppies, and a horn with music in a wreath of holly and clematis. 6.4 cm x 4.2 cm.

17. Six cards from two sets. Three have embossed designs of decorative leaves and ferns, one with a Christmas verse by M F Moss. The others have two designs of two butterflies hovering over a green leaf. 5 cm x 8 cm, 9 cm x 5.8 cm.

18. Three cards, two with a boy in period dress on a flower spray, the third with a bird on a hawthorn branch. 8.3 cm x 4.6 cm.

19. Nine embossed cards with coloured borders, sprays of mixed flowers, and seasonal greetings in verse. 8.3 cm x 4.6 cm.

20. Nine cards, seven designs with roses, convolvulus, lilies of the valley, cornflowers, forget-me-nots, snowdrops. 8.3 cm x 5.1 cm.

21. Three embossed cards, spring flowers in plant pots. 7.7 cm x 4.9 cm.

22. Twelve cards from several sets, flower sprays with greetings. Three cards are marked J B B & Co., a firm listed by Buday as operating in the 1880's. 8.8 cm x 5.2 cm, 8.8 cm x 3.8 cm.

23. Ten cards, found in a packet, five designs with garlands of mixed flowers, probably c1885. 8 cm x 5.3 cm.

24. Five gilt-edged cards, four designs of spring flowers with decorative leaves and ferns, one dated 1883 by the sender. 5.9 cm x 8.9 cm.

25. Ten cards from two sets. Six have four designs of roses, and four have small sprays of spring flowers. 8 cm x 5cm, 6.9 cm x 3.5 cm.

26. "The Wonderful Penny Packet of 6 birthday cards, all different. P.S." Six cards with envelope marked as above, but only four different designs of mixed flower sprays. 8 cm x 4.8 cm.

## VOLUME 229: FLOWERS, FRUIT, FOLIAGE, SMALLER UNBORDERED CARDS

**These cards were published from about 1878-1885. None are marked with the makers' names, but some closely resemble those from S Hildesheimer and S J Saunders.**

1. Six cards, two pleasing designs with autumn leaves and small flowers. There are four versions of one design in two sizes, and the second design has seasonal and birthday greetings, one dated 1878 by the sender. 8.3 cm x 5 cm up to 10 cm x 6.5 cm.

2. Five cards, with sprays of broom, thistles, and flowering or berried branches, one dated 1878 by the sender. The printing resembles that of W Dickes. 11.5 cm x 7.4 cm

3. Four similar cards with narcissus, harebell, ivy, or blackberries. 10.6 cm x 7 cm.

4. Three cards with leaves, heather, and cyclamen, one dated 1879 by the sender. 6.9 cm x 11.9 cm, 9 cm x 11.6 cm.

5. Two cards, variegated leaves on a dark background with greeting in a white panel. 10.6 cm x 6.7 cm.

6. Four cards, small sprays of spring flowers on a grey background with greeting in white panel, one dated 1878 by the sender. 11.2 cm x 7.6 cm.

7. Three similar cards with wreaths of Alpine flowers. 10.9 cm x 7.6 cm.

8/9. Eight cards on shaded grey backgrounds with sprays of heather and Alpine plants, similar in style but in several sizes, one dated 1879 by the sender. The largest card has a Christmas poem signed J P T with flower sprays either side. 5.2 cm x 12.9 cm up to 15.1 cm x 12.7 cm.

10. Four embossed cards, three designs of roses, daisies and forget-me-nots on grey backgrounds, two with couplets by Fannie Rochat. One was dated 1882 by the sender. 11.5 cm x 7 cm.

11. Three embossed cards with bird's nests and flowers on grey backgrounds, and Christmas verses signed M E B. 12.2 cm x 7.8 cm.

12. Four cards (one birthday), three designs, a bee on clover with other flowers and a background country scene, a pink carnation with monochrome bird, butterfly, and roses, and a pink rose and forget-me-nots with two clasped hands in the background. 12.3 cm x 7 cm, 14 cm x 8.5 cm.

13. Two cards, one design of roses and grasses with Christmas or New Year greetings on a lace-bordered scroll. 13.1 cm x 8.1 cm.

14. Five cards (one birthday), flower garlands with greetings on white panels, one a book, two lace-bordered. Two cards were dated 1879, 1880 by the senders, and one is on a decorative mount. 10.6 cm x 6.6 cm.

15. Four miscellaneous cards, colourful flowers on grey backgrounds, one dated 1879 by the sender. 13.3 cm x 6.3 cm up to 14.7 cm x 7.6 cm.

*Numbers 16-21 resemble cards published by S Hildesheimer or S J Saunders.*

16. Six cards, five designs of roses, geraniums, spring flowers, and holly, on brown or green backgrounds, signed J C, with greetings on white scrolls. 10.3 cm x 7.2 cm.

17. Six small grey cards with individual flowers, cornflowers, violets, helianthemum, rose, morning glory, primrose, with appropriate greetings below "May Christmas be as full of joy as the rose of beauty". 6.4 cm x 9.5 cm.

18. Five grey cards, each with an insect or a butterfly and a garland of spring flowers with poetic greeting. 6.4 cm x 9.5 cm.

19. Eight small cards, six designs with sprays of spring and summer flowers. One card is a folder with a patterned cover using two of the designs, and one was dated 1879 by the sender. 4.6 cm x 8.5 cm.

20. Seven grey cards, six designs of flowers growing in a garden urn on a pillar with

colourful flowers beneath, one dated 1880 by the sender. One card is a folder using two of these designs, with children and a vine on the outside. They were probably published by S J Saunders. 5.6 cm x 11.1 cm.

21. Eight cards, including four miscellaneous with spring flowers, one dated 1880 by the sender. The other four are from one set with a single flower and a seasonal verse in a white panel on a grey background. 4.9 cm x 7.5 cm up to 6.9 cm x 10 cm, 6.3 cm x 9.5 cm (set).

22. Three cards, two with grasses or corn and small flowers, one dated 1883 by the sender, the third a garden scene in a garland of flowers. 6.8 cm x 10.2 cm, 10.2 cm x 10.2 cm.

23. Five miscellaneous cards with roses, morning glory, nasturtiums, or violets, on various coloured backgrounds. 4.2 cm x 12.6 cm up to 6.3 cm x 13.6 cm.

24. Seven cards, beige backgrounds. Four from one set have three designs of azaleas, one dated 1882 by the sender; three others have sprays of spring flowers. 9.3 cm x 5.2 cm, 11 cm x 7.3 cm.

25. Four miscellaneous cards, convolvulus, lilies of the valley, snowdrops and heather, sweet peas. Sizes up to 12.5 cm x 8.3 cm.

26. Six cards with colourful designs of violets with spring flowers and a grapevine, one dated 1883 by the sender. 10.3 cm x 6.9 cm up to 11.9 cm x 8.5 cm.

27. Four cards. Two have primulas on a grey background (one birthday), and two have roses or flowers of the cornfield on a brown background, one dated 1885 by the sender. 11.6 cm x 7.7 cm, 11 cm x 6.5 cm.

28/30. Seventeen miscellaneous cards on brown, buff, blue, grey, or cream backgrounds, with designs of spring flowers and roses, six with birthday greetings. 10 cm x 6.8 cm up to 9.5 cm x 12 cm.

## VOLUME 230: FLOWERS, FRUIT, FOLIAGE, COLOURFUL CARDS FROM 1873 TO 1885

1. Six cards, four designs in red, blue, and green of mixed flowers around panels with seasonal verses, one dated 1873 by the sender. 6.3 cm x 9.2 cm.

2. Four cards, pink borders, with seasonal verses in scrolls or panels bordered by trails of leaves and mixed flowers. 10.2 cm x 6 cm, 6 cm x 10.2 cm.

3. Four miscellaneous cards, scalloped borders, two with bouquets of roses and spring flowers, one dated 1879 by the

sender, another with wallflowers. The fourth card has leaves and roses entwined to make four wreaths, each with a greeting, dated 1884 by the sender but probably published earlier. 8.8 cm x 6 cm up to 8.1 cm x 12 cm.

4. Four cards, three from one set with two designs of leaves with violets or lilies of the valley around gilt-edged panels with greetings. The fourth card has a wreath of passion flowers and leaves around a greeting. 10.2 cm x 7.1 cm.

5. Four cards marked "Design V", three designs of waterlilies by a lake, a vine with grapes, and a bird flying to its nest on an oak branch, with greetings in illuminated style lettering. 11.9 cm x 7.7 cm.

6. Four cards, marked "Design IV", various scenes with bird or butterfly set in garlands of flowers. (One of these cards with a different greeting has been included in volume 211 as an example of a scene with ships). 7.6 cm x 11.5 cm.

7. Three birthday cards, with large initial letters for the months May, November, December written on scrolls, each with appropriate flowers - hawthorn, chrysanthemum, holly. These must be three from a series of twelve, one for each month. 8.5 cm x 11.6 cm.

8. Three cards. Two have a gilt cross and anchor with pink and white dog roses or primulas; the third has the sacred symbols of cross, anchor, and pierced heart, with lavish flower displays in gilded vases. 8 cm x 10.9 cm, 7.5 cm x 11.3 cm.

9. Six miscellaneous cards (two birthday), garlands of flowers and leaves around greetings, two in verse. c1880. 9.5 cm x 5.7 cm up to 10.7 cm x 7.2 cm.

10. Six cards, sprays of spring flowers, five with greetings on ribbon scrolls. 3.8 cm x 11.8 cm.

11. Three cards, sprays of mixed flowers. Two from the same set were dated 1884 by the sender; the third card with a blue ribbon tie was dated 1880. 11.8 cm x 7.7 cm, 12 cm x 8.9 cm.

12. Four miscellaneous cards (two birthday). Two have spring flowers with ivy, the third roses, the fourth cornflowers. 9.7 cm x 6.4 cm up to 11.3 cm x 7.5 cm.

13. Five cards. Four from two sets have stylised designs of gentian, waterlily, rose, and arum lily, and the fifth larger card has waterlilies. 6.2 cm x 9.7 cm, 6.6 cm x 9.9 cm, 9.1 cm x 12.9 cm.

14. Nine miscellaneous cards, sprays of spring flowers and roses. Early 1880's. 4.7 cm x 8.2 cm up to 6 cm x 9.2 cm.

15. Seven cards, six colourful designs with sweet peas, fuchsia, roses, cornflowers, pansies, on grey backgrounds with patterned corners, and seasonal verses. One card is in different format with a small added scene in oval vignette. 10.1 cm x 10.1 cm.

16. Five cards, four stylised designs of roses and gloxinia, on grey backgrounds with patterned borders, two dated 1880, 1881 by the senders. 9.4 cm x 12.4 cm.

17. Two octagonal cards with garlands of fuchsia and pansies. 11.5 cm x 15.4 cm.

18. Five cards with spring flowers, roses, china asters or chrysanthemums, arbutus, forsythia, daphne, on dark backgrounds in wide grey borders, one dated 1884 by the sender. They are signed with a monogram E S or S E (untraced). 10.3 cm x 13.6 cm.

19. Three cards, two designs with wreaths of forget-me-nots and violets, one with an appropriate verse. 9.2 cm x 13.2 cm, 13.2 cm x 9.2 cm.

20. Two pale blue cards with seasonal verse on white bordered panels, with flower borders including fuchsias, pansies, passion flowers, and leaves. 12.2 cm x 8.5 cm.

21. Two interesting cards with garlands of china asters or hawthorn, spring flowers, and grasses. Both have the trade registration mark for 29th May, 1883. 13.6 cm x 9.7 cm, 16.5 cm x 12 cm.

22/23. Six cards in two sizes, four designs of holly flowers, campion, apple blossom and catkins, marsh marigold. The four larger cards have cream or green centres with colours reversed for the borders, and one of the smaller plain cards was dated 1882 by the sender. 12.2 cm x 16 cm, 9.3 cm x 12.5 cm.

24/25. Four cards, three designs of Christmas cactus, solanum - perhaps the egg plant(?), and azaleas, on pale green background framed in beige, with greetings in the corners. 15.3 cm x 11.8 cm, 11.8 cm x 15.3 cm.

26. Two birthday cards, azaleas, with greetings by Lewis Novra or Matt C Hale in heart-shaped vignettes, one dated 1886 by the sender. 11 cm x 14.5 cm.

27/28. Six cards, four designs with wreaths of mixed flowers around seasonal verses on pale green or apricot backgrounds, with small flower sprays in each corner. c1885. 12.9 cm x 12.9 cm.

## VOLUME 231:
## FLOWERS, FRUIT, FOLIAGE, SMALLER CARDS IN BRIGHT COLOURS

**These cards have traditional floral designs in sprays, wreaths, or garlands, many on coloured backgrounds, without gilt embellishment except for a few borders. They date from 1879 to about 1885 and are unbordered except where otherwise stated.**

1. Six cards on brown or grey backgrounds, with bunches of mixed flowers, some Alpine, one dated 1879 by the sender. They have hymns or verses by YET, ACW, EAW, EMM on reverse. 7.3 cm x 11 cm.

2/3. Thirteen bordered cards with five designs of spring flowers, heather, or strawberries, one dated 1879 by the sender. There are four texts and nine different greetings on white panels. 8.8 cm x 6 cm, one 11 cm x 7.4 cm.

4/5. Eighteen cards on blue or cream backgrounds, with six designs of summer flowers, two dated 1879, 1880, by the senders. Eight have seasonal greetings and ten have texts. 9.5 cm x 6.4 cm.

6. Six bordered cards, with two designs of roses and one of geraniums with fern, one dated 1882 by the sender. 9.6 cm x 7 cm, one 10.6 cm x 7.8 cm.

7. Six bordered cards from four sets, four with sprays of mixed flowers, two with tulips or nasturtiums, one dated 1881 by the sender. 8.1 cm x 5.5 cm up to 10.2 cm x 6.8 cm.

8. Six cards on cream or grey backgrounds, two designs of crocuses or geraniums, all with different greetings. 10.1 cm x 6.8 cm.

9. Six cards on cream background, four designs of roses, hawthorn, daisies and grasses, one dated 1883 by the sender. 7.5 cm x 10.9 cm.

10. Six small cards, four designs with roses, pinks, and spring flowers around circular vignettes with scenes. 5 cm x 7.8 cm.

11. Four pale blue cards, mixed flowers including roses, poppies, spring flowers, and holly, with grasses. 7.2 cm x 10.6 cm.

12. Two similar with azaleas, carnations, forget-me-nots, daisies, and verses by Cecilia Havergal. 7.4 cm x 11.3 cm.

13. Seven cards on blue backgrounds, some faded, with four designs of a variety of wild flowers and grasses. 7.6 cm x 10.9 cm.

14. Six bordered cards, five designs in bright colours against a dark background, with crocuses, primroses, convolvulus, apple blossom, fuchsia, hawthorn, and greetings on white scrolls. 8 cm x 10.8 cm.

15/16. Fourteen cards (one birthday, one with a text), seven designs on cream ground with red line border of mixed flowers and fruits from garden and countryside. 7.4 cm x 10.8 cm.

17. Five cards from two sets. Three have two designs with butterflies on fuchsia or campanula. Two have fuchsias over a partly rolled cream coloured scroll on a blue background. 7.5 cm x 10.7 cm, 8 cm x 12 cm.

18. Six gilt-bordered cards, three designs of pansies, geranium, or laburnum on dark backgrounds. 7.7 cm x 10.9 cm.

19. Six miscellaneous cards, one with blackberries, the others with various flowers, some Alpine. Sizes up to 10.8 cm x 7.7 cm.

20. Four white-bordered cards, with garlands of fern and roses or spring flowers, and verses by Horatius Bonar, D D, on reverse. 7.6 cm x 11.8 cm.

21. Four cards with gilt line borders, four varieties of asters. 8.3 cm x 13.2 cm.

22/23. Nine grey cards on thin paper with nine designs of spring and summer flowers, perhaps supplied in sheets for cutting up. 8.1 cm x 12.1 cm.

24. Nine cards with sprays of roses, spring flowers, and leaves on green or cream background. 10.2 cm x 6.7 cm.

25. Two cards with white borders, fuchsias or orange lilies on blue background with verse in bordered panel. 7.7 cm x 11 cm.

26. Four miscellaneous bordered cards, three with mixed flowers framing a greeting or scene, the fourth a Scottish New Year card with thistles, all with verses. Sizes up to 8.6 cm x 12 cm.

27. Four miscellaneous cards, three with flowers or leaves around a window, all with verses. The fourth card has a bird's nest and flowers in an arched stone niche. 11.3 cm x 8 cm up to 11 cm x 13 cm.

## VOLUME 232:
## FOLIAGE & BERRIES, 1873-C1885

**The evergreens which brightened the home at Christmas time provided interesting material for greeting card artists, with a colourful contribution from the red berries of the holly. Sets of cards appear with holly, mistletoe, ivy, and oak, sometimes with fruits and berries, and flowers were occasionally seen with the winter foliage.**

1/3. Sixteen cards, one marked Canton, perhaps all from this source. There are

two designs of snow-laden branches with holly or ivy, on eight different coloured backgrounds with twelve distinct poetic sentiments, and two cards were dated 1873, 1876, by the senders.
10.9 cm x 7.6 cm.

4. A large card, holly and snowdrops with gilt background on a green mount with illuminated border. 13.6 cm x 20 cm.

5. Three cards with gilt or red line borders from two sets, with holly, mistletoe and spring flowers. Two cards have greetings printed on a quill pen. 10.1 cm x 7 cm, 11.1 cm x 7.1 cm.

6. Five cards with ferns and ivy, four in silhouette form. Three cards have the same design on different coloured backgrounds with greetings on varied scrolls. Sizes approximately 7.6 cm x 11.9 cm.

7. Five miscellaneous cards with holly, one with a robin. 8.8 cm up to 7 cm x 16.3 cm.

8. Six miscellaneous embossed cards, four with holly, one with oak leaves and acorns, the sixth with ivy and snowdrops.
9.2 cm x 5.6 cm up to 7.1 cm x 11.3 cm.

9. A set of four cards, holly, mistletoe, ivy, and oak on grey background, one dated 1879 by the sender. 8 cm x 14.3 cm.

10. Three cards, two embossed with holly and ivy as in no. 9, one dated 1879 by the sender. The third card has sprigs of holly and mistletoe in a wide grey border.
8 cm x 14.3 cm, 15.2 cm x 11.3 cm.

11. Three gilt-bordered cards. Two have holly or flowers with greeting on a panel by a winter tree. The third card is a folder with these designs on the cover, and a church with angels and a New Year picture within. One was dated 1880 by the senders. 10.1 cm x 13.3 cm.

12. Two large embossed cards, with poetic greetings framed in holly and roses or fir branches and Christmas roses.
11 cm x 15.1 cm.

13. Four cards with two designs of snowdrops with yellow-berried holly and mistletoe with red and yellow-berried holly, both with verses on panels by E J L, M F Moss, and Shirley Wynne. One card was dated 1883 by the sender.
8 cm x 12 cm.

14. Four miscellaneous cards (one birthday) all with holly, red or yellow berries, two with mistletoe, another with Christmas roses. All have greetings in verse.
7.8 cm x 11.4 cm up to 9.5 cm x 14.2 cm.

15. Four cards, two with mistletoe, one with yellow-berried holly, the fourth with holly and snowdrops, one dated 1883 by

WITH BEST WISHES FOR THE NEW YEAR.

**232.12**

the sender.
8.4 cm x 7.5 cm up to 14 cm x 9.5 cm.

16. A large frosted card with a star shining on holly and Christmas roses, dated 1885 by the sender. 12.8 cm x 16.8 cm.

17. A set of four cards with wreaths of fern, ivy and autumn leaves, around greetings in gilt letters, two dated 1883, 1886 by the senders. 11.5 cm x11.5 cm.

18. Two cards, gilt line border, one design of oak leaves, acorns, and harebells, one with birthday greeting. 13.1 cm x 9.5 cm.

19. Four cards, one embossed with oak leaves and acorns, fir and flowers, another with oak leaves and fern. Two from a set have verses on reverse, one signed J M, with gloomy sentiments, perhaps matched by the pictures of ivy and fungus and oak apples on a dead leaf.
Sizes up to 9 cm x 13.5 cm.

20. Three miscellaneous cards with ivy and gilt or silver borders, one a valentine.
14 cm x 8.8 cm, 9.1 cm x 13.2 cm, 8.6 cm x 13 cm.

21. A large card with a Christmas acrostic verse spelling "My Love" wreathed in fir and mistletoe. 12 cm x 15 cm.

22. Three embossed cards, one with Chinese Lantern fruits, another with rowan leaves and berries, the third with black, green, and yellow berries, perhaps laurel. 7 cm x 14.4 cm.

23. Three miscellaneous cards, two with rosehips, the third solanum (?). 7.6 cm x 10.5 cm, 11 cm x 15.5 cm, 12 cm x 9 cm.

24. Four miscellaneous cards, one with blackberries, another with leaves and berries from New Zealand labelled

"Coprosmia Rotundifolia Karania", the third bittersweet. The fourth is unidentified but might be a rose species. Sizes up to 9.8 cm x 13.7 cm.

25. Two cards, a sprig of arbutus with a verse by E I Tupper, and a birthday card with rowan leaves and berries in a blue and gilt line border.
14.2 cm x 10.5 cm, 15 cm x 11 cm.

26. Four cards with wide coloured borders, blackberries, hazel nuts, oak leaves and acorns, dogroses with hips, two dated 1882 by the senders.
14 cm x 9.6 cm, 9.6 cm x 14 cm.

27. Four miscellaneous cards, two with autumn leaves and acorns or hazel nuts, the third dogwood or cornelian cherry, the fourth autumn leaves with red berries.
11.7 cm x 8.9 cm up to 14.4 cm x 9.5 cm.

28. Two cards with coloured borders and background winter scenes framed in branches, one with a bird eating berries.
12 cm x 9.7 cm, 13.5 cm x 11.3 cm.

29. Two cards, branches with apples or blackberries around seasonal verses by Frances Ridley Havergal, one dated 1885 by the sender. 10 cm x 10 cm.

## VOLUME 233:
## FOLIAGE & FERNS, 1880-1885

**These cards might appeal to the botanist, but few express the spirit of Christmas and some of them are rather gloomy, though the technique of highlighting brown leaves with gold is interesting. Some verses are quoted which explain what might be taken as irrelevant pictures.**

1. Three embossed cards on shaded grey background, with leaves of horsechestnut, holly, ivy, with grasses, seed-heads, and a quotation from Shakespeare. One was dated 1881 by the sender. 8.9 cm x 12.7 cm.

2. Three embossed cards, ferns and grasses on beige backgrounds, two with a ladybird or grasshopper.
8 cm x 15.9 cm, 8.4 cm x 14.1 cm.

3. Six embossed cards on brown or green background imitating wood, with five designs of fir, oak, mistletoe, horsechestnut, Virginia creeper with blue berries (Vitis Henryana?) One card is on a mount with patterned border.
11.2 cm x 6.7 cm.

4. Four cards, three designs of colourful autumn leaves with grasses on green backgrounds. 5.8 cm x 12 cm.

5. One card with a bunch of green and dark red ferns on a cream coloured background. 10.1 cm x 15.4 cm.

**234.1**

6. Two cards, one design of a house plant with green and red leaves, one a birthday card with small white greeting card inserted into a leaf. 10.4 cm x 15.2 cm.

7. Five embossed cards from three sets, four designs of ferns and ornamental leaves.
10.6 cm x 7.1 cm up to 7.5 cm x 11.1 cm.

8. One card, with two colour border, ornamental leaves against a blue sky, with a New Year verse. 15.6 cm x 10.5 cm.

9. Nine small cards from three sets, six with leaf motifs and greeting (one a verse by Fanny Rochat) on mottled backgrounds, one dated 1885 by the sender. Three cards have embossed sprays of leaves with ferns or flowers.
9.3 cm x 6.5 cm up to 10 cm x 7.5 cm.

10. Two cards with leaf garlands around Christmas verses, one with a hanging basket. Both have the registration mark for May 29th, 1883. 10.8 cm x 15 cm, 10.2 cm x 4.9 cm.

11. Two cards, one with ferns and a butterfly on pale green background, the other with green and brown ferns, marked Davidson Brothers, London, included here for comparison with similar unmarked cards. 9.5 cm x 14.4 cm.

12. Two attractive cards with wide peach-coloured border, green and brown ferns and grasses on a pale blue background, one frosted. 17.1 cm x 11.1 cm.

13. Three cards, ferns growing on rocks with a background of sea or mountains, with Christmas poems on reverse by E E M. 9.2 cm x 15.3 cm.

14. A large gilt-bordered card with a fern growing in grass on a cream background, and a greeting in gilt letters.
12 cm x 17.5 cm.

15. Five cards, three with ferns, two with ferns and ivy framing a greeting. Two have verses by H M Burnside, one has a text, and another has a poem by Frances Ridley Havergal "Only a leaf, yet it shall bear  A wealth of love ....". 7.2 cm x 10 cm, 9 cm x 11.3 cm.

16. Three cards with ferns, two with vignettes showing sky in the background. Sizes up to 11 cm x 13.2 cm.

17. Two cards, sprays of mixed ferns on grey backgrounds. One with a mosaic finish has a birthday verse by Clara Simmonds; the other has a Christmas poem by H M Burnside. 10.6 cm x 13.8 cm, 9.5 cm x 12.7 cm.

18. Three cards, green leaves with a verse by Frances Ridley Havergal, a jewelled branch of fir with a verse signed E E C, and a branch of lime with leaves and flowers and a poem signed M E R
"O fragile flower, thou art a feeble thing,
Compelled to hold and cling
To some strange sturdy tree.
So, Lord, we cling to Thee."
10.8 cm x 12 cm, 13 cm x 9.9 cm, 14 cm x 9.9 cm.

19. Four embossed cards, three designs, a vine with grapes, a chestnut branch with nuts, and oak leaves and acorns, on blue or buff backgrounds. 8 cm x 15.3 cm.

*The following cards have leaves in shades of brown or autumn colours, some highlighted with gold, a few with flowers.*

20. Two cards, gilt line borders, one with a Christmas poem bordered by gilded brown leaves, dated 1881 by the sender, another with leaves and ferns touched with gold. 7.8 cm x 14 cm, 9.7 cm x 12.6 cm.

21. Two cards, brown leaves, thistles or sea holly and grasses on a cream background, with verses. 11.5 cm x 7.8 cm.

22. Three cards, autumn leaves with grasses and seed heads on brown background, each with a butterfly or insect. The seasonal verses are signed S Ph A. 9.5 cm x 14 cm.

23. Two cards, gilt line borders, ivy on a dark background, and Virginia creeper with bindweed.
11.5 cm x 17.1 cm, 11.2 cm x 15.1 cm.

24. Three cards, two designs of daisies or dog roses with brown leaves touched with gold, one dated 1883 by the sender. 9.1 cm x 13.6 cm.

25. Two cards (one birthday), garlands of autumn leaves with verses, one dated 1884 by the sender. 10 cm x 13.6 cm.

26. Four gilt-bordered cards with leaves, two from the same set with oak or ivy.

*The third card has a verse by Charlotte Murray, and the fourth has ivy with gold highlights and forget-me-nots. Sizes up to 11 cm x 13.6 cm.*

27. Three cards from a set, gilded leaves with white flowers, one dated 1885 by the sender. 13.3 cm x 8.6 cm.

28. Two cards, Virginia creeper with berries, dated 1886 by the sender, and autumn leaves with white flowers.
10.4 cm x 15.8 cm, 18.8 cm x 12 cm.

29. Three miscellaneous cards with autumn leaves, one with a yellow rose. Sizes up to 13.2 cm x 10 cm.

30. Two gilt-bordered cards, one with daisies and brown ivy on a rustic cross, signed with monogram BD, another with roses and a thorny branch shaped like a crown, both with gold highlights.
15.3 cm x 10 cm.

31. Three gilt-bordered cards, two designs of cyclamen or China asters (?) with brown leaves. 15.3 cm x 10 cm.

32. Five cards, four designs of stylised colourful autumn leaves. Two have gilt borders and gold highlights.
6.5 cm x 9.7 cm up to 10.3 cm x 13.7 cm.

33. Two gilt-bordered cards, brown leaves with forget-me-nots or roses.
14.5 cm x 11 cm.

34. Three miscellaneous cards with gilt borders, daisies with ivy and bindweed or bryony, nasturtiums, poppies and cornflowers, all with brown leaves touched with gilt. Sizes up to 15.3 cm x 10 cm.

35. Five miscellaneous cards, all with gold highlights. Three have spring flowers and brown leaves, one a wreath of oak leaves and acorns, the fifth leaves around a circular vignette with snowflakes.
Sizes up to 13 cm x 9 cm.

36. Three cards of a set, with white borders, white flowers and dark brown and gold leaves on pale blue backgrounds. 9.5 cm x 9.5 cm.

37. Three miscellaneous cards with colourful autumn leaves, one with harebells another with holly. Sizes up to 13.7 cm x 10.5 cm.

## VOLUME 234: FRUIT & FUNGI, FLOWERS WITH BIRDS AND INSECTS, 1880-1885

These cards show fruit growing on the branch, sometimes with flowers, and also prepared for the table as part of the Christmas feast. The cards here with birds and insects are those where the flowers appear to be the more prominent subject.

1/2. Ten embossed cards with five colourful designs showing a variety of edible fruits around Christmas greetings in a flower-bordered panel. Four cards are on black backgrounds. c1880. 11 cm x 7.8 cm.

3. Four cards, three designs of branches with apples, cherries, oranges(?) One card is on a decorative bordered mount. 8.5 cm x 5.4 cm, 10.5 cm x 7.5 cm.

4. Four small cards, one with plums or damsons, another wild strawberries, and two with dessert fruits, one wishing the recipient a "fruitful year". 10.1 cm x 6.3 cm.

5. Five cards, four on black backgrounds, four designs with peaches, grapes and a rose, an apple with blossom, and cherries in a paper holder. 11.1 cm x 7.1 cm.

6/7. Nine cards (five birthday), three on gilt backgrounds, four on black, with four designs of cherries, grapes, strawberries, plums, all with greetings on white panels. 11 cm x 6.6 cm.

8. Two cards, with mixed fruit and blossom around a Christmas verse on a buff-coloured background. 8.9 cm x 13 cm.

9. Two cards from one set, grey and gilt borders, one with blackberries, the other with holly, ivy and forget-me-nots. 11.2 cm x 8.6 cm.

10. Four miscellaneous cards, one with blackberries and a bird's nest, another with dessert fruit and a pumpkin, the third strawberries with fir and Virginia creeper. The fourth is a small gilt-edged card with a peach, pineapple, and fig wrapped in a white napkin. 8.2 cm x 4.8 cm up to 9.7 cm x 14 cm.

11. Four cards, two from one set with dessert gooseberries or strawberries on a shelf, another with arbutus flowers and

fruits, the fourth with pumpkin, grapes, and peaches. 10.5 cm x 7.1 cm up to 14.5 cm x 10.5 cm.

12. Two embossed cards, apples or grapes, hanging on a wall of grained wood. 8.6 cm x 11.7 cm.

13. A large card, signed with a monogram O S, with a Christmas verse in a gilt-edged white panel bordered by a grapevine, apples and pear, with an insect. 11.7 cm x 16.9 cm.

14. Four miscellaneous cards, two embossed with strawberries, two with blackberry branches, one dated 1885 by the sender. 9.7 cm up to 15.2 cm x 9.7 cm.

15. Three cards with two designs of red or purple fungi on a dark green background. 11.8 cm x 8.9 cm.

16. One card, fungi and ferns on a grassy bank. 8.2 cm x 12.9 cm.

*The following cards have flowers with birds or insects.*

17. Two birthday cards, one design of primroses and colourful ferns with a butterfly, on a brown background. 15 cm x 7.2 cm.

18. Five gilt-edged cards from two sets. Two have a butterfly or dragonfly hovering over roses or cornfield flowers, one dated 1879 by the sender; three from another set have a ladybird on a dog rose, bees on cherries, and a butterfly on a white ribbon (included as one of the set). 10.8 cm x 7 cm, 10.8 cm x 6.7 cm.

19. Seven embossed cards, pale green with scalloped edges, four designs of various flowers with birds or insects. 6.2 cm x 11 cm.

20. Two cards, one design of a butterfly on forget-me-nots on a gilt or a dark brown background. 10.9 cm x 6.7 cm.

21. Two cards, carnations with bees and a beetle, poppies with bees, one dated 1880 by the sender. 7.8 cm x 14.1 cm.

22. Two cards, arched sprays of cornflower and buttercup with a beetle, and roses and harebells with a bee, both with greetings in verse on a pale grey background. 7.4 cm x 18 cm.

23. Three cards (one birthday), two designs, a butterfly hovering over wild roses and a dragonfly on wisteria, signed with an undeciphered monogram. 12 cm x 9.3 cm.

24. Five cards, four designs of fuchsia, morning glory, rose, daisies or asters, each with a butterfly, on grey backgrounds with greetings on white scrolls. One card has a

gilt border. 10.7 cm x 7.1 cm, 11.9 cm x 8.1 cm.

25. A gilt-edged card with snowdrops, butterflies, and a swallow and a Christmas poem on reverse. 15.7 cm x 10 cm.

26. Three miscellaneous gilt-edged cards, forget-me-nots, heather, camellias and cyclamen, each with a butterfly or moth. Sizes up to 9.2 cm x 13.5 cm.

27. Two embossed cards with brown border, branches of hawthorn, sprays of roses, each with an insect. 13.5 cm x 10.2 cm.

28. Three embossed cards with white border and stylised designs with philadelphus, yellow daisies, and what might be a geranium species, all with butterflies. 11 cm x 9.7 cm.

29/30. Four cards with grey or brown backgrounds, three designs, wild roses with a butterfly, pink convolvulus with a fly, and marguerites with a butterfly, all with Christmas verses below. 10 cm x 17 cm.

31. Five embossed cards from one set, three with flowers, two with leaves and butterflies. 7 cm x 13.5 cm.

32. Seven miscellaneous cards with roses, various flowers and grasses, six with a butterfly, one with a dragonfly. 8 cm x 5 cm up to 8.4 cm x 13.7 cm.

## VOLUME 235: FLOWERS AND FERNS IN POTS AND VASES

"With vases and flowers and sweet happy hours
May Christmas greet all and lovingly fall
To you and to me."

The flower arranger of today would probably think poorly of some of these designs, but they do provide interesting study of Victorian taste in both the flowers and their containers. The cards were published about 1880-1885, and some show the Japanese and Grecian styles much admired at that time.

1. Four cards on dark blue or green backgrounds. Three show roses or lilies in flamboyant pottery vases, the fourth has roses in a glass vase, and the greetings are on white scrolls or on a board on an easel. 8.3 cm x 10.5 cm.

2. Five embossed bordered cards. Four have roses in decorated blue and gold vases; the fifth is a valentine with spring flowers and catkins in a blue and white gilded vase. 7.2 cm x 14.5 cm.

3. Six cards, grey background, four designs with roses, fuchsia, pansies, narcissus, in plain vases with coloured bands. Four cards are embossed. 4.7 cm x 14.2 cm.

4. Three cards, set in borders like picture frames. One has a gilded bowl of roses in a gilt frame with grey border; two have roses or pinks in slender silver vases framed in brown. 9.5 cm x 10.5 cm, 8.6 cm x 10.8 cm.

5. Three cards, grey borders, with vases of flowers on draped tables. One has a bowl of roses and two wine glasses with lilies of the valley, another has two vases with roses, geraniums, daisies and forget-me-nots. The third has a vase with coloured daisies and an easel with a picture and a paint box, and flowers below. 13.5 cm x 10 cm.

6. Two large embossed cards, roses in decorated blue and white pottery vases. 12.6 cm x 17.1 cm.

7. Three cards, mixed flowers in a white bowl, a blue and white mug, and a yellow vase with white figures, one dated 1883. 11.2 cm x 14.1 cm.

8. Three cards, two designs with roses, china asters, geraniums etc., in silver vases, with some blossoms scattered below. Verses by G A are on the backs, one beginning "Sweet summer flowers, supremely fair  Go charm the heart this Christmas day." 10.9 cm x 13.9 cm.

9. Three cards, two designs of an orange lily and a Eucharis lily with fern, in a coloured pottery jug and a glass vase. One is embossed, the other two have poems on reverse by S Ph A. 10.4 cm x 18.5 cm.

10. Two cards (one birthday), roses, geraniums, and other flowers in a decorated jug and a green pottery vase. 11 cm x 14 cm, 10.4 cm x 13.8 cm.

11. Two cards, roses in a wine glass, and roses in a glass bowl with a country scene behind and a poem on the back, perhaps designed by Muckley. 10.2 cm x 13.8 cm, 11.3 cm x 14.2 cm.

12. A card in Japanese style, with cherry blossom in a green vase, a fan, and beads, and a poem by Fannie Rochat on reverse. 14.1 cm x 11.8 cm.

13. Two cards, signed E G Parker, with verses by H Ridley on reverse. One has azaleas in a glass vase, the other chrysanthemums in a decorated green bowl, both on dark backgrounds. 11 cm x 14.4 cm.

14. A bordered card with wild roses, daisies, and ferns in a blue glass swan. These swans, cheaply made by press moulding, were popular ornaments in

**235.2**

Victorian times, and were manufactured by many glassmakers including Burtles Tate & Co., and Thomas Kield, both of Manchester. 15.7 cm x 12.4 cm.

15. A bordered card with tulips in a green vase, and a Christmas verse, quoted at the beginning of this volume. 12.9 cm x 16 cm.

16. Two cards, cyclamen or tulips in plant pots, the latter with narcissi and orchid flowers below. 7.5 cm x 9.6 cm, 11.9 cm x 16.4 cm.

17. Four cards, three designs of roses, two with vases, one with a glass flask. 8.6 cm x 12.6 cm.

18. One card, red and white geraniums in a blue jug, on a green mount with a border of butterflies. 11.7 cm x 17.9 cm.

19. Three cards, each with a single rose in a slender-necked vase. 9.2 cm x 14.5 cm.

20. Two embossed bordered cards, white Japanese anemones, and red flowers resembling single dahlias, in blue and silver patterned jug and tankard, both on identical carved sideboards, with verses by E I T. 10.4 cm x 14.2 cm.

21. A similar unbordered card with azaleas and forget-me-nots in a vase with flower and bird decoration standing on a carved table, with a verse entitled "Flora ever reigns" on reverse. 11.6 cm x 15.5 cm.

22. An interesting card with a dining table holding a variety of objects, including a vase of flowers, a bowl of pot-pourri, two cats, a Japanese parasol, a pair of gloves, and a book, set in an elaborate gilded border. 14.9 cm x 11.2 cm.

23. Three gilt-edged cards each with a broken pot ornamented with flowers, labelled Limoges China, Davenport Ware, Old Chelsea. 9.1 cm x 12.5 cm.

24. A card with a camellia in a handsome mother-of-pearl and gilt vase in Eastern style, with the caption below "Thy Christmas hours be bright as summer flowers", and a long Christmas poem on reverse. 11.5 cm x 16 cm.

25. Two gilt-bordered cards. One has an easel with pansies and a palette, the other has ferns in a decorated bowl on a tripod stand. The first card was dated 1884 by the sender and has a verse by Fanny Forrester on reverse. 11.3 cm x 17 cm, 10 cm x 15.2 cm.

26. An embossed card, pink and yellow bicolour roses in a Grecian style vase with forget-me-not garlands. 11.4 cm x 15.3 cm.

27. One card with roses and forget-me-nots in a slender glass vase. 10.2 cm x 14.3 cm.

28. An embossed card with a rose and bud in a green pottery vase. 12 cm x 18.9 cm.

29. Three cards with two-handled vases. Two have roses or lilies decorating a "Grecian" or "Etruscan" vase, the third has sunflowers in a peculiar vase with a picture of a child's head. 10.6 cm x 14.2 cm, 9.8 cm x 14.5 cm.

30. Two cards with borders imitating grained wood, around pots with house plants, cyclamen and a variety of primula. 15.2 cm x 11.8 cm.

31. Two cards, one with sea holly in a brown jug, and a birthday card with flowers lying before a two-handled vase, both with poems on reverse. 10.3 cm x 15 cm, 15 cm x 11.7 cm.

32. A card marked "Crown Perfumery Co. London", perhaps a trade card, with an embossed scrap of a plant pot with lilies of the valley and a Christmas verse on a white background.  11 cm x 14.3 cm.

33. Three cards, two designs of pottery jugs with ferns. (Compare with volume 100, no. 12, cards by R Rayment for S Hildesheimer & Co). 11 cm x 13.6 cm, 13 cm x 8.3 cm.

## VOLUME 236: FLOWERS, FRUIT, FOLIAGE IN VARIOUS CONTAINERS

**Flowers appear here in pots and vases, boxes and baskets, which range from the dainty handled possession of the lady of the house to the simple garden trug. Few were dated by the sender, but they were probably published in the early 1880's with some exceptions as noted.**

1. Four cards from three sets. Two have spring flowers in bowls signed G B L, with verses by H M Burnside, and two have violets or daisies and forget-me-nots in open boxes. Sizes up to 11.1 cm x 8 cm.

2. Four cards with white borders, violets, snowdrops, or forget-me-nots in open wooden boxes, one dated 1881 by the sender. 15 cm x 7.5 cm.

3. Four miscellaneous cards, roses or spring flowers in decorated or pottery vases, three dated 1881, 1881, 1882 by the senders. Sizes up to 9.5 cm x 13 cm.

4. Two cards (one birthday), with wide beige borders, one dated 1883 by the sender. One has a pot of geraniums in a latticed holder, the other has coleus in a decorated bowl. 11.4 cm x 14.4 cm.

5. Four cards (one birthday), with wide grey borders in three sizes, with flowers in pottery vases, a blue and white bowl, or a glass flask. The flowers include primroses, doronicum, roses, auricula, cornflowers, philadelphus, poppies. 6.6 cm x 9.5 cm up to 9.5 cm x 12.2 cm.

6. Four miscellaneous cards, lilies of the valley and forget-me-nots in a wineglass, poppies in a bowl, azaleas in a green and white pot, and narcissus and geraniums in a three-legged garden stand.
7 cm x 10.2 cm up to 10.5 cm x 13.3 cm.

7. Seven miscellaneous small cards, various flowers in decorated vases, two repeating a design in volume 235 no. 20, but without the sideboards, two dated 1882 by the senders.
Sizes up to 7.1 cm x 11.1 cm.

8. Five cards, ferns, heather, or cactus in bowls or plant pots.
7.4 cm x 11.2 cm up to 8.9 cm x 13.7 cm.

9. Five miscellaneous cards, various flowers in elaborately decorated bowls or vases. One card also has a metal dish and a bowl with begonia leaves.
5 cm x 8.6 cm up to 9.4 cm x 12.1 cm.

10. Four grey-bordered cards, three designs with pansies, narcissus and fern, or roses? in coloured pottery vases.
7.5 cm x 10.7 cm.

11. Five cards, roses or spring flowers in coloured and decorated pottery vases.
7 cm x 11 cm.

12. Seven small embossed cards, elegant baskets, four with roses and spring flowers, three with cherries, strawberries, or raspberries. 8.4 cm x 5 cm.

13. Six embossed gilt-bordered cards, five designs with roses and spring flowers, one dated 1879 by the senders. 10 cm x 6.6 cm.

**235.14**

14/15. Five embossed cards, four designs of rhododendrons with ferns, pink roses, geraniums, begonias in attractive wicker baskets. 14.2 cm x 11.2 cm.

16. Two embossed cards, yellow roses in a garden basket, red campions and convolvulus leaves in a wicker box, with greetings in gilt script. 14.9 cm x 11.4 cm.

17. Two gilt-bordered embossed cards, with flowers in small hampers, red anemones in one, narcissi, fern, and blue anemone blanda in the other.
15 cm x 11.8 cm.

18. Two cards, geraniums and fuchsia in an open gift box, poppies and cornflowers in a garden basket.
11.3 cm x 8 cm, 12.8 cm x 9.6 cm.

19. Two birthday cards, a basket with fuchsia and pansies, another with poppies and forget-me-nots, both standing on a garden parapet against a blue background, one dated 22-8-1883 by the sender.
14.5 cm x 11.3 cm.

20. Two bordered cards (one birthday), dainty baskets holding bouquets of spring flowers. 15.5 cm x 12 cm.

21. Two cards, wicker baskets filled with spring flowers and leaves.
16.5 cm x 13.2 cm.

22. One card, a basket of fruit, with peaches, grapes, gooseberries, and raspberries. 16.6 cm x 12 cm.

23. Three cards with wide cream or grey borders, one with spring flowers in a wicker trug, the other two with flowers in an upturned straw hat. 14.2 cm x 9.8 cm, 12.1 cm x 8.8 cm.

24. Three small cards, two designs of handled baskets with mixed flower bouquets. c1885. 7.1 cm x 7.1 cm.

25. Two grey-bordered cards, baskets with roses and geraniums. c1885.
12.1 cm x 9.5 cm.

26. Four gilt-edged cards, three designs with ferns in hanging ornamental wire baskets, with verses by Sarah Louisa Moore, F E D. Two cards have illuminated designs on reverse and may have been originally joined as a folder. Sizes up to 8 cm x 11.2 cm.

27. Four bordered cards (three with texts), three designs with violets, primroses, or pinks in decorative containers hanging from coloured ribbons. c1885.
7.5 cm x 11.3 cm.

28. Four cards, two designs of carnations or roses and philadelphus with baskets, later 1880's. Sizes up to 11.5 cm x 8 cm.

29. Four cards, three designs of baskets with fuchsias, geraniums, roses, sweet peas, lilac, on dark brown backgrounds.
10.7 cm x 6.7 cm.

## VOLUME 237:
## FLOWERS, FRUIT, FOLIAGE IN CARDS WITH DECORATIVE BORDERS AND BACKGROUNDS

These cards are grouped here as examples of ornamental borders and interesting treatment. Some were inspired by Japanese art and a few have classical themes. They were published in the early 1880's with one or two exceptions as stated, and most of them are good examples of Victorian flower painting and design.

1. A gilt-edged, embossed card with irregular border, and an illuminated greeting in an oval gilt-bordered vignette framed in roses and alpine flowers.
11.2 cm x 15.4 cm.

2. Five elegant cards with four styles of border patterned in gilt and black, one on a black background. There are four designs of flower bouquets, two dated 1877, 1878 by the senders. 7.4 cm x 11 cm.

3. Four similar cards, two with blue and gold patterned borders, one with green and gold and one with purple and gold border, the two latter having an insect on the flowers. One was dated 1879 by the sender. 6.7 cm x 9.6 cm.

4. Seven well-designed cards (two with valentine greeting), with black and gilt patterned borders and five designs of trails of flowers and leaves around the greetings. One was dated 1881 by the sender. 5.9 cm x 12.8 cm.

5. An embossed card with a Christmas verse on a white panel bordered by spring flowers on a gilt background. 14 cm x 9 cm.

6. Six cards on brown or gilt background, with four designs of roses, azaleas, fuchsias, forget-me-nots, pansies, and a gilt or a red line border. 12.8 cm x 8.3 cm.

7. Two interesting cards with flowers and leaves printed in silver and gold on dark brown background in a gold and silver border, one dated 1881 by the sender. 7.8 cm x 12.8 cm.

8. Two cards, snowdrops with garden daisies and hawthorn and appleblossom in a scallop-edged gilt panel with greetings on a similar white panel. 7.2 cm x 11.8 cm.

9. Three cards, roses and fern with snowdrops, lilies of the valley, or white hyacinths, on gilt backgrounds with seasonal verses by Astley H Baldwin. 9.1 cm x 12.4 cm.

10. Two cards, each with a pink rose on a grey background with a bird's nest, and a border patterned in gilt and white. 13.7 cm x 7.8 cm.

11. Three decorative cards with gilt-patterned borders. One has holly in an oval vignette and a Japanese style bird design on reverse, another is embossed with a butterfly on yellow flowers. The third card has an intricate design in Japanese style with flowers in a gilded pot on a stand, with birds flying above and irises on each side. Sizes up to 9.3 cm x 13 cm.

12. Four cards in Japanese style, one with fans and leaves, three with flowers, including the iris and waterlily often seen in these cards. The flowers and leaves have gilt outlines. 8 cm x 12.8 cm up to 10 cm x 13.6 cm.

13. Four cards, one dated 1881, three designs picturing antique themes, on yellow, green, or brown backgrounds. One has Egyptian lotus motifs with a sphinx and a head of Cleopatra unsuitably adorned with roses. Roses also accompany a frieze with putti in a vaguely Pompeian style. The remaining two cards have a Greek tripod before a temple with ten Doric columns on the front, also adorned with roses, and doves. It is interesting to speculate where the artist found his model - the Parthenon at Athens has eight, the Basilica at Paestum has nine Doric columns; the temple at Didyma in Turkey has ten, but these are the later Ionic order. 12.5 cm x 8.3 cm.

14. Three embossed cards, with single flowers, iris, camellia, orange lily, in gilt-bordered oval vignettes in brown borders patterned with gilt motifs. Two have couplets by Eden Hooper. 8 cm x 12.3 cm.

15. Six cards, gilt backgrounds, from two sets. Three have garlands or a bouquet of mixed flowers; the others have trails of flowers around white panels with Christmas verse. 7.5 cm x 10.7 cm, 7.2 cm x 11.3 cm.

16. Four cards with white borders and gilt backgrounds. Two have the same design of spring flowers and leaves with greeting on a long scroll; one has a butterfly on philadelphus, and the fourth has geraniums with a ladybird and a Japanese fan. 7 cm x 16cm, 11.1 cm x 7.8 cm, 12 cm x 8.3 cm.

17. Two cards on backgrounds shaded from gold to brown, with Michaelmas daisies or white field roses. 9.3 cm x 13.6 cm, 10.3 cm x 7.1 cm.

18. An unusual embossed gilt-edged card with dog roses around a clock, with appropriate verse by S K C. 10.4 cm x 13.6 cm.

19. Four cards, one embossed with three sides enclosing a Gothic window and purple Morning Glory. Three from a set have various garden flowers with decorative leaves. 10.2 cm x 10.2 cm, 8 cm x 11.8 cm.

20. Four miscellaneous cards. One is shaped like a shield, with carnations in a blue and gold border, another has garden daisies around a white panel with Christmas verse; the third is tinselled, with ferns and blackberries, and the fourth has forget-me-nots on a slate with gilded border. 8.6 cm x 6 cm up to 10 cm x 11.5 cm.

21. Five cards on gilt backgrounds, geraniums in a blue and white pot, arbutus flowers and berries, roses and philadelphus, harebells and ferns, lilies in a green plantpot. Sizes up to 7.3 cm x 12 cm.

22. Seven cards on gilt backgrounds, with roses, apple blossom, daisies, evening primrose, leaves and grasses, two dated 1884 by the sender. 7.4 cm x 10.8 cm.

23. A large card with blackberry branches over a patterned mosaic background in a border perhaps inspired by Pompeii. 16.3 cm x 11.1 cm.

24. Three cards in Japanese style with bright coloured flowers and leaves and some gilding. 10.1 cm x 15.4 cm, 7.7 cm x 12.2 cm.

25. Two cards, gilt borders, one with flowering branches, butterfly and dragonflies, the other with a spider's web and red and blue flowers. 9.1 cm x 18 cm, 9.8 cm x 15 cm.

26. Two cards with gilt-patterned borders around violets or forget-me-nots. They have verses signed E K D on reverse printed in a style reminiscent of Marcus Ward. 13 cm x 9.7 cm.

27. Five embossed cards, two designs of roses or violets and lilies of the valley on backgrounds in four different colours. Two cards are on illuminated mounts, one with a patterned back, the other with a verse by Fanny Rochat on reverse. 10.9 cm x 7.1 cm, 15.3 cm x 11.3 cm.

28. Three cards (one birthday) with gilt-patterned coloured borders, and a bunch of mixed flowers or a garland with birds. One has a plain back, the others have a patterned back with a verse. 10 cm x 14.4 cm, 9 cm x 13 cm.

29. Five miscellaneous cards with spring flowers on bordered mounts. 6.9 cm x 10 cm up to 9.6 cm x 15.4 cm.

30. A lace-edged card with azaleas and carnations, dated 1887 by the sender. 12.6 cm x 16.1 cm.

31. Four miscellaneous cards with flowers, ferns, and catkins, with interesting coloured and illuminated patterned borders. 6.7 cm x 10.7 cm up to 14.4 cm x 8.8 cm.

32. Four miscellaneous cards with various decorated borders or backgrounds, one with a long poem on reverse, another printed "with Samuel Hamer's Compliments". 12 cm x 7.6 cm up to 14.1 cm x 10 cm.

33. Three cards, one with geraniums in a black, white, and gold patterned border, and two with a gold-patterned border with lilies or pink florets and verses from Longfellow. 15.3 cm x 12 cm, 10 cm x 13 cm.

34. Four cards with patterned grey borders from three sets, one with carnations, the

others with bouquets of flowers.
Sizes up to 8.5 cm x 11.8 cm.

35. Eight miscellaneous cards with silver or gilt backgrounds or gilt decoration, with various flowers.
7.5 cm x 5.2 cm up to 8.1 cm x 12.2 cm.

## VOLUME 238:
## FLOWERS, FRUIT, FOLIAGE, WITH VARIATIONS

**Cards with feathers and fans appear here, with some in trompe l'oeil style showing open books or envelopes and backgrounds like wooden walls. A number have hands, holding flowers or in a handclasp, and three give an interesting selection of feminine fashions in sleeves. Some cards with wide borders are included, and most were published in the early 1880's.**

1/2. Nine embossed cards (four birthday) with four designs of roses and spring flowers on beige or green backgrounds. The greetings are printed on a quill pen. 15.3 cm x 6.9 cm.

3. Three small embossed cards on an imitation wood background, each with a small motif of a feather with fuchsias, carnations, or roses. 9.3 cm x 5.5 cm.

4. Three embossed cards with trompe l'oeil effect, showing books with gilded clasps and tooled covers. One has roses and a cat, another cyclamen and heather, the third violets and lilies of the valley, and all have greetings on white bordered panels. 7.7cm x 11.7 cm.

5. Three embossed cards with the same design of forget-me-nots and an open book, with three different greetings and backgrounds of blue or cream. 10.6 cm x 6.4 cm.

6. Three cards, one an envelope with embossed poppies and cornflower and a quill pen. The other two have open books, one with forget-me-nots, the other with cornfield flowers and a greeting made up of song titles. 10.4 cm x 6.8 cm up to 14 cm x 9.8 cm.

7. Two cards, one a briefcase with a sea scene and forget-me-nots published by M Priester's Continental Printing Co. The other has an open book with a winter scene and daisies, and was published by Albert Marx. 12.2 cm x 8.1 cm, 15 x 10.9 cm.

8. Three cards, two designs in two sizes with a red or yellow rose in an open envelope pinned to a wooden panel, one dated 1884 by the sender. 12 cm x 15 cm, 11 cm x 13.1 cm.

9. Four cards, with fuchsias and asters, ivy and forget-me-nots, poppies and cornflowers, or mistletoe, on brown or cream grained wood backbrounds with greetings on scrolls nailed to the wood. Sizes up to 10 cm x 13 cm.

10. Five cards, two designs. Four cards have a fan with a bouquet in frilled paper or lace and a camellia, a ring, and a pair of gloves, with four different greetings, one for a valentine, and one for a birthday on a gilt-bordered mount. The fifth card, probably from the same set, has a butterfly and roses. 10.1 cm x 6.5 cm, mount 12.5 cm x 8.6 cm.

11. Three cards, two designs of a fan and red and white camellias or hawthorn in a blue circle set in a brown background with orange line borders. 11.5 cm x 11.5 cm.

*Numbers 12-16 have flowers with hands showing part of a sleeve or cuff.*

12. Three small embossed cards on mounts with coloured patterned borders, each with a hand holding a small bunch of flowers. c1880. 10.1 cm x 6.7 cm.

13. Six cards, five designs from three sets showing hands holding flowers. Two have gilt-patterned borders, one dated 1882 by the sender.
8.4 cm x 5.6 cm up to 12.1 cm x 8.2 cm.

14.Two cards, with roses or forget-me-nots around a friendly handshake. 11.6 cm x 7.71 cm.

15. Five cards, one with a vase of violets on a table and two clasped female hands, four with a hand holding flowers, one marked Raphael Tuck, London, included here for comparison with similar unmarked cards. 8.2 cm x 4.7 cm up to 12.7 cm x 9.5 cm.

16. Nine small cards from several sets, including seven with hands and flowers and two with flowers and a bird. Three of these cards are marked Daisy M Craven or S A Craven, and were probably American calling cards. Later 1880's.
8 cm x 4.7 cm up to 10.7 cm x 6.8 cm.

*The following cards have wide coloured borders, some shaded to give a three-dimensional appearance.*

17. Two grey-bordered cards, one design of pale blue plumbago and ferns, with verses by Sabrina and F G on reverse. 9.8 cm x 17.5 cm.

18. Three cards, beige borders, two designs of white flowers, nuts, and autumn leaves. 10.2 cm x 13 cm.

19. Two cards, white geraniums and a variety of double marguerite or pyrethrum(?) in wide grey borders. 14.8 cm x 9.8 cm.

237.12

20. Three miscellaneous cards, mistletoe and Christmas roses with blue border, geraniums and phlox with beige border, roses and forget-me-nots in grey border. Sizes up to 9.8 cm x 13.3 cm.

21. Two cards, violets and lilies of the valley in a beige border, dated 1882 by the sender, convolvulus and forget-me-nots in a grey border.
13 cm x 9.8 cm, 14.3 cm x 11 cm.

22. Four small cards with three designs of spring flowers in wide cream-coloured borders, one dated 1884 by the sender. 10.6 cm x 7.4 cm.

23. Four cards in two sizes with wide beige borders and bunches of spring flowers and grasses, one dated 1890 but probably published earlier.
10.1 cm x 7.1 cm, 9.3 cm x 15 cm.

24. Three cards with stylised flowers and grasses on shaded backgrounds in cream-coloured borders, with poems on reverse. 10.5 cm x 14.4 cm.

25. Six miscellaneous small cards with flowers and leaves and wide beige or grey borders, one dated 1884 by the sender. 8.8 cm x 6.2 cm up to 11 cm x 8.3 cm.

26. Three cards with brown line inside wide border, each with spring flowers and ferns, one with a horseshoe. Sizes up to 8.2 cm x 12.5 cm.

27. Four cards, various flowers in arched vignettes with wide borders. Sizes up to 10 cm x 15.5 cm.

238.4

## VOLUME 239:
## FLOWERS, FRUIT, FOLIAGE, EMBOSSED CARDS, c1879-1885

**The process of embossing is particularly suitable for designs with flowers, and the embossed cards in volumes 239 and 240 have been brought together to give opportunity for the study of this technique, though many more appear in other volumes. Designs were printed both plain and embossed, and some examples appear here of sets in both styles. The process of embossing made printing on the back of the card difficult, so verses and sentiments, usually brief, appeared on the front.**

1/2. Fourteen cards, six designs on three background colours with six different verses on gilt-edged scrolls. The flowers appearing include roses, forget-me-nots, lilies of the valley, cornflowers, pansies, and a possible? rhododendron. Two were dated 1879 by the senders.
7.4 cm x 10.8 cm.

3/4. Nine cards, white embossed borders, six designs of roses, pansies, violets, primulas, camellias, forget-me-nots on cream background, with greetings or texts on small white panel and verse or text below. One is on a bordered mount, and another was dated 1879 by the sender.
7.1 cm x 11 cm, 10.3 cm x 14.2 cm (mount).

5/6. Thirteen cards, with eight formal designs of spring and summer flowers, three dated 1879, 1880, 1881, by the senders. Ten have gilt borders, three are plain with coloured borders and texts.
7 cm x 11 cm.

7. Ten similar small cards (including two plain duplicates), with six designs in formal style, one card on an illuminated mount. Two were dated 1879, 1882, by the senders. 4.8 cm x 8.7 cm, 7.3 cm x 11 cm (mount).

8. Nine cards from three sets, formal designs of spring and summer flowers, two with a moth. 8.6 cm x 5 cm up to 9.5 cm x 6.4 cm.

9. Five cards (one with text), four designs of roses, camellias, forget-me-nots and lilies of the valley, and cornfield flowers, on shaded buff or grey ground, one dated 1880 by the sender. 6.1 cm x 9.3 cm.

10. Six cards from two sets on grey or beige backgrounds. Four have two designs of waterlilies, a lily and forget-me-nots, with greetings in scrolls, one dated 1879 by the sender. Two have bunches of spring flowers. 6.8 cm x 10 cm, 7 cm x 10.5 cm.

11. Eight gilt-bordered cards, six with bouquets or garlands of spring flowers, convolvulus, or heather, two with ivy and birds or a bird's nest. One was dated 1881 by the sender. 6.8 cm x 9.5 cm.

12. Four cards with gilt line borders, three designs of roses, violets, forget-me-nots, one dated 1881 by the sender.
7 cm x 10.5 cm.

13. Four cards from two sets (one birthday). Two have a butterfly with cornflowers or roses, one dated 1879 by the sender. Two have bunches of spring flowers or antirrhinums, one dated 1880 by the sender.
5.5 cm x 13.2 cm, 6.5 cm x 13 cm.

14. Four gilt-edged cards. Three have two designs of bunches of roses and spring flowers, and one from another set has pink roses and a verse by E E R and was dated 1881 by the sender.
7.5 cm x 12 cm, 5.5 cm x 12.7 cm.

15. Six gilt-edged cards from two sets, all with bouquets of mixed flowers. Four are on blue or beige backgrounds, one dated 1882 by the sender; two have two kittens or puppies in a basket hanging above the flowers. 6.3 cm x 11.3 cm, 5.3 cm x 11.9 cm.

16. Five gilt-edged cards from three sets, with flower bouquets. Two are on dark shaded backgrounds, one is a valentine, and two have greetings on a small moveable card. 6.5 cm x 10.9 cm up to 8.5 cm x 11.6 cm.

17. Five cards from two sets. Two have flowers in shell vases, marked copyright L J Alloo, dated 1882 by the senders. Three have two designs of flowers in glass tumblers.
7.6 cm x 10.9 cm, 7.6 cm x 11.1 cm.

18. Four cards, formal designs of iris, morning glory, lilies, and an unidentified blue flower on mottled or shaded grey backgrounds, one dated 1882 by the sender.
9.6 cm x 6 cm up to 11.5 cm x 7.7 cm.

19. Three miscellaneous birthday cards with roses and forget-me-nots and gilt line borders. Sizes up to 8 cm x 10.4 cm.

20. Three cards, two with the same design of morning glory, the third from a different set with violets and a scarf tied in a bow. 11.1 cm x 7.4 cm, 10.8 cm x 7.2 cm.

21. Five cards from four sets. Two have flower bouquets, one with an envelope, the other with a pinned back corner. Another has spring flowers around a nest with eggs, and two have the same design of a wreath of roses and cornflowers with a peacock feather (one with birthday greeting).
6.6 cm x 9.8 cm up to 12.7 cm x 9.3 cm.

22. Eight cards from three sets, seven with gilt line borders, one with grey edge. Four small cards have flower or ivy garlands, with verse or text, three have flower bouquets, and one a butterfly with spring flowers.
5.7 cm x 8.7 cm, 7.1 cm x 10.4 cm, 5.8 cm x 10.2 cm.

23/24. Eleven miscellaneous bordered cards with roses and spring and summer flowers in bouquets, wreaths, or sprays.
5.4 cm x 8.8 cm up to 8.3 cm x 12.7 cm.

25. Eight miscellaneous unbordered cards, including one with the red "Bottle Brush" (callistemon), and two with Alpine flowers and mountain scenery. 4.7 cm x 7.9 cm up to 7 cm x 11.4 cm.

## VOLUME 240:
## FLOWERS, FRUIT, FOLIAGE, EMBOSSED CARDS

**These cards date from 1880 to 1885, with a few of later date, and include some large examples.**

1. Three cards with two designs of bouquets of spring flowers, including narcissi, bluebells, daisies, pinks, forget-me-nots, with leaves and grasses, on blue or ivory background, with verses, two signed G A.
9 cm x 14.7 cm, 7.4 cm x 12.3 cm.

2. Three cards, two designs of roses and spring flowers in wine glasses, on grey, cream, or brown backgrounds. Two have verses by Fannie Rochat, one a birthday greeting, and one was dated 1880 by the sender. 12.3 cm x 9.5 cm.

3. Four attractive cards with wreaths of dog roses, daisies and forget-me-nots, or china asters with Virginia creeper around

verses and greetings, one in Italian.
8.7 cm x 13.3 cm.

4. Two valentine cards with sprays of coloured leaves and flowers on either side of verses headed "Greetings fond and true" and "Love the Charmer".
12 cm x 10.7 cm.

5. Four cards. One has a basket of snowdrops, dated 1883 by the sender, another ferns, forget-me-nots and lilies of the valley. Two from a set have sprays of flowers resembling azaleas and gentians, but not positively identified.
12.8 cm x 10 cm, 11.2 cm x 6.5 cm.

6. Two cards with flowers resembling azaleas, on cream or blue background with greetings in illuminated letters.
9.9 cm x 15.2 cm.

7. Three cards, each with a flower posy lying on a table, made up with a centre rose and rings of spring flowers or rosebuds, in a lace frill. (This type of bouquet appears as an animated card. See Buday, plates 166-8). 11.9 cm x 8.1 cm.

8. Five cards (one birthday) with four designs of holly, roses, forget-me-nots, daisies, leaves and ferns, on blue or grey backgrounds with greetings in decorative panels. 9.1 cm x 12.5 cm.

9. A card with an embossed bouquet of roses and spring flowers on a monochrome country scene, pinned on a background resembling grained wood in trompe l'oeil fashion. 9.4 cm x 13 cm.

10. Five cards from three sets in similar style, with bouquets of spring and summer flowers, leaves and grasses, all with verses, two dated 1881 by the senders. Sizes up to 9.2 cm x 13.2 cm.

11. Three grey-bordered cards, two from the same set with dog roses or pinks, the third with roses and ferns, all with verses. 14.6 cm x 8.8 cm, 15.4 cm x 10.1 cm.

12. Four miscellaneous cards, one a valentine, two with birthday greetings, with irises, dog roses, fuchsias, and geraniums.
13.6 cm x 6.5 cm up to 9.1 cm x 14.8 cm.

13. Two cards, pansies, camellias with forget-me-nots and lilies of the valley, on grey backgrounds. 12 cm x 9.2 cm.

14. Three gilt-bordered cards, cornucopias with roses and spring flowers, and verses or greetings on decorated scrolls, two signed Ada and A R. 17.5 cm x 9 cm.

15. Three cards (one birthday) gilt line borders, one with a rose and a garland of forget-me-nots, another a pansy with lilies of the valley, the third a white single rose with weigela(?) 8 cm x 17.3 cm.

16. Two cards, wide grey borders, anemones or pansies with trails of white flowers and leaves around seasonal verses. 11.7 cm x 13.7 cm.

17. Two cards, ferns and flowers in baskets hanging from rustic framework, with verses below. 10.1 cm x 13.5 cm.

18. Three miscellaneous cards (one birthday), bunches of spring flowers and grasses, one dated 1886 by the sender. Sizes up to 13.8 cm x 10.9 cm.

19. Five cards on cream or fawn backgrounds, three designs of white flowers - narcissi, lilies, snowdrops, fritillaries. 6.4 cm x 13.9 cm.

20/21. Eight gilt-edged cards from two sets, with seven designs of roses, camellias, spring flowers.
10.2 cm x 10.2 cm, 7.8 cm x 12.4 cm.

22. Two cards, white field roses and heather, edelweiss, on grey background with greeting in embossed gilt letters. 10 cm x 13.3 cm.

23. Two cards, various coloured ferns with hawthorn or weigela on cream coloured background with greeting in embossed gilt letters. 10.1 cm x 15.4 cm.

24. Two cards with gilt line borders, violets or forget-me-nots and lilies of the valley arranged in a horseshoe shape, with greeting verses in embossed gilt letters. 10.8 cm x 16.5 cm.

25. A large pale blue card with roses, fuchsia, violets and hawthorn with background of shadowy leaves, a large shell below, and a Christmas verse. 19 cm x 14 cm.

26. Three cards, violets in a paper holder, pink flowers and lilies of the valley on a large leaf, a rose and fuchsias on an open envelope, probably later 1880's. 15 cm x 10 cm, 10.9 cm x 15.5 cm, 14.8 cm x 9.8 cm.

27. Two cards, one a bouquet with roses, pansies, and forget-me-nots on a stand of curious appearance, with greeting on an envelope, the other eucalyptus on a gilt-bordered semi-circle. 12.5 cm x 9.6 cm, 13.5 cm x 9.6 cm.

28. Four cards, two designs, with butterflies hovering over convolvulus and spring flowers, or roses and fuchsia, on beige-coloured backgrounds. Two have birthday greetings and one was dated 1890 by the sender, but they may have been published earlier. 14.3 cm x 10.2 cm.

# VOLUME 241:
# CARDS WITH ROSES, MOST FROM UNTRACED PUBLISHERS

**In the language of flowers the rose is the emblem of love, and its frequent association with the forget-me-not might indicate some use of symbolism in greeting card design as well as giving a pleasing colour contrast. Roses were popular subjects for Victorian artists, and the following three volumes are devoted to roses unaccompanied except by occasional small trails of flowers and foliage; a number of cards with roses together with different flowers appear in other volumes. Most of the cards here portray cultivated garden roses, with some wild roses and moss roses; it is outside the scope of this catalogue to name the Victorian species, but they should provide interesting study for gardeners.**

**The cards in volume 241 are small to medium in size, and were published from 1880-1885 with a few exceptions as stated.**

*Numbers 1-11 are unbordered.*

1. Five embossed cards (two birthday), with three designs of a single red or yellow rose from two sets, one dated 1880 by the sender. 7.1 cm x 10.3 cm, 7.6 cm x 10 cm.

2. Four cards (one birthday), one with a red rose on a brown background, three from another set with red or pink moss roses on green or beige backgrounds, all with greetings on white panels. 12 cm x 7 cm, 11.2 cm x 6.9 cm.

3. Five embossed cards, four from one set with three designs of red, pink or yellow moss roses on brown backgrounds, and one from another set with pink roses dated 1881 by the sender. 6.8 cm x 10.2 cm, 7.1 cm x 9.2 cm.

4. Seven embossed cards from two sets, red, pink, or white roses on blue or cream backgrounds with greetings in gilt embossed letters, two birthday. One was dated 1882 by the sender. 7.3 cm x 11.2 cm, 11.2 cm x 7.3 cm.

5. Four embossed cards, roses and buds, three with red, pink or white flowers on shaded grey backgrounds, and one from another set with pink moss roses on a pale green background. 9.1 cm x 12.6 cm, 11.5 cm x 8.3 cm.

6. Five embossed cards from three sets. Two have pink roses growing in coloured pots, one dated 1882 by the sender; two have pink roses and buds on grey backgrounds, one with valentine greeting, and the fifth has roses and buds with

decorative coloured leaves and a ribbon bow. 7 cm x 11.4 cm up to 13 cm x 10 cm.

7. Four cards, two with pink moss roses, one with red roses and buds, the fourth with a pink and a red rose and ferns. 7.4 cm x 11 cm up to 11 cm x 12.5 cm.

8. Three miscellaneous cards, sprays of pink roses, one with a butterfly, another with Italian greeting. 10.4 cm x 6.1 cm, 11.5 cm x 6.8 cm, 14.8 cm x 8.5 cm.

9. Three cards, two designs of a pink or a white rose with ferns on a pale blue background. 10.7 cm x 7.5 cm.

10/11. Eight embossed cards, four designs in two sizes of red, pink, or yellow roses hanging from a nail, with a white label. One has an appropriate sentiment "Each leaf of these fair roses unfolds a happy day in the New Year". 10.2 cm x 18.1 cm, 8.2 cm x 14.3 cm.

12. Four embossed cards, two with gilt line border and a butterfly on pink or yellow roses, and two others with sprays of pink or yellow buds and roses. 8.5 cm x 12.8 cm, 8.6 cm x 13 cm.

*Numbers 13-28 are bordered.*

13. Three miscellaneous cards, one with a bunch of roses on a parapet, another with roses lying on a cloth on a wooden garden table, the third with pink roses lying on an open book. Sizes up to 14 cm x 10 cm.

14. Two gilt-edged cards, one with two roses in a rectangular vignette on a background scene with birds, the other with two pink roses in a glass bowl in an oval vignette on a grey background, and a poem by C D on reverse. 10.6 cm x 14.2 cm, 11.1 cm x 15.1 cm.

15. Three miscellaneous cards, one with red roses on a blue background, another with moss roses on gilt, the third with embossed roses and ferns in a rustic pot. 12 cm x 7.6 cm, 13.9 cm x 8.6 cm, 10.2 cm x 15.7 cm.

16. Two cards, a birthday card with pink roses trailing round a rustic border, the other a yellow rose and leaves. 9 cm x 12 cm, 10.2 cm x 14.4 cm.

17. Four cards, two from one set with a pink or a white rose and bud lying on grass, another with a beetle on a pink rose and a Christmas poem by Shirley Wynne, the third two red roses, with a long poem by Agnes R Howell on reverse beginning "Fairy flowers are we ...". 14.5 cm x 9.4 cm, 12.2 cm x 8.5 cm.

18. Five embossed cards, one a birthday card with a pink rose, the others with the same design of a red rose on three different coloured backgrounds with three different greetings. 11.3 cm x 6.2 cm.

19. Four miscellaneous cards, two with red roses and spring flowers, one with a red and a yellow rose and buds, the fourth with a red rose and buds. Sizes up to 13.5 cm x 10.2 cm.

20. Five cards, two with grey borders and a pink or a yellow rose, three other miscellaneous gilt-edged cards with red roses. 5 cm x 8 cm up to 12 cm x 8 cm.

21. Five miscellaneous cards with gilt line borders, three with red, two with red, yellow and white roses. Two were dated 1883, 1888 by the senders. 9.5 cm x 6.1 cm up to 12.5 cm x 8.1 cm.

22. Four cards from two sets. Two have birthday verses with pink moss roses and buds; the others have a red or a yellow rose in a glass bottle packed in a wooden box with moss. 7.7 cm x 11.4 cm, 7.9 cm x 11.5 cm.

23. Three grey-bordered cards, pink or red roses with foliage and seasonal poems. 8.6 cm x 8.5 cm.

24. Two silver-bordered cards, a red or a bicolour rose in a circular vignette with silver border. 10.8 cm x 10.8 cm.

25/26. Ten gilt-bordered cards, five designs of various coloured roses on blue or ivory backgrounds. 8.8 cm x 12.4 cm.

27. Four miscellaneous cards, with red, pink, apricot and bicolour roses, one with forget-me-nots. Sizes up to 8.7 cm x 13.2 cm.

28. Six cards from three sets, five designs of white and pink roses, two with a ribbon bow. Sizes up to 11.5 cm x 7.7 cm.

29. Five miscellaneous cards, three with yellow garden roses, two with white field roses and ferns, one dated 1884 by the sender. 8 cm x 9.1 cm up to 10.4 cm x 13.2 cm.

30. Nine small unbordered miscellaneous cards, including three with moss roses and one with roses in a basket. Sizes up to 8.8 cm x 6.3 cm.

31. Eight small unbordered cards from one set, seven designs, each with a single rose, one dated 1883 by the sender. Six are text cards. 6.2 cm x 10.4 cm.

32. Seven small bordered cards, later 1880's, including a rose in a glass vase and another with a scenic background. One is a later version of a card in no. 20. Sizes up to 6 cm x 8.7 cm.

## VOLUME 242: ROSES, LARGE CARDS PUBLISHED IN THE EARLY 1880'S

**This volume demonstrates the number of ways in which roses can be posed for their portraits - standing up, lying down, in vases with lace, hanging, reflected in a lake, and unsuitably frosted. The naive verses accompanying many of the cards link the picture with the season**
**"May dear old Christmas banish all thy woes**
**And make thee bright and blooming as a rose".**

*Numbers 1-21 are bordered.*

1. Three embossed cards, with bunches of pink, red, or yellow roses on dark backgrounds in gilt-patterned borders. 16 cm x 11.9 cm.

2. Three cards with gilt line borders, two designs of pink or pink and white roses on blue, cream, or grey backgrounds with greeting verses, one birthday. 15.6 cm x 11.6 cm.

3. Two embossed cards with grey borders and a red rose, one with a mountain scene in the background. 14 cm x 11.4 cm, 14.4 cm x 11 cm.

4. Two embossed cards, one with two birds perched on a rose branch, the other with a red rose and buds before a stone wall, dated 1882 by the sender. 15.4 cm x 11.9 cm, 15.2 cm x 11.2 cm.

5. Four cards with grey borders, three embossed, three designs of a pink, white, or yellow moss rose, one with birthday greeting. One card was dated 1881 by the sender. 10 cm x 15.3 cm.

6. Two white-bordered cards, one with a hand in a lace cuff holding a pink and white rose, another a shaded pink rose in a glass carafe. 10.2 cm x 15.4 cm.

7. Two cards with red or pink roses and leaves on shaded blue backgrounds with greetings in embossed gilt letters. 13 cm x 17.5 cm.

8. An embossed card with red roses hanging from a nail by a blue ribbon bow, with a ladybird on a leaf. 9.4 cm x 17.8 cm.

9. Three gilt-bordered cards, each with two roses and ferns. 11.6 cm x 14.3 cm.

10. Two embossed cards, each with shaded pink and white roses and moss in an arched panel in a cream-coloured border with gilt decoration. 11.2 cm x 15.6 cm.

11. Two cards, yellow roses in grey borders, one with a poem by J L Richardson on reverse, the other dated 1881 by the sender.
11.5 cm x 15 cm, 11.4 cm x 15.2 cm.

12. Two cards, shaded white roses, one with a poem on reverse, the other dated 1880 by the sender.
10.4 cm x 14.2 cm, 9.8 cm x 13.9 cm.

13. Two cards, one with red roses and white daphne against a country background, the other pink roses on grass.
15.1 cm x 11.5 cm, 17 cm x 12.5 cm.

14. Two embossed cards, a red or a pink rose reflected in a lake. 11.1 cm x 15.8 cm.

15. Two embossed cards with gilt line borders, one a lady in a plumed hat amongst a mass of pink roses and moss, the other unusual single orange roses, perhaps rosa moyesii. Both have greetings in embossed gilt letters.
11 cm x 18 cm, 11.8 cm x 18.2 cm.

16. Two grey-bordered cards, red roses on a background with a house, and a group of white, pink, red and yellow roses on a curved stand.
10.7 cm x 15 cm, 17 cm x 13.1 cm.

17. Two cards, a ladybird on a red rose precariously balanced on a marble stand, with a poem on reverse about the Ladybird and the Rose, and a bunch of roses on a dark background, with a patterned back resembling some seen on Marcus Ward cards, dated 1883 by the sender. 11.2 cm x 15.2 cm, 14.4 cm x 12 cm.

18. A gilt-edged card with a garland of pink roses. 13 cm x 16.6 cm.

19. Two gilt-edged cards, red and apricot roses on a dark background with gilt embossed greeting, and red roses with two white butterflies.
12.5 cm x 17.5 cm, 9.9 cm x 15 cm.

20. Two cards, gilt line borders, a hanging bunch of pink roses and daisies, and an embossed card with pink and white moss roses lying on grass.
11.8 cm x 17.7 cm, 17.2 cm x 11.2 cm.

21. Two gilt-bordered cards, one with yellow roses on a blue mosaic background and a birthday greeting in a silver panel, the other with a bunch of yellow roses, and a verse by M G Watkins MA, dated 1882 by the sender.
13.5 cm x 17 cm, 16.4 cm x 11.9 cm.

*Numbers 22-32 are unbordered.*

22. Two cards, red or pink roses on pale green background. These resemble early Prang cards but are not marked.
10.3 cm x 14.3 cm.

23/25. Eight embossed cards on grey or pale green backgrounds, seven designs, two of moss roses, five of garden roses and ferns, all with rhyming greetings in embossed gold letters. These resemble Emily Whymper's cards for S Hildesheimer.
11 cm x 17.8 cm., 10.2 cm x 16.3 cm.

26. Two embossed cards, one with a red rose in a white lace jabot, the other with a red rose in a lace-edged napkin or kerchief. 11 cm x 16.5 cm, 13.2 cm x 13 cm.

27. Three embossed cards, hanging bunches of roses, leaves, and ferns, with greetings in gold embossed letters.
12.9 cm x 18 cm.

28. Two cards, pink and white roses on a cream background, red roses on a blue background dated 1881 by the sender.
15.7 cm x 9.8 cm, 15.6 cm x 11.5 cm.

29. Two cards, pink and white roses, and frosted pink roses on a pale blue background dated 1883 by the sender.
17.5 cm x 11.8 cm, 20.2 cm x 11.7 cm.

30. Three cards (one birthday), a pink, white, or shaded pink rose with buds or ferns on coloured backgrounds with greeting verses, one dated 1883 by the sender. Sizes up to 11.6 cm x 15.5 cm.

31. Four miscellaneous cards on grey or green backgrounds. Two have red roses and ferns, one has pink shaded roses and white jasmine, the fourth embossed red, pink, and yellow roses. Sizes up to 10 cm x 14.7 cm.

32. Two cards with pink roses and lilies of the valley or daisies. One has a poem on reverse. 11.8 cm x 15.2 cm, 14.5 cm x 11 cm.

33. Three cards, one with a pink and white rose and ferns on blue background. The others have the same design of a pink rose and bud, one a large gilt-edged frosted card, the other small and unbordered.
9.3 cm x 13 cm, 15.3 cm x 9.9 cm, 10.5 cm x 6.3 cm.

34. Two bordered cards, one with a yellow rose dated 1886 by the sender, another with an unusual very dark red rose and berries and a birthday greeting. The first card has a verse signed Sarah Louisa Moore. 9.9 cm x 14.7 cm, 9.9 cm x 15.4 cm.

## VOLUME 243:
## ROSES, LATER CARDS, FROM ABOUT 1885 TO THE EARLY 1890'S

*Numbers 1-8 are bordered, published in the late 1880's.*

1. Two cards, bunches of roses on cream backgrounds. 11.5 cm x 15.4 cm.

2. Two cards, each with a single rose on a cream background.
11.2 cm x 14.4 cm, 11.5 cm x 15.2 cm.

3. Three cards, gilt line borders, red, pink, or yellow roses with a lake in the background and birds or a butterfly.
10 cm x 13.8 cm.

4. Two cards with gilt line borders, sprays of pink roses.
11.4 cm x 15.7 cm, 15.1 cm x 11.1 cm.

5. Two cards with gilt line borders, one with a bird perching on a pink rose in a winter landscape, the other with a white rose and harebells on a scroll rolled back to show a windmill in a country landscape.
10.2 cm x 15.5 cm, 16 cm x 12.5 cm.

6. Two cards, a pink rose reflected in water, and a red and a white and yellow rose with buds.
10.8 cm x 14.7 cm, 10.3 cm x 14.8 cm.

7. Two cards, a white rose on a window sill in a green border resembling a picture frame, and pink moss roses in the shape of a crown.
12.2 cm x 16.5 cm, 14.2 cm x 10.8 cm.

8. Two cards, a yellow rose with ivy, and a birthday card with two yellow roses.
11.7 cm x 15.8 cm, 11.3 cm x 14 cm.

*Numbers 9-26 are unbordered, published in the late 1880's with a few exceptions as noted.*

9. Two cards, shaded pink or white roses on moss, with verses signed Elizabeth Love and SLS. 13 cm x 10.3 cm.

10. Two cards, one design of a red rose and spring flowers slotted through paper, with a verse from "Life Chords" by Frances Ridley Havergal, dated 1886 by the sender.
11.2 cm x 15 cm.

11. Two cards, a red or a pink rose with ivy, and a verse from "Life Chords" in a gilt-edged panel. 10.5 cm x 14.5 cm.

12. Two cards, a pink rose in an open umbrella with quotation from Moore, and red roses in a gilt-edged horseshoe vignette with verse by H M Burnside.
9.4 cm x 12.5 cm, 10.7 cm x 13.7 cm.

13. Three cards in two styles, a red, pink, or white moss rose with buds against a blue sky background with birds.
10 cm x 16 cm.

14. Four cards, one with gilt border repeating the red rose of no. 13, two with pink moss roses on a blue background, the fourth with pink moss roses in an oval vignette. Sizes up to 12.9 cm x 8.2 cm.

15. Two cards, yellow roses with a poem by S K Cowan MA, and a wreath of pink

rosebuds and white daisies in an oval vignette with a birthday verse by Shirley Wynne. 11 cm x 14.9 cm, 10.7 cm x 14.2 cm.

16/18. Ten cards, eight designs of single roses and buds on pale blue backgrounds, with verses by Frances Ridley Havergal. One card is smaller, repeating one design in brighter colours. 15.7 cm x 10.3 cm, 12 cm x 7.5 cm.

19/20. Four cards, two designs of red or pink roses lying on grass, published by Josiah R Mallett, series no 102, two designs. They have four different greetings and three different verses signed F E Eileen Hooper. Buday lists three sets of cards from this publisher of birds, ships, and roses, 1884. 17.6 cm x 13.2 cm.

21. Five cards, four with single pink, red, or yellow roses, one with two white roses and ferns. Sizes up to 8.4 cm x 10.2 cm.

22. Four cards. Two have a yellow rose with ferns or a red rose with elder blossom lying on a white panel with greeting, and the third has two white roses. The fourth card with a yellow rose has a monogram which might be MED. Sizes up to 13.3 cm x 9.7 cm.

23. Four miscellaneous cards, three with white or pink roses and brown leaves, two with gilt highlights. The fourth card has a yellow rose lying on a coloured glass scent bottle. 11.4 cm x 7.5 cm up to 15.2 cm x 9.5 cm.

24. Four miscellaneous cards, two with a red or a pale pink rose, two with yellow roses and ferns. Sizes up to 12.6 cm x 10 cm.

25. Two cards, one with a bunch of pale pink moss roses with a verse by Frances Ridley Havergal, another with a single creamy white rose and a verse signed J L W, dated 1891 by the sender. 11 cm x 15.2 cm, 14.9 cm x 11.3 cm.

26. An embossed card with a pink and yellow rose on a fan with silver decoration and tassel, on a background of embossed silver leaves, dated 1894 by the sender. 14.5 cm x 11 cm.

27. Three gilt-bordered cards with pink or yellow roses and verses by A M H and Frances Ridley Havergal. 9 cm x 12.7 cm, 8.5 cm x 12.2 cm.

28. Four miscellaneous cards with roses, two bordered, with verses by Frederick Langbridge, H S Bainbridge, and Frances Annandale. 7 cm x 9.8 cm up to 10.3 cm x 14.6 cm.

29. Six cards from three sets, three with two designs of single roses, one with pink roses, and two with the same design of a red rose with lilies of the valley over a

country scene in a diamond vignette. 7.5 cm x 10.7 cm, 10.9 cm x 7.4 cm, 11.4 cm x 7.7 cm.

30. Seven miscellaneous bordered cards, two with single roses, four with bunches, and one with dog roses on a Japanese fan. 6.7 cm x 10.2 cm up to 7.7 cm x 12 cm.

31. Five miscellaneous bordered cards with white, pink, or yellow roses. 7.6 cm x 7.6 cm up to 11.6 cm x 11.6 cm.

32. Five miscellaneous cards all with pink roses. 8.3 cm x 8 cm up to 12.6 cm x 8.4 cm.

33. Four bordered cards, one with a bunch of shaded pink and red rosebuds, another with dog roses and a birthday greeting by J P Thomas, and two each with a single rose on a dark background. 8.7 cm x 6.5 cm up to 7.6 cm x 10.8 cm.

## VOLUME 244: PANSIES, WATERLILIES, AND SOME GARDEN FLOWERS

**In the Language of Flowers, the pansy stood for remembrance, and artists used it in this connection as well as for its varied colouring. Some other flowers are included here for comparison, and most of the cards appeared in the early 1880's with a few exceptions as stated.**

*Numbers 1-16 have pansies in many colours.*

1. Five miscellaneous cards, all with gilt borders and decoration, including a variegated flower head in a gilt vignette on a red background dated 1883 by the sender, and another in an oval gilt-bordered vignette with a poem by C D on reverse. 5.1 cm x 7 cm up to 10.1 cm x 13.4 cm.

2. Three unbordered embossed cards (one birthday), two designs of pansies and leaves on a grey background, one dated 1881 by the sender. 10.9 cm x 14.3 cm.

3/4. Six unbordered embossed cards, pansies and moss on a grey background with greetings in embossed gilt letters. 10.1 cm x 14 cm.

5. Three cards, one repeating a design in no. 3 with a greeting in verse. Two others have the same embossed design of purple pansies and lilies of the valley. 10.1 cm x 14 cm, 7 cm x 10.9 cm.

6/7. Five cards, three rather sombre designs of pansies, four on grey and one on light blue backgrounds, with verses by E I T.
"If heartsease in thy bosom reign
 Life's storms shall beat on thee in vain".
16.2 cm x 11 cm, 15.8 cm x 10.6 cm.

8. Three cards, two designs of pansies and laburnum in two sizes, with greeting in a gilt-edged panel in a grey border. 13 cm x 18.4 cm, 7.8 cm x 11.2 cm.

9. Two cards, each with a bunch of mixed pansies, one with brown leaves, the other in a blue and white bowl with a poem on reverse. 12 cm x 15 cm, 15.7 cm x 11.7 cm.

10. Two cards, pansies arranged like a horseshoe, and a spray of pansies with a verse by Charlotte Murray. 10.2 cm x 13.9 cm, 11 cm x 15 cm.

11. Four miscellaneous cards (two birthday), three with pansies and a gauntlet glove, in a square vignette, or in a blue decorated beaker. The fourth card has a bunch of wild pansies. 9.6 cm x 9.6 cm up to 8.8 cm x 17.7 cm.

12/13. Eight miscellaneous bordered cards with pansies, two dated 1884, 1885 by the senders. 9.2 cm x 6.1 cm up to 15 cm x 10.8 cm,

14. Two birthday cards with silver edges, each with a bunch of pansies and ferns, signed BWM, one dated 1887 by the sender. 11.6 cm x 15.5 cm.

15. Two cards, bunches of pansies in a rectangular panel with a Christmas verse, in a wide border, later 1880's. 12.7 cm x 9.8 cm.

16. Three cards, a lakeland scene bordered by blue and purple pansies, a bunch of blue and white pansies, and a mixed bunch of pansies on a card with serrated edge, c1890. 12.8 cm x 12.8 cm, 10.2 cm x 8.5 cm, 13 cm x 10.1 cm.

17. Four cards with gilt line borders (one birthday), three designs of sprays of white, orange, or red azaleas or rhododendrons, with poems on reverse. 14.2 cm x 11.2 cm.

18. Three cards, two with a rose, one with a camellia, against a wall or a hillside background. 14.2 cm x 11.2 cm.

19. Two cards with wide grey borders, crysanthemums on a silver background, each with the same Christmas poem on the back. 15 cm x 12.1 cm.

20. Two cards, sweet peas, on a dark panel in a grey border, or in a cloth with corners pinned back in trompe l'oeil style. 7.4 cm x 10.8 cm, 12.5 cm x 10 cm.

21. Two gilt-edged cards, one design of Christmas roses and forget-me-nots on a grey background with verses for New Year or birthday. 15.5 cm x 10.6 cm.

22. Two embossed gilt-edged cards, reeds and waterlilies in a lake. 16.8 cm x 12.8 cm.

23. Three miscellaneous cards, two with waterlilies, one with an arum lily.
12 cm x 9 cm, 13.5 cm x 9.8 cm,
16.2 cm x 11.3 cm.

24. Two gilt-edged cards, with lilies or fritillaries against a blue sky background, and verses by Cecilia Havergal on reverse in cursive writing. 16.5 cm x 11.9 cm.

25. Two cards, gilt line borders, with pinks or sweet peas, and appropriate verses on reverse.
"Sweet pinks! your perfume shed around
While I a Christmas greeting breathe..."
15 cm x 10.8 cm.

26. Three cards with white borders and pink or red geraniums, one dated 1880 by the sender. 15.4 cm x 9.8 cm.

27. Three miscellaneous bordered cards, two with geraniums, one with cornflowers and sweet sultan.
Sizes up to 14.2 cm x 9.3 cm.

28. Two bordered cards, orchids and daphne, geraniums and white jasmine with decorative leaves and ferns.
10.2 cm x 14.3 cm.

29. Two cards, one a mixed bunch of flowers, leaves and ferns, another with roses, forget-me-nots, and ferns around a gilt-edged oval vignette with greeting.
'9.5 cm x 12.7 cm, 9.5 cm x 13.2 cm.

30. Two cards on brown backgrounds, lilies of the valley with multi-coloured leaves, china asters with verse by Cecilia Havergal on reverse.
12.7 cm x 10.1 cm, 14.5 cm x 11.3 cm.

31. Three miscellaneous cards, spring flowers in a hanging basket, geraniums and ferns, Michaelmas daisies with fir leaves and cones.
Sizes up to 13.6 cm x 10.2 cm.

## VOLUME 245:
## FLOWER CARDS WITH GILT, SILVER AND COLOURED BORDERS, 1880'S

*Numbers 1-22 have gilt borders. Most were published about 1880, with a few later as noted.*

1. Two cards, one with phlox in several colours, the other with roses, both on dark backgrounds with greetings in white scrolls and long poems by MER on reverse.
10.5 cm x 14.2 cm.

2. Three cards, two with roses, one with lilies, on woodland backgrounds.
7.3 cm x 15.9 cm.

3. Three cards (one birthday), daisies or white jasmine on brown or grey backgrounds. 6.3 cm x 16.7 cm.

4. Three cards, white pansies, irises, or crocuses on woodland background.
8 cm x 16.8 cm.

5. Four cards, morning glory, campanulas, roses and pansies, fuchsia, three with verses by EKW, EHB, FEEH, one dated 1879 by the sender. 12.7 cm x 9.5 cm.

6. Three cards with spring flowers, two with a moth or a beetle, all with poems on reverse by E J P. 9 cm x 15.4 cm.

7. Two cards, carnations or narcissi on dark background, one dated 1883 by the sender. 9 cm x 13 cm.

8. Six cards from three sets, five designs including chrysanthemums, crocus, wild rose, helenium, begonia, one dated 1883 by the sender.
9.7 cm x 6.7 cm up to 8.1 cm x 12.7 cm.

9. Two cards, delphiniums, trumpet creeper, on dark backgrounds with rustic borders. 14.5 cm x 9.7 cm.

10. Three miscellaneous cards, all pink and white flowers - geraniums, hawthorn, and gloxinia(?) with alpine phlox. Sizes up to 16.3 cm x 10.8 cm.

11. Two cards. violets, snowdrops and willow catkins, cyclamen with a branch of fir, both with Christmas verses by F Ernest Power. 9.5 cm x 13.8 cm.

12. Two cards, one design of daisies in a gilt-bordered star, one dated 1883 by the sender. 11.6 cm x 14.7 cm.

13. Four cards, probably from a set of six with violets, strawberries, purple vetch, incarvillea(?), three in a rustic frame.
12.4 cm x 9.2 cm.

14. Two cards, cyclamen and ferns, wild roses and strawberries.
15.7 cm x 9.7 cm.

15. Four cards, bittersweet, forget-me-nots, japonica, anemones, with illuminated intitals to greeting verses. 11 cm x 7 cm.

16. Four cards from two sets. Two have a rose or cornflower spray with illuminated capital letter to Christmas verses by F Langbridge; the other two have garlands of roses and spring flowers on a grey background and Christmas verses by FEEH and EHB with decorative capital letters, and a fly or a beetle.
12.2 cm x 9.4 cm, 12.6 cm x 9.3 cm.

17. Five cards with various spring flowers including two from one set. 9 cm x 6 cm up to 7.7 cm x 11.2 cm.

18. Three cards, violets, primroses, japonica, with verses, one dated 1883 by the sender. 9.4 cm x 12.2 cm.

19. Two cards, Christmas roses, Japanese anemones, with verses by TRM, Eden Hooper. 11 cm x 7.3 cm, 12.3 cm x 9.3 cm.

20. Five miscellaneous cards, violets and morning glory, tulips, chrysanthemums, geraniums, and an embossed card with passion flowers.
Sizes up to 10.9 cm x 13.8 cm.

21/22. Eleven miscellaneous cards (two birthday) with various flowers, including three with scenic backgrounds. One card is marked JTSC.
7 cm x 11 cm up to 12 cm x 7.8 cm.

23. Four cards from two sets. Two have red line borders with roses and hawthorn, or anemones and forget-me-nots, with verses in a panel, two have apple blossom or clematis and fuchsia with verses, one signed JE Galliford, in gilt borders.
12 cm x 7.9 cm, 13.2 cm x 8.6 cm.

24. Three cards. One has nasturtiums in a blue line border and an illuminated quotation from Byron marked "copyright 1807"; the other two have primroses or fuchsias in gilt borders. 8 cm x 20.1 cm, 8.3 cm x 17.3 cm.

25. Three cards (one birthday) with verse or greeting in panels wreathed in flowers, two with silver borders, one with red.
9.4 cm x 13.1 cm, 8.5 cm x 13.3 cm.

*Numbers 26-30 have silver borders, c1885.*

26. Two cards, narcissi with ferns and other spring flowers, one with a birthday verse by F R Havergal dated 1884 by the sender. 11.5 cm x 14.8 cm.

27. Five cards with spring flowers, leaves, and wild roses. Two from one set have verses signed LN in a circular silver-edged vignette. Sizes up to 9 cm x 12.3 cm.

28. Three cards with roses, daisies, anemones, harebells, and fern, two with verses by Ben Johnson and Eliza Cook. Sizes up to 13 cm x 10.2 cm.

29. Three miscellaneous cards with rounded corners, two with bunches of spring flowers, the third with Japanese anemones and a mother-of-pearl card case in mosaic style.
Sizes up to 10 cm x 13.5 cm.

30. Three cards from a set, each with a bunch of spring flowers reflected in a lake.
10.7 cm x 7.5 cm.

31. Three gilt-edged cards with rounded corners and wreaths of spring flowers and leaves. Two are frosted and have New Year verses signed SH. c1885.
11.9 cm x 9 cm.

32. Five square cards, four with gilt, one with silver border. Three have bunches of

spring flowers, leaves and grasses, and two have white lilies or carnations on a gilt cross, one dated 1888 by the sender. 8.3 cm x 8.3 cm up to 9.7 cm x 9.7 cm.

## VOLUME 246: LARGE FLOWER CARDS, 1880'S

**These large cards, from unidentified publishers and artists, are well designed in conventional style with some fine embossed examples.**

*Numbers 1-17 have gilt borders and were published in the early 1880's.*

1. Two embossed cards with wreaths of spring flowers and leaves around poems by Ada and AR, one dated 1880 by the sender. 13 cm x 19.8 cm.

2/3. Three cards, sprays with roses, convolvulus, crocuses, apple blossom, and other spring flowers and leaves, by a fence in a background scene with seasonal verses, two with insect or butterfly. 13.2 cm x 20.3 cm.

4. An embossed card with waterlilies and leaves in a basket, reflected in a stream. 12.5 cm x 17.2 cm.

5/6. Four embossed cards (one birthday), three designs of white flowers - arum lilies, waterlilies, anemones, one dated 1880 by the sender. 12.4 cm x 18 cm.

7. An embossed card with dog roses, arum lilies, and spring flowers. 12.4 cm x 18 cm.

8. Three embossed cards (one birthday), with purple vetch, mountain avens, edelweiss, gentians, and cyclamen, and greetings in gilt embossed lettering, one dated 1882 by the sender. 11.1 cm x 16.5 cm.

9. Two embossed cards with apple or pear blossom against a blue sky, with Christmas verses. 11.1 cm x 17.8 cm..

10. Two cards, Christmas roses and fern, saxifraga sarmentosa, with Christmas verses on reverse by A Gill. 13.2 cm x 18.3 cm.

11. Three cards, colourful flower bouquets against a woodland background, one dated 1883 by the sender. 11.1 cm x 17.3 cm.

12. Two embossed cards, wreaths of flowers with heartsease, roses, geraniums, and spring flowers and ferns. 12 cm x 17 cm.

13. Three cards, one design for Christmas, New Year, and birthday of a white tulip and geraniums on a dark background with patterned gilt border, two dated 1882 by the senders. 10.9 cm x 16.4 cm.

14. A card with a stylised design of mauve flowers and pale green leaves on a gilt background, signed Tr C and dated 1884 by the sender. 21.8 cm x 16.5 cm.

15. Two cards, bunches of harebells or lilac hanging over a decorative greeting, with a poem of good wishes on reverse. 13.2 cm x 17.8 cm.

16. Two cards, anemones, azaleas and ferns. 13 cm x 16 cm, 11.6 cm x 15.1 cm.

17. Two cards, butterflies on carnations or white jasmine. 11.5 cm x 18 cm, 12 cm x 18.8 cm.

18. A card with purple passion flowers on a white cross in a gilt background, dated 1886 by the sender. 11.5 cm x 17.7 cm.

19. Two cards, harebells and ferns, ox-eye daisies with a butterfly. 11.5 cm x 17.5 cm, 10.9 cm x 17.3 cm.

20. Two cards with silver borders, one design of anemones with birthday or New Year greeting. 12.5 cm x 16 cm.

21. A silver-bordered card, pansies and Solomon's seal, with Christmas verse by LN on reverse. 12 cm x 16.7 cm.

22/24. Six embossed cards in patterned silver borders, five designs of ox-eye daisies, dog roses, honeysuckle, Christmas roses, wood anemones, one dated 1881 by the sender. 18.3 cm x 13.9 cm.

25. Two cards, one gilt-edged repeating the design in number 24 above, the other with a rose and spring flowers in a gilt-patterned border and an illuminated design on reverse. 15.4 cm x 12 cm, 14.3 cm x 11.5 cm.

26. Three cards, harebells and catkins, wood anemones and catkins, anemones and grasses, in a rustic frame on a blue gilt-edged background. 10.8 cm x 15.8 cm.

27. Two cards, pansies, irises in a gilt frame with grey border, and appropriate greeting verses, one dated 1882 by the sender. 11.3 cm x 18.5 cm.

28. Two bordered cards, orchids, day lilies with Japanese anemones and larkspur and a seasonal verse by Eden Hooper. 11.3 cm x 15.4 cm, 11.4 cm x 17 cm.

29. Two embossed cards, one with apple blossom and forget-me-nots. The other has branches with drooping white or pink flowers, difficult to identify but with some resemblance to the Snowdrop tree (halesia carolina). 12.1 cm x 18.4 cm.

30. Three embossed cards, two designs, one of poppies, cornflowers and spring flowers, the other roses with

forget-me-nots, both on a silver horseshoe around greetings, one birthday. 11.6 cm x 15.5 cm.

31. A birthday card with blue and white anemones, and a poem by JC on reverse. 12.6 cm x 17.4 cm.

32. Two cards, gladioli on a grey background. 11.2 cm x 19.5 cm.

## VOLUME 247: MORE LARGE CARDS

**The publishers and artists of these cards have not been traced. They were published in the early 1880's with one or two exceptions.**

*Numbers 1-13 have gilt borders.*

1. Two birthday cards, oxalis or wood anemones in rectangular vignettes over flowering branches against a blue sky, one dated 1881 by the sender. 10.7 cm x 15 cm.

2. Two cards, a purple gloxinia, and a red carnation and bud. 9.5 cm x 15.3 cm.

3. Two cards, a red geranium and a yellow azalea.10.4 cm x 15.3 cm.

4. Two embossed birthday cards, yellow or white lilies against a background of lace. 10 cm x 15 cm.

5. Two cards, anemones with a birthday verse on a bordered panel, and cornfield flowers with a New Year poem. 10.8 cm x 15 cm, 11 cm x 15 cm.

6. Two cards, roses and wisteria against a stone wall, and roses and forget-me-nots around a New Year verse. 11.8 cm x 17.4 cm, 12 cm x 15.3 cm.

7. Three cards all with seasonal verses. Two are embossed, with crocuses, or a pink flower - perhaps dianthus? The third card has harebells. 9.9 cm x 15.4 cm.

8. Three cards, two designs of honeysuckle with bindweed or harebells, all with Christmas poems on reverse. 10.2 cm x 14.4 cm, 10.9 cm x 14.3 cm.

9. Two cards, cyclamen and ferns, dated 1886 by the sender, and foxgloves with daisies and a verse by Charlotte Murray on reverse. 10.6 cm x 15.7 cm, 11 cm x 13.5 cm.

10. Three miscellaneous cards with butterflies on roses, ferns, or sunflowers, the latter with a poem by AHB on reverse. 10.1 cm x 15.3 cm, 9.9 cm x 17 cm, 10.5 cm x 14 cm.

11. Four cards from two sets with gilt line borders. Two have anemones or honeysuckle, and two have yellow roses or narcissus, one dated 1882 by the sender. 10.4 cm x 15 cm, 10 cm x 14.7 cm.

12. Two cards with flowers and reeds on a background of lake and blue sky. 10 cm x 13.6 cm.

13. Three miscellaneous cards, one with broom, another with cherry blossom, the third with a stylised blue flower. 11 cm x 16.3 cm, 10 cm x 17.4 cm, 9.7 cm x 15.5 cm.

*Numbers 14-23 have various borders.*

14. Two cards, fuchsias, one with silver border and a blue sky background, the other with gilt border. 12.1 cm x 14.5 cm, 9.9 cm x 15.7 cm.

15. Three cards, pink and white mallow in a silver border, a red passion flower in a woodland setting with gilt border, and nasturtiums with a decorative gilded birthday greeting. 10.3 cm x 14.2 cm, 10 cm x 13.5 cm, 10 cm x 16 cm.

16. Four cards, three designs of various flowers including love-in-a-mist, crocus, bindweed, on grey or green background with white border and verses by FR Havergal and FEEH. 11 cm x 15.5 cm.

17. Two cards, carnations with a valentine greeting, a rose and forget-me-nots with New Year verse by RT. 9.3 cm x 15.4 cm.

18. Two cards with wide borders, white jasmine, lilac and pansies. 17 cm x 13.8 cm, 17 cm x 13.5 cm.

19. Three cards, two designs of violets or primroses with a bird's nest, and Christmas verses in gilt-edged panels. 13.6 cm x 9.9 cm.

20. Three similar cards, with hazel nuts, marsh orchid and lady's slipper, oxalis, on dark backgrounds. 9.9 cm x 13.6 cm.

21. Three cards with grey borders, two designs with various flowers including cyclamen and pinks, on green or brown background. 9.5 cm x 13.6 cm.

22. A white-bordered card with white lilies and Christmas greeting in gilt embossed letters. 11.1 cm x 14.4 cm.

23. Three miscellaneous cards, two with spring flowers and leaves, the third with Christmas roses in a pottery shoe. 11.1 cm x 14.4 cm, 10.8 cm x 13.9 cm, 10.4 cm x 13.9 cm.

*The following cards are unbordered, many on dark backgrounds.*

24. Two cards, a butterfly and mixed flowers against a stone wall with verse in an oval aperture, and a bird on a branch with a flower bouquet below. 9.7 cm x 13.6 cm.

25. Two cards with forget-me-nots or lilies of the valley, both with descriptive verses

by E Ridley or SB Bradley. 10.1 cm x 14.5 cm.

26. Two embossed cards, one with camellia, roses, and viburnum, the other with wallflowers, daisies, and forget-me-nots, both on dark backgrounds with greeting verses in pink panels, signed TEM. 11.2 cm x 14.2 cm.

27. Two cards, apple blossom or cherry blossom, both with verse by Cecilia Havergal. 11.3 cm x 14.5 cm.

28. Three cards on grey or beige background with garlands of cyclamen, edelweiss and forget-me-nots, and mixed spring flowers, one dated 1885 by the sender. 10.2 cm x 15.2 cm, 10.2 cm x 14.6 cm.

29. Two cards, gentians and Japanese anemones with verse by FEEH, and spring flowers with Christmas greeting. 9.5 cm x 13.2 cm, 9.6 cm x 14 cm.

30. Three cards, dahlias, begonias, Alpine flowers, on grey or beige backgrounds, one dated 1882 by the sender. 10.3 cm x 14.2 cm, 10 cm x 14 cm.

31. Three cards on beige backgrounds. Two have wreaths of cornfield flowers and leaves or white and red bean plants around a verse of greeting. The third has tulips with appropriate verse. 10.3 cm x 14.2 cm, 10 cm x 13.7 cm.

32. Two cards, each with growing plants, one with ivy, harebells and daisies, the other with a dog rose and fern. 10.1 cm x 14.6 cm.

33. Two cards with colourful bouquets of spring flowers, similar in appearance to "scraps" of the period. 10 cm x 15 cm.

34. Two cards, one with white field roses and a religious verse by FR on reverse, the other with branches of leaves and white flowers against a stone wall. 11.5 cm x 16.3 cm, 11 cm x 14.5 cm.

## VOLUME 248:
## FLOWER CARDS IN "PHOTOGRAPHIC STYLE", EARLY 1880'S

As observed before in cards of children in this style, more information is needed about the technique of production. Some cards are photographic prints coloured by hand, some perhaps reproduced by chromolithography after colouring, and others seem to be drawings imitating photographs, this method producing a more pleasing and artistic effect. Publishers here include William Luks, J Beagles, Davidson Bros, and an untraced HD. Most are in two sizes, large - about

10.7 cm x 16.5 cm, or small - about 6.5 cm x 10 cm, with a few variations as noted.

*Numbers 1-6 appear to be photographs coloured by hand, printed on thin paper mounted on card.*

1. Four cards, three large with leaves, bindweed, and a red rose, and a small birthday card, published by William Luks, two dated 1880, 1881, by the senders.

2. Seven small cards, William Luks, with various flowers and leaves, two with a bird, one with a cross and anchor, another with a horseshoe. Three were dated 1878/9, 1879, 1883, by the senders.

3. Four cards, J Beagles, two large, one a birthday card with a flower wreath around a handshake, the other a memorial card with flowers and ivy round a cross. Two small cards have flower and leaf bouquets.

4. Five cards, including three small with spring flowers, and two others with various flowers and leaves measuring 16.3 cm x 8.3 cm and 9.8 cm x 14 cm.

5. Three large cards, one with leaves and ferns, two with flowers and leaves, two dated 1880 by the senders.

6. One large card, roses and ferns in a white satin slipper; marked HD.

*The following cards appear to be photographs but could be drawings imitating photographs and reproduced in the usual way. They are printed directly on to the cards, within a black, brown, or white border.*

7/8. Six cards, three designs of roses, ferns, and spring flowers. Five are large, in black or white borders, and one measures 9 cm x 13 cm; they have verses by Eden Hooper on reverse. One card is marked Davidson Bros.

9. Two large cards, white borders, one with lilies of the valey in a basket and a verse by Robert Bloomfield on reverse, dated 1884 by the sender. The other has flowers and leaves with a poem and an ornamental design on reverse.

10. Five small black-edged cards with three designs of roses, pansies, and leaves.

11. Eight small cards. Four have bunches of white flowers and leaves in a black and gold border, and four have roses, spring flowers, and ferns in a gold border.

12. Four cards, three small with white flowers in a brown border, (two dated 1884,1885 by the senders), another with pink and white roses measuring 9.5 cm x 12.8 cm.

13. Two small cards. One is a three-page folder with three designs of flower and fern bouquets, and a scroll design outside with verses by Eden Hooper and FEEH. The other has a mixed flower bouquet with grasses and fern.

14. Three large cards, two with roses, one with a tulip and small white flowers, in brown borders with seasonal greetings and quotations from Walter Scott or Frances Ridley Havergal. These cards are probably from drawings.

15. A card with roses and fern in an oval vignette on a black background with white border, and a long Christmas poem on reverse.

16. Three large cards, bunches of flowers, including roses, cornflower, morning glory, in brown or black borders, probably drawings.

17. Three cards, two with wreaths of spring flowers, another with pansies and forget-me-nots in an oval vignette, all with black border and gilt line, one dated 1884 by the sender.
9.5 cm x 11 cm, 9.5 cm x 13 cm.

18. Two unbordered cards, one large with pansies and ferns over two clasped hands, the other with roses and narcissi, measuring 8.9 cm x 13.7 cm.

## VOLUME 249:
## BORDERED CARDS WITH FLOWERS AND FOLIAGE, SMALL TO MEDIUM SIZES, 1880'S

*Numbers 1-18 were published from 1880-1885, most with gilt borders, from unknown makers.*

1. Two cards, one with dog roses dated 1881 by the sender, another with a daisy chain around a panel with a Christmas verse. 9.6 cm x 15.2 cm, 12.7 cm x 9.7 cm.

2. Three cards, tied bunches of primroses, lilies of the valley, or roses, with appropriate verses, one dated 1883 by the sender. 7.8 cm x 11.1 cm.

3. Five cards, with grey and blue or red line borders, four designs of roses, passion flowers, Christmas roses and rosehips, fritillary with ferns. 11.2 cm x 8.2 cm.

4. Four miscellaneous cards, scillas growing in snow, heather, harebells and berries, daisies and heather. Sizes up to 9.7 cm x 13.4 cm.

5. Two cards, a thistle with leaves, blue berries with foliage, one dated 1883 by the sender. 9 cm x 13.5 cm.

6. Two cards, hawthorn or cherry with butterflies or insect, and a lake in the background. 9 cm x 12.8 cm.

7. Seven miscellaneous cards (two birthday) with various flowers including heather, ragged robin, a poppy with holly, and clover. One of the birthday cards has tansy with bulrushes and arum leaves and an ant. Sizes up to 11.2 cm x 7.2 cm and 5.6 cm x 13.7 cm.

8. Four miscellaneous cards, three with spring flowers, leaves and grasses, and one with erigeron in a gold ring and a birthday greeting verse by Montgomery. Sizes up to 9.2 cm x 13.6 cm.

9. Two cards, Japanese anemones or gentians with colourful leaves. 10.8 cm 7.5 cm.

10. Four miscellaneous cards, sempervivum, cherry blossom, wallflowers and forget-me-nots, blackberries, iris seeds and fir. Sizes up to 8.5 cm x 12.7 cm.

11. Four miscellaneous cards (one birthday), with lilac, scillas, gentians, or forget-me-nots in a hanging basket, one dated 1882 by the sender. Sizes up to 9.1 cm x 14 cm.

12. Four miscellaneous cards, with various spring flowers. Sizes up to 13.7 cm x 9.4 cm.

13. Four miscellaneous cards, all with roses and various spring flowers. Sizes up to 9.5 cm x 13 cm.

14. Three miscellaneous cards, all with violets. Sizes up to 9.5 cm x 13.3 cm.

15/16. Ten miscellaneous cards (three birthday), in subdued colours with various flowers, ivy, grasses and leaves, and one of thistles in black and white. 10.4 cm x 7.2 cm up to 11.8 cm x 8 cm.

17/18. Eight miscellaneous cards with various spring and summer flowers. Sizes up to 9 cm x 14.2 cm.

*The following cards were published in the later 1880's.*

19. Two cards, garlands of ivy with stylised flowers around a circular vignette with greeting. 11.1 cm x 14.7 cm.

20. Three cards with grey borders. Two have roses, forget-me-nots and pansies or violets with a birthday verse by Frances Ridley Havergal. The third card has a rose and a wreath of forget-me-nots around a quotation from Tennyson.
"Bless thee for thy lips are bland
And bright the friendship of thine eye"
with Christmas greeting below.
Sizes up to 10.5 cm x 13.5 cm.

21. Two cards, pale blue borders, with chrysanthemums or dog roses and a poem by Charlotte Murray. 15 cm x 11 cm.

22. Three miscellaneous cards, a horseshoe shaped wreath of lilies of the valley and geraniums, daffodils, and a birthday card with purple candytuft, the last two dated 1885 and 1886 by the senders. Sizes up to 12.2 cm x 14.6 cm.

23. Two cards with silver borders, one with yellow clematis (perhaps the variety orientalis?) and a verse by AMH, the other with primulas, pinks and ferns. 11.6 cm x 11.6 cm, 15.4 cm x 12.1 cm.

24. Three cards with dog roses, cyclamen, or narcissi, all with ferns and a valentine greeting. 10.4 cm x 8 cm.

25. Four miscellaneous cards, various spring flowers, one with a verse by Frances Ridley Havergal. Sizes up to 9.2 cm x 13.7 cm.

26. Six cards from four sets with dog roses, anemones and spring flowers, one a valentine with a pink and a scarlet pimpernel. Sizes up to 9.6 cm x 11.5 cm.

27/28. Seven miscellaneous cards with flower sprays, including myrtle, cyclamen, forget-me-nots, snowdrops, narcissi, primulas, violets. Sizes up to 14.7 cm x 9.7 cm.

29. Five miscellaneous cards with white or pale grey borders and sprays of various spring flowers, one with lilies on a rustic cross. Sizes up to 9.1 cm x 11.1 cm.

30. Four miscellaneous cards, three with hawthorn, a yellow rose and fern dated 1886 by the sender and tobacco flowers with a palm leaf. The fourth card is a valentine with a nosegay in a glass holder, perhaps used as a buttonhole. Sizes up to 13.5 cm x 9.4 cm.

31. Three cards, flower sprays over silver hearts with pale green background and border, with Christmas verses, two signed George Withers and Thomas Tusser 1857 - a quotation from his verse as the cards were published in the later 1880's. 11.4 cm x 7.7 cm.

32. Six miscellaneous cards, four with wreaths of spring flowers, one with daisies in a border of moss dated 1886 by the sender, and one with a lily and fern set in an eight pointed star. Sizes up to 10 cm x 11.1 cm.

## VOLUME 250:
## UNBORDERED CARDS IN SMALL TO MEDIUM SIZES, 1880'S AND EARLY 1890'S

1. Four cards (one birthday), from three sets, with crocuses and snowdrops. Sizes up to 7.8 cm x 13.7 cm.

2. Three cards (one birthday), two designs with lilies of the valley and forget-me-nots on envelopes. 10.7 cm x 7.1 cm.

3. Four cards, lilies of the valley, snowdrops, or white hawthorn on fawn background. 7.3 cm x 10.6 cm.

4. Three birthday cards with wild flowers, ferns, and grasses on beige ground, all with texts. 13 cm x 9.9 cm.

5. Two cards with grey backgrounds and illuminated initial to greetings, campanulas or ox-eye daisies and heather, the latter repeating a design in no. 4. 12.9 cm x 9.6 cm.

6. Three cards, roses or azaleas, with greeting in gilt letters in a semi-circular vignette. 10.7 cm x 7.5 cm.

7. Two cards, with cyclamen and ferns or narcissi and fern on grey background, one dated 1883 by the sender. 10 cm x 13.7 cm.

8. Two birthday cards, daisies and foliage or forget-me-nots and fern bordering verses by ELT. 8.6 cm x 15 cm.

9. Two cards with apple blossom or citrus on green background. 8.5 cm x 12.5 cm.

10. Four miscellaneous cards with various spring flowers, ferns, and ivy, three with verses. Sizes up to 7.9 cm x 13.8 cm.

11. Three cards, all daisies, in a straw pottle, with fern, or with knapweed, one dated 1883 by the sender, two with verses by HM Burnside.
Sizes up to 9.2 cm x 13.8 cm.

12. Three cards, one with yellow azaleas, one with yellow dahlias dated 1885, the third dated 1886 by the sender, repeating the dahlia design in a bordered card. 12 cm x 9.3 cm, 11.5 cm x 7.6 cm.

13. Four miscellaneous cards, three designs, campanulas in a shell-shaped hanging pot, white campanulas and forget-me-nots, and a branch of white flowers and leaves, perhaps a variety of clematis. Sizes all about 9 cm x 12 cm.

14. Two cards, white chrysanthemums, yellow roses, with text and greeting. 9.4 cm x 12.8 cm.

15. Three miscellaneous cards, forget-me-nots, anemones, cowslips, the two latter with verses by Frances Ridley Havergal. Sizes about 10 cm x 13 cm.

16. Two cards, camellia, and a variety of hellebore with ivy. 13.3 cm x 10.3 cm, 13.1 cm x 10.5 cm.

17. Three cards, two with cornflowers or forget-me-nots and yellow roses. The third card has a white panel, attached by a pin in the form of a penny-farthing bicycle in trompe l'oeil style, with a violet in one corner. 8.5 cm x 10.6 cm, 7.8 cm x 10.8 cm, 9.2 cm x 6.3 cm.

18. Three cards with trails of forget-me-nots and fern, or hawthorn and campanula, all with Christmas verses. 12.6 cm x 9.8 cm, 12.3 cm x 9 cm.

19. Three cards (one birthday) with spring flowers. One is tinselled and the birthday card has a posy in a glass holder set in a horseshoe. Sizes up to 14 cm x 10.7 cm.

20/22. Fourteen miscellaneous cards with sprays of spring and summer flowers with ferns, grasses, and ivy, one with a battledore and shuttlecock. Two were dated 1886, 1888 by the senders. 8.2 cm x 9 cm up to 12.2 cm x 9.4 cm.

23. Six cards from two sets, with five designs of white flowers on grey or pale blue backgrounds, one dated 1888 by the sender. 12.1 cm x 8.2 cm, 8.5 cm x 11 cm.

24. Five embossed cards (two birthday), three designs of garlands of hawthorn, violets and lilies of the valley, snowdrops and forget-me-nots, around suitable greetings, one dated 1887 by the sender. 11.8 cm x 8.8 cm.

25. Three cards, one a birthday card with a stylised design of a bird on a flowering branch against a harvest moon, dated 1890 by the sender. One with foxgloves is signed Bertha Maguire and dated 1885 by the sender, and the third with carnations is signed ACP, both with verses by Frances Ridley Havergal. Sizes all about 9.5 cm x 13 cm.

26. Five cards from three sets. Two have carnations or daisies and hawthorn, with a verse by Frances Ridley Havergal, one dated 1890 by the sender. Two have sprays of pinks, with forget-me-nots or daisy chains, and the fifth has a garland of anemones and cowslips. Sizes up to 11 cm x 8.5 cm.

27. Two embossed cards, violets with a verse by Frances Ridley Havergal, and apple blossom with a verse by EE Griffin, this dated 1892 by the sender. 10.3 cm x 8.3 cm, 14.9 cm x 11 cm.

## VOLUME 251: UNBORDERED CARDS WITH FLOWERS & FOLIAGE, LATER 1880'S

**These cards are larger than those in the previous volume; many have rounded corners, and some are on thick board with gilt or silver edges.**

1. Three cards (two birthday), two signed with the monogram BM or MB. All have verses, two signed Johnston Beall, and they show pyrethrums or chrysanthemums, irises, and lilies. c1885. 9.7 cm x 13.8 cm.

2. Three cards (one birthday), with everlasting pea, campanulas, or

snowdrops in oval vignettes, all with verses, two from Longfellow. One was dated 1885 by the sender. 10.6 cm x 14.5 cm.

3. Two cards, cherry blossom with a crown of thorns, and snowdrops tied with pink ribbon in a paper holder, both with Christmas greetings - the crown of thorns is more usual for an Easter card, for which this design may also have been used. 9.5 cm x 14.2 cm, 14 cm x 9.7 cm.

4. Three cards with yellow flowers, two with columbines or chrysanthemums. The third card has a sprig of five-petalled blossom which might be inspired by the rock rose. Sizes up to 11.2 cm x 13.9 cm.

5. Two cards, one with narcissi with a religious verse by Canon Bell in a gilt-edged panel, signed with a monogram TMC. The other has rhododendrons and a poem on reverse. 14 cm x 9.8 cm, 15 cm x 11.8 cm.

6. Two cards, a garland of spring flowers, and a bunch of white lilac, both with poems by Frances Ridley Havergal. 11.5 cm x 14.7 cm.

7. Two cards, moss phlox in several colours, white rhododendrons and lilies of the valley, both on shaded pale blue backgrounds with verses by Faith Chiltern and SK Cowan on panels. 11.7 cm x 15.8 cm.

8. Two cards, pink and white petunias against a moonlit background, and a sprig of apple blossom, marked DB. 13.8 cm x 13.8 cm, 14.6 cm x 9.8 cm.

9. Two birthday cards, one with a wreath of forget-me-nots around a poem by Charlotte Murray. The other has blue flowers and ferns with a tennis racquet and a verse by Keble, the flowers modelled on forget-me-nots or linum. 12.8 cm x 15.9 cm, 14.5 cm x 10.7 cm.

10. Two cards, calceolarias and stocks, and a double poppy. 9.9 cm x 14.6 cm, 9 cm x 13.5 cm.

11. Two cards, daisies against blue sky and hills with a poem by Cecilia Havergal, and violets and a poem by Samuel K Cowan MA in a panel over a background with reeds and water dropwort(?). 11.6 cm x 14.8 cm, 10.7 cm x 13.1 cm.

12. Two cards, one with white chrysanthemums, the other with a white rose and mignonette, both with greetings in embossed gilt letters, dated 1885, 1886 by the senders. 11.8 cm x 15.7 cm.

13. Two cards, a birthday card with laburnum and a verse by Frances Ridley Havergal, and white begonias with a Christmas poem by HM Burnside. 11.5 cm x 14.6 cm.

14. Two cards (one birthday), various pink and white flowers with verses by HM Burnside. 12.3 cm x 15.9 cm.

15. Three cards (one birthday), with wreaths of flowers and leaves around greetings, one dated 1886 by the sender, another signed MC or CM - Marian Chase? - with poem on reverse by H Bainbridge. Sizes up to 11.6 cm x 14.4 cm.

16. Three cards on pale blue background. One has a horseshoe with cowslips and primroses, another a yellow rose, dated 1891 by the sender. The third has a bunch of blue flowers, described as lilac in the accompanying verse of greeting, but with five petals instead of the usual four. This card was an interesting find, as so many of these flower cards have been difficult to identify and some, like this one, may have been subject to artistic license. Sizes up to 10.6 cm x 16.3 cm.

17. Two cards with bunches of spring flowers, both with verses, one by HM Burnside. 11.6 cm x 15.5 cm, 10.9 cm x 14.8 cm.

18. Two cards, clematis on a trellis with a poem by Charlotte Murray, and ox-eye daisies and purple vetch, signed JE or EJ, with a poem by Frances Ridley Havergal. 15 cm x 11 cm, 15.7 cm x 11 cm.

## VOLUME 252: CARDS WITH WHITE FLOWERS, LATER 1880'S

**Cards with white flowers were popular in the later 1880's, but their subdued colours, usually green and white, hardly added brightness to the greeting card scene. They were more suitable for New Year or birthday, but a large number in this volume have Christmas greetings and many such appear in albums of the period.**

*Numbers 1-22 are bordered.*

1. Three cards, one birthday, two New Year, various white flowers and ferns, one dated 1883 by the sender. 11.5 cm x 14.4 cm.

2. A card with lilies of the valley and foliage around a New Year greeting. 15.4 cm x 12 cm.

3. Two cards, peonies in a silver border, dated 1883 by the sender, and phlox with ferns. 12.4 cm x 16.2 cm, 12 cm x 15.4 cm.

4. Three cards (one birthday), two designs of snowdrops or campanulas. 10.2 cm x 13.5 cm, 11 cm x 14.7 cm.

5. Two cards, hyacinths, Christmas roses, with Shakespeare quotations for birthday or New Year. 10.5 cm x 14.7 cm.

6. Four cards from a set, three designs of white wild hyacinths, cherry blossom, mock orange, one dated 1885 by the sender. 11 cm x 14.2 cm.

7. Two birthday cards, lilies of the valley in circular vignette with poem by Eliza Cook, and Christmas roses with ivy and a verse by Charlotte Murray. 12 cm x 15.6 cm, 10.8 cm x 14.9 cm.

8. Two cards, snowdrops with a Christmas verse, and jasmine with a New Year greeting by H M Burnside. 10.7 cm x 13.9 cm, 12.5 cm x 15.7 cm.

9/10. Eight cards with gold or silver borders, two designs of carnations or sweet peas from one set, and three designs of roses, lilies or azaleas from another. Two of this second set have the same design with some minor alterations. 8 cm x 11.5 cm, 7.5 cm x 11.5 cm.

11. Four birthday cards, three designs of azaleas, lilies of the valley, and primulas with ferns, all with poems by HM Burnside and gilt borders with rounded corners, one dated 1884 by the sender. 10.5 cm x 13.2 cm.

12. Four miscellaneous cards, two with various flower garlands with ivy or fern, one with a branch of apple, the fourth repeating the primula design in no. 11 in different format. Sizes up to 10 cm x 13.4 cm.

13. Three cards with silver borders, two designs with bouquets of mixed white flowers. 8.7 cm x 12 cm.

14. A birthday card with narcissus and fern in a silver border. 9.8 cm x 15 cm.

15. Four miscellaneous gilt-bordered cards with various white flowers, one with forget-me-nots, another with white and blue violets dated 1884 by the sender. Sizes up to 9.5 cm x 13.7 cm.

16. Two gilt-bordered cards, roses, lilies of the valley, both with ferns. 10.1 cm x 12.9 cm.

17. Six cards with silver borders (two birthday) various white flowers, including three from a set with two designs showing interesting colour variation in the same design. Two were dated 1883, 1885 by the senders. Sizes up to 9.2 cm x 11.8 cm.

18. Four miscellaneous cards (three birthday), sprays of edelweiss, jasmine, lilies of the valley, and ox-eye daisies. Sizes up to 8.3 cm x 12.8 cm.

19. A Christmas card with a stylised white flower in a garland of maidenhair fern, and a poem on reverse by Cecilia Havergal -

"Oh sweet little blossom so tender

Thou bearest a message of love ..." a typical Victorian floral sentiment. 11.7 cm x 14.4 cm.

20. Three cards, two designs of narcissus or Christmas roses in circular vignettes with silver surround. 9.2 cm x 9.2 cm.

21. A Christmas card with white chrysanthemums, ivy, and fern, against a background of a shining cross in a cloudy sky. Late 1880's. 11.8 cm x 17 cm.

22. Three miscellaneous cards, a camellia on a diamond shaped gilt vignette, dated 1887 by the sender, an arum lily on a circular gilt vignette, and lilies of the valley on silver, with a valentine greeting and an apt quotation from Shakespeare. Sizes up to 9.5 cm x 12.5 cm.

23/24. Four miscellaneous cards, (one birthday), with various spring flowers, two bordered, two unbordered, three with verses by Jonathan Beall, Frances Ridley Havergal, EMH. Sizes up to 10.9 cm x 14.5 cm.

*The following cards are unbordered, many on thick board with rounded corners.*

25. Two Christmas cards, one with a wreath of stephanotis and foliage, the other with a wreath of stylised white flowers and decorative leaves, this dated 1885 by the sender. 12.6 cm x 15 cm, 15.2 cm x 12.5 cm.

26. Three birthday cards, two with bouquets of various white flowers and ferns. The third has a bee with a fiddle serenading a white rose. Sizes up to 10.9 cm x 14.5 cm.

27. Two cards, primulas and fern, stephanotis and fern, the first with a verse by Frederick Langbridge MA. 11.9 cm x 15.6 cm, 16.2 cm x 11.2 cm.

28. Two cards, both with Christmas roses and descriptive verses, the drawings signed HLD not very true to nature. 14.5 cm x 10.4 cm.

29. Two cards, one a rose with ivy and daisies, the other with hibiscus or abutilon. 16.5 cm x 12.5 cm, 15.5 cm x 12.2 cm.

30. Two cards, one with narcissus and fern with birds in a blue sky and birthday greeting by AHB, the other lilies of the valley with grasses. 11.8 cm x 15.4 cm, 15.4 cm x 11.2 cm.

31. Four miscellaneous cards, various spring flowers. Sizes about 9.5 cm x 13 cm.

32. Two cards, one dated 1889 by the sender with a mosaic of stylised white flowers and fern. The other has a white rose with a wreath of blue and purple

flowers, clustered like lilac but with five petals. 14.2 cm x 12.3 cm,14.4 cm x 11.8 cm.

33. Two cards, white roses, daisies and foliage, both with verses by HM Burnside, one dated 1889 by the sender.
10.9 cm x 14 cm.

34. Three cards, spring flowers with verses, one dated 1890. Sizes up to 11 cm x 15 cm.

## VOLUME 253: FOLDER CARDS WITH FLOWERS, FRUIT, FOLIAGE

Some folder cards have appeared in earlier volumes with similar single cards from known publishers. These remaining examples from the 1880's are mostly from unknown publishers with a few marked cards for comparison. They come as four-page folders, in triptych style, or as folding screens, with a few envelopes, and usually have illuminated decoration on the cover with verses, and attached single cards or printed pictures within. The cards are measured closed.

1. Two triptych folders with large flower cards within and illuminated decoration on wings and exterior, with a moveable support for standing (one missing), in a style similar to that of S Hildesheimer or SJ Saunders, but unmarked. c1880.
14.3 cm x 11.2 cm.

2. Two triptych folders, with dishes of fruit, vases and Christmas or New Year verses inside, and brown and silver illuminated design with supporting flap outside. 15 cm x 10.7 cm.

3. Four four-page folders with illuminated floral designs on the covers and greeting and attached flower card within, one a birthday card marked Philipp Bros and dated 1884 by the sender. Two cards have alternate verses inside for Christmas or new Year and birthday, one of which could be covered by the attached card. Sizes up to 10.6 cm x 13.2 cm.

4. Four similar cards, three with the same illuminated design of butterfly and roses on the cover. Two have no inside card but display alternate verses for Christmas and New Year or birthday by Frances Ridley Havergal. 11.4 cm x 13.6 cm.

5. Two cards.
a) A folder with gilt-patterned borders, stylised blossom on cover, and flowers with a gilt cross and a Christmas poem by FEEH inside. 8.3 cm x 12.7 cm.
b) A triptych folder with illuminated formal design on wings and outside, and an attached card with dahlias inside.
11.3 cm x 13.4 cm.

6. Two cards.
a) An envelope published by Philipp Bros with illuminated designs of forget-me-nots inside and out, and an attached card, with verses by HM Burnside and Eliza Cook, and a romantic scene on the back.
13.5 cm x 10.6 cm.
b) A four-page folder with birthday verse and attached card inside, published by Ollendorff. The cover has formal gilt flower designs on a pale green ground.
10.8 cm x 14.3 cm.

7. Five miscellaneous folder cards, two in envelope form. Three have illuminated decoration outside, one has an attached card within and a Christmas verse by F Langbridge. One triptych card has unusual decoration imitating a wooden cabinet, with a hand painted flower design inside. Size about 12 cm x 9 cm.

8. Two four-page folders with the same illuminated design outside, each with a different attached flower card within and verses for Christmas or New Year by Frances Ridley Havergal, on pale green background. 10.1 cm x 10.1 cm.

9. Two four-page folders with the same illuminated design outside of holly and mistletoe on pale green background, with attached cards and verses for Christmas or New Year within. 9.1 cm x 11.7 cm.

10. Two cards.
a) A birthday card with rose garlands around a poem by Fannie Rochat inside and a design in white, cream and green of field roses on the cover. 8.2 cm x 14.3 cm.
b) A card with two flower pictures inside and sporting pictures with antlers, horseshoe and hanging game outside.
9.8 cm x 13.8 cm.

11. Three four-page folders with the same blue and gold design in Japanese style outside, and two designs of flower sprays with greetings inside, two being birthday verses signed JG. 6.4 cm x 13.3 cm.

12. Two cards in the form of folding screens.
a) A four-fold screen with scenes of lakes and flowers in circular vignettes on one side, with birthday poems, and formal designs of birds and flowers on the other published by Hildesheimer and Faulkner. This was dated 1909 by the sender, but must have been published in the 1880's.
7.5 cm x 12.4 cm.
b) A three-fold screen with ferns and waterlilies on one side, and leaf and flower designs with scenes in circular vignettes on the other, both in pink borders.
8.3 cm x 14.5 cm.

13. Two cards.
a) A triangular folder with flowers on silver background outside opening to show a forest scene with New Year verse.
17 cm x 12 cm x 12 cm.

b) A four-fold screen with flowering branches on silver background outside and flower pictures by CN (Charles Noakes) inside with a poem by EEM. The screen has brown borders and silver hinges.
9.2 cm x 14.5 cm.

14. Three cards.
a) A triptych folder with illuminated ivy design outside and a flower spray with poem by HM Burnside within.
6.5 cm x 9 cm.
b) A small four-fold screen, published by Ollendorff, with a religious poem by EJ Pope inside and various pictures with cross, flowers, butterfly, and river outside, probably used as an Easter card.
3.9 cm x 8 cm.
c) A four-page folder with music inside and flowers and woodland scene outside, with illuminated corners and clasps.
9.4 cm x 9.4 cm.

15. Two birthday cards.
a) A four-page folder with floral card inside and a pen and ink design of roses and daffodils outside. 12.4 cm x 15.3 cm.
b) A triptych folder with stylised designs of silver flowering branches outside and on wings, with attached flower card and verses by Frances Ridley Havergal within.
12.6 cm x 16.4 cm.

16. Three four-page folders.
a) Gilt flower sprays and patterned border on a pink backgound outside, and a Christmas verse and attached flower card within. 12.7 cm x 12.7 cm.
b) Green and gold illuminated design outside, and two flower pictures with poems by HM Burnside within.
11.7 cm x 15.5 cm.
c) Flowers and scenes in vignettes on a pink background outside, and an attached card with flowers, cross, and a Christmas verse signed AHB inside.
10.3 cm x 14.7 cm.

17. Three four-page birthday folder cards.
a) Blue and gold design on cover, and four flower sprays in lunettes with verses signed Samuel Cowan, MA (no K).
14.8 cm x 11.3 cm.
b) A gilt-patterned cover on red ground, with pressed flower and leaves and verse inside. 11.6 cm x 15.8 cm.
c) Blue and silver design on cover and a river scene with verse by HM Burnside inside. 11.6 cm x 13.7 cm.

18. Four cards.
a/b) Two identical small folders, one with attached card and birthday greeting, the other with flower scrap and Christmas verse, with pink and gold borders.
10 cm x 7 cm.
c) A triptych card with turquoise and gold design on the cover, a river scene inside, and vases of flowers on the wings, with birthday greeting by EMM, dated 1884 by the sender or recipient. 9.7 cm x 11.5 cm.

d) A birthday folder with an attached picture of asters inside and a verse by AHB, and bird and flower designs on the cover. 8.1 cm x 11.8 cm.

19. Six small four-page folder cards.
a/b) Two cards with the same design in gilt on blue or green cover, with a picture of spring flowers in a plant pot and a Christmas poem by the Rev WH Havergal, MA. 6 cm x 8.5 cm.
c/d) Two cards with the same illuminated design on blue or turquoise cover, and flower pictures and verses by AMH or Eden Hooper inside. 6.2 cm x 9 cm.
e) A card with cover design in turquoise on cream background and a flower wreath and a river scene with a verse by Samuel K Cowan MA inside. 8.7 cm x 8.7 cm.
f) A card with brown and gilt design of flowers and birds on the outside and flower garlands with seasonal verse within. 5.8 cm x 8.7 cm.

20. Four four-page folders.
a) Patterned cover in brown and green with fruit in circular vignettes, and a vase of lilies and a lady in classical dress inside. 7.2 cm x 12.3 cm.
b) Black and gilt cover, with Christmas verse by FGH and a spray of carnations set in a patterned turquoise frame. 7.4 cm x 11.1 cm.
c/d) Two cards with the same illuminated design on the cover, but with different flower pictures and verses for Christmas and New Year within. 9.2 cm x 12 cm.

21/22. Nine miscellaneous cards, all four-page folders with silver or gilt designs and patterned borders on the outside on various coloured backgrounds, five with birthday, four with Christmas greetings. Eight have attached flower cards within, and all have poetic greetings. Sizes up to 16 cm x 11.2 cm.

23. Three triptych folders, with two designs of oak and toadstools on the wings with stags or a woodland scene on the outside, opening to show a plain interior with greeting and Shakespeare quotations, one dated 1888 by the sender. They are marked TB & Co. 11.6 cm x 9 cm.

24. A large triptych folder with attached card inside showing a lady's head by E Barnard, with monochrome flower designs on the outside wings, and gilt border and leaf sprays with greeting and verse on the inside. Similar cards appear in the Children and Ladies section, but this is included here for the flower interest on the folder. 11.2 cm x 18.6 cm.

## VOLUME 254: FLOWERS & FOLIAGE, SMALL CARDS, LATER 1880'S - EARLY 1890'S

**Numbers 1-6 are cards with flowers and leaves accompanied by simple greetings in decorative style; these**

**became popular about 1885 and similar examples appear in Volume 257 in correspondence style with spaces for the name of sender or recipient. A few cards have serrated edges. Numbers 9-23 have a miscellany of small cards which could not easily fit in to previous volumes, of no particular artistic quality or interest, but included in this collection to illustrate the response of manufacturers to the growing demand from a wider public for cheaper mass production.**

1. Four cards, embossed flower sprays with simple greetings, dated by the senders 1885, 1886, 1888, 1889. 10.8 cm x 7.2 cm, 11.1 cm x 9 cm.

2. Five embossed cards with gilt and tinselled greetings and decoration. All approximately 11.5 cm x 9.3 cm.

3. Three cards, two with gilt or tinselled flower sprays and greetings, one with a garland of holly and bells and a serrated edge. 12.1 cm x 9.5 cm.

4. Four cards with serrated edges and branches with leaves, one tinselled, two with gilt decorations. 12 cm x 8.8 cm.

5. Four cards with serrated edges and gilded leaves or flowers, one with a verse by Samuel K Cowan MA, another dated 1893 by the sender. Sizes up to 13.8 cm x 10 cm.

6. Six miscellaneous cards, three with leaves, three with gilt flowers or leaf sprays, (one with a cross). One card has an Australian stamp and was dated 1892 by the sender. Sizes up to 12.5 cm x 9.5 cm.

7/8. Nine cards with serrated edges (one birthday), with sprays of spring flowers. Four have verses, two signed by AF Earl, A Matheson. c1890. 8 cm x 6.5 cm up to 13.8 cm x 7.8 cm.

*The following cards are small miscellaneous examples published during the later 1880's. Numbers 9-13 are bordered.*

9/10. Fourteen miscellaneous cards with various flower or leaf sprays, with simple greetings, three birthday. 9.5 cm x 5 cm up to 8 cm x 11.7 cm.

11. Six cards from three sets with flower sprays. 9.1 cm x 6.7 cm, 10.7 cm x 7 cm.

12. Six cards (four square) with sprays or garlands of spring flowers. 6.7 cm x 6.7 cm up to 10.3 cm x 7.2 cm.

13. Six miscellaneous cards with single flowers or sprays, one with a verse by AHB. 8.8 cm x 6 cm up to 7.7 cm x 11.8 cm.

*Numbers 14-23 are unbordered, with a few dated in the early 1880's.*

14. Ten miscellaneous small cards with sprays of spring flowers and leaves, one with a basket, another with a flagon. 8 cm x 4.7 cm up to 10.3 cm x 6.7 cm.

15. Seven cards with sprays or garlands of spring flowers, including three from a set with one dated 1884 by the sender. Sizes up to 7.5 cm x 11 cm.

16. Seven cards from three sets, two with wicker baskets of flowers, two with violets or forget-me-nots on large leaves, and three with hanging baskets. 9.2 cm x 6.5 cm up to 6.7 cm x 10 cm.

17. Seven miscellaneous cards with garlands or sprays of flowers, one with honeysuckle around a circular vignette with a lake scene. Sizes up to 11.5 cm x 7.8 cm.

18. Six cards with garlands or sprays of mixed flowers and leaves. All have verses, four signed by Frances Ridley Havergal and one by Horatius Bonar DD, and two were dated 1892 by the sender. 9 cm x 6.5 cm up to 12 cm x 7.6 cm.

19. Six cards, five from one set with three designs of auricula, cyclamen, periwinkle, and another with primulas and ferns and a small circular vignette with a river scene. 6.5 cm x 10.1 cm, 7.5 cm x 10.7 cm.

20. Six square cards with sprays of flowers and foliage, one with a robin dated 1889 by the sender. Sizes up to 9 cm x 9 cm.

21. Nine small cards from two sets with roses, nasturtiums, pansies, asters, wood anemones. 8.1 cm x 5.2 cm, 5.3 cm x 8 cm.

22. Nine small cards with flowers and foliage. Three have verses by EH Bickersteth, James Montgomery, C Elliott, on reverse. Sizes up to 5.6 cm x 9.2 cm.

23. Nine small cards in rather garish colours with single flowers or sprays. Sizes up to 6.6 cm x 10.1 cm.

## VOLUME 255: LATER CARDS WITH FLOWERS AND FOLIAGE, FROM 1885

**This volume has cards from 1885 to about 1892 of superior quality to those in Volume 254. Most of them are on thick reinforced paper, and a number are on bright coloured backgrounds, often shaded. A few cards are signed by initials or monogram, and two are included from Hildesheimer and Faulkner and S Hildesheimer for comparison with unmarked cards.**

1. Two cards with pale blue borders, with a greeting card in an open envelope and a posy of fern with roses or camellias and a verse by Francis Ridley Havergal. They were dated 1885 and 1886 by the senders. 10.2 cm x 10.2 cm.

2. Two cards, convolvulus or field roses in circular vignettes, one dated 1887 by the sender. 11.5 cm x 11.5 cm.

3. Three decorative cards, lilies or irises with ferns and other spring flowers, with greetings and quotations from Tennyson in bordered bands. One was dated 1889 by the sender. 11 cm x 16 cm.

4. Two cards, camellias or crysanthemums and geraniums in a golden horseshoe, with a poem by HM Burnside. 13.5 cm x 16.5 cm.

5. Two cards, white violets and fern in a vignette with a decorative panel behind, and white florets with ivy on a silver horseshoe with a poem by SK Cowan. 11.3 cm x 13.1 cm, 11.8 cm x 16 cm.

6. A card with a butterfly on honeysuckle and a silver embossed crescent moon. 11.8 cm x 13.5 cm.

7. A birthday card with nasturtiums in a border of forget-me-nots. 13.1 cm x 13.1 cm.

8. Two cards. One has narcissus in a blue circular vignette, dated 1886 by the sender; the other has cut-out embossed blackthorn branches over a green annulet, with a birthday verse by Frances Ridley Havergal. 10.9 cm x 13.5 cm, 10.6 cm x 12.6 cm.

9. Three birthday cards on thick board with sprays or garlands of flowers and fern. One is signed with the monogram MB or BM and has a poem by Frances Ridley Havergal; another is marked Hildesheimer and Faulkner, with a verse by HM Burnside. 7.7 cm x 9.1 cm up to 11 cm x 11 cm.

10. Two cards, one with two white daisies or chamomile on a blackberry cane; the other with orchids in a patterned border. 10.7 cm x 15.9 cm, 16 cm x 11.5 cm.

*Numbers 11-16 have cut-out edges.*

11. A card with yellow roses on a grey background with silk finish, and a Christmas verse signed CS. 13.8 cm x 10.5 cm.

12. Two birthday cards, one with jewelled daisies and ferns and a poem by Frances Ridley Havergal, the other with snowdrops and wood anemones and a verse by Cecilia Havergal. 13.3 cm x 11.3 cm, 14 cm x 10.8 cm.

13. Two cards, one with harebells signed with monogram MB or BM, the other with forget-me-nots on a cross, both with religious verses by Frances Ridley Havergal. 9.2 cm x 13 cm, 15.2 cm x 11.4 cm.

14. Two birthday cards, one with pansies dated 1891 by the sender, the other with lilies of the valley and apple blossom framed in a horseshoe, and a poem by SK Cowan on reverse. 11.7 cm x 15.9 cm.

15. Two cards, clematis on a silver railing with white violets below, and marguerites with a birthday greeting by HM Burnside. 11.5 cm x 15.8 cm, 12.6 cm x 15 cm.

16. An embossed card with a hand holding a wreath of primroses and fir. 12 cm x 17.4 cm.

*Numbers 17-20 are miscellaneous examples, c1890.*

17. Four cards (two birthday), various spring flowers, including two cards with cut out edges and two with gold or silver decoration. 5.9 cm x 9 cm up to 10.1 cm x 10.5 cm.

18. Five cards, various flowers, including one of field roses with silver swallows and a verse by Johnston Beall dated 1890, one tinselled, two with greetings in silver, and the fifth with ferns and narcissus and a verse by SK Cowan dated 1889 by the sender. Sizes up to 13 cm x 9.3 cm.

19. Three cards with serrated edges, one with lilac and embossed birds, another with forget-me-nots, and the third with violets and lilies of the valley in a wicker basket. 13.3 cm x 9.6 cm, 10.1 cm x 13 cm.

20. Six cards with flower sprays including three from one set. All are in similar style on white background with self colour embossed border of ivy or flowers. 8.8 cm x 8.8 cm up to 8.8 cm x 11.8 cm.

*The following cards are on thick board with coloured backgrounds.*

21. Three square cards (two birthday), with coloured flower scraps on black, red, or pale pink backgrounds, one dated 1887 by the sender. 8.2 cm x 8.2 cm.

22. Four cards, dark brown backgrounds with gilded edges. Two are birthday cards with forget-me-nots, one has a sunflower, the fourth a sprig of mistletoe. 8 cm x 12.5 cm up to 14.3 cm x 10.2 cm.

23. Two cards, one with flax on a Japanese fan on shaded orange background. The other has a garland of pansies on a shaded brown background, and is marked S Hildesheimer. As this was the only SH card of this type found for the collection, it was included here for comparison with unmarked cards. 10.8 cm x 14 cm, 10.5 cm x 14.7 cm.

24. Two cards, one a valentine, one a birthday card, with coloured scraps of horseshoes with pansies or roses on black or dark green backgrounds, the first marked "Crown Perfumery, London". These designs were registered by Edith Carrington for S Hildesheimer at Stationers' Hall 4-4-1883 (see Volume 100 no. 17) but may have been used by an another firm. 10.8 cm x 16.4 cm.

25. Three cards, two signed BWM, probably Bertha Maguire with white flowers on shaded green backgrounds and verses by SK Cowan. The third card has marsh marigolds and a crescent moon on a shaded brown background. 11.7 cm x 16.4 cm, 15.3 cm x 11.4 cm.

26. Two cards with flower garlands, Japanese anemones on dark blue, and lapageria (a white variety of the Chilean bell flower), on lighter blue. 11 cm x 15 cm, 11.8 cm x 16.5 cm.

27. Two cards, garlands of white flowers on shaded pink backgrounds, one embossed, the other jewelled, with verses by AM Hone. 10.9 cm x 14.9 cm.

28. Two cards, fans with spring flowers on cream or orange background, and verses by SK Cowan, one dated 1891 by the sender. 14.2 cm x 10.9 cm.

29/30. Four cards in two sizes, three designs of white flowers and ferns, three on shaded blue, one on red background. 14 cm x 10.7 cm, 16 cm x 11.7 cm.

31. Three cards with garlands of primroses, lilies of the valley, or forget-me-nots, with a spider's web and a butterfly, on shaded orange background. 11.7 cm x 16 cm.

32. One card with brown and orange background and stylised flowers bordering a New Year verse by HM Burnside in a bordered diamond-shaped vignette. 14.7 cm x 11 cm.

# THE LATER YEARS

The vast increase in production of greeting cards of all kinds in the latter years of Victoria's reign was accompanied by many innovations in technique. Correspondence and personal cards were developed, with publishers prepared to overprint cards for individual use, and many cards of this period had spaces labelled "To" and "From" for the names of recipient and sender. By 1890 cards appeared in all shapes - flowers, birds, animals, heads, leaves, vases, moons, slippers, baskets, geometric, and many others - and cards were cut out along the edges to outline heads or flowers, with folder cards becoming common. Many of these have already been seen from Raphael Tuck, and some cards from other publishers are seen here with complete volumes for Hagelberg and Nister.

Section

20

Mechanical and three-dimensional cards were a feature of the late 1880's and some ingenious examples by Hagelberg provide useful dates from the patent registrations entered on the cards. The use of coloured paper to reflect light on the scenes was extended to the "Hold to Light" cards. However, artistic merit became increasingly subordinated to the over elaborate decoration of the later 1890's, and this is best summarised by Gleeson White writing in 1894 on Christmas cards and their chief designers - "Probably at no period was mechanical excellence more faultless than to- day, when scarce one design in a thousand has any but the slightest artistic interest. But the low-priced German labour forced the English makers to reduce the prices they paid their artists, and so ultimately they ceased to control the industry".

259.2

## VOLUME 256:
## SMALL PERSONAL & CORRESPONDENCE CARDS

These cards were made by publishers for personal use, some overprinted with the sender's name and address, others in correspondence style with space for the sender's and recipient's names. A few plain cards appear from the early 1880's, but most are small folding cards with decoration in gold and silver published in the later 1880's and the 1890's. It would be interesting to know if sample albums were produced for customers to choose their cards as at present. These were certainly issued in the early 20th century, but none have been found for this collection from the 19th century.

1. Four cards on single sheets, two dated 1881. Three were printed in gold with greetings and the name or monogram and address of the sender. The fourth is a wedding card printed in silver with a mock heraldic device of Cupid and love tokens, giving the name of bride and groom and their new address, dated August 18, 1887. 8.8 cm x 6 cm up to 12 cm x 9.8 cm.

2. Four cards with the sender's name or monogram and address, one with a gilded orchid and ferns, one with a group of children, and two with small scenes (one dated 1887). 11.6 cm x 9 cm.

*Numbers 3-10 are small folders printed with the sender's name and address, many with gilt and embossed decoration.*

3. Six cards, printed in gold, with birds, horseshoes, ivy, monograms, four dated from 1887-1897, showing a variety of styles.
8.5 cm x 5.5 cm up to 11.3 cm x 7.5 cm.

4. Five cards in envelope style. Three are printed in gilt, one has embossed pansies, the fifth has an illuminated tinselled "Xmas". All were dated from 1889-1891.
6.8 cm x 6.8 cm up to 11.5 cm x 9.3 cm.

5. Six cards, two in envelope style with gilt and coloured greeting, one triangular, two with embossed flowers and birds, and one with gilt greeting, all dated from 1891 to 1894.
11.3 cm x 5.6 cm up to 11.5 cm x 6.2 cm.

6. Six cards, five with serrated edges and embossed decoration of bells, flowers, and horseshoes, and one with cut-out embossed border, two dated 1893.
6 cm x 9.5 cm up to 8.5 cm x 11.7 cm.

7. Four cards, one with tinselled flowers and date for 1891/2, two with embossed flowers and birds printed in lilac and gold, the fourth dated 1897 with embossed garlands.
6.8 cm x 10 cm up to 8 cm x 10.8 cm.

8. Three cards with serrated edges, one dated 1894 with cut-out embossed decoration, another with embossed horses and charioteer on lilac ground dated 1889. The third card is a double folder tied with pink ribbon with gilt decoration, and has the names of sender and recipient printed "from William L Mutteen to Mr & Mrs Fred Roff, Manchester, Christmas 1894". Sizes up to 11 cm x 8.3 cm.

9. Four cards with monochrome designs, three of scenes (two in black, one brown tied with ribbon), the fourth with children's heads, dated 1894, 1895, 1895, 1898. Sizes up to 8.8 cm x 11.5 cm.

10. Three cards, folders with inside sheet tied with ribbon or cord. One has an embossed flower design on the cover and a black and white picture inside. The second card has an embossed design of cornflowers on the cover, and is from Mr William L Mutteen, Manchester, dated 1895. The third has a girl's head in an embossed holly design on the cover, and is from Mr & Mrs William L Mutteen, 198 Upper Brook St, Manchester, Xmas 1898.
10 cm x 14.7 cm, 9.1 cm x 12.2 cm, 10.2 cm x 12.4 cm.

*Numbers 11-18 are small folding cards in correspondence style with spaces for the names of sender and recipient.*

11/12. Fourteen cards with embossed gilt decoration of flowers, foliage, bells, etc. Thirteen have serrated edges, and one has gilt edges with embossed cherubs in a gilt frame. c1890.
8.4 cm x 5.4 cm up to 11 cm x 7 cm.

13. Six cards with serrated edges and gilt and silver decoration, including one with a tinselled moon and another with a peacock's feather, c1890.
6.5 cm x 8.1 cm up to 12.9 cm x 7 cm.

14. Six cards, four with elaborate cut-out borders, two with serrated edges. Four have embossed gilt decoration, one silver bells, one a gilt and silver cross.
Sizes up to 12 cm x 8 cm.

15. Six cards in envelope form, two with ivy or oak leaves, two with embossed gilt-edged holly leaves and flowers, one with violets in a tinselled shoe, the sixth with coloured leaves. Late 1880's.
10 cm x 6.3 cm up to 12.3 cm x 7.5 cm.

16. Six cards with serrated edges, decorated with jewelled flowers, one dated 1891 by the sender.
6.5 cm x 8.2 cm up to 11 cm x 7.7 cm.

17. Six cards from three sets with serrated edges. Three have all-over patterns of ivy, daisies or violets, two have coloured gilt-edged carnations, and the sixth has cut-out cornflowers and a poppy. 7.2 cm x 5.8 cm, 9.2 cm x 7.2 cm, 8.6 cm x 9.2 cm.

18. Six cards with various gilt or sepia decoration, including one with a gilded cross opening to show a poem by Eliza Cook, another dated 1895 with frosting, and a birthday card with flowers in a pot. 7.5 cm x 8 cm up to 12.4 cm x 9.5 cm.

19. An unusual folding personal card dated Christmas 1888, printed in gilt with the name and address of the sender, complete with envelope with a Father Christmas head printed in red.
6.8 cm x 10.1 cm.

20. Six cards in similar style to the preceding ones, but only one with space for the sender's name. All have serrated edges with gilt-edged coloured embossed flowers or birds, and two were dated 1893, 1895 by the senders.
9.4 cm x 5.6 cm up to 8 cm x 14 cm.

21. Six cards in similar style, without space for sender's name. All have embossed decoration in gilt or silver and colours and three have patterned lace cut-out insets.
5 cm x 9.7 cm up to 7.5 cm x 11.4 cm.

## VOLUME 257:
## CORRESPONDENCE CARDS, LATE 1880'S-1890'S

These cards have lines for the name of the sender and in some cases for the recipient's name as well. The bulk of the space is taken up for this and for the greeting, usually leaving room for only a small picture in one corner; verses are rarely seen on this type of card. Most of the cards here measure about 11.5 cm x 9 cm, with a few variations as noted, and some are marked with the publisher's name. A few similar cards are included without space for names.

1. Three cards published by Castell Bros., one with pen and ink scenes dated 1885 by the sender, another with a sprig of mistletoe, the third with a stag's head lifting to show a hunting scene.

2. Four cards by Castell, two with winter scenes, two with Georgian figures, one dated 1886 by the sender.

3. Three cards published by Wirth Brothers, two with country scenes, the third a shepherd with his flock in winter.

4. Three cards published by AH Bunney, Liverpool and Llandudno, with views of Lime St, Liverpool, Conway Castle, and Llandudno Bay. All are marked "Printed in Bavaria".

5. Five cards, two from Davidson Bros., three Hagelberg, all with scenes, one dated 1889 by the recipient.

6. Four cards with small mother-of-pearl motifs of a cupola, fan, buoy, and a panel with butterflies. Three are marked Hagelberg and the fourth is printed with a name and address and the date, New Year 1889.

7. Four cards, black and white pictures of birds and animals. Two are signed AT (one dated 1886 by the sender), and two are marked H S G & Co London and G F & S (neither is listed by Buday).

8. Four cards, two with scenes in vignettes, two with pictures of Durham and Norwich Cathedrals, signed F E B.

9. Four cards. One has a mountain scene "Bristen Stock", one a jewelled garland of flowers with a country scene, another sea birds. The fourth card with a sailing ship is signed BDS and faintly marked Hildesheimer and Faulkner, included here for comparison with unmarked cards.

10. Six cards. Five have country scenes including three of waterfalls, one of a castle by a lake, all framed in garlands of leaves or flowers. The sixth card is smaller with Medmenham Abbey in a vignette and measures 9.7 cm x 6.7 cm.

11. Three cards. Two are larger, one a winter scene with a farm and church and a poem by Charlotte Murray, the other a country house in moonlight, measuring 11.4 cm x 15 cm, 14.2 cm x 11.2 cm. The third card has a Biblical scene and a text and was dated 1887 by the sender.

12. Three cards, little girls climbing over fences, printed on sepia backgrounds.

13. Six cards, all with children, including two smaller ones measuring 11 cm x 8.5 cm and 11 cm x 7.4 cm.

14. Three cards with embossed patterned edges and designs of flowers, bells, and ivy with silver and gilt decoration. Two cards have the same design, but one has tinselled decoration.

15/17. Twelve embossed cards with serrated edges and various designs of flowers, holly, foliage, mistletoe with bells, moon, star, or horseshoe. All have some tinselled decoration and two have cut-out greetings.

18. Four cards with flowers. Three have serrated edges and tinselled lettering; the fourth has tinselled flowers and a poem by MA Jarvis.

19. Four embossed cards, one with a tinselled flower, one with 1892 on gold banners hanging from a silver holly branch, and one with a gold oak leaf. The fourth card has a gold ivy leaf and is signed "from Laurence Alma Tadema".

**259.5**

20. Three cards, serrated edges, with birds. One card is larger, 13 cm x 10 cm, with birds in a shield shaped vignette.

21. Four cards, one with blackberries and a bird in monochrome, another with two kittens in a gilded basket, the third with embossed gilt birds on a branch over a greeting in blue print. The fourth card has a procession of bags with arms, legs, and faces, perhaps containing sweets, though there might be some deeper significance.

22. Five cards with birds. Two with serrated edges and embossed robins and holly measure 12.8 cm x 7.3 cm.

23. Four cards, three with holly, one with mistletoe.

24. Four cards, two with ferns, one with mistletoe, one with oak.

25. Four cards, three with flowers, one with ivy. Three have serrated edges and two were dated 1888, 1893 by the sender.

26. Five cards, four with flowers, one with ivy. Three are smaller, measuring 9 cm x 6 cm up to 11.3 cm x 7.3 cm.

27. Four cards with violets, forget-me-nots, or roses.

28. Three cards. Two have serrated edges and embossed pansies outlined in gilt; the third has a patterned edge in art nouveau style with an embossed robin.

29. Three larger cards on thick gilt-edged board, nasturtiums signed Ada Hanbury, mistletoe, or stylised flowering branches, all with gilt lettering. Sizes up to 13 cm x 10.5 cm.

*Numbers 30-33 are in similar style to the correspondence cards but without space for names. All have gilt edges and lettering.*

30. Five cards. One has a mother-of-pearl lute, two have tinselled flowers, one has a church, and the fifth has a poem signed E E G.

31. Four cards, two with embossed and tinselled flowers, one with a golden ivy leaf, the fourth with golden bells and ivy.

32. Four cards, three designs, a soldier on a camel, a tennis net with balls, and five men on penny-farthing bicycles.

33. Four cards, two with embossed, gilded and tinselled flowers, one with a clown, the fourth with two Georgian figures in a circular vignette.

## VOLUME 258: CARDS PUBLISHED BY WOLFF HAGELBERG OF BERLIN c1885-1895

Hagelberg supplied cards for the English market from the 1860's, often sold with the imprint of other publishers. He was highly regarded for artistic merit, and S Hildesheimer invited him to share in judging the 1881 prize competition. Some Hagelberg marked cards have appeared in previous subject sections and in Volume 257, and cut-out, folding, and shaped cards appear here. They include some interesting examples which can be opened into three-dimensional scenes or models, for which patents were taken out in England, Germany, and USA. Most of the cards are numbered and marked "Berlin", indicating that they were made in Germany, and marketed from 1885 through their London branch at 12 Bunhill Row. Some unmarked cards are included which were probably, from similarity of style, published by Hagelberg. Most of the poetic sentiments were by E E

258.9

**Griffin or MS Haycraft, abbreviated in the text to EEG and MSH. Many of the cards are in correspondence style with spaces for the names of sender and recipient.**

*Numbers 1-7 are shaped cards, late 1880's-1890.*

1/3. Twenty-two cards, including thirteen crescent moons in two sizes, three palettes, one oval, and five rectangular cards repeating the designs. There are five moonlight country scenes, three with ships and lighthouses, and two other country scenes, with various captions, all in subdued colours on pale grey backgrounds with silver highlights. Numbers 106 (rectangles), 121, 212 (moons), 122, 170 palettes. Some cards are signed LD, probably Lucien Davis, RI. Sizes: moons 11.5 cm x 9.5 cm, palettes 9.5 cm x 12.5 cm, oval 12.7 cm x 9 cm, rectangles 6 cm x 9.8 cm.

4. Four cards. Three are bell-shaped, with Gothic ruins, numbers 381, 157, 157 (dated 1889 by the sender). The fourth card is a lute with a country scene printed in sepia, no. 413. 10 cm x 10.5 cm, 8 cm x 9.3 cm, 25 cm x 9 cm.

5. Six cards, two hexagons with birds, no. 168, a ship scene on a fan or battledore, no. 266, two sails with yachting scenes, numbers 517, 160, and a triangle with a winter scene, no. 112. The last three are signed LD. Sizes up to 10.5 cm x 11.8 cm.

6. Seven cards, two crescent moons with flowers, no. 412, a five-pointed star with flowers, no. 439, two circles with the same country scene, no. 335, a small palette, no. 148, and an oval with a sickle and a harvest scene, no. 620. 6 cm x 4.8 cm to 13.5 cm x 12 cm.

7. Five cards. Two are circular with a little girl or cherubs in Summer scenes, nos. 341, 607. The other three, with children or a castle view, have slots so placed that the cards may be made into three-dimensional models. They are marked Patent 6359, USA 8-3-1887, German 37390. 9 cm x 9 cm up to 12.7 cm x 12.7 cm.

*Numbers 8-11 have children, birds and animals, in various shapes and with edges cut-out around heads or figures, many with humorous verses, made about 1890.*

8. Seven cards.
a) A puppy jumping through a barrel, with a poem by EEG on reverse, no. 274.
b) Three kittens before a floral screen, with a verse by EEG, no. 735.
c/e) Two designs of kittens by a bandbox and puppies with a muff.
f) A poodle looking in a mirror on a barrel-shaped card with a verse by EEG, no. 302.
g) Two kittens in lace-edged caps, with verse by EEG, no. 326.
Sizes up to 9.5 cm x 11 cm.

9. Six cards.
a) Three elephants in hats holding black babies in their trunks, with a verse by EEG containing a topical reference to Barnum's show. No. 776.
b) A stork holding an ink pot, with verse by EEG. No. 344.
c) An elephant in ceremonial trappings, cut-out like a scrap. No. 734.
d) A frog blowing a trumpet, on a folder card with verse by EEG on reverse.
e) Two frogs on a shell with a sea scene. No. 116.
f) Frogs climbing a ladder with ducks below, the incident described in a humorous verse by F Ernest Power. 7.2 cm x 5.8 cm up to 11.5 cm x 9.2 cm.

10. Seven cards.
a) A girl in a hat on a scallop-edged card. No. 604.
b/c) Birds, cat with a robin, on gilt ground with greeting in a panel. Nos. 509, 510.
d) Kittens on an autumn leaf, with a verse signed Elbetee on reverse.
e) An open purse with notes or money.
f) Five children by a fence holding a cloth showing a poem by EEG. The reverse of the card shows the children's backs. No. 428.
g) Three overlapping circles with dogs and kittens, dated 1887 by the sender. 6.4 cm x 7.1 cm up to 15.3 cm x 8.5 cm.

11. Nine cards.
a/b) Two folders with a boat on the cover, opening to show a rowing four of dogs with cox, and an appropriate poem signed Nemo, one dated 1891 by the sender. Nos. 364.
c) Two peaches, one open showing a grub with a curious verse by EEG on reverse, marked copyright 1890 Hagelberg.
d) Bellows decorated with forget-me-nots, no. 337.
e/f) Two small bats or fans, each with a dog's head.
g) A wheatsheaf, opening to show a country scene and a verse by AM Hone.
h) A wheelbarrow, opening to show a country scene and a verse by EEG.
i) A "kid" glove, with appropriate poem by EEG. 5 cm x 8.4 cm to 11.8 cm x 14 cm.

*Numbers 12-21 show folding cards, many with cut-out and pierced decoration; a few similar single cards are included.*

12. Six cards, five folders one plain, with embossed flower, foliage, and ivy decoration, three with horseshoes, one with a silver bell. Two cards use the same design in different ways. 8.7 cm x 6 cm up to 13.2 cm x 10 cm.

13. Three elaborate folding cards. Two have an outside flap with cut-out and pierced designs of swallows or owls, and a second flap with a scene, opening to show pansies or a tinselled winter scene with a poem by MSH. The third card has lost its outside flap but has the same winter scene and a different poem by MSH. They are not marked but are attributed to Hagelberg from similarity of style. 15.2 cm x 11 cm.

14. Six cards. Five are folders with four designs of birds, one marked, the others attributed from similarity and the characteristic small scene or floral spray on reverse, all with verses within, four signed by EEG. The sixth card is circular. Sizes up to 13.2 cm x 9.2 cm.

15. Five folding cards, two marked. All have outside flaps with cut-out bird pictures, and four have a second flap with a country scene, opening to show further pictures and verse by FRH, EEG, or MSH. The largest card has a tinselled picture of Father Christmas within. 8.5 cm x 6.5 cm up to 11.2 cm x 15.1 cm.

16. Three cards.
a) A folder with a picture of girls and a verse signed TWM inside and birds on the cover.
b) A pale grey card with flowers on two flaps, opening to show a scene and a poem

by MSH.
c) Another similar with flowers and two clasped hands opening to show more flowers and a poem by EEG.
Sizes up to 13.4 cm x 10 cm.

17. Four cards (three marked), with elaborate embossed and tinselled flower and leaf decoration. Two are folders with two flaps, opening to show greeting or another tinselled card; two are single cards with shaded pink and red borders with flowers around scenes with sailing ships.
Sizes up to 14.5 cm x 11 cm.

18. Five single cards. Two have scenes in gilt borders in Art Nouveau style, one has a cut-out border of forget-me-nots, another a winter scene with a verse by EEG. The fifth card has a wreath of flowers around a panel with greeting and is numbered 509.
7.3 cm x 6.2 cm up to 11.4 cm x 9 cm.

19. Three cards, a fan with birds, no. 207, a folder with gilt "Auld Lang Syne" and winter scene, and a single card with blue tits and sparrows in a silver border with tinselled daisies, no. 828.
11.8 cm x 7 cm up to 15.5 cm x 10.2 cm.

20/22. Sixteen folding cards, 1890's. Ten have embossed flower decoration, and one has an interesting mixture of a church scene, cherubs, and a row of chickens with Art Nouveau border. Two have children, one an angel, one a cat, another a dog, and all open to show verses or greetings.
8.3 cm x 6.5 cm up to 9.6 cm x 12.5 cm.

*Numbers 23-27 are mechanical opening cards which can be made into three-dimensional scenes, most marked with patent numbers, dated from 1889-1891.*

23. Two cards.
a) Souvenir of Colonial and Indian exhibition, 1886, signed CM or MC, with pictures of men from the Colonies against a sailing ship background. There is an attached booklet of colonial views which can be opened by pulling a tab. It is numbered 173, a useful guide to dating.
16.5 cm x 11.3 cm.
b) A three-tier winter scene which can stand up in three-dimensional form, marked Patent 11400/90, USA Patent 27-1-1891, with an indistinct verse on the back. Coloured paper reflects light on the sky and snow. 16.5 cm x 11.5 cm.

24. A tinselled card which can be opened out to make a model of a farmhouse with four walls, snow and robins outside and pictures of birds within, and a poem by MSH. It is marked Patent no. 16254//89, USA Patent 4-3-1890. (The bird designs appear in no. 35). 17.5 cm x 16 cm.

25. Two similar cards.
a) An attic window with puppies and cats on the roof, opening out to make a square pyramid, with an appropriate poem by EEG. 11 cm x 11 cm.

258.17

b) A woodland scene with frosted snow and branches, opening to show pictures of owls inside, marked Patent no. 16264/89, USA Patent granted. 15.5 cm x 14 cm.

26. Three cards, unmarked, but probably Hagelberg.
a) A horseshoe edged with snow framing a country house in moonlight, with a device enabling it to stand up like a photoframe, with light reflected through coloured paper behind moon and windows. Patent 14013/91, German patent 61857, USA applied for. This card is a forerunner of the cards much sought after by postcard collectors known as "Hold to Light".
10 cm x 10.7 cm.
b) A similar card with a boat framed in icebergs, light being reflected through the transparent background from coloured paper behind. Patent numbers as for a).
9 cm x 12.5 cm.
c) A frosted winter scene in two tiers with farmhouse and hilly background. A cardboard lever turns it into a three-dimensional scene. Patent 14175/90, designed in England, made in Germany.
12.5 cm x 9.7 cm.

27. Two cards.
a) A town in winter, perhaps German or Swiss, framed in snow-covered branches and wooden palings, opening to make a three-dimensional model. Patent 14175/90, designed in England, made in Germany.
9.1 cm x 13 cm.
b) A similar single card with a child in bed, seen through a window framed in snowladen branches with birds.
9.1 cm x 13.3 cm.

*Numbers 28-33 are single cards, with one exception, featuring cut-out borders with greetings and pierced decoration.*

28. Four frosted unmarked cards.
a/b) Scenes bordered by cut-out greetings

and mounted in rustic frames, one signed FCP. 12.5 cm x 12.5 cm, 10 cm x 10 cm.
c) A similar folder card with verse inside. 13.8 cm x 9.3 cm.
d) A winter scene in a cut-out border of snow-covered branches with birds, signed F Corbyn Price. 11 cm x 14.7 cm.

29. Four cards.
a) A house by a lake seen through a church window, with cut-out border.
b) A winter scene on a blue background, with cut-out tinselled Christmas greeting, and verse by EEG on reverse, no. 933.
c) A country scene with flowers and robins on a silver border and a cut-out greeting, with a poem by SKC on reverse, no. 789.
d) A winter scene bordered by embossed tinselled white flowers with a verse by EEG on reverse. Sizes up to 11 cm x 15 cm.

30. Four cards.
a) A winter scene with cut-out tree branches in one corner, no. 307.
b) A snow scene on a panel set in a gilded wheel, no. 592.
c) Shakespeare's song "When icicles hang by the wall" with a cut-out picture of owls on a crescent moon, no. 430.
d) A verse in a panel in silver border with cut-out Christmas greeting on a tree branch, no. 790.
Sizes up to 14.8 cm x 10 cm.

31. Three cards, all with poems by EEG.
a) Santa Claus and three children in a snow-covered village with a cut-out border of silver ivy leaves, no. 416.
9.3 cm x 13.5 cm.
b) A plain card from the same set with another view of Santa Claus and children.
7.2 cm x 11.2 cm.
c) Children on a flowering branch, in a patterned border. 16.4 cm x 9.7 cm.

32. Four cards.
a) A curly haired girl in a green hat and

dress, with a border of cut-out branches and greeting. 10 cm x 13 cm.
b/d) Three small cards, two designs each with two winter scenes set on a bamboo screen. 6.3 cm x 6.7 cm.

33. Five cards.
a/c) Pen and ink country scenes on a card threaded through a wreath of jewelled roses (one birthday). 13.6 cm x 9.5 cm.
d) A moonlight scene with church, with a cut-out rose spray and a poem by EEG, no. 634. 9.8 cm x 13.2 cm.
e) Cattle by a stream, signed LD, with cut-out flower border, no. 847.
14.7 cm x 10.5 cm.

*The following cards are similar and attributed to Hagelberg, but have no marking or numbers.*

34. Four cards with scenes and cut-out borders of branches, leaves, or stonework, one with a verse by ES on reverse.
7.5 cm x 9 cm up to 16 cm x 11.2 cm.

35. Three cards.
a) A continental town in moonlight, with daisies and a cut-out border of a tree with silver leaves, and a poem by EEG on reverse.
b) A country scene in a silver border with a cut-out cottage roof and chimneys and a birthday greeting and poem on reverse, dated 1890 by the sender.
c) A New Year poem by MSH with a church roof and spire above and a cut-out border with bells and holly.
Sizes up to 15.5 cm x 11.5 cm.

36. Four cards, all with the same border of birds on silvered branches. Three are from a set with two designs of birds on shaded pink backgrounds. The fourth card has a moonlight view of a church by a lake.
9.1 cm x 13 cm. These bird designs, without the border, are used in no. 23.

37. Four frosted cards with scenes, three in cut-out borders of branches, one dated 1892 by the sender, the fourth in a circular cut-out border with leaves. Sizes up to 10 cm x 14 cm.

38. Two cards, pen and ink country scenes, one in a cut-out border of ivy leaves, the other with birds on branches. The first card has a poem by Elizabeth Love on reverse.
10 cm x 13.6 cm, 15.5 cm x 11.3 cm.

39. Four cards, winter scenes, two with cut-out borders (one with a verse by Isa J Postgate on reverse), two with cut-out Christmas greeting. Sizes all about 13 cm x 9.8 cm.

40. Four cards, with various interesting trellis-like cut-out borders, three with scenes, one with a gilded bird and jewelled flowers.
11 cm x 8 cm up to 14.7 cm x 10 cm.

41. Four cards with cut-out borders of branches with birds. Two are from one set

with winter scenes and a poem by Clara Simmonds on reverse, the third has a winter scene and a verse by EJP on reverse, and the fourth card has blue tits flying over snow and a verse by AL Salmon. Sizes up to 16 cm x 11.7 cm.

42. Two cards, pen and ink river scenes with cut-out coloured pansies or daffodils at two corners. 11.6 cm x 15.2 cm.

43. A frosted card with a greeting "A Happy Christmas with best wishes", the Christmas in the centre of the card contrived from cut-out branches and snowdrops. It has a pen and ink design of flowers and a quotation from Shakespeare on the back. 16.2 cm x 12.2 cm.

44. Six cards (three birthday) with various cut-out borders of flowers or ivy around summer scenes.
9.7 cm x 8 cm up to 10 cm x 13 cm.

## VOLUME 259: CARDS PUBLISHED BY ERNEST NISTER,1890'S

**Most of these cards are marked Ernest Nister, London, printed in Bavaria, with series numbers. A few also have the caption "printed at Nuremberg, Bavaria", and the name of EP Dutton & Co, 31 West Twenty Third Street, New York, with Nister's address given as 24 St Bride St, EC. It is possible that a second number sequence might have begun in co-operation with this firm as some later cards appear to have early numbers. Some typical datings by senders might help to give more accurate timing though it must be remembered that a date as given by a sender only means that the card was issued before that date. Numbers 1287, 1481 were sent in 1894, no. 2419 in 1895, no. 2121 in 1896, no. 4901 in 1896 and nos. 6523, 7065 in 1900. Many of these cards were designed for children's use, and are reminiscent of the large number of children's books published by Nister. Some of the earlier cards have the Nister trademark of a palette and brushes with a child's head.**

1. Two cards.
a) Two flaps, with a cut-out girl holding a sheaf of corn in a country scene, signed F Hines, open to show a long poem by Clifton Bingham. No. 942.
10.4 cm x 13.2 cm.
b) An opening card with a cut-out inn and stage-coach on the front, and a long poem inside continuing on the back. This card is marked Nister & Dutton, unnumbered.
14.7 cm x 10.5 cm.

2. Five folding and mechanical cards.
a) A croquet box with frogs inside, no. 827.
14.4 cm x 3.7 cm.

b) A folding card with mice, no. 1495.
11.7 cm x 5.4 cm.
c) A cat with a jug of milk. Pull tab to make its head move, no. 1222.
11.9 cm x 9.2 cm.
d) An opening card with a Cat Harlequinade, Harlequin and Columbine on stage in the centre and clown and pantaloon on the side flaps.
14.6 cm x 10.3 cm.
e) A card with owls in men's clothing on side flaps, opening to show a verse of greeting by LLW (number missing).
10.8 cm x 9.5 cm.

3. Four cards.
a) A mechanical card with cut-out girl and dog. Pull tab to make the dog jump, no. 1232. 10.3 cm x 13.6 cm.
b) An opening card, with hounds and huntsmen in three tiers on springs, no. 5419. 9 cm x 13.5 cm.
c) A folding card with Georgian girl and boy on triangular flaps, opening to show a verse by Ellis Walton, no. 925, dated 1894 by the sender. 8.8 cm x 8.8 cm.
d) A cut-out picture of a toy town with shops and figures, no. 1051.
10.2 cm x 6.7 cm.

4. Five opening cards with cut-out birds or animals.
a) A duck pulling a toy yacht, dated 1894 by the sender, no. 1481. 12.4 cm x 6.4 cm.
b) Two bears at school, no. 1075?
7.1 cm x 6.7 cm.
c) Two owls at a window, no. 1470.
11 cm x 8.3 cm.
d) A dog in a man's suit and hat on a weighing machine, dated 1895 by the sender, no. 2419. 6.6 cm x 11.8 cm.
e) A stand-up card with owls and a shop selling mice, with a verse by LLW, no. 2242. 8 cm x 11.8 cm.

5. Seven shaped and cut-out children's cards with cats in various pursuits, including one driving a cart pulled by a dog, one riding a bicycle, a cat in a boot, another drinking milk from a pail, two kittens on a plate, two holding a card with a feline band, and three tabbies in lace caps, gowns and aprons drinking tea.
Nos. 1087, ?, 1628, 1533, 830, 715, 1551.
Sizes up to 11.5 cm x 11 cm.

6. Six shaped and cut-out cards, a leaf with moonlight scene, no. 706, a frog and a duckling, no. 877, a dog in a dunce's cap, no. 1560, two squirrels and a handcart with nuts at 6d a lb, no. 1055, two birds under an umbrella, no. 5719, a hen and chickens, no. 1548. Sizes up to 10.5 cm x 11.5 cm.

7. Six shaped and cut-out cards with children, a little girl in a summer scene, no. 1012, children skating with a dog, no. 1063, four little girls in frosted white bonnets and pelisses, no. 1479, a girl with dolls and a cat, no. 1566, a girl and a cat in snow, no. 1062, a girl and two boys in sailor suits, no. 4627.
Sizes up to 13 cm x 9.6 cm.

8. Seven small cards with children. Two are folders with a fairy or children, nos. 864, 1516. Two have cut-out flaps with children and embossed borders, no. 1546, with another plain card repeating one design, no. 1556. The sixth card is a very small imitation post-card with stamp and postman, no. 813, and the seventh is a plain card with a girl and dogs and a message printed in cursive writing for the sender to sign, no. 1562.
6 cm x 5.2 cm up to 11 cm x 8.3 cm.

9. Five cards with patterned or serrated edges. Four are folders, two with children, nos. 2229, 2310, one with Santa Claus in red robe, no. 2446, one with a country scene, number erased. The fifth card has a small girl stirring the Christmas pudding, no number.
8.2 cm x 8.9 cm up to 9.5 cm x 12.3 cm.

10. Five well-designed frosted cards, with folding cut-out flaps, two with robins, three with little girls in fur-trimmed winter coats and hats. Three are numbered 2233, 4315, 4412. Sizes up to 9.2 cm x 11.8 cm.

11. Six cards with robins, including two folders, one with embossed tinselled border and greeting, no number the other with triangular flaps, no. 1187. The other four have serrated or patterned edges, two numbered 1093, 4702.
Sizes up to 12.7 cm x 7.5 cm.

12. Six cards with patterned cut-out edges. One has three little girls in white bonnets and pelisses in a holly border, no. 5742, another a country scene in a border of ivy, four have young people in Georgian or shepherdess style dress, nos. 1085, 5736, 5811, 5811. 8.3 cm x 9.5 cm up to 9.5 cm x 12 cm.

13. Four folder cards with serrated edges, one with a girl in Regency dress, no. 5531, another in shepherdess costume with a poem by FGS, no. 5547. The third card has a girl in a muslin dress with embossed forget-me-not border (no number), the fourth has a girl crowned with daisies and embossed daisy decoration, no. 5513. Sizes vary between 7 cm x 13.2 cm and 8.4 cm x 12 cm.

14. Four folder cards, one with a girl in fur-trimmed coat and hat carrying holly, dated 1900 by the sender, no. 6523, another with two boy soldiers and a flag, no. 6547. The third card has a cat in an embossed flower border, no. 6623, and the fourth has a cat and dog under mistletoe, with a descriptive verse by HGH.
Sizes up to 8.6 cm x 13 cm.

15. Two cards with patterned edges, one with the Virgin Mary and the Babe in the Manger, no. 6843, the other with three angels' heads, no. 6837.
9.5 cm x 13.5 cm, 9 cm x 14 cm.

*The following cards all have floral or foliage designs.*

16. Eight miscellaneous folding cards in various styles. Six have spring flowers, one holly, nos. 1072, 1079, 1138, 1287 (dated 1894 by the sender), 1271, 1505, 6903. The eighth card has birthday greeting with an apple branch on two flaps opening to show a girl picking apples and a verse signed Marion Wallace, no. 1042.
6.8 cm x 8 cm up to 11.6 cm x 11.6 cm.

17. Seven cards, four with serrated edges. One has birds on a flowering branch, no. 1555, another is shaped like an easel, no. 1097, two have violets, nos. 825, 858, one has roses, no. 1056. The sixth is an Easter postcard with lilies on a cross of ferns, no. 1054, and the seventh has an illuminated quotation from Charles Dickens with holly decoration, no. 108, both marked Nister & Dutton, perhaps with a later series of numbers.
6.1 cm x 8.3 cm up to 14 cm x 8.8 cm.

18. Five elaborate folder cards, four with cut-out tinselled lace decoration, three numbered 1434, 2010, 2121 dated 1896 by the sender. The fifth card has embossed flowers and ivy with a bordered oval framing a country scene, no. 4236.
10.9 cm x 7.8 cm up to 9.5 cm x 13.5 cm.

19. Four folding cards, three with violets. One is an Easter card with verse signed CB, another has a Christmas verse by Frank Mayhew, no. 4341, the third a birthday card on springs which opens out to make an interesting three-dimensional model with four tiers. The fourth card has an Easter greeting with stars, a cross, and flowers, no. 7065, dated 1900 by the sender.
9.1 cm x 9.5 cm up to 10 cm x 12.5 cm.

20. Four Easter cards, folders, one with lilies and a poem by Marion Wallace, no. 1295, another with embossed snowdrops dated 1898 by the sender, the third with passion flowers, these two with verses by

258.23

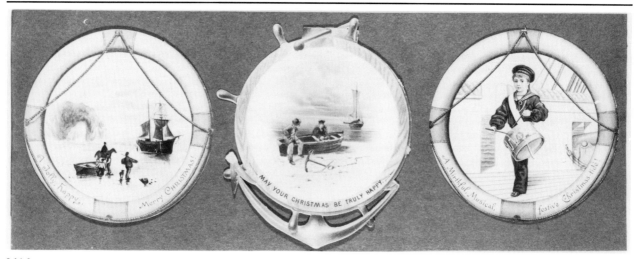

261.3

Charlotte Murray. The fourth card has a cross with lace and tinselled decoration and a poem by Frances Ridley Havergal, no. 4642. Sizes up to 11 cm x 15 cm.

21. Four elaborate folding cards. Three have birthday greetings and ribbon ties, one with forget-me-nots dated 1898 by the sender, no. 4901, two with embossed and cut-out floral borders, one no. 2743. The fourth card has a New Year verse by HM Burnside and embossed and tinselled flowers on lace background on the cover, no. 2006. Sizes up to 10.3 cm x 13.5 cm.

22. A small booklet in the shape of a butterfly, shown on the front and back covers, with a poem of greeting on several pages each adorned with a small spray of flowers. This was dated 1914 by the sender but may have been made earlier.
9.7 cm x 7 cm.

## VOLUME 260: CARDS FROM MORE PUBLISHERS, WITH SOME MECHANICAL CARDS, MOST PRINTED IN GERMANY

The shaped, cut-out, and folding cards, numbers 1-23, are marked with publisher's names, and some of the unmarked cards in subsequent volumes might be attributed by comparison with these. Numbers 24-30 are interesting mechanical and three-dimensional opening cards, most in surprisingly good condition after a century's use, though a few small heads are missing. Only one of these is marked.

1. Three religious folder cards, tied with tasselled cord. The first dated 1892 has a long poem "God Knows the Best", in a cover with a robin and snowdrops, published by Walter G Wheeler, 21a Warwick Lane, Paternoster Row, EC, and John G Wheeler, 88 Mildmay Park, N, London. The two others with embossed flower design have religious poems, and

are marked Walter G Wheeler, 17 Paternoster Row, London EC, one Keswick Series no. 2111, the other no. 643 dated 1897. They were all printed in Germany, and continue the series of "Mildmay" cards in Volume 128, probably through members of the same family. Sizes up to 10.7 cm x 17.6 cm.

*Numbers 2-7 were published by Castell Bros. Only one is numbered.*

2/3. Six folding cards for children written like letters with pictures replacing some words in rebus style, featuring toys, cards, books and Christmas goodies, one dated 1891 by the sender, with an envelope. 9 cm x 11.6 cm.

4. Five similar cards written as riddles with pictures - "What animals do you always take to bed with you?" Answer - "Calves". 11.3 cm x 10 cm.

5. Four folding cards with leaves, holly, flowers and a robin, one marked "The Peniel" with a verse by Lucy A Bennett. 8.3 cm x 5.5 cm up to 13.2 cm x 8.4 cm.

6. Six shaped cards. Three (two designs) have spring flowers in baskets, one has flowers in a slipper, another flowers in a tub and the sixth is a circle with edges folded over flowers.
8 cm x 8 cm up to 8.8 cm x 12.6 cm.

7. Five shaped cards, donkeys by a fence, birds pecking a cottage loaf, a banjo, a sail and a cracker opening to show a couple in Georgian dress, numbered JTF 136 38138. 8.1 cm x 7.5 cm up to 6.4 cm x 16 cm.

*Numbers 8-13 were published by Davidson Bros, London, 1890-1900.*

8. Two cards, one oval with a harbour scene and a verse by SK Cowan, the other an octagonal folder with winter scenes and a poem by HM Burnside. 11 cm x 14.6 cm, 9.7 cm x 9.7 cm.

9. Five folding cards with pictures of children. One has a trademark of a palette on a globe. Sizes up to 6.4 cm x 13 cm.

10. Four folding cards. Two are in Art Nouveau style with children or cats, the third has a puppy in a glove, the fourth kittens in a wheelbarrow.
Sizes up to 9 cm x 13.2 cm.

11. Five embossed cards with flowers or holly. One has an elaborate cut-out border with forget-me-nots and butterflies. c1895. 10 cm x 7.5 cm up to 9.3 cm x 14 cm.

12. Four folding cards c1900 with embossed flowers, three tied with ribbon. Two have verses by HMB, one a greeting by Isabel Warry.
7.5 cm x 9.8 cm up to 9.7 cm x 13 cm.

13. Three folding cards, printed in England, early 20th century (included for comparison). Two have humorous pictures of gentlemen imbibing or suffering nightmares, the third has two children by a window with a golliwog.
Sizes about 9 cm x 11.5 cm.

*Numbers 14-15 were published by Wirth Brothers.*

14. A collection of 10 cards of various shapes, with scenes, birds, or animals, with an envelope marked "10 Beautiful Christmas Cards, all different designs, for 10 cents". This came from Canada, indicating that Wirth's cards of the late 1880's were sold there.
4.2 cm x 9.5 cm up to 13.6 cm x 8.3 cm.

15. Four shaped cards with scenes. Two are marked Wirth Bros, one a shield, one a parallelogram. The other two are circular, marked Wirth Bros & Owen, one dated 1884, the other no. 2350.
Sizes up to 10.2 cm x 10.2 cm.

*Numbers 16-19 were published by Meissner & Buch, some marked Leipzig. Their cards may have been made there but Buday gives a*

*London office address as well as Leipzig.*

16. Six cards. One has a watermill scene on a palette, no. 8810, late 1880's. The other five are folders, four with flowers, one a three-fold card with a cut-out border of cats, 1890's.
6 cm x 8.7 cm up to 9.4 cm x 13.2 cm.

17. Two cards with cut-out edges. One opens to show cats on a wall and dogs on a ladder, the other has children in nursery rhyme costume carrying gilt letters.
11.7 cm x 12.8 cm, 14.8 cm x 8.3 cm.

18. Five interesting cards with scenes and cut-out gilt and silver borders with flowers and leaves. All have verses, four signed OB, MSH, ALS, VJB. Possibly 20th century.
8 cm x 12 cm up to 9.5 cm x 14.5 cm.

19. Three folding cards with heraldic motifs and verses in mediaeval style, two designs. Perhaps 20th century.
8.8 cm x 12.4 cm.

*Numbers 20-21 were published by Sockl & Nathan (S & N), late 1880's.*

20. Four cards, an oval with a country scene dated 1887, and three circular, two with scenes, one with a robin.
7.3 cm x 7.3 cm up to 13.7 cm x 11 cm.

21. Five cards with flowers. Two are circular, three oval, two of these with birthday verses by I IM Burnside.
Sizes up to 14 cm x 10.5 cm.

22. Two cards with pierced patterned borders, one marked S & N with a child at prayer, the other marked "Court" with a wreath of flowers. 9.6 cm x 11.8 cm, 12.4 cm x 14.8 cm.

23. Four cards. Three were published by Misch & Stock, one an oval with flowers c1890, the other two folders with children and a winter scene, all with a trademark of a horseshoe and bells. The fourth card is heart-shaped with a puppy and a kitten in a hat, published by M Priester's Continental Printing Co, series no 191.
9.5 cm x 10.3 cm up to 11.3 cm x 15 cm.

*The following cards were folded flat for sending by post; some open out to three-dimensional models and others are movable.*

24. Three cards.
a) A hunting scene, opening into three tiers on springs. 14 cm x 7.5 cm.
b) A card with German greeting, opening to show a brown-clad Santa Claus in a three-tiered winter scene. 9.2 cm x 13 cm.
c) An elaborate cut-out card printed in sepia, with ladies of the late 90's in a river scene with boats and swans.
11.5 cm x 10.7 cm.

25. Three cards.
a) A dog by a kennel, opening to three-dimensions showing puppies in the kennel. 11.5 cm x 5.8 cm.
b) A gherkin, opening to show a cat eating a fish from a plate. 4.3 cm x 14.8 cm.
c) A cat on a ladder with a dog at the foot. 6.7 cm x 14 cm.

26. Four fine cards in mint condition, opening to show various scenes mounted on springs.
a) Jameson's Ride.
b) Highland dancers with bagpipes.
c) Highland soldiers.
d) A band of negro minstrels.
Sizes up to 10.1 cm x 9.8 cm.

27. Two fine opening cards which stand up to show:
a) Three tiers of yachts, dated 1896 by the sender. 15 cm x 18 cm.
b) A seaside scene with boats and jetty, and a poem by Nemo on reverse.
13.6 cm x 9.7 cm.

28. Four cards with children.
a) A girl on a swing. 8.2 cm x 11.5 cm.
b) Four little girls at bedtime, dated 1893 by the sender. 12 cm x 10 cm.
c) A girl and boy posting letters.
7 cm x 14.3 cm.
d) Roses round a window, which opens to show a small girl with a letter.
10 cm x 7.1 cm.

29. Three cards.
a) A lady with a parasol and two children. 12 cm x 13 cm.
b) Four girls at a teatable. 12.8 cm x 8.3 cm.
c) A fan with flowers, and two boys peeping over it at a girl writing letters.
14 cm x 9.3 cm.

30. Three cards with animals, all movable.
a) Four puppies, on movable mounts with descriptive verse by Elbetee.
13.1 cm x 10 cm.
b) Two feline crossing sweepers with movable heads. 8.8 cm x 10.5 cm.
c) Three cats at the teatable, with movable heads and descriptive verse by EEG.
10 cm x 7.2 cm.

## VOLUME 261:
## FOLDING, SHAPED AND CUT-OUT CARDS WITH CHILDREN AND LADIES, AND SOME HUMOROUS EXAMPLES

**Most of these cards were designed for children, some with intricate devices for conversion to three-dimensional models. One Raphael Tuck card is included here for comparison with the unmarked examples.**

1. Two cards, each with a girl or boy nestling in a leaf on a scrap attached to a white card, one dated 1883 by the sender.
16.3 cm x 10.7 cm, 15.7 cm x 11.7 cm.

2. Six shaped cards with children. Three are Japanese fans, two are palettes, one

SANTA CLAUS wishes you a merry CHRISTMAS.

**261.40**

dated 1886, and the sixth is a dish with handles with small fairy figures in vignettes and a birthday greeting, dated 1885 by the sender.
Sizes up to 13 cm x 9.2 cm.

3. Five shaped cards. Two are balls with a cricket or football scene, two are lifebelts with a seashore scene or a sailor boy. The fifth is a wheel and anchor with another seaside view. Sizes up to 9 cm x 10.5 cm.

4. Five cards with children and cut-out edges. Four have verses, three by Frank Ferndale or Lewis Novra, the other by EEG dated 1890 by the sender.
Sizes up to 11.2 cm x 14 cm.

5. Four cards. Two are shaped like cups, with small children in high chairs, one of these designs repeated in a plain card. The fourth card is a basket of washing, the lid lifting to show two children and an appropriate verse by SK Cowan MA.
Sizes up to 11 cm x 12.5 cm.

*Numbers 6-9 were made c1890.*

6. Six cut-out cards (one birthday), with children dancing by a wall or fence, with a toy yacht, in a go-cart.
Sizes up to 12.5 cm x 8 cm.

7. Two cut-out cards from a set, children playing before a white fence.
12.5 cm x 8.7 cm, 12.5 cm x 7.2 cm.

8. Three cut-out frosted cards with children in white fur-trimmed hats and coats, one with a girl and boy, another with four boys, the third with four girls.
9 cm x 10 cm, 11 cm x 9.2 cm.

9. Six cards, four shaped with small girls in a basket, in a posy of flowers, on a

tambourine, in a gilt-edged oval. Two are cut-out, with a boy holding a posy and two small children playing with a dog.
Sizes up to 11 cm x 9.5 cm.

*Numbers 10-24 were probably published c1895.*

10. Three intricate folding cut-out cards with children, all made to stand up, two with verses by Clifton Bingham.
Sizes up to 11.9 cm x 9 cm.

11. Three frosted folding cards, two with children, one with Father Christmas.
Sizes up to 9.5 cm x 10.6 cm.

12. Two cards, opening out to stand up, one with a winged cherub and a robin, the other with an angel watching over a sleeping child.
10 cm x 6.5 cm, 14 cm x 11 cm.

13. Five cut-out folder cards wtih children playing, one with a girl and boy on bicycles.
9.5 cm x 9 cm up to 15.2 cm x 8 cm.

14. Six folding cards with serrated edges, all with children. Four have verses by E Love, SK Cowan, CD.
6.3 cm x 9 cm up to 11.3 cm x 7.3 cm.

15. Seven folder cards with serrated edges, showing children dressed in Kate Greenaway style. Three have verses by MS Haycraft and AO Harris.
6.8 cm x 8.6 cm up to 11.5 cm x 8.5 cm.

16. Three cards opening to stand up, with children, the edges cut-out around the heads. Sizes up to 8.9 cm x 12 cm.

17. Four folder cards from two sets, with greetings in gilt and small pictures of children in long dresses. 8.8 cm x 11.6 cm.

18. Four folder cards with patterned borders, two with a boy and girl in party dress, one with a girl holding a flower, the fourth two small girls reading a book under an umbrella.
7 cm x 10.2 cm up to 8.9 cm x 11.8 cm.

19. Seven folder cards from four sets with children in various activities, three with verses by S Herbert, EEG, or AO Harris. Three have serrated borders, four have embossed patterned borders.
Sizes up to 7 cm x 11.3 cm.

20. Two trick cards. One shows a girl on a bicycle but opens out to show her on a donkey or playing tennis. The other shows two men and two girls in sporting costume standing still, but opens to show them dancing, with a descriptive verse by SKC.
8.8 cm x 12.8 cm, 11.3 cm x 6.9 cm.

21. Two folding cards, a lady riding a bicycle, a girl and a boy on bicycles, both with patterned borders.
9 cm x 11.5 cm, 9 cm x 12 cm.

22. Three folding cards with decorative embossed borders, one with Red Riding Hood riding a bicycle, two with girls in pretty bonnets with flowers.
Sizes up to 8.7 cm x 12.5 cm.

23. Four folder cards, one with two Japanese girls, another a small girl holding flowers dated 1894 by the sender, a third a couple in Georgian dress, the fourth a lady in a pierced silver border with forget-me-nots. Sizes up to 9.2 cm x 11.5 cm.

24. Four cards with elaborate pierced decoration and patterned borders, all with children. One opens to show a boy and girl dancing, in black party dress, the boy in a Fauntleroy style suit.
Sizes up to 10.2 cm x 14 cm.

*Numbers 25-33 were published in the later 1890's.*

25. Eight miscellaneous folding cards with children, and serrated or patterned borders.
5.8 cm x 6.3 cm up to 6.6 cm x 14.4 cm.

26. Six cards with Art Nouveau decoration, three folders, three single. Two have children in Georgian dress, one has a baby framed in a gilded border with verse by Agnes O Harris.
7.5 cm x 9 cm up to 13.5 cm x 10 cm.

27. Five cards with pictures of ladies or children in monochrome, three dated 1897, 1897, 1899. This style was extensively used for 20th century cards.
7.5 cm x 10 cm up to 11 cm x 14 cm.

28. Five folder cards with children in period costume. Two have cut-out figures and open to stand up.
7.5 cm x 13 cm, 11.5 cm x 10 cm.

29. Six miscellaneous folder cards, four with children in period or shepherdess costume, one with a girl in a daisy hat dated 1903 by the sender, the sixth with two children feeding rabbits.
Sizes up to 9.2 cm x 11.7 cm.

30. Five cards with Chinese or Japanese figures. Two plain cards have the same boy in a coolie hat but in different backgrounds, with a verse by JGF. The third has a mother and child with a parasol and a dog, the fourth has an elaborate arrangement of fans around a girl's head, and the fifth is a cut-out figure of a child in a kimono with greeting on a fan under her arm. Sizes up to 8.7 cm x 12.8 cm, cut-out card 14.3 cm x 6.5 cm.

31. Three single frosted cards with children in white fur-trimmed garments.
6.3 cm x 11 cm, 9.2 cm x 13.5 cm.

32. Three covers from folding cards with elaborate cut-out borders, and children in Georgian dress.
8.5 cm x 14.8 cm, 10 cm x 14.2 cm.

33. Eight cards with children. Five are covers from folding cards, three are single cards. Sizes up to 11.6 cm x 7.8 cm.

34. Six folder cut-out cards with children, including a baby and a cat in a lace-trimmed cradle, and a girl looking at her dog in a cradle. c1900.
5.8 cm x 8.3 cm up to 8.4 cm x 13.5 cm.

35. Five miscellaneous cards. One has two children on a snowball and a robin, c1895, another has a boy in a tent with a Union Jack above and a patriotic verse by HM Burnside. The other three are folders with small figures, probably early 20th century.
Sizes up to 9.6 cm x 12 cm.

36. Three folder cards for children with riddles and answers in rebus style with pictures for some words. c1890.
6.5 cm x 14 cm.

37. Two three-fold cards, cut as found in albums, with pictures of wooden dolls and a letter written as from a doll to its owner.
1890's. 9 cm x 11.5 cm.

38. Two three-fold cards for children, one with scenes at the zoo, the other "All about the Three Little Kittens", published by Raphael Tuck c1890 and included here for comparison. 7.3 cm x 11.3 cm.

39. A three-fold card with a house on the front, opening to show dolls inside preparing Christmas dinner, perhaps early 20th century. 9 cm x 10.8 cm.

40. Three cut-out cards, two negroes in top-hats carrying an umbrella bearing a greeting and a descriptive verse, and two cards with Father Christmas, one marked Pain Bros, Wholesale Art Traders, Hastings. Sizes up to 14 cm x 10.3 cm.

41. Five cards for childrez, four with Father Christmas dressed in red, one with a greeting in German, the fifth a cut-out wheel barrow containing toys.
Sizes up to 12.5 cm x 10 cm.

42. Three cards, horseshoes, two with negro hunting scenes, one with forget-me-nots and a greeting in French, one dated 1889. 13 cm x 11 cm.

43. Six shaped or cut-out humorous cards, including a clown's hat, a top hat, a collar and tie, and a stiff collar, these with appropriate punning greetings. The other two are cut-out figures of a postman and a sailor. Sizes up to 11 cm x 8.2 cm.

44. Seven shaped cards, a willow pattern plate, a cup and saucer, a card tray, a pot of jam, a glass of beer, a dish with handles and an egg cup dated 1890 by the sender.
Sizes up to 8.5 cm x 11.3 cm.

45. Five shaped folding cards, a purse with money advertising Pears soap, a handbag

opening to show violets, a box of ferns, a basket of flowers, and a travelling bag opening to show flowers and a verse by EE Griffin. Sizes up to 9.5 cm x 9 cm.

46. Six cards. Four are shaped like a violin, a Japanese parasol, a coal scuttle and a boot containing fruit. The fifth card is a pair of boots with fruit and the sixth is a slate with attached duster.
Sizes up to 7 cm x 11 cm.

47. Four shaped cards, a drum, a tambourine, a box of sardines and a churn opening to show two cats, with appropriate poem on reverse.
Sizes up to 8 cm x 13.5 cm.

48. Five humorous cards, probably for the adult market. One is an opening card with boys listening to a band playing in the snow; two have Highland pictures with "the Cock o' the Walk" and a kilted dancer, dated 1897, and the fourth has a boy and a policeman in a border of cut-out helmets. The fifth card is a regrettable example of sick humour showing a cat with a 50lb weight tied to its tail and the caption "For here I send you 50 pounds, you see!" Sizes up to 9.8 cm x 13.2 cm, cat 15.5 cm x 4.5 cm.

49. Four festive cards, one a silver horseshoe round a winter scene, another a patterned dish with a bird's nest and eggs, and two small folding cards in the shape of bells with holly. c1890. 9.8 cm x 11.2 cm, 13.3 cm x 7 cm, 5 cm x 6 cm.

# VOLUME 262:
## SHAPED, CUT-OUT AND FOLDER CARDS WITH BIRDS, BUTTERFLIES AND ANIMALS

**Most of these cards were published in the 1890's with a few, as indicated, from the 1880's. They are unmarked with the exception of numbers 19 and 20, though many might be attributed to Hagelberg.**

*Numbers 1-7 were published in the 1880's.*

1. Six shaped cards with birds, robins on a star and a horseshoe, a blue tit on an envelope, a crested lark in a circle, birds on a spray of flowers with a moonlit scene, and ducks on a scallop shell with a poem by Cecilia Havergal on reverse.
Sizes up to 14.7 cm x 9.4 cm.

2. Four cards with birds, two shaped like Japanese fans, another with cut-out birds on a fence, the fourth a cut-out swallow carrying a small card with silk inset.
Sizes up to 13 cm x 8.3 cm.

3. Six shaped cards. Three of a set are shaped like paper posy-holders with embossed robin, blue tit or cat with holly or mistletoe, one dated 1883 by the sender. Another has birds on a drum, the fifth has robins sheltering in a hat, the sixth a

robin posting a card. The post-box has seven times of clearance.
9 cm x 9.5 cm up to 14 cm x 11.5 cm.

4. Four shaped cards. Two are handbags holding cards with blue tits, and two are decorative easels holding pictures of winter scenes with robins.
6 cm x 8 cm, 6.3 cm x 10.5 cm.

5. Five cut-out cards. Three open out to stand up, with a hen and chicks, a robin and a canary in a muslin cap. The fourth has an owl in a muslin cap and the fifth has an owl in a frilled bonnet with opening wings and a greeting in German.
Sizes up to 15.8 cm x 6.5 cm.

6. Six folder cards with birds. Five are frosted, with serrated edges, and two have verses by HM Whitlow and HM Burnside.
6.4 cm x 9 cm up to 15.6 cm x 7 cm.

7. Three elaborate cut-out and frosted cards with birds in winter scenes, one with a verse by EE Griffin.
Sizes up to 10.6 cm x 14.4 cm.

*Numbers 8-18 were published in the 1890's.*

8. Five cards with birds and cut-out and frosted decoration, one dated 1891 by the sender. Two have verses signed JB and Fannie Rochat.
6.7 cm x 8.1 cm up to 11.5 cm x 16 cm.

9. Four embossed folder cards with serrated edges, two with robins on snow-covered branches, two with robins and other birds with holly or mistletoe.
9.3 cm x 11.9 cm, 9.3 cm x 11.6 cm.

10. Four folder cards with patterned borders. Two have humanised robins on a tandem or in Georgian dress in the style of R Dudley and two have robins or bullfinches on winter branches, with verses by JS. Sizes up to 12 cm x 8.9 cm.

11. Six opening cards. Three with serrated edges from one set have robins in winter scenes, two from another set with coloured patterned borders have robins or bullfinches, and the sixth has robins in a country scene. 10 cm x 7.5 cm, 12.7 cm x 7.8 cm, 13 cm x 6.8 cm.

12. Six elaborate cut-out opening frosted cards. Two have robins on a boot with tinselled cut-out greeting; the other four have cut-out winter scenes with robins, blue tits, or thrushes.
Sizes up to 12.4 cm x 9 cm.

13. Five cards, four folder, one single, with birds and elaborate borders and cut-out decoration, including one with a white dove on a background of flowers and bells and a verse by Frances Ridley Havergal, dated 1896. Another has a poem by Lily Oakley. Sizes up to 13 cm x 7.5 cm.

14. Eight cards. Four small folders have serrated edges with various birds, a single card has owls, a folder dated 1891 by the sender has bullfinches and a larger card with blue tits, holly and a horseshoe opens to show a verse signed JB.
9.5 cm x 7.1 cm up to 10 cm x 13.9 cm.

15. Four cards with birds, including three folders, one dated 1897 by the sender and two with verses by EE Griffin, AF Earl, and a single card with perforated border dated 1895 by the sender.
5.6 cm x 7.2 cm up to 12.9 cm x 8.3 cm.

16. Six folder cards. Five have elaborate cut-out embossed designs of birds, including one with an attached envelope with a verse by Gertrude E Shaw. The sixth card has an embossed design of blue tits in a blue border and a verse by SK Cowan within, and was dated 1902 by the sender.
6 cm x 10.6 cm up to 9 cm x 11.4 cm.

17. An eight-page folder with robins and a winter scene in an Art Nouveau style border and a poem by AE Lemprière Knight within. 11 cm x 15.5 cm.

18. Four folder cards. Two are tied with cord and have birds with flower decoration, one a birthday card dated 1898 by the sender. The third has a ribbon tie and a picture of birds with a bell and a verse by Frances Ridley Havergal. The fourth has a cut-out design of birds with a nest and a greeting in French, dated 1896 by the sender. Sizes up to 9.7 cm x 11.8 cm.

19. Two early 20th century cards, included here for comparison, issued by the Society for the Protection of Birds, 3 Hanover Square, London W1.
a) Two pictures of a rabbit and a robin, and a blackbird, by J MacWhirter RA with a verse by Ella Wheeler Wilcox.
9 cm x 11.5 cm.
b) The Bird Waits, by FCG, with a verse by MM Hadath and a calendar for 1907.
11.4 cm x 8.7 cm.
The second card has the prefix "Royal", so presumably the first card was issued before 1907.

20. Four shaped cards. One is an embossed butterfly opening to show a greeting, perhaps 20th century, another is a cut-out butterfly carrying a postcard with a birthday greeting. Two are shaped like a butterfly and a shell with angels, and have verses inside by JLW and FDW, and indistinct markings which might be MW & Co. Sizes up to 11 cm x 9.5 cm.

*Numbers 21-30 have animals with an occasional bird, published in the 1890's.*

21. Three cards with cut-out edges. Two have an umbrella sheltering ducks or rabbits with a punning verse on reverse; the third dated 1890 by the sender shows

mice stealing cheese from a table.
12.5 cm x 9.5 cm.

22. Six cards, cut-out animal designs, five
with cats, one with cats and puppies, two
dated 1891, 1892 by the senders.
Sizes up to 9.8 cm x 12.8 cm.

23. Five shaped and cut-out cards,
including a puppy on a leaf, two muzzles
with dogs and two boxes with kittens and
puppies. Sizes up to 12.5 cm x 10.5 cm.

24. Six shaped cards. Three from one set
are drums, each with a cat or dog playing a
trumpet, cymbals, or a drum, one dated
1897 by the sender. One is a top hat with a
white kitten and another has two cats in a
pan. The sixth card is a blue fan with two
cats playing battledore and shuttlecock
and a descriptive poem on reverse.
7.5 cm x 10 cm up to 16.7 cm x 9.5 cm (fan).

25. Five cards. Four from one set are
palette shaped with pictures of a dog, a
hare, a sailing ship and a mountain scene
and the fifth is circular with a cat reading a
book. 10.3 cm x 7.5 cm, 7.3 cm diameter.

26. Three embossed cards, two designs of a
horse's head in a gilt or silver horseshoe.
10.3 cm x 11.5 cm.

27. Four cards. Three have cut-out designs
of a greyhound pulling two dogs in a two-
wheeled cart, a cat pulling a two-wheeled
cart with two cats, and a mechanical card
in two pieces with cats and dogs riding
bicycles. The fourth card shows a cat
wedding described in a punning verse.
Sizes varying from 11.3 cm x 9 cm to
15 cm x 7.3 cm.

28. Three shaped cards.
a) A fish, opening to show frogs fishing,
with a descriptive poem by EEG on
reverse. 15.5 cm x 6 cm.
b) Two frogs in Highland dress on a
tam-o-shanter. 13 cm x 7.4 cm.
c) A cut-out lady frog drinking tea, in a
waterlily border. 6.5 cm x 7.3 cm.

29. Six cards with dogs or puppies and
patterned embossed borders or cut-out
edges, including a dog on a bicycle and
another with pierced decoration. Two are
folders, one dated 1898 by the sender, two
are the covers of folders, and two are
single cards, one with a poem by Jane
Marsh. Sizes up to 14.7 cm x 7.3 cm.

30. Five miscellaneous cards, three with
cut-out edges. Two have cats, one has
dogs, a small folder has a cat, and a
three-fold gilt-edged card opens to show
a mouse fishing.
7.8 cm x 7.8 cm up to 12.7 cm x 10 cm.

31. Six folder cards with patterned or
serrated edges, with dogs, rabbits, pigs
and donkeys, and a card with cut-out
bears and the caption "With Fur-vent
Wishes". c1900. Sizes up to 8 cm x 11.5 cm.

32. Six folder embossed cards, three with
cut-out edges, showing cats, dogs and a
circus pig. c1900.
Sizes up to 8 cm x 14.5 cm.

33. Two shaped cards, racquets with
kittens. 7 cm x 17.2 cm.

## VOLUME 263:
## SHAPED AND CUT-OUT
## CARDS WITH SCENES,
## FLOWERS AND FOLIAGE

**These cards are unmarked except for
numbers 23 and 33 and most were
published in the late 1880's with a
few exceptions as stated. This
volume includes some unusual
shapes with hats, shoes, vases,
moons, lavishly decorated with
flowers, and a collection of rare
leaf-shaped cards.**

*Numbers 1-15 are shaped and cut-out cards
dated in the late 1880's, with country scenes,
many showing churches.*

1. Four gilt-edged cards, two diamond
shapes with the same design of a castle
and ferns, an eight-pointed star with a
church in winter in a wreath of ivy and
forget-me-nots, and a circle with a country
farm, dated 1883 by the sender.
11 cm x 17 cm, 12.5 cm and 12.2 cm
diameter.

2. Two oval silvered shells with scenes of
churches in winter. 15.6 cm x 11.5 cm.

3. Seven cards with country scenes, one
circular, one oval, two horseshoe shaped, a
terracotta vase, a circle with a scroll and a
rectangular seaside scene on a black circle
with daffodils.
6.2 cm x 8.7 cm up to 13 cm x 13 cm.

4. Six circular cards, two with sailing ships,
one a sunset country scene, two with river
views wreathed in flowers, and one with
birds flying over winter trees.
9 cm x 11.8 cm diameter.

5. Six fans, two from a set with birds and
sunset scene, three with flowers and
various scenes, and a frosted view of a
church amidst trees.
5.7 cm to 9.8 cm radius.

6. Six circular cards (one birthday), five
designs of sea and country views in sepia.
7.4 cm diameter.

7. Five crescent moons, four with views of
churches and bells and Christmas verses
on reverse, the fifth gilt-edged with a lake
in moonlight. Sizes up to 13 cm x 6 cm.

8. Eight cards with various scenes,
including a sail shape, an oval, a bell, a
leaf, a shield and three triangles, one of
these with a poem by Charlotte Murray on
reverse.
5 cm x 7.8 cm up to 12.7 cm x 13 cm.

9. Five cards with moonlight scenes,
including a bell, a horseshoe, two circles
and a rectangle with folded corners in
trompe l'oeil style, this signed LD. The bell
has a verse by HM Burnside on the back
and was dated 1889 by the sender.
10 cm x 10 cm up to 14.5 cm x 14.5 cm.

10. Five oval cards, four with sea and river
scenes, the fifth with a view of Greenwich
Hospital signed WHST.
Sizes up to 14 cm x 10 cm.

11/12. Nine palettes (one birthday), with
scenes, seven oval, two rectangular,
including one with a country house in a
silver crescent moon with a poem by
S K Cowan.
7.5 cm x 9.7 cm up to 11 cm x 14.3 cm.

13. Five cards like scrolls drawn in trompe
l'oeil style, one dated 1889 by the sender,
two with verses by H S Bainbridge or
Frederick Langbridge, all with winter
scenes.
9.6 cm x 7.4 cm up to 12.2 cm x 11.5 cm.

14. Three shaped cards, a silver bell, a
lighthouse, and a crescent moon, all with
pictures of sailing ships. 9.4 cm x 11 cm,
10.2 cm x 19 cm, 8.5 cm x 10 cm.

15. Three cards with cut-out edges, a
church with a poem by SKC on reverse, a
house by a lake with a verse by Clara
Simmonds, and a snow-swept house in
moonlight. Sizes up to 11 cm x 14.7 cm.

*Numbers 16-23 are shaped like leaves, some
with a picture on one side and a leaf on reverse,
a few with plain backs and greetings. Later
1880's.*

16. Three cards, leaves with gilded serrated
edges and leaf backs, two with winter
scenes, one with a castle and chapel.
19 cm x 11 cm.

17. Two frosted leaves with rectangular
views of a lake or a snowbound farm and
plain backs. 15 cm x 12.3 cm.

18. Three cards from two sets, two with
river views, one with a winter landscape,
all with greetings on leaf-patterned backs.
14 cm x 13 cm, 18 cm x 8.2 cm.

19. Four cards, oak leaves. Three have lake
or winter scenes with leaf backs; the fourth
has a lake in an oak leaf border with a
Christmas poem on reverse.
11 cm x 8.8 cm up to 18 cm x 11.3 cm.

20. Five cards. Four are ivy leaves, three
with scenes, one with blue tits perched
under icicles, signed A F L. The fifth card
is a holly leaf with a winter landscape. All
have leaf backs and two have sentiments
by H M Burnside.
13 cm x 12 cm, 17 cm x 10 cm.

21. Three ivy leaves with snowdrops, violets, or primroses, and greeting on leaf backs. 14 cm x 13 cm.

22. Five cards, two with the same frosted scene on an ivy leaf with greeting on plain back. The third is an ivy leaf with a Christmas poem on reverse, the fourth a holly leaf with greeting on reverse, and the fifth has flowers and greeting on a leaf with plain back.
7 cm x 9 cm up to 11 cm x 14 cm.

23. Three ferns with white flowers and leaf back with greeting, signed with an undeciphered monogram. One is marked S Hildesheimer, included here for comparison. 10 cm x 15 cm.

24. Two cards, a gilded feather with a moonlit landscape, and a leaf with a riverside house set in a rectangular patterned frame with a robin.
20.7 cm x 7 cm, 13 cm x 10.5 cm.

*Numbers 25-38 are shaped cards with flowers or greenery, most from the later 1880's with exceptions as stated.*

25. Six cards, two gilt-edged circles, one dated 1881 by the sender, with forget-me-nots or carnations, two crescent moons with roses and cut-out floral borders, a horseshoe with cut-out floral border, and a scallop-edged semicircle with buttercups signed N A W and a birthday greeting by J Ellis. Sizes up to 11 cm x 11 cm.

26. Six cards, a leaf with lilies of the valley and a poem by S K Cowan M A, three scallop-edged circles with flowers, a scalloped oval, and an attractive card in the form of a decorated plate with cut-out border.
5.8 cm x 7.5 cm up to 13 cm x 13 cm.

27. Six cards with flowers, including a kite shape, a parallelogram, two hexagons, a semicircle, and an envelope sealed with a rose. Sizes up to 14.2 cm x 14.2 cm.

28. Two fans with forget-me-nots and narcissi in a cut-out lace border with mosaic decoration. Radius 9 cm.

29. Two fans with autumn leaves and scalloped borders. Radius 9.6 cm.

30. Five fans with flowers, including two in Japanese style.
7.5 cm x 5 cm up to 7.4 cm radius.

31. Five cards, four with flowers, including a hat, a slipper, and two bowls. The fifth card is a Yule log decked with mistletoe. Sizes up to 9 cm x 14.5 cm.

32. Seven cards in the shape of flower decorated vases, including six designs from three sets. Sizes vary from 6 cm x 12 cm to 10 cm x 10 cm.

33. Seven cards with cut-out edges, including three baskets of flowers (two designs), a pair of bellows with primroses, a wicker box of violets, a bunch of pansies, and a shell. The last two have greetings on reverse. 8.5 cm x 8 cm up to 14.5 cm x 8 cm.

34. Five small folder cards in the shape of flowers, leaves, or fruit, opening to show verses, one dated 1891 by the sender. One card shaped like a carnation is marked H & F no. 267 and dated 1890 by the sender, and is included here for comparison with similar unmarked cards. 6 cm x 8 cm up to 12.5 cm x 8.5 cm.

35. Four oval cards with flower sprays. Two are palettes, (one birthday), with poems by Charlotte Murray or Cecilia Havergal, one is a birthday card with a quotation from Moore, and the fourth is frosted, with a blue border.
Sizes up to 11.7 cm x 16 cm.

36. Two oval cards, each with a frosted sea view framed in flowers.
13 cm x 16 cm, 16 cm x 13 cm.

37. Seven cards with flowers or ferns, three circular, one a hexagon, and three oval. One oval card was dated 1889 by the sender, another has a jewelled border. 7.7 cm x 9 cm up to 14 cm x 11 cm.

38. Six cards with flowers, two shaped like shields, two crescent moons and two horseshoes, one with sentiments by S K Cowan MA. Sizes up to 9.5 cm x 12 cm.

*Numbers 39-58 have cut-out borders and decoration, published in the late 1880's and early 1890's, a few later.*

39. Four embossed cards in correspondence style with cut-out borders and decoration, and holly, ivy, or mistletoe. 11.3 cm x 9 cm. See volume 257.

40. Five cards with elaborate cut-out flower decoration. Two from the same set have a verse by Charlotte Murray in a central oval, another has jewelled daisies, the fourth has flowers on a gilded lattice, and the fifth has a moonlight scene on a background of blossom.
Sizes up to 12.5 cm x 9.7 cm.

41. Three cards. One is a birthday card printed in sepia with a flower spray and a cut-out border of branches, another has flowers in a rustic cut-out border. The third card has jewelled flowers and a star with robins on a cut-out crescent moon. Sizes up to 10.7 cm x 14.5 cm.

42. Three cards, two with cut-out greetings and forget-me-nots, the third with cut-out bell and window and Christmas roses. All have greetings, one by Frances Ridley Havergal.
11.9 cm x 8 cm up to 14.4 cm x 10.7 cm.

43. Three cards with cut-out decoration, one with holly round a winter scene, another with lanterns. The third card has tinselled flowers and a birthday greeting. 8.7 cm x 11.5 cm, 15.5 cm x 7.2 cm.

44. Six cards with cut-out edges. Two from one set have gilded leaves, one has ivy, and the others have pansies, roses, or chrysanthemums.
9 cm x 5.5 cm up to 12.7 cm x 8 cm.

45. Four cards (one birthday), with small floral cut-out motifs, all with verses, three signed by Eliza Cook, Charlotte Murray, E N. According to biographer Julia Briggs, E Nesbit painted cards for Raphael Tuck. She might also have contributed sentiments to the Christmas card trade. Buday lists E N as writing in 1900.
Sizes up to 13 cm x 10.2 cm.

46. Two attractive cards with leaf and floral cut-out borders around Christmas poems, one signed Edward Capern.
9.6 cm x 13.6 cm.

47. Five birthday cards, all with cut-out spring flowers, one jewelled. All have verses, three signed by Elizabeth Love, Clara Simmonds, and M S H, and three were dated 1890, 1895, 1897 by the senders. Sizes vary from 13 cm x 7 cm to 6.5 cm x 14 cm.

48. Four cards, with cut-out flowers or ivy leaves. One dated 1892 has a verse by Charlotte Murray, another a verse by Mrs Hemans. Sizes up to 11.7 cm x 15 cm.

49. Seven cards, four with cut-out flowers, two with ivy, one with gilt border and decoration. Sizes up to 9 cm x 12 cm.

50. Six cards (four birthday). Four have cut-out flowers, one has ivy and the sixth has jewelled oak leaves.
Sizes up to 12 cm x 9 cm.

51. Four floral cards, three with serrated edges, one with patterned border and lace corners. Sizes up to 12.5 cm x 10.2 cm.

52. Five birthday cards, all jewelled with flowers, four with patterned borders. Sizes up to 9 cm x 12 cm.

53. Five birthday cards. Four have patterned borders with cut-out flowers, and one has a plain cut-out border. Four have verses, two signed by Charlotte Murray and one by E Love, and one card was dated 1895 by the sender. Sizes up to 13 cm x 9 cm.

54. Six floral cards with serrated or cut-out patterned edges, five with poems by Frances Ridley Havergal or M S Haycraft. Sizes up to 12 cm x 9 cm.

55. Six floral cards, three with cut-out flowers, two tinselled, and one with a fan

with hand-painted silk inset.
Sizes up to 11.5 cm x 9.2 cm.

56. Two birthday cards with flower decoration and sea scenes.
14 cm x 10.2 cm, 15.7 cm x 11 cm.

57. Seven small cards with flowers or scenes. Sizes up to 11 cm x 8 cm.

58. Five religious cards. Two are Scripture Union Mottos for 1897 and 1900, two are Easter cards dated 1892 and 1894 by the senders, and one is a Christmas card with flowers on a gilt-edged cross.
Sizes up to 13 cm x 9 cm.

# VOLUME 264:
# FOLDER CARDS, LATE 1880'S TO 1900, WITH SCENES AND FLOWERS

These cards, mostly published in the later 1890's, reflect the changes in popular taste towards the end of the century and while some can be said to have interesting design and technique their artistic merit does not compare with that of earlier cards. With one exception, no publishers are marked, and most of the cards appear as single examples from what must have been sets. One interesting card in number 1 is a well-drawn picture of Manchester Town Hall, showing a blue sky and trees in the background, of particular interest for this collection with its permanent home in Manchester.

*Numbers 1-6 illustrate various plainer styles from the late 1880's to 1900.*

1. Nine small cards, one with ivy on the cover opening to show a winter scene and a verse by E E G, eight with various scenes including an Egyptian scene with a pyramid and a view of Manchester Town Hall with a verse by E E G.
6.3 cm x 6 cm up to 10 cm x 8.6 cm.

2. Nine cards with cut-out flowers and leaves, some opening to show scenes, with greetings or verses, one by Rev. J W Myers BA. 9.3 cm x 6.4 cm up to 12.3 cm x 8.3 cm.

3. Six cards, including a palette, a pentagon with three triangular opening flaps, a fan opening to show a country scene and a verse by S K Cowan, a butterfly over lilies of the valley, a sunset seen through a cut-out letter, and a birthday card with tinselled seaweed and a poem by S K C and a pink rose inside.
8 cm x 10.2 cm up to 9.3 cm x 13 cm.

4. Four cards with scenes in monochrome, three with birthday greetings on embossed backgrounds, the fourth dated 1892 by the sender with a Christmas poem by E Matheson. 11.7 cm x 6.2 cm up to 13.5 cm x 8.9 cm.

5. Five miscellaneous cards. Two are on brown paper imitating wood, one with flowers dated 1896 by the sender, the other with the picture of a girl inside. Another is in triptych form with gilt decoration, the fourth is a green envelope with gilt horseshoe and whip dated 1898 by the sender, and the fifth has cut-out roses on a fence. Sizes up to 8.5 cm x 13 cm.

6. Four miscellaneous personal cards, perhaps samples, showing the fin-de-siècle fashion for dark colours, in purple, green and brown, three dated 1898, one 1899.
7.3 cm x 8.4 cm up to 8.8 cm x 11.7 cm.

*Numbers 7-13 have scenes and flowers, with embossed and gilded decoration on white backgrounds.*

7. Five cards. Four are from one set, with two designs and three different greetings showing country views in two small gilt-edged vignettes on embossed paper. The fifth is similar with one circular vignette.
9.2 cm x 9.5 cm, 10.5 cm x 8.5 cm.

8. Four miscellaneous cards with scenes in small vignettes, three with serrated edges, two with verses by H M Burnside and Janet Marsh. The fourth has embossed flower decoration and a birthday greeting by M S H.
5.8 cm x 8.6 cm up to 10 cm x 13.7 cm.

9. Six cards with various monochrome scenes in vignettes and embossed flower or ivy decoration, with greetings or verses by E E G, A O H, C A Griffiths.
Sizes up to 12.5 cm x 8.2 cm.

10. Seven cards with patterned edges and embossed flower decoration around scenes, including one viewed through a cut-out star. Three have verses by E Love, H M Burnside, M S Haycraft.
9.5 cm x 7 cm up to 9.2 cm x 12.8 cm.

11. Seven cards with serrated or embossed patterned edges, with various scenes and flowers, one a view of Newark signed G B. Two have verses by J Ellis and M S H.
7.3 cm x 8.5 cm up to 11 cm x 12.5 cm.

12. Three cards. One has a cut out shell border opening to show a sailing ship and a lighthouse, another has robins at a window, the third shows a room with a cat by the fire and has a poem by Ellis Walton inside. Sizes up to 8.7 cm x 11.4 cm.

13. Six miscellaneous cards. Four have gilt decoration and embossed leaves and flowers, one dated 1897. The fifth has an embossed motif with golf clubs, ball and flag, and the sixth has a greeting in silver and a Nativity picture inside.
8.3 cm x 8.6 cm up to 12.3 cm x 9.2 cm.

*Numbers 14-39 have flower decoration, many in Art Nouveau style, nearly all heavily embossed.*

14. Three cards, one with anemones on an opening fan, another with embossed pansies. The embossed violet cover on the third card opens to show a seven-page folder marked "Guess Who", with the sender's name appearing on the final fold.
Sizes up to 11.7 cm x 8.6 cm.

15. Six cards with Art Nouveau style borders around various flowers, two dated 1894, 1897, three with verses signed K M B, H S H, H M Burnside.
5.5 cm x 12.5 cm to 9 cm x 12 cm.

16. Seven cards with serrated or cut-out borders and various flowers, two with pierced decoration, one with a cut-out tinselled waterlily. One was dated 1897 by the sender. Sizes vary from 10 cm x 7.8 cm to 5.4 cm x 14 cm.

17. Five cards with various pink, blue, or white flowers and patterned or serrated borders. Three are hand painted and two have verses by S K Cowan and M S Haycraft.
11.1 cm x 7.6 cm up to 11.2 cm x 15 cm.

18. Six cards with various embossed flowers, five with serrated edges, one cut-out. One opens to show a view of Killarney; another has a poem by Coombes Davies and two have verses by H M Burnside (one dated 1892 by the sender). Sizes up to 9 cm x 11.8 cm.

19. Four cards with forget-me-nots and elaborate pierced, gilded and tinselled decoration, one with a verse by A B M, another dated 1894 by the sender.
Sizes up to 12.5 cm x 9.3 cm.

20. Four cards with forget-me-nots, all tinselled, with cut-out borders and decoration, one with a poem by H M Burnside. Sizes up to 14.5 cm x 9.5 cm.

21. Five cards with forget-me-nots in patterned cut-out borders.
8.3 cm x 7.5 cm up to 11 cm x 8.5 cm.

22. Eight cards with forget-me-nots in serrated or patterned borders. One has a gilded horseshoe, another a glass tumbler and two have verses by M S Haycraft and Isabel Warry.
9.7 cm x 5.2 cm up to 13.7 cm.

23. Three cards from one set, embossed forget-me-nots with gilt greetings and serrated edges. 9 cm x 11.7 cm.

24. Seven miscellaneous cards with violets and serrated or patterned edges. One card marked Hagelberg is included for comparison and three have verses by M S Haycraft, J May Barnes, A L S.
10 cm x 5.5 cm up to 12.7 cm x 9.5 cm.

25. Five cards with violets and patterned cut-out edges, one dated 1900 by the sender. Two cards have the same design of clasped hands in a ring of violets, with two

different verses by H M Burnside.
Sizes all about 8.5 cm x 11.8 cm.

26. Six cards with serrated edges and various spring flowers, three with tinselled greetings. Two have verses by S K Cowan and M S Haycraft.
8.8 cm x 11.7 cm, 8 cm x 11.7 cm.

27. Five cards, two bordered with cut-out pansies, two with a girl's head in a pansy hat, another dated 1898 by the sender.
9 cm x 7.5 cm up to 10 cm x 13.7 cm.

28. Six cards with pansies, three with tinselled decoration, one with greeting in French. Sizes vary from 6 cm x 11.3 cm to 7.2 cm x 9.8 cm.

29. Six cards with pansies in decorative borders, one with a verse by C D.
Sizes up to 9.5 cm x 12.5 cm.

30. Four cards with white or yellow flowers in cut-out edges.
Sizes up to 12.7 cm x 8.5 cm.

31. Five cards, one with narcissus, four with daisies including two with verses by H M Burnside and E E G and another with elaborate lace tinselled decoration.
11 cm x 6.5 cm up to 9.5 cm x 14 cm.

32. Five cards with elaborate lace or patterned borders, one with ivy, two with snowdrops, two with forget-me-nots. Two have verses by F R Havergal, one a poem by H M Burnside and another has a photograph of the sender.
8 cm x 10.5 cm up to 12.3 cm x 9.4 cm.

33. Six cards with patterned and cut-out borders, five with various flowers, one with holly. One card has a verse by Frank Ferndale and was dated 1895 by the sender, another has a verse by A F Earl, and one was dated 1898 by the sender.
8 cm x 8.5 cm up to 11.2 cm x 9.5 cm.

34. Six cards with various spring flowers and patterned or cut-out borders, one with a poem by H M Burnside.
Sizes up to 12 cm x 9 cm.

35. Four tinselled cards. One with leaves has a verse by Osburn Blackburn, another dated 1895 by the sender has a small booklet under flaps with cut-out flowers. One with cornflowers has a verse by A M H and the fourth with a forget-me-not border has a poem by F R Havergal. Sizes up to 14 cm x 9 cm.

36. Six cards in envelope form, one with ivy, the others with various spring flowers.
Sizes up to 15 cm x 7.5 cm.

37. Five cards in envelope style with spring flowers, including two with serrated edges from one set with poems by Coombes Davies. Sizes up to 12.5 cm x 8.8 cm.

38. Five cards, serrated or patterned edges, one dated 1897 by the sender. Four cards have china with floral decoration, one with a fan, and the fifth has primulas in a glass vase. 7 cm x 9 cm up to 8.8 cm x 11.6 cm.

39. Four cards (one birthday), three with cut-out flowers and gilt decoration, one with serrated edges and a flower garland around two clasped hands. 9.1 cm x 5.8 cm up to 12 cm x 8.5 cm.

## VOLUME 265: FOLDER CARDS OF THE 1890'S WITH FLOWERS AND FOLIAGE

**These cards are in similar style to those in Volume 264, but include a number with more elaborate decoration and tinselling. Some have holly and mistletoe and other foliage, and all the cards are embossed, a few having scenes or flowers printed on silk insets. Some Easter and birthday cards have been grouped together at the end.**

1. Seven cards with holly and mistletoe or ivy. Two are tinselled and two from one set have scenes in small vignettes.
10 cm x 6.4 cm up to 11.8 cm x 8 cm.

2. Four cards with holly decoration. Two have scenes in small vignettes, one with a verse by Isabel Warry, and another has an elaborate cut-out border.
9 cm x 9.7 cm up to 14 cm x 9.2 cm.

3. Three cards, one with an envelope. Two have holly decoration, the other ivy.
8 cm x 10.2 cm, 10.7 cm x 6.2 cm, 11.7 cm x 6 cm.

4. Five cards. Two from one set have holly or ivy in a floral border, two are tinselled with ivy or holly and horseshoes on folded side pieces. The fifth card has a tinselled greeting and a sailing boat with flowers in an ivy border. Sizes up to 11.5 cm x 10 cm.

5. Two elaborate three-fold tinselled cards with cut-out greetings and scenes viewed through a cut-out circle, one with holly, the other with forget-me-nots and bells.
12.7 cm x 9.4 cm, 13.7 cm x 10.6 cm.

6. An eight-page folder with holly and robins on embossed paper with a cut-out oval showing a winter scene beneath. This is marked W & K, Wildt and Kray, a firm listed by Buday as issuing postcards in the 1900's. The verse inside is by Clifton Bingham, listed by Buday as writing for Tuck 1880-90. The card appears to be in an early 20th century style. 11.5 cm x 16.8 cm.

7. Five cards with embossed patterned borders and ivy or leaf decoration, including one from R Tuck included for comparison with a verse by W H Seal. Three others have greetings signed S K C,

Osburn Blackburn, M S Haycraft.
11 cm x 6.5 cm up to 9 cm x 13.5 cm.

8. Four similar with leaf decoration. Two are tinselled with opening side flaps and one is an eight-page folder with a greeting by H M Burnside.
10.3 cm x 8.1 cm up to10 cm x 14 cm.

9. Four cards (two birthday) with embossed patterned borders of flowers and ivy, three with scenes printed on silk, one with a vase of forget-me-nots. Three are eight-page folders with ribbon ties and two were dated 1897 by the senders.
8 cm x 10 cm up to 10 cm x 13.5 cm.

10. Two cards. One has floral wreaths on side flaps which open to show a verse by H S and the other has a country scene printed on silk in a border of pansies on the cover of an eight-page booklet.
10.7 cm x 13.7 cm, 15 cm x 10.7 cm.

11. Three cards. Two are eight-page booklets with flower decoration on lace or silk insets. The third has flower decoration threaded with ribbon and was dated 1897 by the sender.
Sizes up to 10.5 cm x 14.2 cm.

12. A booklet mounted on embossed board with tinselled flowers on the cover and a long poem "Devotion" by Frances Ridley Havergal inside, dated 1892 by the sender.
13.5 cm x 17 cm.

13. Another booklet with ribbon tie entitled "A Garland of Greeting", with flowers and ivy in a patterned border on the cover and suitable quotations from Byron, Cowper and Wordsworth within, probably used as a birthday card.
12.8 cm x 18.5 cm.

14. Five cards. Two are eight-page folders tied with cord; one has a mother-of-pearl shell and was dated 1892 by the sender, the other mother-of-pearl flowers and silver bells and a long poem by E E G. The third has silver leaves, the fourth flowers and silver leaves, the fifth tinselled flowers and a scene in vignette, these two dated 1892 by the senders.
6.5 cm x 12.5 cm up to 9.8 cm x 12.9 cm.

15. Two elaborate tinselled cards with cut-out flower edges on folding wings, one opening to show a country scene.
14.5 cm x 15 cm, 12.5 cm x 17 cm.

16. Two similar with flowers and ivy on tinselled trellised wings which open to show a verse by H M Whitlaw on one dated 1895 by the sender and a greeting by M S Haycraft on the other.
12.5 cm x 14 cm, 12.5 cm x 16.4 cm.

17. Six cards with elaborate cut-out embossed borders and tinselled pierced decoration and flowers, one dated 1896 by the sender. Sizes up to 9.3 cm x 13.4 cm.

18. Four similar birthday cards, one with a tinselled lattice framing a scene in a circular vignette dated 1897, another with a verse by H M Burnside, the third with a silver anchor on ivy, and the fourth with flowers on a silver lattice over a verse by Coombes Davies.
Sizes up to 9.3 cm x 13.4 cm.

19. Two pierced tinselled cards, one with ivy round a country scene, the other with a garland of bells, forget-me-nots and narcissi over a verse by M S Haycraft.
10.3 cm x 17 cm, 12.6 cm x 9.9 cm.

20. Three cards with pansies, chrysanthemums, or daisies, and pierced and tinselled decoration, one dated 1895 by the sender, the others with verses by Coombes Davies and Frances Ridley Havergal. Sizes up to 9.2 cm x 15.4 cm.

21. Seven cards with various pink flowers and tinselled decoration, one dated 1895 by the sender.
10 cm x 7.5 cm to 13 cm x 9.5 cm.

22. Five cards with various white or yellow flowers and pierced decoration, four tinselled. Two have verses by Eliza Cook and Frank Ferndale.
Sizes up to 9.5 cm x 13 cm.

23. Four cards, three tinselled, with ivy or flowers in patterned borders. Three have verses by Charlotte Murray, A F Earl and H M Burnside.
Sizes up to 9.3 cm x 13.5 cm.

24. Four tinselled cards with various flowers, three showing scenes through cut-out vignettes, one with a leaf handle opening side flaps to show a picture of Loch Katrine. Three have greetings by S K C, A F Earl, Frank Mayhew.
Sizes up to 11.5 cm x 11.5 cm.

25/26. Ten cards with various flowers and tinselled decoration, two with bells, one with a horseshoe, another with an anchor. Sizes up to 12 cm x 8.5 cm.

*Numbers 27-32 are Easter cards showing mainly white flowers with crosses.*

27. Three elaborate tinselled cards, two with silver crosses and verses by M S Haycraft and F R Havergal. The third with cut-out flower border dated 1896 by the sender was published by R Tuck and is included here for comparison with unmarked cards.
13.3 cm x 17 cm, 9.5 cm x 14 cm.

28. Three tinselled cards with white flowers and crosses. One with a poem by M S Haycraft was dated 1898 by the sender, and another was dated 1900.
8 cm x 13 cm up to 10.8 cm x 15.5 cm.

29. Five cards, four with crosses and white flowers, one dated 1896, another with a verse by L H Sigourve dated 1895 by the sender, another with a greeting by M S Haycraft. The fifth card is a booklet tied with cord, in a cover with tinselled flowers and ivy, opening to show a long poem "Beyond" by A F Earl.
8.5 cm x 6.5 cm up to 12.7 cm x 11 cm.

30. Six small cards with flowers and various sacred symbols. One with a tinselled anchor has a verse by H M Burnside. Sizes up to 7.8 cm x 10 cm.

31. Three cards, one an eight-page folder with a winter scene in a circular vignette and verses inside by F R Havergal and Margaret Haycraft. Another has narcissi with a silver cross and the third has white flowers with a verse by H M B and was dated 1906 by the sender.
10.2 cm x 7 cm up to 9.5 cm x 14.5 cm.

32. Six cards. Four are cut-out crosses, one dated 1894 by the sender; the remaining two are folders with crosses and flowers.
7 cm x 9.3 cm up to 8 cm x 13.3 cm.

*Numbers 33-37 are birthday cards.*

33. Four cards with decorative borders and tinselled forget-me-nots, violets and pansies. One is an eight-page folder with ribbon bow and a poem by M S Haycraft, one was dated 1897 by the sender, and two other eight-page folders with cord ties have verses by Ellis Walton and E E G.
Sizes up to 11.5 cm x 14.5 cm.

34. Six cards. Five have tinselled flowers and pierced decoration, four with verses by S K Cowan, H M Burnside, or A F Earl. The sixth has a cut-out ivy leaf and a scene viewed through a window.
7 cm x 10.2 cm up to 13.3 cm x 9.5 cm.

35. Six cards with various spring flowers, four with verses by A F Earl, M S Haycraft, Fannie Goddard, Charlotte Murray.
Sizes up to 12.5 cm x 8.2 cm.

36. Four cards with various pink and white flowers. Three with verses by M S Haycraft, Clara Dubois, Charlotte Murray, were dated 1894, 1898, 1898 by the senders and the fourth, an eight-page folder, has a verse by H M Burnside.
8 cm x 10.5 cm up to 10 cm x 14 cm.

37. Six cards with serrated borders. One has an ivy branch and a verse by Marion Wallace; the others have various flowers and three open to show scenes inside.
11.4 cm x 6 cm up to 13.9 cm x 8.5 cm.

## VOLUME 266:
## HOLD TO LIGHT AND CELLULOID CARDS

**"Hold to light" cards appeared in quantity about 1890 though some may have been published earlier. The technique of the earlier cards was to print another picture on the back which appeared on the front when a light shone through; angels, Santa Claus, animals and flowers were used in this way. Towards 1900 a new technique was used, making a cut-out pattern usually from windows and lights, which were illuminated by coloured paper usually inserted between the front picture and the postcard style back. A few of these from the early 1900's are included here, with an early one from Hagelberg.**

**The use of celluloid, or ivorine, became popular in the 1890's. The earlier cards in the section with painted flowers have some charm, but embossing and colour were perhaps used to excess in the later folder cards. These have two sheets, tied by cord or ribbon, with greetings inside; they continued in popularity well into the twentieth century, a few later cards being included here for comparison. Two cards relating to Queen Victoria conclude this section.**

*Numbers 1-10 are "Hold to Light" cards.*

1. A Raphael Tuck card, Artist series (before 1893) with two boys chasing something, which appears as a dog with a pan tied to its tail when light shines through. A descriptive verse signed "Helen of Troy" tells the story (included here for comparison with similar cards).
12 cm x 8 cm.

2. Two cards published by W Hagelberg, probably c1890. One has a child asleep with Santa Claus appearing through the light, no. 782. The other shows the Holy Family in Egypt, with guardian angels seen through light, no. 843.
9.9 cm x 13.2 cm, 14.7 cm x 10.8 cm.

3. Three cards designed by Helena Maguire, one dated 1890 by the sender. One shows a mother and baby, another a lady under the mistletoe, the third a sleeping child, revealing when held to light a guardian angel, a gentleman waiting for a kiss and a cat ready to wake the child.
10.2 cm x 14.2 cm, 14.2 cm x 10.2 cm.

4. Three cards by Bertha Maguire in similar mounts with plain borders. Two have ivy, showing snowdrops through the light and one has a rose which opens out, dated 1890 by the sender.
10.1 cm x 14.1 cm, 14.1 cm x 10.1 cm.

5. Two cards. One has a picture of the Virgin and Child in the Stable, opening to show a view from outside with the shepherds and sheep, which shows angels with the Star when held to light. The other shows a village in winter snow framed in a border with tinselled daisies. The same village in spring appears on the reverse so that winter can disappear when the card is held to light. This card is marked Patent

no. 18582/89 and USA Patent May 20th 1890, which suggests that these cards first appeared around 1889.
14.5 cm x 10.8 cm, 15.6 cm x 10.2 cm.

6. Two cards on mounts with patterned borders. The first has a winter scene on the front with summer on reverse and the second, dated 1893 by the sender, has a mediaeval maiden under the mistletoe with attendant knight revealed by light.
10.2 cm x 14.4 cm, 11.7 cm x 15.5 cm.

7. A postcard with monochrome landscape, revealing angels when held to light, postmarked 1906. 13.8 cm x 9 cm.

8. A view of Windsor Castle and town in embossed forget-me-not border has cut-out windows which show red when held to light. This is an early example of the later technique, perhaps c1895.
13 cm x 9.1 cm.

9. Four postcards. Two dated 1908 have children with Father Christmas or a snowman and the third has Father Christmas in green robe delivering toys. The fourth card is marked W Hagelberg and shows Father Christmas in purple robe carrying a tree and a sack of toys through the night. This card is interesting, as the name of Hagelberg is not prominent in postcard literature and Buday lists the firm as publishing from 1870-1890's. The card however does have the appearance of the early 20th century and was found in an appropriate album, unused. No other postcard marked Hagelberg appears in the Seddon Collection. 8.7 cm x 14 cm.

10. Three postcards, one with a ship with Edwardian stamp, one of a church postmark 1906, the third a winter scene postmark 1911, with light seen through cut-out portholes or windows.
14 cm x 9 cm, 8.7 cm x 14 cm.

*Numbers 11-24 are on celluloid or have celluloid insets. The later ones were probably made in the early 1900's.*

11. Three cards, a hand-painted spray of flowers and leaves with a valentine verse, a lily of the valley scrap tied with a blue ribbon bow to a painted background, and an embossed bronze flower motif with Italian greeting. 8 cm x 16.3 cm, 5.7 cm x 8.2 cm, 9.7 cm x 6.3 cm.

12. A card with a greeting and a sea scene in a serrated border with painted ships on a celluloid sail. 10.4 cm x 11.4 cm.

13. Two cards with embossed silver borders and celluloid insets with attached paper scraps.
9.8 cm x 13.7 cm, 13.7 cm x 9.8 cm.

14. Three bordered cards, two with flowers painted on celluloid insets and greetings (one birthday). The third card has a gilt-patterned border but has lost its inset.
13.2 cm x 10.7 cm, 10.9 cm x 8.1 cm.

15. Six cards with elaborate pierced designs, one with painted flowers on celluloid. Five cards are paper but resemble celluloid and are included here for comparison. Two of these were published by Hagelberg and have a Greek key cut-out border round flower sprays; the remaining three from one set have flower scraps on lace backgrounds.
11.3 cm x 7.7 cm, 8.1 cm x 12.7 cm, 12.7 cm x 6.9 cm.

16. A card with serrated edges on buff-coloured paper with a hand painted rose in embossed patterned border stapled to the background card with silver-headed pins, dated 1893 by the sender. The card is included here as this stapling technique is frequently seen on cards with celluloid attachments. 11.5 cm x 15.7 cm.

17. Two folding embossed cards with celluloid pieces stapled to the covers, one with pansies, one with ivy. Both have a tinselled greeting "For Auld Lang Syne" on the cover and a verse inside and are tied with ribbon bows.
10.3 cm x 14.5 cm, 14.5 cm x 10.3 cm.

18. Two cards. One has forget-me-nots on celluloid with a cut-out patterned border and a stapled Christmas greeting; the other is a folder with a celluloid motif with painted flowers and tinselled greeting stapled to the background.
11 cm x 17.5 cm, 13.3 cm x 10.2 cm.

19. Two cards. Both have stapled celluloid motifs with painted flowers, one a horseshoe dated 1890 by the sender, the other a star and crescent moon. The sentiments are printed in silver, and one was dated 1890 by the sender.
14.5 cm x 10.2 cm, 14.7 cm x 10.6 cm.

20. Four cards.
a) An elaborate folder with pierced embossed decoration, silver lettering, and an attached celluloid motif with painted pansy and forget-me-nots.
14.5 cm x 11.3 cm.
b) An ivy spray on blue transparent gilt-edged celluloid, marked "Wm Strain & Sons, entered Stationers' Hall.
11.7 cm x 4.3 cm.
c) A celluloid bell with country scene stapled to a blue card with silver greeting.
9.2 cm x 11.7 cm.
d) A folder card with a Christmas verse by H S B on the cover and a celluloid cross inside. 8.2 cm x 11 cm.

21. Three folder cards with celluloid covers, tied with coloured tasselled cords. One has embossed violets, another ivy and the third has a dove pulling a cart piled with purple fabric pansies, all in obtrusive garish colours mainly green and purple. Verses inside are signed by H M Burnside,

Vera Arlington, and C A Dubois.
9.2 cm x 14.3 cm, 13.5 cm x 7.7 cm.

22. Four similar, three with roses, one with holly. All have verses inside, two signed Vera Dale, C H Collins.
7.3 cm x 13 cm up to 9.6 cm x 14.6 cm.

23. Four similar. Two have flowers, one has holly around a pair of boots with a message and a seal in silver. The fourth card has forget-me-nots and a tinselled greeting with a heart, a horseshoe, and two hands clasped over a boot, and is marked Philco, a firm well know for 20th century postcards.
10.3 cm x 7.2 cm up to 9.7 cm x 12.7 cm.

24. Two cards.
a) A celluloid motif with painted rose stapled to an octagonal card with turned over edges. 12.5 cm x 12.5 cm.
b) A folder with velvet roses and forget-me-nots on a celluloid cover with a verse by H M Burnside inside, dated 1907 by the sender. 9.7 cm x 16.4 cm.

25. Two cards, fitting postscripts to the final volume of Victorian cards, dated 1897.
a) A personal card from R of 23 Wilson Patten St., Warrington, marking Queen Victoria's Diamond Jubilee, a plain folder with the verse from Austin ending
"And long the prayer resound
God Save our Gracious Queen".
7.5 cm x 10.2 cm.
b) A folder printed in gilt with a crown over a picture of Queen Victoria, probably at the marriage of Prince George to Princess Mary of Teck, showing the bride kneeling before the Queen and bridesmaids nearby. 14.3 cm x 10.5 cm.

# INTO THE 20TH CENTURY

*Section*

*21*

A small selection of 20th century cards is included here showing changes of style and popular taste and some innovations of the later 1890's. Many of the publishers noted here are new to this catalogue, though a few Victorian names still appear. Perhaps the continuing influence of Morris, Art Nouveau, fin de Siècle styles and possibly even the Silver Studio might be traced, with a hint of the coming of Art Deco. Few designs, however, are remarkable for artistic merit, but it must be remembered that by now cards were universally bought and used and publishers, as always, catered for popular taste. Three sample albums of 1913 and 1914 give a cross-section of some techniques and styles available at the time, including paper like parchment, celluloid, hand-coloured photographs, and some quite well designed lace paper.

By 1910 postcards had taken over much of the production, and a small selection with greetings is included; the high series numbers give some idea of the vast quantity made. A volume of First World War cards brings reminders of the trenches, and includes a few examples of the hand embroidered silk cards much treasured as souvenirs by the folk at home. The 1914 War ended the printing of cards in Germany for firms based in Britain, and by 1918 many card manufacturers prominent in Victorian times had disappeared or been taken over, or had directed production into other channels.

**267.12**

# VOLUME 267:
# 20TH CENTURY PUBLISHERS AND ARTISTS AND SOME MISCELLANEOUS CARDS

**These cards are folders, 1900-1914, with some exceptions as noted.**

1. Five cards, one with illuminated verse signed G S Hollings, one with a holly wreath, two with flowers, one with a fisherman, all published by Hills & Co. 9.1 cm x 9.1 cm up to 14 cm x 8.8 cm.

2. Six cards published by W McKenzie & Co, London EC, one dated 1903. Two cards have black and white scenes in small vignettes, another has roses, one has dogs, another children, and the sixth is an embossed 18th century scene with forget-me-not sprays. 8.7 cm x 9.5 cm up to 10 cm x 14.3 cm.

3. Four cards published by Mowbray with religious pictures and verses. Sizes up to 10.3 cm x 12.8 cm.

4. Four cards published by Wildt & Kray, one with bells and ivy made in Bavaria, the other three with robins on celluloid, pansies, or a greeting and verse in decorative lettering marked British manufacture. 8.5 cm x 11.5 cm up to 10.2 cm x 15 cm.

5. Six cards. Two were published by Delgado, London, one a comic picture of prehistoric times, the other a clock wreathed in ivy. Two were published by B B, London, one showing world maps, the other a rural scene with violets. The others are from Misch & Co, one with illuminated text, the other a motor car with Father Christmas. 8.5 cm x 8.5 cm up to 8.5 cm x 11.7 cm.

6. Two cards, an eight-page folder with a sketch of a lady "Erma" by E Barnard on the cover, and a card with pen and ink portrait of a lady by Lewis Baume, dated 1910 by the sender. 10.8 cm x 13 cm, 11.4 cm x 14.8 cm.

7. Four cards. Three were published by C W Faulkner, perhaps about 1920, and include two designed by Ethel Parkinson with a gentleman in silhouette or Japanese ladies, and another with Japanese ladies signed I M J. The fourth card has a comic fisherman, signed Phil May (cover only). He died in 1903, but the card might be later. 6.2 cm x 12.4 cm up to 10 cm x 14 cm.

8. Four cards.
a) Elizabethan dancers, signed Ludovic.
b) Two dogs, signed Louis Wain.
c) A Medici card with a Nativity scene by Margaret Tarrant.
d) A plump smiling baby face by Mabel Lucie Attwell. Numbers c) and d) were probably issued in the later 1920's but are included as examples of artists popular in

the post-war period. Sizes up to 12.2 cm x 12.7 cm.

9. Four personal cards with photographs, two in drab dark brown covers. Two cards were personal greetings from Mr & Mrs Charles Dyer, the first with pictures of their children Doris and Frank (in a frock and knickers) dated 1900, the second perhaps about 1905 showing the children again. The third card dated 1903 has a picture of a baby Rosemary, and the fourth a river scene. 8.7 cm x 12.5 cm up to 11.5 cm x 15.7 cm.

10. Two hand-made cards, sketches mounted on brown paper.
a) A watercolour view of a rocky harbour with a sailing ship. 11.6 cm x 11.6 cm.
b) A booklet with six pen and ink caricatures of dogs, babies, a motor-car, a Gibson girl, signed I M Hopps. 13.6 cm x 17 cm.

11. Six cards, four with children in winter or summer scenes, one with a girl in Kate Greenaway dress blowing bubbles, the sixth dated 1908 by the sender with two girls and dolls by the fireside. Sizes up to 9.4 cm x 11.6 cm.

12. Eight cards with children, including one showing Father Christmas, and a personal sample card dated 1912 with two boy scouts and a plum pudding. Sizes up to 10.6 cm x 8.3 cm.

13. Four cards, all with aeroplanes. Three are personal cards with line drawings, one showing letters dropped from a plane dated 1913, another dated 1914 showing a plane flying over a silhouetted castle. The fourth card has a youthful Santa Claus in a flying machine, probably published later. 7.3 cm x 11.8 cm up to 10.2 cm x 15.4 cm.

14. Four humorous cards, two opening out to show mishaps to a soldier on horseback and a maidservant, the third with golfers and the caption "May this Christmas suit you to a Tee". The fourth card, with a moustached "masher" opens out to show a huge bow tie. Sizes up to 11.3 cm x 10 cm.

15. Five cards with motor cars, two driven by pigs or cats. One card has children with a toy car, another shows an early model coming to grief, and the fifth is a single card showing a goggled chauffeur at the wheel. 8.9 cm x 7 cm up to 8.4 cm x 12.2 cm.

16. Three humorous cards, with various festive scenes involving food and drink. All about 8.4 cm x 12.6 cm.

17. Four humorous cards. One shows a lighted cigar with a festive poem by Bertram Hope, another two dwarfs with a pipe and cigarette. Another opens to show a kitten in bed, and the fourth is a single card with Father Christmas firing a

**267.15**

champagne cork with small puddings as ammunition. Sizes up to 12.5 cm x 9.5 cm.

18. Six humorous cards with cats, dogs, and an owl, four having the covers only. Sizes up to 13 cm x 9.5 cm.

19. Five humorous cards. Three have birds (one with cover only), another has elves with holly and mistletoe headdresses. The fifth is a letter card with gummed edges and perforations for opening. Sizes up to 8.8 cm x 11.5 cm.

20. Five cards showing the "Good Old Days" in Georgian and Stuart times. Sizes up to 9.2 cm x 11.8 cm.

21. Three cards, one shaped like a jug with holly, and two with Chinese or Japanese figures. Sizes up to 12 cm x 9.6 cm.

22. Five cards, including two single Easter cards, one with the Virgin Mary in a circular vignette with silver stars, the other marked Y W C A 1913 with the Good Shepherd. Two cards have angels watching over children, and the fifth has a bell which lifts to show two angels. 6.4 cm x 11.8 cm to 10.3 cm x 14.2 cm.

23. Six single cards with religious verses in illuminated style. Four have gilt edges, and two are marked Girls Friendly Society. Sizes up to 7.3 cm x 11.7 cm.

24. Five cards. Two are single with verses and decorated initial letter, one dated 1908 by the sender, and another has a Venetian scene dated 1910. A folder card with flowers on the cover and texts and verses inside was dated 1915 by the sender and marked Mildmay. The fifth card on paper resembling parchment has illuminated greetings and verses and was dated Christmas 1913 from Minnie Howard,

Stockport Road, Marple.
8.8 cm x 11.3 cm up to 10 cm x 15.5 cm.

25. Four cards, three with printed greetings, one dated 1904 from the head Master of Central School, Wimbledon Common, another dated 1902 from H S Mele-Shaw of the Engineering Dept, University College, Liverpool, to his students, the third dated 1909-10 from Mr & Mrs George Lambert to their friends. The fourth card has a Pre-Raphaelite lady in black and white with illuminated greeting, dated 1908 by the sender.
9.5 cm x 12.8 cm up to 12.2 cm x 15.8 cm.

26. Two Masonic Christmas cards, dated 1908, 1925, both with the compasses and square insignia in gilt.
12 cm x 15.7 cm, 15.2 cm x 11.4 cm.

27. Three American cards with tinselled and jewelled decoration. Two are postcards, one with two doves mounted on a blue silk inset.
10.8 cm x 8.3 cm, 14 cm x 9 cm.

28. Six "cards" made from silver metal. An early example from Scotland, marked "Foyers Loch Ness" has the date 1896-7. The others might be 1920's, and have painted flowers or holly, one shaped like a bookmark. Sizes up to 7.5 cm x 12 cm, bookmark 5 cm x 15 cm.

## VOLUME 268: MORE 20TH CENTURY CARDS

**These cards are folders, usually tied with ribbon or cord, and dated 1900-1914, with a few exceptions as noted. Some are dated sample cards.**

1. Eight cards, c1900, five with holly, mistletoe, or ivy, three with flowers.
5.8 cm x 9 cm up to 8.3 cm x 11 cm.

2. Seven cards, including two with birds, two with floral designs and one with illuminated greeting, 1900-1903. Two others have ships, one marked 1901.
7.3 cm x 10.5 cm up to 13.7 cm x 10.2 cm.

3. Eight cards, seven with designs of forget-me-nots, ivy, four leaved clover, lilies of the valley and one with holly. Early 1900's. Sizes up to 8.3 cm x 10.3 cm.

4. Eight cards (five with covers only). Six have holly designs, one has ivy with bells, and one a decorative gilded greeting. Early 1900's. Sizes up to 9.3 cm x 10.5 cm.

5. Seven cards, six with various illuminated or heraldic designs, dated 1900-1902 by the senders. The seventh card was published by Raphael Tuck, and is in booklet form inscribed "Friendly Greetings for the New Century".
7.5 cm x 8.5 cm up to 12.6 cm x 9 cm.

6. Eight cards, including one with a geometric design of forget-me-nots and

another with clover leaves around cattle in a circular vignette. The others have gilt greetings, monograms, or the date 1903 in gilt lettering, and all were dated 1902 or 1903.
8.8 cm x 6.7 cm up to 12.8 cm x 10.2 cm.

7. Four personal cards, all dated 1904 or 1905. One white card has an embossed figure of a man entitled "A Brown Study", another on deckle-edged paper has a simple greeting. A single card has a Christmas poem probably composed by the sender, Robert Hyde of Sunnywood, Didsbury, and the fourth is a sample card with a lady in a muslin dress in an oval frame with Art Nouveau border in purple, green, and silver.
9 cm x 11.5 cm up to 8.4 cm x 18 cm.

8. Seven personal or sample cards dated from 1905 to 1908. Five have simple designs with lettering or holly, one has a country village scene; the seventh card has a Scottish theme with gilded sword dancer and thistles on a dark background.
Sizes up to 12.2 cm x 10 cm.

9. Five personal or sample cards, including one with holly, another with ivy, and Father Christmas with two children dated 1910, 1909, 1912. The fourth card is another from Sunnywood, Didsbury, with a Christmas poem by the sender in a Japanese border. The fifth card has an attractive illuminated cover reminiscent of the 1870's designs, with Tennyson's poem "New Year Bells" inside, dated 1908, and printed on paper resembling parchment.
9.3 cm x 7 cm up to 10.5 cm x 14 cm.

10. Five cards dated 1911. Four were probably sample cards, two having scenes in vignettes on the covers and two gilt lettering and flowers. The fifth card was sent from India and has the insignia of the Lancashire Fusiliers on the covers.
10.9 cm x 7.7 cm up to 12.5 cm x 15.7 cm.

11. Four cards. Two have pictures of sheep or children in tinselled borders, dated 1912 and another with a floral design in gold and green was dated 1910, probably all sample cards. The fourth has a calendar for 1912 attached, with greeting for Christmas 1911, on brown board, with a small picture of a boat by a seaside village.
7.3 cm x 10.2 cm up to 11.3 cm x 16.2 cm.

12. Seven miscellaneous cards dated from 1911 to 1913 with scenes, flowers and gilded lettering. Five were sample cards.
5 cm x 7 cm up to 8.5 cm x 13 cm.

13. Two large cards. One dated 1911 was from Mr & Mrs Leckie, with a portrait inside of Mr Leckie who was the manager of the Grand Theatre, Stalybridge, and a small oval print of a rural scene in a decorative border with a calendar. The other has three lovely ladies in muslin draperies on the cover and was from Mr & Mrs George Thornton, 24 Trafalgar Road,

Birkdale, at Christmas 1909, obviously an expensive card on thick handmade paper.
12.5 cm x 17.9 cm, 17.7 cm x 12.7 cm.

14. Five cards, including two with scenes, one with clasped hands in a border of forget-me-nots, and a sample card dated 1913 with festoons of roses around a Wedgwood style oval vignette. The fifth card has roses and a cut-out oval showing birds and a greeting in German, dated 1903 by the sender.
Sizes up to 9.4 cm x 11.2 cm.

*Numbers 15-21 have monochrome prints or vignettes on embossed or coloured backgrounds. This technique appeared in the late 1890's but continued well into the 20th century.*

15. Five cards (two single), with rural scenes mounted on embossed white backgrounds, one dated 1898 by the sender.
7.4 cm x 9.5 cm up to 14.5 cm x 12.2 cm.

16. Five cards with rural scenes, one coloured, with birthday greeting, another dated 1903 by the sender.
Sizes up to 13.7 cm x 10.3 cm.

17. Six cards with country scenes, one a personal card dated 1897. Three have pink, blue, or red mounts.
9.8 cm x 6 cm up to 8.6 cm x 12.7 cm.

18. Four cards with prints of elegant ladies on embossed patterned mounts.
Sizes up to 9.4 cm x 12.4 cm.

19. Six cards, five designs of ladies on white or coloured backgrounds, c1900. One coloured print shows a lady and gentleman riding bicycles.
Sizes up to 9 cm x 11.7 cm.

20. Five cards with prints of cats, horses, or deer on plain or embossed white backgrounds, c1900.
Sizes up to 13 cm x 10.5 cm.

21. Seven cards with prints of various scenes, four on embossed white backgrounds, two on plain white and one on green. Three cards were dated 1896, 1901, 1909. Sizes up to 11 cm x 8.5 cm.

22. Five cards for hunt followers, two with coloured prints of the chase, two with black and white scenes, the fifth with a fox's head on the cover and a picture of a stage coach inside signed W J Wollen.
12.4 cm x 7.5 cm up to 14.5 cm x 10 cm.

23. Five cards, c1900. Three have embossed white designs in Wedgwood style on coloured backgrounds, one enclosing a photograph. Two from one set show a lady with a Cupid, in white on dark green background. Sizes up to 8.4 cm x 12.2 cm.

24. Seven cards c1900 on red, brown, blue or green paper with simple greetings or

motifs on the covers.
6 cm x 8 cm up to 7.2 cm x 12.6 cm.

25. Four cards with silk decoration. One has painted flowers on silk set on a white embossed background, another a lake with swans printed on silk. The third has applied velvet flowers and leaves, and the fourth a vignette with an embroidered holly spray on a hand-painted background.
9.7 cm x 7.8 cm up to 8.9 cm x 12.4 cm.

26. Six cards. Four have cut-out decoration (two dated 1914 and 1916), one a single card. The fifth has gilt embossing around a panel with greeting, and the sixth has two ivy leaves which pull back to show the greeting.
10 cm x 7.1 cm up to 8.8 cm x 14.6 cm.

27. Six cards with covers of material resembling celluloid, one with an initial on mother-of-pearl dated 1913. One has an illuminated greeting with holly, another dated 1896 has a greeting in a small gilded motif. Two others have flowers, and the sixth dated 1911 has bells and holly.
6.3 cm x 9.6 cm up to 7.6 cm x 13.4 cm.

28. Five cards. Two have flowers in vases, marked "Golden Series", and three have hand painted flowers, one dated 1914 by the sender. 6 cm x 8 cm up to 8 cm x 12 cm.

## VOLUME 269:
## ALBUM OF CARDS FOR PERSONAL USE, CHRISTMAS 1913

**The album has no publisher's name, and orders for the printing of name and address were meant to go through the retailer who stocked the album, which is labelled "Best & Cheapest, The Premier Ideal, Private Greeting Cards". Prices vary from 2s 6d per dozen for small cards to 5s 6d per dozen for a large calendar. The cards are all folders, tied with silk ribbon or tasselled cord, with brief greetings or verses, some quotations from the classics.**

**Many cards have coloured pictures which are all labelled "Real photographs, hand coloured", which means that the photographs were coloured and then processed for reproduction. The pictures are in romantic style, with lovely ladies, rural or mountain scenes, and the good old days.**

1. Four cards, two with hand coloured photographs, two with gilt initial or greeting, all on shaded grey paper.
10.7 cm x 6.7 cm up to 8.1 cm x 11.7 cm.

2. Two cards on brown paper with hand coloured photographs, one a ship with calendar below, the other an elegant lady in a garden.
9 cm x 15.5 cm, 11.5 cm x 14.7 cm.

3. A calendar with coloured photograph on white embossed mount, with pink ribbon for hanging. 12 cm x 17.7 cm.

4. Four cards tied with pink silk cord. They have white embossed covers with pierced decoration showing the pink inside sheet. Sizes up to 10.7 cm x 9 cm.

5. Two embossed cards with coloured photographs, one on shaded cream paper, the other on brown.
11.3 cm x 14.5 cm, 14.8 cm x 11.3 cm.

6. Four cards with embossed floral decoration on celluloid.
7 cm x 10.3 cm up to 9.5 cm x 11.6 cm.

7. A card with a hand coloured photograph of a village street mounted on white embossed paper. 15.5 cm x 13.8 cm.

8. Four cards, three with hand coloured photographs, one with a gilt initial, all on cream shaded embossed paper.
Sizes up to 11 cm x 9.2 cm.

9. Four cards, with name or initial on white embossed paper.
Sizes up to 11 cm x 9.1 cm.

10. A card with hand coloured photograph in an oval vignette in an elaborate cream and green embossed border.
15.4 cm x 13.7 cm.

11. Four cards, two with hand coloured photographs, two with gilt initials, on white embossed patterned backgrounds.
8 cm x 5.7 cm up to 6.2 cm x 12.2 cm.

12. Four cards with gilt cut-out decoration and greeting on white paper resembling moiré silk. Sizes up to 8.4 cm x 12 cm.

13. A combined blotter and calendar with picture of a lady in a garden mounted on embossed patterned white card with shaded grey border and cord.
14.7 cm x 21 cm.

14. Four cards with elaborate gilt embossed decoration, two having coloured photographs, two with gilt initials.
Sizes up to 9.5 cm x 11.7 cm.

15. Four cards with gilt initials or greetings, two with photographs, on dark green embossed mounts with cord and tassels to match.
12 cm x 8.8 cm, 8 cm x 12 cm, 7.4 cm x 12 cm.

16. Two cards, photographs mounted on pink and green or white and green embossed backgrounds.
15 cm x 11.2 cm, 11.2 cm x 14.5 cm.

17. Four cards with embossed flower designs and gilt greetings on "Dainty Fine

Art Celluloids", mounted on embossed white paper. Sizes up to 8.2 cm x 12 cm.

18. Two cards "Real Photogravures", with rural scenes in sepia. 8.8 cm x 12.6 cm.

19. Four cards with designs of small trails of roses and leaves and quotations from the poets with illuminated initial letters. One card has a hand coloured photograph. Sizes up to 9.5 cm x 11.8 cm.

20. A calendar with coloured photograph mounted on embossed brown card.
14.7 cm x 20.3 cm.

21. Three cards with simple greeting or name and address on the cover of a plain white folder. Sizes up to 9.2 cm x 15.3 cm.

22. Four cards with gilt cut-out decoration on shaded background.
10.7 cm x 6.7 cm up to 8 cm x 12 cm.

23. Two cards, one with a coloured photograph of a child and dog over a calendar for 1914, another with a hunting scene mounted on white embossed background.
9 cm x 15.4 cm, 11.2 cm x 14.7 cm.

24. Four cards on shaded green and white paper, three with hand coloured photographs, one with verse.
7 cm x 10.5 cm up to 9.5 cm x 12 cm.

25. Four cards on embossed green and white paper with cord and tassels to match, two with coloured photographs, two with gilt initials.
8.2 cm x 8.8 cm up to 8 cm x 12 cm.

26. A card with two hand coloured photographs of mountain scenes on shaded embossed background.
15.5 cm x 13.8 cm.

27. Four cards with gilt motifs on patterned embossed white paper. Sizes up to 11 cm x 9 cm.

28. Three cards with hand coloured photographs mounted on dark brown paper.
7.7 cm x 11.5 cm up to 11.3 cm x 14.2 cm.

29. A card with a river scene mounted on white card with a patterned border.
12.3 cm x 17.8 cm.

30. Three cards "Real photogravures", pictures in sepia of a stage coach, sheep on a cliff, and a lady spinning, with brown silk cord and tassels to match.
Sizes up to 9 cm x 12.6 cm.

31. Four cards with gilt motifs on shaded blue, white, and pink paper, with pink cord and tassels.
Sizes up to 10.9 cm x 9 cm.

32. Three cards on embossed paper patterned in grey and white, two with gilt

initials, one with mountain scene and calendar.
12 cm x 8.7 cm up to 12 cm x 17.4 cm.

33. A calendar with hand coloured photograph of a river scene mounted on cream embossed paper with red backing and ribbon for hanging. 15.7 cm x 21 cm.

34. Four cards, three with scenes, two with gilt initials, on embossed white paper. 7 cm x 10.3 cm up to 9.6 cm x 11.7 cm.

35. Four cards. Two of these with silver motif and greeting on shaded grey and white paper are described as "Half-Mourning" cards, but the greetings inside differ very little from others in this book. The other cards are children's cards, with brightly coloured pictures on the front, and from the greetings inside appear to be bought for children to send.
8.2 cm x 9 cm up to 8 cm x 12 cm.

## VOLUME 270:
## ALBUM OF CARDS FOR PERSONAL USE, CHRISTMAS 1913

This album, also for Christmas 1913, is labelled "Orient series of Private Greeting Cards", again with no clue to the manufacturer. It is interesting to observe in the instructions for ordering that the latest dates for receiving orders for Christmas and New Year cards were Saturdays December 20th and 27th respectively. The final date for cards ordered from a Raphael Tuck album of 1976 was December 3rd. The pictures in this album are described as "Real Bromide, hand coloured". The cards are tied with coloured tasselled cord or ribbon with one or two exceptions. On the back cover is a note "All cards contained in this book guaranteed of British manufacture".

1. Four cards, three with pictures seen through cut-out vignettes in white embossed paper, one with gilt initial. One picture of Christmas waits is the same as one in Volume 269, on a different style of card. 6 cm x 8 cm up to 8 cm x 12.5 cm.

2. "The Duchess of Gainsborough", (sic), reproduced on a large card after Thos. Gainsborough, R A. 14 cm x 19.4 cm.

3. Four cards, two with inset pictures, one with verse, one with gilt initial, on shaded background.
7.7 cm x 8.3 cm up to 8.2 cm x 10.5 cm.

4. Four cards with embossed flowers in shades of green and purple, two with small scenes viewed through a cut-out circle. 7 cm x 8 cm up to 7.8 cm x 12 cm.

5. Two cards, one with the picture of a girl seen through a cut-out oval vignette, the other with stags by a waterfall over a calendar, both on shaded cream paper. 10.5 cm x 16.5 cm, 10 cm x 15.5 cm.

6. Four cards with embossed gilded and tinselled decoration, three with scenes of stage coach, stag, or sheep.
8 cm x 8.5 cm up to 12 cm x 8 cm.

7. A Novelty Calendar, with a rural scene set on an easel. 15.5 cm x 17 cm.

8. Three cards on shaded blue and white paper, two with inset scenes, one with gilt initial over senders name and address. 8.3 cm x 10.5 cm up to 10.5 cm x 14.7 cm.

9. Four cards with gilt greeting or initial on embossed white paper.
6 cm x 7.9 cm up to 7.5 cm x 10.3 cm.

10. Four cards on embossed patterned shaded paper, two with small inset scenes, two with gilt initials and purple flowers. 7.5 cm x 8.1 cm up to 11.5 cm x 8 cm.

11. Three "Genuine Photogravure" cards, printed in brown, with a romantic river and castle scene, a lady in Georgian dress, and a village in winter.
10.2 cm x 7.7 cm up to 8.4 cm x 15.3 cm.

12. A card and a book marker, the card with gilt initial and greeting and address on the front, the book marker with an oval inset picture and gilt border.
12 cm x 16.7 cm, 6.5 cm x 17 cm.

13. Four cards with inset pictures on shaded paper, three with sea or country scenes, one with a lady's portrait.
10 cm x 7.3 cm up to 8.3 cm x 15.3 cm.

14. A shaded single card with gilt initial, greeting and name and address of sender in an embossed border. 15.3 cm x 12 cm.

15. Three cards with photogravure or bromide pictures mounted on shaded card. 7 cm x 10 cm, 8.3 cm x 15.1 cm, 12.5 cm x 10 cm.

16. Two cards with coloured pictures on shaded mounts and embossed flower decoration and greeting below.
10.6 cm x 14.5 cm, 15.5 cm x 12 cm.

17. Four cards with shaded green and white embossed covers, two with scenes, two with gilt initials seen through cut-out vignettes. Sizes up to 11.5 cm x 8.3 cm.

18. Three cards. One has a lady in Georgian dress in a floral border with gilt initial on an embossed white background. Two are marked "Mourning Cards", on shaded grey and white embossed paper, but have Christmas greetings attuned to memories of the past. 8 cm x 15.2 cm, 8 cm x 11.3 cm, 10 cm x 7 cm.

19. A large card with birds over a country scene mounted on shaded grey and white paper. 12 cm x 16.5 cm.

20. Four cards on embossed white paper, one a smaller version of the larger card in no. 18, another with a rural scene. The others have a gilt initial and the name and address of the sender, one with 1913, 1914 in coloured floral wreaths. 6 cm x 12.5 cm, 9.7 cm x 7 cm, 11.6 cm x 8 cm.

21. A "Real Photogravure, hand coloured" picture of a stage coach in an autumn setting. 18.3 cm x 13.3 cm.

22. Four cards with flower designs on celluloid.
6 cm x 7.5 cm up to 10.5 cm x 8 cm.

23. Two cards with humorous designs by Lawson Wood, one a schoolmaster and a snowman, the other a policeman and a man with a stolen goose, both on cream shaded embossed background.
13 cm x 16.5 cm, 10.7 cm x 14.5 cm.

24. Four cards on embossed silver patterned backgrounds with gold motifs and greetings.
6 cm x 8 cm up to 10.5 cm x 7 cm.

25. A card with a picture of a lady in a teagown, and a calendar with a village scene, both on dark brown mounts. 8.2 cm x 15 cm, 11.9 cm x 16.6 cm.

26. Three cards on shaded grey and white paper, two with inset pastoral scenes, one with gilt motif and initial.
8 cm x 8.4 cm up to 11.6 cm x 8.2 cm.

27. Two cards. One has a cock and a holly branch in a cream border with illuminated greeting, the other a coloured line drawing of a village by a lake in an oval vignette set in an illuminated border.
10.7 cm x 14.4 cm, 12 cm x 16.8 cm.

28. Four cards, two with gilded motif or decorated initial, and two with a sea or country scene set in an embossed border. Sizes up to 11.4 cm x 8 cm.

29. Two cards on shaded grey and white backgrounds, one with holly and horseshoes, the other with an inset river scene over a gilt initial in an ivy wreath. 12.5 cm x 10.2 cm, 10 cm x 12.5 cm.

30. Four cards, two with pictures of a rural scene or a young lady set in shaded backgrounds with gilt initial. The third has an embossed design of bells and holly on a cream shaded background. The fourth has a picture of a family in a drawing room with grand piano and a village scene below.
7.2 cm x 9.7 cm up to 10 cm x 12.2 cm.

31. Four cards. Three have pictures seen through cut-out rectangles or oval with gilt

borders, and the fourth has a gilt initial and motifs. Sizes up to 8.1 cm x 12.8 cm.

32. Three cards. One has a picture of a mother and child mounted in a circular border over a greeting, and another a village scene viewed through a cut-out vignette in embossed paper. The third card has a line drawing of a number of flying machines including all kinds of aeroplanes, a balloon, and a Zeppelin. 10.3 cm x 16.7 cm, 11.6 cm x 8.2 cm, 7.1 cm x 9.8 cm.

33. A business calendar, with a print of sailing ships mounted on grey paper with black border. 25 cm x 15.5 cm.

34. Four cards. Two are children's cards, one with Dutch girls dancing, the other with children snowballing. The third card has a stamp with a black cat and the fourth shows a Dutch boy smoking a cheroot. 9.8 cm x 7.6 cm up to 10 cm x 12.5 cm.

## VOLUME 271:
## ALBUM OF CARDS FOR PERSONAL USE, CHRISTMAS 1914

**This volume is labelled "The R A series of Private Cards", for Christmas 1914 and was obviously put together after the outbreak of war in August as a collection of greetings is supplied for "those who have friends or relatives serving their country". The cards are folders tied with silk ribbon with a few exceptions as noted, and the designs are more restrained than those in volumes 269 and 270, with no cut-out lace paper or celluloid. The flower designs and motifs are mostly small delicate coloured line designs in a style which continued in popularity in the 1920's and 30's. The cheapest price was 3/- per dozen, but most were priced at about 7s/6d.**

1. Three cards, two with greetings in coloured motifs on white cards with green shading, the third a lady in flower trimmed hat and befrilled muslin dress. Sizes up to 9.3 cm x 14.8 cm.

2. Two cards, both with the same motif of a festoon of roses, one a large folder with a picture of a coaching inn inside, the other an envelope containing a personal card. 12.5 cm x 15.9 cm, 11 cm x 8.3 cm.

3. Three cards with monochrome scenes, one with sheep, another with a little girl by the sea, the third a picture of fisher folk. The first two are probably photographs. 13.5 cm x 7 cm, 6.7 cm x 10 cm, 15.2 cm x 9.2 cm.

4. Two cards, one with sailing ships in sunset mounted on grey card, and another with a festoon of roses over a greeting on plain white card. 13.5 cm x 18.7 cm, 9.9 cm x 12.7 cm.

5. A calendar with a vase of flowers on plain white card, and a card showing a collection of Japanese Bonzai trees in green pots. 7.6 cm x 15.5 cm, 14.6 cm x 12 cm.

6. Two cards. One has a small rose festoon around an initial over greeting and name and address of sender, on a white folder; the other has a butterfly and flowers on embossed white paper. 12.5 cm x 18.6 cm, 8.1 cm x 14.2 cm.

7. Missing, probably a large calendar judging by the price of £2 per dozen.

8. Two cards, one with a print of sailing ships on dark grey mount, another a girl's portrait on brown mount. 11.8 cm x 16 cm, 12 cm x 15.2 cm.

9. Two cards. One has a pen and ink rural scene over greetings of personal details, on a white folder; the other has the same coaching inn picture as no. 2, this time in colour, on a white folder. 12.5 cm x 18.6 cm, 9.2 cm x 15.5 cm.

10. Two cards with small motifs over greetings on plain white paper, one a line design with conventional rose festoon around a garden with sundial, the other a pen and ink drawing of a rustic scene. 9.7 cm x 15 cm, 9.1 cm x 15 cm.

11. Two cards, one a photograph of a river, the other a sepia drawing of Regency ladies skating, signed Kingsley. 15.3 cm x 11.3 cm, 13.5 cm x 10.2 cm.

12. One card (one removed), a hydrangea in a blue pot on plain white card. 10.1 cm x 15.4 cm.

13. Two cards. One has a print of a rural scene mounted on grey paper, the other a drawing of a lighted lamp with appropriate verse below. 15.6 cm x 11.8 cm, 8.4 cm x 13.8 cm.

14. Two cards with prints of a windmill or a lady with a bandbox waiting outside an inn, mounted on brown or grey paper. 13.5 cm x 18.5 cm, 11.8 cm x 15.4 cm.

15. Three cards, one reproducing the "Laughing Cavalier" in black and white. The other two are similar in style, one showing birds taking letters from one side of the globe to the other, the second with two fireside pictures. 7.7 cm x 9.8 cm, 11.3 cm x 9 cm.

16. Two cards with prints of Elizabethan and Georgian scenes on plain white paper. 8.7 cm x 14.1 cm, 12.6 cm x 18.4 cm.

17. Two cards, one with a booklet calendar, the other with a black and white sketch of an old inn yard, both on plain white paper. 8 cm x 14 cm, 11.1 cm x 14.5 cm.

18. Three cards, one with a scroll bearing Christmas greetings, another with an aeroplane, the third with "Best Wishes" bordered by a small rose garland. Sizes up to 13.8 cm x 9.5 cm.

19. Two cards, one with a coloured line drawing of a maiden in Victorian dress, the other with a print of a mother and baby beneath a garland of roses. 11.5 cm x 15.2 cm, 9.6 cm x 15.2 cm.

20. A card with a black and white picture or photograph of seven dogs on a church pew. 18.7 cm x 13.8 cm.

21. Two cards, one single with a small wisteria motif over greeting and personal details, the other a folder with a small picture of sailing ships printed in blue. 15.3 cm x 12 cm, 8.2 cm x 14.7 cm.

22/23. Four cards, three with greetings in small motifs on pale blue or white paper, the other a vase with forsythia on black background. Sizes up to 10 cm x 14.5 cm.

24. Three cards, one a stage coach, another a Georgian family walking in winter, the third with a small ivy wreath around a gilt initial on a white card with blue shading. 11.3 cm x 9 cm, 12.5 cm x 10.1 cm, 8.3 cm x 13.2 cm.

25. Three cards, two girls with muffs in a winter landscape, a fan with violets, and a small decorative design of roses in a hanging basket. 14.5 cm x 12 cm, 11.5 cm x 7 cm, 8.6 cm x 14.2 cm.

26. Two cards, a coloured line drawing of a Georgian gentleman writing, and a cat and a dog eating from the same plate. 8.9 cm x 13.9 cm, 15.4 cm x 11.7 cm.

27. Two cards, a blue vase with carnations, and a plain card with verse, greeting and personal details only. 8 cm x 14 cm, 14.7 cm x 11.7 cm.

28. Another similar plain card with different verse. 14.7 cm x 11.5 cm.

29. Missing - probably a calendar, priced at £2 per dozen removed by former owner.

## VOLUME 272:
## 20TH CENTURY CHRISTMAS AND NEW YEAR POSTCARDS

**These cards were published before the First World War and nearly all were made in Germany. A few come from firms active in Victorian times, some are American and a number with English captions have "postcard" printed on the back in several European languages. They all measure about 14 cm x 9 cm and many are heavily embossed and tinselled, obviously made to catch the eye. The dates on the postmarks are given where present and a few**

**have a decorative date worked into the design. It is interesting to note in the light of present day postal procedures the halfpenny stamp, one seventy-second part of the 15 pence of today, and the postmark which is often dated December 24th.**

1/3. Nine cards. Four have embossed flowers and gilded greetings on a brown background. Five are from Stewart & Wolff, all with silver borders; two have birds and holly, series 606, another has dogs, series 633, one has children, series 685, and the fifth has a river scene framed in holly, series 654.

4/5. Six cards on silver backgrounds from Stewart & Wolff. Four show children in winter outdoor pursuits, series 628, one has a winter scene framed in holly, series 657, the sixth postmarked 1910 has girls in Japanese dress blowing bubbles, series 405.

6. Three cards, Stewart & Wolff. One has birds and holly, series 466, another a pig dressed as a country gentleman, series 624. The third, signed Ellen H Clapsaddle and postmarked 1906, has a red-robed Father Christmas speaking on the telephone to an expectant small girl.

7. Three novelty cards. Two are from Woolstone Bros, "Milton Mechanical" series, with pull out flaps altering the greeting from "Xmas Joy" to "Be Yours"; one has a tinselled basket of violets, no. 0521, the other dated 1911 has holly and a floral bell, no. 055. The third card has a tinselled picture of a huntsman framed in a horn and is marked "Penmenmawr".

8/9. Six unmarked cards, probably foreign origin with English captions and "Postcard" on reverse in 17 European languages, with various subjects - children, dogs, holly, a market and violets with gilt date 1907.

10/11. Six similar cards with children, angels, a Christmas tree, holly and a family scene.

12. Three cards with greetings in French, one dated 1902-1903 showing the Old and New Years as old woman and child, another a tinselled card with flowers and birds, the third with white doves on holly.

13. Three cards, two tinselled with forget-me-nots and clasped hands or angels and bells. The third has a scrap with flowers and a hand holding a pen mounted on celluloid.

14/15. Three cards, two with velvet leaves or holly mounted on embossed background, the third with a black velvet pig on a background with shamrock.

16. Three cards with silk roses set in an embossed background of doves and forget-me-nots.

*Numbers 17-33 are all marked "Popular Series".*

17/18. Five cards with country scenes and embossed flowers in silver borders, no. 163.

19. Three cards, two similar to above no. 151, the third with poppies and daisies on silver background, no. 136.

20. Three tinselled cards with holly decorating a hearth with hanging kettle or an outdoor scene, no. 315.

21. Three fanciful tinselled cards with forget-me-nots, pansies, violets and snowdrops decorating an engine, an anchor and a bell, no. 455.

22/23. Three tinselled cards with angels ringing bells, no. 597.

24/25. Four tinselled cards with wreaths of flowers and small children delivering letters, no. 600.

26/27. Four embossed cards with birds and flowers on scenic backgounds, no. 608.

28/29. Six cards. Four are series 614 showing angels decorating Christmas trees; one has a winter scene with holly, no. 770, the sixth has tinselled flowers and "Greetings from London", no. 415.

30. Three tinselled cards with flower decorated fans, no. 744.

31. Three cards, two with children playing no. 788, the third showing father and children with a Christmas tree, no. 904 dated 1906.

32/33. Four fanciful tinselled cards showing a young lady driving a flower-decked motor car with the help of a small Cupid, no. 615.

*Numbers 34-37 were published by Misch & Co.*

34. Three cards. Two have 1907 and 1908 worked into the designs of four-leaved shamrock and tinselled roses, nos. 796, 979, and the third postmarked 1911 has a red-robed Father Christmas sitting on top of a globe, no. 796.

35. Three cards. Two from series 955 have winter scenes with holly or fir, and the third has Father Christmas in a motor car laden with holly, no. 1386.

36. Two cards with winged angels in a starry sky, no. 988.

37. Three cards, Father Christmas lighting a candle on a tree no. 318, an Easter card with flowers on a cross no. 423 dated 1909 and a winter scene framed in holly, no. 1797 dated 1910.

272.43

*Numbers 38-46 were published by BB London.*

38/39. Four cards, three with religious scenes on a gold and silver background, dated 1907, 1908, 1911, the fourth showing a handclasp under the verse "I value no gift that good fortune may send Like the grip of the hand of a dear true friend", dated 1908.

40/41. Five miscellaneous cards with cats, holly, flowers, a Scottish girl with plaid and heather, and a dog reading a letter, nos. A33, X253, E25, X301, X58.

42/43. Six cards. Three from series S3 have a red-robed Father Christmas (one in a motor car) on a gold and silver background, two similar cards series S4 have robins, and the sixth has a Father Christmas head framed in holly, no. 171.

44. Three cards, two with winter scenes, one with holly and a clock, two dated 1914, nos. E339, X31, X350.

45. Three cards, one with a Canadian scene no. X1104, two with aeroplanes flying over a map of the world decked with holly, dated 1911, no. X14.

46. Two cards dated 1909, a winter scene with holly in purple and gilt, no. 177, and a boy in pierrot costume, no. 110.

47. Three cards with Father Christmas in red robe delivering presents to small girls, marked M S B with trademark E in a circle.

48. Three cards, one from H V & Co, no. EC1392 dated 1910 with bells and holly round a winter scene, and two marked Shamrock with Father Christmas in a brown robe, dated 1910, no. 4069.

49. Three cards. One is from Valentine, with Father Christmas on a broomstick, dated 1903, no. 5905. Two are from Artotype and have robins on holly branches, dated 1907.

50/53. Seven cards published by Nister. Four have holly decorating pictures of children, dogs, cats and the cow that jumped over the moon, dated from 1905 to 1909, three numbered 544, 222, 473. One has angels, no. 828 dated 1905 another children singing carols, no. 233 dated 1906 and the seventh has a church with a Christmas verse.

*Numbers 54-65 were published by Wildt and Kray.*

54/55. Six cards. Two have tinselled holly around a winter scene in a holly leaf vignette, another has Father Christmas on a sleigh, another two children exploring their Christmas stockings. Two have embossed birds and holly on a silver background, dated 1906, 1908.

56. Three cards with silver backgrounds and holly, one with Father Christmas in a blue robe, one with angels ringing bells, the third with a swallow and a winter scene, nos. 961 dated 1907, 847, 960.

57. Three cards, a winter scene with holly in a black border, no. 1635, and two humorous cards, one with walking pots and pans, the other with holly and mistletoe, nos. 2779, 3114, dated 1913, 1914.

58. Three cards. Two are tinselled, with flower decorated camera or balloon, nos. 850, 1103. The third has a leaflet shaped like a bell with a verse by H M Burnside inside, mounted on a holly background, no. 1901.

59. Three cards, one with acorns and winter scene, one with holly around a gilded bell, the third with robins dated 1914. Nos. 2858, 3089, 3096.

60. Three cards. One by Ellen H Clapsaddle has two children looking at a picture book, no. 3081 and another shows two children with their Christmas stocking, no. 2077. The third card, no. 1699, has a humorous coat-of-arms made up of Mother Goose, crackers, a Christmas pudding and a turkey, with holly and mistletoe.

61. Three cards, one a banjo decorated with forget-me-nots, no. 1147. The other two dated 1908 have ships and sea views with appropriate verses, no. 1190.

62/63. Six cards, three with scenes in vignettes, no. 849 dated 1907, no. 2352, no. 2132 dated 1911. Another has a cart of holly dated 1914, no. 1468, a fifth a vase of flowers dated 1915, no. 1532, and the sixth card has a plum pudding with a hungry teddy bear, series 1915.

64/65. Six cards, four with scenes, nos. 1476, 1480, 1965, 4906, one with a horse-drawn sleigh, the sixth with birds and a nesting box, nos. 1912, 721.

66/67. Six cards from the Philco Publishing Co. Two have angels with holly, series X 903, 14426, and another has children and holly no. 1643. A card with a poor girl selling violets to a well-dressed lady, no. 2331F, was dated 1910 and another with a winter scene, no. X911 was dated 1912. The sixth card has a comic picture of a doctor and patient, no. 4011 dated 1906.

68. Two cards from S Hildesheimer, birds on a branch no. 5511 and a small girl on a drawing room chair, no. 5314.

69. One card from E A Schwerdtfeger, a winter scene in a small vignette on a dark green background with holly and mistletoe, dated 1912.

70/71. Six cards from E A Schwerdtfeger. Two have Father Christmas in a red robe, another an angel with a Christmas tree. Two show gramophones of the period covered in roses or violets, dated 1910, and the sixth is a photograph of roses.

72. Two cards. One from Eustace Watkins dated 1909 shows a tired Santa Claus taking a rest in a nursery, no. 1003; the other from W S Bradford, shows a hand holding a tinselled bunch of flowers, dated 1906.

73. Two cards. One from Schaefer and Scheibe has an angel and holly no. 2008, the other marked R K & Co has holly framing a winter scene.

74/75. Six cards. Two with Father Christmas at a window and a small girl with a horseshoe are from Julius Bendix, nos. 804, 871. Two are from the Novelty P C Co, Liverpool and have angels and dwarfs outlined with silver, and the remaining two are from E S, London, one with a girl sitting on a letter H, the other with a tinselled bicycle covered in flowers dated 1906.

76/77. Five cards from P F with English captions (probably foreign as "postcard" appears on reverse in 17 different languages). Two have scenes in vignettes, nos. 6150, 6985, one a sunset view of a snowbound schloss, no. 6144 dated 1906. Another has an embossed pansy, no. 7404 and the fifth Santa Claus with parents and baby, no. 6481 dated 1906.

78/79. Six cards by Giesen Bros, London, marked "made in Austria". Three have gilded angels, another a moonlit church, nos. A540, A547 (dated 1909) A543, G329 (dated 1906). Another has holly on a silver background, no. X93, and the sixth has a Christmas tree in a grey and green border, no. G129.

*Numbers 80-91 were published by Davidson Bros.*

80/81. Six cards with scenes in vignettes in silver borders with holly, series 84 nos. 1, 2, 3, series 87 nos. 1, 2, 3.

82/83. Six cards with silver backgrounds. Three show cottages by a river with illuminated greeting in a scroll with holly, mistletoe, or ivy, series 81 nos. 1, 2, 3. Three others have scenes in vignettes with sprays of holly or heather, nos. 88, 3013 dated 1909, 3020.

84. Three cards with silver borders, sunset or moonlight scenes with capital letters to greetings drawn in embossed holly wreaths, series 83.

85. Three cards with silver borders, one with robins and a winter scene marked 1909, no. 1404, another with holly and a moonlit cottage, marked 1909 no. 1412, a third with greeting written in forget-me-nots, no. 86, dated 1911. (These two cards with printed dates give useful clues to number sequence).

86/87. Three cards, robins perching on a greeting spelt in holly, a heart with forget-me-not border dated 1910, no. 109X, and a "Humorous Proverb" with man facing a bulldog barring the way to his fair lady.

88/89. Two embossed cards with silver backgrounds showing motor cars carrying robins and blue tits perched on holly and mistletoe, one dated 1908. Series 75 nos. 1 and 2.

90/91. Six cards with photographs of children and Father Christmas on Christmas Eve and Christmas morning. These are marked "printed in England" unlike those before and have no postmark, but could be pre 1914. The photographs are numbered 3529-3534.

92. Three cards, one with bells and holly from Woolstone Bros, dated 1911, two with scenes dated 1913 from Rotary Photo and Minton & Shore.

93. Three cards, one marked with monogram M A B showing a foreign church and holly spray, another with children and a Christmas tree, the third with a Christmas street scene.

94/95. Two humorous cards from Bamforth, a photograph of a man by an empty cottage grate, and a band playing in the snow with angry householders at their windows.

96/97. Six miscellaneous crudely designed cards embossed with flowers or holly, dated 1905-1908.

98/99.  Six miscellaneous cards, two with holly, four with flowers, dated 1904-1908.

100/101. Six miscellaneous cards, three with children, one with pierrot, one with a goose girl and a mail coach, the sixth a lady playing a guitar, dated 1904-1908.

*Numbers 102-111 were for American or Canadian use, with stamp price quoted in cents, but some were marked "made in Germany", with others from American sources.*

102/103 Six cards, three with scenes in vignettes and holly, one with a robin and holly, one with holly sprays dated 1906 and one marked John Winsch 1910 showing an elegant lady.

104. Three cards, one with holly border, another with a fir branch on a silver background dated 1900, the third with poinsettias on moiré silk.

105. Three cards with holly sprays and scenes in vignettes, one marked E Nash 1910.

106. Three cards, Father Christmas, a bell and holly, and a slipper filled with roses with a Jewish greeting.

107. Three cards from S P C Co, dated 1905, showing men and women in humorous domestic situations.

108/109. Six cards, including one with jewelled ivy leaves marked John Winsch 1913 and another with holly and a winter scene from Whitney, Worcester, Mass. Two dated 1906 and 1907 are imitation cheques, one from the Syndicate Publishing Co., Chicago, and two have scenes with holly.

110/111. Six cards. Four have embossed pictures of Father Christmas and two from Canada have a robin or violets.

112/113. Six cards, dated 1907. One has gilded bells and holly, another a small girl holding a fir branch in a border of forget-me-nots with 1907 outlined in flowers. Four from a set have curious designs of a maiden in continental costume with baskets of babies.

114/115. Six cards dated from 1907-1912. Two have winter scenes and holly sprays, one has robins and holly, and three have children, one with Father Christmas.

116/117. Six cards dated 1910, 1911. Two have Cupids with hearts, one has angels watching over a village, another has angels with a mother and baby, the fifth has

**272.60**

robins, and the sixth a ship festooned wtih violets and forget-me-nots.

118/119. Four cards dated 1912. Two have the date marked in flowers, one has an angel with a holly spray, the fourth a nativity scene with Dutch stamp.

120/121. Five cards. Two are from Beagles, one a tinselled picture of St Pauls, the other a cats' Christmas party dated 1906 with scores of cats in human apparel. Two are from the Carlton Publishing Co, one a dog in a hat, the other a lady in fur trimmed coat. The fifth card shows boys snowballing, from a photograph, dated 1908.

122. Three cards dated 1913, two with Father Christmas and gilt decoration, one with two children carrying the date outlined in fir branches.

123. Three cards, one with two children snowballing, and two from a set with birds and holly on a scroll with Christmas verse below.

124/125. Five cards, one with Father Christmas, two with children, one with robins in a holly border, and one with an angel flying over a village.

126. Three cards with tinselled flowers, two marked with monogram P F B, one from Meissner and Buch.

127. Two humorous cards with snowmen, one dated 1913.

128/129. Six cards, one with a winter scene, another of Lincoln Cathedral's nave. Four from one set have winter scenes and holly set in gilded borders with illuminated greetings.

130/131. Seven cards, Popular Series, six from a set no 828, one no 3202, all showing

children with dogs, cats, or dolls, taken from coloured photographs, printed in Saxony.

132/133. Five cards, two with scenes in vignettes, one with an angel, another a small girl with hoops. The fifth card has a caravan in a holly-decked horseshoe with a postmark 1915 but was marked "printed in Germany".

134/135. Four cards, one with cats from the "Wrenck Series" dated 1906, two with children. The fourth card has Father Christmas with two children and a German greeting, dated 1905.

136. Two cards from Max Ettlinger, one dated 1908, a lady with white muff, the other a girl in party dress.

## VOLUME 273: BIRTHDAY AND EASTER POSTCARDS, 1900-1914

*Numbers 1-23 have birthday greetings, most printed in Germany.*

1. Four cards with spring flowers or roses, Misch & Co, nos. 1615 dated 1908, 1631, 1633, 1822.

2. Four cards, published by Meissner and Buch, pictures in vignettes on shaded grey background, dated 1909-1910, nos. 1555, 1557, 1569.

3. Two cards, Wildt & Kray, flowers on silver background, dated 1906.

4. Three cards, Philco, a garland of flowers round a slipper, pierrot and pierette, a punt with man and woman on a moonlit river, nos. 2118A, 2347B, 2264E dated 1909.

5. Three cards, Philco, with scenes in vignettes on coloured backgrounds, nos. 2214F dated 1908, 2245A and C.

6. Three cards, H Vertigern & Co, flowers probably from photographs, nos. 6079, 5821, 5901 dated 1908.

7. Three cards, E A Schwerdtfeger, a kitten, a basket of forget-me-nots, and a boy with flowers, two numbered 940, 1876.

8. Four cards, Davidson Bros, printed in England, flowers, dogs, kittens, from photographs, dated 1909-1911.

9. Three cards, Aristophat Co, children with flowers, from photographs, printed in France, one dated 1908.

10. Three cards, Rotary, Photo, one with the letters of "Birthday" filled with faces, and two with country scenes, two dated 1909, 1912.

11. Three cards with flowers from photographs, two from Rotary, one from the Rapid Photo Co, dated 1907.

12/13. Six cards, two from Solomon Bros, with scenes in vignettes and flowers dated 1911, 1914, two from photographs with flowers and scenes indifferently coloured from A & G Taylor, one dated 1907, and two from Beagles with scenes in vignettes dated 1909, 1910.

14. Three cards with flowers, two from P F B with lilies of the valley or tinselled roses, one W S series with a hand holding tinselled pansies.

15. One card, Max Ettlinger & Co, a riverside scene on a green background with embossed roses and gilt decoration, dated 1908.

16. Three cards marked G D & D, G G M B, B V & Co (dated 1909) the first two showing clasped hands with floral decor, the other a gold and silver ship against a sunset.

17. Three cards with children, one on a tree branch, two with forget-me-nots or shamrock, all with gilded outlines and decoration, one dated 1908.

18/19. Five cards, two with tinselled flowers, one with doves and roses, two with applied velvet rose or ivy leaves.

20/21. Five cards wth scenes from photographs in vignettes, four with flowers in border, two dated 1911, 1912.

22/23. Six miscellaneous cards with flowers, one with a swallow, another with a scene in vignette, dated from 1906-1914.

*Numbers 24-36 have Easter greetings.*

24/26. Seven cards from Wildt & Kray, dated from 1908-1914. Three have crosses with flowers, one has chickens and lilac, another has lilies, and two have children with chicks.

27. Two cards, Alfred Stiebel, with the same design of two girls holding an outsize Easter egg, but with different colouring and greeting, no. Alpha 861.

28/29. Three cards from Philco. Two have fanciful scenes of children in an egg chariot drawn by cocks or goats, no. 2275 B & D. The third has ladies apparently in a large egg on a carriage pulled by rabbits, an interesting example of a trick photograph, no. 6016c dated 1906.

30. Two cards, E A Schwerdtfeger & Co. One has rabbits with coloured eggs, the other a girl with a basket of eggs, dated 1914.

31. Two cards, one from B G Co with children on a large egg and small chicks, the other with two chicks and a basket of coloured eggs from M Ettlinger, no. 4776, both dated 1906.

32. Two cards. One from Misch & Co shows a satin egg tied with ribbon, dated 1908. (These eggs were filled with sweets or chocolates). The other, from S Langsdorff & Co, New York, has a small girl with a large egg in an inset dress of real silk.

33. Two cards, one with a floral cross from Lonsdale and Bartholomew, Accrington, the other with daisies on a silver background from Stewart & Wolff, dated 1905.

34/35. Four cards. One has tinselled chicks and forget-me-nots in a top-hat. Two have chicks as gipsies, living in a hut made out of an egg shell, and the fourth has a gilded egg with flowers. The last three have "postcard" on reverse in a number of foreign languages and were probably made abroad.

36. A well-designed card with flowers on a silver cross on a patterned background.

## VOLUME 274:
## CARDS OF THE FIRST WORLD WAR, A SMALL SELECTION

**These are of two kinds, cards sent by soldiers from the fighting zones and those from the folks at home. Many of the regimental cards bear lists of the battles fought; some are humorous, some are poignant reminders of the tribulations suffered by soldiers and sailors and of the devastation in France. The silk embroidered cards in number 25 are examples of a very large production, including woven cards and printed silk cards, which were sent mainly as souvenirs from the forces to their friends and relations.**

*Numbers 1-6 were sent by people at home.*

1. Six folder cards with patriotic motifs of flags, soldiers and sailors, one from Philco, four dated 1914.
Sizes up to 11.7 cm x 9.4 cm.

2. Two folder cards with flags. One was dated 1914, printed with the name of the sender and has a long patriotic poem by I E Fitzgerald. The other has an attached silk Royal Navy flag.
12.5 cm x 15.5 cm, 12 cm x 15.3 cm.

3. Two folder cards, one dated Christmas 1916 with printed greetings inside from Derbyshire and Nottinghamshire public figures. The other was from the Lord Mayor of Birmingham, dated December 1915. The greetings imply that these were meant to be sent to the fighting forces.
11.5 cm x 15.5 cm, 10.1 cm x 13 cm.

4. Four folder cards. Two have flags, one from Canada 1914, the other 1918 celebrating victory. The third card has soldiers as ancient Egyptians and was sent by the congregation of St Andrew's Church, Alexandria, Egypt. The fourth card is in memory of the execution of Edith Cavell in 1915 and the greeting on the cover is "May Christ be with you this sad Christmastide", signed Geo G Whitney.
11.5 cm x 8 cm up to 9 cm x 14 cm.

5. Three cards. Two are folders showing cheerful soldiers, from the Golden Series and Regent Series; the third is a postcard from J Beagles & Co, no. 118B, with flags guarded by two British bulldogs and a patriotic verse.
Sizes up to 15.3 cm x 10.3 cm.

6. A folder card from the British Red Cross Society and Order of St John, Christmas 1918, with a heraldic border and flags outside and Father Christmas pictures with soldiers and ships and a verse ending "Please God, I'll bring Peace next year". This must have been designed before the Armistice on November 11th.

*Numbers 7-24 were for the use of servicemen.*

7. Three cards. Two are folders and have flags and regimental insignia marked British Expeditionary Forces in France, decorated with holly or mistletoe and signed J Prudhomme. The third is a single card marked Dardanelles Xmas 1915, with well printed appropriate motifs and coat-of-arms of the Printing Section, Royal Engineers.
9.5 cm x 12.2 cm, 9.7 cm x 14.1 cm.

8. Two monochrome folder cards, one "With Good Wishes from General Mitford and the Head Quarters 72nd Infrantry Brigade, Christmas 1915", the other from the 2nd Indian Cavalry Amm. Park, In the Field, Xmas 1915.
9.7 cm x 14.1 cm, 12.3 cm x 9 cm.

9. A folder card with a woodcut of a country scene, marked "From the Artists, France 1916".

10. Two cards showing the real side of war. One depicts the N E corner of Delville Wood, captured 27th August 1916, with the initials of the various corps involved, published by R Tuck. The other signed J P Beadle, with Christmas greetings from the 7th Division, 1916, shows a soldier in a trench by a brazier dreaming of his homecoming.
13.7 cm x 9.8 cm, 15.3 cm x 10 cm.

11. Two folder cards, pen and ink. One has a soldier in the field, thinking of home, from the 38th Welsh Division, 1917, the other has the insignia of the London Rifle Brigade with pictures of recent battles in vignettes, sent Christmas 1916.
12.5 cm x 16 cm, 8.8 cm x 14 cm.

12. Two cards, a folder from the 106th Field Company with appropriate tools of the trade, 1917, and a single card with a battle scene in red and black from the 41st Division, Christmas 1917, signed G Thompson.
12.5 cm x 16.6 cm, 11.1 cm x 16 cm.

13. Two folder cards. One signed L Ravenhill from the 20th Light Division, New Year 1917, has a comic picture "A few days rest in billets" outside and a sketch of a wounded soldier with a German helmet inside. The other has an elaborate pen and ink design, from the Second Army School of Musketry, Christmas 1917.
10.6 cm x 14 cm, 11.5 cm x 15.2 cm.

14. Three folder cards with regimental insignia, all 1917, from the Royal Regiment of Ireland, the 147th Trench Mortar Battery, and the Third Battalion S Lancs, Egypt. Sizes up to 9.5 cm x 11.8 cm.

15. Three folder cards with monochrome designs, two dated 1917 from the 61st Division and the Royal Engineers. The third card has the insignia of the Royal Engineers Inland Water Transport and two ships marked AS98, A105, and was signed by D McC Brown, 1918.
Sizes up to 10 cm x 14 cm.

16. Two cards. One Christmas 1917 from the 24th Division has a humorous pen and ink sketch of England and France pulling out the feather of the German Eagle, with America in the background. The other signed Leonard Kirley marked T M B s, 143, 144, 145, Italy 1918, shows a cheerful soldier and Italian scenes.
11.3 cm x 17.5 cm, 11 cm x 16.5 cm.

17. Four cards. Two are folders, one with the badge of the Royal Inniskilling Fusiliers, another from the Royal Navy. The third from the 15th Scottish Division shows a resigned Highlander leaning against a huge thistle "Still Here", signed Geo M Ward 1917. The fourth from the

B E F 1919, has various scenes from France, Gallipoli, Egypt, and Palestine, and Highland soldiers within, probably a New Year card for a Scottish division.
Sizes up to 10.4 cm x 15 cm.

18. Two folder cards, one 1917-18 with a wreath bound with ribbon bearing the names of battles and a black spade token mark. The other, printed by G Falkner & Sons, Manchester, has a picture of the trenches with a bomb bursting to show Christmas fare, "An Unexpected Burst of Greetings from the 46 Div".
10.2 cm x 15.5 cm, 9.9 cm x 15.4 cm.

19. Two folder cards, one 1917 from the East Yorkshires showing a vanquished enemy, the other 1918 from the 56th London with a Union Jack on a wreath of holly and laurel.
10.9 cm x 13.8 cm, 14 cm x 11.5 cm.

20. Two folder cards, one 1918 from the Royal Berks Regiment with a picture of soldiers in Italy, the other a French card with English greeting and calendar for 1918 sent as a souvenir.
11.4 cm x 13.9 cm, 12.4 cm x 9.4 cm.

21. Two folder cards with pen and ink sketches on the cover. One from the 30th Division has pictures of battlefields inside, and the other with a sketch of the ruined Cloth Hall at Ypres in 1918 was from the 33rd Division.
14.5 cm x 16.8 cm, 18.2 cm x 12 cm.

22. Three folder cards, all 1918. One was from the 2nd Australian Tunnelling Company with appropriate border decoration; another from the 212th Field Company, R E, shows a bridge being repaired and the third from the 41st Division, published by Raphael Tuck, has wartime scenes inside.
Sizes up to 10.4 cm x 16.6 cm.

23. Four folder cards dated from 1916-1918. Two were from the 8th B Manchester Regiment (The Ardwicks) with crest on the front, one was from the B E F, Italy, the fourth has the Welsh National Anthem and the Welsh Dragon, B E F.
Sizes up to 8.7 cm x 12.5 cm.

24. Four cards, 1918. Two were from the 8th Field Survey Co, R E, one with a winged victory figure in a Macedonian scene, the other with greetings from the Salonika Army. The third has a picture of the Balkans by G D Armour, marked Survey Co R E, B S F no 364, and the fourth is a folder from the 25th Division.
All approximately 9 cm x 14 cm.

25. Three hand embroidered silk cards probably made in France, all with Christmas greetings. One is in envelope form with a small card inside, and embroidered French and English flags with holly sprays. Another has a blue bird

carrying holly and mistletoe, and the third has a church. These cards were made in large quantities for the English troops in France. 14 cm x 9 cm, 9 cm x 14 cm.

# A BRIEF NOTE ON ARTISTS, PUBLISHERS, WRITERS

Many designers of greeting cards were established book illustrators, and some, like J C Horsley and W M Egley of the "first" two Christmas cards, were artists of national repute. Charles Bennett, a regular contributor to Punch, did two sets of cards for Goodall in 1865 and 1866. He died in 1867 leaving his family destitute, but Punch staged a benefit night for them in Manchester supervised by Sir Arthur Sullivan. A scrapbook in Manchester City Art Gallery compiled by Birket Foster, who also designed some Christmas cards, contains some amusing sketches by Bennett. Other early cards, most in humorous vein, were designed by Luke Limner (John Leighton), Alfred Crowquill (the Brothers Forrester), Robert Dudley, and Ernest Griset, all book illustrators of note.

Royal Academicians included J Moyr Smith and H Stacy Marks, whose sets for Marcus Ward are sought by collectors. Cards from E J Poynter, W F Yeames, Marcus Stone and many others appeared in Tuck's Royal Academy Series, but these, although they raised the reputation of Christmas card art, were not received with much enthusiasm. The set of three angels' heads by Rebecca Coleman, which critics said had broken the record for popular success, quite outdid those by James Sant, RA. Her brother W S Coleman, a noted naturalist and illustrator of bird and animal books, designed cards for De La Rue with the half-clad youthful beauties that prompted Punch's comment that they should not be out at Christmas.

Marcus Ward published cards by Walter Crane and Kate Greenaway, as well as a number of books illustrated by them, but Kate left this firm in 1877 though her designs were used by Marcus Ward for many years afterwards, often with small alterations and different backgrounds. Walter's brother, Thomas Crane, was the Artistic Director for Marcus Ward, and his style is evident in many of the unsigned floral and illuminated designs from this firm.

The prizewinners in the competitions organised in 1881 and 1882 included Alice Squire, H M Bennett, E A Lemann, J M Dealy, Linnie Watt, Emily Barnard, Eleanor Manly, and Alice Havers - all women. Many of these artists produced pictures of charming idealised children which accorded with the sentimental Victorian view of Christmas. A new name in Christmas card literature appears here in Volume 147 with cards by Felix Dussert for Augustus Thierry, showing children and young folk in bright colours of blue, russet, green and gold. These are not marked but have been positively identified from Stationers' Hall records.

Portraits of birds were provided by Harry Bright, Harrison Weir and Hector Giacomelli with birds and animals in comic situations from Robert Dudley, H H Couldery, S T

Dadd and A M Lockley. Cards by Beatrix Potter appeared about 1890; a fine collection of these is held by The National Trust in Cumbria, from which the few examples here were identified.

Flower illustration, so important as an accomplishment for the Victorian young lady, appeared on all kinds of greeting cards, sometimes inappropriately with roses in full bloom at Christmas. Artists included many women, Emily Whymper, Marian Chase and Kate Sadler perhaps the most prolific. The painter W J Muckley, who worked in Manchester and Wolverhampton, designed many fine cards for Albert Hildesheimer and Hildesheimer and Faulkner as well as glass decoration for the firm of Richardsons.

Topical cards and humour came from Alfred Gray, W G Baxter, the Ludovicis, R F McIntyre, and Harry Payne. Town and country scenes were contributed by A Glendenning RBA, Albert Bowers, and A F Lydon, with cathedrals from F Corbyn Price and Palestine pictures by Louisa F Bewlay RBA. Families appear, with two Maguires, three Woodward sisters, three Colemans, two Cranes, three Ludovicis, and several Bowers, Sadlers, Vernons who may have been related, as well as husband and wife teams - the Duffields, Mr & Mrs Fred Morgan (Alice Havers), and others.

The artists mentioned above and many more made considerable contributions to the improvement in the standards of popular art. More research is needed in the attribution of unsigned designs, but caution should be used when considering style alone without factual evidence.

Publishers have already been mentioned in the foreword but a brief resume of the more important names and development might be helpful. By the 1860's the commercial possibilities of the Christmas card trade had appeared and firms already in the printing trade such as Goodall, De La Rue, and the early valentine makers Sulman, Canton, Wood, Windsor, J Mansell, Rimmel were entering the market. These were soon joined by Marcus Ward and Raphael Tuck; Louis Prang in USA diverted his considerable colour printing output to greeting cards in the early 1870's, and these found a market in Britain through the firm of Ackermann, already noted for sporting prints.

Many firms originated in Germany. The Hildesheimers set up business in Manchester, and Wolff Hagelberg supplied cards in the 1870's to Marcus Ward and S Hildesheimer. Bernhard Ollendorff and Wirth Bros. & Owen made cards with silk insets, and Thomas Stevens and Bollans used their machine made designs on greetings cards as well as for bookmarks and silk pictures. Fine lace-edged cards, decorated with silk and mother-of-pearl, were imported from French firms, including Aubry.

Eyre and Spottiswoode and Castell Bros kept up the high artistic standards fostered by Marcus Ward, and firms including Charles Caswell, H Rothe, Campbell and Tudhope catered for the growing demand encouraged by the Sunday School movement for cards and texts with distinct religious flavour. William Dickes, an early Baxter licensee, had produced cards for the Religious Tract Society, Sunday School Union, Society for the Promotion of Christian Knowledge etc, from the 1860's, and Riddle and Couchman printed cards for these bodies.

Alfred Gray published and designed political and topical cartoons in the 1880's, and Angus Thomas was a popular supplier of comic cards with punning humour. By 1900 most of the earlier firms had been taken over or gone out of business, with many new names catering for the early 20th century postcard trade; up to the First World War printing was done mostly in Germany. Many of the early greeting card designs were used for 20th century postcards, and some were probably pirated by firms in USA, notably designs by Kate Greenaway and W S Coleman (see Volume 51).

Greeting cards were prized for the messages or "sentiments" as well as for their pictorial content. The first cards had only a brief seasonal greeting, but by 1870 this was extended to verses. Texts from the Bible of course appeared, and extracts from established writers and the classics were often used; about 30 names have been noted in this collection with Shakespeare, Tennyson, Burns, Wordsworth and Shelley most often quoted. These are not listed in the appendix of writers, with one or two exceptions. Frances Ridley Havergal was a celebrated writer of religious verse, and her poems appeared as well as the greetings she wrote specially for cards. S C Hall who wrote verse for Marcus Ward and Eyre and Spottiswoode was well known as the editor of the Book of British Ballads, published by Routledge. Cards in this collection with verses by S K Cowan MA and F R Havergal come from ten different publishers; Helen M Burnside, Astley H Baldwin, Rev Frederick Langbridge, Charlotte Murray, appear with from five to seven different publishers. Other names frequently appearing include Fanny Goddard, Julia Goddard, Eliza Cook, Sarah Doudney, Eden Hooper, Lewis Novra, and a number of clerics including several bishops.

Sentiments of a high poetic standard were not often seen on the cards, but they were written to satisfy popular taste. They ranged from the simple greeting on the early cards to elaborate poems, sometimes in narrative style describing the pictures, with long sentimental poems on the inside folder of the elaborate cards of the '90s contrasting with the punning greetings on the comic cards. Many poems were unsigned, or initialled by writers so far untraced.

Some examples of sentiments are given in the catalogue and a few more typical examples are given here.

Little Robin Redbreast, to the window comes
Seeking warmth and shelter, asking us for crumbs
Shall we not remember all outside our door
Whom the chill December finds hungry, sad and poor.


Ring out the Bells, this music tells
Of joy and hope and home
The Sounds we hear let Fancy bear
To friends, where'er they roam.

Blossoms sweet the message tell
That I love thee, love thee well.

(With puns on the pictures)
The pillar box does more for you
Than any box of pills.

Christmas pleasure may you meet
Unimpeachable and sweet

(In wartime)
Who so worthy of a greeting when old Christmas comes once more
As the lads whose hearts are beating to defend our native shore.

# NOTE ON APPENDICES

Lists of publishers, artists and writers are provided here
instead of the usual alphabetical index. The list of
headings to be found in the Contents should provide
ample material for subject study. While it is appreciated
that it is unorthodox to list names as read rather than with
surname first, the large number of compound names,
monograms, and initial signatures would make the
conventional approach difficult. The present procedure
follows Buday's example in his **History of the Christmas
Card**.

Variations of spelling, title, or location from those given by
Gleeson White or Buday are taken directly from cards in
the collection. Obviously not all the Victorian and early
20th century artists or publishers listed by those
authorities can be found in the collection; conversely some
new names appear here, both in the artists' and publishers'
lists. The references given in those lists are to volumes and
page number; for instance 26.2 means Volume 26 sheet 2,
and 26.2, 3-14 means Volume 26, sheet 2, sheets 3 to 14
inclusive. Where initials appear by evidence of style and
probability to belong to a listed name, they are put with
this name, otherwise untraced initials or monograms are
put under their surname initial after the full names.
Untraced initials of writers are not listed.

# ARTISTS AND DESIGNERS

R J Abraham. 67.5
Adams. 159.12
T H Allchin. 78.1; 88.15; 112.1; 116.6
L J Alloo. 239.17
Will Anderson. 113.23
Emily Andrews. 94.28
Helen C Angell. 35.27; 46.7
G D Armour. 274.24
Harry Arnold. 32.19-23; 33.15-17; 38.25;
40.2; 94.9-15; 148.10-11; 170.23
Susan Annie Ashworth. 100.6
Mabel Lucie Attwell. 267.8
Aubert. Introduction Section 7; 50.11;
53.8
E C A. 70.22
H A. 163.32
L A. 89.14-15
M A. 81.25

E A Bailey. 78.4
Wilfred Ball. 210.2
J Edward Barclay. 116.2
Hannah B Barlow. 37.1-3
Emily Barnard. 68.12-14; 253.24; 267.6
H W Batley. 116.1
Lewis Baume. 267.6
W G Baxter. 173.1, 17-25
J P Beadle. 274.10
Harry Beard. 95.3, 34
Hermann Beck. 135.11
J G F Belbeder. 20.9, 10 (F) 189.23; 201.11
Charles H Bennett. 24.1
Harriet M Bennett. 67.3, 29, 30-38; 189.23
(HMB). 98.24
H Berkely. 108.21
Louisa F Bewley. 98.1-8
M L Bewley. 82.22
H Binbeck. 185.20
G H Birch. 203.1
George Bishop. 94.16
Matilda Maria Blake. 94.31
Alfred Bouchette. 73.2, 9; 91.11
Albert Bowers. 81.1-7; 90.1-3; 113.24;
201.6; 207.1-3, 5, 6, 11, 13-23
Fanny Bowers. 75.9, 10
Georgina Bowers. 39.13-17
S Bowers. 114.20; 114.21; 207.24
Gertrude M Bradley (see Woodward)
Fidelia Bridges (FB). 64.33; 65.16, 18, 19
Harry Bright. 79.7; 90.5; 186.2-10
D McC Brown. 274.15
Gordon Browne. 58.14
H K Browne (Phiz). 64.27; 169.23
Mr Buckley. 18.32
W Burton. 112.15
B. 183.2
A B. 172.11
A W B. 210.21
B B(?) monogram. 220.10-17; 214.15-18
E I B. 97.23
F E B (?). 207.7; 257.8
G B 264.11
M B or B M (monogram). 85.16-31; 87.29,
30; 89.8, 23, 26; 214.19; 251.1; 255.9, 13
P F B. 272.126
S B or B S (monogram). 119.21
W B. 113.22

E Carrière. 31.18; 33.29, 30
Edith Carrington. 96.6, 32; 110.17-19;
255.24

Jessie Chase. 80.24; 100.16
Marian Chase. 96.32; 97.1-3, 18; 98.21, 22;
100.28; 101.1-19; 197.6; 251.15
Charles Chumleigh. 95.29-31
F C Church. 64.20
J S Churchill. 134.29
Ellen H Clapsaddle. 272.60
J Clark. 108.21
W Claudius. 166.5
A M Clausen. 75.13
George Clausen RA. 67.9
G Clements. 208.1
B Coble. 93.17
C C Coleman. 65.29; 66.23
Rebecca Coleman. 55.1-13; 67.7, 8; 94.22,
23; 200.6
William Stephen Coleman. 55.14-34;
59.18, 22, 24, 25; 68.10; 93.24; 164.20;
200.6, 7
Lisbeth B Comins. 64.15, 24
Eliza Ann Cook. 68.33-35; 91.12, 15;
159.15
Horatio H Couldery. 111.15, 16, 18, 19;
180.17, 18; 182.1, 33
Thomas Crane. 30.34; 34.3, 15, 20; 37.3;
38.13, 25; 39.10; 41.4, 6, 9, 10; 46.1-6; 47.9,
14; 48.20, 21; 50.30; 52.17
Walter Crane. 51.23-27; 52.34-41
Helga von Cramm. 40.13-15; Volume 125
(all)
Marian Croft. 67.11, 13
Alfred Crowquill. 24.9, 10
(Pseudonym of Alfred Henry Forrester,
who drew the pictures, and his brother
Charles Robert who perhaps wrote the
verses. This name is variously spelt as
Forrestier, Forester, in reference books)
George Cruikshank Junior. 73.12; 74.15,
16; 90.5
A M C. 76.4
H O C. 79.33
H W C. 186.12, 13
J C (perhaps T C) monogram. 201.25;
222.24
J B C. 174.27
J V F C. 54.36
J W C. 119.37
M C or C M (monogram). 69.15; 71.18, 19
O H C. 210.4
T G C. 182.15
T M C. 251.5
Tr C. 246.14
W F C. 71.14

S T Dadd. 37.14-20
A Daudin. 35.30, 32; 38.4
J Daudin. 35.28, 31
Fanny Elton Davies. 98.30; 100.15
J A Davis. 169.35
Lucien Davis (LD signature). 205.16, 20,
24; 258.1-3, 5, 33
Louis F Day. 48.26
Jane M Dealy. 34.36; 106.8-17; 198.1
W C T Dobson RA RWS. 68.3
Anna Maria Donnelly. 18.30
E A S Douglas. 60.8
Richard Doyle. 31.16
Robert Dudley. 24.5, 11-25, 34, 35; 26.4-6,
11, 13, 14, 23; 27.1-3; 53.22-38; 137.20;
174.2-11; 179.4; 262.10
Mrs M E Duffield. 100.10; 109.12; 115.1;
116.22, 29; 117.8-28; 243.22

William L Duffield. 110.4, 6
E Duncan RWS. 24.26
Cel Dusser. 94.17
Felix Dussert. 69.2; 147 (all); 163.30;
200.9; 210.12
B D. 233.30
C T D. 113.29
F D. 222.28
H D. 134.13
H L D. 252.28
L D (monogram). 263.9
W N D. 82.1

C Eade. 5.18
Louis Edouin (Edwin?) Edouard. 95.27
M Ellen Edwards. 68.21, 22; 108.13; 115.1
William Maw Egley. 1.2
Ellam. 73.24; 91.10; 171.5; 174.25
E J Ellis. 34.25
Rosina Emmet (Emmett?). 64.12
J C Erhard. 1.11
A Erskine. 75.16
R M Erskine. 75.17
Eustace. 172.2
John Eyre. 94.33
G E (see O and G E)
J E or E J (monogram). 87.13; 251.18
J E E (?) (monogram). 135.19
M E (monogram). see E M
S E (monogram). see E S

Edward H Fahey. 53.16; 58.1-15
Robert Faulkner. 108.14, 15
Frank Feller. 110.30, 31
Fred Fitch. 80.36
John Auster Fitzgerald. 94.32
Elizabeth Folkhard. 69.17; 106.19
Edwin Forbes. 1.3
Forrester (see Crowquill)
Myles Birket Foster RWS. 163.1-9
W Gilbert Foster. 68.31; 80.34
M S Fraipunt (?). 208.25
Alfred Fredericks. 63.5
Catherine Frances Frere. 94.18, 19
F L Fuller. 79.19; 91.5
Harry Furniss. 173.25
C D F. 190.27

Thomas Gainsborough RA. 270.2
Edwin Gardener. 94.34
E C Gardner(?). 70.8, 18
Valentine T Garland. 111.13, 14
Arthur J Gaskin. 78.27
Mrs Georgie C Gaskin. 133.15
H Giacomelli. 65.18; 79.8-14
A Glendenning Jr RBA. 113.1
A Gobran. 33.30
Thomas Goodman. 33.6
Maud Goodwin. 175.31
Alfred Gray. 173.2-15
C Green. 107.8
Kate Greenaway. Introduction Sections 4,
6; 51.1-22, 28-48; 52.1-33
References to cards similar to K G etc.
31.16; 33.34; 41.17-19; 42.21-27; 68.29;
106.27; 107.38; 154.33; 155.22-29; 163.12,
13, 28; 167.26; 173.5, 6; 204.3, 7; 267.11
J W Grey. 68.30
Ernest Griset. 54.1-6, 25, 28, 31, 33, 35;
58.11, 12; 74.18; 95.36; 180.13
D Guy. 135.4
C I G. (see W C S and C I G)

G S (not Sadler). 209.29
M S. 180.25
O S. 234.13
W C S & C I G - artists or publisher? 154.6

Margaret Tarrant. 267.8
Percy Tarrant. 34.10; 46, 8-10
K Terrell. 67.6
G Thompson. 274.12
Isa Thompson. 89.16
J K Thompson. 33.10
E G Thomson. 55.35, 36; 60.1-7
Patty Townshend. 34.10; 40.4, 5; 67.4;
106.22; 158.1
William Henry Tuck. 96.14; 99.5
Alice Turner. 100.22
J M W Turner RA. 82.1, 2; 208.1
A T. 180.25; 257.7
H S T. 108.18
L T (monogram). see T L
M T. 123.4
T R T (monogram). see J R J
W H S T. 210.1; 212.29; 263.10

Florence K Upton. 69.29

A L Vernon. 67.26
Frank Vernon. 200.2
R Warren Vernon. 93.12
I Vickery. 91.5
E Vouga. 220.18-22

Louis Wain. 93.9; 267.8
F S Walker RE. 56.28
Seitz Wandsbeck. 182.1
Alfred Ward. 33.43
E Warwick. 202.1, 2
Louisa Marchioness of Waterford. 68.11;
81.23
Linnie Watt. 81.23; 94.1-3; 106.33-46;
148.6, 7
Miss M Webb. 148.39
W J Webb. 68.30; 75.6-8; 90.7
Harrison Weir. 169.10; 186.1; 197.11
A West. 88.24; 109.22; 112.16-22; 115.24,
27
G F Wetherbee RI ROI. 71.15
Dora Wheeler. Introduction to Section 8
Miss C White. 79.15-18; 80.33; 81.27;
88.24; 90.4; 91.14; 175.13; 186.14
L H White. 80.35; 90.4; 97.26
Mrs O E Whitney. 65.6
Mrs Emily Whymper. 94.35, 36; 96.21, 22;
97.14-16; 98.19,20; 99.4; 100.25; 102 (all);
103.4; 104.9; 126.15; 201.20
W J Wiegand. 72.17-30; 201.10
E Wilson. 114.13-15; 118.20; 120.17
W J Wollen. 268.22
Lawson Wood. 270.23
Alice Woodward. 204.1
E C (Nellie) Woodward. 204.1
Gertrude Woodward (Bradley). 204.1
Creswell Woollett. 71.27; 75.11; 162.34, 35
H S Wright. 40.11
W L Wyllie. 80.25-28
C H W. 182.19, 20
E W. 109.15; 120.10, 16
E W (monogram). 120,6
E W? (monogram). 136.13; 170.19;
175.4, 12
E A W? 120.13
J W. 69.27

K W. 87.13, 14
N A W. 263.25

W F Yeames. RA 68.1

Henry Zimmermann. 94.26, 27

# PUBLISHERS AND PRINTERS

This list may include some selling agents. The firms have London addresses unless otherwise noted, though some worked as well in Germany where many cards were manufactured later in the 19th Century and up to the outbreak of the First World War.

A Ackermann. 60.1-17; 61.5, 17-19, 23; 62.5, 19; 169.23
Adam & Co, (Newcastle). 226.1-4
Alpha Series, Alpha Publishing Co. 177.22, 25
American Baptist Publication Society. 200.1
Aristophat Co. 273.9
F Appel, (Paris). 151.5
Artistic Stationery Co. (A S Co). 165.10; 167.4-27; 185.17; 201.27; 222.29.
Artotype. 272.49
Aubry (Paris). 151.1; 194.1-4; 196.1-16; 202.10

Baddeley Bros (B Bros). 174.16, 17
Baillard (Paris). 196.23
Bamforth (Holmfirth). 146.16; 272.94, 95
Harvey Barton (photographer?). 213.27
Maison Bassel (Paris). 121.33-37
George Baxter. Introduction Volume 2; 6.1; 209.11
J Bazine (Paris). 195.12
Beagles. 145.10; 248.3; 272.120; 273.13; 274.5
Julius Bendix. 272.74
Bennet & Co (Montreal). 200.19
Benziger Frères (Paris). 196.25
Bertin. 121.33-37
Bertini Seymour & Co. 172.14
Birds - see Royal Society for the Protection of Birds
Birn Bros. 166.5; 180.1
Bishop & Co. 2.5
Blot (Paris). 196.24
J Bognard (Paris). 151.12
E Bollans & Co. Introduction Volume 13; 14.4; 16.8; 22.37; 23.23; 164.5; 225.6
Bollen & Tidswell. 165.12; 185.18, 19
Bonamy (Poitiers). 121.33-37; 196.22
Book Society. 133.11-14
Bouasse-Lebel et Fils et Massin. 121.33-51; 196.24
W S Bradford. 272.72
J Brady & Co. 208.29
J H Bufford & Sons. 60.29-31. 200.6
Burland Lith Co. 200.20 (see J T Henderson)
A H Bunney (Liverpool and Llandudno). 257.4
B & S. 177.9, 10
B B (London and New York). 267.5; 272.38-46
D B. 251.8
G G M B. 273.16
J B B & Co. 150.3; 186.2; 228.22
M A B. 272.93
M J B. 177.12
M S B. 272.47
P F B. 272.126; 273.14
T B & Co. 171.17; 204.14; 222.34; 253.23

James Campbell & Son (Canada). 200.16
Campbell & Tudhope (Glasgow and London). Volumes 122, 123; 144.5, 19; 179.31
Robert Canton. Introduction Volumes 5, 11, 14; 7.10-17; 8.22-25; 10.13-16; 15.21; 16.2; 18.1-30; Volume 19; 20.1-23; 25.26; 30.40; 99.1, 2; 136.1
Carlton Publishing Co. 272.121
Castell Bros. Volume 134; 137.20; 149.1-6; 171.19; 174.2-13; 179.4; 185.20, 21; 206.1-6; 221.1-3; 257.1, 2; 260.2-7
Charles Caswell (Birmingham). Volumes 124, 125; 142.24
Charles, Reynolds & Co. 200.8, 9; 135.4; 168.9; 185.16; 208.29
M Chatterton. 8.6; 166.15 (also Montague, Chatterton at the same address)
G & W Clarke (Montreal). 200.13, 14.
William J Clarke (Montreal). 200.15
David C Cook. 200.2 Agent?
Couchman (see Riddle & Couchman)
Court Greeting Cards. 140.11; 260.22
H S C & Co. 172.2; 177.11
J C & S (Sons?). 177.11 ✗
S P C Co. 272.107

Davidson Bros. 135.36; 152.32; 161.5-11; 172.19; 174.25; 180.2-5, 22; 186.17-19; 207.5-12; 222.11-14; 233.11; 248.8; 257.5; 260.8-13; 272.80-91; 273.8
Day & Son. 8.2, 3
Thomas De La Rue & Co. 1.4, 16; 3.30; Volumes 53-59; 164.14; 189.31; 200.6
De Labarrie et N Genoux (Paris). 195.6; 195.5-8 (De L et G N)
Dean & Son. 6.25-41; 7.20; 8.26, 27; 10.26-28; 20.24-29; 121.11; 138.1
Delgado. 267.5
Dennison. 176.30
Deulin (or Drulin). 201.1
William Dickes. 8.5; 126.1-15; 127.27; 141.4, 5, 9-12, 14, 15; 219.1; 226.25; 229.2
H Dobbs & Co. 15.8
Dobbs Kidd & Co. 1.9
H Dorn. 1.15
Drummond's Tract Depot (Stirling). 133.5; 142.24
Dupuy & Son (also Thomas). 85.1; 132.7, 21
E P Dutton (New York). see Nister & Dutton.
D & Co. 177.7
G D & D. 273.16

F Edwards & Co. 133.8
Max Ettlinger. 272.136; 273.15, 31
L Eudes (Tours). 196.25
Ewens. 16.4
Eyre & Spottiswoode. 48.17-19; 135.1-3; 148.2-27; 162.3; 164.14; 165.9; 166.4, 25, 31; 167.1-3; 168.17; 179.1-3; 185.3-10; 193.6; 194.1-5; 197.5; 201.20; 205.1-11; Volumes 217, 218

Ernest Falck & Co. 23.16, 17; 108.2; 148.28, 29; 156.36; 174.1; 185.1, 2; Volumes 223, 224
George Falkner & Sons (Manchester). 274.18; 257.7 (G F & S)
Faudel Phillips & Sons. 98.6-8
Faulkner - see Hildesheimer & Faulkner

C W Faulkner & Co. 108.30; 115.29-34; 145.10; 267.7
E Fuller. 8.1
F & S. 12.31
F F & Co. 213.33
P F. 272.76, 77

Gall & Inglis. 141.24
Galpin - see Petter & Galpin
N Genoux (Paris). 195.6, 7 - see De Labarrie et N Genoux
Ben George. 148.39 Agent?
Gibbs Shallard & Co (Sydney). 171.20; 200.25-29
Giesen Bros. 272.28, 29
Girls Friendly Society. 267.23
Golden Series. 268.28; 274.5
Charles Goodall & Son. 3.2-14, 36; Introduction to Volumes 11, 14; 18.9; Volumes 24-29; 52.31, 32; 164.14
Gotto - see Parkins & Gotto
Alfred Gray. Volume 173
Mrs E Grimke (Prestwich, Manchester). 133.2-4
F Guy (Cork). 168.8
B G Co. 273.31
H S G & Co. 257.7

Wolff Hagelberg (Berlin, London, New York). Introduction Volume 21; 21.12; 44.1-5; 45.1-5; 99.1, 2; 100.1, 2; 135.5-13; 149.7-15; 169.22; 174.18-20; 179.5-16; 186.22-27; 198.8, 9; 205.12-32; 211.15; 221.4-11; 257.5, 6; Volume 258; Introduction Volume 262; 264.24; 266.2, 9, 15
Halford Bros. 202.1, 2, 5
Hallmark Cards. 1.5, 6
W T Harris. 2.14
J E Hawkins, Yapp & Hawkins. Volume 127
J T Henderson (Montreal). 200.20
Albert Hildesheimer. 23.22; Volume 105; 219.20, 21
Siegmund Hildesheimer. 15.18; 18.23; 30.40; 44.1-5; 45.1-5; Volumes 94-104; 155.6; 164.14; 183.3; 184.21; 197.6; 199.6; 201.16, 20, 29; 206.5; 229.16-21; 235.33; 242.23-25; 253.1; 255.23-24; 263.23; 272.68
Hildesheimer & Faulkner. Volumes 106-120; 163.3; 164.14; 198.1; 199.19; 200.8, 10; 201.16; 211.33; 253.12; 255.9; 257.9; 263.34
Hills & Co. Hamilton Hills & Co. H H & Co. 136.31; 169.31; 177.1-5; 202.6, 7; 267.1
Hodgson - see Matthews & Hodgson
Houghton (Blackpool). 178.1
E H. 177.7, 8
J G H. 200.29

Inglis - see Gall & Inglis

M L J (Jonas?). 208.25

Kaiser - see Vogelbank & Kaiser
Kelly - see Rolls & Kelly
Kilburn (Nottingham). 172.2
Jonathan King. 1.8; 16.17; 52.13; 148.1, 28: 156.36; 176.1; 185.1, 2; Volumes 223, 224
Kinze Bros, Meissner (Leipzig). 30.22, 24
Kray - see Wildt & Kray
J M Kronheim & Co. 6.1-7; 132.4; 201.2

John Windsor & Sons. 1.10; 4.1-3; 14.1;
17.5, 6; 145.3, 6
John Winsch. 272.102, 108
Wirth Bros & Owen, also Wirth Bros (New
York & London). 135.25, 26; 149.22-25;
167.15, 16; 179.25-27; 186.8, 9, 20, 21; 197.7,
8; 198.20; 201.16; 206.7-23; 222.9, 10;
257.3; 260.14, 15
Wolff (see Stewart & Wolff)
J T Wood & Co. 11.2; 15.22; 16.12, 13;
17.5; 145.3-5
Woolstone Bros. 272.7, 92
Wrenck Series. 272.134
W & Co. 153.23; 222.31
D W. 225.7, 8
J W & Co. 204.23
V O W. 211.32

Yapp & Hawkins (see Hawkins)
Y M C A (see Manchester)
Y W C A. 267.22

# WRITERS

Identified writers have been listed here with the publishers who issue the cards they signed, where these are known. Untraced initials have not been listed. Classical writers and authors whose works were quoted on cards but not specifically written for them, are not included, with one or two exceptions. Initials are used here for those publishers with lengthy names which can be readily identified.

Achespé (Caswell)
Ada (Stevens)
Adams
H Alford (Dickes)
F Annandale
Vera Arlington

H S Bainbridge
E F Baker (Raphael Tuck - RT)
Astley H Baldwin (Prang, Hildesheimer & Faulkner - H & F, S Hildesheimer - S H, Marx, S J S, Ollendorff)
Jonathan Beall (Meissner & Buch)
Thomas Beaumont (H & F)
Canon Bell (R T, Caswell)
Lucy A Bennett (Castell)
Rev E H Bickersteth (R T, Caswell)
Clifton Bingham (R T, Nister)
Osburn Blackburn
A M Bode (R T)
J L B Bodycomb (R T)
H Bonar D D (Caswell, Religious Tract Society - R T S)
S B Bradley
Braham (H & F)
Katherine A Brock (R T)
T Brown
H M Burnside (H & F, Caswell, Ollendorff, Nister, Philipps, Sockl & Nathan - S & N, Davidson)

Alice Cary (H & F, Eyre & Spottiswoode - E & S)
M Cather (H & F)
Jessie Chase (R T)
E MN Chettle (R T)
Edith Helena Cooke (R T, Wirth Bros & Owen)
Eliza Cook (R T, Philipps)
J N Cooper
Samuel K Cowan MA (R T, S H, H & F, R T S, J F Schipper - J F S, Davidson, Philipps, S & N, Meissner & Buch - M & B, Hagelberg)
J E Cox (H & F)

Vera Dale
Coombes Davies
Francis Davis (Marcus Ward - M W, H & F)
Sarah Doudney (M W)
H Daunton
W Drummond (R T)
W H Drummond

A F Earl (S H)
Elbetee (Hagelberg)
C Elliott
J Ellis

Marianne Farningham (Caswell)
Frank Ferndale
G A Finlayson (R T)
Fanny Forrester (H & F, R T)
Charles Fox (Caswell)
J L E Freeman (E & S)
J Hain Friswell (M W)

J E Galliford
A Gill
Fanny Goddard (R T)
Julia Goddard (M W, S H)
Meta Going
Mary Gorges (R T)
J H Goring
J Green (M W)
E E Griffin (Hagelberg)
C A Griffiths

M M Hadath (Royal Society for the Protection of Birds - R S P B)
Rev Newman Hall (R T)
S C Hall (M W, E & S)
Lady Laura Hampton (H & F)
F E Eileen Harper - signed F E E H (R T, S H, Caswell, E & S)
A O Harris
W Harris (Dickes)
M E Hatton (H & F)
Cecilia Havergal (R T, H & F, Caswell, Davidson)
Frances Ridley Havergal (M W, R T, S H, R T S, Caswell, Castell, Philipps, M & B, Hagelberg, Nister)
M S Haycraft - Margaret? (R T, Hagelberg, Ollendorff, S & N, M & B)
"Helen of Troy" (R T)
Enis Herne (M W)
J C Holland (H & F)
F S Hollings (H & F)
G S Hollings (HIlls & Co)
A M Hone (Hagelberg, R T)
Eden Hooper (R T, E & S)
N Hope
J S H Horton (Davidson)
W Walsham How
Agnes R Howell - signed A R H (M W, R T, A H, H & F)

M R Jarvis (R T)
W Cairn Jones (R T)

E Kennedy - signed E K (R T, M W)
E A Lemprière Knight (R T, H & F)

Lavinia M Lancaster (R T, Caswell)
Rev. Frederick Langbridge (M W, R T, R T S, signed F L also S H, Caswell)
Horace Lennard
Sydney Lever (R T, Castell)
Elizabeth Love (Hagelberg)

Dr. George Macdonald (Wheeler, Caswell, R T)
Rev. J R MacDuff, DD
Charles Mackay (S H)
Dr. Mahlenberg (R T S)
Nora Manning (Ollendorff)
Dr. Mansell (R T)
Janet Marsh
A Matheson
E Mathison

Handley G G Maule MA
Frank Mayhew (Nister)
Hart Milman
R N Milner (Dickes)
James Montgomery
Sarah Louise Moore
M F Moss (Albert Hildesheimer - A H)
Charlotte Murray (R T, Davidson, Nister, Ollendorff, S & N)
Rev. J W Myers BA (H & F, Hagelberg)

Needham (H & F)
"Nemo" (Hagelberg)
Newton (R T S)
Nicolai
Hon Mrs Norton (Alfred Gray)
Lewis Novra (S H, E & S, Ollendorff, Davidson)

Lily Oakley
Ouseley

E A C Pearson (R T)
Mrs Picton
E J Pope (Ollendorff)
Isabella J Postgate
Ernest Power ( H & F, Hagelberg)
Kate Price (R T)
Adelaide Proctor (Dickes, R T)
A A Proctor (H & F, Dickes, R T)

Faith Quiltern (H & F)

Thomas Randolph (Prang)
J L Richardson
E Ridley (A H, H & F)
H Ridley (A H, H & F)
Arthur Rigby (R T)
M S Mae Ritchie (Ollendorff)
Rev C W Roberts (John Sands)
Fanny(ie) Rochat (R T)
M E Ropes (R T S)
Charles J Rowe

Sabrina
A L Salmon (R T, Hagelberg, M & B)
J M Saxby (R T)
R P Scott (Ollendorff)
W H Seal (R T)
Epes Sergeant
G or Gertrude E Shaw (R T)
"Sigma" (R T)
Ernest Sigourney
L Sigourne
Silesius (R T S)
Clara Simmonds (R T, Hagelberg)
Eliza Simmonds
A Smith (Dickes)
C H Spurgeon
Arthur Steine
J Stirling
Hesba Stratton (M W, H & F)
Elton Summers (R T, E & S)

G M Taylor (Caswell)
Jeremy Taylor (S H)
Celia Thaxter (Prang)
F Thomson
Thring
R C Trench (Dickes)
Ellin Isabelle Tupper (H & F, Ollendorff)

Jetty Vogel (R T, Caswell)
"Veni" (John Sands)

Marion Wallace (Nister)
Ellis Walton (R T)
Isabel Warry (Davidson)
M G Watkins MA
Edwin Waugh (Nister)
D E Weatherly (H & F)
Fred E Weatherly (A H, H & F)
J L Wharton
J E Whitby (R T)
Leonard Whitby (R T)
H M Whitlaw
S Wigley (H & F)
Ella Wheeler Wilcox (R S P B)
Alice C Wilkinson (S & N, Caswell)
Wilfred Woffam BA (R T)
Mrs E Wolstenholme (Gibbs Shallard)
Bishop Wordsworth (Caswell)
H B Worth
Shirley Wynne (A H, H & F)